MICROBIOLOGY AND HUMAN DISEASE

MICROBIOLOGY AND HUMAN DISEASE

SECOND EDITION

George A. Wistreich, Ph.D.

Chairman, Life Sciences Department
Director, Allied Health Sciences Programs
EAST LOS ANGELES COLLEGE
LOS ANGELES, CALIFORNIA

Max D. Lechtman, Ph.D.

Instructor
Microbiology Consultant
GOLDEN WEST COLLEGE
HUNTINGTON BEACH, CALIFORNIA

GLENCOE PUBLISHING CO., INC.
Encino, California
Collier Macmillan Publishers
London

GLENCOE PUBLISHING CO., INC.
17337 Ventura Boulevard
Encino, California 91316
Collier Macmillan Canada, Ltd.

Library of Congress Catalog Card Number: 75–14932

3 4 5 6 7 8 9 RRD 80 79 78 77

ISBN 0-02-479190-3

To our respective families,
whose encouragement, patience, and sacrifices
helped to make this book possible.

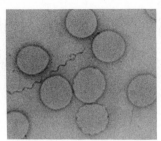

DIVISION 1

AN INTRODUCTION TO MICROBIOLOGY

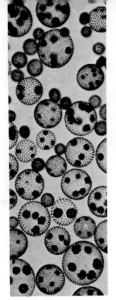
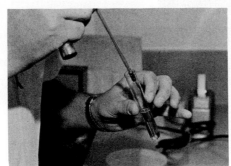
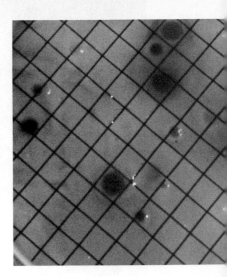

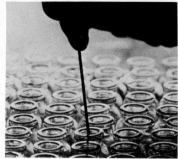
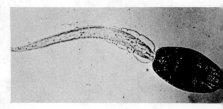

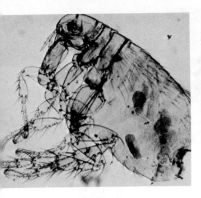

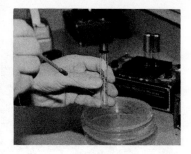

DIVISION 8

AN INTRODUCTION TO MEDICAL PARASITOLOGY

FOREWORD

Microbiology and Human Disease is not written for the specialist but for the student who is in need of a broad foundation in microbiology and who wants to obtain some insight into the role microorganisms play in health and disease. By using this text the individual should achieve these objectives and specifically be able to:

1. Recognize the position microorganisms occupy in the biological world, as well as their various biological functions.
2. Note the basic similarities and differences, from structural and functional standpoints, of microbes compared to higher forms of life.
3. Gain an appreciation of the problems and methods involved in the cultivation and identification of microorganisms.
4. Obtain a deeper understanding of the means used by microorganisms to cause disease and of the human mechanisms of defense.
5. Recognize the various ways in which disease agents can be transmitted.
6. Gain familiarity with microbial-caused diseases.
7. Critically evaluate methods used to control microorganisms.
8. Acquire a larger and more functional vocabulary.

The realization of these objectives cannot be easily accomplished. It will demand a genuine effort on the part of the student. However, through such effort he will grow to appreciate the important position microorganisms hold in his world.

January, 1973

G. A. Wistreich
M. D. Lechtman

PREFACE TO THE SECOND EDITION

Microbiology has seen a rapid period of growth in the last few decades as a result of extensive research that has provided knowledge of many new microorganisms and their activities. It has also become increasingly evident that numerous exciting and significant discoveries in such areas as biochemistry, genetics, medicine, molecular biology, pharmacology, and physiology rely on an understanding of microorganisms and an application of microbiological principles. In a text intended for an introductory course, it would be impractical, if not impossible, to treat each and every facet of microbiology in detail. The intent of the second edition of *Microbiology and Human Disease,* therefore, is to emphasize selected basic principles, concepts, and descriptive data. With this background, the reader can then assimilate information about new developments into a general frame of knowledge and can more readily understand how each new pertinent discovery resembles, differs from, extends, or refutes existing principles and concepts. A textbook for today's students must do justice to the newer principles and concepts pertinent to microbiology without neglecting the older and proven ones that provide the foundation upon which the new body of knowledge rests.

As in the previous edition of *Microbiology and Human Disease,* the chapters have been arranged so as to facilitate the reader's efforts to study and identify the various types of microorganisms, to recognize their fundamental similarities and differences, and to learn the techniques and methods used in the control of microorganisms and their activities. Toward this end each division is introduced by a set of behavioral objectives to help readers understand exactly what they should expect to achieve in reading the chapters in the division.

The general organization of the second edition of *Microbiology and Human Disease* has not been changed significantly from that of the first edition. However, certain changes and additions have been made in the majority of chapters and in the "Atlas of Color Plates" not only to update the presentation but also to make it more understandable.

With the realization that cancer is a leading cause of death and disability throughout the world and with the increasing attention being given to the role of viruses in the disease state, a new chapter entitled "Oncogenesis and Microorganisms" has been added to this edition. In addition, the references section at the end of the text contains a list of publications carefully selected to provide readers with introductory as well as more advanced and detailed material pertinent to the subjects discussed in the chapters.

We would like to take this opportunity to thank all those persons who contributed to the second edition of *Microbiology and Human Disease*. In particular, we would like to again acknowledge the expertise of Mr. Charles Righter, who executed a large portion of the artwork and coordinated the color photographs with admirable skill. We would also like to thank Mrs. Janis Long and Mrs. Ruth Rodney for the effort and care they exercised in typing the latest portions of the manuscript, and the respective members of the editorial and production staff of Benziger Bruce & Glencoe, Inc., for their untiring and imaginative efforts expended in the preparation of the second edition for publication. In addition to the contributions of these persons, this edition of *Microbiology and Human Disease* was also greatly influenced by the many enthusiastic comments of students; the wise guidance and counsel offered by numerous instructors, students, colleagues, and health-care professionals; and the many contributors from various countries who willingly provided us with photographs and diagrams. To all of these persons we are especially indebted.

PREFACE TO THE FIRST EDITION

Selecting the subject matter to be included in an introductory microbiology textbook, or more specifically the material that must be omitted, presents a most difficult problem. This is especially true not only because of the rapidly amassing body of knowledge, but also because of varied approaches and areas of emphasis observed by instructors of microbiology. In light of these problems, the authors have selected a broad range of basic properties of microorganisms and microbiological principles and concepts, and arranged this material in a manner which will help students to understand the functioning of microorganisms in relation to other living systems. Toward this end we have relied quite heavily on illustrations (both black and white and color) to support the difficult and important portions of the text, and constructed reference charts and tables not only to emphasize the significance of an assortment of related facts, but to provide quick access to relevant facts and terminology.

Microbiology and Human Disease is organized along the lines of a division or unit system. The first four divisions are devoted to the characteristics of microorganisms and a broad spectrum of activities involving microbial life. The remaining three divisions are primarily concerned with host defense mechanisms, disease transmission, and disease states. All of these topics are heavily supplemented with illustrative material. "Questions for Review" at the end of each chapter are provided to aid the student in reviewing the material presented and in testing his comprehension of the principles and facts discussed. The text's appendix includes a reference bibliography to provide both general and specific sources of additional information and a glossary of operational definitions. An atlas of color photographs depicting cultural and diagnostically significant characteristics of microorganisms, specific morphological features, and representative clinical disease states is placed in the center of the text for easy reference.

A more detailed description of the individual divisions, emphasizing the major features of each, follows.

Division 1. The chapters in this division provide a general survey and definition of the microbial world, together with brief presentations of selected historical events which have contributed to the development of microbiology. Additional points of historical importance are interwoven with appropriate subject matter in later chapters. The authors feel that all too often the general tendency to concentrate history into one or two chapters of a textbook overpowers the student and interferes with his appreciation of the development of the science. Attention also is given in this division to current representative activities of microorganisms and their interrelationships with other biological systems.

Division 2. This division spotlights microbial structure and function. One specific chapter is provided which describes, in a significant but not overly burdensome manner, the various techniques used in the preparation of specimens for most types of microscopy, including bright-field, dark-field, transmission, and scanning electron microscopy. A chapter also is included in this section which presents, in summary form, the structural features of higher biological forms. This was done in order to provide a frame of reference for students so as to enable them to make comparisons between familiar biological systems and microorganisms.

Division 3. The first chapter in this division briefly presents basic terminology and explanations of biochemical compounds so as to give the student some familiarity with preparations used to grow microorganisms. Representative techniques and the results of microbial cultivation are discussed in the remaining chapters in this division.

Division 4. The chapters in this unit are devoted to discussions of the basic principles and various processes associated with microbial growth, metabolism, and genetics. Newer concepts of cellular regulation, techniques, and comparisons between microorganisms and other biological systems are also presented.

Division 5. Because of the practical significance of the control of microorganisms, chapters in this division present discussions of basic principles as well as descriptions of particular techniques employing them. The practical application

of heat, disinfectants, and chemotherapeutic agents are emphasized.

Division 6. The principles and techniques associated with immunology are quite extensive and have extreme practical importance. The division opens with a chapter devoted to defense mechanisms against disease agents. This is followed by a consideration of the factors responsible for a microorganism's disease-producing capability. The next two chapters deal with the characterization of antigens and antibodies, and the techniques used to isolate and identify them. This division also includes chapters which discuss blood groups and typing, new concepts concerning the Rh baby, hypersensitivity, and auto-immune diseases. The final chapter presents the preparation of immunizing materials, their administration, and certain side effects which can occur.

Division 7. This is the largest division in the text and is unique in several respects. The first chapter here stresses the various routes and means of transmission for disease agents. This is followed by a chapter describing the collection of specimens and representative approaches to the identification of pathogens. The majority of the remaining chapters are devoted to microbial diseases arranged in relation to specific tissues and/or organ systems attacked. A specific chapter is included which deals with dental microbiology. The final chapter presents a large group of disease agents that are transmitted by warm-blooded animals and arthropods.

Division 8. This division has been organized along classic lines. The two chapters contained here present the ways in which medically important protozoa and helminths are transmitted and identified, the diseases they cause, and the measures used for their control.

Microbiology and Human Disease is an appropriate text both for introductory and intensive courses, such as are found in junior (community) and four-year colleges and universities. This text may contain somewhat more subject material than is covered in certain microbiology courses —subjects that an instructor cannot consider in his formal lectures. Their inclusion, however, enables each instructor to select and to emphasize the areas he believes to be the most important, and yet provides the interested student with the opportunity to read about topics that were either omitted or briefly discussed in lectures. Thus the arrangement and the number of chapters in each division allows for flexibility in the use of the book and the specific needs and interests of students. The inclusion of an exceptionally large array of black and white and color photographs, functional tables and charts, and a glossary to explain the technical terminology used throughout the text provide an excellent means of familiarizing students with the properties of microorganisms and microbial principles.

The authors hope that this text will significantly contribute to the efforts of instructors of microbiology to motivate students into increasing their knowledge concerning the activities and importance of microorganisms, and to establish a firm foundation that will be of value to students in related coursework.

The scope and content of *Microbiology and Human Disease* were greatly influenced by numerous instructors and students, colleagues, technologists, and technicians. We are especially indebted to these individuals for their instruction, wise guidance, and counsel.

We would like to thank Mr. Charles Righter, who aided in a large portion of the artwork found in the text. Particular acknowledgement is due to several persons who exerted meticulous care, and spent many hours in the typing of the original manuscript and its revisions. These include Miss Gloria Medrano, Mrs. Ruth Rodney, Miss Janis Cutting, and Mrs. Priscilla Jorden. The authors wish to thank Mr. L. Isaksen for technical assistance, and Mr. John Devaney and Mr. Ken Evans (Jet Propulsion Laboratory) for several of the scanning electron micrographs. We are also extremely grateful to those numerous contributors from various countries who have willingly provided us with photographs and diagrams.

The authors are especially indebted to Ms. Sharon Millman, who devoted a great deal of her patience, time, and editorial expertise to the preparation of our text. We would also like to acknowledge the efforts of Mr. Chuck Alessio in the selection, guidance, and coordination of the text's illustrative material.

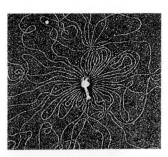

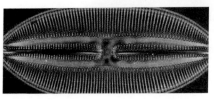

An Introduction to Microbiology

DIVISION 1: Behavioral Objectives

After reading the chapters in this division, the individual should be able to:

1. Describe the major divisions of microbiology and the components of each.

2. Recognize the value of the various publications available on microbiology and related areas.

3. Identify selected important contributors and their contributions to microbiology.

4. Recognize the respective positions of microorganisms in the biological world.

5. List and illustrate some of the significant activities of specific microorganisms.

6. Recognize the interrelationships among humans, other higher life forms, and microorganisms.

The Scope of Microbiology

The Microbial World

Microscopic forms of life can be found in vast numbers in nearly every environment known to man. They are found in the soil, in bodies of water, in the food and water we consume, and even in the air we breathe. Fortunately, the greater number of such microorganisms are not harmful to man nor to the various forms of life in his world. The microbial world includes in its membership microscopic forms of life as well as those that are too small to be seen with an ordinary microscope.

Many microorganisms occur as single cells, some are multicellular, and still others (such as viruses) do not have a true cellular appearance. Certain organisms, called *anaerobes,* are capable of carrying out their vital functions in the absence of free oxygen. However, the majority of organisms, referred to as *aerobes,* require free oxygen. Microbes are known which can manufacture the essential compounds for their physiological needs from atmospheric sources of nitrogen and carbon dioxide. Other microorganisms, such as viruses and certain bacteria, are totally dependent for their existence on the cells of higher forms of life. The branch of science known as microbiology embraces all of these properties of microorganisms and many more. For the most part, microorganisms are unicellular and exhibit the characteristic features common to biological systems. Such properties include:

Reproduction. The ability to multiply. Many microorganisms are capable of both *asexual* and *sexual* forms of this basic process. (Sexual reproduction is simply defined as the union of nuclear material from two different cells, resulting in a new individual.)

Metabolism. The ability to utilize a variety of substances as food and to obtain from them the needed energy for numerous cellular activities, the sum total of the chemical reactions associated with these activities. Metabolic reactions can be grouped into two categories, namely, *anabolism,* or constructive metabolism, and *catabolism*, or destructive metabolism. Reactions of the former type are associated with the synthesis of cellular components, needed for growth, reproduction, and repair, while those of the latter category include digestion and degradation of harmful substances.

Growth. Most microorganisms, as well as other forms of life, generally increase in size due to materials produced intracellularly, a process of growth from within. This is in contrast to accretion, which is the accumulation of material from the external environment onto surfaces.

Irritability. The ability to respond to environmental stimuli, including temperature, acidity, intense light, and toxic substances.

Adaptability. Adjustment to environmental stimuli. Several microbial types survive unfavorable environments because they are capable of altering certain of their activities, for example the direction of their movement (motility), and because they secrete substances to detoxify harmful substances in their environments.

Mutation. The susceptibility to genetic change. Certain environmental factors, of either a normal or an experimental nature, can not only bring about changes in the genetic apparatus, but can increase the frequency of such reactions. Mutations, in general, appear with a definite degree of frequency.

Organization. It is clear from the processes performed by microbial forms of life that they must possess a certain level of organization and precision. Hence, it is quite appropriate to refer to microbes as small, organized units or *microorganisms*.

Microbiology and Its Subdivisions

Taxonomic Arrangement

Included among the subjects for study in the field of microbiology are algae, bacteria, fungi (molds and yeasts), protozoa, and viruses. As a matter of convenience, the general branches of microbiology frequently are designated accordingly (Figures 1–1 and 1–2). This terminology, referred to as the taxonomic approach, includes:

Bacteriology. The study of bacteria. Bacteria represent a large group of microscopic organisms in terms of both variety and numbers. They are found in numerous types of environments, ranging from the soil and bodies of water to the external and internal surfaces of humans, lower animals, and plants. The activities in which bacteria are involved include the causation of disease, the decomposition of decaying or dead organic matter, the digestion of food in humans and other forms of life, and the production of various chemicals, foods, and other useful products.

Immunology. The study of a host's defense mechanisms (resistance) against disease. In general, this involves determining the contributions to resistance made by the specific activities of certain body cells, e.g., lymphocytes and phagocytes, and the various chemical components of body fluids such as antibodies, complement, and lysozyme. Modern immunology also is concerned with the diagnosis, prognosis, and prevention of disease.

Mycology. The study of fungi. Included in this group are molds, mushrooms, and yeasts. Fungi are widely distributed in nature and exhibit a wide variety of sizes, colors, and shapes. These organisms are not photosynthetic. Many live in the soil and take an active part in the decomposition of organic matter. In addition, fungi are involved in the production of several kinds of food and antibiotics and in the causation of disease in humans, lower animals, and plants. Ringworm, for example, is a fungous infection.

Phycology (algology). The study of algae. These organisms range in size from microscopic unicellular forms to the multicellular giant kelp, commonly referred to as seaweed, which can reach lengths of 150 feet or more. The pigments in algae, which span the colors of brown, green, red, and yellow, give these organisms their noted ability to carry out photosynthesis. Algae are also useful as decomposers of organic matter in sewage and as food sources for humans and for livestock. Agar, an ingredient in preparations used to grow bacteria and other microorganisms, is obtained from a com-

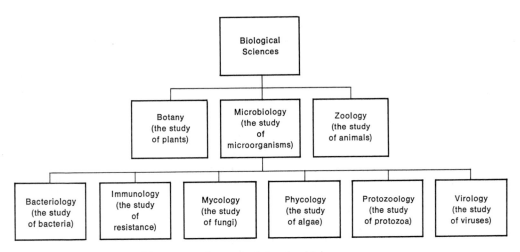

FIG. 1–1. Representation of the taxonomic approach to microbiology.

mon seaweed alga, *Gelidium.* Not all of the activities of algae are beneficial to higher life forms, however. For example, algae have recently become quite a problem as water pollutants. There have been dramatic increases of high concentrations of organic matter in the form of wastes in ponds, lakes, and other bodies of water, a process of nutrient enrichment known as *eutrophication* (Color photograph 3). With appropriate environmental temperatures this process results in an increased microbial productivity that commonly upsets the normal ecological balance and creates such problems as algal scums, terrible odors, and the death of fish caused by oxygen depletion.

Protozoology.   The study of protozoa. These organisms are larger than most other microorganisms and are quite complex in structure and activities. They are found in sewage, in various bodies of water, and in damp soil. Although most protozoa live on rotting or dead organic matter, or even on bacteria, and are mainly harmless, some types of protozoa are responsible for several of the most severe diseases of humans and other ani-mals, such as African sleeping sickness and malaria.

Virology.   The study of viruses (from the Latin term meaning poison). This specialized area of investigation also may include the study of rickettsia. At one time it was thought that these microorganisms represented forms of life intermediate between viruses and bacteria. Recent findings have demonstrated the rickettsia to be a specialized type of bacterium.

The Status of Viruses

Before the actual visual demonstration of viruses, these agents were surrounded by an "aura of mystery" because of their apparent invisibility, as well as their disease-producing capabilities. Initially, combatting the effects of these invisible producers of disease proceeded along the lines of prevention through vaccine development. Representative of this disease-prevention approach are the studies of Edward Jenner (Figure 1–3) in 1798 of vaccination against smallpox, and the investigations of Louis Pasteur in 1884 in the development of a vaccine against rabies (hydrophobia).

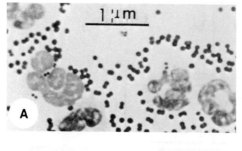

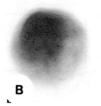

Bacteriology

FIG. 1–2. The branches of microbiology. _A_. A photomicrograph of the bacterium _Staphylococcus aureus_ in the presence of several white blood cells. This microorganism has a spherical or coccus shape. _S. aureus_ is noted as the cause of several infections, including boils, food poisoning, impetigo, and pneumonia. (From Melly, M. A., Duke, L. J., Liau, D. F., and Hash, J. H.: _Infect. Immun._, **10**:389, 1974.)

Immunology

_B_. One example of immunologic procedure, blood typing. The reaction on the left occurs when blood to be used in a transfusion is of the correct type, while the reaction on the right, referred to as agglutination, can result when blood of a group different from the recipient is used in a transfusion. (Courtesy of USDA.)

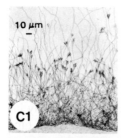
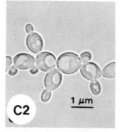
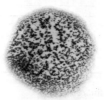

Mycology

_C1_. Fungi. The typical appearance of the mold _Penicillium notatum,_ one of the producers of the antibiotic penicillin. (Courtesy of Abbott Laboratories.)

_C2_. Brewer's yeast, _Saccharomyces cerevisiae,_ a fungus. This microorganism is frequently used in baking. (Courtesy of Standard Brands, Fleischmann Laboratories, Stamford, Conn.)

Phycology

_D_. A typical phytoplankton algal community from the Antarctic pack ice area. (Courtesy of Dr. Paul E. Hargraves, Narragansett Marine Laboratory, Kingston, Rhode Island.)

Protozoology

_E_. A scanning electron micrograph of _Euplotes_ species. This protozoan is commonly found in marine and fresh waters. Note the tuft-like brushes of cilia (short structures used for movement) at one end of the organism. (From Frankel, J., and Ruffolo, J. J.: _J. Protozool._, **20**:8–18, 1973.)

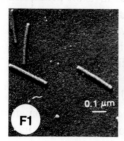
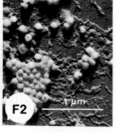

Virology

_F1_. An electron micrograph of tobacco mosaic virus. (Courtesy of Dr. Robley C. Williams and the Virus Laboratory, University of California, Berkeley.)

_F2_. An electron micrograph of influenza virus, type B. (Courtesy of Lederle Laboratories, Pearl River, N.Y.)

filters, he concluded that here was a form of life hitherto unknown to humans. Some seven years later, in 1899, M. W. Beijerinck independently discovered the same phenomenon, to which he gave the designation *contagium vivum fluidum* (a contagious living fluid).

With the discovery of several viruses responsible for diseases in animals, including foot-and-mouth disease (FMD) by Löffler and Frosch (1898), yellow fever by Reed and his associates in 1900, and the subsequent demonstration of viruses

FIG. 1–3. The original vaccination procedure conducted by Edward Jenner (1749–1823). It was performed by removing and transferring some vesicular fluid from a lesion of cowpox on the hand of a dairymaid (seen on the left bandaging her hand) to the arm of a small boy. The successful outcome of Jenner's vaccination against smallpox established a firm basis for the value of artificial immunization. (Courtesy of Fisher Scientific Co.)

It was actually Louis Pasteur who proposed that the designation *vaccine,* from the Latin word *vacca,* meaning cow, be applied to all immunizing agents (immunogens). Furthermore, he suggested that procedures employing such material be referred to as *vaccinations*.

The discovery of viruses, or at least the recognition of a nonbacterial infective agent, was made by Iwanowski in 1892. While he was working with diseased tobacco plants (Figure 1–4), he detected the infectious nature of the sap from these plants. As Iwanowski could not demonstrate the agent microscopically, nor prevent its activity by passing infectious plant sap material through bacterial retaining

FIG. 1–4. A leaf of a tobacco plant infected with tobacco mosaic virus (TMV). Note the variation in color shown on the infected leaf. (Courtesy of the U.S. Department of Agriculture.)

capable of attacking and causing the destruction of bacteria in 1915 by Twort and in 1917 by D'Herelle, interest in these agents began to grow. In 1935, W. Stanley reported the crystallization of tobacco mosaic virus (TMV) to the scientific world.

This discovery, in the words of W.

Hayes, "gave birth to the romantic idea that viruses are a kind of missing link between living and nonliving material," a type of borderline of life. Differences of opinion still exist as to whether these are living forms. Nevertheless, viruses have gained a prominent position in the world of man, not only because of their obvious etiologic relationship to disease, but also because of their value as research tools in unlocking the intricate mechanisms of life's processes. In the words of Sir Christopher Andrewes (somewhat paraphrased), the position achieved by viruses no longer limits them to a merely parasitic existence, but establishes them as a separate category of living things.

Integrative Arrangement

Another approach to the study of microorganisms is the "integrative arrangement," as referred to by Luria and Darnell. Here the subdivisions of microbiology are directed toward analyzing the common or specialized characteristics or properties of microbes and their various interactions. Examples of these areas of study include:

Microbial cytology. The study of microscopic, as well as submicroscopic, details of microbial cells. The latter type of investigation usually involves the techniques of electron microscopy (see Chapter 6).

Microbial ecology. The study of the relationships between microorganisms and their environments. An investigation of the way microorganisms respond to unfavorable situations would be an example of this area of specialization.

Microbial genetics. The study of inheritance. This area of investigation concerns itself with the activities of the nuclear elements of microorganisms and how they regulate the growth and development of these forms of life; determining the effects of mutation-causing agents, i.e., mutagens; altering the genetic makeup of microorganisms; and uncovering the basis of antibiotic resistance in various microbes.

Microbial physiology. The study of the functioning of microorganisms. Metabolic activities, the effects of the environment on microbial synthetic pathways, and determining the nutritional requirements of different groups of microbes are a few of the types of investigations involving microbial physiology.

The extremely important and exciting area of molecular biology has been a recent outgrowth of the advances in knowledge and technology made in microbial genetics, physiology, and in the technology of microbiology. The principal aim of molecular biology is directed toward determining the relationship between chemical structure and the genetic makeup or constitution of microbial and higher forms. Microorganisms have played a central role in the development of the solid foundation on which current studies of the intracellular regulatory mechanisms and the expression of genetic information are based (Figure 1–5). Among the advances that contributed to this foundation were the discoveries relating to the structures and functions of deoxyribonucleic acid (DNA) and ribonucleic acid (RNA) and the mechanism by which genetic information in DNA controls the synthesis of proteins. In fact, how genetic information flows from DNA to RNA and finally results in the formation of a protein molecule is referred to as the "central dogma" of molecular biology.

Microbial taxonomy. This specialized area includes the naming and classifying of microorganisms. Microbial taxonomy involves determining the similarities and differences among microbial species and using these data to formulate a classifica-

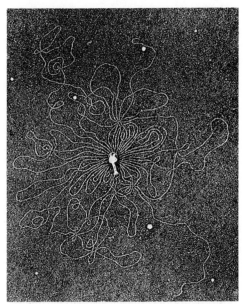

FIG. 1–5. A special preparation of a bacterial virus (bacteriophage) showing its DNA, which contains the genetic information of the virus. The virus particle is located approximately within the center of the nucleic acid. The bar marker equals 1.0 micrometers. (Courtesy of Dr. A. K. Kleinschmidt; from Kleinschmidt, A. K., Lang, D., Jacherts, D., and Zahn, R. K.: *Biochem. Biophys. Acta,* **61**:857, 1962.)

tion system which shows the relationship of microorganisms to one another.

Mention should also be made of two other areas of investigation, biochemistry and biophysics. Biochemistry is concerned with the chemical basis of living matter and the various reactions associated with them, while biophysics is devoted to the study of the principles of physics as they apply to all living matter.

These specialized fields are "reductionist" sciences, analyzing basic processes in terms of electrons, atoms, and molecules. Many of these branches overlap. Moreover, one subdivision can include a number of others, each of which is concerned with a particular microbial group. For example, microbial genetics may be further divided and restricted to bacteria or to bacterial viruses, i.e., bacteriophages.

The education of a microbiologist today includes a background of general information in the majority of subdivisions. However, because of the tremendous accumulation of information in each specialization—which the individual cannot hope to master—the microbiologist must limit himself to one, or a select few, of the branches of microbiology. The branches he chooses to specialize in depend upon the type of microbial work he wishes to pursue. There are many different areas of applied microbiology.

Applied Areas of Microbiology

Many substances used by man in his everyday life are actually products of microbial activity. Microbe-dependent activities such as fermentation have been used since ancient times, but the improvements brought about by modern technology and the information obtained from the various areas of microbial specializations have made possible a closer control of microorganisms and their activities in the field of industrial microbiology. This area of microbiology involves the efforts of chemists, engineers, and microbiologists toward efficient control of the conversion of raw materials into desirable end products by carefully selected microorganisms.

The welfare of man is also affected by the particular activities of certain microbial species that interfere with the normal processes of the human body. Investigations concerned with such harmful effects of microorganisms (pathogens) form the basis of medical microbiology. The following types of studies are included in this area of specialization: (1) determining the properties and disease capabilities of microorganisms; (2) developing procedures to detect the presence of pathogens (diagnosis); (3) attempting to discover an antibiotic or antibiotics which will eliminate the disease agent or prevent it from exerting its harmful effects (antibiotic sensitivity testing); (4) developing vaccines against pathogens; and (5) incorporating both chemical and physical methods for the management and control of infectious diseases in the population as a whole. Today an ever-increasing number of health team specialists are being trained in the principles of this specialized area.

Many animal parasites, such as hookworms and tapeworms, have microscopic stages in their life cycles, and courses concerned with the medical aspects of microbiology may include the study of these forms. Ordinarily, however, these *metazoan* (multicellular) *parasites* are considered separately in the specialized branch of *Parasitology*. In this textbook the parasitic protozoa, e.g. causative agents of diseases, including amebic dysentery and malaria, and the parasitic helminths will be considered in a specific division devoted to medical parasitology.

Microbiology and the Scientific Method

One goal of microbiology, as well as of every other branch of science, is to find explanations for observed phenomena and to show interrelationships between them and related events. To achieve this aim, a type of organized common sense approach, referred to as the "scientific method," is used in one form or another. While all of the steps of this procedure may not be applicable to every aspect of microbiology, the essence of the method does direct the microbiologist to pose pertinent questions and to look for testable answers.

The scientific method involves making careful observations of a particular event and arranging them so that a generalization can be made to account for the observed phenomenon. This particular step is called an *hypothesis*, or simply a "well-calculated guess." Once a hypothesis has been formulated, its validity must be tested. This phase of the scientific method is called *experimentation*. The simplicity or complexity of the hypothesis will determine the type and degree of experiments needed. Such experiments must be designed to test the pertinent point of the hypothesis, to include adequate controls for purposes of comparison, and to avoid the subjectivity or bias of the scientist himself. Experimental results must be repeatable by others. Experiments which cannot be repeated by other competent investigators are discarded.

The next stage of the scientific method is the *theory*. This is an explanatory hypothesis that has been supported by various types of observations and experiments. A good theory can be used to predict new facts, to show relationships between phenomena, and to relate new information as it is uncovered. Quite often the term *law* is used interchangeably with *theory*. A distinction must be made, however, for a law is a theory which has attained universal acceptance. Many theories do not achieve this distinction.

The Vast Literature of Microbiology

Within a relatively few years an enormous collection of experimentally determined data has accumulated, and has been recorded in numerous periodicals. Discussions and interpretations of these data also form an impressive number of publications. Obviously, the need to communicate knowledge and ideas is vital to any phase of scientific endeavor. Such knowledge of important developments constitutes a most powerful and necessary tool for scientific methodology.

In beginning the study of any new area of specialization, some understanding and information about publications in the field

FIG. 1–6. An array of representative periodicals pertinent to microbiology.

is essential. Representative periodicals are shown in Figure 1–6.

Scientific periodicals are produced by scientific societies, individuals, institutions, private companies, and commercial publishing firms. They range in frequency from weeklies like *Science* to annuals such as *Annual Review of Microbiology*. The content of periodicals also may vary. Certain journals, such as *Applied Microbiology* and the *Journal of Bacteriology*, are devoted to providing short or detailed reports of recent research developments covering the pure and the applied aspects of microbiology. Other publications, such as *Advances in Immunology* and *Bacteriological Reviews*, provide review articles covering specialized areas. Such reviews are especially important to individuals being introduced to a new field of interest or a specialized topic. Still other types of periodicals, including *The American Scientist* and *The Sciences*, combine both these approaches and may add additional items such as book reviews, society devel-

opments, and announcements. Quite often periodicals contain advertisements of products useful for the microbiologist.

The majority of publications provide an annual index of subjects and authors, either in a separate issue or as a part of the last issue of a particular volume. The contents of most journals are given on the front or back cover or near the front in the form of a table of contents. Mention should be made also of certain reference publications which are devoted solely to providing brief summaries or article titles for specific subjects (e.g., *Biological Abstracts, Index Medicus*) and others which list the titles of articles contained within selected periodicals *(Current Contents).*

To list all of the available sources of information pertaining to microbiology would be impractical, not only because of space limitations, but also in view of the fact that new specialized publications appear each year. Medical or related types of libraries should be consulted for further information.

QUESTIONS FOR REVIEW

1. What are the characteristic features of a biological system? Must all of these properties be present before a microorganism can be considered as living? Explain.

2. Which of the properties of a biological system would you consider essential to the well-being of microorganisms in the following situations?
    a. pathogenic bacteria in the bloodstream
    b. a microorganism stranded on the surface of the moon
    c. bacteria in the small intestine of man

3. What contributions did the following individuals make to the development of microbiology?
    a. Edward Jenner
    b. Iwanowski
    c. Louis Pasteur
    d. Beijerinck
    e. D'Herelle and Twort
    f. Leeuwenhoek
    g. Walter Reed
    h. Alexander Fleming

4. Compare the taxonomic and integrative approaches to microbiology.

2

Early Events in the Development of Microbiology

Microorganisms cannot be seen with the naked eye. Although several microbial forms—algae, bacteria, protozoa, and yeasts—had been observed by Anton van Leeuwenhoek as early as the year 1674, it was not until the development of the modern compound and electron microscopes and specialized techniques that biologists the world over became aware of the tremendous numbers and kinds of microorganisms. As information accumulated, not only from microscopic examinations but from other types of studies as well, it became clear that significant and numerous differences exist among the members of this microbial world, including chemical composition, modes of nutrition, size, and structure.

Microbiology, like most other scientific disciplines, had its origin deeply rooted in curiosity. At first microorganisms were considered to be mere objects for speculation, with little if any other significance. However, with the contributions of numerous individuals, including Pasteur, Koch and Lister, this limited view of microbes changed drastically during the latter part of the nineteenth century. The world became aware of the capabilities of microorganisms to produce both desirable and undesirable changes in their environments, which of course included disease. And so investigators unleashed a tremendous burst of studies in microbiology.

This chapter will present many of the early historical landmarks associated with the growth of microbiology, while the following chapter will introduce the major groups of microorganisms studied in this most fascinating branch of the biological sciences.

Early Development of Microbiology

Leeuwenhoek

In 1673, in Delft, Holland, a successful linen merchant by the name of Anton van Leeuwenhoek first observed and consequently introduced man to the mysterious and exciting world of microorganisms. For fifty years, until his death at the age of 90 in 1723, Leeuwenhoek (Figure 2–1) continued to make countless observations with the aid of small, simple microscopes. Even though compound microscopes had been developed long before (1590), Leeuwenhoek found his optical device more suitable for observing specimens with transmitted light. The magnifying power of his early instruments ranged from approximately 50 to 300 times the diameter of a particular specimen.

Anton van Leeuwenhoek's position in the development of microbiology has been firmly established, not because he constructed microscopes with improved lenses, but because of his remarkable observations and descriptions of microscopic forms of life. Due to his unending curiosity about the world around him, he spent hours upon hours examining specimens that he col-

FIG. 2–1. Anton van Leeuwenhoek (1632–1723), the Father of Bacteriology and Protozoology. (Courtesy of Fisher Scientific Company, Chicago.)

lected from lakes, rain barrels, and even from his own teeth and those of other people. Among his first observations can be found descriptions of protozoa, the basic shapes of bacteria, yeasts, and algae. Because of the importance of these observations, Leeuwenhoek is considered by many to be the Father of Bacteriology, and the Father of Protozoology.

Leeuwenhoek's discoveries went beyond the "microbial" world for he made numerous other contributions of biological significance. For example, he provided confirmatory evidence for William Harvey's theory of blood circulation by constructing an aquatic microscope ("aalkijer"). This instrument enabled him and others to observe the flow of erythrocytes through the capillaries of a fish's caudal fin. Some of Leeuwenhoek's other observations included the demonstration of muscle fiber striations (1682), nuclei of fish erythocytes (1682) and the myelin sheath of nerve fibers (1717). No wonder such discoveries were provocative to investigators and inquisitive amateurs everywhere. Unfortunately, the investigations of microorganisms were neglected for some time after Leeuwenhoek's death. This was partly due to difficulties encountered in

the construction of better microscopes, and partly to the fact that many still consider microorganisms to be nothing more than little oddities.

Pasteur

Except for Leeuwenhoek, French and German scientists dominated the field of early microbiology. One of the first scientists to impart a true biological function to microbes was Louis Pasteur (Figure 2-2), truly one of the major figures in the development of biology and medicine. A chemist and physicist, Pasteur was born on December 27, 1822, in the little French village of Dôle. The discoveries of this man were destined not only to provide additions to existing knowledge, but to bring to light dramatic new concepts and approaches to age-old problems. Pasteur's contributions have been responsible for new and more effective measures for the prevention of disease, the improvement of health in general, and the understanding of basic aspects of microbial life. The latter includes such things as the processes

FIG. 2–2. Louis Pasteur (1822–1896), the freelancer of science, working in his laboratory. (Courtesy of Chas. Pfizer & Co., Inc., New York.)

of fermentation, pasteurization, and the development of effective vaccines against such dreaded diseases as rabies and anthrax. As mentioned in Chapter 1, the term "vaccine" itself originated with Pasteur.

The Germ Theory of Fermentation

Nonvitalist vs Vitalist

Fermentation is a process in which alcohols and organic acids such as vinegar or lactic acid are formed from sugar-containing fluids. The results of fermentation reactions, including the souring of milk and the preparation of alcoholic beverages, have been observed and used by people all over the world throughout history. Yet, despite the recorded descriptions of microorganisms by Leeuwenhoek, the true biological basis of fermentation was not formulated until well into the nineteenth century. Basically, two major schools of thought evolved as explanations for these processes, namely, the nonvital (non-biological) and the vital (biological) theories.

According to the nonvital view, the yeasts seen in fermenting materials were considered to be the by-products rather than the causes of fermentation. During the period from approximately 1839, to 1869, supporters of the nonvital theory, including the three influential chemists Berzelius, Liebig, and Wöhler, maintained that essential, unstable chemical entities called *ferments* produced the reactions in question as catalysts, enzymes, or simply activators of chemical reactions. These unstable substances came into being as a consequence of the action of air upon sugar-containing fluids. The resulting ferments transmitted their property of instability to sugar molecules, which in turn decomposed, thus forming the products of fermentation. Liebig used as support for this nonvital theory his observations showing the ab-

sence of yeasts in acetic and lactic acid fermentations. Unfortunately, the nonvitalists neglected to consider that other microorganisms could be the producers of these "essential ferments." Several years later these reactions were shown to be caused by bacteria.

The basis of the biological theory of fermentation was established independently and almost simultaneously during the years of 1836 and 1837 by three scientists—the German algologist Kützing, the French physicist Cagnaird-Latour, and the German physiologist-pathologist Schwann. Schwann clearly demonstrated the role of yeasts in alcoholic fermentation and their sensitivity to heat and chemical agents. Treating these microorganisms by such means stopped all fermentative activity. In addition, Schwann described the asexual form of reproduction (budding) of yeasts, and showed that this "sugar fungus" *(Saccharomyces cervisiae)* was needed in large numbers for the fermentation reaction to proceed. Needless to say, these observations were not readily accepted by the nonvitalists. Thus the stage was set for a bitter controversy which was not settled until Louis Pasteur provided the crucial experimental proof for the microbial nature of fermentation in 1857.

Pasteur's Contributions

Pasteur's studies involving fermentation occupied a major portion of his scientific career, extending from approximately 1854 to 1876. His entry into this field came about through a request for help in finding the basis for the souring and spoilage of beer and of wines. Pasteur was a professor at the University of Lille, France, in a city where the production of wine and beer was a very important industry. Pasteur found that the problem was caused by a type of fermentation process other than one involving normal yeasts. In short, sugar was converted to lactic acid rather than alcohol, by lactic acid fermentation. The microscopic examination of sediments from wine vats in which the undesirable reactions occurred showed the presence of microorganisms which eventually were recognized as bacteria and unwanted ("wild") yeasts. The classification of such organisms was difficult since the so-called "formal rules" of taxonomy were not yet developed. The obvious solution to the problem was to find a way to eliminate and/or destroy these microbes without altering the quality of the alcoholic beverages.

On further experimentation, Pasteur came to realize that wines could be heated and held for some time without spoiling at a temperature intermediate between 50° and 60° C (122° and 139° F). This procedure came to be known as *pasteurization*. It was subsequently applied to a variety of products, the best known of which is milk. Contrary to popular opinion, pasteurization was not applied to milk first. Today routine pasteurization can be performed by heating milk or other beverages at 63° C (145° F) for 30 minutes. This exposure, generally speaking, is sufficient to kill pathogenic (disease-causing) microorganisms.

In investigating many other fermentative processes, Pasteur discovered that:

1. Each type of chemical fermentation, as defined by the particular organic end product or products formed, is associated with a specific microbial type.

2. Specific environmental conditions are necessary for the development of each microorganism, such as a definite degree of acidity or alkalinity.

While studying a particular fermentation, Pasteur discovered microorganisms that could live only in the absence of free oxygen, and named them *anaerobes*. He became aware of this fundamental biological phenomenon during microscopic ex-

amination of bacteria causing butyric acid fermentation. While these organisms normally are motile, he noticed that certain ones in a preparation, specifically those in close contact with air, ceased to move, i.e., became immotile. Pasteur quickly realized the possibility that air might exert an inhibitory effect on these bacteria, and confirmed his suspicion by introducing a stream of air into fermentating systems. The effect was obvious. The process was either totally stopped or slowed down considerably. The terms "aerobic" and "anaerobic" were coined by Pasteur to distinguish between microbes capable of living in the presence and absence of free oxygen, respectively.

The contributions of Pasteur were to have a pronounced effect on the control of microorganisms and demonstrated the relationship of numerous organisms to "disease." As pointed out by Stanier, Doudoroff, and Adelberg, Pasteur referred to the spoilage processes of beer and wine as "diseases." Perhaps in his own mind the association between microorganisms and the infectious diseases of animals and plants was firmly fixed.

The Spontaneous Generation or Abiogenesis Controversy

The spontaneous appearance of life from inanimate or decomposing organic matter was a belief commonly held by man since at least 346 B.C. This concept appears to have been proposed by the Greek scholar Aristotle and perpetuated by his students and numerous others well into the nineteenth century. The "Aristotelian doctrine of spontaneous generation" met little opposition, because man constantly saw what he thought to be examples of the process. The appearance of snakes, frogs, and related forms of life from the mud of river banks, and the development of maggots in, and the emergence of flies from, decaying food supported the unquestioning acceptance of this doctrine. It was thought that lower forms of life could not originate by any other means. Thus, before any relationship of microorganisms to various natural processes, including disease, could be shown, the concept of spontaneous generation would have to be disproved.

Francesco Redi

Among the first notable demonstrations that the doctrine of spontaneous generation did not apply to highly organized animals was made by the Italian naturalist Francesco Redi. In approximately 1665 he showed that maggots did not emerge spontaneously (de nova) from putrefied (decayed) meat. Redi put meat into three separate containers or flasks. One of these was stoppered, another was left uncovered, and the third was covered with a gauze or veil-like material. Naturally the meat readily putrefied and attracted flies. Redi made the following observations:

1. The stoppered container showed no evidence of any form of flies, whether larvae or adults.

2. Flies laid their eggs on the meat in the uncovered container. And, within a short period of time, the larval stages or maggots and newly emerging adult flies appeared.

3. Although no maggots were present in the meat in the gauze-covered flask, they did appear on the covering. Apparently the aroma of the putrefying meat attracted the flies, but because they were unable to gain access to it, they simply laid their eggs on the gauze.

Thus Redi dealt a crushing blow to the myth that flies were spontaneously generated from meat. However, even with his evidence in hand against the doctrine of spontaneous generation, Redi still believed that insects in a type of plant tumor called galls arose spontaneously.

The "War of Infusions"

Leeuwenhoek's discovery of bacteria—so-called animalcules—revived the arguments for the occurrence of spontaneous generation, but on a microscopic level. Although he felt that his newly discovered forms came from the surrounding air, Leeuwenhoek performed no systematic study to prove it. Another view shortly developed. Many individuals believed that inanimate animal or vegetable matter held a "vital" or life-generating force which could be transformed so as to give rise to animalcules. The appearance of bacteria and protozoa, the so-called infusoria, in boiled preparations of hay or meat after standing was considered as ample supportive proof. This type of solution is known as an infusion. In 1711 Louis Joblot, a French contemporary of Leeuwenhoek's, carried out a study which showed this was not the case. Basically, he observed that infusions stoppered tightly immediately after boiling remained free of microorganisms. However, if such boiled and stoppered preparations were later opened and exposed to the air of the environment, animalcules soon appeared. Joblot's findings were challenged, and thus the "war of infusions" began.

John Needham. This Roman Catholic priest in 1749 reported the results of his experiments which he felt proved that bacteria arose spontaneously in an environment where no such living forms existed before. His studies primarily consisted of tightly corking flasks containing boiled mutton broth and periodically observing them for cloudiness as an indication of microbial growth. While some containers remained clear, most of them eventually became cloudy or turbid. Upon examining a few drops of fluid from these preparations with the aid of a microscope, he found them teeming with microorganisms. Since boiling was known to destroy microorganisms as well as any other living cells, Needham felt justified in concluding that his experiments clearly demonstrated the existence of spontaneous generation. He postulated that the organic matter in his flasks possessed a "vital or vegetative force" which could confer the properties of life on the non-living elements present.

Lazzaro Spallanzani. Some years later, in 1765, the Abbé Lazzaro Spallanzani, an Italian naturalist, reinvestigated Needham's findings and conclusions. He primarily questioned the heating procedure used by his predecessor. Spallanzani found that heating hermetically sealed flasks containing any one of several types of organic matter for one hour did not cause them to become cloudy within a reasonable length of time. This experiment was repeated several times with the same results occurring every time. Needham argued that the prolonged boiling procedure destroyed the life-rendering "vegetative force." Spallanzani responded to this argument by taking heated, closed flasks and breaking the seal allowing exposure to air. Within a short time the contents of these flasks became turbid, thus showing that the long-heated organic matter still was capable of supporting life.

Spallanzani's experiments appeared to have dealt the doctrine of spontaneous generation a crucial blow. However, the effect was short-lived. This was largely because of the discovery of oxygen by Joseph Priestley, a Unitarian Minister, and the demonstration of its importance to life by Lavoisier in 1775. The arguments for spontaneous generations began once again, as Spallanzani's findings were criticized from the standpoint that sufficient air was not present in his sealed flasks to support microbial growth.

T. Schwann and F. Schulze. Additional experiments now were necessary to show that bacterial growth in nutrient-containing flasks was brought about through an exposure to air containing these organisms, and that the result was not a case of spontaneous generation. Theodor Schwann in 1836 arranged separate series of flasks, one of which held an infusion of some type, to prove this point (Figure 2–3). Air entering one such experimental system was passed through a tube device heated red-hot. Following this exposure, the air was introduced into the flask containing the nutrient material. Another system received untreated air and thus served as the experimental control. Soon growth developed in the control, while the system receiving heated air remained sterile (free of any living organisms). Similar experiments were performed by Franz Schulze in 1836. However, his approach involved the use of the chemical agents sulfuric acid and potassium hydroxide. Air was allowed to enter flasks with nutrients only after it had passed through these compounds.

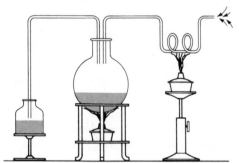

FIG. 2–3. A diagrammatic representation of Schwann's experimental system to disprove spontaneous generation. If the center flask, containing an infusion or other nutrient material, were exposed to heated air, growth would not occur in this system. Note the coiled glass tubing and the heating device on the right-hand side of the drawing.

Schröder and von Dusch. Upon hearing the results of these experiments, the proponents of spontaneous generation contended that the drastic treatments to which the air systems were subjected in the studies of Schwann and Schulze destroyed all possible "life-rendering power." This obviously would prevent life from being spontaneously generated. This objection was countered in 1854 by Schröder and von Dusch, who introduced the practice of using cotton plugs for bacteriological culture flasks and tubes. While their experimental design was similar to that of Schulze and Schwann, these scientists did not treat air in any way other than simply filtering it through cotton wool which had been previously baked in an oven (Figure 2–4).

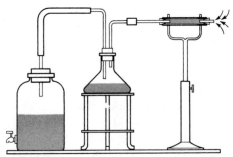

FIG. 2–4. A diagrammatic representation of the experimental system used by Schröder and von Dusch in 1854 to demonstrate the removal of living organisms from air by filtration. The bottle on the left was used to produce a suction which would draw air through the long tube containing cotton wool (at left). This air would then flow over the flask containing nutrient material. (After Burdon, K. L.: *Textbook of Microbiology*. The Macmillan Co., New York, 1958.)

The results of these experiments were the same. Flasks which received "filtered" air showed no signs of growth, while those systems exposed to unfiltered air clearly demonstrated the presence of microorganisms. These studies confirmed that the treatment of air with chemicals or with heat in reality was unrelated to the development of growth in nutrient-containing flasks. Moreover, these findings demonstrated not only the sensitivities of living forms in air to chemicals and heat, but the fact that they could be removed from air

by filtration through cotton wool. Pasteur later demonstrated the presence of bacteria in the cotton wool used for filtration, showing that these organisms were trapped in the material.

The Final Blows to Spontaneous Generation. The Contributions of Pasteur and Tyndall

Although these various experiments might seem conclusive, the issue was far from settled. This was evident from the 1859 and later writings of one of Pasteur's principal antagonists, Felix Pouchet. Pouchet claimed to have carried out experiments which conclusively showed that microbial growth could occur in the "absence of atmospheric contamination." About this time the studies of Pasteur were becoming public knowledge and several other scientists began to recognize the roles of microorganisms in fermentation and putrefaction processes. However, the acceptance of his views on the biological functions of microbes was threatened by the claims of Pouchet and other supporters of spontaneous generation. Irritated by these arguments, Pasteur was determined to disprove spontaneous generation once and for all.

Slightly altering the procedure of Schröder and von Dusch, Pasteur passed large volumes of air through a tube which held a plug of guncotton serving as a filter. A portion of this material was then disolved in an alcohol-ether mixture and the sediment remaining was examined microscopically. Pasteur found small round or oval bodies which resembled the spores (reproductive structures) of plants. To show that the guncotton not only stopped the passage of microorganisms, but was heavily laden with these forms of life, Pasteur simply added a little of the used filter to sterile meat infusions. Soon microbial growth appeared. Thus Pasteur confirmed how microbes gained access to and also how they could be prevented from entering fermentable and related types of nutrients.

Despite his obvious success, Pasteur was not fully satisfied. He then performed what has been referred to by Stanier, Doudoroff, and Adelberg as "perhaps his most elegant experiment on the subject" to show that air lacking in microbes could not create life from organic infusions. Special swan-neck or gooseneck, flasks (Figure 2–5) were made to which liquid nutrient media was added. No plugs of any type

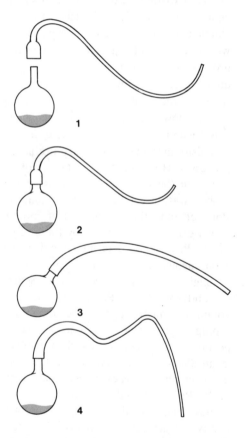

FIG. 2–5. "Swan-neck" flasks used by Pasteur in his experiments to disprove the doctrine of spontaneous generation. Note how the curvature of a flask would prevent the access of microorganisms into the nutrient fluid of the system. The flask with the detached neck (1) was used to show that the nutrient material was able to support microbial growth. (Redrawn from the works of Pasteur.)

were used to prevent the passage of microorganisms into these systems. The flasks and their contents were first sterilized by boiling. Despite the fact that these systems were open to the external environment, growth did not develop. Because of the length and the bend of the flask's gooseneck, microorganisms present in the air could not be transported into the flask proper. However, if the top of a system were broken off, or if a flask were tilted so that the sterile liquid nutrient ran into the exposed part of the neck and then returned, microbes soon appeared in the fluids.

Pasteur also demonstrated that the distribution of microorganisms is not uniform in the atmosphere. During a summer holiday, he took several hermetically sealed flasks containing sterile nutrient fluids to many localities in France. A certain number of these flasks were opened at each location, exposed to the environment, and then quickly sealed. Flasks that were exposed to the atmospheres of deep wine cellars or mountain air in the Alps mostly remained free of microorganisms. However, the experiments carried out in the streets of Paris, or on the road to Pasteur's home town, Dôle, produced several contaminated flasks. Thus Pasteur showed in a semi-quantitative fashion that microorganisms, although present in the atmosphere, are not evenly distributed.

Most authorities agree that the "final blow" to spontaneous generation was given by British physicist John Tyndall in 1877. During the course of his studies concerned with the optical properties of atmospheric dust, he observed that a beam of light passing through air lacking dust particles could not be seen. On the other hand, Tyndall found that a light beam passed through a "dust-laden" environment was readily visible. Moreover, the dust particles within such an atmosphere could also be seen. Aware of Pasteur's conclusions regarding the presence of microorganisms on dust, and the greater likelihood of microbial contamination in a dusty environment, Tyndall devised a system (Figure 2–6) to determine if air lacking dust particles ("optically empty air") contained microorganisms. He built a specialized culture chamber equipped with vents through which bacteria could not enter, lateral windows, and test tubes in racks. In addition, the sides of this box were coated with glycerol in order to trap the dust particles in the chamber which sooner or later would come to settle on the surfaces. When the chamber was found to be optically devoid of floating matter, as determined by shining a beam of light through its lateral windows, the test tubes were filled with a broth medium, which was then sterilized by placing the bottoms of these tubes in a pan of boiling brine. Tyndall observed that the broth remained sterile even though it was in direct contact with the air of the chamber. When dust-laden air was introduced, microbial growth appeared after a brief incubation period. Thus, with his specialized chamber and techniques, Tyndall demonstrated that bacterial life occurred in sterile broth only after it was introduced from an outside source.

During the course of his studies, Tyndall also became aware of incredibly resistant bacterial structures. These forms, which are now known as *spores,* were named and independently demonstrated in 1877 by the German botanist-bacteriologist Ferdinand Cohn. While attempting to repeat his experiments with dust-laden environments, Tyndall found he was unable to obtain similar results after a bale of hay (used in broth preparations) was brought into his laboratory. This situation arose largely because of the presence of spore-forming bacteria in the hay which interfered with the sterilization of nutrients in test tubes. Only when tests were performed in different rooms could the results of his original experiments be duplicated. The major difficulty was eliminated by boiling nutrient-containing solutions for short periods of time on each of three successive days, and incubating them between sterilizations at favorable temperatures to allow microbial growth to occur. This process of intermittent sterilization subsequently became known as *tyndallization.* Today, spores are destroyed in bacteriology laboratories by more rapid means, with the apparatus called the *autoclave* (Figure 18–1). This device incorporates steam under pressure, usually at a temperature of 121.5°C.

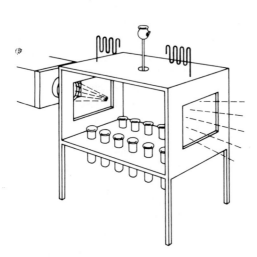

FIG. 2–6. A schematic representation of the culture chamber designed by John Tyndall to investigate the relationship of bacteria and dust particles. Note the lateral windows, the specialized vent system, and the thistle tube for the introduction of nutrient medium into the test tubes located in the bottom of the chamber.

Antiseptic Surgery

The introduction of anesthetics into surgery and obstetrics during the 1840s contributed greatly to the development of efficient surgical techniques, enabling surgeons to perform complex and lengthy operations which previously were not feasible to undertake. Unfortunately, the incidence of wound infections from surgical procedures increased and quite often resulted in the death of patients. Confronted with this problem and the desire to prevent wound infections, the young English surgeon Joseph Lister, (Figure 2–7) undertook the task of combating them.

FIG. 2–7. Dr. Joseph Lister (1827–1912). (Courtesy of National Library of Medicine, Bethesda, Maryland.)

Impressed with Pasteur's studies showing the involvement of microorganisms in fermentation, putrefaction, and spontaneous generation, Lister reasoned that the very basis of surgical infection, *sepsis*, might be microbial in nature. Consequently, he devised a series of procedures designed to prevent the access of microorganisms to wounds. This system came to be known as *antiseptic* surgery. It included the heat sterilization of instruments

and the application of carbolic acid (phenol) to wounds by means of dressings. Lister's procedures were critically received at first, but ultimately proved to be an effective means of preventing surgical sepsis, thus establishing modern surgery. Although Lister was not aware of the exact nature of the microorganisms involved, antiseptic surgery did provide an indirect source of evidence in support of the germ theory of disease.

The Germ Theory of Disease

In developed countries today, most of the major pestilences, including cholera, plague, smallpox, typhoid, typhus, and yellow fever, which were responsible for the deaths of millions of people in the past, are controlled by means of prophylactic vaccination, environmental sanitation and the destruction of arthropod vectors ("bugs" such as fleas, lice, mosquitoes and ticks that serve to transmit specific infections). Unfortunately, in socalled "undeveloped" countries, many of these diseases still take a heavy toll of life, and also cause significant disability in the population. Needless to say, the discovery of the causative agent of a particular disease is a major stepping stone in its control. Individuals such as Robert Koch (Figure 2–8), Louis Pasteur, and others who established the specific relationship between a disease agent and a disease state, and who developed methods for the control of infections, deserve to be heralded as major contributors to the well-being of mankind.

From the earliest times, diseases were associated with natural phenomena, such as earthquakes and floods, mysterious and supernatural forces, and poisonous vapors called *miasmas*. Although ancient Greek and Roman physicians suspected that certain types of disease were caused by invisible, minute agents, no direct proof for

FIG. 2–8. Robert Koch (1843–1910), one of the trail-blazers of microbiology. This German-born bacteriologist was responsible for the identification of numerous human pathogens, the development of specialized bacteriological techniques, and the discovery of tuberculin. (Courtesy of National Library of Medicine. Bethesda, Maryland.)

this view was found until the nineteenth century. The concept of contagion—the discovery of how infectious diseases were spread from a diseased individual to others —preceded the demonstration of the existence of pathogenic agents by many centuries.

Fungi were the first microorganisms shown to be pathogenic. Agostino Bassi proved experimentally that an agent of this type caused an infection in silkworms. This discovery was followed in 1839 by the first isolation of a fungus from a human skin disease by Schönlein. As later chapters will show, many fungi are recognized as a serious threat not only to man, but to the plants and other forms of animal life in his environment. Protozoa also were among the first microorganisms shown to have an association with disease. This relationship is credited to Pasteur, who in 1865 discovered that an infection of silkworms, which were vital to the silk industry in Europe, was "protozoan" in nature. The disease was called *pebrine*.

Koch's Postulates

The direct demonstration of an etiologic role of bacteria as agents of an infectious disease was given by Koch in 1876, and confirmed by Pasteur and Joubert. The organism used was *Bacillus anthracis* (Color photograph 81), the cause of anthrax. Although rod-shaped structures had been observed by Davaine several years earlier in the blood and organs of sheep dying of anthrax, there was no clear-cut proof at that time that these bodies were the cause of anthrax.

Koch established a definite sequence of experimental steps or rules with which the causal relationships between a specific organism and a disease state could be proved beyond a doubt. Although this procedure is known as "Koch's Postulates," it is important to note that Jacob Henle, a German scientist, offered the theoretical basis for the demonstration of the germ theory of disease in 1840. In showing the causal relationship of *B. anthracis* to anthrax, Koch first had to isolate the organism from a case of the disease and ultimately obtain similar cultures from laboratory-inoculated animals exhibiting symptoms of the infection.

The steps of Koch's Postulates can be generalized as follows:

1. The causative agent must be found in every case of the disease.

2. This microorganism must be isolated from the infected host, or patient, and grown in a pure culture containing no other kinds of microorganism (Koch utilized the aqueous humor of the eyes of cattle for this purpose).

3. A pure culture of the suspected agent must reproduce the specific disease after its inoculation into a new normal, healthy, susceptible animal.

4. The same microorganism must be recovered again from the experimentally infected host.

With relatively few exceptions, the causal relationship of pathogenic bacteria to a particular disease state has been shown according to the dictates of Koch's Postulates. One notable exception is the causative agent of human leprosy, *Mycobacterium leprae*, for which man is the only natural known host. Attempts to reproduce the disease with organisms isolated from actual human infections have met with repeated failures and only a few successes under experimental conditions.

Rivers' Postulates

At the time Koch formulated his system, true viral pathogens were unknown. The need for criteria to demonstrate their relationship to diseases became apparent shortly after their discovery. In 1937, Rivers created a group of rules similar to those of Koch for this purpose. Rivers' Postulates briefly are as follows; applicable to both animal and plant viruses:

1. The viral agent must be either demonstrated in the host's body fluids, e.g., blood and spinal fluid, or plant sap, at the time of the disease, or present in the cells of the host showing specific lesions.

2. Filtrates obtained from the tissues or body fluids of an infected host must produce the specific disease in a suitable healthy animal or plant or provide evidence of infection in the form of antibodies against the viral agent. It is important to note that all filtrates used for inoculations must be free of any bacteria or other microscopic cultivable microorganisms.

3. Similar filtrate material from such newly infected animals or plants must in turn be capable of transmitting the specific disease in question to other hosts.

The Microbiologist

Today, elaborate equipment and procedures play an important role in microbiology, but the most important instrument must still be the mind of man. Scientific investigators must exercise great care in not allowing their views and feelings to influence them. This becomes extremely difficult when the findings of a study are contrary to the beliefs of the person conducting the research experiment. Nevertheless, all scientists are bound by principles of integrity. Failure to observe this responsibility may have dire consequences, especially in the eyes of the scientist's fellow workers.

Public recognition of the contributions by scientists takes many forms. The Nobel Prize is one example. These awards were established by Alfred Bernhard Nobel, the inventor of dynamite. From his discovery Nobel became an extremely wealthy industrial magnate. In 1896 he died, leaving most of his accumulated fortune ($31.5 million) for use in the awarding of the Nobel Prizes. Nobel prizes are awarded to individuals "who, during the preceding year, shall have conferred the greatest benefit on mankind." The categories for consideration include chemistry, economics, literature, medicine or physiology, peace, and physics. A selected list of Nobel Prize winners whose contributions have had an influence on the development of microbiology is given in Table 2–1.

Table 2–1   Selected Nobel Prize Winners and their Contributions
to the Development of Microbiology

Year	Category of Prize	Nobel Laureate	Contribution to Microbiology
1901	Physiology or Medicine	Emil A. von Behring	Development of diphtheria antitoxin and other forms of serum therapy
1902	Physiology or Medicine	Ronald Ross	The transmission and life cycle of malaria in man
1905	Physiology or Medicine	Robert H. Koch	Studies concerning tuberculosis and the development of Old Tuberculin, OT. The latter material was the forerunner of the preparation used today in skin testing tuberculosis
1907	Physiology or Medicine	Charles L. A. Laveran	*Plasmodium vivax*, and the role of protozoa in producing human disease
1908	Physiology or Medicine	Paul Ehrlich	The humoral theory of antibody formation and related aspects of immunity
		Elie Metchnikoff	Phagocytosis and its role in immunity
1912	Physiology or Medicine	Alexis Carrel	Studies concerned with the transplantation of blood vessels and organs
1913	Physiology or Medicine	Charles R. Richet	Anaphylaxis
1919	Physiology or Medicine	Jules Bordet	Complement fixation and immunity
1927	Physiology or Medicine	Julius Wagner-Jauregg	The use of "malaria inoculation" for the treatment of mental deterioration resulting from syphilis infection
1928	Physiology or Medicine	Charles J. Nicholle	Studies on typhus fever
1930	Physiology or Medicine	Karl Landsteiner	Discovery of human blood groups
1931	Physiology or Medicine	Otto H. Warburg	Studies concerning the nature and mode of action of respiratory (cellular) enzymes
1937	Physiology or Medicine	Albert Szent-Györgyi von Nagyrapolt	Studies in cellular metabolism
1939	Physiology or Medicine	Gerhard Domagk	Antibacterial effects of the drug prontosil
1945	Physiology or Medicine	Ernst B. Chain	The discovery and subsequent development of the antibiotic penicillin for use in the treatment of infectious diseases
		Sir Alexander Fleming	
		Sir Howard W. Florey	
1946	Chemistry	John H. Northrop	The preparation of enzymes and viral proteins in pure form
		Wendell M. Stanley	
		James B. Sumner	Crystallization of enzymes
1946	Physiology or Medicine	Hermann J. Muller	The production of mutations by x-ray irradiation
1948	Chemistry	Arne W. Tiselius	The development of electrophoresis, and discoveries demonstrating the complex nature of serum proteins
1951	Physiology or Medicine	Max Theiler	Development of yellow fever vaccine
1952	Physiology or Medicine	Selman Abraham Waksman	Discovery of streptomycin
1953	Physiology or Medicine	Hans A. Krebs	Discovery of citric acid cycle
		Fritz A. Lipmann	Discovery of coenzyme A and its role in intermediary metabolism
1954	Physiology or Medicine	John F. Enders	The cultivation of poliomyelitis virus in tissues other than nervous (i.e. extraneural) tissue culture
		Frederick C. Robbins	
		Thomas H. Weller	

Table 2–1–*Continued*

Year	Category of Prize	Nobel Laureate	Contribution to Microbiology
1958	Physiology or Medicine	George W. Beadle	Various contributions to microbial genetics
		Edward L. Tatum	
		Joshua Lederberg	
1959	Physiology or Medicine	Arthur Kornberg	Mechanisms involved in the biologic synthesis of RNA and DNA
		Severo Ochoa	
1960	Physiology or Medicine	Sir F. Macfarlane Burnet	Acquired immunological tolerance
		Peter B. Medawar	
1962	Physiology or Medicine	Francis H. Crick	The molecular structure of DNA and its relationship to information transfer in living organisms
		James D. Watson	
		Maurice H. F. Wilkins	
1965	Physiology or Medicine	Francois Jacob	Regulatory processes that contribute to the genetic control of enzymes, including the "operon concept"
		Jacques Monod	
		André Lwoff	
1966	Physiology or Medicine	Francis Peyton Rous	Regulatory processes associated with viral replication (synthesis). Discovery of tumor-causing viruses in chickens
1968	Physiology or Medicine	Robert W. Holley	The relationships of genetic code components in determining cellular function
		Har Gobind Khorana	
		Marshall W. Nirenberg	
1969	Physiology or Medicine	Max Delbrück	Viral genetic structure and mechanisms involved in viral replication
		Alfred D. Hershey	
		Salvador D. Luria	
1972	Physiology or Medicine	Gerald M. Edelman	The determination of the chemical structure of an antibody
		Rodney Porter	
1974	Physiology or Medicine	Albert Claude	Discoveries concerning the structural and functional organization of the cell
		Christian de Duve	
		George Palade	

The Growth of Organized Microbiology

In approximately three-quarters of a century microbiology has become a significant influence in our society and one of the most dynamic and important branches of the biological sciences. Because any functional and growing field requires a formal means of communication with which to exchange ideas and experimental findings, it is not surprising to find the appearance of numerous journals (Figure 1–6) and the establishment of several organizations representing the various specialties of microbiology. The activities of these professional organizations are directed toward the advancement of the particular specialties and the interests of its members.

There are also organizations that are directed toward the advancement of microbiology in general. In the United States, for example, there is the American Society for Microbiology. Originally es-

FIG. 2–9. The official emblem of the American Society for Microbiology. This medallion was adopted in 1974 to commemorate the 75th anniversary of the organization's founding. The various microbial forms, namely algae, bacteria, fungi, protozoa, and viruses, are shown in the center, with four symbols that represent important applications of micrology surrounding them. The structures of deoxyribonucleic acid (DNA) and an immunoglobulin molecule appear at the upper left and right positions, respectively. At the lower left, the basic core structure of penicillin is shown. This symbol emphasizes the discovery of antibiotics and their numerous applications to the control of infectious diseases. Another important chemical structure, that of para-aminobenzoic acid (PABA), is depicted at the lower right. This compound is an essential nutrient for many bacteria. The specific antibacterial effectiveness of sulfanilamide and its numerous derivatives depends upon the close chemical and physical similarities between PABA and sulfanilamide. (With permission of the American Society for Microbiology.)

tablished in 1899 as the Society of American Bacteriologists, in 1961 the society changed its name in order to emphasize the inclusion of areas other than bacteriology (Figure 2–9). Several monographs, laboratory aids, and journals are published by this organization. Among the journals they publish are *Applied Microbiology, Bacteriological Reviews, Infection and Immunity,* and most recently, the *Journal of Clinical Micro-*

biology. In addition to the American Society for Microbiology, there are also organizations in the United States that are limited to specialties such as immunology, infectious diseases, and protozoology.

Comparable organizations are well established and recognized in other countries. Among these are the Society for General Microbiology (Great Britain), the British Society for Immunology, the Japanese Society for Bacteriology, the Netherlands Society for Microbiology, and the Society of Japanese Virologists. Because all of these organizations are concerned with the advancement of microbiology or one of its subdisciplines, particular attention is given to maintaining the highest professional and ethical standards.

QUESTIONS FOR REVIEW

1. What contributions did Leeuwenhoek make to the development of microbiology? Did his discoveries go beyond the microbial world? Explain.

2. Why weren't the findings of Leeuwenhoek extended for almost 100 years after he made them?

3. Who demonstrated the biological significance of microorganisms?

4. What were the major arguments used to support the nonvital (non-biological) and the vital (biological) theories of fermentation? What are "essential ferments"? What were the contributions of Kutzing, Cagnaird-Latour, and Schwann to demonstrating the role of yeasts in alcoholic fermentation?

5. What consistent patterns did Pasteur find in studying different fermentative processes? How did he show the microbial basis for fermentation?

6. What is pasteurization? What types of microorganisms are destroyed by this process?

7. What is the "doctrine of spontaneous generation"? How would you attempt to disprove it? Why did the discovery of oxygen in 1775 provide new support for the proponents of this concept?

8. Describe the experiments of Pasteur and Tyndall, and explain how they dealt the final blow to spontaneous generation.

9. What is antiseptic surgery?

10. What were the early concepts of the cause of diseases? What were some of the first indications of the role of microorganisms in the causation of disease?

11. Explain Koch's Postulates. What significant contributions did Koch make to demonstrating the basis of the germ theory of disease? What are Rivers' Postulates?

3

Microbial Classification

Classification of organisms serves several purposes, including: (1) establishing the criteria necessary for identification; (2) arranging organisms with similar characteristics into groups; (3) determining evolutionary relationships; and, above all, (4) lessening or eliminating confusion.

The classification of bacteria presents special problems, and may be based on a few characteristics or on many. Several bacterial classification schemes are *artificial*: they do not attempt to represent natural or evolutionary relationships among organisms, as is done in classifying higher animals and plants. *Natural classifications* of microorganisms are possible, however.

This chapter will present selected problems of microbial classification, some schemes to resolve them, and certain evolutionary aspects, including theories of the origin of life.

For centuries men have customarily classified various forms of life visible to their unaided eyes as either animal or plant. This practice was eventually adopted by biologists as a scientific basis for separating the living world into the two well-known kingdoms, *Animalia* and *Plantae*. Carolus Linnaeus, the Swedish naturalist, subdivided these kingdoms into readily identifiable and related groupings. His *Species Plantarum* of 1753 and *Systema Naturae* of 1758 are still used as the primary classification schemes for plants and animals, respectively.

According to the Linnean system, all life forms can be placed into one of two *kingdoms*, Plantae and Animalia. The animal kingdom is divided into general groupings or taxonomic ranks called *phyla* (singular *phylum*), while for plants the groupings are called *divisions*. For both kingdoms these ranks are subdivided into *classes*, classes into *orders*, orders into *families*, families into *genera* (singular *genus*), and finally the genera are composed of *species* (singular *species*). Thus, taxonomically, man comprises the species *sapiens*, genus *Homo*, in the family Hominidae, order Primate, class Mammalia, phylum Vertebrata, and the Animal kingdom. An essential feature of the Linnean or *binomial* (two-name) *system of nomenclature* is that each plant and animal is designated by a *genus* name and a *trivial* or descriptive name referred to as the *species designation*. (Each species grouping consists of individuals capable of interbreeding.) Thus man is known as *Homo sapiens*.

Linneaus was detailed in his classification of bacteria; however, he placed all bacteria into a large group called Vermes and the genus *Chaos*. We should note here that at the time Leeuwenhoek's description of protozoa in 1674 and bacteria in 1676 were less than 100 years old, and it was not until 100 years later that Pasteur reported a function for several of these animalcules.

The Position of Microorganisms in the Living World

In general, animals are characterized as lacking the typical structures of plants such as leaves, stems, and roots. In addition, they are noted as being actively motile, nonphotosynthetic, and quite complex. Plants, on the other hand, are regarded as being the opposite of animals in all of these properties.

Until approximately 1830, the taxonomic status of most forms of life remained fairly constant. However, the exploration of the microbial world and the subsequent discovery of numerous types of microorganisms confronted the traditional approach to classification with several problems. While certain microorganisms could be categorized as either plant or animal, many could not. Additional properties had to be used. One of these was the possession by plant-like microorganisms of an outer structure called a *cell wall*. Animal cells, such as protozoa, did not have this feature and were able to capture and to ingest solid foods, such as smaller protozoa and cell fragments. Thus microscopic algae, bacteria, and fungi (molds and yeasts) were grouped into the Plantae, while the protozoa were considered to be members of the Animalia. Unfortunately, other problems soon became apparent. Microorganisms were discovered which had properties of both animals and plants. Even though biologists of the time continued to arbitrarily place these microscopic forms into the two kingdoms, it was obvious that a suitable classification of microorganisms could not be derived from those features which were characteristic of larger animals and plants.

Early Bacterial Classification Schemes

Due to the usually artificial means by which bacteria have been classified, their taxonomy has been quite flexible. Linnaeus apparently was justified in creating a new category for them. Later, bacteria were incorrectly shifted about into various other categories, as a result of insufficient knowledge. In 1773 Mueller placed all bacteria into a single species, *Monas termo,* believing that these organisms were highly pleomorphic and essentially the same in all other characteristics. The next year, Mueller decided that a second genus, *Vibrio,* was justified. Sixty years later, in 1838, Ehrenberg placed all bacteria into the class Infusoria. Nageli, in 1857, placed all bacteria into the class Schizomycetes ("splitting fungi"), a designation still in use today.

The arrangement of bacteria into various genera and species took place after Pasteur, in 1857 and in 1860, began to show that these organisms were more than just curiosities. The next step in bacterial classification was taken in 1890–1900 by Migula, who considered bacteria to belong to two major divisions, the Eubacteria (true bacteria) and Thiobacteria (autotrophs). The first major attempt to coordinate the characteristics of bacteria was finalized in 1903 in the *Atlas and Handbook* by Lehmann and Neumann. The publication contained hand-colored photographs and drawings of bacteria and their growth characteristics. These growth properties were utilized in developing the scheme for their identification and classification.

The beginnings of a formalized manual for classification purposes began with the publications by Chester in 1901, followed by the work of Lehmann and Neumann in 1903, and the significant addition of physiological traits by Winslow in 1908 and Orla-Jensen in 1909. These contributions served as the basis for the efforts of the Society of American Bacteriologists (now the American Society for Microbiology) to formulate the first edition of *Bergey's Manual of Determinative Bac-*

teriology in 1923. With each subsequent edition, significant advances have been made, including the addition of new species and improved schemes for classification (Table 3–1).

The Botanical Approach

In 1957, the authors of the seventh edition of *Bergey's Manual* grouped the more primitive forms of microorganisms under a separate division. This division of *Protophyta* contained the following classes: I, Schizophyceae, or blue-green algae; II, Schizomycetes, or bacteria, actinomycetes, and mycoplasma; and III, Microtatobiotes, or rickettsia, chlamydia, and viruses.

The second division, *Thallophyta,* according to this scheme contained two main groups of microorganisms, algae (other than the blue-green) and the fungi. These microorganisms have as their basic unit a *thallus,* which is a plant-like structure that is not differentiated into roots, stems, or leaves. A limited characterization of the true fungi (Eumycetes) is given in Table 3–2.

The remaining microbial group, the protozoa, are placed within the phylum of the same name, in the animal kingdom. The classes of protozoa are presented in Table 3–3.

Unfortunately there is no classification scheme that is entirely satisfactory to everyone. Depending on the authority consulted, various inconsistencies exist. New systems are proposed from time to time, but have as yet not been internationally accepted. Throughout this text we will endeavor to use the most widely accepted terminology whenever possible.

A Third Kingdom: The Protista

In considering the variety of microbial metabolic and structural characteristics, some of which are plant-like or animal-like, it is indeed difficult to decide in which category they belong. One case in point is *Euglena.* Members of this genus are motile, possess chloroplasts, synthesize starch, and do not have cell walls. Botanists consider the *Euglena* a type of algae, the division Euglenophyces. Zoologists, on the other hand, believe *Euglena* to be protozoan in nature. When members of this genus are subjected to antibiotic treatment, or when a certain mutation occurs, the ability to synthesize chlorophyll is lost, thus providing more of a basis on which to classify the organisms as protozoa.

The science of taxonomy has been faced with similar difficulties as far back as 1830. In 1866, one of Charles Darwin's students, Ernst Haekel, proposed the establishment of a third kingdom to eliminate the existing confused status of microorganisms, and to provide a logical position for them in the living world. This division, called *Protista* from the Greek word meaning primitive, or first, has gained in popularity through the years since its introduction, but is not universally accepted.

Since the original concept of a third kingdom, numerous criteria have been developed with which to more adequately determine where to classify microorganisms. The protists are separated from typical animals and plants on the grounds that organisms in this category are biologically and biochemically independent. There is, generally speaking, no dependence upon other cells, such as the arrangement found with the tissues and organs making up higher plants and animals. This definition precludes classifying viruses as protists; however, many microbiologists add this group as a matter of convenience. In general protists are: (1) widely distributed, (2) unicellular, (3) capable of rapid growth, and (4) biochemically versatile. (The last property refers to their independent synthetic capabilities.)

Table 3–1　A Description of the Bacteria (Division II in the 1974 Edition of *Bergey's Manual*)

Part[a]	Category	General Description	Selected Human Pathogens	Disease Produced
1	Phototrophic Bacteria	Gram-negative, spherical or rod-shaped bacteria. Multiplication is by binary fission and/or budding. They are photosynthetic without producing oxygen. Pigments are purple, purple-violet, red, orange-brown, brown, or green.	None	None
2	Gliding Bacteria	Gram-negative rods typically embedded in a tough slime coat. They are capable of a slow gliding movement. Reproduction is by binary fission. Gliding bacteria sometimes form colorful fruiting bodies.	None	None
3	Sheathed Bacteria	Gram-negative rods that occur in chains within a thin sheath. They sometimes have a holdfast cell for attachment to surfaces.	None	None
4	Budding and/or Appendaged Bacteria	Bacteria with rod-, oval-, egg-, or bean-shaped filamentous growth. Multiplication is by budding or binary fission. These bacteria sometimes have a holdfast cell.	None	None
5	Spirochetes	Slender, flexible, coiled cells. They may occur in chains and exhibit transverse fission.	*Borrelia recurrentis* *Treponema carateum* *T. pallidum*	Relapsing fever Pinta or carate Syphilis
6	Spiral and Curved Bacteria	Rigid, helically curved rods with less than one complete turn to many turns.	*Campylobacter fetus subspecies intestinalis*	Septicemia
7	Gram-Negative Aerobic Rods and Cocci	Included are rods that are usually motile, with polar flagella; bluntly rod-shaped to oval cells, some of which are motile by polar (at one end) or peritrichate (surrounding) flagella and some of which are cyst formers; and rods and cocci that require high concentrations of sodium chloride for growth.	*Bordetella partussis*[b] *Brucella melitensis*[b] *Francisella tularensis*[b] *Pseudomonas aeruginosa*	Whooping cough Brucellosis Tularemia Urinary tract and wound infections
8	Gram-Negative Facultatively Anaerobic Rods	Included are straight and curved rods. Some are nonmotile; others are motile by polar or peritrichate flagella. All members are non-sporeformers; some have special growth requirements.	*Escherichia coli* *Salmonella typhi* *S. typhimurium* *Serratia marcescens* *Vibrio cholerae* *Yersinia pestis*	Gastrointestinal and urinary tract infections Typhoid fever Food poisoning Respiratory and urinary tract infections Asiatic cholera Plague
9	Gram-Negative Anaerobic Rods	Obligate anaerobic, non-sporeforming organisms. Some members are motile. Pleomorphism (variation in shape) occurs.	*Bacteroides fragilis*	Abscess formation, appendicitis, and heart valve infections
10	Gram-Negative Cocci and Coccal Bacilli	Cocci characteristically occur in pairs, and adjacent sides of the cells may be flattened. Organisms are not flagellated.	*Neisseria gonorrhoeae* *N. meningitidis*	Gonorrhea One form of bacteria meningitis
11	Gram-Negative Anaerobic Cocci	Cocci vary in size and characteristically occur in pairs. They are not flagellated.	*Veillonella parvula*	Central nervous system diseases
12	Gram-Negative Chemolithotrophic Bacteria	Pleomorphic rods. These organisms use inorganic materials for energy.	None	None
13	Methane-Producing Bacteria	Rods or cocci. Some members are Gram-positive; others are Gram-negative. All are anaerobic and produce methane.	None	None
14	Gram-Positive Cocci	Various arrangements of cocci that are aerobic, facultative, or anaerobic.	*Staphylococcus aureus* *Streptococcus pyogenes*	Food poisoning, boils, and pneumonia Strep throat, scarlet fever, and rheumatic fever
15	Endospore-Forming Rods and Cocci	Members are aerobic, facultatively anaerobic, or anaerobic. Also, some members are Gram-positive, and others Gram-negative.	*Bacillus anthracis* *Clostridium botulinum* *C. tetani*	Anthrax Botulism Tetanus (lockjaw)

Table 3–1—*Continued*

Part[a]	Category	General Description	Selected Human Pathogens	Disease Produced
16	Gram-Positive Asporogenous (non-spore-forming) Rod-Shaped Bacteria	Members may be aerobic, facultatively anaerobic, or anaerobic.	*Listeria monocytogenes*	Abscess formation, encephalitis, and endocarditis
17	Actinomycetes and related organisms	Rods or pleomorphic rods, with filamentous and branching filaments. Included are aerobic, facultatively anaerobic, and anaerobic rods. These organisms are generally Gram-positive, and some are acid-alcohol-fast (acid-fast).	*Actinomyces israelii* *Corynebacterium diphtheriae* *Mycobacterium tuberculosis* *M. leprae*	Lumpy jaw Diphtheria Tuberculosis Leprosy
18	The Rickettsias	The majority of cells are Gram-negative coccoid or pleomorphic rods. Most are obligate intracellular parasites transmitted by arthropods.	*Chlamydia psittaci* *Rickettsia prowazekii* *R. rickettsii*	Parrot fever Epidemic typhus Rocky Mountain spotted fever
19	The Mycoplasmas	Highly pleomorphic, Gram-negative organisms that contain no cell wall. They reproduce by fission, by production of many small bodies, or by budding. Members may be aerobic, facultatively anaerobic, or anaerobic.	*Mycoplasma pneumoniae*	Atypical pneumonia

[a] Based on the divisions and descriptions in Buchanan, R. E., and Gibbons, N. E. (eds.): *Bergey's Manual of Determinative Bacteriology*, 8th ed., Williams & Wilkins, Co., Baltimore, 1974.
[b] The position of these organisms is uncertain.

Cellular Organization. The development of the electron microscope and associated techniques for the preparation of biological specimens has clearly demonstrated the existence of two types of cellular organization, namely, the *procaryotic* (primitive nucleus) and *eucaryotic* (true nucleus). The procaryotic group, which includes blue-green algae and bacteria, is characterized by: (1) lack of a nuclear membrane and nucleoli; (2) the absence of membrane-bound, organized structures, e.g., endoplasmic reticulum, mitochondria, chloroplasts, Golgi apparatus, and lysosomes; (3) flagella which do not have the complex organization of higher forms of life; (4) the absence of a mitotic spindle or apparatus during nuclear division; and (5) the presence of a single chromosome. This structure consists of the genetic

Table 3–2   A Description of the Eumycetes (True Fungi)

Class	Description	Selected Human Pathogens
Zygomyces	Mycelium usually composed of aseptate (coenocytic) hyphae. Sporangiospores are produced. Sexual reproduction is by the fusion of gametes.	*Absidia* spp. *Mucor* spp.
Ascomycetes	Mycelium is usually septate with conidia production. There is rare reproduction by budding of unicellular, yeast forms. Ascospores are produced in sacs or asci. Sexual reproduction is by fusion of gametes or somatic hyphae.	*Allescheria boydii*
Basidiomycetes	Mycelium usually septate and may be structurally simple or complex. Basidiospores are produced. Sexual reproduction is usually by fusion of somatic hyphae.	*Amanita* spp. (Poisonous mushroom)
Fungi Imperfecti (Deuteromycetes)	Mycelium usually septate when present with conida on isolated conidiophores or in aggregations. Sexual reproduction is not known.	*Histoplasma capsulatum* *Madurella* spp. *Phialophora* sp. *Candida* spp. *Cryptococcus* spp.

Table 3–3   A Description of the Protozoa

Subphylum	Superclass	Selected Differentiating Properties	Selected Human Pathogens
Ciliophora	Ciliata	These are protozoa having cilia during some stage of their life cycle. Some organisms in this group also form resistant structures. Sexual reproduction is by conjugation. Asexual reproduction is by binary fission.	*Balantidium coli*
	Opalinata	These protozoa contain many nuclei of one type. Their movement is by cilia arranged in oblique rows. Sexual reproduction is by syngamy with asexual reproduction by binary fission.	None known
Sarcomastigophora	Sarcodina	Members of this group are amoeboid in shape and the organisms may form resistant structures called cysts. Their movement is by pseudopods (false feet). Reproduction is by binary fission.	*Entamoeba histolytica*
	Mastigophora	These organisms may be amoeboid in shape. They are generally covered with a pellicle, and adult forms move by means of one or more flagella. Reproduction is by binary fission.	*Giardia intestinalis* *Trichomonas hominis* *Trypanosoma gambiense* *T. cruzi*
	Sporozoa	This group of protozoa is composed of organisms without organelles of locomotion throughout entire life cycle. They possess a cyst stage in their life cycle. Sexual reproduction is by fusion of gametes with asexual reproduction by binary fission.	*Plasmodium falciparum* *P. malariae* *P. ovale* *P. vivax* *Toxoplasma gondii*

SOURCE: Adapted from Barnes, R. D., *Invertebrate Zoology,* 3rd ed., W. B. Saunders, Philadelphia, 1974.

material deoxyribonucleic acid (DNA) but lacks the basic group of proteins called *histones*.

Eucaryotic organization is found in various protista, including fungi, protozoa, and certain algae, as well as typical animals and plants. In addition to containing all of the membrane structures absent from the procaryotes, eucaryotic cells possess histones and more than one chromosome. Additional details of procaryotic and eucaryotic differences with respect to chemical composition, structure, and related functions are presented in Chapters 8 and 10.

The Monera.   Another approach to microbial classification was offered by Stanier and Van Niel in 1941. They proposed another third kingdom designation, Monera, which would contain solely the blue-green algae and the bacteria. Other algae and protozoa would remain in Protista. Viruses, however, still remained an enigma.

The Procaryotae.   The eighth edition (1974) of *Bergey's Manual* proposed the

Procaryotae kingdom as an official designation for bacteria and blue-green algae. The Cyanobacteria, or blue-green algae, are included in Division I; Division II contains the Bacteria. The Cyanobacteria are characterized as ". . . phototrophic procaryotic organisms that use water as an electron donor and hence produce oxygen in light." The Bacteria are organized into 19 parts (Table 3–1) on the basis of specific distinguishing characteristics. This approach avoids some of the confusion associated with previous editions, in which organisms were placed into discrete classes.

Natural Classification of Microorganisms

Computers have permitted microbiologists to compare organisms on the basis of many characteristics at once, rather than the relatively few properties usually considered in classification. This type of approach is called *numerical taxonomy* since it deals with large numbers of properties, usually more than 50. Some taxonomists believe that certain features should be given more value than others. For example, the Gram stain or microscopic morphologic properties might be considered as more significant than the fermentative capabilities of a microorganism in assigning it to a class. However, *Adansonian analysis,* which gives all characteristics equal weight, is generally the method followed, to avoid bias.

With appropriate programing, a computer can compare the various traits of many organisms and produce the information necessary to relate similar organisms into taxonomic groupings or clusters. Each organism is classified as an *operational taxonomic unit* or OTU. The computer determines the percentage of similarity between OTUs and then arranges the clusters of organisms according to the highest mutual similarity. Such clusters are called *phenons.* The clusters showing highest similarity are called *taxospecies,* to differentiate them from groups of organisms that are shown to be related genetically, *genospecies,* and from organisms named according to the current method of binomial classification, which are known as *nomenspecies.* As more characteristics of organisms are analyzed, the possibility increases for a natural classification scheme of procaryotic microorganisms.

Genetic relatedness is an attractive addition to taxonomy, since it indicates very close relationships among organisms by comparing various characteristics of the genetic material, DNA. This aspect of taxonomy will be discussed in Chapter 16.

The Trend in Microbial Classification

The formulation of a more natural, rather than an artificial, classification of microorganisms has significantly modified our way of thinking. The only semiofficial classification scheme currently available is that published in the eighth edition of *Bergey's Manual.* This publication was issued in 1974. Several studies have pro-

duced new information and uncovered new relationships among microorganisms. For example, sufficient evidence has accumulated to show quite convincingly that rickettsia, chlamydia, and mycoplasma are, in essence, bacteria. Further aspects of viral classification are discussed in Chapter 9.

The wealth of knowledge relating various organisms by numerical taxonomy will make a vast difference in the future publications dealing with microbial classification. From the medical standpoint, the use of computers in classification also offers potential for the identification of clinically significant pathogenic agents of diseases. It does not seem impossible that in the near future an instrument will be available to obtain a pure culture, perform 50 to 100 rapid biochemical, morphological, and antibiotic sensitivity tests, and within a short time identify a pathogenic organism and suggest the appropriate chemotherapy for it.

Possible Origins of Life

Few, if any, theories concerning the origin of life fail to suggest the guidance of a supernatural force to persons attuned to that philosophy. An opposite view can be taken by persons with an atheistic philosophy. This discussion takes a neutral viewpoint.

Before Pasteur's brilliant experiments disproving the spontaneous generation of life under certain conditions (Chapter 2), it seemed obvious that the multitude of worms, snakes, and insects arose from dirt, soil, water, decaying material, and so forth. Anaxagoras (510–428 B.C.) believed that life came to earth from clouds as seeds in rain. The better-known Greek philosopher Aristotle (384–322 B.C.) proposed that all forms of life came from the soil and from refuse.

After experimental results disproving

spontaneous generation were accepted by the scientific world, man looked to other planets as a possible source for the origin of life. Helmholtz suggested in 1864 that live microorganisms were brought to earth in meteorites. The following year, Richter proposed that spores traveled through space on any of a variety of particles until they reached a planet with the proper conditions for their germination and growth.

Probably the best-known hypothesis of this type was the *panspermia* theory offered by the Swedish physical chemist Arrhenius in 1908 (five years after winning the Nobel Prize for his electrolytic theory). He calculated that transfer of particles between planets was indeed possible. Once spores were thrown into the upper atmosphere by air currents, they would travel throughout the universe, propelled by electrical activity and the forces of light rays, until they reached a habitable planet. The majority were destroyed by the heat of blazing stars, but some few found new homes after years or ages of space travel. Until and unless space missions find a basis for proof of this hypothesis, the consensus is that we must look for the origins of life here on Earth.

Probably the first thorough presentation of a theory of the origins of life was published in 1936 by Oparin, based on a series of writings and lectures that began in 1922. Oparin held that the primitive Earth had an atmosphere composed of simple hydrocarbons and superheated steam. This description was derived from the theory that the various chemicals were formed in and on Earth and in the atmosphere as a result of chemical reactions at extremely high temperatures.

As the Earth cooled, and steam condensed into large bodies of water, a "hot dilute soup" was formed, consisting of many different organic compounds that are required by living organisms today. As proteins formed, aggregates accumu-

lated, thus creating colloidal particles. This is an important aspect of Oparin's theory, since colloids have the "catalytic" characteristics of enzymes. Colloidal particles are absorptive in nature, and thus can bring chemical compounds into intimate contact with one another. In this manner, according to Oparin, various organic chemicals came into contact on the colloidal particles. Ultimately a droplet formed that was able to: (1) increase its stability, (2) develop inheritable traits which were subject to mutation, and (3) incorporate enzymatic activities, including various metabolic pathways which allowed for the rapid synthesis of various compounds and the production of the energy required for these reactions. At this point a living cell had formed.

During the period when Oparin was developing his theory (1922–1936), Haldane suggested that the primitive atmosphere contained carbon dioxide, ammonia, and water vapor. Upon exposure to ultraviolet light, these gases interacted and produced a variety of organic compounds. Although Haldane's 1928 concept could have been tested by simple experimentation at that time, it was not until the significant studies of Miller and Urey, first reported in 1953, that an extensive study was begun.

Miller exposed methane, ammonia, hydrogen, and steam to electrical discharges, simulating lightning in the primitive atmosphere over a long period. Chemical analyses of the yellowish fluid that accumulated showed that it contained a variety of amino acids, organic acids, and urea. With properly controlled experiments, Miller ruled out microbial contamination as a source of the organic compounds.

Using slightly different conditions, other organic compounds have been synthesized, including deoxyribose, ribose, certain purines and pyrimidines, and various nucleotides. Thus, it does not seem impossible for any or all of the simple compounds necessary for life to have been synthesized in the primitive atmosphere of the earth and to form the "hot dilute soup" proposed by Oparin and Haldane. The next probable step in the series of events would be the synthesis of macromolecules and ultimately their incorporation into a distinct system.

Probably the most significant experiments on macromolecular synthesis were those of Fox and his co-workers, reported from 1955 to 1963. These investigations undertook the synthesis of protein under primitive conditions. When amino acids are heated in a dry state at 150° to 200°C for 30 minutes to 3 hours, a linear polypeptide is formed. This *proteinoid* generally has a gram molecular weight of 4,000 to 10,000, depending on temperature. Its formation requires an excess of two amino acids, glutamic and aspartic. A proteinoid is virtually indistinguishable from natural proteins or polypeptides of the same molecular weight.

Among the most significant properties of these proteinoids is their capacity to form microspheres, with dimensions similar to those of bacterial cells. When proteinoid material is placed in hot water and allowed to cool for a few minutes, membranous structures appear. Their diameter size ranges from 1 to 80 μm. Some of the microspheres appear to be budding, and their membranes seem to be doublewalled. These walls act as semipermeable membranes.

On primitive earth with superheated steam (approximately 200°C) before the formation of the oceans, amino acids forming on hot, dry rocks could plausibly yield proteinoids. Subsequently, as temperatures dropped below 100°C, the oceans formed, which could have transported proteinoid material into areas where conditions were favorable for microsphere

formation. It is quite possible that Oparin's coacervates and Fox's microspheres coexisted, and may have combined to yield double-walled membranes surrounding a coacervate or primitive cytoplasm. This arrangement would provide greater stability to the structure. If we assume that the membranes could rupture and reform, then Oparin's concept of coacervate mixing could function within the protection of the membranes. It would appear, then, that the first organisms could easily have been of microbial size and spherical shape enclosed within a limiting membrane.

Paleontology

Paleontology is the study of ancient life based upon the features of fossil remains. Such material may be in a petrified state, and therefore observed as solid objects, or it may be in the form of an imprint in rock left by a particular structure which has long since deteriorated. While it is a simple matter to visualize the fossil remains of leaves, footprints, or bones, it is exceedingly difficult to imagine the appearance of micro-fossils. Today, modern techniques such as electron microscopy and microchemical analysis, are making it possible to study microbial genera in existence during Pre-Cambrian times, two to three billion years ago. A major problem is distinguishing between actual microfossils and other objects of comparable size and shape.

Paleomicrobiology. The evolution of man and lower animals has been deduced largely from the study of fossils. According to the present understanding of Darwin's theories of evolution and natural selection, life forms are constantly changing, usually very slowly, due to mutation. Such a change in a specific property of a particular species—such as its pigmentation, metabolic pathway, or structure—

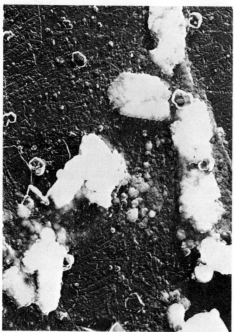

FIG. 3–1. Clumped and isolated fossil "bacteria" observed in Pre-Cambrian iron formations. (From Schopf, J. W., Barghoorn, E. S., Maser, M.D., and Gordon, R.O.: *Science,* **149**:1365–1366, 1965. Copyright 1965 by the American Association for the Advancement of Science.)

might add to its chances for survival in its particular environment, giving it a selective advantage over others favoring the survival of its offspring. This would prevail until another change occurred either in organisms or in the environment that upset the relative survivabilities. In discussing advantageous mutations, we should not forget that mutations can also be harmful—indeed, most mutations are harmful and only a few are helpful.

By studying fossil remains, we see changes in the body structure and appendages of animals and the vascular systems of plants when ancestral forms are compared with their modern counterparts. In making such comparisons, it must be assumed that life as we know it today evolved from simpler forms to more complex ones, presumably from a single-celled ancestor.

The small size and similar structure of microorganisms make it very difficult to obtain significant details of their evolution. However, with recent advances in the specialized area called *paleomicrobiology,* microbial fossils have been discovered which indicate that certain microorganisms existed three billion years ago.

In 1965 Schopf and his co-workers reported the presence of well-preserved rod-shaped and coccoid "bacteria" in Pre-Cambrian iron formations. Their age was estimated to be two billion years, or two eons. By the use of surface replicas of ultrathin sections, rod-shaped "organisms" approximately 1.1 μm by 0.55 μm and coccoid "organisms" 0.35 μm in diameter were observed. Figure 3–1 shows clumped and isolated rod-shaped "bacteria." The clumps of these "organisms" closely resemble the microcolonies of certain modern soil bacteria.

The proof for the bacterial nature of these structures included: (1) their existence in both preserved and imprint forms, (2) their orientation in various positions and in different planes with respect to one another and to other materials in the rock specimen, and (3) the consistency in appearance of these structures when prepared by a variety of methods.

Bacterial Evolution

Several hypotheses concerning the evolution of bacteria have been postulated. Among the first and probably the most generally accepted is the "theory" (really a hypothesis, as proof is lacking) proposed by Kluyver and Van Niel in 1936. According to them, the first or *proto-bacterium* possessed a spherical shape, and served as the ancestral source of four bacterial lines (Figure 3–2). Following Figure 3–2 in a clockwise manner, *A* represents the evolution of bacteria with peritrichous flagellation, resulting in the Enterobacteriaceae (1); other Gram-negative organisms, and the Bacillaceae (2); *B* represents the evolution of diplococci, streptococci, and non-motile rod-shaped bacteria such as corynebacteria, mycobacteria, and the actinomycetes; *C* represents the evolution of polar flagellated bacteria of the pseudomonadales, possibly resulting in the spirochaetales; and *D* represents the development of the grouped cocci, including tetrads, cubical packets (sarcinae), and clusters.

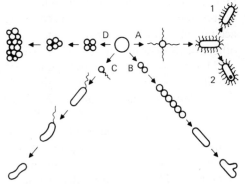

FIG. 3–2. An adaptation of the Kluyver and Van Niel theory of bacterial evolution.

In addition to the morphological aspects of evolution, the pattern appears to be applicable to microbial metabolism. Presumably, the first organisms were anaerobic, since molecular oxygen did not accumulate until about two billion years ago. Fossil data indicate the presence of microorganisms on earth at least three billion years ago. Anaerobes today appear to have a primitive metabolism.

QUESTIONS FOR REVIEW

1. Define, describe, or explain:
   a. natural versus artificial classification
   b. panspermia
   c. Coacervate versus microsphere
   d. paleomicrobiology
   e. binominal classification
   f. taxospecies, genospecies, and nomenspecies
   g. numerical taxonomy

2. What types of instrumentation and scientific breakthrough in microbiology have been and are critical to improvements in classification?

3. How were the following individuals involved in obtaining information concerning possible origins of life and microbial classification and evolution?
   a. Leeuwenhoek
   b. Fox　　　　　c. Pasteur
   d. Schopf　　　 e. Koch
   f. Kluyver and Van Niel
   g. Arrhenius　　h. Linneaus
   i. Oparin　　　 j. Adanson
   k. Miller　　　 l. Neumann
   m. Bergey　　　 n. Lehmann

4. Compare attempts at the development of a third kingdom for microorganisms, considering the advantages and disadvantages of each.

5. How does the "fossil" evidence for ancient microorganisms compare with the theory of microbial evolution presented in this chapter?

A Survey of the Microbial World

Several of the groups which make up the kingdom of Protista will be briefly described here to provide an introduction to the microbial world: algae, bacteria, fungi, viruses, and related forms. It is important to note that viruses are listed here simply for the purpose of convenience, although these forms do not fall into the classification of protists, as they are not considered to be true cells.

Algae ("The Grass of the Waters")

These organisms, generally speaking, are photosynthetic aquatic protists. Most algal forms are non-embryo-producers, free-floating and free-living. Certain species, however, participate in symbiotic associations, living together with other organisms. Lichens (which are discussed later in the chapter) are a primary example of this type of symbiotic relationship.

Algae frequently are found in bodies of water used by man—lakes, ponds, reservoirs, rivers, streams, and swimming pools. Unfortunately, in certain cases algae may be quite troublesome, giving drinking water a disagreeable taste and odor and clogging water filtering systems. Occasionally, when water temperature, nutrients, and associated factors reach a favorable level, certain algae multiply very rapidly, resulting in what is referred to as an "algal bloom" (Color photograph 3). When this occurs the waste products of such algae accumulate and may seriously affect the other forms of water life.

Many algae form an important part of the planktonic population, which is composed mainly of microscopic forms of life floating near the surfaces of most bodies of water. The term *phytoplankton* is used to designate the algae of the group, while *zooplankton* is applied to the animal-like organisms. Plankton form the basis, or starting point, of several food chains. These organisms are eaten by progressively larger forms of life which in turn may be consumed by man himself (Figure 4–1).

Algae range in size from microscopic dimensions to several which may attain lengths of 60 meters. Some are unicellular (diatoms), while other algae are highly differentiated multicellular forms. Unicellular types are found in all algae divisions with the exception of the brown algae (Table 4–1).

Major divisions of algae are shown in Table 4–1. Representatives of unicellular

FIG. 4–1. An example of a food chain beginning with plankton.

Table 4–1   Major Divisions of Algae

Division	Common Name	Habitat	General Structural Arrangement	Pigments Contained	Selected Reserve Materials
Bacillariophyces	Diatoms	Fresh and salt water	Mainly unicellular	Chlorophylls *a* and *c*, carotenes, xanthophylls	Chrysolaminarin (leucosin), oils
Chlorophyces	Green algae	Fresh water and moist environments	Unicellular to multicellular	Chlorophylls *a* and *b*, carotenes, xanthophylls	Starch, oils
Chrysophyces	Golden algae	Fresh and salt water	Mainly unicellular	Chlorophylls *a* and *c*, special carotenoids, xanthophylls	Oils, leucosin
Cyanophyces	Blue-green algae[a]	Fresh water, soil	Unicellular to multicellular	Chlorophyll *a* carotene, carotenoids, phycobillins	Starch
Euglenophyces	Euglenids[b]	Fresh water	Unicellular	Chlorophylls *a* and *b*, carotenes, xanthophylls	Fats, paramylum
Phaeophyces	Brown algae	Salt water (cool environment)	Multicellular	Chlorophylls *a* and *c*, special carotenoids, xanthophylls	Fats, laminarin
Pyrrophyces[c]	Dinoflagellates	Fresh and salt water	Unicellular	Chlorophylls *a* and *c*, carotenes, xanthophylls	Starch, oils
Rhodophyces	Red algae	Salt water (warm environment)	Multicellular	Chlorophyll *a*, phycobillins, carotenes, xanthophylls	Starch, oils
Xanthophyces	Yellow-green algae	Fresh and salt water	Unicellular	Chlorophyll *a*, carotenes, xanthophylls	Chrysolaminarin, oils

NOTE: The scheme shown is the one used by botanists.
[a] This is the only group on the list having a procaryotic organization.
[b] These microorganisms possess characteristics of both animals and plants. Euglenids seem intermediate between algae and protozoa.
[c] One genus, *Gonyaulax*, occurs in algal blooms referred to as the "red tide."

organisms are discussed in the following sections, with particular attention paid to their prominent features and various beneficial and harmful activities.

Green Algae

Five to six thousand different species of green algae are known today. Like other microscopic algae, they are found in abundance in the upper portions of aquatic and marine environments. All the essential nutrients needed by them for growth and reproduction are right at hand, dissolved in the surrounding areas. Few of these microorganisms are found at depths greater than 7 meters, largely because sunlight does not penetrate to that depth. Green algae are autotrophic organisms; they synthesize all of the organic compounds they require from inorganic substances, such as carbon dioxide, water, and minerals.

In general, green algae are considered to be closely related to higher forms of plant life because of certain properties shared in common with them. These include: (1) cellulose (a complex polysaccharide) in their cell walls; (2) a definite nucleus; (3) chlorophylls *a* and *b*, and other pigments in well-defined chloroplasts (i.e., pigment-containing structures of higher plants); and finally (4) the production of starch in photosynthesis. Several botanists hold the view that embryo or land plants evolved from green algae. In this context, an embryo is a multicellular young form of a plant which develops from a fertilized egg cell, i.e., zygote. The young plant is contained within the female reproductive structure, the ovary. Both forms are grouped into the same division of Chlorophyces (*Chloro*, green; *phyta*, plants). However, the green algae and embryo-producing plants are placed in separate subdivisions, the Chlorophycophytina (*phyco*, algal), and the Embryophytina, respectively.

Morphologically, the green algae exhibit a wide diversity in body types. Many are unicellular (Color photograph 2), while others may appear as filaments. Aggregated colonies are commonly found.

Diatoms

These microorganisms comprise the division of Bacillariophyces. Over 10,000 different species are known. Diatoms comprise a major portion of the large floating populations in fresh and salt water referred to as *plankton*. This accumulation of organisms is composed of trillions of algae which as a group produce more food through photosynthesis than all the rest of the plant world combined. Diatoms are found even in arctic regions (Figure 1–2D).

One of the obvious characteristics of diatoms is their intricately sculptured bilateral and radial patterns (Figures 4–2A and 4–2B). Diatoms are generally classified on the basis of the shape, symmetry, and structure of their cell walls, called *frustules*. The walls of diatoms consist of two halves, referred to as *valves*, which overlap each other much like the parts of a pillbox. The organisms with circular valves (Figure 4–2A) are called *centric* diatoms, while those characterized by boat-shaped structures with essentially bilateral symmetry are the *pennate* diatoms (Figure 4–2B). The structural details of their siliceous skeletons provide a basis for more detailed classifications.

Chemically these organisms are unique in that their cell walls contain large con-

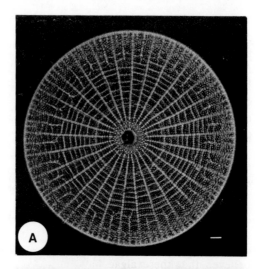

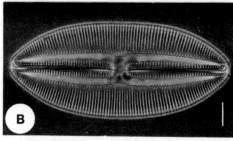

FIG. 4–2. Representative diatoms from the orders of Centrales and Pennales. *A*. *Arachnoidiscus,* a marine, centric diatom. *B*. *Navicula,* a marine pennate diatom. (Courtesy of Dr. Paul E. Hargraves, Narragansett Marine Laboratory, Kingston, Rhode Island.)

centrations of silicates. These substances are the basic components of glass, granite, and sand. Diatoms continuously absorb these silica-containing compounds and deposit them in their cell walls. Generally, when a diatom dies, silica in the cell wall begins to dissolve rapidly. However, under favorable conditions this does not occur, and an accumulation of these glassy structures forms deposits of fossil diatoms called *diatomaceous earth*. Such deposits have been gathering for thousands of years, so that in some parts of the world they have been found to measure 900 meters in depth.

Diatomaceous earth has many important functions. For instance, because of its abrasive quality, it is used as a polishing agent in many toothpastes and in metal polishes. It also is employed in the manufacture of both insulating materials for buildings and dynamite sticks. Several other types of industries use diatomaceous earth for the filtration of beer, oil, and other fluids.

Diatoms possess chlorophylls *a* and *c* and fucoxanthin. These organisms, as well as the members of the golden algae (i.e., Division Chrysophyces) and the yellow-green algae (i.e., Division Xanthophyces), produce and store the reserve food substances, chrysolaminarin and oils. It is believed that these algae have been significant sources of petroleum.

Blue-Green Algae or Cyanophyces
(from the Greek *Kyanos,* Meaning Blue)

These algal forms are found in a wide variety of environments. Some grow freely in snow on high mountain tops, whereas others thrive in thermal springs, such as those found in Yellowstone National Park, where the temperature may be as high as 85°C. Still others are found in marine and fresh waters, in soil, and even in wet flower pots. Certain blue-green algae are capable of growing on volcanic rock where most plant life fails to develop. The explanation lies in the ability of these microorganisms to utilize gaseous (elemental) nitrogen, carbon dioxide, and water vapor from the air for their nutritional needs. This process, referred to as *nitrogen fixation,* contributes to the nitrogenation of soil and thereby to the maintenance of soil fertility. In addition to this valuable reaction, certain blue-green algae produce toxic substances that have been implicated in the death of various forms of aquatic life and even of man.

Blue-green algae may, in reality, be green (Color photograph 1), purple, red, yellow, or even colorless. (Certain investigators consider such nonpigmented or colorless forms to be bacteria.) These variations are brought about by the presence of different kinds and proportions of pigments. Blue-green algae contain a form of chlorophyll, namely chlorophyll *a,* within a continuous system of flattened membranes (Figure 4–3). (These photosyn-

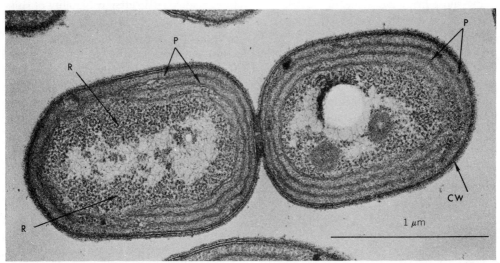

FIG. 4–3. Electron micrograph of a blue-green algae showing the protocaryotic cellular arrangement. Note the presence of photosynthetic layers (*P*), ribosomes (*R*), cell wall (*CW*), and the absence of a true nucleus. (From Kunisawa, R., and Cohen-Bazire, G.: *Arch. Mikrobiol.,* **71**:49–59, 1970.)

thetic membranes are not discrete, and should not be confused with the chloroplasts of higher forms of plant life.) The algae also contain two water-soluble bile pigments collectively referred to as *biliproteins* or *phycobilins*. The latter pigments may be either blue (phycocyanin), or red (phycoerythrin).

Blue-green algae occur most commonly as colonial and filamentous forms (Color photograph 1), which may be branched or unbranched. These organisms are procaryotes and therefore do not possess the eucaryotic cellular organization with chloroplasts, mitochondria, and a nucleus, so characteristic of higher forms of plant life (Figure 7–7). Therefore, several investigators consider blue-green algae to be an advanced form of bacteria. However, significant differences, including the types of chlorophyll pigment and aspects of photosynthesis, as well as the form of motility, appear to argue against this view. Blue-green algae-like specimens have been uncovered in rocks which are at least one and a half billion years old. These organisms are believed to be the most primitive algae in existence today.

Euglenids (The Intermediates)

Several of the organisms classified as members of the Division Euglenophyces have a combination of characteristics of both animals and plants, such as photosynthetic capacity and the ability to ingest. Accordingly, both zoologists and botanists have laid claim to these microorganisms, each with some justification. Like green plants, many euglenids possess the same forms of chlorophyll *a* and *b* and some are photosynthetic, while others are nonpigmented. However, obvious differences are apparent. Euglenids have a tough outer cell membrane similar to that found in most animal cells. A cell wall is definitely absent. Because of the difficulty in de-

ciding the true nature of these organisms, many prefer to call them simply eucaryotic protists.

Euglenids are widely distributed in bodies of water, especially fresh water. They are present most often in regions with high organic nitrogen, such as ponds, polluted streams, and wet barnyards. One of the better known of the euglenids is *Euglena,* which is commonly studied in general biology classes. Euglenids are extremely important experimental tools, but have no other economic importance.

Bacteria (From the Greek for "Little Rod")

These microorganisms, first discovered by Leeuwenhoek, are among the most widely distributed forms of life. Well over 1,700 species are known at the present time, found in air, water, the upper layers of soil, internal and external regions of the human body, and those of lower animals and plants. In short, these microorganisms are *ubiquitous.* As later chapters will show, bacteria are almost completely at the mercy of their environments. Temperature, acidity (pH), the availability of suitable nutrients, and the presence of toxic substances greatly affect the survival of these and other microorganisms.

Bacteria are generally unicellular, and appear in one of three shapes, namely rod-like (Figure 4–4*A*, 4*B*, and Color photograph 14), coccus (spherical) (from the Greek "berry") (Figure 4–4*C* and Color photograph 63), and spiral-shaped (Figure 4–4*D* and Color photograph 95). The various patterns of arrangements associated with these microorganisms and certain of their important structures are discussed more fully in Chapter 8.

A characteristic feature of bacteria is their highly rigid cell wall. However, within recent years a group of organisms called *Mycoplasma* that lack this outer cellular component have been isolated from animals and from certain plants (Figure 4–5). These bacteria were first isolated from cattle having a contagious disease, pleuropneumonia. Subsequently, all organisms resembling them in relation to their variations in shape were first designated as *pleuropneumonia-like organisms* (PPLO). Microorganisms that exhibit varying shapes and are grown under favorable conditions are now often referred to as being *pleomorphic*.

Bacteria grow and reproduce when they are provided with a favorable enviroment. In the laboratory the cultivation of these microorganisms involves supplying nutrients in a suitable form or culture medium and appropriate conditions of oxygen tension, pH, and temperature. A wide variety

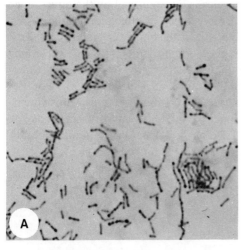

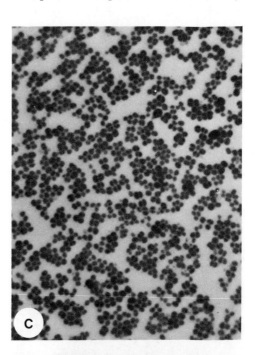

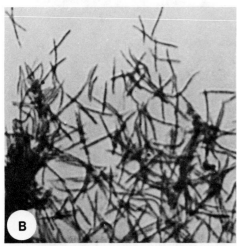

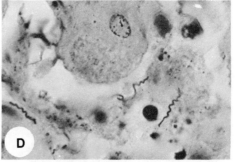

FIG. 4-4. The basic shapes of stained bacteria. A. A preparation of the rod *Lactobacillus* spp. (Courtesy of Dr. Richard Parker.) B. Another rod, with tapered, pointed ends. The organisms shown are fusobacteria. (Courtesy of Dr. Richard Parker.) C. A microscopic field of the spherical or coccus form of bacteria. The grape-like clusters of this organism, *Staphylococcus*, are evident. (Courtesy

CCM: General Biological, Inc., Chicago.) D. This photograph shows one type of spiral, the spirochete *Treponema pallidum*. It is the etiologic agent of syphilis. Organisms in this genus seldom exceed 15 micrometers in length. (Courtesy of the Armed Forces Institute of Pathology, Neg. No. 54-22493-(745-1).)

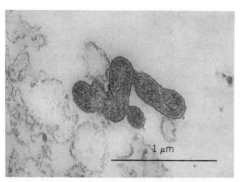

FIG. 4–5. The appearance of *Mycoplasma* HT grown in tissue culture. Note the variation in shapes—rod, oval, and spherical. (From Dmochowski, L., Dreyer, D. A., Grey, C. E., Hales, R., Langford, P. L., Pipes, F., Recher, L., Seman, G., Shively, J. A., Shullenberger, C. C., Sinkovics, J. G., Taylor, H. G., Tessmer, C. F., and Yumoto, T., The University of Texas, M. D. Anderson Hospital and Tumor Institute at Houston, Texas Medical Center: *Ann. N. Y. Acad. Sci.,* **143**:578–607, 1967. © The New York Academy of Sciences; 1967; Reprinted by permission.)

of culture media is used in bacteriology. Newer ones are constantly being developed. The choice of a particular one may be determined by a specific growth requirement of a bacterial species. The resulting growth, or *culture,* as it is called, appears after a sufficient incubation period. The resulting accumulation of bacteria on a solid nutrient is called a *colony* (Figure 4–6). Quite often a bacterial species is distinguished by the appearance of its colonies (Color photographs 4, 47, and 91) or the ability or inability to break down certain compounds or substrates contained in a growth medium. (Color photographs 39, 41, and 49). For example, the colonies of the previously mentioned "wall-less" mycoplasma have a "fried-egg" appearance (Color photograph 4*B*).

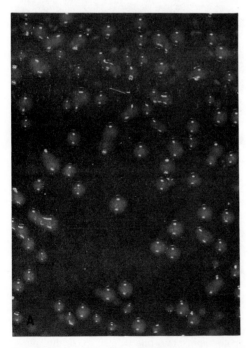

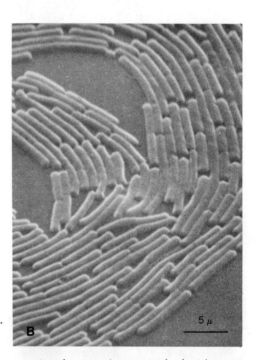

FIG. 4–6. Bacterial colonial morphology. *A.* Colonies of clover nodule bacteria growing on a solid medium contained in a Petri dish. Each colony is composed of several million bacteria. (Courtesy of The Nitragin Company, Inc.) *B.* A scanning electron micrograph of colonial growth showing the arrangement of bacterial rods at the periphery of a colony. (From Afrikian, E. G., St. Julian, G., and Bulla, L. A., Jr.: *Appl. Microbiol.,* **26**: 934–937, 1973.)

Bacteria, as indicated earlier, are ubiquitous. In their natural habitats these microorganisms are generally associated with either other bacteria or microbial types. Such symbiotic relationships may be of a beneficial or harmful nature. Fortunately, in the majority of cases bacteria are considered harmless, and many perform beneficial functions for man and other forms of life.

It has been said that if the activities of bacteria and certain other microbial types were to stop, all animals and plants would soon become extinct. This would occur because these microorganisms are responsible for the decomposition of dead organic material and of the wastes of humans and lower animals. By means of the decomposition process, certain chemical elements are returned to the soil, after which they are utilized by plants for growth and other basic processes. Eventually all types of organic material are returned to the soil or to the sea. In short, bacteria can be looked upon as nature's microscopic garbage disposal and recycling units. An example of the importance of bacteria in this process is nitrogen fixation. Animals and higher plants are characterized by their inability to use atmospheric or free nitrogen. This chemical element is vitally needed by numerous forms of life for the production of protein and other nitrogen-containing compounds. Certain bacterial species are able to convert free nitrogen into a utilizable form (See Chapter 15). Bacterial fixation of nitrogen can be classified as being either of a symbiotic or nonsymbiotic type. The former is carried out by bacterial species which inhabit the root systems of various common legume plants, such as alfalfa, beans, clover, peas, and soybeans.

Bacteria participate in the digestive processes of humans and other animals. For example, a sufficient quantity of the vitally needed vitamin K is supplied to humans by the enzymatic activity of bacteria found in the large intestine. This organic substance is used in the body to aid in blood coagulation. Additional beneficial effects of bacteria will be discussed in later chapters.

Other activities of bacteria are utilized commercially for the production of various pure chemical substances, foods, and other useful products. Some of these will be mentioned in Chapter 5.

The antagonistic or harmful activities of bacteria are well known. Certain bacterial species are able to invade, multiply, and carry out their life processes at the expense of a susceptible animal, plant, or other microorganism. Recently a bacterial species, *Bdellovibrio* (Figure 4–7), was discovered which is capable of invading and parasitizing other bacteria. Examples

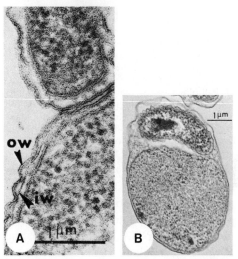

FIG. 4–7. *Bdellovibrio,* a bacterium capable of parasitizing another. <u>A</u>. An electron micrograph showing *Bdellovibrio* attached to its host. The inner and outer walls of the host are indicated by *IW* and *OW*, respectively. <u>B</u>. The parasite inside its host. After the parasite has penetrated into its host's cytoplasm, it will use the nutrients there for reproductive purposes. Eventually the host will lyse (break open) and newly formed *Bdellovibrio* will escape. (From Abram, Castroe, Melo, and Chou, *J. Bacteriol.,* **118**: 663, 1974.)

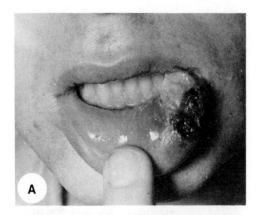

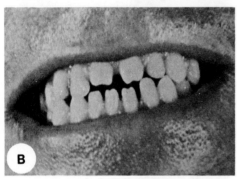

FIG. 4–8. Some pathogenic effects of bacteria. *A*. The primary chancre of syphilis. This venereal disease is produced by the spirochete *Treponema pallidum*. (Courtesy of the Armed Forces Institute of Pathology, Neg. No. 44251-B.) *B*. Syphilis contracted during early pregnancy can affect the fetus. One such effect, Hutchinson's Teeth, manifests itself later in life. (Courtesy of the Armed Forces Institute of Pathology, Neg. No. 218547-4.)

of diseases caused by bacteria in humans include actinomycosis, anthrax (Color photograph 81), boils, gonorrhea, impetigo (Color photograph 69), pneumonia, and syphilis (Figures 4–8*A* and *B* and Color photographs 97–101). It should be noted at this time that certain microorganisms are not harmful in their normal habitats. However, if the environment is changed or if these organisms are introduced into a new region, a disease process may develop. Moreover, several of these microorganisms are referred to as *opportunists,* meaning that under normal conditions they do not cause disease, but

if an opening should present itself an infection would occur. The effects of pathogenic bacteria, together with the regions of the human body affected, are discussed in Division 7.

The harmful activities of bacteria are not necessarily limited to causing fullblown infections in man, other animals and plants. Certain microorganisms of this type can cause spoilage of various substances, including fruits, vegetables, fish, and meats.

Rickettsia

For centuries these microorganisms have been responsible for the deaths of countless millions during times of war and natural disasters. It has been claimed that Napoleon's defeat in Russia in 1812 was brought about by typhus fever (a wellknown rickettsial disease). This infection struck again during World War I, when over three million soldiers and civilians died because of it. Even during World War II and the Korean conflict, epidemics threatened the outcome of several military operations.

These microscopic forms were named after Dr. Howard Taylor Ricketts, who. isolated the agent causing Rocky Mountain spotted fever. He died in Mexico City in 1910, while studying typhus fever. The genus designation for most of these agents is *Rickettsia*. At one time rickettsia were considered to occupy a position among microorganisms between bacteria and viruses. However, within the last fifteen years it has become exceedingly clear that they are a highly fastidious form of bacteria having absolute requirements. All rickettsia, with the exception of the causative agent of Trench fever, *Rickettsia quintana,* are obligate intracellular parasites. They must have living susceptible cells for their growth and multiplication (Figure 4–9). This property distinguishes them from most other bacteria.

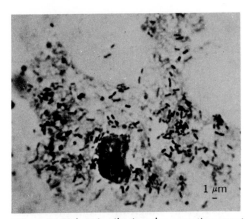

FIG. 4–9. *Rickettsia siberica,* the causative agent of Siberian tick typhus fever. Note the typical rod shape of these organisms. These rickettsia are generally located intracellularly. The large structure shown is a cell nucleus. (Courtesy of Rocky Mountain Laboratory, U.S. Public Health Service, Hamilton, Montana.)

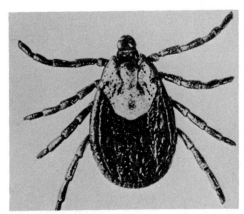

FIG. 4–10. A hard-shell tick, *Dermacentor andersoni.* This arthropod can transmit Rocky Mountain spotted fever and other rickettsial diseases. (Courtesy of Rocky Mountain Laboratory, U.S. Public Health Service, Hamilton, Montana.)

Rickettsia differ from viruses in several features, including chemical, metabolic, reproductive, and structural differences. The characteristic properties of these microorganisms are presented in much greater detail in Chapter 39.

Another important property of rickettsia is the wide range of natural hosts that they are able to infect; these include arthropods, e.g., fleas, mites, and ticks (Figure 4–10), birds, and mammals. Members of the genera *Cowdria, Erlichia,* and *Neorickettsia* are pathogenic for some mammals. For example, *E. canis* causes a serious disease in dogs (Figure 4–11). *Cowdria* species cause heartwater of cattle, goats, and sheep. *Neorickettsia* are involved in a complicated helminth (worm)-borne disease of canines. Characteristically most of these microorganisms are transmitted from vertebrate host to vertebrate host by an arthropod, referred to as a *vector.* Some rickettsia may be passed on from one generation of arthropods to the next, by means of *transovarial passage,* i.e., by being introduced into eggs during their formation.

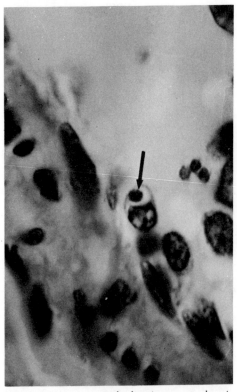

FIG. 4–11. A micrograph showing a cytoplasmic inclusion of *Ehrlichia canis,* the rickettsial causative agent of ehrlichiosis in dogs. This microorganism is spread by ticks. (From Hildebrandt, P. K., Conroy, J. D., McKee, A. E., Nyindo, M. B. A., and Huxsoll, D. L., *Infect. Immun.,* 7: 265–271, 1973.)

While the pathogenic natures of several rickettsia are well known, it should be noted that there are several of these microorganisms that are apparently nonpathogenic. Rickettsia belonging to the genera of *Rickettsiella* and *Symbiotes* do not harm their insect hosts. This state of affairs may be due to the establishment of a mutually beneficial relationship (*mutualism*). Relatively little is known about these nonpathogenic rickettsia.

Rickettsia have been of major concern because of the public health dangers they pose. These concerns have stimulated studies involved with the production of antibiotics, insecticides, and vaccines.

Fungi

The true fungi, or Eumycetes (Eumycophyta), are a large group of eucaryotic, nonphotosynthetic microorganisms. Microscopically, these organisms frequently are thread-like or filamentous (Figure 4–12), but in some cases are single-celled (Figure 1–2C2). The colloquial terms

mold and *yeast* are used for the filamentous and unicellular stages, respectively, and are convenient descriptive terms that do not have any taxonomic significance. The tubular filaments of fungi, called *hyphae,* branch widely and interweave with one another to form a visible mass referred to as a *mycelium* (Figure 4–13 and Color photographs 30–34). It is this cottony, hairy, white or colored growth that is popularly called mold. New mycelia can develop either from the fragmentation of hyphae or by outgrowth from the reproductive bodies called *spores.* These latter structures can be produced either asexually or sexually. It is important to note that not all fungi exhibit the type of mycelial appearance described thus far. This is es-

FIG. 4–12. The microscopic appearance of *Rhizopus nigricans,* the common bread mold, as shown by scanning electron microscopy. Note the characteristic thread-like hyphae and the spores. (Courtesy of Dr. R. F. Baker, U.S.C. Medical School.)

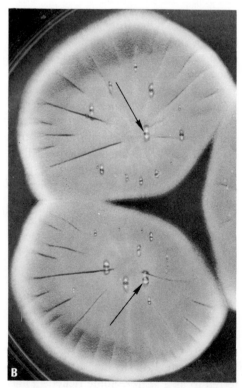

FIG. 4–13. The mycelia of *Penicillium chrysogenum.* Note the droplets (arrows), probably the antibiotic penicillin on the surface of these masses of hyphae. (Courtesy of Lederle Laboratories.)

pecially true for mushrooms, puffballs, and rusts, which are examples of the class Basidiomycetes. Five major classes of fungi are recognized: Ascomycetes, Basidiomycetes, Deuteromycetes (Fungi Imperfecti), Myxomycetes, and Zygomycetes. The structural features of several species belonging to certain classes are given in Chapter 10.

Fungi are widespread in nature. Most are terrestrial saprophytes, dependent on the products of other organisms either living or dead for nutrients. About 250 marine species also have been described. Many molds are active producers of a variety of hydrolytic enzymes. These substances enable them to decompose and utilize a wide variety of chemically complex compounds found in decaying plants, paint, paper, rubber, and wood products. Fungi, especially the molds, carry out many useful functions, including the production of several different types of antibiotics (e.g., penicillin and streptomycin); the ripening and flavoring of Roquefort and Camembert cheeses, and the restoration of important elements to the soil through their decomposition of organic matter.

Yeasts

Yeasts are commonly employed in the manufacture of various alcoholic beverages and in baking. The importance of these organisms in such processes lies in their ability to ferment sugars. As the application of sugar fermentation to the production of alcoholic products will be discussed in Chapter 5, it will be considered here only in relation to baking. In the production of alcoholic beverages carbon dioxide is a by-product. However, in baking, this compound is an essential ingredient. For the preparation of various bakery goods, yeasts (Figure 1–2C2) are mixed with dough in which they multiply and produce their sugar-fermenting enzymes. The ensuing fermentative activities of these microorganisms result in the production of alcohol and carbon dioxide, which fill the dough and cause it to rise. Upon baking, the gas expands and the alcohol escapes.

In addition to their fermentative capabilities, certain yeasts also serve as important sources of the B complex vitamins and ergosterol. The latter compound is used in the production of Vitamin D.

Destructive Effects of Fungi

Although some fungi are beneficial to humans, others are capable of causing widespread destructive diseases of plants (Figure 4–14 and Color photograph 5) and animals. Each year millions of dollars are lost in damage caused to fruits and vegetables.

FIG. 4–14. The fungus disease of dry beans called bean rust. The causative agent *Uromyces phaseola typica* produces destructive lesions on the surfaces of the plant's leaves. (Courtesy of the U.S. Department of Agriculture's Bureau of Plant Industry.)

Several pathogenic fungi, primarily belonging to the Deuteromycetes, may produce two general types of infections, namely those which involve the superficial tissues, such as hair, nails, and skin, and those which affect the deeper tissues and organs. Examples of the former include the variety of infections called ringworm (Color photographs 70–72). Some of these microorganisms are limited to causing only one of the general forms of disease states, while others can produce both types of infection (Figures 4–15*A* and *B*). Many of these mycotic infections are described in detail in several chapters of Division 7.

There are several fungi that are toxic to humans, including some common and widely distributed mushrooms (Color photograph 6). Mycotoxicoses (fungal poisonings) result from the ingestion of fungi that produce toxic compounds called mycotoxins. Among the better known of the poisonous mushrooms are members of the genus *Amanita*. In Europe from 90 to 95 percent of all human deaths from mushroom poisoning have traditionally been attributed to *Amanita phalloides*. The toxins of this fungus, namely amatoxins and phallotoxins, are complex molecules. Their physiological effects in humans and other vertebrates have recently been shown to involve metabolic disturbances and disruption of nuclei of certain cells.

Other mycotoxins, principally those produced by species of *Aspergillus* (Color photograph 32) and other fungi known as aflatoxins, have been shown to be quite toxic to many animal species. The real and

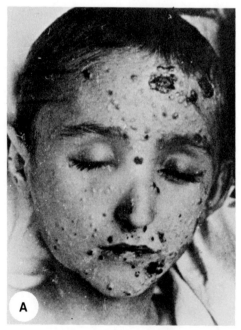

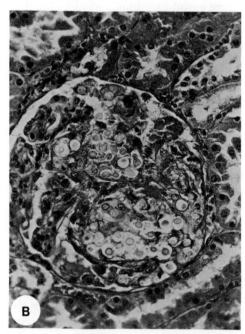

FIG. 4–15*A*. The destructive effects of the yeast pathogen Cryptococcus neoformans, cryptococcosis of the face. (Photograph given to Dr. Zimmerman by Bilgisi Sheseti, Istanbul, Turkey. Courtesy of the Armed Forces Institute of Pathology, Neg. No. 55-8225.) *B*. An example of deeper tissue involvement, cryptococcosis of the kidney. Note the large numbers of C. neoformans (arrows) in the glomerulus. These organisms are surrounded by capsules, i.e., a surface covering structure composed of a complex polysaccharide, which have not been stained. (Courtesy of the Armed Forces Institute of Pathology, Neg. No. 57-17776.)

potential danger of these poisonous fungal compounds was dramatically shown in 1960 by the development of a large-scale trout poisoning in commercial fish hatcheries where the fish had been fed rations later shown to be contaminated by fungi and by concurrent outbreaks of turkey X disease in poultry in England. (The name "turkey X disease" was given to the disorder because the cause was not yet known.) The occurrence of mycotoxins in food is not too surprising considering the wide distribution of fungi and their growth during storage and handling of food and food crops. The recognition of aflatoxins accelerated investigations in several countries. This led to the isolation and identification of many additional ones, some of which were demonstrated not only to be toxic to many animal species, but also to be hepatocarcinogenic (cancer-producing in the liver).

Mycotoxicoses assume worldwide significance in view of population groups suffering from protein deficiency diseases such as Kwashiorkor, in which additional liver injury may develop from dietary insults from mycotoxins. Corrective measures for malnutrition sometimes focus on protein sources such as peanuts and cereals, which may be contaminated by mycotoxin-producing fungi. The World Health Organization (WHO) has been a leader in directing attention to the serious health hazards associated with fungus-contaminated foods.

Slime Molds (Fungi)

The organisms belonging to the Myxomycophyta are commonly called slime molds because of the slimy appearance of their vegetative forms, called *slugs* or *plasmodia* (singular, *plasmodium*). Slime molds have at times been classified as both fungi and protozoa, largely because their vegetative (actively feeding) structures are composed of masses of amoeba-like cells, which do not possess cell walls, and their fruiting (reproductive) structures resemble those of fungi. Approximately 500 species of slime molds are recognized. Usually these organisms are saprophytic, feeding on decaying plant life, and can be found exhibiting various colorations on decaying logs, dead leaves in dense, shaded forests or in damp soil. Certain slime molds, such as *Plasmodiophora brassicae,* are parasitic and cause significant injury to several types of cruciferous plants, such as cauliflower, radish, rutabaga, and turnip. This organism causes club-root disease of plants. Usually the roots of the plant increase in size and provide an environment for slime mold growth and development.

The slime molds can be divided into two groups, the cellular and the acellular slime molds. The vegetative forms of the cellular mold consist of single amoeba-like cells, whereas naked masses of protoplasm of indefinite size and shape (plasmodia) comprise the vegetative structures of the acellular slime molds.

One of the outstanding features of this group of microorganisms is their rather unique life cycle. This can be illustrated by briefly considering the cycle of a cellular slime mold (Figure 4–16). (Sexual reproduction apparently does not occur in these forms, whereas it does in the acellular slime molds.) Cellular elements of slime molds live and multiply in soil habitats as uninucleated amoebae. Bacteria within these environments are used as food. However, when the supply of bacteria is exhausted, the amoebae combine their efforts and collect into multicellular aggregates (pseudoplasmodia). The cells comprising this structure lose some of their individuality but do not fuse. The aggregation process is initiated by the production of acrasin, a chemical recently identified as cyclic adenosine monophosphate (cAMP). The number of cells which make up these new structures may easily reach 100,000 amoebae. Each aggregate undergoes a complex and precisely regulated development cycle resulting in the formation of a "fruiting body" (Figure 4–16). The latter structure consists of a base, a slender stalk, and a cluster of spores contained within a capsule at the head. The fruiting body is composed of two specialized types of cells, namely *stalk cells* and *spores*. The former elements are concerned with lifting the spore mass off from the substratum, the surface on which the slime mold is situated. Environmental factors apparently play an important role

in the development of the fruiting structure.

The spores of the slime mold germinate upon being moistened and give rise to single cells called *myxamoebae*. These forms, which closely resemble typical protozoan amoebae, divide or reproduce by simple fission, or splitting. Eventually, under the conditions mentioned earlier, pseudoplasmodia again are formed and the development cycle begins once more.

Lichens

Many an interesting relationship exists between various microorganisms. One of these is the symbiotic association between certain algae and fungi, the combination of which is called a lichen (Color photographs 7 and 8). While the relationship is of benefit to both types of organisms, it doesn't occur with all algae and fungi. Only appropriate blue-green or green algae and certain fungal species belonging to the class of Ascomycetes (sac-forming fungi) are capable of forming such unions.

In the resulting plant body, called a *thallus*, the fungus produces a tightly interwoven foundation composed of its filaments. Algal cells usually are housed and protected within this basic structure. The function of algae, according to one commonly held view, is that of providing nutrients through the photosynthetic process. Fungi absorb water and minerals from their environments. These substances then are utilized by the companion algae. Since lichens are capable of living in environments that cannot support most other forms of life (e.g., on rocks, and in the arctic), it may well be that this association is formed as a matter of utmost necessity for survival. It is interesting to note that although lichens are remarkably resistant to drying, cold, heat, and other variations in environmental conditions, they are extremely sensitive to air pollu-

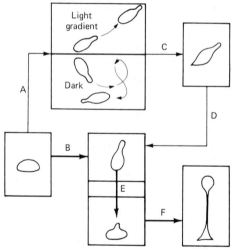

FIG. 4–16. A schematic representation offered by Newell, Telser, and Sussman of the alternative pathways open to a developing cellular slime mold. An aggregate of cells may form a migrating slug (*A*) or it may begin to fruit without migration (*B*). In a dark environment a migrating slug moves about in a random fashion. When exposed to a light source it generally migrates toward it. If the migrating slug receives illumination from an overhead light, it stops migration and begins the fruiting process (*C* and *D*). Formation of the fruiting structure can be suspended by a migration stimulus up to approximately 16 hours after it has begun. After the seventeenth hour (*E*), however, the completion of the fruiting process cannot be stopped. (From Newell, P. C., Telser, A., and Sussman, M., Brandeis University, Waltham, Mass.: *J. Bacteriol.*, **100**:763–768, 1969.)

tants and quickly disappear from heavily polluted urban regions. Apparently lichens absorb and concentrate the pollutants from rain water and do not have the means to excrete them. Thus, lethal concentrations of toxic air pollutants can be gradually reached.

At least 15,000 different lichen species have been identified. Fungi generally are the dominant organisms and therefore determine the shape and size of the basic structure. Many different arrangements and colors are displayed by lichens. These differences largely determine their type or category. Three major types of lichen are recognized.

(1) *Crustose* (crust-like): usually found on rocks or bark as irregular, flat patches. The colors include black, grey, green, yellow, and brown (Color photograph 7).

(2) *Foliose* (leaf-like): curled, leafy, usually greenish-grey, possessing rootlike structures for purposes of attachment and the absorption of minerals.

(3) *Fruticose* (shrub-like): a highly branched form, that either hangs from different tree parts or originates from the soil (Color photograph 8).

Although the uses of lichens are few, they are economically important. They can serve as food for arctic caribou and reindeer. In addition, lichens are used in the preparation of litmus paper, a well-known indicator in chemistry and related sciences. Recent investigations have demonstrated that certain of these organisms are capable of producing antibiotic substances effective against particular bacteria and fungi. From such reports it appears that lichens may have great potential uses in the treatment of certain diseases. Another role of lichens, which is occasionally overlooked, is their contribution to the organic content of soil. Quite often the activity of their root-like structures aids in the decomposition of rocks. The decaying remains of dead lichens become intermixed with the small rock particles, providing nutrients and a foundation for plant development.

Protozoa

These organisms are animal-like protists. Approximately 30,000 different species of them are known. Several protozoa, as Chapter 41 will show, are known for their pathogenic activities. However, many protozoa can be beneficial. For example, protozoa contribute to maintaining soil fertility and can function as a natural means of controlling microbial populations by feeding on various types of microorganisms. Other functions and properties of protozoa are presented in the descriptions of their respective taxonomic classes (Chapters 3 and 10).

Because protozoa propel themselves in distinctive ways, they can be differentiated from one another on the basis of locomotion. The following groups are representative of this arrangement. Refer to Chapter 3 for additional classification details.

Sarcodina

In this group the locomotion, as well as the capture of food, is accomplished by means of temporary protoplasmic extensions called *pseudopodia* (Greek *pseudes,* false; *podion,* foot). The cell moves as a whole when the organism extends an area of its protoplasm and then the remaining portion of the cell flows into that extension. This process is quite frequently called "ameboid motion," since the amoeba is a well-known example of this type of locomotion.

The kinds of protozoa that comprise Sarcodina are quite numerous, and can be encountered in all bodies of water. One of the most interesting is the large subgroup called the Foraminifera (approximately 18,000 different species, found mostly in salt water). These microscopic forms have the ability to form shells made of lime material or substances from the surrounding waters, such as sand. Since Foraminifera have inhabited the seas for millions of years, their shells have accumulated on the ocean floors and form a dominant portion of certain layers of sedimentary rock. Deposits of these organisms form a grayish ooze which may be transformed into chalk. The "White Cliffs of Dover" represent such an accumulation.

It is also interesting to note that the pyramids near Cairo, Egypt, were carved from limestone deposits composed of the remains of these microorganisms. The presence of Foraminifera has also proved useful to the petroleum geologist concerned with finding new oil fields.

Mastigophora

Members of this group of protozoa usually possess one or more long, whiplike structures called *flagella* at some or all stages of their life cycle. In addition to being used for locomotion, these specialized structures, or organelles, can be utilized for obtaining food and as sense receptors. The flagellates are an extremely variable group of organisms. Most of these protozoa are unicellular; however, some, such as *Volvox* (Figure 4–17), form colonial aggregates.

The free-living Mastigophora are found in large numbers in both fresh and salt water. In addition, many of these organisms inhabit the soil, and others live in the intestinal tracts of some animals. Flagellates are medically important. One disease caused by representative members of this class is African sleeping sickness (Figure 41–5). The protozoans involved here are called *Trypanosoma gambiense* (Color photograph 112) and *Trypanosoma rhodesiense*. These flagellates enter the bloodstream of man through the bite of the tsetse fly. In an untreated case of the disease,

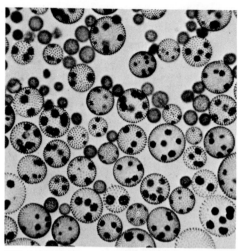

FIG. 4–17. *Volvox*, a colonial aggregation of cells belonging to the class of Mastigophora. (Courtesy CCM: General Biological, Inc., Chicago.)

the victim becomes drowsy, and passes into a deep sleep (coma) which is followed by death.

Another genus of this class which parasitizes humans and other animals is *Leishmania*. The human skin disease known as cutaneous leishmaniasis is commonly found in the Mediterranean region and elsewhere. Uncomplicated cases do not present any problems, and infected persons usually recover within one year's time. However, when bacteria complicate this condition, a tropical ulcer develops (Figure 4–18). The details of this disease state, as well as others caused by mastigophorans, are discussed more fully in Chapter 41.

A beneficial and interesting relationship exists between certain members of Mastigophora and termites. This association is a mutualistic one, the term used when two different forms of life live together for mutual benefit. The termite is an insect which ingests wood, but cannot digest the cellulose in it. Protozoa living in the intestine of the termite digest the cellulose, thereby providing sugar for the nutrition of the insect as well as for themselves.

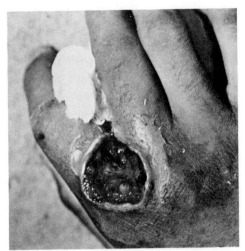

FIG. 4–18. A tropical ulcer of the hand. (Courtesy of the Armed Forces Institute of Pathology, Neg. No. A–43127–1.)

Ciliophora

The Ciliophora possesses fine protoplasmic hairs called *cilia* (Latin, *cilium*, eyelid or eyelash). These hairs extend through pores in the outer covering (*pellicle*) and function in moving the organism and obtaining food. The movement of the cilia is such that the cell revolves as it swims. Ciliophora are found in both fresh and salt water. Some are free-living, whereas others are either parasitic or commensal, the term used when two or more different organisms live together, and one benefits while the other is neither benefited nor harmed.

Of all the protozoa, the members of Ciliophora are the most specialized, because of their various organelles which carry out particular vital processes. These structures are discussed in Chapter 10.

Suctoria

These protozoans represent an interesting group of ciliated organisms. The young Suctoria are free-swimming. In the process of developing into adults, these young organisms lose their cilia, and subsequently attach themselves to some object with the aid of a stalk or disc. Suctorians can be found in fresh and salt waters and on aquatic plants and animals.

Their food is obtained by means of delicate protoplasmic "tentacles," some of which are pointed in order to spear unsuspecting prey, while others are rounded and function as suckers to catch food (Figure 10–19).

Sporozoa

The last class of protozoa to be considered is the Sporozoa, which possibly comprises the most widely occurring of animal parasites. Some are intracellular, i.e., live within the host's cells, while others can be found in body fluids or various organs of the body. These protozoa usually do not have any locomotor organelles, and therefore must depend upon their victims for food.

One of the most familiar of sporozoan infections is malaria. The term "malaria" (meaning "bad air") came into common use several centuries ago when people thought that the night air carried the agents of this disease. Today we know that this illness is caused by the protozoan, which is transmitted to man by the bite of infected female anopheline mosquitoes. Malaria, a scourge of mankind since ancient times, has played a decisive role in the history of civilization. Today, this disease is largely found in tropical and subtropical areas, although cases may occasionally occur in other parts of the world.

Viruses

The formulation of a functional definition of a virus has posed numerous problems in recent years. This is obvious from the variations in definitions which have appeared since their initial discovery. Viruses do not readily lend themselves to the type of common-sense rules used in the classification of animals and plants. Consequently, they have been defined on a rather arbitrary basis. However, regardless of the criteria used, or the priority in which these are placed, certain properties of viruses generally are emphasized. Specifically, these features include: (1) the non-cellular nature of viruses (these agents do not possess the typical parts of procaryotic or eucaryotic cells such as a cell membrane, mitochondria, nucleus, and ribosomes); (2) the viral dependence on the metabolic system of the host it invades; and (3) the presence of genetic material referred to as the *viral genome*, which is capable of directing the host to synthesize mature infectious particles which are called *virions*. These particles serve as the means by which the genetic machinery of the virus is transferred from one cell to another. In short, the virion represents an extracellular infective state. Other properties of viruses, such as their submicroscopic size and the types of hosts infected, are also included in describing them. It should be noted, however, that the size of viruses is no longer considered an essential feature of these agents.

A suitable functional definition of viruses would be one which distinguishes them from all other types of biological forms. This appears to be possible with the definition proposed by Lwoff and Tournier in 1966, listing the following five specific properties of a virion, i.e., a mature virus particle: (1) the possession of only one type of nucleic acid, either deoxyribonucleic acid (DNA) or ribonucleic acid (RNA); (2) the replication (production) of viral particles directed by the viral nucleic acid; (3) the absence of binary fission, the splitting form of division which is characteristic of bacteria and related microorganisms; (4) the lack of the genetic apparatus necessary in the synthesis of high-potential energy yielding

cellular systems; and (5) a dependence on the ribosomes (cellular particles important in the production of protein) belonging to the cell which hosts the virus. Ribosomes (Figure 4–19) are utilized in the biosynthesis of special proteins which form the *capsid* (coat or shell around the nucleic acid of the virus). A complete virus consists of a nucleic acid-nucleoprotein core surrounded by a protein capsid or by other coverings called *envelopes*. Additional details of viral structure are presented in Chapter 9.

It is customary to group true viruses into relatively broad categories according to the types of hosts they infect. On this basis the following groups are recognized: (1) animal viruses, specifically affecting vertebrates; (2) microbial viruses, e.g., bacteriophages, cyanophages, etc.; (3) insect viruses; and (4) plant viruses.

Animal Viruses

Many diseases of man now recognized as caused by viruses, such as smallpox (Figure 4–20) and yellow fever, have been known for centuries. Many additional major illnesses of man and other animals, both domestic and wild, are viral in nature. These include canine distemper, foot-and-mouth disease (Figure 4–21*A* and *B*), influenza, measles, mumps, poliomyelitis, rabies, and various types of encephalitis. The latter diseases represent virus-induced sleeping sickness, e.g., Eastern equine encephalitis (EEE) and Western equine encephalitis (WEE). These infections should not be confused with the protozoan disease, African sleeping sickness, which is spread by the tsetse fly. In 1911, Rous discovered the ability of viruses to produce malignant tumors (Rous sarcoma) in chickens. This finding was the first of many which recognized the viral nature of such neoplasma in both animals and plants.

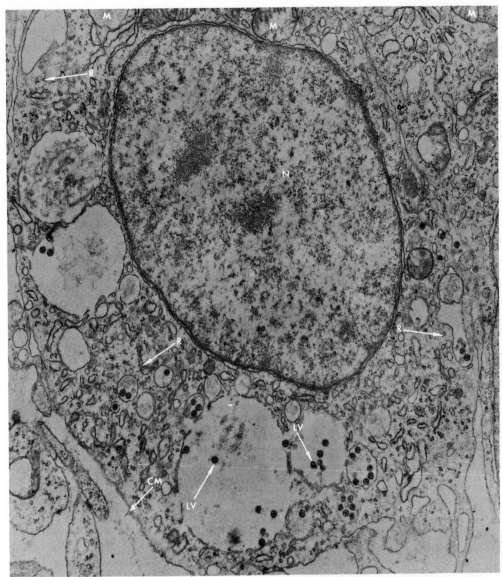

FIG. 4–19. An electron micrograph showing the presence of fowl leukosis virus (LV) in a cell from a 9-day-old chick embryo. This virus is the cause of a form of leukemia in birds. Note the various parts of this cell and the complete lack of a cellular organization in the viral particles. Symbols: *CM*, cell membrane; *M*, mitochondria; *N*, nucleus; *R*, ribosomes. (Courtesy of the U.S. Department of Agriculture.)

The effects of animal viral agents can range from the production of mild skin rashes and upper respiratory symptoms to tissue destruction and death. Several of the later chapters will discuss the various viral infections.

Bacterial Viruses (Bacteriophages)

Almost all of the large group of readily cultivable bacteria have been found to serve as hosts for bacteriophages. The host range of these phages may be limited to a specific bacterial species, or may extend

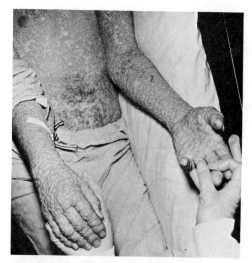

FIG. 4–20. The manifestations of smallpox. (Courtesy of the Armed Forces Institute of Pathology, Neg. No. 53–19850–1.)

to several bacterial genera. Relatively recently, phage-like viruses have been reported to attack several blue-green algal species (Figure 4–22). Their morphological features greatly resemble those of bacterial viruses (Figure 4–23). This observation provides additional support for the view held by many microbiologists of the close relationship between blue-green algae and bacteria.

Many bacterial viruses have proved to be extremely useful tools in studies concerned with uncovering the mechanisms involved with cellular infections. Other phages have been valuable aids in diagnosis and epidemiological investigations.

In recent years several other viruses of microorganisms have been reported,

A

B

FIG. 4–21*A*. One of the first electron micrographs of foot-and-mouth disease (FMD) virus. The disease agent is one of the smallest viruses affecting animals. Foot-and-mouth disease is a potential threat to the beef and dairy industries of the world. (Courtesy of the U.S. Department of Agriculture.) *B*. An acute case of foot-and-mouth disease in a Hereford steer. Note the drooping and salivation. (Courtesy of the U.S. Department of Agriculture.)

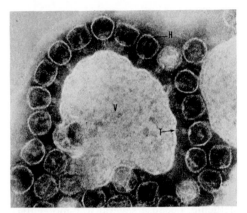

FIG. 4–22. Phage-like particles from blue-green algae. Head (*H*) and tail (*T*) parts are quite evident. Compare these structures to those in Fig. 9–11. (From Padan, E., Shilo, M., and Kislev, N.: *Virology*, **32**:234–246, 1967.)

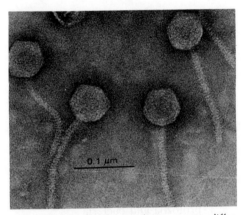

FIG. 4–23. Certain bacterial viruses are differentiated into head and tail components. (Courtesy of Drs. L. Kemp and A. F. Howatson.)

including fungi, protozoa, and green and brown algae.

Insect Viruses

Among the invertebrates (animals without backbones) only insects have been found to be attacked by viruses. A wide variety of such diseases are known. Some are of economic importance, as they involve useful insects, such as honey bees and silkworms. Still other viruses attack pests and consequently may be of value as control devices.

In many insects, virus infections cause the formation of specific intracellular protein products or inclusions. These inclusions may be either granular or polyhedral (many-sided) (Figure 4–24). Diseases associated with them are referred to as granuloses or polyhedroses, respectively. The polyhedral type of inclusion may be formed in either the cytoplasmic or nuclear region of the cells of infected animals. Granular productions, which are either capsules or oval grains of protein, generally have been observed in the cytoplasm.

Plant Viruses

Diseases caused by these agents are of great importance and many are major agricultural problems. A large number of plants are subject to viral infections, including beets, fruit crops, sugar cane, and tobacco (Figure 4–25).

Viroids

In 1971, T. O. Diener introduced the term *viroid* to represent a newly discovered category of subviral plant pathogen (Color photograph 9). The first member of this unique class of disease agent was found during investigations by Diener and W. B. Raymer concerning the agent of potato spindle tuber disease. Two additional plant diseases, chrysanthemum stunt and citrus exocortis (CEU), are now recognized as viroid-caused conditions.

The currently known viroids consist of low-molecular-weight ribonucleic acid (RNA) and are found primarily in the nuclei of infected cells, in close association with cellular chromatin material. Just how viroids produce their effect is not known. However, several hypotheses have been offered, such as the possibility that the viroids specifically interfere with host metabolic functions. A situation of this

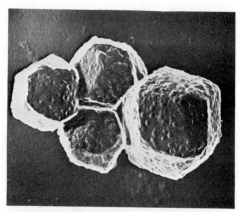

FIG. 4–24. An electron micrograph of a cytoplasmic polyhederosis virus. Spherical viral particles can be seen in the polyhedra shown. (Courtesy of Dr. R. Markham, Agricultural Research Council, Cambridge, England.)

FIG. 4–25. An electron micrograph of tobacco mosaic virus negatively-stained. (Courtesy of Dr. R. Markham, Agricultural Research Council, Cambridge, England.)

type, for example, could result in cellular production of faulty proteins. The transmission of agents such as the potato spindle tuber viroid (PSTV) can occur through the pollen or ovules (a part of the plant's ovary) of infected plants.

The recognition of the existence of viroids poses several questions that have potentially important implications for molecular biology, virology, plant pathology, and veterinary and human medicine. This is especially true in the case of medicine, because several low-molecular-weight ribonucleic acid molecules have been found in association with a number of viral infections.

QUESTIONS FOR REVIEW

1. Distinguish between the following types of organisms.
   a. procaryotic and eucaryotic cells
   b. PPLO and viruses
   c. blue-green algae and bacteria
   d. bacteria and viruses
   e. molds and yeast
   f. diatoms and protozoa
   g. bacteria and rickettsia
   h. Ciliophora and Sarcodina
   i. protozoa and bacteria
   j. Sporozoa and Mastigophora
   k. viruses and viroids

2. What are the protista? Is there any particular advantage or disadvantage in using this category?

3. Explain or define the following terms:
   a. bacteriophage
   b. mycelium
   c. coccus
   d. bacterial colony
   e. hyphae
   f. lichen

4. Differentiate between symbiosis and parasitism.

5. List several of the beneficial functions of the following microbial types.
   a. bacteria
   b. viruses
   c. molds
   d. yeast
   e. green algae
   f. protozoa
   g. rickettsia
   h. diatoms

6. Is any one particular type of microorganism more essential than others to human existence? Explain.

7. Do all groups of microorganisms contain pathogenic species for man or the various other forms of life in his environment?

8. How could the pathogenicity of a microorganism suspected of producing an infection be determined?

9. Where in your general immediate environment would you expect to find the following types of microorganisms?
   a. viruses
   b. green algae
   c. bacteria
   d. protozoa
   e. fungi
   f. rickettsia

10. Why are the rickettsia considered to be bacteria rather than a form of life intermediate between bacteria and viruses?

11. What similarities do you find between blue-green algae and bacteria? List any differences between these microorganisms.

Selected Aspects of Applied Microbiology

Many substances used by man in his everyday life are products of microbial activity. Several of these substances have been used since antiquity. Through the combined efforts of chemists, engineers, and microbiologists, modern technology has improved upon the procedures of old so that microorganisms can be purposefully directed to do man's bidding. This chapter briefly describes a selected number of such microbial applications.

Industrial Microbiology

Industrial microbiology refers to the use of microorganisms, or a microbiological technique, in a commercial enterprise. Beneficial microbial activities vary from the production of antibiotics, enzymes, and various organic chemicals, to the preparation of alcoholic beverages, blood plasma substitutes, and steroids such as hormones. Examples of microbiological techniques of importance in this area of specialization include microbial contamination control, various procedures for sterilization and for the determination of the effectiveness of sterilization, and vitamin assays. Usually clinical microbiology is not considered to be a part of industrial microbiology. However, the advent of numerous, highly profitable laboratories concerned with aspects of medical microbiology and chemistry suggests that a new addition has been made to this area of specialization by the so-called clinical

testing laboratories associated with the allied health sciences. The purpose of the following brief section is to familiarize the reader with the more classical examples of industrial microbiology, including fermentation and the aerobic conversions of raw materials into commercial products.

Aside from disease states, natural fermentative activities are probably the oldest known microbial processes in human experience. Fermentation can be defined as the process of converting simple or complex sugars into different biochemical compounds by the action of microorganisms in environments of decreased oxygen. A classical example is the relationship between the growth of yeasts and the production of alcohol under conditions which are aerobic (having little or no free oxygen) and anaerobic (having a low level of free oxygen). When yeasts first are grown in a medium containing some form of carbohydrate, such as glucose, and then cultured under aerobic conditions, the decomposition (catabolic metabolism) of this sugar results in the release of a considerable quantity of energy, chemical compounds for the yeasts' reproduction, and large amounts of carbon dioxide (CO_2) and water (H_2O). This reaction can be expressed in a simple equation:

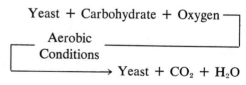

Yeast + Carbohydrate + Oxygen $\xrightarrow{\text{Aerobic Conditions}}$ Yeast + CO_2 + H_2O

Subsequently, when yeast is grown under anaerobic conditions, the overall metabolic activities of the microorganism are quite different. Not only is the resultant microbial growth less, but the production of energy, CO_2 and H_2O also is reduced. The biochemical compounds formed differ from those produced under aerobic conditions. Using alcohol fermentation as an example, the following equation represents the overall fermentation process.

Yeast + Grapes
          (Source of carbohydrates) ⌐
       Anaerobic
⌐   Conditions
└─────────→ Alcohol (wine)

The term *fermentation* should never be used in reference to any microbial process, unless the process is performed under anaerobic conditions. Bear in mind that these examples are oversimplified and have been used simply to emphasize the difference between aerobic and anaerobic metabolism. A more complete discussion of microbial metabolism will be presented in later chapters.

Anaerobic Microbial Processes

The Dairy Industry

The fermentation of milk sugar (lactose) is used in the production of various food products. Milk usually contains a wide variety and number of microorganisms. In order to ensure a high-quality dairy food, such organisms must be eliminated. After this step, pure cultures of reliable microorganisms, called *starter cultures*, are introduced into the starting material, which usually is high-quality, pasteurized milk or cream. The characteristic flavors and textures of butter, buttermilk, cheeses (Figures 5–1 and 5–2), yoghurt, and related foods are due to the types of micro-

organisms, i.e., bacterium or fungus, used in the fermentation and subsequent processes. For example, in the production of butter a bacterial culture, either *Streptococcus cremoris* or *S. lactis,* is introduced into cream and rapidly produces citric acid. This compound then coverts the lactose into lactic acid, causing the cream to sour. When the level of acid reaches a point that prevents both the growth and lactic acid metabolism of the streptococci,

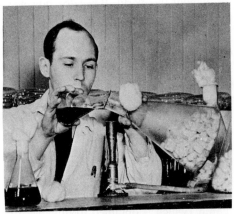

FIG. 5–1. Cubes of sterilized whole wheat bread are inoculated with *Penicillium roqueforti* by a laboratory technician. Eventually the cubes will be removed from the flasks, dried, and powdered for use in making blue cheese. (Courtesy of Borden, Inc.)

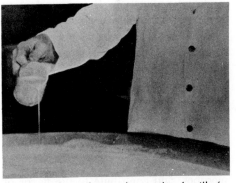

FIG. 5–2. Three thousand pounds of milk for making Swiss cheese are in this circular vat. The milk is held at a temperature of 34.2° to 35.8°C. Rennet has been added. The cheese-maker is adding the hole-forming culture *Propionbacterium shermanii*. (Courtesy of Borden, Inc.)

a second bacterial culture, *Leuconostoc citrovorum,* is added. This organism ferments the citric acid to the compound diacetyl, which is responsible for both the aroma and the flavor of butter. Subsequent to the fermentation reactions, churning is used to produce butter and buttermilk. Commercial buttermilk also can be obtained without churning.

The production of most cheeses is the result of microbial activity. Vast numbers and kinds of cheeses are manufactured throughout the world. Basically, however, they can be divided into three types: *soft* (such as cottage cheese or cream cheese); *hard rennet-curd* (such as cheddar or Swiss); and *soft or semi-soft rennet curd* (such as Camembert).

Most cheesemaking processes start with cow's milk, either whole or skimmed. The customary first step is to curdle the milk, producing curd. By adding an appropriate bacterial culture to the starter material, a firm curd and a watery fluid portion (called *whey*) are formed. If the enzyme rennin (which is obtained from calves) is added, the process is hastened. (A variation of these reactions is used in the identification of bacterial species—see Color photograph 50.)

Moisture removal is the second step in cheese production. It is important to note that the particular extent to which moisture is reduced depends upon the type of cheese to be produced. Heat, pressure, or cutting and compression of the curd are used for this purpose. When suitable amounts of whey have been removed, the resulting curds are molded into characteristic shapes. Salt is sometimes added during cheese production, as it can reduce moisture, prevent the growth of unwanted microbes, and contribute to the flavor of particular cheeses.

Another important step in cheese production is ripening. Certain cheeses obtained after milk curdles are called unripened cheeses. A good example of this type of product is cottage cheese. When cheeses undergo ripening by bacteria or fungi, protein or fat is usually degraded, depending upon the dairy product desired. For instance, in the case of Camembert and Limburger cheeses, proteins are broken down, whereas in the case of Roquefort and blue cheese, fat is degraded. Swiss cheese presents another situation: With this latter product the activity of bacteria brings about the fermentation of lactic acid, which results in the characteristic holes in the cheese.

Ripening can be conducted in one of two ways. The particular procedure depends, again, on the type of cheese desired. In the case of hard cheeses, e.g., cheddar and Swiss, the microorganisms are introduced and distributed into the interior of the cheese, while in the case of soft cheeses, e.g., Camembert and Limburger, the microorganisms are encouraged to grow on the surface and not in the interior of the product. These ripening methods also affect the sizes of cheese bricks or other units. Hard cheeses can be prepared in rather large dimensions, while soft ones are usually found in small sizes.

The Food Industry

The fermentation of natural vegetable sugars is used in the manufacture of such items as sauerkraut, ripe olives, and pickles. Sauerkraut is the product resulting from the lactic acid fermentation process occurring in cabbage over a period of six weeks. The general procedure involves the layering of shredded cabbage with salt in a deep vat. The salt inhibits the growth of undesirable bacteria and promotes the fermentation process by the bacterium *Leuconostoc mesenteroides.* This organism produces large quantities of lactic acid from the cabbage juices within the first week of the fermentation. As acidity increases, the *L. mesenteroides* decrease in numbers, and are replaced by various species belonging to the genus *Lactobacillus*. In most cases *L. brevis* predominates and carries on the fermentation, producing acetic and lactic acids and alcohol. In addition, a variety of additional organic acids and related compounds are formed which give sauerkraut its distinctive flavor.

Alcoholic Beverages Industry

The production of alcoholic beverages constitutes a significant division of industrial microbiology in many countries. The three major categories of these products are beer, wine, and spirits (distilled alcoholic beverages). Brief descriptions of the processes involved in the production of these beverages will be presented.

Historically, several lines of evidence indicate that the making of wine and beer on a professional basis was well established at least 3,000 years before Christ. For example, an Assyrian tablet dating back to 2000 B.C. states that Noah took beer with him aboard his ark. Documents of Egyptian and Chinese origins describe the production and use of beer in 2500 and 2300 B.C., respectively.

Beer. Beer is the result of a yeast fermentation process which uses barley or other grains as the source of sugars and various nitrogen-containing compounds. As yeasts cannot ferment starch (the complex form of sugars contained in grains) a preliminary step, called *malting,* must be used. In this process the grain is kept in a moistened state which causes it to sprout, thus initiating the production of the enzyme amylase. The enzyme breaks starch down into various simpler sugars that can then be fermented by the yeast. The sprouting malt grains are removed and readied for the fermenting process by drying, followed by mashing with water. Prior to the introduction of yeast, the fermentation medium is heated to eliminate undesirable microorganisms. Hops, i.e., dried petals of the vine *Humulus lupulus,* also are added to enhance the color and flavor of the final product and to stabilize it. Hops contain, among other chemical compounds, two antibacterial substances, *humulon* and *lupulon,* which prevent bacterial contaminants from spoiling the beer. The fermentation process is completed when sufficient alcohol is produced. The beer then is filtered and pasteurized, or filtered through a very fine screen to remove bacteria.

Wine. Winemaking is probably a less complicated process than brewing beer. Wine is made by the fermentation of almost any ripe fruit juice or certain extracts from vegetable products, such as dandelions. As these starting materials contain sufficient sugar (12 to 30 per cent), as much as 15 per cent alcohol may be obtained with certain yeast strains. The grapes used for wine usually range in sugar content from 12 to 30 per cent, and in water content from 70 to 85 per cent. Several other kinds of constituents are found in grapes, including acids and minerals. Generally, it is these substances and their respective quantities that account for the different color, taste, and sometimes bouquet of wines.

As soon as the skin of the grape is broken the fermentation begins. Commercially, the fruit is crushed and pressed mechanically. The resulting pressed grape juice, called *must,* can be fermented naturally by the enzymatic activity of wild yeasts that grow on the grapes. In Europe, yeasts which normally are on grapes are used to perform the fermentation, while in the United States, grape juice and other fermentable substances usually are sterilized to prevent the growth of undesirable microorganisms. Specific yeast cultures then are introduced and the mixture of fruit juice and microorganisms is aerated to promote yeast growth. Anaerobic conditions are instituted when yeasts are present in sufficient numbers to carry out the fermentation.

When the process is complete, as determined by the alcohol content of a sample (Figure 5–3A), the wine is placed into vats to clarify and age (Figure 5–3B). The aging process involves continuing enzymatic activities under anaerobic conditions until the flavor and aroma for that particular type of wine have developed. While aging takes place, the wine slowly clears and the suspended solid material settles to the bottom of the container in the form of a sediment. Normally, the product is separated from its sediment, and transferred several times to smaller containers. This procedure, called *racking,* is continued until the aging process reaches its limit in the tanks. To prevent spoilage, the resulting product is pasteurized or filtered.

Several different types of wines are produced, the majority of which are used in association with meals, either before (appetizer), during (red and white table wines), or after (dessert wines).

Distilled beverages. Beverages obtained through distillation include whiskey, brandy, and rum. The type of product is generally dependent upon the material used in the fermentation. The whiskeys are prepared from different types of grains, brandy from fruit juices, and rum from sugar cane. Rye whiskey is produced from distilled fermented rye grains, bourbon from corn, and Scotch from barley malt. The various flavors of whiskeys are dependent upon the presence of several types of minor ingredients known as congenerics. These substances include aldehydes, esters, ethers, higher alcohols, and volatile acids.

The whiskey distillation process can be performed by the use of vacuum and heat, which causes the separation of the volatile products from most of the water and solids present. The resulting distillate varies in alcohol content from 90 to 96 per cent. The raw product then is aged or matured in wooden casks or barrels. The distillate also is diluted with water to reduce the alcohol content to approximately 51.5 per cent. However, during the period of aging the per cent of alcohol increases because of the evaporation of water.

FIG. 5–3A. A cellarman using a wine-thief to extract wine samples for laboratory testing. B. Redwood aging vats capable of holding 63,000 gallons. (Courtesy of The Taylor Wine Company, Inc., Hammondsport, N.Y.)

Aerobic Microbial Processes

Many industrial processes rely upon the aerobic metabolic activities of microorganisms. Bacteria are noted for their manufacture of various enzymes, vinegar, and antibiotics, while fungi are notably involved in the production of citric acid, antibiotics, and steroids (e.g., hormones). You will recall that the initial step in the fermentation procedure for alcoholic beverages was aeration to promote yeast growth. In the case of aerobic microbial processes, all activities are performed under highly aerated conditions.

Microbial Enzymes

Enzymes of fungi and bacteria have applications in a wide variety of industrial areas, including alcoholic beverages, food, and detergents. Enzymes are primarily protein, but may be associated with other components in order to carry out a particular activity. These substances are generally named after the type of material (substrate) which is acted upon. Thus, amylase is the enzyme that decomposes starch, protease affects proteins, and lipase breaks down lipids, i.e., fats.

In the production of alcoholic beverages, microbial amylase and protease may be used instead of the enzymes from barley malt to prepare grains for fermentation. Proteases and lipases are utilized in the cleaning of animal hides, a necessary step in leather production. Proteases are also used commercially for meat tenderizing, as they are capable of breaking down some of the tough meat protein.

One commercial application of microbial enzymes has been for the removal of various stains from clothing. Many of the substances which stain clothes either are made of lipids, proteins, or starches, or they are held in a fabric by these types of compounds. Certain enzymes, under suitable conditions, can decompose stains or the cementing substances associated with them, and thereby help to clean the soiled fabric. Needless to say, stains can be made of a large variety of substances, and appropriate enzymes may not be available or, if available, they may not be incorporated into detergent or pre-soak compounds used in laundering. Thus, one should not be too surprised if all stains are not removed by commercial products. Moreover, such enzyme-containing products have been associated with the development of allergies.

Microbial enzymes are obtained by processes carried out either in shallow pans for optimum aeration by diffusion, or in tanks where aeration is produced by bubbling air through the growth medium. Usually rich organic wastes from dairy or canning plants are used as the growth medium. When microbial growth is judged to be complete on the basis of an analysis for the desired enzyme, the microorganisms are removed by filtration, thus leaving the culture filtrate which can be processed for the particular enzyme.

Vinegar

Commercial vinegar usually is made from wine or cider. It contains approximately 3 to 5 per cent acetic acid, which is responsible for its sour taste. In one process, fruit juice is fermented by brewer's yeast, *Saccharomyces cervisiae,* until it contains 10 to 12 per cent alcohol. It is then sprayed onto the surfaces of wood shavings, or other suitable material, contained in a tall cylindrical tank. These shavings are then inoculated with a bacterial species such as *Acetobacter aceti,* which rapidly converts alcohol to acetic acid. The entire process must be carefully controlled, especially in relation to aeration and temperature. The oxidation of the alcoholic fluid produces so much heat that bacterial growth may be stopped if the system is not cooled properly.

Steroid Transformations

Steroid hormones are extremely important in contraception and in the treatment and management of various conditions including arthritis and shock. Corticosterone, an adrenal cortex hormone, has been extremely useful in the treatment of shock. Supplies of this compound generally were obtained from cattle and were in limited supply until studies showed that microorganisms could transform other steroids into corticosterone. Investigations also showed that a combination of chemical and microbial reactions could be used to produce another steroid hormone, cortisone, widely applied in the treatment of arthritis and in control of other types of inflammatory states.

Industrial fermentative processes, such as the production of beer, wine, and rum, involve numerous enzymes in the conversion of the sugar substrate to the alcohol product desired. Furthermore, several microorganisms capable of fermenting glucose or saccharose may bring about the formation of the same product. In the case of steroid transformations the situation is quite different. A single specific enzyme is utilized to change one particular chemical component on a steroid molecule, thus creating a new compound. Such an enzyme may be associated with only one microbial species. An example is the synthesis of cortisone from the sex hormone progesterone involving the fungus *Aspergillus orchraceus.* Several other common fungi, like *Penicillium* and *Rhizopus,* and funguslike bacteria like actinomycetes also carry out steroid transformations. These microbial transformations are the only practical means for the large-scale production of selected steroids.

Antibiotics

The discovery of penicillin was reported by Alexander Fleming in 1929, and the subsequent development of this compound in the early 1940s by Chain and Florey provided the basis for a multi-billion-dollar antibiotic industry. Antibiotics are usually produced by growing a specific bacterial or fungus species in a submerged culture in large, well-aerated tanks (Figure 5–4*A*). In the case of penicillin production, for example, a suitable medium (which usually contains by-products of the distilling industry) is aseptically inoculated with fungi such as *Penicillium chrysogenum* or *P. notatum* (Color photograph 30). In one or two weeks of growth, conditions develop which interfere with the production of penicillin. At this time the fungal, i.e., mold growth, is removed by centrifugation, or a combination of this process and filtration, followed by the complex extraction and purification of the antibiotic (Figure 5–4*B*).

Commercial antibiotics have been obtained from similar activities of bacteria, e.g., *Bacillus polymyxa, B. subtilis, Actinomyces* spp., and fungi, e.g., *Aspergillus fumigatus* and additional species of *Penicillium.* The antibiotics produced by these and many other microorganisms are largely responsible for the successful treatment of many dreaded bacterial diseases including anthrax, gonorrhea, meningitis, strep throat, syphilis, and tuberculosis. Research by the pharmaceutical industry is constantly uncovering new and modified antibiotics which already have broadened the application of these "wonder drugs" (Figure 5–4*C*). Details of these compounds' mode of action, applications, sensitivity patterns, and related properties are presented in a later chapter.

Waste Treatment

Microorganisms abound in nature and serve a significant role in the conversion of waste materials into useful by-products.

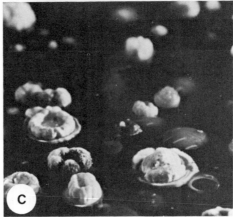

FIG. 5–4. Antibiotic production. $\underline{A}$. Production fermentors. These huge fermentation tanks, filled with sterile nutrient media, are inoculated with a high-antibiotic-yielding fungal culture. (Courtesy of Chas. Pfizer & Co., Inc., N.Y.) $\underline{B}$. High-rotary vacuum filters used to remove the fungal growth. (Courtesy of Chas. Pfizer & Co., Inc., N.Y.) $\underline{C}$. From just such fungal colonies (mycelia) the first "broad-spectrum" antibiotic was produced after years of screening and testing of samples from all over the world. (Courtesy of Lederle Laboratories.)

In this scavenger role, microorganisms are present in the enormous accumulations of decaying and rotting animal and plant matter. Their capacity for digesting a wide variety of complex organic materials and producing simpler organic and inorganic substances is clearly demonstrated by the role these forms of life play in sewage treatment.

Sewage usually consists of several components, including garbage, the excrement of humans and other animals, and various forms of inorganic and organic debris. Usually this material is diluted by domestic and industrial waste waters as well as by rain.

Different types of problems arise when industries empty huge quantities of their wastes into the sewage system. Sometimes the materials are toxic for animals, plants, and microorganisms. Other times, even though industrial wastes are nontoxic, the discarded material increases the load of solids that must be stabilized by treatment. Although in most large cities in the United States the collection of domestic sewage is more or less carefully controlled, often the disposal of wastes is far from adequate. In many smaller communities the problems of waste disposal are even less efficiently handled. Unfortunately, the increases in comfort and convenience that develop from industrial and technological advances have all too often increased both biodegradable (organic substances that can be broken down by normal environmental processes) and nonbiodegradable waste materials within the environment. Moreover, such accumulations have increased the need for more and better methods of waste disposal.

Effective sewage treatment should decrease the biochemical oxygen demand (BOD), which refers to the oxygen-consuming property of waste water samples, or indirectly, the degradable organic materials present. In addition, it should remove poisonous and other objectionable substances. Sewage treatment represents human attempts to speed up natural processes so that the large volumes of wastes generated by community living can be adequately controlled. The methods of treatment chosen depend on several factors, including the presence of toxic substances, the quantity of material and its BOD, and the nature of the bodies of water into which the resulting products of treatment are emptied (Figure 5–5).

Primary treatment. As mentioned earlier, sewage consists of numerous components. Domestic and industrial waste waters as well as rain usually dilute this material. The water content of the mixture usually is over 90 percent, which permits relatively easy pumping of sewage to treatment plants for disposal purposes (Figure 5–5). Primary sewage treatment relies on the force of gravity and a few screens to take out the heavier materials;

thus it begins with the removal of solids, including cardboard, plastics, glass, wood, and gravel, from the more readily digestible components (Figure 5–5). The large solids, grease, and scum caught in this manner are raked off by hand or by mechanical means. Some plants use a shredding device in place of screens to chop up the heavier items, which thus stay in the sewage water until the next stage of treatment.

Screened or shredded sewage is then passed through a *grit chamber,* which serves to remove cinders, sand, and small stones. Removing such items also serves a protective function in that pumps and other equipment used in later stages are protected from damage. The use of grit chambers is particularly important to communities that use combined storm and sewage systems.

Following this stage the sewage water with its suspended material is ushered into a sedimentation tank. Here, because there is a reduction in the velocity with which the sewage flows, suspended solids settle to the bottom. Depending on tank size and quantity of sewage, more than one tank could be necessary for this phase of the operation. The settled material, known as *sludge,* is removed either manually or by mechanical means. In certain cases sludge is dried in beds and disposed of on land. However, because sludge itself could present a pollution problem, it is preferable to initiate microbial decomposition in sludge digestion tanks before drying.

The liquid portion of the sedimentation tank is treated with chlorine to kill microorganisms and to reduce objectionable odors. Once this occurs, primary treatment is complete, and the effluent is released into some natural water environment, *e.g.,* lake, river, stream, or ocean. It is estimated that approximately 30 percent of the municipalities in the United States do not go beyond primary treatment of their sewage.

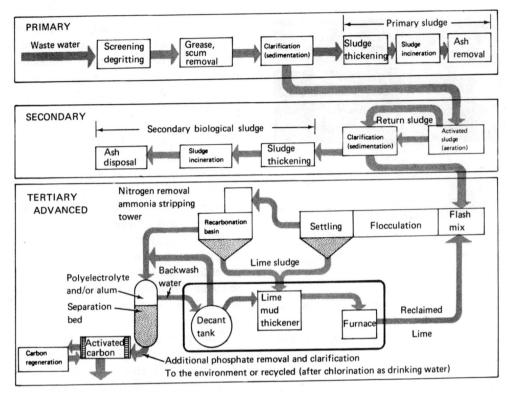

FIG. 5–5. Diagrammatic representation of primary, secondary, and tertiary sewage treatment.

(After Odum, *Fundamentals of Ecology*, Philadelphia: W. B. Saunders, 1971.)

Secondary treatment. Because of the objectionable properties of the effluent from primary treatment, it is in most cases put through a secondary treatment (Figure 5–5). This type of operation involves the biological degradation of organic material by microorganisms under controlled conditions. It is generally performed in two phases, aerobic and anaerobic digestion. In the aerobic phase, suspended solids are mixed with previously treated material, and then are pumped to aeration tanks. This mixing of *raw sewage* with treated sewage assures the presence of the proper microorganisms to carry out the digestion process. The mixed sewage then is aerated by compressed air, mechanical belts, or other suitable devices, thus enabling aerobic organisms to convert wastes into highly oxidized and generally much less offensive by-products. These include carbon dioxide, nitrates, phosphates, sulfates, and water.

Secondary treatment is designed to stabilize the greater portion of the organic materials, thereby reducing the BOD. The mode of stabilization by populations of aerobic organisms, most often employed in larger sewage disposal plants, is called the *activated sludge method*. While this is the most satisfactory approach to treating domestic sewage, the process can be ruined by the presence of toxic industrial waste products.

An alternative to aeration tanks is the trickling filter approach. In this process, suspended solids are sprayed onto the surfaces of artificial beds of broken stone, cork, plastic balls, or another supporting matrix contained in tanks. Microorganisms subsequently form a living film on the components of the matrix and digest the or-

FIG. 5–6. A trickling filter with a spraying or distributing device. This type of filter is commonly used in sewage treatment plants. (Courtesy of the National Medical Audiovisual Center, Atlanta.)

ganic matter of the sewage as it filters or trickles through the bed. Figure 5–6 shows a typical trickling filter equipped with spraying arms.

During this aerobic digestion or stabilization phase, many different types of microorganisms, e.g., bacteria, fungi, and protozoa, are actively engaged. These organisms, along with other particulate matter, are held together by a slimy bacterial secretion. This combination thus forms a *"floc."* The particulate content of the floc is very important to high activity, for it is well known that materials in solution or in suspension are adsorbed onto the surfaces of particles. The floc in essence acts as a means for concentrating wastes which subsequently are digested by the microorganisms present. Thorough mixing of the system is essential at this point; if the mixing process is inadequate, the oxygen content is soon depleted and the system becomes septic in nature. Anaerobic conditions develop, foul odors are produced, and the wastes are not properly digested.

While anaerobic conditions are not desirable under the aerobic phase of sewage treatment, they are necessary for another phase, namely, *sludge digestion*. In this

process raw sludge is pumped into a contact tank (Figure 5–7) and mixed with previously treated material. Microorganisms are again actively involved, but this time they produce related compounds that include ammonia, hydrogen sulfide, and methane in addition to carbon dioxide and water. The gaseous by-products, such as methane and ammonia, are combustible and are used as sources of power in larger treatment plants to run the electrical generators that power the sewage treatment equipment and provide electric lighting.

The partially digested solid materials are processed through a secondary clarifier or settling tank, where they settle out. The sediment containing the microbial growths and their by-products is called *activated* or *secondary sludge*.

This procedure removes larger particles which can either be returned to the contact tank (Figure 5–7) or be mixed with raw sludge before being pumped into the contact tank. The remaining clarified fluid may simply be disinfected, or may also be digested further by being discharged into soil or various bodies of water. It also is possible for such clarified material to be processed prior to its release under the aerobic condition described earlier.

When sewage treatment is judged to be complete according to analyses for solids and oxidizable materials, the resultant fluids are released. The processed material then may be chlorinated and discharged into various bodies of water, allowed to filter into porous soil through drainage ditches or irrigation pipes. In either case, the by-products of sewage treatment can serve as a source of needed food material for plants, and subsequently for animals. Sludge which remains after the overall treatment is usually dried and incinerated, or may be heat-sterilized and sold as fertilizer.

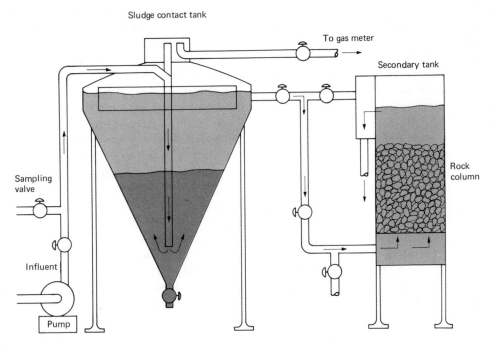

FIG. 5–7. Cross-section of a pilot plant for sludge digestion. (Courtesy of the National Medical Audio-visual Center, Atlanta.)

Tertiary treatment. *Advanced* or *tertiary treatment* refers to the use of any form of treatment to further purify waste water over and beyond the primary and secondary operations. The primary purpose of advanced treatment is to remove the contaminants of waste water that remain behind after secondary treatment. Such contaminants include inorganic nitrates and phosphates, dissolved organic compounds, and suspended solids. Unfortunately, a thorough treatment of sewage water is both difficult and costly. Yet if the water needs of communities are to be met, methods for improving the efficiency of sewage treatment and disposal must be found and implemented.

Sewage and disease. The proper disposal of processed sewage liquids or solids requires disinfection, either before or during the release of such materials into the environment. Chlorination or filtration of liquids and the heating of solids will kill the pathogenic microorganisms which can be transmitted by sewage. Included in this group of pathogens are the causative agents of bacterial diseases such as cholera (*Vibrio cholerae*) and typhoid fever (*Salmonella typhi*), as well as enteric viruses such as poliomyelitis and coxsackie.

Sewage treatment plants are capable of processing millions of gallons of sewage every day. It is a mixed blessing for the residents of coastal cities that salt water is so readily available as a means of diluting and disinfecting the processed sewage which might otherwise not be so thoroughly processed and disinfected upon its release. This process of dumping treated sewage into the ocean undoubtedly adds to the evergrowing problem of environmental pollution.

Lagooning. Aerobic waste stabilization does not have to be performed in large buildings and concrete reservoirs, but is being done in the so-called "algae lagoon." These are actually very shallow ponds, into which wastes are pumped for treatment. If the proper slime- or floc-forming bacteria are present, along with others necessary for aerobic stabilization, one requirement for suitable treatment is present, namely, suitable flora. Since mixing and spraying are impractical in a situation of this type, algae are used as a source of oxygen for the organisms. Here we have a sound ecological system, with groups of different organisms working for mutual benefit. The algae require carbon dioxide, water, and other compounds which the bacteria supply by the digestion of the sewage. The bacteria require the oxygen that the algae now are able to produce. This concept of combining algae and other microorganisms in waste treatment has been considered both for the production of food and oxygen for astronauts, and as a means of disposing of their waste materials.

Eutrophication. An ecosystem is a natural unit of living and nonliving components that interact to produce a stable system in which the exchange of materials between these parts follows a circular path. Water not only serves as an essential "vehicle" through which nutrients are recycled in any ecosystem, but it is also vital to the continued existence of organisms and for the continued functioning of any ecosystem. The concentrations of two chemicals, nitrates and phosphates, are of special concern. In soil, nitrates and phosphate compounds (provided in the form of agricultural fertilizers) are beneficial to plants; however, their introduction into lakes, rivers, streams, etc., can cause several undesirable consequences.

While the effluent of modern sewage plants can be treated to remove basic nutrients, including phosphates, ammonia, nitrates, and other nitrogen-containing compounds, it is more difficult and expensive to control the pollution caused by agricultural sources. The growth of algae and various other forms of plant life in lakes, streams, etc., depends on the concentration of inorganic nutrients. As these materials become more abundant, algal growth is stimulated, resulting in rapid growth and the formation of thick, slimy algal mats—called *algal* or *plankton blooms*—over the surface of the water (Color photograph 3). Toxic metabolic products and undesirable odors frequently are associated with them. In addition, with time oxygen supplies beneath the slimy surfaces decrease substantially and aquatic forms of life useful to humans cease to survive.

A lake or stream into which considerable amounts of nutrients are released with a resulting acceleration of ecosystem productivity is said to be of a eutrophic (well-fed) type. The process by which this type of accelerated aging occurs is called *eutrophication.* It has several effects, one of which is the elimination of many fish species. Excessive nutrient concentration in aquatic systems also may cause human illness and the extensive growth of aquatic weeds which can affect shellfish production, interfere with fishing and bathing, and constitute a hazard to navigation. Eutrophication has been accelerated drastically in several areas by the increased dumping of industrial wastes, phosphate detergents, etc., creating a situation referred to as cultural eutrophication.

Other Applications of Microorganisms

Microbial Insecticides

Numerous insects associated with the destruction of agricultural products or with the transmission of various disease agents to man, other animals, and plants appear to be susceptible to the effects of certain microorganisms. Agostino Bassi in 1838 first proposed the use of microorganisms in the control of insect pests. In order for a prospective insect pathogen to be an effective "microbial insecticide" it should meet certain requirements, including: (1) the capability to cause sufficient injury to the specific insect host so that its "competitive" activities are inhibited; (2) the ability to be fast-acting; (3) the possession of a specificity for a particular insect pest, (the insect pathogen should be harmless to useful insects and invertebrates); (4) the microbial insecticide should be relatively unaffected by environmental factors, such as drying, sunlight, or by the manner in which it is dispensed in the field (dust or spray); and, finally, (5) the production of large quantities of such microbial insecticides should be economically feasible. Unfortunately, taken as a whole, the majority of microorganisms isolated from diseased insects do not seem to fulfill these requirements, thus making microbial control of agricultural pests a most difficult task.

In general, only certain spore-forming bacteria have been used seriously as microbial insecticides. Two examples of such organisms are *Bacillus thuringiensis* Berliner and *B. papilliae* Dutky. The latter bacterial species causes type A milky disease in the larvae of the Japanese beetle, *Popillia japonica*. The former organism belongs to a group of bacteria which are referred to as being *crystalliferous*. This designation has been applied to several *Bacillus* spp. which produce a discrete inclusion, or crystal, in cells undergoing sporulation (formation of the resistant structures, spores) (Figure 5–8). Normally a sporulated culture will contain both crystals and spores. The significance of these crystals lies in the fact that the protein which comprise them functions as a toxin capable of injuring the mid-gut

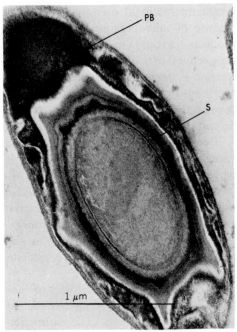

FIG. 5–8. A photograph of a thin section (slice) of a young spore of *Bacillus popilliae* obtained with the techniques of electron microscopy. The spore (S) and parasporal body (PB), or crystal, are quite apparent. (Courtesy of Dr. S. H. Black, Baylor University College of Medicine, Houston.)

cells of susceptible insects. The activity of these crystals may inhibit the feeding of the pest, or may cause other harmful effects.

The use of microorganisms as effective agents in the biological control of insects needs further investigation. Studies of this nature are part of an experimental and applied speciality called *insect pathology*.

Biological Warfare (BW)

Many individuals today look upon the aggressive use of microorganisms with distaste and would choose to ignore it. This military implication of modern microbiology cannot be overlooked, in view of the availability of commercial equipment for the propagation of disease-producing microorganisms, and the variety of methods for their dissemination. Relatively recent international agreements banning the use of microorganisms and/or their products (toxins) in warfare have decreased efforts to develop offensive weapon systems. Such agreements, however, have not decreased attempts to develop the means with which an efficient defense system can be established.

Because microorganisms constitute a varied weapon system rather than a single type of weapon, the development of appropriate defense systems is difficult, and presents problems such as the detection and rapid identification of microorganisms, decontamination and disinfection, and the development of effective vaccines and chemotherapeutic agents.

At least two major categories of biological weaponry are recognized—*lethal* and *incapacitating*. The exact distinction between these two forms of weapons is not clear. Moreover, according to Meselson, international law and international custom apparently do not distinguish between them.

Lethal biological weapons could be introduced into a particular area by a variety of means. For example, a spray could be delivered by an airplane flying over the target area. Thus, the individuals in the region would quite readily inhale the disease-producing agents. Even though protective measures such as vaccines and antibiotics are available to combat pathogens of various kinds, these would be limited in effectiveness in situations produced without warning. Several microorganisms could function as lethal biological weapons. However, because of the danger of creating widespread epidemics which could involve both friend and foe, agents of a contagious nature probably would be avoided. Another potential danger associated with a lethal agent is that, once introduced into a populated region, organisms with greater disease-producing capabilities might emerge. In short, the outcome of using such agents is quite unpredictable.

Incapacitating or nonlethal biological agents would be spread in a manner similar to that for lethal biological weapons, and with the same disadvantages. In general, the "contagiousness" of such microorganisms would be low or lacking. Examples of pathogens which could be used here include: (1) viruses of dengue fever (breakbone fever) and Venezuelan equine encephalitis; (2) the causative fungal agent of coccidioidomycosis; and (3) the bacterial causative agent of brucellosis (undulant fever). These nonlethal agents could be employed in a variety of situations ranging from incapacitating city populations to hampering the advance of an enemy army. Although some investigations in this area of specialization are directed to finding possible means of protection against conceivable microbial weapons, valuable information relevant to the control of diseases from natural causes is also obtained.

Single-Cell Protein

As difficult as it may be to believe, milligram for milligram bacteria and many other microorganisms have as much protein as steak. Even though it may be some time before this source of protein, referred to as single-cell protein (SCP), is used to replace various human foods, more and more attention is being directed toward the ability of microorganisms to grow rapidly on materials previously thought not to be food sources, or on edible but not nutritious substances. Bacteria and fungi can be utilized to eliminate or alter various weeds and other unwanted plants, urban solid wastes, oil, and almost anything with carbon in it. There have been reports of bacterial strains, for example, that can be used to assist in the cleaning operation in cases of oil spillage.

The substances used by microorganisms in the production of SCP are supplemented with other nutrients such as inorganic nitrogen compounds. Through microbial enzymatic activities the energy contained within the carbon sources is converted into biomass, i.e., the total weight of living matter. This resulting SCP is harvested, usually dried, and subsequently used for animal feed. With further processing most SCP can be used as a source of food for humans.

Single-cell protein could replace high-protein grains used for animal feed and free these grains for human consumption. Various animals, such as cattle and hogs, although excellent sources of amino acids, must eat an extremely large amount of plant mass to produce their own smaller mass. The fattening of livestock requires unbelievable quantities of human-edible plant material. This often involves feeding such animals one of the best protein sources known, namely, soybean meal. In contrast, the people in poor and developing countries often have to subsist on a protein-deficient plant diet. SCP has the potential to correct this situation by serving as a replacement for the human-edible supplements used in the livestock industry, thereby making these supplements available for human consumption. In addition, single-cell protein can be a direct source of human protein.

SCP may have an unpleasant ring to it for many people, because they frequently associate microorganisms with disease and spoilage only. Nonetheless, precedent for the presence of microbes in several types of food and beverages consumed by humans is not lacking, as sections of this chapter have shown.

QUESTIONS FOR REVIEW

1. What is industrial microbiology? Describe briefly at least two examples of anaerobic microbial processes used in this area of specialization.

2. What types of microorganisms are used in the following processes?
   a. Swiss cheese production
   b. blue cheese manufacture
   c. the production of beer and wine
   d. the manufacture of pickles and olives
   e. antibiotic production
   f. SCP production

3. What types of aerobic microbial processes are used for industrial purposes?

4. Describe the involvement of microorganisms in waste treatment. Is there a need for disinfection in this process?

5. What are microbial insecticides? How are they used?

6. What is biological warfare? What are its shortcomings? Distinguish between lethal and incapacitating biological weapons; give at least two examples of each category.

7. Differentiate between the following:
   a. primary sewage treatment versus secondary treatment
   b. lagooning and eutrophication

8. a. What is single-cell protein?
   b. What is the potential value of SCP?

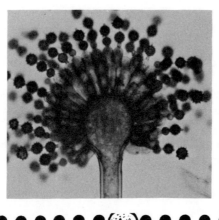
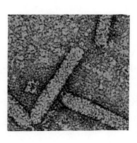
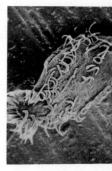
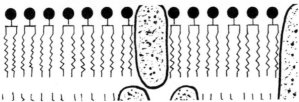

Microbial Structure and Function

DIVISION 2: Behavioral Objectives

After reading the chapters in this division, the individual should be able to:

1. Describe the major techniques used in visualization of microorganisms.

2. Apply the metric system of measurement to the structures of typical animal and plant cells and microorganisms.

3. Recognize the advantages and limitations of techniques and microscopes used in the study of microorganisms.

4. Summarize the structures and associated functions of the major components of typical animal and plant cells.

5. Describe the arrangements, structures, and associated functions of the major components of typical bacteria, fungi, and protozoa.

6. Distinguish between procaryotic and eucaryotic cells.

7. Summarize the basic structural differences between viruses and viroids, and between viruses and the other microbial types.

8. List the distinguishing biochemical differences among microorganisms.

6

Techniques Used in the Observations of Microorganisms

Technical advances in the sophistication of materials and equipment used to examine microbes have been a key element in the development of microbiology. One example of this dependence of microbiology on advancing technology is the evolution of the microscope. Since the time of Leeuwenhoek's discovery of certain microorganisms, the methods for viewing such forms of life have greatly improved. The general appearance of bacteria and some of their structures, for example capsules and flagella, could be demonstrated with suitably prepared specimens and adequate bright-field microscopes. However, only within the past 20 years or so have details of microbial internal organization been uncovered. Although the existence of submicroscopic infectious agents was known since the turn of the century, not until the electron microscope came into being were they actually seen.

General Principles of Microscopy

A wide variety of microscopes and associated techniques are currently available to enable one to see microorganisms in considerable detail. As the main portion of this chapter will demonstrate, these instruments have undergone significant modifications (Figures 6–1, 6–17, 6–22, and 6–31) since the time of Leeuwenhoek and his simple microscopes. Depending upon the principle involved in magnification, microscopes can be grouped into one of two categories—light and electron microscopes. The former group includes *bright-field, dark-field, fluorescence,* and *phase-contrast* instruments, while the latter category includes the *transmission* and *scanning electron* microscopes. This chapter will introduce a representative number of fundamental techniques and equipment used by microbiologists and workers in allied scientific areas for the observations of cells and their component parts. Before considering the various forms of microscopy, attention will be given to the units of measurement used in describing the morphologic characteristics of microorganisms and other microscopic and submicroscopic objects, and to some fundamentals of optics.

Units of Measure

In microbiology, as well as in other branches of the biological sciences, several common metric units are used to express the dimensions of microscopic objects under study. Recently, new prefixes to express lengths, volumes, and weights have been adopted by the scientific community. In the case of lengths, *micrometers* (μm) and *nanometers* (nm) are used instead of microns (μ) and millimicrons (mμ), respectively. The micrometer measures one-thousandth (0.001 or 10^{-3}) of a millimeter (mm). It can be subdivided into one thousand units, each of which is a nanometer (nm). One nm is made up of 10 Ångstrom units (Å).

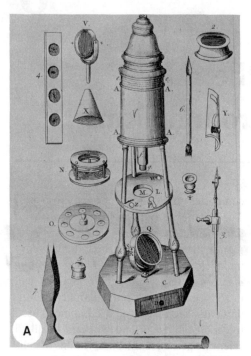

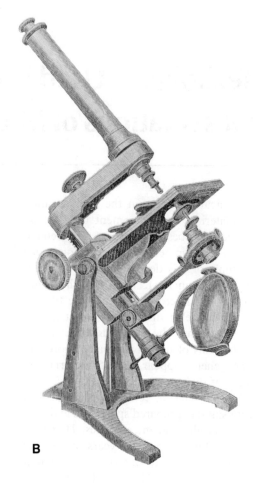

FIG. 6–1. Modifications of light microscopes through the years. _A_. Scarlett's microscope of approximately 1760. Note the large number of microscope parts. Do any of them bear a resemblance to the components of a modern-day instrument? _B_. A later model (1854), known as the Spencer's Trunnion Microscope. Note the adjustment knobs (arrows). (Courtesy of the American Optical Instrument Company, Buffalo.)

B

Table 6–1   Equivalents for Selected Units of Measurement
and their English System Equivalents

Angstrom (Å)	nanometer (nm) or millimicron (mμ)	micrometer (μm) or micron (μ)	millimeter (mm)	inch (″) (approximately)
1	0.1 (10^{-1})	0.0001 (10^{-4})	0.0000001 (10^{-7})	0.000000004 (4×10^{-9})[a]
10	1	0.001 (10^{-3})	0.000001 (10^{-6})	0.00000004 (4×10^{-8})
100	10	0.01 (10^{-2})	0.00001 (10^{-5})	0.0000004 (4×10^{-7})
1,000	100 (10^{2})	0.1 (10^{-1})	0.0001 (10^{-4})	0.000004 (4×10^{-6})
10,000	1,000 (10^{3})	1.0	0.001 (10^{-3})	0.00004 (4×10^{-5})
100,000	10,000 (10^{4})	10	0.01 (10^{-2})	0.0004 (4×10^{-4})
1,000,000	100,000 (10^{5})	100 (10^{2})	0.1 (10^{-1})	0.004 (4×10^{-3})
10,000,000	1,000,000 (10^{6})	1,000 (10^{3})	1	0.04 (4×10^{-2})
100,000,000	10,000,000 (10^{7})	10,000 (10^{4})	10	0.4 (4×10^{-1})
254,000,000	25,400,000 (25.4×10^{6})	25,400 (25.4×10^{3})	25.4	1

[a] This value is the same as 1/25,000,000 of an inch. In other words as the last entry in the Angstrom column shows, approximately 254,000,000 Å are needed to make one inch. How many Å make a meter?

The relationships of these various units to one another, as well as to other components of the metric system and equivalent values of the English system, are given in Table 6–1. To prevent confusion both old and new types of metric system designations are included.

It should be noted that each type of microscope possesses a definite limit of visibility: each instrument can be used to observe cells or other objects of a certain size and none below this size. For example, an ordinary light (bright-field) microscope can be employed to observe objects with dimensions down to approximately $0.2\,\mu m$. However, if an electron microscope is used to examine specimens, the sizes of objects which can be observed are approximately down to 15 nm. The limitations of these and other instruments are compared in Figure 6–2, and the advantages and disadvantages of each form of microscopy are given in the sections which follow.

Optical Fundamentals

To understand microscopy, it is important to be aware of certain fundamental properties of light and optics. With this foundation explanations of many of the problems encountered in using a microscope will become more readily apparent.

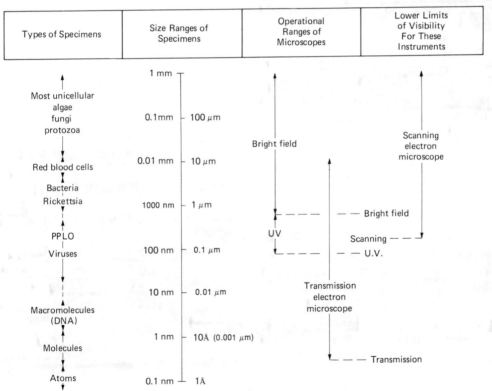

Types of Specimens	Size Ranges of Specimens	Operational Ranges of Microscopes	Lower Limits of Visibility For These Instruments

FIG. 6–2. A diagrammatic representation of the types of specimens which can be viewed by three different instruments commonly used in microbiology and related areas, and one microscope which is being used with increasing frequency, the scanning microscope. The operational ranges are also indicated. (Adapted in part from Rhodes, A. J., and Van Rooyen, C. E.: *Textbook of Virology.* Williams & Wilkins Co., Baltimore, 1968.)

Properties of light. Light is transmitted from one point to another with a velocity of approximately 186,300 miles or 3×10^{10} centimeters per second. According to the wave theory, light is propagated as waves traveling in a hypothetical medium called the *luminiferous ether* or simply the *ether,* extending throughout space.

Amplitude. Light waves are described in terms of their amplitude, frequency, and wavelength. (Figure 6–3*A*). This is readily seen by an analogy between a light wave and a skip rope. When two people pull on the rope and stretch it tight, a position of equilibrium is established. Now if the rope is swung, a wavelike effect is produced. The maximum displacement of the rope as represented by the crests and troughs of the curves produced constitutes the amplitude (Figure 6–3*A*).

Frequency. This property of a light wave refers to the number of vibrations that occur in one second. Specifically, frequency is the number of times a wave crest or trough passes a particular point per second (See Figure 6–3*B*). If two people take a rope and shake it, the frequency of the wave can be regulated by the speed with which the rope is shaken.

Wavelength. A property of waves inversely associated with frequency is the *wavelength.* A simple definition of wavelength is the distance between two corresponding points on a wave, the distance between two successive peaks or crests.

The wavelengths of light rays which make up the so-called visible spectrum range from approximately 4000 to 7000 Å (400 to 700 nm). The colors we see result from a combination of factors including amplitude, frequency, and wavelength. The colors and their corresponding wavelengths are shown in Figure 6–4. Waves possessing lengths either less than or

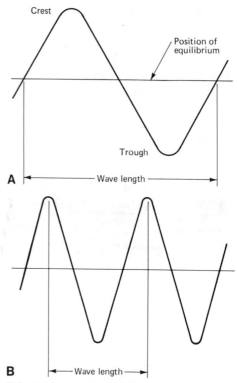

FIG. 6–3. Properties of light waves. *A.* The anatomy of a wavelength. Note the position of equilibrium. *B.* A representation of frequency.

greater than the limits of the visible spectrum also exist. Ultraviolet light rays, for example, have dimensions ranging from approximately 1000 to 3850 Å (100 to 385 nm), while the measurements for infrared are greater than those of visible light.

The resolving power of a microscope—its ability to reveal the fine details of a specimen—depends on wavelength. As a general rule, the shorter the wavelength of light used, the greater is the resolving power. Thus, with ultraviolet light as the source of illumination, finer details can be seen in specimens than with visible light.

Refractive index and refraction. The nature of the material or medium through which light passes during the operation of a microscope plays a prominent role in the image seen. The rate at which light moves through transparent media is not the same for all cases. Denser materials exert a slowing effect on light rays. This fact makes it possible to determine the effect of various media on the movement of light through them. Values for this determination are expressed in the form of a *refractive index,* or index of refraction. This property is defined by the formula:

$$\eta \text{ (refractive index)} =$$

$$\frac{\text{the speed of light in a vacuum}}{\text{the speed of light in the medium being tested}}$$

In making such determinations, it is important to keep the temperature constant during the testing period. The indexes of some commonly used materials are 1.00003 for air, 1.33 for water, an average of 1.6 for various glass preparations, and 1.55 for immersion oil.

Light rays traveling in a single-medium generally move along a straight path. However, if these rays pass from one material with a particular refractive index into another having a different refractive index, the light wave changes direction. This phenomenon, called *refraction,* takes place at the boundary between the two media. The importance of refraction and the refractive indexes of materials is clearly indicated in the use of the oil immersion objective and other forms of microscopy.

The individual or individuals responsible for the invention and early development of the compound microscope are still in dispute. However, most experts acknowledge the basic contributions made by Hans and Zaccharias Janssen. Around 1590, the Janssens introduced a second lens to magnify the image formed by a primary lens, and provided the principle upon which today's compound microscopes are based.

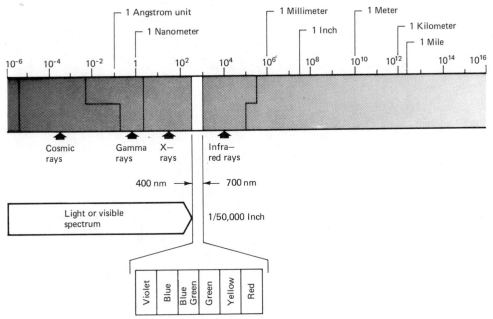

FIG. 6–4. Relative wavelengths of representative forms of radiation. Which of these are of importance in studying microorganisms? Would any type of radiation be harmful to these and other forms of life?

A compound microscope consists of two lens systems: the objective, which magnifies the specimen and is close to it, and the ocular or eyepiece, which magnifies the image produced by the objective lens. The total magnification thus obtained is equal to the product of the magnifying powers of the two sets of lenses (the initial magnification of each part is usually engraved on the piece). Under optimal conditions, maximum magnifications ranging from approximately 1,000 to 2,000 times ($\times$) the diameter of a specimen being observed can be obtained. The greater magnifications are usually obtained by highly trained microscopists using auxiliary equipment.

Successful operation of a microscope depends upon an understanding of: (1) the principles involved in its operation, (2) the functions of the instrument's components, and (3) the procedures for proper maintenance and use.

Light Microscopes

Bright-Field Microscopes

One of the tools essential for studying microrganisms is the bright-field microscope. Two types of this instrument are known—the simple microscope (Figure 6–5A) and the compound microscope (Figure 6–5B). Simple microscopes, those containing a single lens held in a frame-like

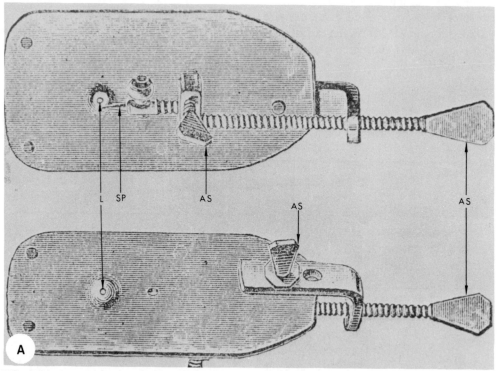

FIG. 6–5A. Leeuwenhoek's simple microscope. Front and back views are shown. A single magnifying lens (L) was held between two thin metal plates. Objects for examination were mounted on a specimen pin (SP) which could be moved by adjusting screws (AS). Specimens were viewed by holding the microscope close to the eye and placing a source of illumination in back of the lens. B. A cutaway diagram of a representative compound monocular microscope. The various components of the instrument and the pathway followed by light waves through the microscope during use are shown. (Courtesy of the American Optical Instrument Company, Buffalo.)

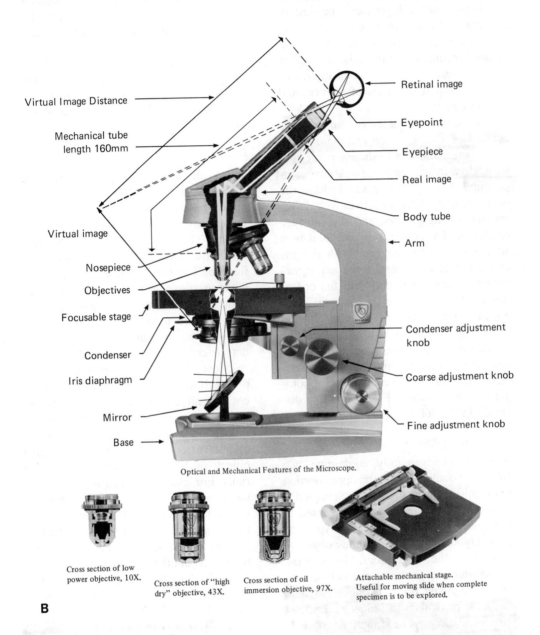

Virtual Image Distance

Mechanical tube length 160mm

Virtual image

Nosepiece

Objectives

Focusable stage

Condenser

Iris diaphragm

Mirror

Base

Retinal image

Eyepoint

Eyepiece

Real image

Body tube

Arm

Condenser adjustment knob

Coarse adjustment knob

Fine adjustment knob

Optical and Mechanical Features of the Microscope.

Cross section of low power objective, 10X.

Cross section of "high dry" objective, 43X.

Cross section of oil immersion objective, 97X.

Attachable mechanical stage. Useful for moving slide when complete specimen is to be explored.

B

device, have been in use for centuries as magnifiers or reading glasses. However, the instrument was not used as a research tool until the middle 1600s. Leeuwenhoek, who is considered largely responsible for establishing the foundation of microbi-

ology, used the simple microscope effectively, and developed the technique for specimen viewing by transmitted light. His observations of protozoa and bacteria were made known to the scientific world for the first time in 1674 and in 1676, respectively.

Unfortunately, the effectiveness of the simple microscope is restricted because of its limited magnification, crude construction, and other disadvantages. The compound instrument, on the other hand, has had widespread application in microbiology, associated branches of science, and a variety of industries.

The ordinary compound microscope consists of a series of optical lenses (systems), mechanical adjustment parts, and supportive structures for its various components. The optical lenses include the ocular, usually three objectives with different magnifying powers, and the substage condenser. The coarse, fine and condenser adjustment knobs, together with the iris diaphragm lever, comprise the major mechanical parts concerned with the operation of the instrument. The various components of the scope are held in position by, or are contained within, supportive structures such as the base, arm, pillar, body tube (barrel), and revolving nosepiece. Several of these microscope components are shown in Figure 6–5 and discussed in the following sections.

Ocular or Eyepiece

A short tube generally containing two lenses, the ocular fits into the upper portion of the microscope's body tube. Several different types of eyepieces can be used to examine specimens. The specific type used generally depends upon the objective lenses on the instrument. In general, the magnifying power of the ocular usually is engraved on it. Common magnifications for oculars include $1\times$, $2\times$, $5\times$, $10\times$, and $15\times$. The functions of eyepieces generally are to magnify the image of the specimen produced by the objective and to correct certain aberrations or distortions associated with the objective. Commonly used oculars include compensating, Huygenian, and hyperplane eyepieces. The compensating type is designed

to neutralize distortions due to different wavelengths of light produced by certain types of objectives. The Huygenian is used with low-power objectives. The hyperplane eyepieces generally are used with objectives of intermediate power. This type of ocular produces a flatter microscope field than the previously mentioned eyepieces.

Objectives

These microscope components are considered to be the most important of the optical parts, primarily because they affect the quality of the image seen by the observer. Three major types of objectives are in use: achromatic, apochromatic, and fluorite. The first of these objective types is the least expensive and simplest in construction. The latter two are more expensive and are used in more critical types of work, as they are corrected for most defects commonly encountered.

Most laboratory instruments are equipped with three objectives that have different magnifying powers: the low-power, high-power (or high-dry), and the oil-immersion lenses. Several microscope manufacturers differentiate the individual objectives by sets of differently colored rings. For example, green is used for the low-power, yellow for the high-dry, and red or black for the oil-immersion objective. If not color-coded, the individual objectives commonly can be distinguished from one another on the basis of their respective lengths (low-power is the shortest, while the oil-immersion lens is the longest).

The primary functions of the objective lenses include: (1) gathering or concentrating the light rays coming from the specimen being viewed; (2) forming the image of the specimen; and (3) magnifying this image. Several important properties of a microscope are directly associated with the objectives. One of these is *resolving power* (RP) or *resolution,* which is defined as the ability to distinguish clearly two points that are close together within the structure of a particular object. This feature is largely determined by the wavelength of the light source (with a shorter wavelength providing finer detail) and the angular aperture of the lens system being used. The resolution is also affected by the refractive index of the medium through which light passes before entering the microscope objective. The relationship of these factors is expressed in the combined formula:

$$\text{Numerical Aperture (NA)} = \eta \sin \theta$$

where η represents the refractive index of the medium through which light passes before entering the objective lens, and sin θ is the trigonometric sine of half the angle formed by light rays (in the shape of the cone) coming from the condenser and passing through the specimen. Light in this form frequently is referred to as "a pencil of rays." Figure 6–6 diagrammatically depicts the explanation of numerical aperture. Values for NA are engraved on the barrel of objectives and are used to determine the maximum resolution obtainable.

Another important feature of modern-day instruments is the property of *parfocal.* Stated simply, this means the changing of objectives without major focusing adjustments. Thus, if a higher magnification is needed during the course of examining a specimen, one would just rotate the desired higher objective into place and make some minor focusing adjustment to bring the specimen into view.

Table 6–2 lists various uses of different objectives. One objective, the oil-immersion lens, is an important tool for individuals studying microorganisms. Therefore, the principle involved in its use must be considered.

The highest-magnification microscope objective utilized in general courses is the oil-immersion objective. It can magnify specimens about 100 times. In order to obtain the best possible results, the objective is immersed in a medium which has approximately the same index of refraction as glass, specifically, 1.6. One medium commonly employed for this purpose is cedarwood oil. Other materials containing mineral oil also are in common use. Oils have the advantage of not drying out when exposed to air for long periods of time. Further, oil provides an "optically homogenous path" for light rays to pass from the specimen, through the oil, and into the front lens of the oil-immersion objective (Figure 6–7). An entirely different picture results if air is present between the specimen and the objective. In this case, as some light is lost due to the air, the image observed usually is fuzzy, and the finer details cannot be seen (Figure 6–8A). The resolving power of the oil-immersion objective definitely is enhanced by the oil medium (Figure 6–8B). Individuals using this objective for the first

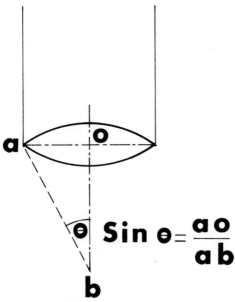

FIG. 6–6. A diagrammatic representation of numerical aperture.

Table 6–2   Representative Uses of Microscopic Objectives

Objective	Uses
Low-Power	1. Observations of microscopic features of certain algae, fungi, and protozoa 2. Examination of bacterial colonies and fungus mycelia 3. Detection and identification of helminth ova 4. Determination of agglutination (clumping) of bacteria, red blood cells, etc., in certain serological tests 5. Location of stained areas on a slide. (This procedure is used first by many persons before the oil-immersion objective)
High-Power	1. Examination of living cells in hanging-drop or wet mount preparations[a] 2. Detection of bacterial motility 3. Examination of blood smears 4. Examination of tissue specimens
Oil-Immersion	1. Detailed examination of blood smears 2. Examination of bacterial smears 3. Detailed examination of tissue specimens

NOTE: These are not the only uses of objectives.
[a] These techniques are discussed later.

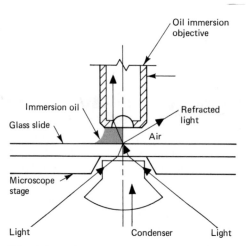

FIG. 6–7. A diagrammatic representation of a comparison between the effects of oil and air on the passage of light rays from a specimen to the front lens of the oil-immersion objective. (Adapted from Carpenter, P. L.: *Microbiology.* W. B. Saunders Company, Philadelphia, 1967.)

time have a tendency to use large quantities of oil. One good drop of this medium usually is sufficient.

The oil-immersion objective is used in various phases of microbiology. To insure the effectiveness of the microscope component, care should be exercised to remove the oil from the objective and all other parts after use. Lens paper is usually employed for this purpose.

The Condenser, Iris Diaphragm, and Mirror

A condenser is found under the microscope stage between the source of illumination and the specimen or object to be viewed. This microscope component frequently is called a *substage condenser*. One of the most commonly used is the Abbé condenser (Figure 6–14*A*). It consists of two lenses which illuminate specimens with transmitted light. The condenser is an important adjunct to high-resolution microscopy. Microscopic examinations of specimens with the aid of either high-power or oil-immersion objectives

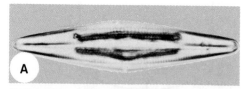

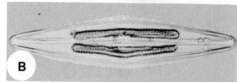

FIG. 6–8. A comparison of an observed image of a diatom when viewed with the oil-immersion objective. *A.* No oil was used here. Air was present between the objective and the specimen. *B.* The effect with immersion oil. Note the clearer image and the greater detail.

require adequate illumination. It is the condenser which serves this purpose. In addition to the Abbé, the variable-focus and achromatic condensers are also commonly used.

Occasionally, too much light may pass through the specimen and into the objective lens, significantly decreasing the contrast of the specimen. Microscope condensers generally are equipped with an iris diaphragm to control light intensity. This component functions as a shutter to increase or decrease the amount of light entering the condenser. When unstained material, such as living protozoa or hanging drop preparations of bacteria, is to be examined, the opening of the iris diaphragm generally is reduced. This component is regulated by the iris diaphragm lever. Many newer microscopes are equipped with fixed condensers and iris diaphragms, regulated for general use.

An adjustable mirror can be used with microscopes to reflect light up into the instrument's condenser, thus aiding in the illumination of a specimen. Today, however, many instruments do not utilize a mirror.

Micrometry

In certain aspects of microbiology, it is necessary to measure the respective dimensions of cells or, if possible, of their components. With light microscopy, this type of procedure generally can be performed with the aid of a special ocular containing a graduated scale (*ocular micrometer*) and a *stage micrometer*. The latter device is a glass slide $3'' \times 1''$ on which a millimeter (mm) scale usually is imprinted. Graduation of this scale is in hundredths of a millimeter.

The measurement procedure first requires that the ocular micrometer be calibrated with the stage device. This is done by replacing the normal eyepiece of the microscope with the ocular micrometer

and determining the exact number of divisions i.e., hundredths of a millimeter, which correspond to those of the millimeter scale on the stage micrometer. In addition, the microscope body tube length and the objective used should be noted, as these components are important to the accuracy of the measurements taken: the manipulation or exchange of these parts will change calibration values. With the calibration of the ocular micrometer completed, the stage micrometer is removed and the specimen to be measured is placed in position.

Variations of this procedure utilizing photographic methods also are known. With photography, permanent records of the dimensions or organisms can readily be made. Electron microscopy and related procedures (see later sections of this chapter) have provided both a means with which to study the structural details of specimens and techniques for obtaining more accurate size measurements.

Defects of Microscopes

Optical defects or aberrations of microscopes occur when light from a point in the specimen being examined does not converge to a point in the image observed. Ideal or "first-class" microscopes are free of such problems, but are expensive.

Basic lens defects include chromatic aberration, coma, curvature of the field, distortion, and spherical aberration. A brief discussion of a select number of common defects follows. It is important to note that, although the light microscope is emphasized here, several of these aberrations also occur with the electron microscope.

Spherical aberration. This is probably the most common geometric aberration (error or defect) inherent in the lens. Serious distortion of the image occurs with spherical aberration. This problem exists when light rays passing through a region near the lens edge (nonaxial) are not brought to the same focus as those near the center of the lens (axial) (Figure 6–9). The result is a blurred image. This defect can be corrected by grinding the lens to a shape which will permit the axial and non-axial rays to have a common focus.

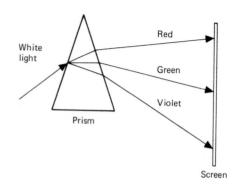

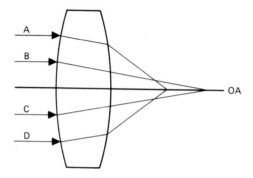

FIG. 6–9. A simple illustration of spherical aberration. Note that the rays A, B, C, and D are refracted differently at several points along the lens. Unless a correction is made, spherical aberration will result. (*OA*. Optical axis.)

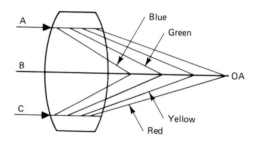

FIG. 6–10<u>A</u>. When white light is passed through a prism its various components, such as red, green, and blue light rays, can be seen. <u>B</u>. An illustration of chromatic aberration. Note that the resulting rays of different wavelengths, A, B, and C, come to focus at a different point along the optical axis (*OA*).

Chromatic aberration.   This defect is caused by the varying extent to which light rays of different wavelength, having different color, are refracted. As such rays pass through a lens they will be brought into focus at different points. For example, red rays, because they are less refracted in passing through a lens than blue rays, are brought to focus farther from the lens (Figure 6–10). In general, images seen in instruments with this defect also are blurred and may exhibit colors different from those of the specimen.

Chromatic aberration can be corrected by properly combining lenses having different light dispersive capabilities, so that the various components of white light are recombined and not separated. Lenses used to achieve this effect are known as *achromatic* lenses.

Specimen Preparation Techniques Used in Bright-Field Microscopy

The procedures used to prepare microorganisms for microscopic examination can be placed in two general groups. The *hanging-drop* and *temporary wet-mount* (TWM) techniques are used with living organisms. The second group of procedures, *staining,* employs *smears,* which are thin films of microorganisms spread on the surface of a clean glass slide which has been air-dried and heat-fixed by passing the specimen through the flame of a Bunsen burner. This step not only kills but coagulates the proteinaceous substances of cells and thereby fixes the organisms to the slide.

The Hanging-Drop and Temporary Wet-Mount (TWM) Techniques

The direct examination of microorganisms in the normal, living state can be extremely useful in the determination of size and shape relationships, motility, and reactions to various chemicals or immune sera. The hanging-drop and temporary wet-mount techniques both maintain the natural shape of organisms and reduce the distorted effects which can occur when specimens are dried and fixed. Because the majority of microorganisms are not very different from the fluid in which they are suspended in terms of either color or refractive index, a low-intensity light source is used for viewing them.

Hanging-drop preparations (Figure 6–11) are made by placing a drop of a microbial suspension onto the center of a cover slip, usually ringed with petroleum jelly or a similar material. This type of sealing material is used primarily to reduce evaporation, and to eliminate air currents. A depression slide (hollow-ground slide with a concave central area) in an inverted position is lowered onto the prepared cover slip. Slight pressure is applied to the slide in order to insure contact between the cover slip and the depression slide. The finished preparation then is turned right side up and ready for examination. Certain microorganisms, such as protozoa, move too quickly to be studied. A 2 per cent solution of carboxy-methyl-cellulose can be used to slow down such rapidly moving organisms. Another difficulty which sometimes presents itself is the actual locating of the specimen. Making a wax-pencil mark close to the edge of the droplet of the microbial suspension and diminishing the intensity of the light source help greatly in eliminating most problems in locating specimens.

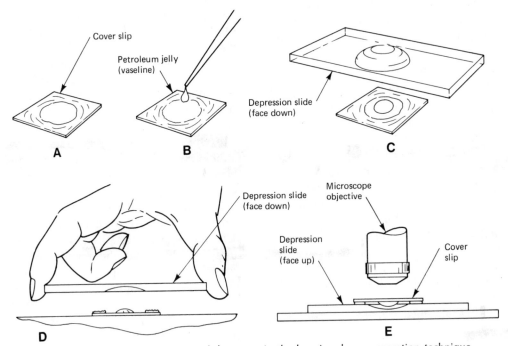

FIG. 6–11. A schematic representation of the steps in the hanging-drop preparation technique.

Temporary wet-mounts of specimens are prepared by placing a drop of microbial suspension on the center of a clean glass slide, and placing a cover slip over the preparation. The procedure for locating microorganisms in a specimen is similar to the one described for the hanging-drop technique.

Staining

The microscopic study of live cells is limited, in that usually only the outline and structural arrangement of cells are revealed by bright-field microscopy. Stained preparations of fixed cells permit: (1) a greater visualization of cells; (2) observation of internal cellular components; and (3) to some extent, a differentiation of microbial species.

The nature of dyes. Dyes may be categorized into two groups, the natural and the artificial. As few natural compounds are still in use, the discussion here will primarily be concerned with a brief characterization of synthetic dyes. Certain fundamental principles of dye chemistry are presented to provide a background for the various procedures used by microbiologists. All too often individuals perform these techniques without really understanding the basis for, or the nature of, the staining reactions.

The first artificial dyes were obtained from aniline, a coal-tar derivative. Consequently, all dyes of this class and many newer ones that bear no relationship to this starting compound are referred to as *aniline dyes*. This term, however, is being replaced by the designation *coal-tar dyes,* since all of these dyes are obtained by chemical reactions from coal-tar substances.

All coal-tar dyes are derivatives of benzene, a hydrocarbon having the chemical formula C_6H_6, and structurally represented as

A form of the compound commonly used in writing is

The value of benzene lies in its ability to combine with various elements (for example, nitrogen, oxygen, and sulphur) or combinations of elements, i.e., radicals such as NO_2 (nitro group). Certain combinations result in a particular structural arrangement of the molecule, producing a colored substance. Certain additional alterations of this colored compound produce a dye. It should be noted that imparting color to a benzene derivative does not cause it to act like a dye. In other words even if a benzene compound is colored, it is not necessarily capable of staining tissues or other materials to any great extent.

Color is associated with certain definite atomic groupings referred to as *chromophores*. Examples of these groups include $C=C$ (ethenyl), $C=N$ (imino), $C=O$ (carbonyl), $C=S$ (thiocarbonyl), $N=N$ (azo), $N=O$ (nitroso), and NO_2 (nitro). The more such groupings a particular compound possesses, the more intense its color. Benzene compounds with such chromophore groupings (radicals) are called *chromogens*. As mentioned earlier, the possession of color by these compounds does not indicate they are able to stain tissues and other substances. The dye property is imparted to a chromogen by the presence of additional groups, referred to as *auxochromes*. These auxiliary groups enable the compound to undergo electrolytic dissociation (i.e., the separation of the molecule of an electolyte into its components or atoms) and to form salts with either acids or alkalies. The yellow dye picric acid is a good illustration of the basic differences and properties of the chromophores and auxochromes. In using three chromophore groups of $-NO_2$ (nitro radical) to displace three hydrogen atoms of a benzene ring, a yellow chromogen, trinitrobenzene, is formed. This compound is represented by the structural formula

The chromogen, although it has color, still does not behave like a dye. It has neither acidic nor basic properties and it cannot form salts. However, if another hydrogen atom is replaced, for example with the auxochrome, the result is formation of a hydroxyl group, $-OH$, and acid compound. This is represented by the following formula.

The addition of the auxochrome imparted the dye properties, electrolytic dissociation and salt formation, to the trinitrobenzene.

A dye, then, is defined as an organic compound containing both auxochromic and chromophoric groups attached to benzene rings. Currently available dyes are obtainable in the form of salts and are

of two general types, basic and acidic. The electric charge on the dye ion determines the type of dye. Basic dyes are positively charged. Substances of this kind stain or react with nuclear components. Acid dyes are negatively charged. Compounds of this type stain cytoplasmic material and certain kinds of granules and other related materials.

Simple staining. Various bacteriological procedures utilize staining solutions which contain one and only one dye dissolved in either a dilute alcoholic solution or water. Such preparations are referred to as *simple stains*. The concentrations of the commonly used dyes are quite low, approximately 1 to 2 per cent. Simple staining solutions include carbolfuchsin, crystal violet, methylene blue, and safranin.

This type of staining procedure involves applying the simple stain to a fixed bacterial smear for a length of time which may range from a few seconds to several minutes. Such stains should never be allowed to dry on the smear. Before the microscopic examination, preparations are rinsed to remove excess stain and dried by blotting between layers of filter paper or other appropriate material. Bacterial cells to which these simple staining solutions are applied take the color of the dye preparation (Color photograph 14).

Simple stains can be used: (1) to demonstrate the shapes and sizes of microorganisms; (2) to differentiate or distinguish bacterial cells from nonliving structures; and (3) to show the presence of bacterial spores.

Differential staining. The preliminary grouping of bacteria is usually based upon their gross morphology and the manner in which they react to certain staining techniques referred to as *differential staining methods*. Procedures of this type employ more than one dye preparation, which, when properly applied, will differentiate (distinguish or separate) nearly all bacteria into major groups. The two most widely used of these methods in bacteriology are the *Gram* and *acid-fast staining techniques*. The differentiation principle also is utilized for the demonstration of bacterial structures located intra- or extracellularly. These components include spores and capsules.

Gram stain. The Gram staining reaction was developed in approximately 1883 by Christian Gram, a Danish physician. He chanced on it while trying to stain biopsy (pathologic) specimens so that microorganisms could be differentiated from the surrounding tissue. Gram noted that some bacterial cells exhibited an unusual resistance to decolorization, and used this observation as the basis for developing his differential staining technique. The diagnostic significance of the tech-

nique was realized probably for the first time in 1886.

The Gram differentiation is based upon the color reactions exhibited by bacteria in a fixed smear preparation when they are treated with the primary dye crystal violet (a purple or violet preparation) followed by an iodine-potassium-iodide solution. Certain organisms lose the violet color rapidly when a decolorizing agent such as ethyl alcohol or a mixture of acetone and alcohol is applied, while others lose their color more slowly. After this decolorization step, a counterstain, usually the red dye safranin, is used. A standardized procedure listing the specific reagents and respective staining times is given in Table 6–3. Bacterial cells resistant to decolorization will retain the primary dye and exhibit a blue or purple color. They will not take the counterstain. Such organisms are referred to as *Gram-positive* (Color photo-

Table 6–3   A Representative Standardized Gram Staining Procedure

Reagents in their order of application[a]	Length of time applied	Reactions and appearance of cells[b]	
		Gram-positives	Gram-negatives
Crystal violet (CV)	1 minute	1. Dye is taken up by cells in two forms, bound and unbound 2. Cells appear violet	1. Same 2. Same
Iodine solution (I)	1 minute	1. Iodine reacts, i.e., fixes probably both the unbound and bound crystal violet[c] 2. A CV-I precipitate (CV-I complex) is formed 3. Cells remain violet in color	1. Same 2. Same 3. Same
Decolorizer (ethanol or an acetone-ethanol mixture)	Applied cautiously drop by drop until a purple color no longer comes from the smear	1. The decolorizer causes the dissociation of the CV-I precipitate, CV-I = CV + I 2. The components of the complex are now soluble 3. Dehydration of the thick cell wall occurs 4. Diffusion of dye proceeds slowly	1. Same 2. Same 3. Dehydration of the thin cell envelope occurs 4. Diffusion of dye proceeds faster
Counterstain (safranin or a dilute solution of carbol fuchsin)	½ - 1 minute	1. Some displacement of CV possibly occurs, but in general cells are not affected 2. Cells appear purple or blue	1. Displacements of any CV left occurs 2. Cells take up counterstain 3. Cells appear red or pink

[a] Note that wash steps are used after the application of each reagent.
[b] Based on information provided by Bartholomew, J. W., Cromwell, T., and Gan, R.: "Analysis of the Mechanism of Gram Differentiation by Use of Filter Paper Chromatographic Technique," *J. Bacteriol.*, 90: 766, 1965.
[c] Iodine is called a *mordant* in this capacity.

graph 15). Those microorganisms unable to retain the crystal violet stain, the decolorized cells, will take the counterstain, and consequently exhibit a pink or red color (Color photograph 16). The term *Gram-negative* is used to describe these organisms. Several characteristic properties of the Gram-positive and Gram-negative groups appear to be correlated with their staining reactions; these include chemical composition, sensitivity to penicillin, and relative cell-wall thickness.

In addition to the two major categories of bacteria, Gram-variables and Gram non-reactives have also been recognized. *Gram-variables* include bacteria which under ordinary conditions may be either Gram-positive or Gram-negative. This type of variation in staining may be due, in large part, to improper technique, i.e., lack of attention to decolorization, etc. The Gram non-reactive category includes those microorganisms which do not stain, or which stain very poorly. Members of the genus *Mycobacterium* and various spirochaetes may fall into this group.

When properly performed the Gram stain can be useful in the diagnosis of a large number of infectious diseases. The reactions of a wide variety of bacteria, both pathogenic and nonpathogenic, are listed in Table 6–4.

The general procedure is quite simple perhaps deceptively so. It involves, in order of application, a primary dye, iodine solution, decolorizer, and a counterstain (Table 6–3). Customarily, each reagent is removed after its period of application by rinsing with water. Excessive washing, however, can remove the dye or dye-iodine complexes within the cells and consequently greatly affect the overall staining reaction. As the decolorization step probably is the most critical, precautions should be taken to guard against misleading results. A commonly employed control is the use of a mixed smear of cultures of a Gram-positive coccus and of a Gram-negative rod on a portion of the same slide containing an unknown specimen. The final step in the procedure, the application of the counterstain, must be performed very carefully. Given too much exposure time, the counterstain will replace the primary dye in Gram-positive organisms, thus affecting the stained appearance of these cells.

Since the original work of Gram, many investigators have attempted to determine the mechanism involved in Gram differentiation, with little success. The concepts offered to explain the Gram-positive state can be grouped into at least three specific categories: (1) the existence of a specific Gram-positive substrate; (2) the presence of different affinities for the primary dye crystal violet, by Gram-positive and Gram-negative cells; and (3) the existence of permeability differences between Gram-positive and Gram-negative microorganisms.

At the present time, Gram differentiation appears to be a permeation phenomenon. Both the thickness of an organism's cell wall and the dimensions of the interstitial spaces, i.e., "pore size," are important determinants of the final outcome of the Gram stain procedure.

Acid-fast stain procedure. This staining technique was developed by Ehrlich in 1882. The property of acid-fastness, demonstrated by this method, is the most important property differentiating mycobacteria from other bacterial species. Among the better-known members of this acid-fast group are *Mycobacterium leprae,* the causative agent of leprosy, and *M. tuberculosis,* the causative agent of tuberculosis. Acid-fastness generally is defined as a resistance by cells stained with a basic dye to decolorization by a 3 per cent solution of acid alcohol—a hydrochloric acid (HCl) and ethyl alcohol mixture.

Table 6–4   Gram Stain Reactions of Various Bacterial Pathogens and
Commonly Encountered Nonpathogenic Organisms

Microorganism	Gram Reaction[a]	Morphology	Disease Caused or Habitat
Actinomyces bovis	+	Rod	Lumpy jaw, actinomycosis
Bacillus anthracis	+	Rod	Anthrax
B. subtilis	+	Rod	Saprophytic organism widely distributed in nature; recently associated with abscesses after tooth extraction
Bacteriodes spp.	−	Rod	Members of normal flora in gastrointestinal tract; causative agents of brain abscesses and wound infections
Bordetella pertussis	−	Rod	Whooping cough
Branhamella (Neisseria) Catarrhalis	−	Coccus	Normal inhabitant of the upper respiratory tract; however, has been known to cause meningitis
Brucella melitensis	−	Rod	Brucellosis (Malta Fever)
Clostridium botulinum	+	Rod	Botulism (fatal food poisoning)
C. tetani	+	Rod	Tetanus (Lockjaw)
Corynebacterium diphtheriae	+	Rod	Diphtheria
Enterobacter (Aerobacter) aerogenes	−	Rod	Widespread in nature; nonpathogenic
Escherichia coli	−	Rod	Normal inhabitant of the intestinal tract; certain strains can produce infant (summer) diarrhea
Francisella tularensis	−	Rod	Tularemia in humans and several other warm-blooded animals
Hemophilus aegyptius	−	Rod	Pink-eye
Klebsiella pneumoniae	−	Rod	Pneumonia; urinary tract infections
Micrococcus (Sarcina) lutea	+	Coccus	Widely distributed in nature; nonpathogenic
Mycobacterium tuberculosis	+[b]	Rod	Tuberculosis
M. leprae	+[b]	Rod	Leprosy
Neisseria gonorrhoeae	−	Coccus	Gonorrhea
N. meningitidis	−	Coccus	Meningitis; upper respiratory tract infections
Pseudomonas aeruginosa	−	Rod	Can cause infections of the respiratory and urogenital systems
Rickettsia rickettsii	−	Rod	Rocky Mountain spotted fever
Salmonella typhi	−	Rod	Typhoid fever
Serratia marcescens	−	Rod	Widespread in nature; has been the cause of respiratory infections
Shigella dysenteriae	−	Rod	Bacterial dysentery
Staphylococcus aureus[c]	+	Coccus	Causes boils, carbuncles, pneumonia, and many other types of diseases
Streptococcus lactis	+	Coccus	Sours milk
S. (Diplococcus) pneumoniae	+	Coccus	Lobar pneumonia
Treponema pallidum	−[d]	Spirochete	Syphilis
Vibrio cholerae	−	Vibrio	Asiatic cholera
Yersinia (Pasteurella) pestis	−	Rod	Plague

[a] Note that the Gram staining reactions listed for each organism are based on results of the test with 24-hour-old cultures. It also is important to remember that Gram positivity with certain organisms disappears with older cultures. In other words, cells of cultures exhibiting a Gram-positive reaction can become Gram-negative upon aging.

[b] The significance of the Gram stain reaction is debatable here. However, the fact that these organisms are acid-fast is of diagnostic importance.

[c] Pathogenic staphylococci usually are detected on the basis of a positive coagulase test. The details of this procedure are discussed in the chapter concerned with these organisms.

[d] The staining of this organism requires special techniques. Dark-field microscopy and even stained tissue preparations produce more convincing indications of infection.

Most bacterial cells can be easily stained by general techniques. However, certain microorganisms possess cell walls containing substantial quantities of fatty or waxy substances, and staining or decolorizing them by the usual methods can prove to be difficult. Ehrlich's observation of such difficulties was responsible for his development of the acid-fast staining procedure. He found that preparations of tubercle bacilli resisted decolorization by strong hydrochloric acid solutions and retained the color of a dye reagent composed of aniline oil in water and an alcoholic solution of crystal violet. Bismarck brown Y was used as the counterstain in his procedure. On microscopic examination, the tubercle bacilli, or the acid-fast organisms, were purple, and all remaining material was stained brown.

Later changes in methodology resulted in the formulation of the Ziehl-Neelsen procedure. This modified method, although essentially similar to Ehrlich's, is the one used in laboratories for the identification of acid-fast organisms. One advantage of the Ziehl-Neelsen procedure is the use of reagent having a better preserving quality than those employed in the original method. Basic fuchsin in aqueous 5 per cent phenol (carbol fuchsin) is the primary staining reagent, while methylene blue is used as the counterstain.

The acid-fast staining procedure is performed by applying the primary dye, carbol fuchsin, to a heat-fixed bacterial smear. Next, the preparation is steamed over a Bunsen burner or similar device for approximately 5 minutes. More dye is added as needed to prevent drying. After heating, the slide is allowed to cool, and then it is rinsed gently in running tap water. Acid alcohol, the decolorizing agent, is then applied to the smear drop by drop, until a red color (the primary dye) no longer runs off from the smear.

The preparation is rinsed again immediately and then is covered with the counterstain, methylene blue. After one minute this reagent is rinsed from the slide. On microscopic examination, acid-fast cells are red (Color photograph 17) and non-acid-fast cells (Color photograph 18) are blue.

The mechanism of the acid-fast staining reaction is unclear at the present time. Certain individuals hold to the concept that mycolic acid is solely responsible for the property of acid-fastness. However, there is no conclusive evidence to support this view. One general requirement for the reaction to occur appears to be intact cells. Disrupted cells of normally acid-fast organisms will become non-acid-fast.

Spore stain. Bacterial spores are known for their resistance to high temperature, radiation, desiccation, chemical disinfection, and staining. These structures, which are formed within the cell (*endospore*) cannot be stained by ordinary methods, such as simple and Gram staining procedures. The dyes do not penetrate the spore's wall. Stained smears of spore-containing cells appear to have oval holes, or colorless spheres, within them. Drastic procedures are necessary in order to demonstrate the presence of spores. A modified Ziehl-Neelsen method (Color photograph 23) can be used for this purpose, but the Schaeffer-Fulton procedure is more commonly employed (Color photograph 22).

In this procedure the primary stain, malachite green, is applied to a heat-fixed smear and heated to steaming for approximately 5 minutes. The steaming is done to enhance the penetration of the dye into the relatively inpermeable spore coats. Next, the preparation is washed for approximately 30 seconds in running water. The wash step mainly removes the malachite green from the cellular parts other than the spores. A counterstain, safranin, is then applied to the smear. This compound displaces any residual primary dye in the vegetative cells, but not in the spores. In adequately prepared smears one can readily observe green spores within red or pink cells, and free green spores (Color photograph 22).

Spore staining techniques are of taxonomic importance in that they can be used to aid in the identification of spore-producing bacteria belonging to the genera *Bacillus* and *Clostridium*. The genus of *Bacillus* includes the causative agent of anthrax, *B. anthracis,* while the genus of *Clostridium* contains a wealth of human pathogens, including *C. botulinum, C. perfringens,* and *C. tetani.* These organisms are the causative agents of botulism (fatal food poisoning), gas gangrene, and tetanus (lockjaw), respectively. The intracellular location, shape, and size of endospores are relatively constant and characteristic for a given bacterial species (note Color photograph 23). Consequently, these properties can be used to establish the identification of a newly isolated, unknown organism.

Dark-Field Microscopy

Specimens examined with this technique usually are seen as bright objects against a black or dark background (Figure 6–12). This is an effect opposite to the one obtained with bright-field microscopy, where specimens usually appear darker against light backgrounds. The dark-field procedure commonly is performed by fitting an Abbé condenser with an opaque disk or "dark-field stop" (Figure 6–13*A*). This dark-field stop is placed below the condenser, thus eliminating all light from the central portion of this microscope component. A thin cone of illumination, how-

ever, does reach the specimen, which in turn scatters this light (Figure 6–13*B*). In reality the specimen becomes a secondary source of illumination, thereby appearing as a glowing object against a dark background.

The examination of objects that do not require high magnification usually incorporates the Abbé condenser and the low-power objective. For higher magnification, additional condensers, such as the cardoid and the paraboloid (Figure 6–14) are employed with other objectives. A source of intense light generally is required for procedures involving these microscope components. Care should be exercised to insure that the microscope slides and cover slips used in the performance of dark-field examinations are free from dirt, dust, and scratches. Unwanted objects and marks are capable of reflecting light and could easily brighten the background.

Dark-field microscopy is used for the examination of unstained microorganisms, the contents of hanging-drop preparations, and colloidal solutions. These procedures have diagnostic importance, especially in the case of syphilis (Figure 6–12).

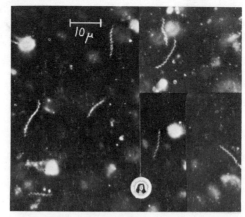

FIG. 6–12. Photomicrographs showing the dark-field image produced with *Treponema pallidum*, the causative agent of syphilis. Note the bright spirochetes against the dark background. (Courtesy of Dr. Theodore Rosebury, A.S.M. LS-327.)

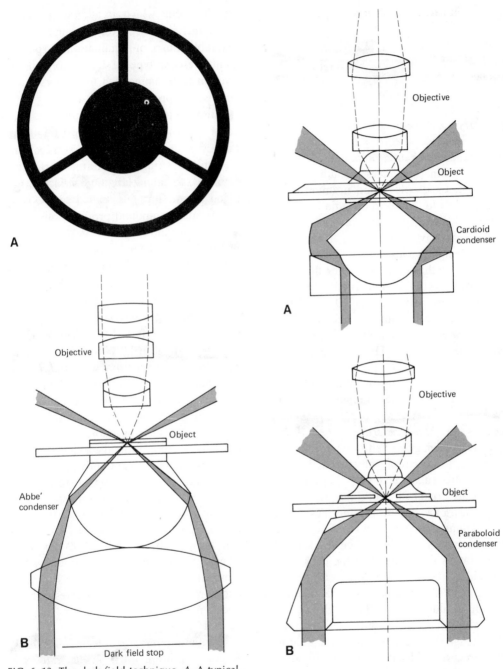

A

B

Dark field stop

FIG. 6–13. The dark-field technique. _A._ A typical dark-field stop. _B._ A schematic representation of the application of the dark-field stop and the subsequent effects. It is evident from this diagram that a specimen only is illuminated by oblique rays of light. An Abbé condenser is also shown. (Courtesy of Bausch & Lomb Incorporated, Rochester, N.Y.)

Objective

Object

Cardioid condenser

A

Objective

Object

Paraboloid condenser

B

FIG. 6–14. Schematic diagrams of microscope condensers. The solid lines represent the path of light through the condensers and objectives; the broken lines represent the diffracted light rays. _A._ A cardioid condenser. _B._ A paraboloid condenser. (Courtesy of Bausch & Lomb Incorporated, Rochester, N.Y.)

Objective

Object

Abbe' condenser

Fluorescence Microscopy

This type of microscopy provides a means of studying structural details and other properties of a wide variety of specimens. Such materials differ in "fluorescing power" from their surroundings. This property of *fluorescence* is noted when such substances become luminous upon their exposure to ultraviolet light (UVL). When certain substances, including some dyes, fat, oil droplets, and uranium ores, are exposed to this form of radiation, they absorb the energy of the invisible ultraviolet light waves and emit it in the form of visible light waves.

The fact that particular dyes fluoresce is utilized in studies concerned with some tissues, cells, and bacteria. Dyes of this nature include acridine orange R (Color photograph 111*B*), auramine O, primulin, and thiazo-yellow G. These substances apparently also possess a particular selective action for microorganisms and their components. For example, the fluorescent dye auramine O is used in a detection procedure for *Mycobacterium tuberculosis*. The dye, which glows yellow when exposed to UVL, has a strong selective action for the wax-like substances which in part comprise this organism. Auramine is applied to a smear of a sputum specimen suspected of containing *M. tuberculosis*. Excess dye is removed by washing. Then the stained preparation is examined in the dark with the aid of the so-called "fluorescence microscope." The presence of the tubercle bacilli is indicated by the bright yellow organisms against a dark background. (Although the effect produced is similar to that observed with a dark-field microscope, the principles involved differ significantly.)

Instruments used in this type of microscopic application do not differ optically or mechanically from the conventional microscope, but do require special filter systems. Many manufacturers provide complete units which, in addition to these filters, include objectives, condensers, and a suitable source of illumination. A special nonfluorescent type of immersion oil or glycerin is recommended for fluorescence microscope procedures.

Immunofluorescence is another adaptation of this type of microscopy. Fluorescent dyes, such as fluorescein isothiocyanate and lissamine rhodamine B, are employed to chemically label (react with) blood serum proteins, called *antibodies*. The former compound produces an apple green color, and the latter an orange one. Antibodies, as later chapters emphasize, are noted for their ability to react with protein or protein-polysaccharide components or products of various types of cells, including bacteria. Such chemical substances are referred to as *antigens*.

Antibodies can be obtained by injecting antigens into a suitable animal. After a sufficient length of time, the injected animal is bled to obtain the antibodies which it produced. Subsequently, a fluorescent dye such as fluorescein is combined with these antibodies, thus creating a fluorescein-labeled antibody preparation. When this material is applied to a specimen smear containing the antigen responsible for the initial production of the antibody, a specific antigen-antibody reaction will occur. The antibody will fluoresce when a treated smear is examined by fluorescent microscopy. The details of antibody production as well as fluorescent antibody methods can be found in Chapters 22 and 23, respectively.

Immunofluorescence techniques have several important uses, including the detection of disease agents in tissues, cells, and other specimens, and the products of various types of microorganisms. The chemical structure of cells can be effectively investigated with the aid of such procedures.

Quite recently, a simple but limited method for the "direct fluorescent labeling" of microorganisms and selected protein substances was reported. Such preparations were found to be readily distinguished from nonprotein substances by their forming stable linkages with fluorescein isothiocyanate (FITC) (Figure 6–15), or with proteins which have been labeled with this dye (Figure 6–16).

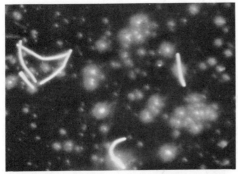

FIG. 6–15. The fluorescence of *Bacillus anthracis,* the causative agent of anthrax, when stained with fluorescein isothiocyanate (FITC). Such cells appear apple-green in color. (From Pital, A., Janowitz, S. L., Hudak, C. E., and Lewis, E. E.: *App. Microbiol.,* **14**:119–123, 1966.)

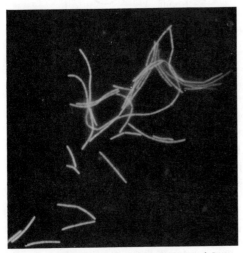

FIG. 6–16. The fluorescent appearance of *B. anthracis* when cells are stained with the FITC-labeled protein β-glucosidase. (From Pital, A., Janowitz, S. L., Hudak, C. E., and Lewis, E. E.: *App. Microbiol.,* **15**:1165–1171, 1967.)

(These are protein compounds other than antibodies.) The method has great potential in detecting biological material in soil and atmospheric specimens containing nonliving débris.

Phase Microscopy

This form of microscopy can be quite useful in examining the internal structures of microorganisms or in distinguishing them in certain fluid environments. The phase microscope (Figure 6–17) functions by intensifying the differences in the refractive indices of certain cellular structural components from the protoplasmic material surrounding them. The incorporation of this phase-contrast principle makes these structures visible so that their shapes, sizes, and other features can be studied.

FIG. 6–17. The inverted research phase microscope. This instrument, while incorporating the phase-contrast principle, differs from similar instruments by having its objectives and oculars in a reverse position (below the stage). (Courtesy of Unitron Instrument Company, Newton Highlands, Mass.)

The demonstration of microorganisms in suspending fluids (Figure 6–20) having slightly different refractive indices is accomplished similarly.

The phase-contrast principle was discovered by Fritz Zernike, who was recognized for his achievement by being awarded the Nobel Prize in physics for the year 1953. As discussed earlier in this chapter, light waves have several variable characteristics, including frequency and amplitude. The human eye cannot perceive a situation when one of two light waves, both of which exhibit equal amplitude and frequency (Figure 6–18A), differ with respect to phase (that is, the crest of one wave doesn't coincide with the other) (Figure 6–18B). A special type of optical device is needed to make these phase differences visible to the human eye. (Figure 6–19).

The condenser in a phase-contrast instrument or a common general microscope has a special *annular diaphragm*. This component allows only a ring of light to pass through the condenser and strike the specimen being viewed. The microscope objective also contains a transparent disk, called the *phase-shifting plate* or *element*. A ring on this disk is used for focusing the light from the annular diaphragm. Depending on its composition, this ring can alter the phase of light waves passing through it by either delaying or advancing them. Thus, by briefly retarding one wave it is forced out of phase with another one which has not been delayed. In actual practice, when a single ray of incident light strikes a particle in a specimen, two rays develop. One of these, the direct (not diffracted) ray, originates from the annular diaphragm, passes through the specimen, and is focused on the phase-shifting element. (Note that the latter will either delay or advance this light ray). The second ray, originating from the incident light ray, is

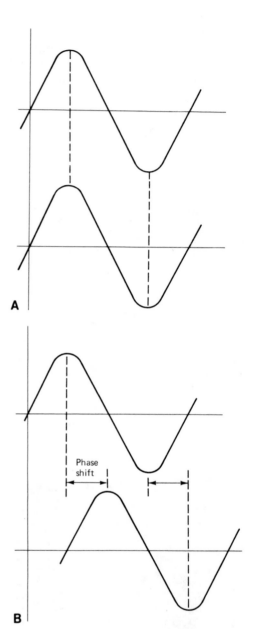

FIG. 6–18. The properties of light wave amplitude and frequency with respect to the characteristic of phase. *A*. Two light waves exhibiting equal frequency and amplitude in phase. *B*. Light waves showing the same properties of amplitude and frequency but differing from one another by being out of phase. The phase-contrast microscope transforms this difference into a visible phenomenon. (After Wren, L. A.: *Understanding and Using the Phase Microscope*. Unitron Instrument Company, Newton Highlands, Mass., 1963.)

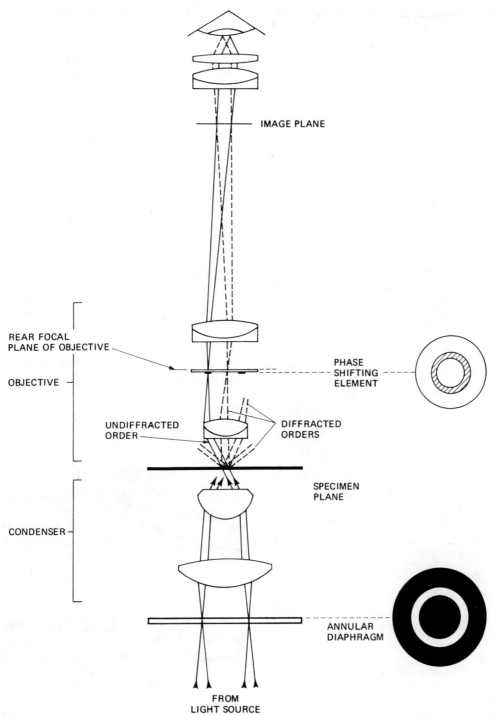

FIG. 6–19. The operation of the phase-contrast principle. (Courtesy of Bausch & Lomb Incorporated, Rochester, N.Y.)

scattered or diffracted as a consequence of its passage around the margin, but not through, the specimen. Because this ray deviates from its normal path it does not strike the phase-shifting element, and its phase is not affected. Upon the subsequent focusing of both the diffracted and undiffracted rays an "optical difference" becomes evident.

Specimens may appear lighter against a dark background (*dark contrast*) or darker against a light background (*bright contrast*) (Figure 6–20). These effects are dependent upon the type of phase-shifting element employed.

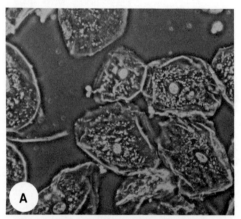

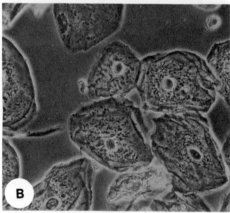

FIG. 6–20<u>A</u>. An example of dark contrast using squamous epithelial cells. The cells are lighter against a dark background. <u>B</u>. The same cells showing bright contrast. (Courtesy of the American Optical Instrument Company, Buffalo.)

Electron Microscopes

The Transmission Electron Microscope (TEM)

The realization that the light microscope had reached its theoretical limit of resolution (0.2 μm) and that further improvements in optical microscopy could not increase resolution was primarily responsible for the development of the electron microscope. "It was inevitable" as Wyckoff states, "that the realization of the exceedingly short wavelength of electrons would give microscope research quite a new direction." Acceleration of these negatively charged particles through 50,000 volts, for example, produces a wavelength of approximately 0.05 Å. The theoretical resolution attainable in this case would be approximately one-half of this value. In actual practice, the resolving power achieved is about 4 Å.

Development of the TEM

Several investigations were important to the development of transmission electron microscopes. Among these were the experiments of J. J. Thomson, who, in 1897, proved that cathode rays consisted of electrons and showed that such streams of negative electricity in a sufficient vacuum could be deflected by both electrical and magnetic fields. This discovery suggested the possibility of constructing lenses with which to manipulate electrons. However, such so-called "electron lenses" were not built until about 1927. Lenses can be made using either electrical or magnetic fields for purposes of concentrating and consequently focusing electrons.

In 1931, Max Knoll and Ernst Ruska, at the High Tension Laboratory of the Technical University in Berlin, constructed and demonstrated the first transmission electron microscope. Since its initial introduction to the scientific world, this expensive and delicate laboratory tool has undergone numerous improvements that make it, in the words of Fernandez Moran, "not only an invaluable research and clinical instrument, but a unifying discipline of the natural sciences."

While the transmission electron microscope clearly has continually provided a wealth of visual data concerning biological systems, the instrument does have its limitations. For example, it cannot be used to view tissue in the living state. Futhermore, the accurate interpretation and correlation of TEM findings to biological systems requires the application of natural science specialities, such as biochemistry and biophysics.

Design of the TEM

Most transmission electron microscopes are similar in basic design to the light microscope (Figure 6–21). However, certain distinct differences exist (Table 6–5). The basic components of the TEM include a source of illumination, optical, viewing, and vacuum systems, and electronic voltage-stabilizing circuits (Figure 6–22).

The source of illumination (electron gun) for the TEM generates an electron beam from a V-shaped thin tungsten cathode filament. This metal wire must be heated to a high enough temperature

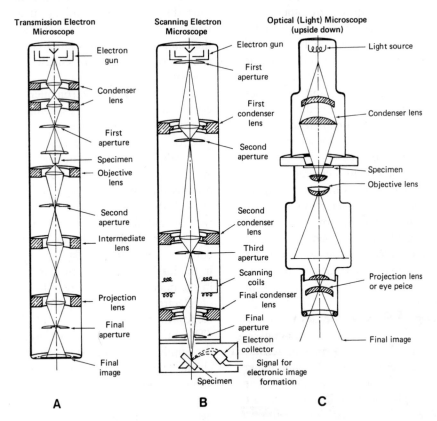

FIG. 6–21. A comparison among diagrammatic representations of: A. The transmission electron microscope, B. The scanning electron microscope, and C. The optical or bright-field microscope.

Table 6–5   Differences between the Ordinary Light Microscope and a
Typical Transmission Electron Microscope

Property or Procedure	Light Microscope	Transmission Electron Microscope
Source of radiation for image formation	Visible light	Electrons
Medium through which radiation travels	Air	Vacuum (approx. 10^{-4} mm Hg)
Specimen mounting	Glass slides	Thin films of collodion or other supporting material on copper grids
Nature of lenses	Glass	Magnetic fields or electrostatic lenses
Focusing	Mechanical (i.e., raising or lowering objectives)	Electrical, i.e., the current of the objective lens coil is changed
Magnification adjustments	Changing of objectives	Electrical, i.e., changing current of the projector lens coil
Major means of providing specimen contrast	Light absorption	Electron scattering

to accelerate a sufficient quantity of electrons from the surface at the tip of the filament by thermionic emission. These electrons are concentrated by other components of the electron gun, producing a fast-moving narrow beam to these negatively charged particles. In order for the TEM to function properly, the components of the electron gun and the lenses must be aligned with one another.

The lens of an electron microscope consists of a lens coil formed by several thousand turns of wire encased in a soft iron casing. A magnetic field is created by passing a current of approximately 1 ampere through the coil. The electron beam is concentrated within the soft iron casing and additional lens components also made of soft iron, called *polepieces*. The latter are specially constructed for maximum effectiveness and are situated centrally in the lens coil.

Three general types of lenses are found in an electron microscope: (1) condenser, (2) objective, and (3) projector lenses. The latter serves to project the final image of the specimen onto a viewing screen. Essentially this lens functions in place of the ocular or eyepiece of a conventional light microscope (Figure 6–21). The components of a typical electron gun include two circular metal plates with centrally

located holes. One of these plates, the *anode,* is positively charged and serves to pull the electrons from the filament toward it. The concentration of these electrons is increased by the second plate, the *cathode shield*. This latter component is negatively charged and encases the electron gun.

The screen of an electron microscope is coated with a phosphorus compound so that it fluoresces upon being irradiated by electrons. Permanent records of an image are made on photographic plates or film. A camera or other suitable device is used for this purpose. Specimens are generally viewed through lead-treated thick glass with the aid of a binocular microscope.

The functioning of the TEM is dependent upon maintaining a sufficient vacuum in the instrument's column. Air molecules in the microscope interfere with the paths of electrons and consequently the efficiency of viewing. To prevent this, the TEM must be evacuated for use. This is accomplished by high-performance mechanical and oil-diffusion pumps. As the latter component must be heated, a cooling device also is needed. The vacuum needed for the instrument's operation is approximately 10^{-4} mm Hg (mercury).

The electrical components of the electron microscope are quite complex; these

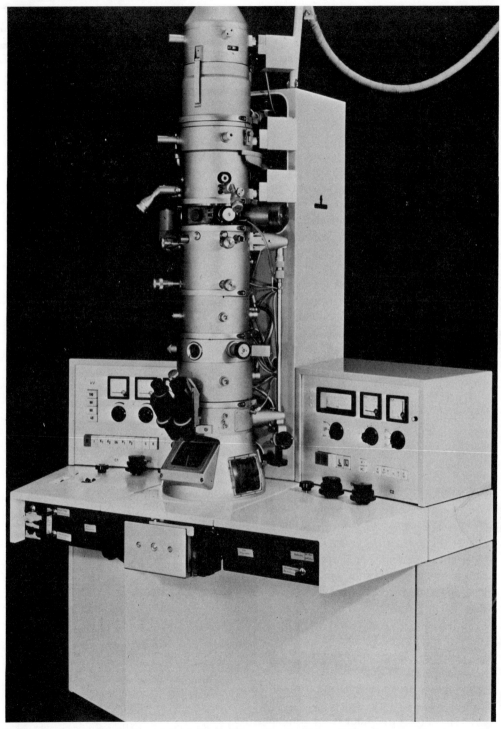

FIG. 6–22. One representative of the large number of currently available electron microscopes, Siemens Elmiskop I. (Courtesy of Siemens America Incorporated, N.Y.)

include the high-voltage supply for the electron gun and the various circuits for the individual lenses.

Further details of operation and related subjects can be found in the several texts listed in the Appendix.

Specimen Preparation for Electron Microscopy

In order to study the structural aspects of various purified biological preparations, including cellular and subcellular components, the basic anatomy of microorganisms, and the intracellular development of microorganisms, with the electron microscope, specimens must be specially treated so that they can be easily recognized. In short, the contrast of specimens must be greatly enhanced. Chemically speaking, biological materials are composed mainly of the elements carbon, hydrogen, nitrogen, and oxygen. As these elements have low atomic weights, they also have "low electron density" or in more appropriate terms, low "electron scattering power." When a biological preparation is placed on the usual type of plastic supporting film used in electron microscopy (collodion or formvar) the contrast between the specimen's electron image and its supporting film is very poor. Techniques developed to correct this problem include shadow-casting, surface replica, and electron staining. The basic principles of these methods, together with the technique of ultrathin sectioning, will be briefly discussed.

Shadow-Casting

This procedure involves depositing a thin film of an electron-dense material at an angle onto a specimen. Substances employed for this purpose include chromium (Cr), nickel (N), platinum (Pt), uranium (U), or alloys of gold and palladium (Au-Pd) and platinum and palladium (Pt-Pd).

The specific material to be used is placed on a tungsten filament or other device, which is heated sufficiently to cause the electron-dense material (metal) to atomize. Figure 6–23A is a diagrammatic representation of the shadow-casting apparatus, and Figure 6–23B shows the effect of the procedure on a specimen.

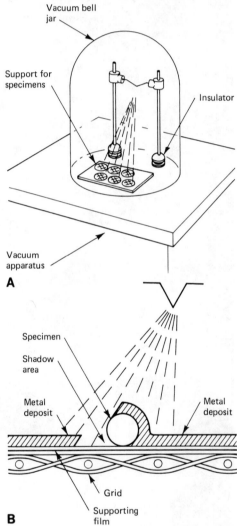

FIG. 6–23A. A diagrammatic representation of the shadow-casting apparatus. B. The distribution of metal evaporated onto a specimen. The shadow area is transparent and consequently appears light in viewing the specimen. It registers as a dark region in electron micrographs. Most electron micrographs are printed in this case as negatives.

The shadow-casting technique decidedly increases the specimen's contrast. This is illustrated by the electron micrograph shown in Figure 6-24A. Double shadowing from two different angles has also been used (Figure 6-24B).

Surface Replicas

Surface replicas have been widely used in certain specialized areas of microbiology. The technique is of great value in studying the surfaces or topography of specimens, including algae, bacterial spores, and viruses. Surface replicas are generally prepared by a "single-stage" technique (Figure 6-25A). In this technique, a thin layer of a coherent material having a low molecular weight (carbon), is deposited onto the surface of a specimen *in vacuo*. The newly coated specimen then is floated onto a water surface from which it is transferred to a strong acid or alkali solution capable of dissolving away the specimen without damaging the replica. The resulting cleaned replica is washed in water and placed on a specimen grid for viewing in the electron microscope (Figure 6-25B). Replicas generally are shadow-cast in order to emphasize certain aspects of surface detail. This procedure may be performed before the application of carbon or after the digestion step. Replication techniques vary, as the type of specimen may require special treatment.

Electron Staining

Electron stains are solutions which contain heavy metal elements. These preparations are used to increase the contrast of specimens. Commonly employed electron stains include osmic tetroxide, phosphotungstic acid (PTA) and uranyl acetate. Most electron stains function by either being absorbed on the surface—a form of embedding the specimen—or by combining with specific chemically reactive groups of the specimen. Two general types of staining techniques are known—positive and negative staining. *Positive staining* makes electron-transparent particles visible against a relatively transparent background, while *negative staining* sets specimens against

FIG. 6-24A. An electron micrograph demonstrating the effect of shadow-casting. The specimen here is vaccinia virus. This microorganism is used in vaccinations against smallpox. (Courtesy of Dr. Robley C. Williams and the Virus Laboratory, University of California, Berkeley.) B. An example of a variation in technique, double shadowing. This is a preparation of *Tipula iridescent* virus, which can cause disease in the crane fly. (Courtesy of Dr. R. Markham, Agricultural Research Council, Cambridge, England.)

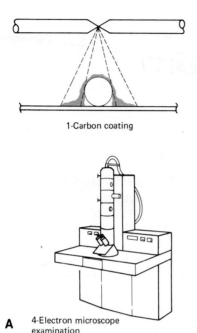

1-Carbon coating

2-Dissolving specimen   3-Wash step

A   4-Electron microscope
        examination

B   1 μm

FIG. 6–25A. A diagrammatic representation of the single-stage replica technique. _B_. The result of carbon replication showing the surface of resting spores of *Bacillus megaterium*. Note the particular surface detail. (Unpublished electron micrographs by L. J. Rode and Leodocia Pope, Department of Microbiology, The University of Texas at Austin, Austin, Texas 78712.)

an electron-dense background. In 1959, while studying preparations of turnip yellow mosaic virus S. Brenner and R.W. Horne introduced this simple negative contrast technique into general use for electron microscopy. The procedure employs potassium phosphotungstate (KPT) or the other compounds mentioned earlier and provides a high resolution for the examination of viruses (Figure 6–26A) and other specimen types. One advantage of this technique is that it does not require any specialized vacuum equipment. Negative staining in electron microscopy is often used as a quantitative device as well as a diagnostic tool.

Thin Sectioning (Microtomy)

Many biological specimens are too thick for direct examination in the electron microscope. To make them suitable for investigation, either surface replication or thin sectioning is usually employed. The latter procedure seems applicable to a larger variety of specimens. With the aid of this technique, structural arrangements of tissue (cellular interconnections), the internal organization of cells, developmental cycles of microorganisms, and many other items of biological interest can be effectively studied.

The microtome.   Microtomes used for the sectioning of specimens for light microscopy are generally unsuitable for electron microscopic investigations. This is largely because the older microtomes are rarely capable of cutting sections of less than one micrometer (μm) in thickness. Modern-day instruments ("ultra-microtomes" Figure 6–27) employed in specimen sectioning for electron microscopic examinations are capable of producing sections ranging in thickness from 50 to 320

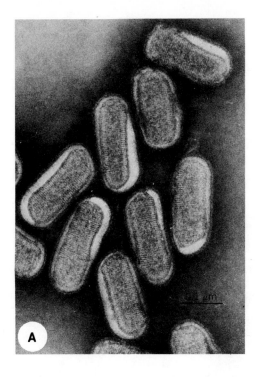

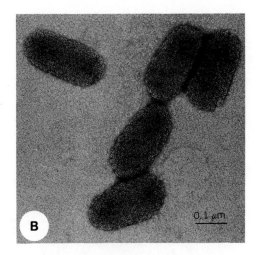

FIG. 6-26. Two different negative staining procedures involving sowthistle yellow vein virus. _A._ The appearance of the virus when stained with phosphotungstic acid. _B._ A similar viral preparation stained with uranyl acetate. The surface proteins of the virus particles are quite evident. (Courtesy of D. Peters and E. W. Kitajima.)

nanometers (nm). With the "ultra-microtome" the specimen is advanced toward the cutting knife much more slowly. This reduced rate of advance makes it possible to obtain sections of varying thickness ranging from ultrathin to thick. In older microtomes the advance of specimens was mechanical, but more recently designed instruments employ a thermal mechanism. The forward movement of a specimen is controlled by the rate of heating of the rod holding the specimen. At the present time, this mechanism is the most precise one known. The rate of heating and the sectioning speed are two important factors controlling section thickness.

The actual cutting of materials is performed with glass or diamond knives, because specimens embedded in plastic (Araldite or Epon) can be more readily sectioned with these tools. Glass knives are made by scoring a selected strip of plate glass at a desired angle and then breaking it. Although glass knives can be

prepared with the aid of a glass cutter and two pairs of glass-breaking pliers, commercial "Knife-Makers" also are available. With a commercial device, the exact scoring angle and the breaking of glass are easily controlled. As glass knives lose their sharpness, they are discarded. This, of course, is not the case with diamond knives. These cutting tools eliminate many of the difficulties encountered in glass knife-making and are essential for the sectioning of hard specimens, such as teeth and bones. Diamond knives must be kept sharp for good results. When one becomes dull, it must be carefully sharpened.

As specimen sections are cut, they are floated onto a liquid surface in a trough (water bath) which is either attached to the microtome or to the knife itself (Figure 6–28). The trough usually is filled with a water-acetone or water-alcohol mixture. The floating specimens are fished from the water bath onto specimen grids. Depending upon the type of investigation,

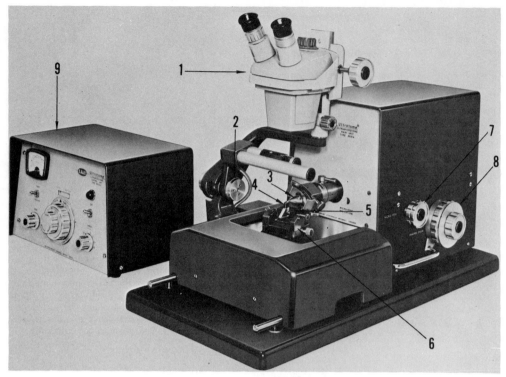

FIG. 6–27. A representative "ultra-microtome" used for specimen sectioning. A photograph of the Ultrotome III showing many of its component parts. (1) high-powered optical system; (2) knife evaluator with dual illumination (fluorescent tube and focused lamp) used in knife inspection and specimen trimming; (3) specimen holder; (4) collecting trough (water bath); (5) glass knife; (6) knife stage; (7) "micro-feed" knob; (8) "macro-feed" knob; (9) ultrotome control unit, which controls specimen sectioning. (Courtesy of LKB Instruments, Inc., Rockville, Maryland.)

they may be processed further. Such preparations can provide detailed information on the internal arrangements of cells (Figure 6–29B).

Specimen preparation.   Before sections of biological materials can be obtained with the aid of microtomy, the specimens must be treated in some manner to preserve a specific structure or structures. This treatement includes fixation, dehydration, and embedding in plastic. The reliability of the final appearance of preparations is dependent upon these steps, as the reagents used may easily affect the physical and chemical properties of specimens. Following is a brief description of

the general specimen preparation procedure for microtomy.

Fixation.   *Fixation* is primarily directed toward the preservation of biological structures. The process can utilize such fixatives as osmium tetroxide, potassium permanganate, and various aldehydes (e.g., glutaraldehyde). In addition to their preserving properties, some fixatives (such as chromium and uranium salts and lead compounds) are capable of staining specimens. The effects of fixating reagents vary depending upon many factors, including their chemical natures, the time of exposure, the penetrating capabilities of the fixative, and the chemical composition of the structure to be preserved. All of these factors and more must be taken into consideration before adequate fixation can be achieved.

Dehydration. The *dehydration* process is performed after specimens have been washed to remove any excess fixative solutions. Usually specimens are dehydrated by passing them through a series of alcohol solutions of increasing strength, proceeding from 25 per cent to absolute alcohol. After the specimen has been through these solutions, all water should have been removed. The presence of water

in the specimen would result in poor embedding and, consequently, inferior sections would be obtained.

Plastic embedding. As discussed earlier, thin sections are desired for electron microscopic investigations. To obtain such preparations, biological specimens are infiltrated with a plastic embedding agent. This procedure will impart sufficient strength to the biological material to maintain it structurally during sectioning. In other words, the presence of the plastic embedding agent will prevent the collapse of the specimen.

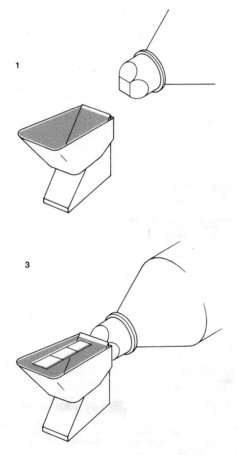
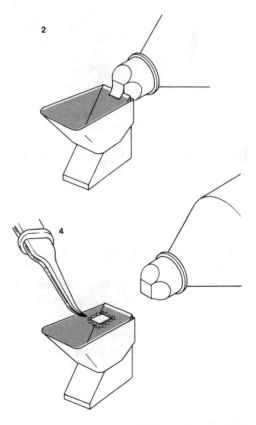
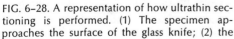

FIG. 6-28. A representation of how ultrathin sectioning is performed. (1) The specimen approaches the surface of the glass knife; (2) the beginning of a section; (3) the appearance of several sections; (4) the removal of a specimen for viewing on a coated grid.

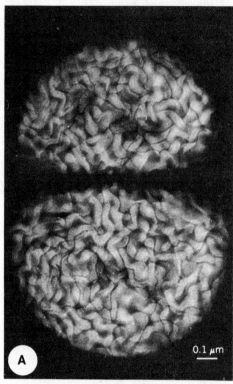

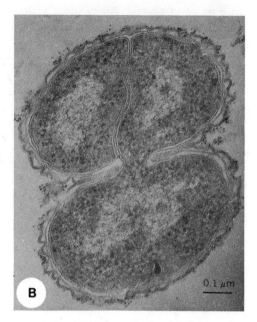

FIG. 6–29. Electron micrographs of *Veillonella* sp. comparing two techniques used in electron microscopy. _A_. A negatively-stained whole cell preparation. Note the convoluted surfaces of the diplococci. _B_. A thin section. Note the internal appearance of the organisms as well as their convoluted outer regions. The cell on the right has developed a cross wall which will eventually result in division. (From Mergenhagen, S. E., Bladen, H. A., and Hsu, K. C.: *Ann. N.Y. Acad. Sci.*, **133**:279, 1966. © The New York Academy of Sciences; 1966; Reprinted by permission.)

Embedding usually takes place in gelatin capsules of various sizes, filled almost to the top with a thick liquid embedding material. These agents also contain specific substances which are involved with their polymerization or hardening. The biological material to be embedded is introduced into the capsule and allowed to sink slowly through the thick fluid, allowing for good infiltration of the specimen. The polymerization of currently used embedding materials can be accomplished by keeping preparations in an oven set at 60° C for 24 to 48 hours.

Freeze Etching

This technique has great applicability for the biological sciences. With this technique, unfixed specimens can be examined and the production of artifacts can be prevented. Briefly, the freeze etching method involves supercooling a specimen in a drop of water so that a solid block of ice is formed. A sharp, cooled cutting blade is used to cleave the specimen. The resulting preparations are placed in an evaporating unit such as a shadow-casting instrument and cooled by liquid nitrogen. Following this step, specimens are removed for a short time to allow a sublimation or etching of the ice block to occur. This treatment exposes the surface specimens, which are then shadowed with metal to provide contrast. A replica (impression of the surface) is then prepared, after which the specimen is dissolved by acid treatment or other technique. The final result is a more elaborate form of replica preparation (Figure 6–30).

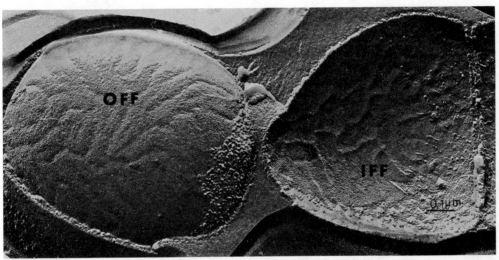

FIG. 6–30. An example of the freeze-fracture technique. With membranes, two complementary fracture faces are produced, *OFF*, the outer fracture face, and *IFF*, the inner (concave) fracture face. Both faces of this cell membrane of *Streptococcus faecalis* show particles. (From Tsien, H. C., and Higgins, M. L.: *J. Bacteriol.*, **118**:725–734, 1974.)

The Scanning Electron Microscope (SEM)

This instrument is comparatively new and quite different in principle as well as in application from the conventional Transmission Electron Microscope (TEM) described earlier. The SEM (Figures 6–21 and 6–31) has gained wide usage in studies concerned with the examination of rough surfaces of specimens from such diverse fields as biology, geology, and metallurgy. Specimens for examination require little preparation. Furthermore, large portions of surfaces can be seen in detail (Figures 6–31 and 6–32) with excellent contrast.

The possibility of a scanning instrument apparently was first suggested by Knoll in 1935. Through the intervening years investigators in several countries improved the early models of the instruments to the point where in 1965 commercially produced microscopes with approximately 250 Å guaranteed resolution became available.

Normally, the instrument is operated by scanning a metal-coated specimen surface with a fine electron probe (beam of electrons) 50 Å to 100 Å in diameter, or less. A cathode ray is synchronously scanned with this electron probe, in order to have each point on the cathode tube correspond to a point on the specimen. The cathode tube's intensity is varied in proportion to the intensity of various impulses generated by the electron probe. Such impulses include secondary electrons and back-scattered electrons. A photographic record is made of the cathode display, which consists of several points representing an area of the specimen's surface.

Applications of the SEM are increasing rapidly in the biological sciences, especially because of the remarkable contrast obtainable with this instrument in comparison with the TEM, and also because of the relatively minimal preparation necessary for specimens for surface examination.

Specimen preparation. Cell collapse in specimens is a major problem encountered

FIG. 6–31. An overall view of the Model 700 High Resolution Scanning Electron Microscope with a dispersive x-ray spectrometer and x-ray readout equipment in place. (Courtesy of Materials Analysis Company (MAC), Palo Alto, Calif.)

in SEM specimen preparation. It can, however, be prevented by any of several methods, such as critical-point drying, freeze drying, or quick freezing followed by observation on an ultra-cold specimen stage in the microscope. Of these methods, critical-point drying is perhaps the one most commonly employed. It involves, after appropriate fixation, solvent dehydration of a specimen and replacement of the dehydrating material with a second solvent that will mix with a liquefied gas which is used to remove the solvent from (to dry) the specimen. A series of ethyl alcohol or acetone solutions of increasing strength (graded systems) are used for specimen dehydration. Liquefied gases used for critical-point drying include carbon dioxide, certain types of Freon, and nitrous oxides. After all the steps of critical-point drying are carried out, specimens are generally coated with a heavy metal such as gold, platinum, or an alloy.

In microbiology, the SEM is receiving considerable attention, especially in studies concerned with the surface characteristics of bacterial cells (Figure 6–33), spores, and fungi. The SEM is also becoming important in studies of morphological changes in tissues infected with microorganisms, and in studies of the organization and structure of microbial communities in various environments (Figure 6–33).

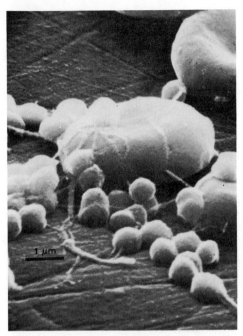

FIG. 6–32. Scanning micrograph showing the hemagglutination of red blood cells by cells of the bacterium *Neisseria catarrhalis*. Note the difference in size between the red blood cells and the bacteria. (From Wistreich, G. A., and Baker, R. F.: *J. gen. Micro.*, **65**:167, 1971.)

QUESTIONS FOR REVIEW

1. Define or explain the following:
   a. simple microscope
   b. Gram-variable
   c. compound microscope
   d. wet-mount
   e. micrometer
   f. scanning microscope
   g. nanometer
   h. auxochrome
   i. mordant
   j. acid alcohol

2. Distinguished between resolving power (RP) and magnification.

3. What is parfocal?

4. What are the functions of the following microscope components?
   a. condenser
   b. iris diaphragm
   c. low-power objective
   d. coarse adjustment knob
   e. ocular
   f. condenser adjustment knob

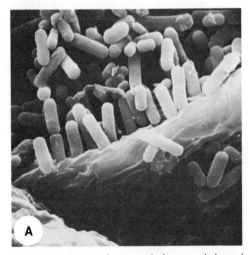

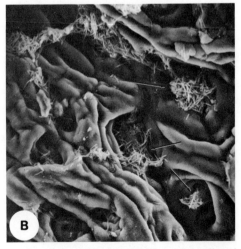

FIG. 6–33. _A._ Attachment of short, rod-shaped bacteria to the epithelial surface of an adult mouse's stomach. _B._ A scanning electron microscopic view of a crypt of Lieberkuhn in the colon of an adult mouse. Note that the opening to the crypt (arrows) is filled with masses of spiral- and fusiform-shaped microorganisms. (From Savage, D. C., and Blumershine, R. V. H.: *Infect. Immun.*, **10**:240–250, 1974.)

5. Compare the types of microscopes listed below in relation to sources of illumination, specimen preparation, limits of magnification, and general uses. The construction of a table with these categories will be quite helpful.
   a. bright-field microscopy
   b. fluorescence microscopy
   c. dark-field microscopy
   d. transmission electron microscopy
   e. phase-contrast microscopy
   f. scanning electron microscopy

6. Compare the results which can be obtained in using the hanging-drop procedure with those associated with simple stains.

7. What is the purpose of differential staining procedures? What are common examples of this type of technique?

8. What are the respective functions of the reagents used in the Gram stain?

9. What factors play prominent roles in determining Gram positivity?

10. What are the specific color characteristics of the cell types or microbial structures listed below after the performance of the standard Gram, acid-fast, and spore stains?
    a. *Staphylococcus aureus*
    b. *Escherichia coli*
    c. Gram-positive bacteria

    d. *Mycobacterium leprae*
    e. Gram-negative bacteria
    f. acid-fast bacteria
    g. spores and associated vegetative cells
    h. Gram variable organisms
    i. non-acid-fast cells
    j. Gram non-reactives

11. What factors contribute to the resolving power of a microscope?

12. What function is associated with immersion oil? How is this material applied?

13. Indicate the general range of sizes of the following microorganisms.
    a. bacteria
    b. protozoa
    c. rickettsia
    d. viruses
    e. fungi
    f. mycoplasma

14. Define "dye." What are the components of this type of chemical compound?

15. What is meant by an acid dye?

16. What types of cellular structures are stained by a basic dye?

17. Do dyes have functions other than staining?

Structural Properties of Typical Animal and Plant Cells

Woods, in his introductory contribution to the fifteenth symposium of the Society for General Microbiology, points out that, in the construction of buildings, the correlation of structure and function is deliberately planned; yet, in the case of a microorganism, its distinctive design "has emerged through the trial and error of mutation and selection." With the development of the electron microscope and associated techniques, the organization of microbial cells has been continually and effectively unveiled. The microbiologist, however, is still confronted with the task of clearly defining the function or functions of newly discovered components of microorganisms. Chapters 8, 9, and 10 will present the various known structural components (together with their functions) which contribute to the distinctive architecture of certain representative microorganisms. However, consideration will first be given to the characteristic cytological features of typical cells of higher animals and plants. This approach to microbial cytology is being used for several reasons, which include: (1) the desire on the part of the authors to clearly show basic structural differences between higher forms of life and microorganisms; and (2) the need to provide a basis for readers to understand certain features of resistance and pathologic processes presented in later chapters.

Historical Background

In 1665, more than three hundred years ago, the pioneer English microscopist, Robert Hooke, observed that cork consisted of small, box-like units which were suggestive of the living quarters used by monks. To these microscopic spaces, he applied the designation of *cell,* from the Latin word *cella,* meaning "small enclosure." What Hooke saw during his examinations was nothing more than the remains of cells—their cell walls. The fact that living cells contained "juices" became evident from other studies he performed.

Several years passed before microscopes were developed to the point where they were capable of magnifications sufficient to yield more detailed knowledge of cells (See Chapter 6). Up to 1833, a plant cell was known to be composed of a wall and green-colored bodies (now called *chloroplasts*). In this year the Englishman Robert Brown discovered that all cells, whether animal or plant, contained a large oval to round structure which he designated the nucleus (Figure 7–1). Within a short time after, the German botanist Matthias Schleiden uncovered a smaller intranuclear body. This structure was named the *nucleolus* (Figure 7–1). Schleiden also is known for his contribution to the formulation of the cell theory. While discussing the thinking of the times with

Theodor Schwann, a zoologist, he developed the concept that all organisms consisted of cells. This theory, which with some exceptions (such as viruses) is accepted today, also held that the cell represented a fundamental unit of both structure and function. The formulation of the cell theory gave rise to an important question, namely, where do cells come from? The answer was provided by Rudolf Virchow in 1855, who generalized the situation by stating that "cells come only from cells." In other words, new cells can only come into being through the division of previously existing cells.

By the turn of the century several of the specialized parts of the cell which are now referred to as *organelles* were known. However, their functions remained a mystery. From the late 1930s to the present day, procedures have been and are being developed to unravel the relationships of organelles to the functioning of the whole cell. Moreover, additional structures and processes are being discovered as a consequence of these studies.

Animal Cells

The cell is far from being simple, yet it is the basic unit of organization for relatively independent biological activity. Individual animal cells can differ substantially from one another in various properties, including function, shape, size, and structural components (see Color photographs 10 and 11). In essence a "typical" animal cell does not exist. Nevertheless, certain organelles are common to most cells (Figure 7–1). These and other cellular components, together with their functions and chemical composition, are discussed in the following section. The parts of the cell are organized into: (1) the cell membrane, (2) the nucleus and nucleolus, and (3) membrane-associated structures. The flagella and cilia of animal cells are included in the part of Chapter 8 dealing with bacterial flagella. The cells of higher animals and of plants are organized and differentiated into specific tissues (Color photograph 13). This topic will not be considered here to any great extent because

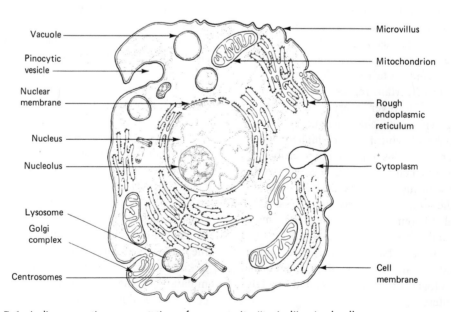

FIG. 7–1. A diagrammatic representation of a composite "typical" animal cell.

of space limitations. Readers are advised to refer to a general biology text for more information.

The Cell Membrane

The outer surface of an animal cell is bounded by a sharply defined elastic covering, sometimes referred to in a general sense as "skin." This portion of the cell, which can be called the *cytoplasmic membrane, plasma membrane,* or just *cell membrane,* is an integral functioning structure.

Membranes serve as partitions to subdivide the cellular space into many self-contained compartments in which biochemical reactions may occur. Structures similar to, if not identical to, the cytoplasmic membrane also surround intracellular organelles such as the nucleus, mitochondria, and endoplasmic reticulum. The plasma membrane of a eucaryote is "continuous" with the cell's internal membrane systems.

The cell membrane regulates the passage of molecules into and out of cells in a selective or differential manner, both passively and actively. When a cell membrane acts as a passive barrier, substances pass through it by simple diffusion, moving from an area of greater concentration to one of lesser concentration until an equilibrium is reached. Recent studies have shown that the membrane also contains certain regions which are capable of performing work in order to bring about the accumulation of certain molecules within the cell or causing the extrusion of others. This so-called "osmotic work" involves the expenditure of energy and is generally referred to as *active transport.* Cells that are actively involved in the transport of substances, such as certain ones in the intestine, frequently form elongated, slender processes called *microvilli* (Figure 7–1). As a consequence of such formations, the surface area is greatly increased, aiding absorption.

Mention should also be made here of the cell's ability to "trap" small quantities of the solution or liquid surrounding it. This transport process, called *pinocytosis* or "drinking-in," enables a cell to acquire high molecular weight compounds, such as proteins. The pinocytic mechanism begins by the invagination (folding-in) of the membrane, resulting in the formation of a sac, referred to as a *vacuole* or *vesicle.* The emptying of the vacuole's contents is controlled by its membrane. Reverse pinocytosis is referred to as *emeiocytosis,* or cell vomiting. This type of process may be involved with cellular secretion.

With the development of ultrathin sectioning and appropriate staining procedures, biologists were provided with means to obtain direct visual evidence for the structural arrangement of membranes. One of the current theories of membrane structure, proposed by Davson and Danielli in final form in 1954, holds that it is a three-layered (protein-lipid-protein) sandwich. Robertson in 1959 extended this biomolecular model concept to form the basis of his "unit membrane" theory. According to this concept, all membranes associated with a typical cell possess the protein-lipid-protein sandwich arrangement. Supportive evidence has been provided by x-ray diffraction and electron microscopy studies. In electron micrographs one can indeed see two electron-dense lines, each approximately 2.5 nm (25 Å) wide, enclosing a much lighter layer also about 2.5 nm (25 Å) wide. This membrane would be 7.5 nm (75 Å) thick. One serious drawback to such electron microscopy studies was the possibility that the use of chemical fixatives in preparing tissues might introduce artifacts. However, recent studies of membranes with the newly perfected freeze-etching technique, which does not employ chemical fixatives, also have shown a three-layered structural arrangement for membranes.

Recent studies have confirmed the classic model of membrane structure proposed by Danielli and Davson. In 1971 the lipid bilayer was confirmed by M. Wilkins working at Cambridge University in England. Some modifications, however, have been noted by several investigators with respect to the position and arrangement of proteins to the lipid bilayer. These modifications are as follows: (1) protein molecules are not arranged in an orderly array upon the lipid bilayer (Figure 7–2); (2) protein molecules actually penetrate the lipid region and may extend through it completely; and (3) protein molecules constantly move and reorganize their molecular configuration (shape).

Chemically, cell membranes are composed almost entirely of proteins and lip-ids. The proteins are enzymes that perform specific roles: the selective permeability property of membranes is associated with proteins. The lipids provide strength and other structural properties for the membrane. Membrane lipids constitute a category of compounds referred to as phospholipids. The molecules of these compounds are amphipathic, because one end is repelled by water (hydrophobic) and the opposite end is attracted to water (hydrophilic). The hydrophilic end, which carries an ionic charge and is polar, consists of glycerol attached to phosphate and other chemical groups. The nonpolar end consists of hydrocarbon chains of fatty acids (Figure 7–2).

Chemically, membranes differ from one cell type to the next. Analyses have

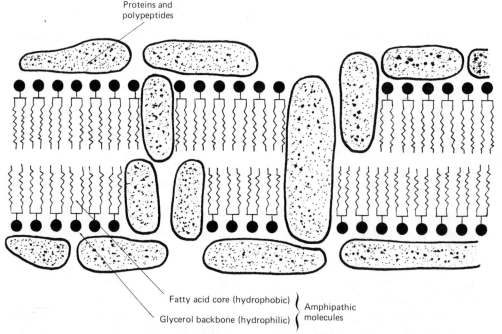

Proteins and polypeptides

Fatty acid core (hydrophobic) } Amphipathic
Glycerol backbone (hydrophilic) } molecules

FIG. 7–2. The structural arrangement of proteins and lipids in a plasma membrane. This cellular structure is described as a lipid bilayer sandwiched between layers of protein molecules. The proteins penetrate, and may even extend through, the membrane. (After Hickman, C. P., Sr., Hickman, C. P., Jr., and Hickman, F. M., *Integrated Principles of Zoology*, 5th ed., the C. V. Mosby Company, St. Louis, 1974.)

clearly demonstrated differences in types of lipids and in the protein-lipid ratios of membranes obtained from different cell types, i.e., erythrocytes and bacteria. The enzymic compositions also varied considerably.

From a functional standpoint membrane systems are involved with a large number of biological functions. Such activities include: (1) the active transport of substances across the membrane; (2) an involvement in protein synthesis; (3) phagocytosis (a process involving engulfment of foreign matter); (4) pinocytosis; (5) wound healing; and (6) increasing the movement of small molecules across the membrane.

The Nucleus and Nucleolus

Each cell of higher animals usually contains one small, generally spherical or oval structure known as the *nucleus* (Color photograph 10). The shape of the nucleus generally conforms to the particular shape of the cell in which it is found. During their maturation, certain cell types, e.g., mammalian erythrocytes (Color photograph 10), lose this organelle. Some cells found in the liver and stomach contain more than one nucleus, that is, they are *multinucleate*.

Structurally, the animal cell nucleus is basically similar to that of the plant cell. The nuclear sap, referred to as the *karyolymph* or *nucleoplasm*, is separated from the surrounding cytoplasm by a delicate nuclear membrane (Figure 7–3). This latter structure resembles the plasma membrane, but has large gaps. These so-called "nuclear pores" (Figure 7–3) provide for an easier passage of cellular substances. Chemically, the nuclear membrane is composed of lipid and protein. Slender threads of nuclear material called *chromosomes* occur within the karyolymph. These structures are quite thin and usually are evident during specific stages of mitosis (Figure 16–1). Chromosomes are composed of submicroscopic hereditary factors known as genes, i.e., *deoxyribonucleic acid (DNA)* and certain closely associated proteins.

Functionally, the nucleus is the cell's control center for its physiological processes. Included in these activities are the synthesis of nucleic acids, cell growth, and duplication.

The karyolymph of cells that are not undergoing reproduction usually contains one or more small bodies called *nucleoli* (singular *nucleolus*). The electron micrograph of a plant cell shown in Figure 7–7B shows these structures well. It is interesting to note that the total volume of the nucleoli within a nucleus is relatively constant. For example, if one nucleolus is present, it is generally quite large. However, if more than one such structure is present, the total volume of all nucleoli is approximately that of a single nucleolus. Chemically, these structures consist of protein and ribonucleic acid (RNA). Functionally, nucleoli may serve as storehouses of messages for the control of cellular activities. Such important information is generated by the DNA of the nucleus and is contained within a special form of nucleic acid referred to as *messenger ribonucleic acid* or *mRNA*. Eventually the mRNA passes into the cytoplasm.

Membrane-Associated Structures

Mitochondria (singular, mitochondrion). These organelles were first observed at approximately the turn of the century by the German cytologist R. Altmann. The mitochondria represent one class of cellular organelles that are primarily concerned with energy conversion. Chloroplasts constitute another type of specialized group of structures concerned with this cellular activity. They are discussed in the plant cell section. Mitochondria appear in the form of filaments, granules, or spheres (Figure 7–4A). Although the larger

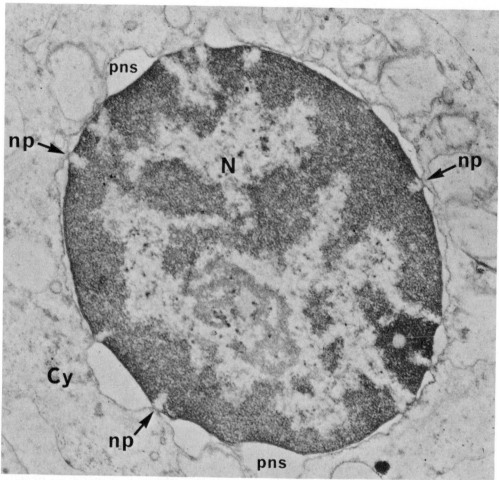

FIG. 7–3. A normal human lymphocyte which has been irradiated. Nuclear pores (*np*) are quite evident in this electron micrograph. Other regions and structures shown include the cytoplasm (*Cy*), nucleus proper (*N*), and perinuclear space (*pns*). (From Stefani, S., and Tonaki, H.: *Arch. Path.,* **89**:440–445, 1970. Copyright 1970, American Medical Assn.)

mitochondria can be viewed by light microscopy, the electron microscope and associated techniques are necessary for investigation of their ultrastructure.

Structurally, a mitochondrion is bound by a double membrane, the outer layer of which separates it from the surrounding cytoplasm. The inner layer is folded repeatedly into parallel ridges or plates, called *cristae* (Figure 7–1). These structures may extend to meet other cristae and actually fuse with them. Recent studies in-

volving electron microscopy have demonstrated the presence of stalked particles, or so-called "lollypops," at approximately 10 nm (100 Å) intervals along cristae surfaces (Figure 7–4B). These particles consist of: (1) a hollow stalk or stem portion, measuring 3.0 to 3.5 nm (30–35 Å) in width, and 4.5 to 5.0 nm (45–50 Å) in length; and (2) a spherical head structure having a diameter of 7.5 to 8.0 nm (75–80 Å). Although the exact function of these particles is not known, they are be-

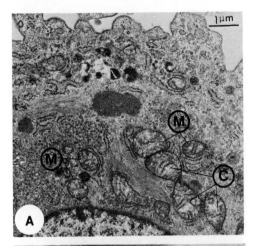

FIG. 7–4. Mitochondria (M). _A_. An electron micrograph showing the characteristic features of this organelle. Note the cristae (C) within the mitochondria. The Golgi complex (G) also is evident. (From Murad, T. M., _ACTA Cyto._, **17**: 401–409, 1973.) _B_. The enzyme-containing particles associated with membranes (the cristae), shown by negative staining and electron microscopy.

lieved to contain the enzymes needed for oxidative phosphorylation (a series of reactions in which oxygen is utilized and energy-containing compounds are formed and released) (Chapter 15).

The inner compartment of the mitochondrion contains a semifluid material, referred to as a _matrix_. Certain of the enzymes involved with the oxidation of fatty acids and those associated with the Krebs (citric acid) cycle are found here. The location of the enzymes as well as the functions of mitochondria have been determined to a large extent by biochemical procedures. Biochemists can separate these organelles from other cellular components by differential high-speed centrifugation. The rupturing of mitochondria

and the subsequent separation of their components provides additional material for analysis. From studies involving these and related types of procedures, the chemical nature of mitochondria has been determined, and it has been found that these organelles can produce a number of proteins, consume fat, and respire. Their primary function, however, still remains the release of utilizable energy. Hence, the designation of cell "powerhouse" has been given to these organelles. Chemically, mitochondria primarily consist of lipid, protein, and nucleic acids. So-called "satellite chromosomes," i.e., deoxyribonucleic acid-containing components, are present in mitochondria. Furthermore, recent studies have shown that mitochondria replicate independently within cells undergoing division.

Endoplasmic reticulum, ribosomes, and polysomes. The cytoplasm of cells actively engaged in the synthesis of proteins has been found to be heavily endowed with the components of a complicated system of membranes known as the _endoplasmic reticulum_ (ER). Other types of cells also have endoplasmic reticulum components, but generally fewer. This "membranous labyrinth" consists of canals and vesicles extending from the cell membrane deep into the interior of the cell (Figure 7–1). Continuous connections between it and certain cellular components, for example the double nuclear membrane and the Golgi complex, also have been demonstrated. Two general types of endoplasmic reticulum are known: rough-surfaced or _granular,_ and smooth-surfaced or _agranular_. The latter type consists primarily of membranes only, while the former is also associated with numerous small ribonucleoprotein particles called _ribosomes_ (Figure 7–5). These particles are bound to the endoplasmic

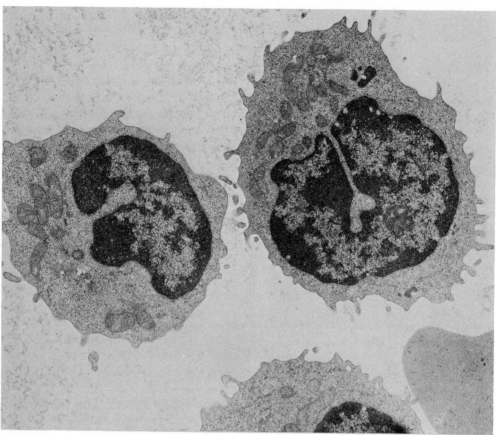

FIG. 7–5. An ultrathin section of two lymphocytes. Note the numerous dot-like ribosomes within these cells. What other organelles are obvious? (Courtesy of Dr. T. M. Murad.)

reticulum facing the cytoplasmic matrix, which is the semifluid ground substance of a cell, consisting of a variety of chemical compounds including amino acids, nucleic acids, and proteins.

Both types of endoplasmic reticulum may be present in the same cell. Functionally, the granular form is associated with protein synthesis, while the agranular ER is believed to have a secretory role of some type. The smooth endoplasmic reticulum (SER) is believed to be involved with lipid or fat synthesis and with detoxification of potentially harmful substances. Under certain circumstances, portions (vesicles) of the SER and the Golgi complex are almost indistinguishable. In fact,

the Golgi complex is sometimes considered as a specialized form of smooth endoplasmic reticulum. Other functions that have been suggested for the endoplasmic reticulum include: (1) providing a means for the transport of amino acids, carbohydrates, and related compounds to organelles such as mitochondria; (2) supplying needed nuclear membrane components during the specific stages of cell division; and (3) offering "preferential" pathways for the diffusion of the products of metabolism through the cytoplasm. Additional studies are being conducted to confirm these particular functions.

As will be emphasized in the chapter concerned with bacterial cytology, protocaryotic organisms, e.g., blue-green algae and bacteria, do not have an endoplasmic reticulum.

Chemically the ER primarily is composed of protein and lipid.

Ribosomes, as mentioned earlier, are associated with the endoplasmic reticulum. In addition, these submicroscopic structures can exist freely in the cytoplasm (Figure 7–5). Chemically, ribosomes are approximately one-half ribonucleic acid (RNA) and one-half protein. (Refer to Chapters 15 and 16 for a discussion of RNA and protein synthesis.) Physically, after chemical extraction treatment with phenol, the ribosome separates into two different-sized components. An aid in determining the size of the components is their sedimentation behavior in a high gravitational field produced by a centrifuge. The sedimentation characteristic is expressed in S (Svedberg) units, which reflect this property. Generally, the larger the particle being tested, the greater the S value.

Functionally, ribosomes are important participants in protein synthesis. Rich and his associates demonstrated that the most active ribosomes are those in clusters of four or more, called a *polysome* or *polyribosome* (Figure 7–6A). The individual components of such aggregrations are held together by a strand of another type of ribonucleic acid referred to as messenger RNA (Figure 7–6B). The ribosomes "collaborate" with this nucleic acid in the formation of protein molecules.

Golgi complex (golgi apparatus or bodies). Named after the Italian cytologist Camillo Golgi, this tightly packed assemblage of "membrane-limited vesicles" or sacs is generally found near the cell's nucleus (that is, it is *juxtanuclear*). The number of such cellular components per cell varies. These vesicles usually occur in two forms—as small spheres and as broad, flattened structures, frequently referred to as *cisternae* (singular *cisterna*). In electron micrographs of ultrathin tissue sections, the latter appear as networks of elongated, parallel, membrane-enclosed spaces which are stacked closely together (Figure 7–4). The membranous portions of the Golgi apparatus always are smooth, i.e., agranular.

The exact cellular function of the Golgi

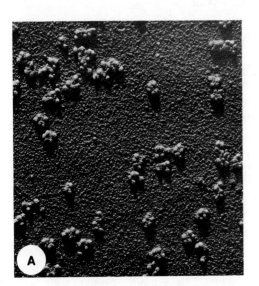

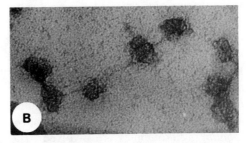

FIG. 7–6. Polyribosomes isolated from rabbit reticulocytes which were actively engaged in the synthesis of hemoglobin. _A_. An electron micrograph of platinum-shadowed polysomes. Note the clusters of ribosomes. _B_. Similar polysomes which have been negatively stained with uranyl nitrate. Thin strands of messenger RNA connecting these submicroscopic structures are evident. (Courtesy of Dr. Alexander Rich, Massachusetts Institute of Technology, Cambridge, Mass.)

complex is not completely understood. However, cytologists postulate that it functions as the temporary storage depot for certain cellular products before their secretion.

Lysosomes. Animal cells have recently been found to have among their membrane-bounded organelles small membranous vesicles containing a number of hydrolytic enzymes. These enzymes are capable of degrading nucleic acids, proteins, and other macromolecular constituents. In a normal, intact cell these enzymes are segregated in vesicular structures called *lysosomes* to prevent them from digesting cellular components. Upon the rupture of the lysosome, the hydrolytic enzymes are released and proceed to participate in the lysis and digestion of dying or dead cells. This type of activity is believed to be part of several processes, including pathological necrosis and phagocytosis (Chapter 20). Often confused with lysosomes are peroxisomes, membrane-bounded organelles with oxidative enzymes for the decomposition of hydrogen peroxide and for other functions.

Microtubules. Recent electron microscope studies have revealed a class of subcellular organelles, the *microtubules,* found in a variety of eucaryotic cells. These structures are long, straight cylinders with a diameter of 24 ± 2 nanometer (nm) and a hollow core approximately 15 nm in diameter. The walls of microtubules are composed of protein subunits called *tubulins*. Microtubules are involved in a wide variety of cellular processes. Their major functions include transport of material within a cell, ciliary and flagellar movement, development and maintenance of cell form and of chromosomes during mitosis. Microtubules are often grouped into two broad classes, based on sensitivity to antimitotic agents, temperature,

pressure, or other treatments. Easily disrupted tubules, called labile microtubules, include those that form the spindle fibers during mitosis, and are randomly distributed throughout the cytoplasm during other stages of the cell cycle. Stable microtubules (those that are more difficult to disrupt) are the usual components of cilia, flagella, centrioles, and related structures.

Plant Cells

The cells of higher plants (Figure 7–7) have several of the same organelles commonly found in animal cells, organized and differentiated into tissues. Brief descriptions of the four recognized main tissue types, fundamental, meristematic, protective, and conductive, together with the cells which comprise them, are given in Table 7–1. Representative light-microscopy stained preparations are shown in Color photographs 12 and 13. The discussion in this section will be concerned with plant organelles, their functions, and, in certain cases, their ultrastructure (Figure 7–7).

Cell Wall

Plant cells characteristically have an outer structure called a *cell wall* (Figure 7–8) that encloses the plasma membrane and the various organelles contained within it. Cell walls vary in both morphology and chemical composition, depending upon the age and type of cell. For example, the structure surrounding a young cell is single and is referred to as a *primary* wall; it is thin (approximately 1 to 4 μm thick) and relatively elastic. Its elasticity enables the cell to grow. In older cells, as growth ceases, a *secondary* wall forms between the primary structure and the remainder of the cell. This newly formed structure differs in chemical composition and physical properties from the primary wall. Sec-

Table 7–1   Main Plant Tissues

Type	Description
Fundamental	Three general forms of this plant tissue are recognized: parenchyma (Color photograph 5) collenchyma, and sclerenchyma (Color photograph 6). The *parenchymal* tissue cells are thin-walled, and contain large vacuoles. A modified form of this tissue, called *chlorenchyma,* is made up of cells with chloroplasts. Photosynthesis and food storage are the major functions of parenchyma, which makes up most leaves. *Collenchyma* tissue primarily is supportive in nature. Its cells have walls with especially thickened corners, and can be found in most plant stems. *Sclerenchyma* tissue provides support and mechanical strength to the roots, stems, and seeds of many plants. The cells of this form of tissue are greatly thickened (Color photograph 6).
Meristematic	The major function of this plant tissue type is to provide cells for the other types of tissue which make up a plant body. Most of the meristematic tissue becomes differentiated into other plant tissues. The cells here are small and thin-walled. A large nucleus is present. Meristematic tissues are present in the tips of roots and stems. This type of tissue makes possible the increases in length and diameter of certain plant parts.
Protective	As the name of this plant tissue states, its function is a protective one. The cells which make up this tissue have thick cell walls. They serve to prevent loss of water from the underlying tissues in a plant and to limit or prevent injury from mechanical abrasions, e.g., rubbing. The outer layer of leaves, the epidermis, and the cork layers found in roots and stems are examples of protective tissue.
Conductive	Two forms of conductive tissue are recognized, *xylem* and *phloem* (Color photograph 5). The former through the plant, while the latter transports water and dissolved salts conducts dissolved nutrients and products produced by the plant. Xylem cells also may function in a supportive way as they have rather thick cell walls.

ondary walls provide additional strength. Most plant cells have primary walls, but not necessarily secondary ones. Tissues which transport substances through a plant are made up of cells having both types (Color photograph 13). The ultrastructures of cell walls, as demonstrated by electron microscopic examples, are composed of strands referred to as *microfibrils*

within a complex mixture of compounds called a *matrix.* A common layer between the primary structures of cells, known as the *middle lamella,* serves to hold groups of cells together. Pits or small holes in cell walls permit the passage of materials from one cell to another.

Chemically, the polysaccharide cellulose, a compound composed of thousands of repeating units of the six-carbon saccharide glucose, is the primary structural component of cell walls. This is especially true for the primary wall of young cells and the middle lamella. Additional compounds found in these structures include derivatives of other six-carbon sugars, i.e., hexoses, called *hexuronic acids.* Secondary walls contain lignin, a compound which imparts rigidity and strength. It should be noted that the cell wall is not a living component of the plant cell.

Plasma Membrane

This structure, which also is common to animals, surrounds the cytoplasm of a plant cell, and separates it from the cell wall. The plasma membrane differs substantially from the wall in chemical composition, function, and structure. These differences are summarized in Table 7–2.

Plastids

Most plant cells contain specialized structures involved in the synthesis and storage of nutrients. These cellular bodies are called *plastids,* and include chromoplastids, leucoplastids, and chloroplastids (chloroplasts).

Chromoplastids.   These bodies contain carotenoid pigments which account for the color changes of flowers, fruits, and leaves, and are important in photosynthesis.

Leukoplastids.   In general, leukoplastids are colorless components of cells not exposed to light, which serve as storage

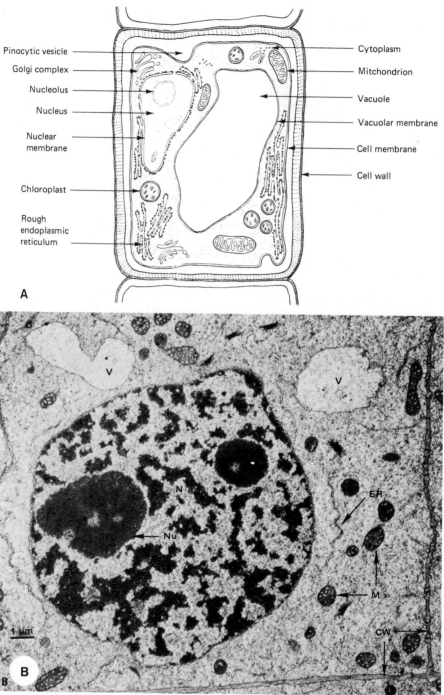

Pinocytic vesicle

Golgi complex

Nucleolus

Nucleus

Nuclear
membrane

Chloroplast

Rough
endoplasmic
reticulum

Cytoplasm

Mitchondrion

Vacuole

Vacuolar membrane

Cell membrane

Cell wall

A

FIG. 7–7. The plant cell. _A._ A composite dia-
grammatic representation of plant ultrastructure.
Note that many of the organelles found in ani-
mal cells are present here. Which ones are not?
_B._ Ultrathin section of an onion root cell. The var-
ious components of this cell include the cell wall
(*CW*), endoplasmic reticulum (*ER*), mitochondria
(*M*), nucleus (*N*), nucleolus (*Nu*), and vacuoles
(*V*). (Courtesy of Dr. R. B. Park, Department of
Botany, University of California, Berkeley.)

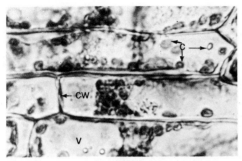

FIG. 7–8. A temporary wet mount preparation of a leaf of the common water plant *Elodea*. The cells shown are of a parenchymal type. Certain of the cellular components evident in this preparation for light microscopy include ones which distinguish plant cells from animal cells. Note the following structures: cell wall (*CW*), chloroplast (*C*), and sap vacuole (*V*).

centers for starch and related compounds. The structures can be found in the cells of roots and underground stems. Starch-containing leukoplastids are called amyloplasts.

Chloroplasts. These organelles are probably the best-known plastids of higher plants. Leeuwenhoek first observed these so-called "green-colored bodies" in plant cells.

Structurally, chloroplasts (Figures 7–8 and 7–9) are disc-shaped and measure approximately 2 to 4 μm in diameter and 0.5 to 1.0 μm in thickness. Ultrathin sections of these organelles examined in the electron microscope reveal the existence of an elaborate internal organization.

Within chloroplasts, series of parallel membrane layers situated close to one another can be observed (Figure 7–9). These membranes, which extend throughout the length of this organelle, are referred to as *lamellae*. In certain areas densely packed and highly oriented lamellae form *grana*. The lighter regions of the chloroplast are termed *stroma*. The membranes in the stroma and connecting the various grana are referred to as the *lamella of intergranum*. A double membrane delimits the chloroplast from the remaining portions of the cell's cytoplasm.

The internal arrangement and structure of chloroplasts differ among the various forms of life possessing these organelles. Generally, the type of organelle (i.e., structures with a double limiting membrane, lamellae, and grana) shown in Figure 7–9 is common to seed plants, mosses, and ferns. The chloroplasts of green, brown, and red algae are similar to these plastids, but grana are lacking. Algae which possess phycobillins (accessory photosynthetic pigments) also possess granules attached to their lamellae (Figure 7–10). Blue-green algae and photosynthetic bacteria have organelles containing photosynthetic pigments that are quite different from the structures which have been described for higher plants. No limiting double membranes are present in their pigment-containing organelles.

Table 7–2   Differences between a Plant Cell Wall and its Plasma Membrane

Property	Cell Wall	Plasma Membrane
Chemical Composition	Primarily carbohydrate. Secondary walls contain lignin	Lipid and protein
Function	Imparts rigidity and strength to the cell	Regulates the passage of substances into and out of cell, maintaining the integrity of the cell
Structure	Rigid and relatively thick. Primary walls range from 1 to 3 μm, while secondary structures exhibit thickness of 5 to 10 μm	Flexible and thin, approximately 7.5 nm (75 Å)[a]

[a] Other structural features of plasma membranes are described in the earlier section dealing with animal cells.

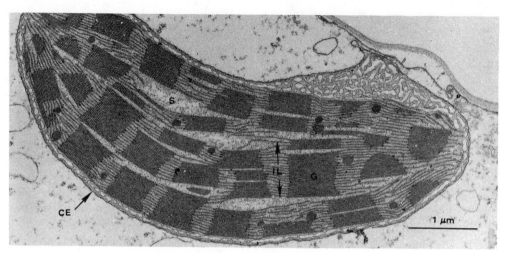

FIG. 7–9. An ultrathin section of a chloroplast (or chloroplastid) from a corn leaf (Zea mays). Note the closely packed lamellae which form the grana (G). Other portions of the chloroplast shown include the envelope or membrane (CE), the lamella of the intergranum (IL), and the stroma (S). (Courtesy of L. K. Shumway, Genetics and Botany, Washington State University.)

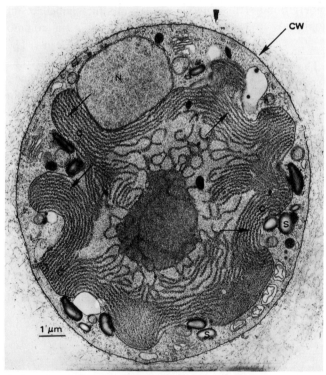

FIG. 7–10. An ultrathin section of the red algae *Porphyridium cruentrum*. Small granules (arrows) are attached to the chloroplast lamellae (C). These granules have an approximate diameter of 35 nm (mμ). These structures may be major sites of phycobillins (accessory photosynthetic pigments). Other structures shown include a nucleus (N), cell wall (CW), and the storage product, starch granules (S). (From Gant, E., and Conti, S. F., Datrmouth Medical School, Hanover, N. H.: *J. Cell Biol.*, 25:423–434, 1966.)

Chemically, chloroplasts primarily contain lipids, pigments, protein, and both ribonucleic and deoxyribonucleic acids. The pigments are perhaps the most distinctive of these compounds. These substances are universally found, and are of major importance in photosynthesis. Two major classes of pigments are usually present, the chlorophylls and the carotenoids. Carotenoids are yellow pigments, quite different in molecular structure from the green chlorophylls. Animals utilize carotenoids as a source of Vitamin A. Phycobillins also can be found in certain cases. These compounds are accessory photosynthetic pigments.

From the functional viewpoint, chloroplasts have one primary role, and that is to participate in the process of photosynthesis. This process forms the most important set of reactions. It involves the conversion of light energy into chemical energy, synthesizing carbohydrates from carbon dioxide, photosynthetic pigments, and water. The general over-all photosynthetic process can be expressed as follows:

$$6\,CO_2 + 6\,H_2O \xrightarrow[\text{chlorophyll}]{\text{light energy}} (C_6H_{12}O_6 + 6\,O_2 \uparrow)$$

Photosynthesis generally is divided into two parts. The first of these incorporates chlorophyll and light, and results in the conversion of light energy into chemical energy. This part of the photosynthetic process is called the *light reaction.* The second portion of photosynthesis is referred to as the *dark reaction,* since it is not light-dependent. Here the converted or trapped chemical energy is used for carbohydrate synthesis. It is important to note that oxygen generation occurs during the light reaction. This most important by-product is released into the atmosphere.

The relationship of chloroplasts to photosynthesis involves their internal structure. Chloroplast lamellae contain the photosynthetic pigments, which are actually composed of closely packed spherical structures called *quantasomes.* The light reaction is associated with the lamellar structures. The stroma contain the numerous substances necessary for the dark reaction. The details of the photosynthetic process can be found in several of the general references listed in the Appendix.

Vacuoles and Granules

In the majority of mature plant cells most of the central areas are occupied by bubble-like cavities called *vacuoles* (Figure 7–11). These cellular components are bordered by a vacuolar membrane, which resembles the plasma membrane in both structure and function—the regulation of the passage of materials into and out of the vacuole. In general, vacuoles are small in developing, growing plant tissue. However, they enlarge substantially as cells mature. As these vacuoles are located near the center of the cell, the general components of the cytoplasm are then pushed toward the cell's periphery and against the wall (Figure 7–11). The contents of vacuoles are mostly water, but other substances are sometimes found.

Various forms of inclusions called *granules* may be evident in the cytoplasm of plant cells (Figures 7–10 and 7–11). The most common of these perhaps is starch (Figure 7–10). These granules are storage centers of various solids, including fat, protein, and, as indicated earlier, starch.

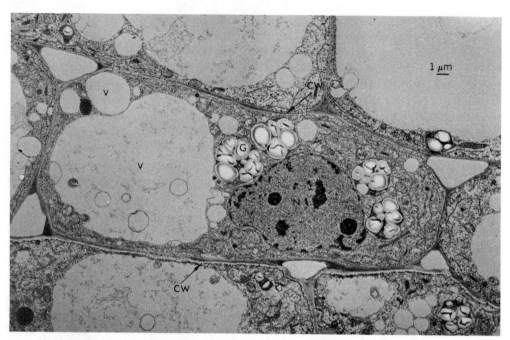

FIG. 7–11. An electron micrograph of a parenchymal cell from a cotton plant. Note the various
components which include granules (G), nucleus
(N), and vacuoles (V). The thin cell wall (CW) is
also evident. (Courtesy of Dr. R. B. Park, Department of Botany, University of California, Berkeley.)

QUESTIONS FOR REVIEW

1. Compare a typical plant cell with one
   of the animal variety as to structural
   similarities and differences.

2. Construct a table listing the functions
   and chemical composition of the following organelles.
   a. chloroplast
   b. cell wall
   c. polyribosomes
   d. cell membrane
   e. endoplasmic reticulum
   f. nucleus
   g. mitochondrion
   h. nucleolus
   i. microtubule

3. Describe the organization of the cell
   membrane according to the most recent theories.

The Arrangements and Anatomy of Bacteria

Bacterial cells are distinguished by morphological features which include shape, size, patterns of cell arrangement, and ultrastructure, or so-called "fine structural detail." Many of these properties are of great importance for: (1) the identification of a particular bacterial species; (2) uncovering specific structures and their related functions; and (3) correlating or integrating the various intracellular structures with the overall functioning of the organisms. This aspect may be referred to as *biochemical* and *biophysical anatomy,* since biochemistry, biophysics, bacterial cytology, and physiology are all involved. It is important to note that these bacterial properties can be affected by various factors, including temperature and the presence or absence of nutrients and toxic substances.

Shapes and Patterns of Arrangement

As noted in Chapter 4, the individual members of different bacterial species have one of three principal shapes, these being spherical or coccus (plural, *cocci*), rod-like or cylindrical, and spiral. The spherical bacterium can exhibit a number of different patterns.

Cocci can appear in the following arrangements:

diplococci: pairs of cells (Figures 8–1 and 8–2*A*)

streptococci: chains of four or more cells (Figure 8–1 and Color photograph 15)

tetrad: four cocci in a boxlike or square arrangement (Figure 8–1)

sarcinae: cubical packet consisting of eight cells (Figure 8–1)

staphylococci: irregular, grapelike clusters of cocci (Figure 8–1 and Color photograph 63)

On examination, cultures of cocci (as well as other organisms) will show a wide variety of different arrangements (Figure 8–2 and Color photograph 15).

Rods or *bacilli* (singular, *bacillus*), as they are sometimes called, generally are cylindrical or relatively long ellipsoids (Figures 8–1 and 8–2*B* and Color photograph 14). These cells may occur singly, in pairs (*diplobacilli*), or in chains (*streptobacilli*). With certain species the cells may appear to be rather small rounded rods. In other words, these cells are difficult to designate clearly as rod or coccus. Such cells are referred to as *cocco-bacilli* (Figure 8–2*B*).

Certain bacterial species may produce unique groupings of their cells. *Corynebacterium diphtheriae* is one example of this. The palisading property (arrangement of cells resembling a picket fence) of this organism and other members of the genus is well known. Spiral organisms (singular *spirillum,* plural *spirilla*) exhibit, depending on the species, significant differences as to the number and amplitude of spirals and the length and rigidity of the spiral turns or coils (Color photograph 95). Vibrios (Figure 8–3) are bacteria

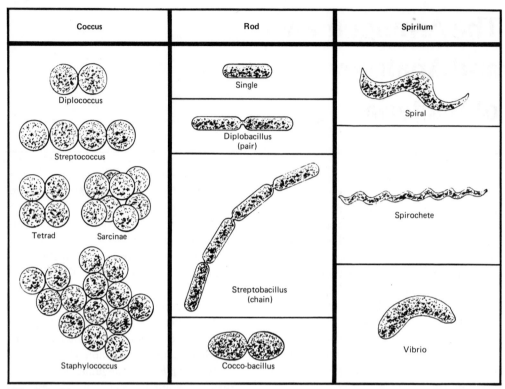

FIG. 8–1. Diagrammatic representation of the characteristic patterns of bacterial morphology and cell arrangement.

which consist of only a portion of a spiral. Other organisms possess several loose turns (Figure 8–3). The etiologic agent of syphilis, *Treponema pallidum* (Color photograph 95 and Figure 6–12) has a corkscrew appearance caused by the coils of the organism being compressed.

The majority of bacteria, as well as

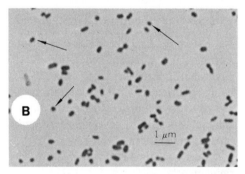

FIG. 8–2*A*. Electron micrograph showing the diversity in coccal arrangements found in a *Branhamella (Neisseria) catarrhalis* culture. Note the presence of diplococci, tetrads, and chains of cells. *B*. A photograph of a light microscope preparation showing rods and cocco-bacilli (arrows).

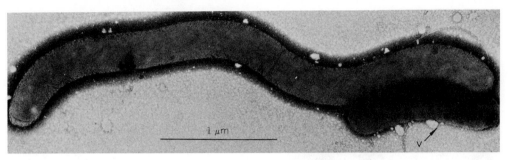

FIG. 8–3. Examples of the spiral organism *Rhodospirillum rubrum*. A vibrio (v) is also shown in this electron micrograph, clearly indicating the differences in these two forms.

other microorganisms, exhibit variation in their shapes and sizes. Such cells are referred to as *pleomorphic* forms when organisms are grown under generally normal conditions of growth and division cycles. The variant shapes may be either temporary or permanent. The mycoplasma are one group of organisms noted for their temporary pleomorphic nature (Figure 8–4). These organisms do not possess a rigid cell wall, which is characteristic of other bacterial cells. Permanent variation in shape is due to genetic change. *Involution* forms generally develop in response to unfavorable environmental conditions, such as the presence of toxic products or alterations in osomotic pressure. Cells of this type exhibit swollen, degenerative features.

Before microbiologists could begin their investigations of the molecular architecture of cells and the functional interrelationships of cellular components, knowledge of the chemical composition as well as arrangements of cell parts had to be obtained. Coordination and accurate, well-thought-out interpretations of the results obtained from extremely sensitive microanalytical chemical procedures, as well as extensive electron microscopic examinations of intact cells and isolated intracellular components were essential.

Several procedures can be used to disrupt microorganisms and obtain from these preparations the cell component or components to be studied. In general, "mechanical" means of cell disintegration are successful for such purposes. Techniques of this type include: (1) grinding or violent agitation with abrasive materials, e.g., alumina, glass beads, sand, or syn-

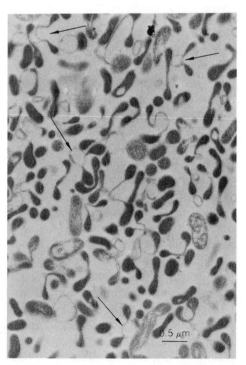

FIG. 8–4. The pleomorphic nature of the mycoplasma. Note the various shapes these organisms exhibit in this electron micrograph. (From Boatman, E. S., and Kenney, G. E.: *J. Bacteriol.,* **101**:- 263–277, 1969.)

FIG. 8–5. The Ribi cell fractionator. This instrument is used for the disruption of microorganisms. Generally, suspensions of cells are forced through a cooled needle valve under pressure. (Courtesy of I. Sorvall, Inc., Norwalk, Conn.)

thetic zeolite; (2) pressure cell disintegration (Figure 8–5); and (3) sonic and ultrasonic disintegration. With these methods disruption of cells generally occurs, releasing the intracellular contents. Combinations of centrifugation and washing of resulting preparations usually are employed to remove unwanted substances, for instance abrasives. The separation and subsequent isolation of particular cellular components, such as cell membranes, cell walls, enzymes, and ribosomes can be achieved through the use of a "regimen" of different centrifugation speeds (differential centrifugation). For example, bacterial cell walls can be removed from a suspension of disrupted cells by first employing low-speed centrifugation, speeds of approximately 3,000 to 4,000 times gravity ($\times g$), for ten minutes, followed by high centrifugation speeds of 10,000 to 20,000 $\times g$ for 15 to 30 minutes. Low-speed centrifugation generally will remove most unbroken cells and coarse debris in

the form of a sediment, leaving cell membrane components, the bulk of cell wall material, and soluble components, e.g., enzymes and ribosomes, in the supernatant (non-sedimented portion). The speeds specified for the high-speed centrifugation have been demonstrated to remove bacterial cell walls from this type of suspension.

The Bacterial Surface

Within recent years, the surfaces of bacterial cells have attracted the attention of various microbial specialists, including biochemists, geneticists, immunologists, molecular biologists, and physiologists. The results of numerous diverse and intriguing studies have provided knowledge of the transport of substances across surface barriers, the formation of surface structures, the effects of antibiotics, and the respective roles of bacterial surface components in the causation, diagnosis, and prevention of infectious diseases. This section will describe the currently recognized structures: (1) surface appendages (flagella and pili); (2) surface adherents (capsules and slimes); (3) the cell wall; (4) the protoplast membrane; and (5) axial filaments.

Flagella

These filamentous appendages of bacteria are responsible for their motility. It was the movements of bacteria which aroused the interest of Leeuwenhoek and drew his attention to the very existence of these microorganisms. In addition to being observed microscopically, motility today can be demonstrated in various semisolid media, i.e., those preparations which contain approximately 0.3 per cent agar. Motile organisms are recognized by the visible spreading of their growth throughout the medium.

In studying or identifying a bacterial

species, determining whether the organisms are motile or not can be significant. Care must be taken to distinguish true movement from the quivering or to-and-fro motion known as Brownian movement. The latter is caused by a bombardment of the bacteria by various molecules of the fluid in which they are suspended.

The formation or synthesis of flagella and their associated activity do not necessarily correlate with other bacterial physiological properties. However, it appears that flagellation does bear a direct relationship to growth rate. Both the logarithmic and maximum stationary phases of a growth cycle favor flagellar synthesis (see Chapter 14 for a discussion of growth cycles). Furthermore, Leifson indicates that several factors may affect flagellation, among them the chemical composition of media, pH, and the liquid or solid state of the medium. More flagellation occurs in liquid preparations. This finding also holds true for the formation of another type of filamentous appendage, pili (fimbriae).

The existence of locomotor organelles, i.e., flagella, has been inferred, according to Van Iterson, since the mid-1800s. Yet their visualization was not possible without the aid of electron microscopy and the Leifson flagella stain, used in light microscopy (Figure 8–6).

The flagella stain of Einar Leifson generally has been satisfactory for the demonstration of the majority of bacteria. In this procedure tannic acid, basic fuchsin, methylene blue, and sodium chloride are applied to bacterial smears. The methylene blue is used as a counterstain. In preparations utilizing this dye, bacteria stain blue and the flagella are red. However, in general all portions of cells appear red (Color photograph 19).

Flagellar shape and arrangement. These locomotor organelles are extremely delicate structures, as indicated by the relative ease with which they can be detached from their bacterial cells. Flagella in a stained preparation (Color photograph 19) generally exhibit an undulating appearance, and are long and slender. With most bacterial species the shape of these organelles is fairly uniform and constant.

The thickness of flagella has been observed to vary from species to species. In addition, differences as to the number and arrangement of these locomotor orga-

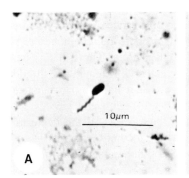 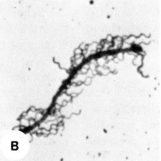 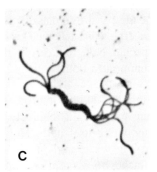

FIG. 8–6. Various shapes and arrangements of bacterial flagella. The magnification is the same for all preparations. (All micrographs are through the courtesy of E. Leifson. Preparations were stained by the Leifson flagella staining procedure.) A. *Pseudomonas diminuta* exhibiting polar monotrichous flagellation. The wavelength of the flagellum is quite short and very unusual. B. A fresh-water isolate, *Spirillum* sp. The lophotrichous form of flagellation. C. *Flavobacterium* sp. showing peritrichous flagellation.

Table 8–1   A Comparison of Classification Schemes Based on the
Number and Arrangements of Flagella

Scheme	Terminology	Brief Explanation
I	Atrichous	Absence of flagella
	Monotrichous	One flagellum at one end of a bacterial cell
	Amphitrichous	One flagellum located at each end of the organism
	Lophotrichous	Two or more flagella at one or both ends of a bacterium
	Peritrichous	Flagella surrounding the bacterial cell
II[a]	Polar	Two categories exist: a) *monotrichous,* the presence of a single flagellum at one or both ends of the bacterium b) *multitrichous,* two or several flagella at one or both ends of the cell In both categories, the bases of individual flagella are parallel to the long axis of the bacterium to which they belong
	Subpolar (rarely found)	Two categories also are recognized in this division. However, the distinguishing point is that the bases of individual flagella are situated at right angles to the long axis of the of the bacterial cell a) *monotrichous,* a single flagellum located near the pole or end of the cell b) *multitrichous,* several flagella near the pole of the bacterium
	Lateral	Flagella associated with this category appear to arise predominantly from the middle portion of the bacterial cell a) *monotrichous,* one flagellum b) *multitrichous,* several flagella in the form of a tuft originate from the mid-portion of the bacterium
	Peritrichous	A random, haphazard arrangement of flagella scattered around the bacterial cell
	Mixed	The presence of two or more flagella exhibiting distinctly different physical properties in different regions of the bacterial cell

[a] Adapted from Leifson, E.: *Atlas of Bacterial Flagellation.* Academic Press, New York, 1960.

nelles exist between bacterial species. Some organisms do not possess flagella, a condition referred to as *atrichous,* while others may have one (*monotrichous*) or several (*multitrichous*).

The terminology of classification has varied. Table 8–1 presents two sets of terms which are currently in use. It will be observed that classification scheme I is general, while scheme II is somewhat more specific. Note that certain designations are common to both systems.

Flagellar ultrastructure. A typical flagellum possesses a relatively uniform diameter along its length. However, near the region where this locomotor organelle attaches to a *basal granule* or *body,* just beneath the cytoplasmic membrane, a thickened, hook-shaped portion, the *basal hook,* can be observed (Figure 8–7*A* and *B*). Flagella are believed to originate in the basal body. In certain negatively-

stained preparations of various bacterial species, basal flagellar ends were found to be connected with a broadened body, designated by Hoeniger and Van Iterson as a *collar,* which in turn was connected by means of a constricted region, or neck, to a disc- or cup-shaped part (Figure 8–7*C*). The latter structure, which may have a paired disc appearance, is considered by certain investigators to be a detached segment of the basal body. The collar is believed to be a cell wall fragment. It should be noted here that a flagellum originates in the cytoplasmic region and pierces the cell wall as it emerges from the bacterial cell. In short, the locomotor organelles of bacteria are not appendages of the cell wall.

Bacterial flagella are much thinner than the cilia of vertebrates or the flagella of protozoa. The organelles of bacteria generally range in thickness from 12 to 15 nm (120 to 150 Å). Furthermore, bacterial

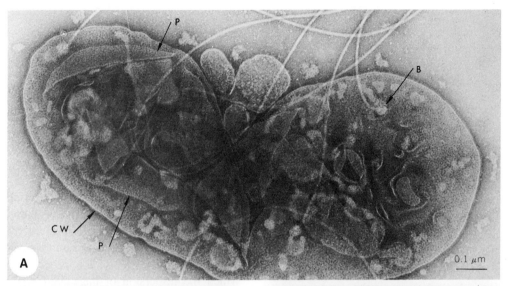

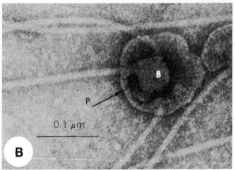

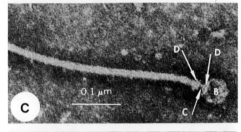

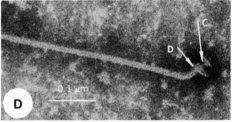

FIG. 8–7. Negatively-stained (PTA) preparations of *Proteus mirabilis* showing the origin of flagella and other components of bacterial cells. *A*. An electron micrograph of an osmotically shocked bacterial cell (suspended in distilled water after treatment with penicillin). Most of the cytoplasmic content of the cell has been eliminated, except for remnants of the plasma membrane (*P*) and basal bodies (*B*). The relatively fine structure of the cell wall (*CW*) can also be seen. *B*. Portions of plasma membrane (*P*) surrounding basal bodies (*B*) *C*. A micrograph showing the relationship of a basal body to its flagellum. Note the presence of a collar-like structure (*C*) on the flagellum, and a narrowing region where the flagellum is attached to the basal body (*B*). At this region of attachment in the basal body a more or less solid, disc-shaped structure can be seen (*D*). *D*. A clearer presentation of the flagellar collar (*C*), narrowed region of attachment, and disc-shaped structure (*D*). (From Hoeniger, J. F. M., Van Iterson, W., and Van Zanten E. N.: *J. Cell Biol.*, **31**:603–618, 1966.)

flagella do not possess the 9 (peripheral) + 2 (central) subfibrils characteristically found in the cilia and flagella of higher forms (Figure 8–8). Electron micrographs have demonstrated that the flagella of bacteria consist of an intertwining of three parallel protein fibers in a triple helical structure.

Chemically, the aforementioned fibers are composed of a single kind of protein, called *flagellin*. The molecular weight of flagellin is relatively low, approximately

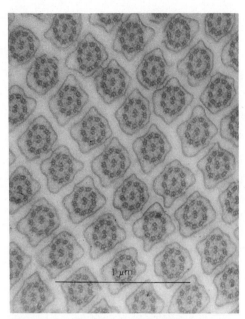

FIG. 8–8. An electron micrograph of a cross-section through the cilia of a rumen ciliate. Note the presence in each cilium of an outer ring of 9 pairs of fibrils surrounding 2 centrally located fibrils, characteristic of higher animals and plants. (Courtesy of L. E. Roth and Y. Shigesaka, Kansas State University.)

20,000 to 40,000. A unique amino acid, ε (epsilon)–N-methyl-lysine has been associated with this protein compound. Although a similarity in the amino acid composition and molecular weight exists among the flagellins obtained from different bacterial species, these compounds are by no means identical. This fact is demonstrated by the immunological specificity, i.e., the production of different antibodies, associated with flagella preparations from different bacterial species, sub-species, and strains. From a medical diagnostic standpoint, such differences are important in the identification of certain pathogens.

The motility observed with flagellated bacteria is believed to be associated with certain mechanical changes in the basal body. The mechanism or mechanisms responsible for movements of the nonflagellar species, such as spirochetes, certain

blue-green algae, and some slime bacteria (the myxobacteria), are not well understood.

Function. The advantages derived by bacterial cells from the possession of flagella are not thoroughly understood. Several investigators have suggested flagellar functions which include: (1) an ability to migrate toward environments favorable for growth and away from those which might be harmful; (2) a means of increasing the concentration of nutrients or decreasing the concentration of poisonous materials near the bacterial surfaces by causing a change in the flow rate of environmental fluids; and (3) a process by which the dispersion of flagellated organisms to uninhabited areas for purposes of colony formation can be achieved. In the case of pathogens, the suggestion also has been made that flagellated organisms may be able more readily to penetrate certain host defense barriers, such as mucous secretions.

Fimbriae or Pili

These structures are described as filamentous surface appendages that exhibit varying diameters and lengths. Their presence on bacterial cells can be detected directly with the aid of standard electron microscopy procedures, e.g., shadow-casting (Figure 8–9A) and negative staining (8–9B) or indirectly by hemagglutination tests (HA) (Figure 6–32).

Hemagglutination alone—which involves the clumping (agglutination) of red blood cells (erythrocytes) from a variety of laboratory animals—is not always a reliable indicator of the filamentous appendages, as the reaction can be caused by mechanisms other than those associated with fimbriae (known as "non-fimbrial hemagglutination"). Moreover, certain fimbriated organisms are known not to produce this reaction.

In general, pili (fimbriae) are differen-

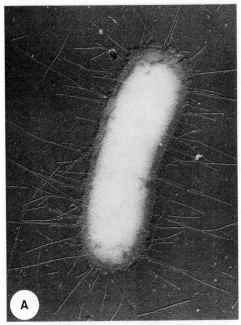

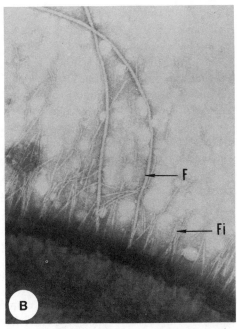

FIG. 8–9. Bacterial pili (fimbriae). _A_. Type I pili-
ated _Escherichia coli,_ strain K-12F. (Courtesy of
Drs. C. C. Brinton, Jr., and J. Carnahan, University of Pittsburgh.) _B_. A negatively-stained preparation showing a clear distinction between the
thin fimbriae (_Fi_) and the thicker flagella (_F_) of
Proteus spp.

tiated from bacterial flagella on the basis
of several properties, including: (1) their
smaller diameter; (2) the absence of the
snakelike appearance which is so characteristic of flagella; and (3) the apparent
lack of association with an organism's
motility. Two general classifications for
pili have been reported. One of these was
suggested by Brinton in the United States,
and the other by Duguid in England. Both
schemes propose the establishment of six
pilus types. The basic criteria used for
these classifications include physical dimensions, hemagglutinating properties,
and the sensitivity of hemagglutination
to the presence of the carbohydrate D-
mannose.

Chemical analyses of pili, specifically
Type I, have shown them to be primarily
protein. Specific homogeneous protein
subunits, called _pilin,_ interlock and form
the rigid, helical, tubelike pilus. The pro-

duction of Type I pili is under genetic
control.

These filamentous surface structures
have been found primarily in association
with Gram-negative bacteria. Included in
this group are members of the following
genera: _Escherichia, Klebsiella, Neisseria,
Pseudomonas, Shigella,_ and _Vibrio._ Recently, reports have appeared demonstrating the existence of pili in numerous
strains of the Gram-positive organism
Corynebacterium renale.

Function. The functions of pili include:
(1) adherence to most surfaces, cellular
or otherwise; (2) transfer of nucleic acids;
(3) formation of surface films of organisms (_pellicles_), which could enhance
microbial growth in still-culture situations
when the oxygen supply is limited; and
(4) use as receptor sites for bacterial
viruses.

Capsules and Slimes

Bacterial capsules have been described as organized or "distinctly oriented" accumulations of gelatinous material adhering to cell walls, in contrast to slime layers, which are unorganized accumulations of similar material. The presence of a slime layer usually is indicated when cultures demonstrate a stringy consistency when touched with an inoculation loop. With the aid of India ink and bright-field microscopy, capsules usually can be demonstrated as uncolored halos (clear zones) between the opaque background and the individual bacterial cells (Color photographs 20 and 21). Common procedures utilize suspensions of bacteria and India ink either in the form of a wet mount, or as a smear preparation. In the latter, safranin commonly is employed to stain the bacteria. The wet mount procedure tends to provide a more accurate indication of the true shapes and sizes of capsules.

Special staining and immunologic procedures also are used for the demonstration of these structures. The fact that capsules can be antigenic, i.e., cause the production of antibodies, has proved to be very important. For example, in the Quellung reaction specific anticapsular antibodies are used not only for the detection, but for the identification of unknown capsule-producing bacteria. In this technique, identification can be established if exposure of a particular bacterial agent to specific antibodies causes its capsular structure to swell. One application of this procedure is the differentiation of the large group of *Streptococcus (Diplococcus) pneumoniae* strains, which number more than seventy. The capsules are immunologically distinct.

Capsular antigens can be detected and localized using electron microscopy and ferritin-antibody conjugate preparations. Normally, antibody molecules do not possess a high electron-scattering capacity.

In order to increase this property, a protein molecule, ferritin, which has a high content of iron, is coupled to an antibody molecule. Specimens containing the specific antigenic material will combine with the ferritin-antibody conjugate. In the electron microscope the antigen plus ferritin-antibody conjugates are indicated by the accumulation of ferritin in the form of dark spots (Figure 8–10). In other words, wherever ferritin molecules are evident, specific antibodies and antigens have combined.

The production of capsules is greatly influenced by the genetic constitution of a bacterial species, as well as by environmental conditions. Consequently, a wide range in density, thickness, and adhering properties are found among strains of organisms. Capsule formation also can be dependent on the presence or absence of capsule-degrading enzymes and various growth factors. Electron micrographs of these structures generally do not show any

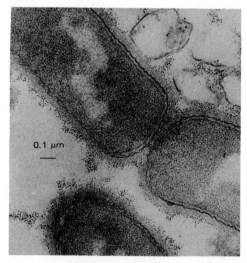

0.1 µm

FIG. 8–10. Detecting the presence of bacterial capsules with the aid of ferritin-antibody conjugates and electron microscopy. Note the concentration of ferritin (dark dots) surrounding the capsules of *Salmonella typhimurium*. (From Shands, J. W.: *N.Y. Acad. Sci.*, **133**:292–298, 1966. © The New York Academy of Sciences; 1966; Reprinted by permission.)

specific structural features; however, many of the so-called "true capsules," as opposed to slime layers, have been shown to possess definite borders.

Chemically speaking, capsules exhibit a varying composition. However, homologous structures have been found. Complex polysaccharides, either alone or in combination with nitrogen-containing mucin-like substances and polypeptides, are the most common constituents of bacterial capsules. Uronic acid is one type of compound commonly found in capsules but not frequently in cell walls. The characteristics of capsules associated with particular pathogenic microorganisms will be given in later chapters.

Encapsulation, i.e., capsule production, is quite important to certain pathogenic bacteria, as it influences their disease-producing capabilities. Capsules provide protection to such organisms against phagocytosis and bactericidal factors in the body fluids of their host. The loss of the capsule-producing property often results in reduction, if not a total disappearance, of disease-causing capacity. Many pathogens on their initial isolation from a diseased individual will form capsules. Examples of bacteria whose virulence is associated with capsulation include *Bacillus anthracis* (the etiologic agent of anthrax), *Clostridium perfringens* (the etiologic agent of gas gangrene), and *Streptococcus pneumoniae* (the etiologic agent of lobar pneumonia) (Color photograph 21).

Cell Walls

According to Nathan Sharon, the presence of bacterial cell walls was implied in Leeuwenhoek's descriptions of these microorganisms. Apparently he recognized the need for some type of structure which would not only preserve a bacterium's shape, but hold its cellular contents together. The rigid cell wall is the main structural component of most microorganisms, with the exception of L-forms, mycoplasma, and certain protozoa. Its presence was first demonstrated by placing bacterial cells in a very concentrated sucrose solution, which exerts a high level of osmotic pressure. The cellular membrane and its contents were seen to shrink away from an outer, bounding, rigid envelope. Thus the bacterial cell's outer structural limit was defined. Cell walls have several functions, including: (1) preventing the rupture of bacteria due to osmotic pressure differences between intra- and extracellular environments; (2) providing a solid support or "fulcrum" for flagella; and (3) as indicated earlier, maintaining the characteristic shape of microorganisms. The sites of attachment for the majority of bacterial viruses, i.e., bacteriophages, are associated with cell walls.

The cell wall may account for approximately 20 to 40 per cent of a bacterium's dry weight. Several factors can affect this contribution to the cell, including the organism's particular stage of growth and its nutritional deficiencies.

In recent years, the development of various types of equipment and techniques for the isolation and characterization of bacterial cell walls has provided much information on the chemical and ultrastructural features of these walls. Generally, this type of data is presented on a comparative basis showing the similarities and differences between Gram-positive and Gram-negative bacteria. A brief account of certain essential features is presented here.

The first chemical analysis of bacterial cell walls was carried out in 1887 by Vincenzi. His studies showed the presence of substantial amounts of nitrogen, and that this structure was not composed of cellulose, the common component of plant cell walls. During the 1950s and later years, Salton and others performed a number of analyses and observed the following general cell wall properties.

1. The presence of two simple sugars related to glucose (Figure 8–11) N-acetylglucosamine (NAG) and N-acetyl-muramic acid (NAM) (from the Latin word *murus,* meaning wall). The latter compound occurs only in bacteria and organisms closely related to them, such as blue-green algae and rickettsia. Both NAG and NAM are interconnected to form the glycopeptide or mucopeptide layer of the wall.

2. Cell walls may contain a variety of the naturally-occurring amino acids that form proteins. Included in this group are alanine, glycyine, glutamic acid, and lysine. (See Chapter 11 for a discussion of such compounds.) Differences exist in the amino acid composition of Gram-positive and Gram-negative cell walls.

3. Bacterial cell walls also have so-called "unnatural" forms of amino acids. In other words, the atoms which make up these molecules are organized differently than in "natural" amino acids.

4. Certain organisms contain a compound unique to them, namely, diaminopimelic acid (Figure 8–12). It is present in walls lacking lysine.

Certain chemical differences are known to exist between the walls of Gram-positive and Gram-negative bacteria. The latter structures are more complex, and contain a wide range of amino acids, significant amounts of lipid and polysaccharide, and protein constitutents. Combinations of these components, e.g., lipoprotein and lipopolysaccharide, also are present. Such compounds have antigentic and toxic properties.

The cell walls of Gram-positives are relatively thick, measuring approximately 15 to 18 nm. Moreover, they are uniformly dense (Figure 8–13*A*). The struc-

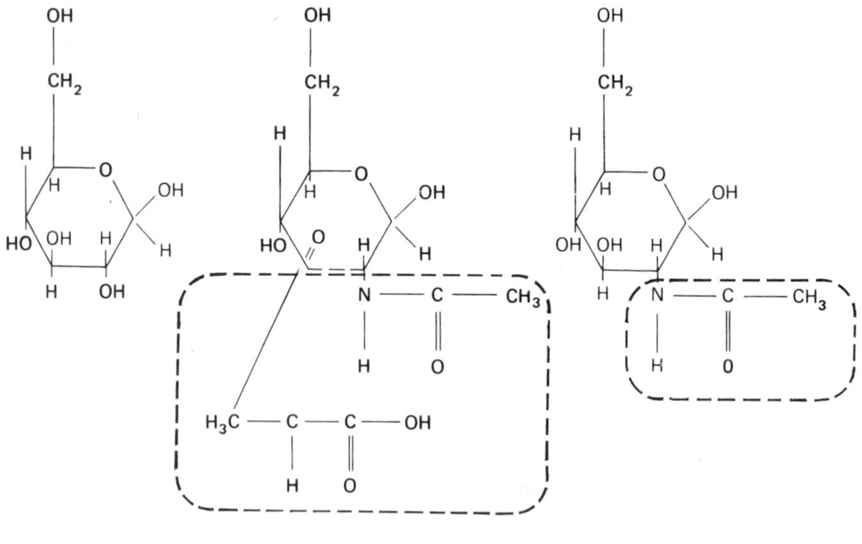

Glucose   N — acetylmuramic acid   N — acetylglucosamine

FIG. 8–11. The structural formulas of the amino sugars found in bacterial cell walls. For comparison glucose is included. The encircled portions of N-acetylmuramic acid (NAM) and N-acetylglucosamine (NAG) indicate where these compounds differ from glucose. (After Sharon, N.: *Sci. Amer.,* **220**:92, 1969.)

tures of Gram-negative bacteria are relatively thinner, approximately 10 nm thick (Figures 8–14 and 8–15).

A so-called "backbone layer" or membrane in both types of walls imparts the mechanical rigidity or strength to these structures. It is the innermost part of the cell wall, next to the cell membrane, and is composed of N-acetylglucosamine and N-acetylmuramic acid. The term *murein sacculus* has been given to the backbone or rigid layer (Figure 8–16). Additional layers composed of proteins and lipopolysaccharides apparently cover this cell wall component of Gram-negative organisms. The Gram-positive bacteria may have special polysaccharides such as teichoic acids associated with their cell walls.

Protoplasts (Gymnoplasts) and Spheroplasts (Semi-gymnoplasts)

Under certain conditions bacterial cells may lose all or a portion of their walls. Two general procedures are known which can bring about this state, namely: (1) culturing organisms in the presence of a poisonous substance, such as penicillin, or depriving cells of essential nutrients needed in the formation of their cell walls; and (2) treating cells with enzymes capable of hydrolyzing linkages in the

rigid layer, the murein sacculus, of bacterial walls. When the cytoplasmic membrane is found either to contain only trace amounts of cell wall or to be completely free of such material (Figure 8–13B), the term "protoplast" usually is used to denote the remaining unit. This designation customarily is employed in relation to Gram-positive organisms. In the event that cell wall material is not completely removed from the bacterium, the word "spheroplast" is employed. Usually this term is used for rounded Gram-negative organisms which have developed as a consequence of the treatments mentioned above.

Penicillin, when introduced in proper concentrations and under appropriate culture conditions, can transform growing cells of several species, e.g., *Escherichia coli* and *Salmonella typhimurium*, into spheroplasts. The antibiotic functions in this manner by inhibiting cell wall synthesis at a particular point in the process.

The enzyme lysozyme has been used by numerous investigators to produce cells either completely or almost free of wall material. The classic studies of Tomcsik and Guex-Holzer in 1952, and those of Weibull in 1953, demonstrated that rod-shaped cells are converted as a result of such treatment into osmotically sensi-

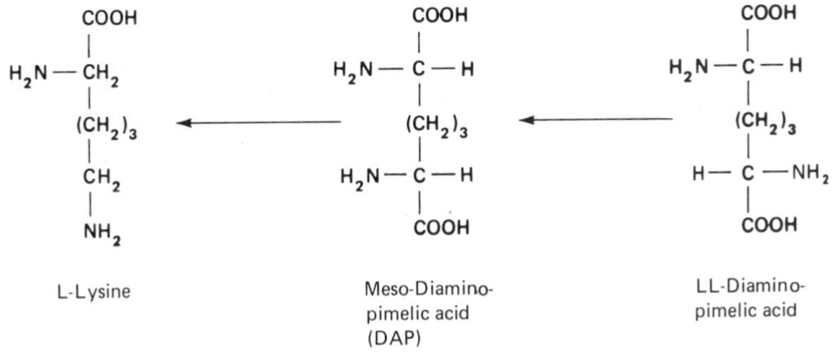

FIG. 8–12. The structural formulas of L-lysine and meso and LL-diamino-pimelic acids. Certain organisms utilize LL-DAP in their cell walls, while others convert its derivative meso DAP into lysine for wall formation. A specific decarboxylase accomplishes this step by removing a carboxyl group (COOH).

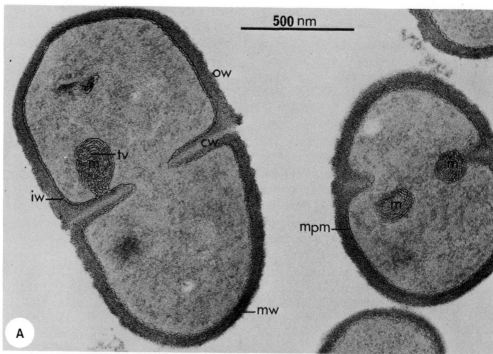

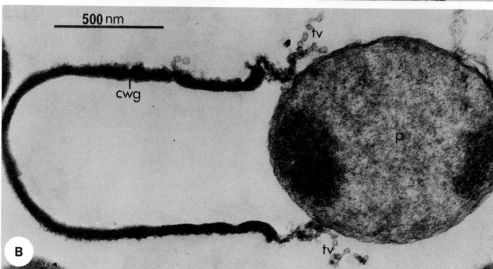

FIG. 8–13A. An electron micrograph of dividing cells of *Lactobacillus casei* showing thick outer walls (*ow*) and middle cell walls (*mw*) extending into the areas of cross-wall or septum formation (*cw*). The darkly stained inner cell wall (*iw*) of the cell on the right is seen in the peripheral region but not in the cross wall. The cell membrane (*mpm*) of the cell on the left is closely applied to the wall and cross wall, and can be seen to extend into and to surround the meso-some (*m*) boundary. Mesosomes, together with their tubular-vesicular (*tv*) components, are quite evident. *B*. A protoplast (*p*) of *L. casei*. Note the absence of a cell wall and of mesosomes. The tubular-vesicular (*tv*) components of the meso-somes are attached to the cell wall ghost (*cwg*) with protoplast formation. (Courtesy of Thorne, K. J. I., and Barker, D. C.: *J. Gen. Microbiol.*, **70**:87–98, 1972.)

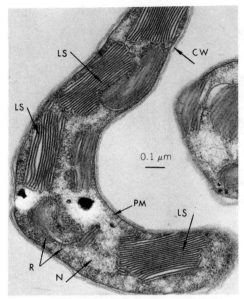

FIG. 8–14. An electron micrograph of a thin section of *Ectothiorhodospira mobilis* showing its general internal arrangement. Included are: multilayered cell wall (*CW*), lamellar stacks (*LS*), nucleoplasm (*N*), plasma membrane (*PM*), and ribosomes (*R*). This organism is classified as a photosynthetic, Gram-negative, motile bacterium. (From Remsen, C. C., Watson, S. W., Waterbury, J. B., and Truper, H. G.: *J. Bacteriol., 95*:- 2374–2392, 1968.)

tive spherical structures. In order to prevent the lysis, i.e., disruption, of such cells, procedures of this type are performed in stabilizing solutions, such as polyethylene glycol or sucrose. Precautionary measures of this type are necessary regardless of the method used for protoplast or spheroplast production.

Studies concerned with the removal of cell walls from intact bacteria have clearly shown that, in an osmotically stable medium, or protective environment, treated cells generally assume a spherical shape, regardless of the original shape of the cell. The investigations of Weidel and his associates in 1960 demonstrated that it is the rigid mucopeptide layer in bacterial cell walls that is responsible for their shape.

Morphologically, isolated protoplasts do not contain mesosomes (Figure 8–13*B*). The latter cell components are intracytoplasmic membranous organelles which usually are present in dividing vegetative cells and which are associated with various important processes, e.g.,

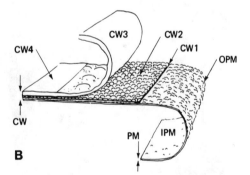

FIG. 8–15. The ultrastructure of the cell envelope of the Gram-negative bacterium *Escherichia coli* as shown by freeze-etching. *A.* A cell envelope fractured along a convex surface. The cell wall portion (*CW*) shown has a wavy appearance, with small particles and fibrils attached to it. The region underlying the cell wall is the outer surface of the plasma membrane (*OPM*). Note the smoother region with occasional blunt protrusions in associate with the plasma membrane. *B.* A schematic representation of the envelope

of *E. coli.* The structural detail shown has not been drawn to scale. Looking from the outside inwards, four cell wall surfaces can be seen· *CW*1, the mucopeptide layer; *CW*2, the globular protein layer; *CW*3, the inner surface; and *CW*4, which includes two aspects of the outer surface—the smooth and wavy varieties. The wavy region represents the lipoprotein and lipopolysaccharide complex. (From Nanninga, N.: *J. Bacteriol.,* **101**:297–303, 1970.)

FIG. 8–16. An electron micrograph of a normal rod-shaped murein sacculus. (Courtesy of Schwarz, U., and Leutgeb, W.: *J. Bacteriol.*, **106**: 588–595, 1971.)

nucleoid division, sporulation, and transverse septum development.

L-forms. Certain bacteria can spontaneously give rise to variants that can increase their numbers (replicate) in the form of small filterable cells with defective or absent cell walls (Figure 8–17). These organisms, called *L-forms,* can also be formed by several other species when their cell wall synthesis is inhibited or impaired. L-forms can occur both *in vitro* and *in vivo*. Penicillin and other antibiotics, specific antibody, and lysosomal enzymes that degrade cell walls are specific agents that can create the environment necessary for L-form production in the tissues of a suitable host. The role of these organisms

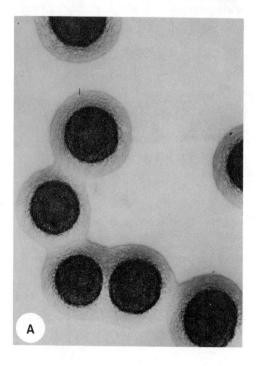

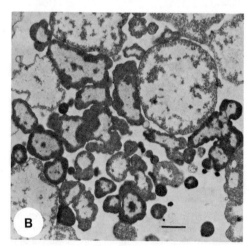

FIG. 8–17. L-forms. _A._ Photomicrograph of L-form colonies of *Bacillus subtilis*. _B._ Electron micrograph of an ultrathin section cut through an L-form colony. Note the absence of cell walls and the irregular shapes of the cells in the photo. The bar marker represents 1μm. (Wyrick, P. B., and Rogers, H. J.: *J. Bacteriol.*, **116**:456–465, 1973.)

in the causation of disease remains unclear. However, L-forms have been isolated from several disease states in humans, lower animals, and plants.

L-forms are morphologically equivalent to protoplasts and spheroplasts (Figure 8–17). However, the designation of L-form is restricted to cells that can multiply. Some L-forms revert to normal cell-wall-containing vegetative cells in a suitable host or in favorable media, whereas others maintain their morphological property. Special media must be used for the isolation and growth of all L-forms.

Structures Interior to the Cell Wall

Bacterial Plasma Membrane

This structure lies just beneath the organism's cell wall. It is a "discrete and differentiated" cellular component. The plasma membrane, in addition to serving as an osomotic barrier that passively regulates the passage of materials into and out of the cell, participates in the active transport of various substances into the bacterial cell. Active transport provides bacteria as well as other microorganisms with certain advantages, including the ability to maintain a fairly constant intracellular ionic state in the presence of varying external environmental ionic concentrations and the means with which to capture nutrient materials present in low concentrations in media. Membranes contain several types of transport systems for such substances as amino acids, mineral ions, sugars, and related compounds.

The bacterial plasma membrane also participates in the outward transport of molecular waste products, certain "building block" substances necessary in the formation of surface structures, and exoenzymes. The membrane and membrane-associated structures, e.g., mesosomes, are important to the energy-producing reactions of the cell.

Chemically, the plasma membrane of bacteria consists of both proteins and lipids. Sterol, a type of high molecular alcohol compound, characteristically is not found in the bacterial or blue-green algal membranes, but is a common constituent of higher forms. The exact structural arrangement of bacterial membranes remains undetermined at this time. However, they range from 5 to 8 nm in thickness and comprise 10 to 20 percent of a bacterium's dry weight.

Axial Filaments

Spirochetes, which have flexible cell walls, move by unique structures called axial filaments. Electron micrographs have revealed that each filament is composed of two fibrils identical in structure to flagella. The fibrils originate from either pole of the organism and extend toward the other pole between two layers comprising the cell wall (Figure 8–18). There is an apparent overlap in the organism's mid-region.

Mesosomes

Bacterial membranous structures were observed in *Mycobacterium avium* (the cause of tuberculosis in birds) by Shinohara, Fukushi, and Suzuki in 1957. Since then, many other investigators have found organelles of this type in various bacterial species. Several terms have been used to designate such membranous structures; these include chondroid, intracytoplasmic membrane, plasmalemmosome, and mesosomes. The last-named term has been widely accepted and consequently will be used in this textbook.

Mesosomes have been reported to occur primarily in species of various Gram-positive bacterial genera. Included among this group of organisms are members of

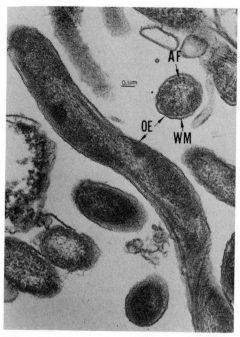

FIG. 8–18. Electron micrograph of a treponeme cross section showing the following: the outer envelope (*OE*), the cell-wall membrane (*WM*), and axial filaments (*AF*). (Courtesy of Johnson, R. C., Wachter, M. S., and Ritzi, D. M.: *Inf. and Immun.*, **7**:249–258, 1973.)

Bacillus, Lactobacillus (Figure 8–13), *Staphylococcus*, and *Streptococcus*. Membranous structures similar to the mesosomes of Gram-positives are seldom seen in Gram-negative bacteria. The appearance of their organelles differs substantially. Mesosomes in Gram-positive bacteria generally appear as pocket-like structures and contain tubules, vesicles (Figure 8–13), or lamellae (folded membrane arrangement). Gram-negative organisms primarily exhibit the lamellar form.

It is important to distinguish mesosomes from the extensive intracellular membranous systems associated with the specific functions performed by nitrogen-fixing, nitrifying, and photosynthetic bacteria (Figure 8–14). The discussion which follows will concentrate on mesosomal structures of Gram-positive organisms.

Fine structure and function. The variations in the morphology of mesosomes observed in electron micrographs appear to be caused by the fixative and fixation procedure used in specimen preparation. In general, using *Lactobacillus casei* as our example, a mesosome pocket results from the in-folding of a membrane (invagination) (Figure 8–13). Frozen-etched preparations of bacilli have clearly shown that mesosomes are morphologically different from the cell's outer membrane. Chemical and functional differences have also been noted. A single coiled tube is believed to occupy the membrane invagination.

Functionally, mesosomes appear to be utilized in several bacterial processes, essentially, to increase the cell's membrane surface, which in turn increases enzymatic content. A relationship seems to exist between the "enzymatic needs" of cells and the formation of new mesosomes.

The activities with which mesosomes have been associated include: (1) cell wall synthesis; (2) division of nuclear material; (3) cellular respiration; and (4) sporulation. With respect to nuclear division, which involves the segregation of DNA, and cell wall synthesis, mesosomes do not seem to be indispensable. These procedures have been observed to occur in the absence of such membranous organelles.

Bacterial Nucleus
(Chromatin Body, Nucleoid)

Procaryotic cells lack the distinct structure known as the nucleus in eucaryotic cells. In addition, bacteria and blue-green algae, i.e., procaryons, do not possess other features and structures characteristically associated with higher forms, such as a mitotic apparatus, nuclear membrane, and nucleolus. The bulk of the DNA in procaryons appears to be concentrated in one or several regions within them. No membrane specifically surrounds this concentration of nucleic acid. Because of this difference in the internal organization of the nuclear region, the DNA-containing structures are not considered to be true nuclei. The terms used to designate them vary, and include *bacterial nucleus, nucleoid, chromatin,* and *nuclear body.*

Nucleoids can be observed by several means. With light microscopy such structures can be observed using special procedures such as the use of DNA-specific stains (Feulgen, or the fluorescent dye acridine orange) (Color photograph 120) and the use of hydrochloric acid (HCl) or ribonuclease (RNase) for the hydrolysis of the ribonucleic acid (RNA) in fixed bacterial cells. The latter technique tends to remove the RNA which is densely packed around the DNA of the cell's nuclear region. Thus, when a basic dye is applied after this treatment the nucleoids can be readily recognized.

The techniques of electron microscopy also have provided means with which to study the nuclear regions of bacteria in more detail. The appearance of nucleoids can be affected by various factors. For example, depending on the procedure used for fixation, nuclear regions may appear as coarse, dense bodies, or as bundles composed of relatively fine fibrils. The condition of the culture also can alter the features of nucleoids in electron micrographs.

Ribosomes

In bacteria and in related microorganisms, e.g., blue-green algae, a large portion of the ribosomes appear to be free in the cytoplasm. In ultrathin sections these submicroscopic structures appear as fine granules within the cell's interior. Ribosomes can be obtained from bacteria by first disrupting them with acid then centrifuging the resulting homogenate at high speeds (100,000 × *g*) for 1 to 3 hours.

FIG. 8–19. Tungsten-shadowed 50 S ribosomes of *Escherichia coli*, including interpretive drawings of the surface features of the ribosomal subunits. Bar marker represents 0.01 μm (μ). (From Bassel, A. R., and Campbell, L. L.: *J. Bacteriol.*, **90**:811–815, 1969.)

The recovered bacterial spherical particles generally have a sedimentation coefficient of 70 S. Each ribosome is composed of one 30 S and one 50 S particle (Figure 8–19). By weight these ribosomes are somewhat smaller than those found in eucaryotic cells and other microbial types. They are estimated to account for approximately 40 per cent of a bacterium's dry weight. The ribosomes of green algae, fungi, and protozoa have values of 80 S. Such structures are made up of one 40 S and one 60 S particle.

Chemically, ribosomes are composed of approximately 40 per cent protein and 60 per cent RNA; 90 per cent of a bacterial cell's total RNA is associated with these structures.

As with other forms of life, ribosomes are important components of the protein synthesizing process. Groups of these units, held together by strands of messenger RNA, i.e., polyribosomes or polysomes (Figure 8–20), are the sites where such activity takes place.

Chromatophores, the Photosynthetic Apparatus of Procaryons

Blue-green algae (Color photograph 1) and certain algae-like species of bacteria carry out the essential steps of photosynthesis in pigment-bearing granules. These structures differ from the complex cellular component, the chloroplast (Figure 7–9), which is found in eucaryotic plants: procaryons lack true chloroplasts. The photo-

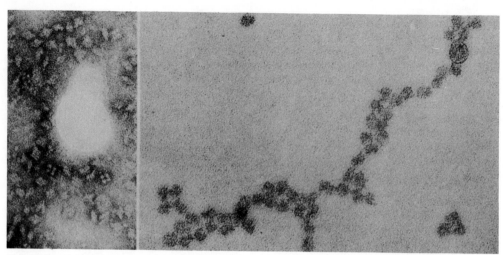

FIG. 8–20. Electron micrographs of negatively stained polyribosomes of *Escherichia coli*. These preparations were obtained by high-speed cen-trifugation. (Courtesy of Dr. A. Rich, Massachusetts Institute of Technology, Cambridge, Mass.)

synthetic membranes of bacteria, called *chromatophores,* and those of blue-green algae, *thylakoids,* are not membrane-enclosed nor are they self-duplicating structures. Furthermore, they are heavier and larger than ribosomes. The organelles of a similar pigment-containing nature in brown algae, diatoms, and in dinoflagellates are called *phaeoplasts.* Red algae have *rhodoplasts.* The photosynthetic membranes of blue-green algae and several photosynthetic bacteria extend through these organisms in a parallel arrangement (Figure 8–14). Spherical vesicles (i.e., spindle-shaped bodies) connected by narrow constrictions also have been observed in some photosynthetic procaryons. The photosynthetic apparatus of these microorganisms is apparently associated with their cytoplasmic membranes, and possesses oxidative and synthetic enzymes.

Photosynthetic bacteria do not contain pigments which are characteristically found in the blue-green algae or in higher plants, but possess *bacteriochlorophylls.* The chlorophylls found in these organisms are bacteriochlorophylls *a*—the main chlo-rophyll found in photosynthetic bacteria —and *b* and *Chlorobium* chlorophylls 650 and 660. The latter two pigments are found in the green sulphur bacteria.

Selected Cytoplasmic Inclusions

During respective growth cycles certain bacteria can accumulate several kinds of reserve materials, water-insoluble and water-soluble. Such accumulations, which are "non-living bodies," are called *inclusions,* and include metachromatic granules, lipids, polysaccharides, and certain inorganic substances. Some of these cellular inclusions are common to a wide variety of microorganisms, while others appear to be limited to a few, and can be extremely useful in the identification of certain bacterial species. For example, metachromatic granules (Figure 8–21) are quite conspicuous as characteristically found in *Corynebacterium diphtheriae,* the etiologic agent of diphtheria. Obviously, such cytoplasmic inclusions are of diagnostic importance. The demonstration of these various accumulations can be achieved by several methods. The choice of procedure is generally deter-

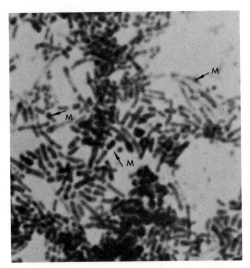

FIG. 8–21. A preparation of *Corynebacterium diphtheriae* stained by an aged methylene blue solution. Note the characteristic arrangements of the bacterial cells. Such formations are associated with members of the genus *Corynebacterium*. Metachromatic granules (M) can also be seen. (Courtesy of J. Mosley, East Los Angeles College.)

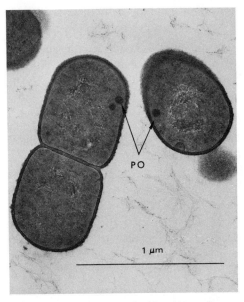

FIG. 8–22. A section of *Microbacterium thermosphactum* showing polymetaphosphate inclusions (PO). (From Davidson, C. M., Mobbs, P., and Stubbs, J. M.: *J. Appl. Bact.*, **31**:551–559, 1968.)

mined by the chemical nature of the inclusion type in question.

Cytoplasmic inclusions have been divided into two major groups based on the presence or absence of a surrounding membrane.

Non-Membrane-Enclosed Inclusions

Metachromatic granules. These inclusions are found in several types of microorganisms, including algae, bacteria, fungi, and protozoa. The actual chemical composition of metachromatic granules (also called Babes-Ernst granules or volutin) has been disputed for some time. Certain investigators hold that they are polymerized inorganic phosphate. Others contend that the granules are composed of nucleic acid, lipid, and protein. Metachromatic granules are considered to be used for the temporary storage of reserve food material.

Traditionally, these inclusions have been identified with the aid of staining procedures using an aged solution of methylene blue or toludine blue. When volutin-containing cells are stained with the former reagent, the granules take on reddish-blue and violet tones, thus producing the phenomenon of *metachromasia*. The age of the dye preparation used is important. As the dye ages, dimers and trimers of methylene blue molecules are formed. These are responsible for the multiple staining effect. Unstained, such inclusions appear refractile in the light microscope and opaque in the electron microscope (see Figure 8–22).

Polysaccharide granules. Examples of these granules include glycogen and starch. Iodine solutions generally have been used for their demonstration. Those areas producing a bluish coloration are considered to be starch-containing, while those with a reddish-brown color generally are designated as glycogen.

Membrane-Enclosed Inclusions

The barrier surrounding all of these inclusions is of a non-unit membrane type. Current evidence indicates it is composed entirely of protein. Examples of these inclusions include lipid inclusions, sulfur globules, and gas vacuoles.

Lipid inclusions.

Lipid droplets have been reported to occur in numerous bacteria, including species of the genera *Azotobacter, Bacillus, Corynebacterium, Microbacterium, Mycobacterium,* and *Spirillum.* Generally speaking, fat granules appear most regularly in Gram-positive species. These inclusions become more prominent as the bacterial cell ages.

Lipids may take the form of either neutral fats or granules of polymerized β-hydroxybutyric acid (Figure 8–23). The latter is an important "sole storage lipid" in certain organisms.

For light microscopy, lipid or poly-β-hydroxybutyrate granules can be stained easily with fat-soluble dyes such as the Sudan series. With simple stained preparations of fat-containing cells, colorless areas or vacuoles representing these inclusions usually are evident.

Gas vacuoles.

Gas vacuoles are complex organelles composed of an array of substructures referred to as gas vesicles (Figure 8–24). These vesicles are hollow cylinders with conical ends that measure

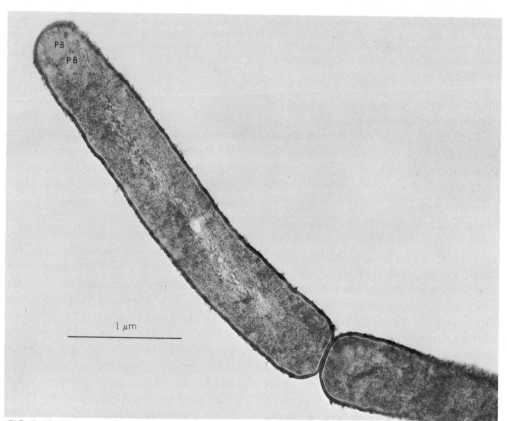

FIG. 8–23. A section of *Microbacterium thermosphactum* showing the presence of poly-β-hydroxybutyrate inclusions *(PB)*. This bacterial species has been frequently isolated from a variety of pork sausages. (From Davidson, C. M.: Mobbs, P., and Stubbs, J. M.: *J. Appl. Bact.,* **31**:551–559, 1968.)

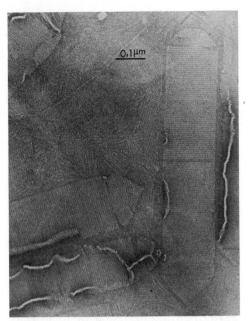

FIG. 8–24. Collapsed gas vesicles of the blue-green alga *Anabaena flos-aquae* negatively stained with phosphotungstic acid, x200,000. (Courtesy of Branton, D.: *Bact. Revs.*, **36**:1–32, 1972.)

from 65 to 115 nm in diameter and from 0.2 to 1.2 μm in length. The gas vacuoles occur in several aquatic procaryotic organisms, including blue-green algae, photosynthetic green and purple sulfur bacteria, and certain other related microorganisms. Among the functions that have been attributed to the vacuoles are the regulation of cell buoyancy, light shielding, surface-to-volume regulation, buoyancy provision, and various combinations of these functions.

Dormant Bacterial Structures (Endospores, Cysts, and Conidia)

The production of dormant structures by certain bacteria is comparable to the process of seed formation in plants. According to several authorities, this type of activity may represent cellular differentiation at a primitive level. In bacteria, dormant structures of three kinds can be produced: *endospores, cysts,* and *conidia* (Table 8–2). The first two of these resting bodies are formed asexually, i.e., without the union of nuclear material from two different types of cells. Usually only one such structure is produced per cell. Conidia present a different situation, as several are formed and are utilized for purposes of reproduction.

Several species of four bacterial genera are capable of forming endospores (Table 8–3). However, this property is more common among the members of *Bacillus* and *Clostridium*. The rare occurrence of endospore formation in other genera suggests that the process was not a characteristic of very many organisms early in their evolutionary development. This point is borne out by the results of genetic studies which have demonstrated *Sporosarcina* and *Sporovibrio* to be more closely related to active spore-forming species than to the members of the genera of *Sarcina* and *Vibrio*.

A comparison of cross sections of endospores, cysts, and conidia is presented in Figure 8–25. The gross mor-

Table 8–2   Selected Characteristics of Bacterial Dormant Structures

Property	Structures		
	Endospore	Cyst	Conidia
Heat resistance	Characteristically present	May be present	To a limited degree
Cortex	Present	Absent	Absent
Dipicolinic acid (DPA)	Present	Absent	Absent
Number formed per cell	1	1	Formed in chains

Table 8–3   The Occurrence of Dormant Structures in Bacteria Genera

	Structures		
	Endospores	Cysts	Conidia
	Bacillus	*Azotobacter*	*Norcardia*
	Clostridium	*Myxococcus*	*Actinomyces*
	Sporosarcina	*Sporocytophaga*	*Streptomyces*
	Sporovibrio		*Micromonospora*

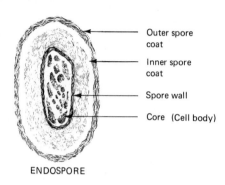

Outer spore coat

Inner spore coat

Spore wall

Core (Cell body)

ENDOSPORE

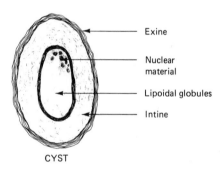

Exine

Nuclear material

Lipoidal globules

Intine

CYST

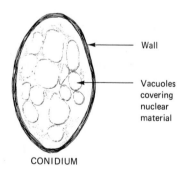

Wall

Vacuoles covering nuclear material

CONIDIUM

FIG. 8–25. Representative cross-sections of bacterial dormant structures.

phology of these structures appears to be quite similar, with their central cytoplasmic regions surrounded by thick outer layers.

Bacterial endospores.   An *endospore* is a dormant or resting structure formed within individual bacterial cells. This term refers to the specific structure present in a parent cell or sporangium during the spore formation period (Figure 8–26). Upon disintegration of these cells, the endospores are released or freed (Color photograph 22). The terms *exospore* and *free spore* are used to describe such structures (Figure 8–27*B*).

The dehydrated state of a bacterial spore is such that its refractility, i.e., ability to bend light rays, and its physical density approach those characteristic of dried protein. Additional properties of

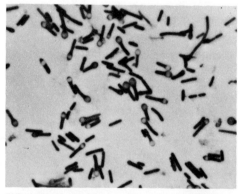

FIG. 8–26. Typical terminal spores of *Clostridium tetani,* the causative agent of tetanus. These endospores are the clear to grayish areas near the end portion of the bacterial cells shown. These organisms range in size from 0.3 to 0.8 μm (μ) by 2 to 5.4 μm. (Courtesy of CCM: General Biological, Inc., Chicago.)

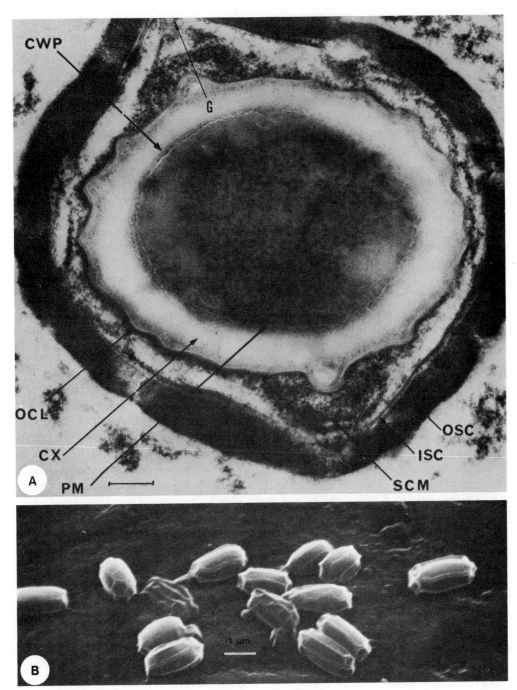

FIG. 8–27A. An electron micrograph showing a thin section of a *Bacillus megaterium* mature spore. Symbols: *CWP*, cell wall primordium or spore wall; *G*, germination groove; *OCL*, outer cortical layer; *CX*, cortex; *PM*, plasma membrane; *SCM*, subcoat material; *ISC*, inner spore coat; *OSC*, outer spore coat. The bar marker represents 0.01 μm. (From Freer, J. H., and Levinson, H. S.: *J. Bacteriol.*, **94**:441, 1967.) *B.* Scanning electron micrograph showing the spores of *Bacillus polymyxa*. (From Murphy, J. A., and Campbell, L. L.: *J. Bacteriol.*, **98**:737, 1969.)

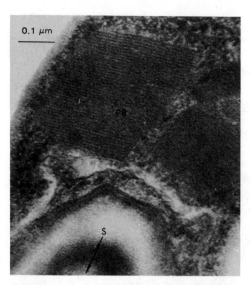

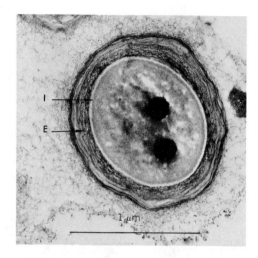

FIG. 8–28. An ultrathin section showing both a spore (S) and parasporal body (PB) of *Bacillus thuringiensis* within a sporangium. (Courtesy of Drs. J. R. Norris and H. M. Proctor, Shell Research Ltd., Milstead Laboratory of Chemical Enzymology, Sittingbourne, England.)

FIG. 8–29. An ultrathin section through a cyst of *Azotobacter vinelandii*. This preparation has been stained with ruthenium red, which demonstrates capsular material. The cyst coat shown clearly demonstrates the exine (E) and intine (I) layers. The latter is homogenous in appearance, while the former shows lamination. (From Pope, L. M., and Wyss, O.: *J. Bacteriol.*, **102**:234–239, 1970.)

spores include an unusual resistance to the effects of heat, drying, chemical disinfection, and radiation, and an impermeability to common stains. Several of these characteristics are used not only to detect the presence of spores, but to determine when these structures give rise to bacterial cells.

The process by which bacteria form spores is called *sporulation,* whereas the process by which spores develop into bacteria is called *germination.* Chapter 14 presents these events in more detail, especially with respect to the metabolic, structural, and chemical changes which occur, and their relation to spore resistance.

In certain species of the genus *Bacillus,* the process of sporulation is accompanied by the deposition of an inclusion known as a *parasporal body* or *Restkörper.* One such inclusion body occurs in a cell and usually appears as a single large crystal (Figure 8–28). The chemical composi-

tion of such structures is protein. The function of parasporal bodies to the bacterial cells in which they form and their relationship to the process of sporulation is unknown. However, these structures have been used in the control of certain insects (Chapter 5, "Bacterial Insecticides").

Bacterial cysts. The cysts produced by *Azotobacter* spp. and various myxobacteria in general are somewhat spherical and possess a contracted cytoplasm and thick structured wall. The cytoplasm of *Azotobacter* spp. usually contains evident nuclear material, lipoidal globules, and electron-dense bodies (Figure 8–29). The thick wall of this organism consists of an inner layer, or *intine,* and an outer layer, or *exine.* Cysts of *A. agilis* are not heat-resistant, while those of another species, *A. chroococcum,* exhibit resistance comparable to bacterial spores. As in the case of bacterial spores, cysts are resistant to drying, and are formed singly within vegetative cells. Unlike bacterial spores, they are not highly refractile, and do not possess an obvious cortex or dipicolinic acid (DPA).

Conidia. The dormant structure of the actinomycetes is the *conidium,* an asexual spore which is formed at the end of aerial mycelia by a process of fragmentation. These resting bodies are comparable to the conidia produced by various genera of fungi (e.g., *Aspergillus* and *Penicillium*). A mild thermal resistance appears to be the only common characteristic of conidia and of bacterial spores. Among the differences know to exist between these two types of dormant bodies are the absence of a cortex, DPA, a lack of refractility, and the external formation of multiple conidia.

Bacterial Size

The small size of bacterial cells is certainly obvious from microscopic examination. The dimensions of the smallest bacterial species border on the limits of the resolution of the bright-field microscope. The majority of pathogens range in size from approximately 0.2 to 1.2 μm in diameter, and 0.4 to 14 μm in length. The dimensions of particular causative agents of disease are given in the chapters in which they are discussed.

The size relationships of bacteria to the cells of higher forms of life are shown in Figure 8–30. A comparison of certain cellular components also is made here. It is readily seen that bacterial cells approximate the size of mitochondria.

QUESTIONS FOR REVIEW

1. Distinguish between procaryotic and eucaryotic cells and give representative examples of each.

2. Compare a typical plant cell with one of the animal variety as to structural similarities and differences.

3. Construct a table listing the functions and chemical composition of the following organelles.
   a. bacterial cell wall
   b. capsule
   c. mesosome
   d. pili
   e. bacterial cell membrane
   f. cilia
   g. bacterial flagellum
   h. chloroplast
   i. chromatophore
   j. endoplasmic reticulum
   k. bacterial genome
   l. nucleus
   m. ribosome
   n. nucleolus
   o. polyribosome
   p. mitochondria
   q. gas vacuole

4. Compare the cell walls of Gram-positive and Gram-negative bacteria.

5. Describe the different arrangements exhibited by bacteria. Can these arrangements be utilized for purposes of classification?

6. What procedure or procedures must be taken to observe the following organisms or organelles?
   a. bacterial spores
   b. cell membranes
   c. flagella
   d. ribosomes
   e. capsules
   f. endoplasmic reticula
   g. mesosomes
   h. mitochondria

7. How does the bacterial nucleus differ from that found in a typical animal cell?

8. Compare a bacterium flagellum to

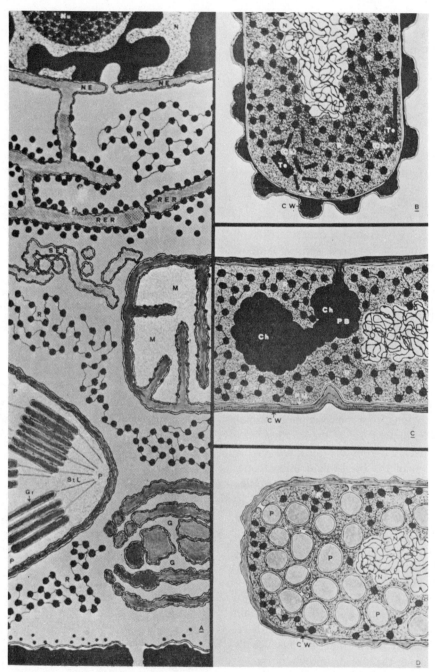

FIG. 8–30. A diagrammatic representation of a typical cell of a higher form of life and a bacterium. Structures are generally drawn to scale. _A._ A generalized cell. _B._ Gram-negative bacterium treated with tellurite. _C._ A Gram-positive rod. _D._ A photosynthetic bacterium. Symbols: _CW,_ cell wall; _Gr.,_ granum of chloroplast; _G,_ Golgi complex; _M,_ Mitochondrion; _N,_ nucleus; _NE,_ nuclear envelope; _Nu,_ nucleolus; _PB,_ peripheral body; _P,_ plastid; _PM,_ plasma membrane; _RER,_ rough endoplasmic reticulum; _SER,_ smooth endoplasmic reticulum; _R,_ ribosomes; _StL,_ stroma lamellae. (From Van Iterson, W.: _Bact. Rev.,_ **29:**-299–325, 1965.)

one of a protozoan nature as to composition and function.

9. a. What is a bacterial spore?
    b. Discuss the process of sporulation.
    c. How could bacterial spores be destroyed?

10. Differentiate between a protoplast and a spheroplast. What does *gymnoplast* mean?

11. Which is the importance of the following structures to the virulence of a microorganism, disease transmission, or diagnosis?

    a. bacterial flagella
    b. capsules
    c. pili
    d. cell walls
    e. spores
    f. ribosomes

12. How could one obtain a preparation of cell walls from a bacterial culture?

13. What are L-forms?

14. Identify the bacterial structures indicated in the electron micrograph shown in Figure 8–31.

FIG. 8–31. An ultrathin section of *L. plantarum*. (From Kakefuda, T., Holden, J. T., and Utech, N. M.: *J. Bacteriol.*, **93**:472–482, 1967.)

Viral Structure

Basic Architecture of Extra-Cellular Viruses

In a typical viral life cycle, intracellular and extracellular phases occur. The intracellular phase involves replication of viral components leading to the formation of mature virus particles. Most mature infective viruses (*virions*) exhibit a characteristic structural arrangement. Based on studies employing electron microscopy-associated techniques and x-ray diffraction analysis, the basic structure of virions has been found to consist of a nucleic acid inner core surrounded by a protein outer coat, called a *capsid* (Figures 9–1, 9–2).

The viral nucleic acid, which contains the viral *genome* (which specifies the essential properties of the virus), may be of either a single- or double-stranded variety and assumes a long, filamentous, folded or coiled form (Figure 9–2). Viruses recognized today contain either RNA or DNA, but not both.

The Nucleocapsid

The protein coats of simple viruses are constructed from protein molecules

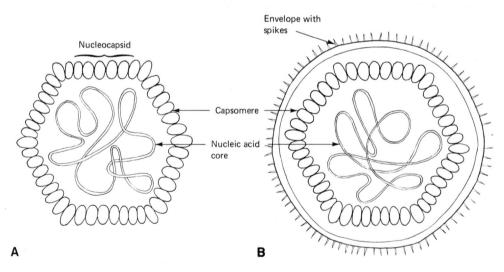

A

B

FIG. 9–1. A diagrammatic representation of viral architecture. <u>A</u>. A so-called naked virus particle. Note the folded appearance of the nucleic acid, and the capsomers. <u>B</u>. An enveloped nucleocapsid. The envelope itself has spike structures. (Modified from Davis *et al.: Microbiology*. Hoeber Medical Division, Harper & Row Publishers, Inc., Scranton, 1968.)

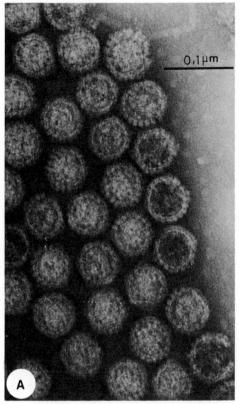

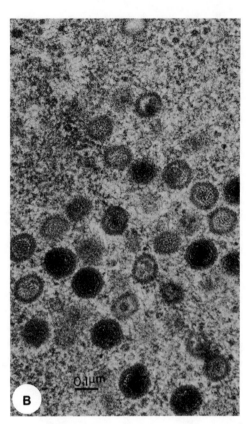

FIG. 9–2 <u>A</u>. A negatively stained preparation of wound tumor virus. This plant virus contains RNA. Note the coiled appearance of the nucleic acid in individual viral particles. (Courtesy of L. M. Black and R. Markham.) <u>B</u>. An electron micro-

graph of an iguana virus-infected cell. Several stages of capsid formation are shown. (From Zeigel, R. F., and Clark, H. F.: *Inf. Imm.*, **5**:570–582, 1972.)

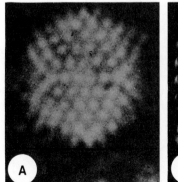

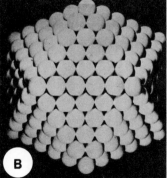

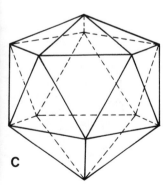

FIG. 9–3. Cubic symmetry. <u>A</u>. An electron micrograph showing the capsomere structure of adenovirus, type 5, in a negatively stained preparation. <u>B</u>. A capsomere model of an adenovirus.

(Courtesy of Dr. R. W. Horne, The John Innes Institute, Electron Microscope Laboratory, Norwich, England.) <u>C</u>. An icosahedron (20-sided figure).

(*structural subunits*) which, in clusters or aggregates, form the morphological subunits referred to as *capsomeres*. In electron micrographs, these capsomeres are the visible portions of viruses, appearing in several recognizable forms. Initial, relatively crude observations of viral particles indicated that viruses exhibited one of three broad structural forms: elongated rod-shaped, spherical, or tadpole-shaped with a head and tail. It is now known that the structure of a virus particle has one of several symmetries (form). Included among these basic shapes are cubic (Figure 9–4*A*), helical (Figure 9–4*C*), a combination of symmetries known as binal (Figure 9–4*D*), bullet-shaped (Figure 9–4*F*), filamentous (Figure 9–8*E*), and no obvious discernible symmetry. The latter form has been called *complex*.

The capsid, together with its enclosed viral nucleic acid core, comprises the nucleocapsid (Figure 9–1*B*). Virions may consist of nucleocapsids alone or nucleocapsids enclosed by a portion of host cell-derived membrane.

Enveloped Viruses

Several animal viral particles, as a consequence of their intracellular development pattern, acquire an outer coat or covering from the cytoplasmic or nuclear membranes of infected cells as they pass through or as they are extruded from them (Figure 9–5). The term *envelope* has been given to this outer coat (Figure 9–1*B*). (It has been suggested that the envelope be called a *peplos* and its subunits be called *peplomers*.) Viruses lacking such envelopes are commonly referred to as "naked." In 1968, F. Fenner suggested the use of "non-enveloped" as a substitution for the latter term. Chemically, envelopes consist of carbohydrates,

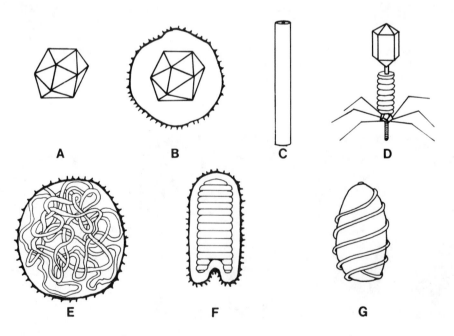

FIG. 9–4. A diagrammatic representation of the shapes of selected viruses. *A*. Adenoviruses. *B*. Herpesviruses. *C*. Plant viruses such as tobacco mosaic viruses. *D*. T (type)-even bacteriophages. *E*. Mumps virus. *F*. Rabies virus and certain plant pathogens. *G*. Orf virus.

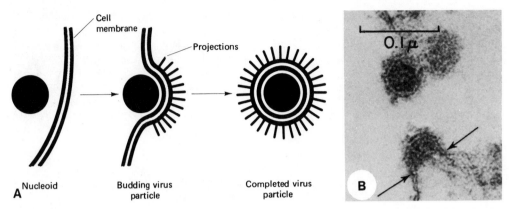

FIG. 9–5. Development of an enveloped virion. _A._ A schematic diagram showing the process of Semliki Forest virus particle formation. _Left,_ a virus nucleoid, assembled elsewhere in the cell's cytoplasm, approaches the cytoplasmic membrane. _Center,_ budding of the nucleoid through the membrane. The developing particle also acquires a coating of projections associated with the membrane portion through which it is bud-ding. _Right,_ the complete virus particle, consisting of a nucleoid wrapped in a membrane coat containing projections. Viral particles like this one appear free in extracellular spaces or within vacuoles. _B._ An electron micrograph showing both a developing (arrows) and a complete virus particle. (From Acheson, N. H., and Tamm, I.: _Virology,_ **32**:128–143, 1967.)

lipids, and proteins. The molecular organization of these structures remains largely unknown. Membranes generally range in thickness from 10 nm (100 Å) to 15 nm (150 Å). Depending on the viral agent, envelopes may or may not be covered with projecting spikes (Figure 9–1_B_ and 9–6_F_), which in profile appear as a fringe. The physical characteristics of such fringes differ among viral groups and may be used for identification purposes. The ability of viruses such as influenza to agglutinate red blood cells is associated with these spikes.

Variations in Shape and Size

Virions vary not only in size, but also in shape (Figures 9–4 and 9–6). The capsomeres of different viruses are arranged in definite geometric patterns. In the case of tobacco mosaic virus the morphological units form a helical structure. This arrangement is shown diagrammatically in Figure 9–7. The virus particle itself is a long rod and is referred to as a _helical virion._

Several animal, plant, and bacterial viruses exhibit a polyhedral shape; that is, they are many-sided. Their capsids are commonly in the form of an icosahedron, a structure having 20 triangular faces, 30 edges, and 2 corners (Figure 9–3).

The capsomeric arrangement of an adenovirus (causative agent of such diseases as pharyngitis and conjunctivitis), shown in Figure 9–3_B_, amply demonstrates this type of geometric pattern. Such viral particles are called _icosahedral virions._ The size of this type of virus is determined by the number of capsomers it has.

When virions of either helical or icosahedral shape are enclosed by envelopes, the respective descriptive terms "enveloped helical" and "enveloped icosahedral" may be employed to designate them. Examples of the former would be herpesviruses, e.g., the causative agents of fever blisters (Figure 9–4_B_), while the myxoviruses, e.g., the causative agents of influenza (Figure 9–6_F_) and mumps, exemplify enveloped icosahedrals. Figure

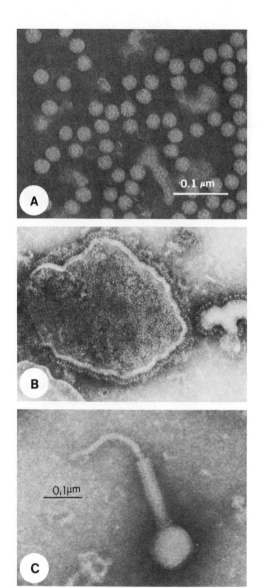

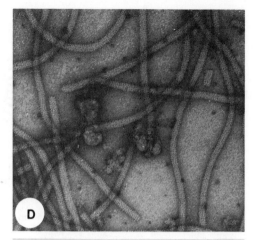

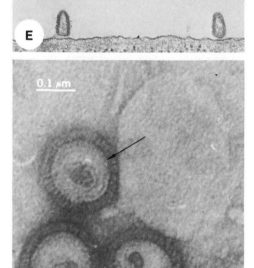

FIG. 9–6. Electron micrographs of negatively stained preparations of viruses demonstrating variations in shapes and relative sizes. Note the variety of hosts represented. _A._ Foot and mouth disease (FMD) virus. The host for this agent typically is the horse. (Courtesy of Dr. S. S. Breese, Jr., and the Plum Island Animal Disease Laboratory, ADP, ARS, U.S. Department of Agriculture, Greenport, Long Island.) _B._ Infective respiratory syncytial (RS) virus, one of the causes of the common cold. The size of the viral particles is variable. Note the spikes along the viral envelope. (Courtesy of Bachi, T., and Howe, C.: _J. Virology,_ **12**:1173–1180, 1973.) _C._ Bacteriophages of *Clostridium botulinum,* type C. This virus strain (3C^tox+) plays an active role in the production of toxin by C. *botulinum,* type C. (Courtesy of Eklund, M. W., and Poysky, F. T.: *Appl. Microbiol.,* **27**:251–258, 1974.) _D._ A negatively stained preparation of potato x virus. (Courtesy of Dr. R. Markham, Agricultural Research Council, Cambridge, England.) _E._ Bullet-shaped rabies virus particles. (From Iwasaki, Y., Wiktor, T. J., and Koprowski, H.: *Lab. Invest.,* **28**: 142–148, 1973.) _F._ An electron micrograph of a negatively stained preparation of the Asian type of influenza virus. Note the presence of spikes of these virions, and the variations in shape (arrows). (Courtesy of Lederle Laboratories, Pearl River, N.Y.)

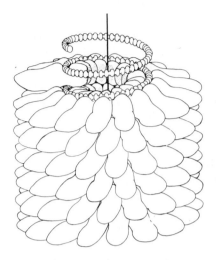

FIG. 9–7. Tobacco mosaic virus. A diagrammatic representation of this virus showing how its RNA chain is arranged within the supporting framework of the capsid. (From Caspar, D. L. D., and Klug, A.: *Adv. Virus Res.,* **7**:225, 1960.)

9–5 shows the development of an enveloped virion.

The Basic Architecture of Bacteriophages

More complex arrangements of viral components are also known. This is demonstrated by the basic morphological types of bacterial viruses (Figure 9–8). Bacteriophages have been isolated from a large number of bacterial genera. According to D. E. Bradley, these viruses demonstrate a greater variation of form than any other viral group. At the time of writing, numerous basic morphological types have been recognized, with no particular form being restricted to a specific bacterial genus. A newly discovered heli-

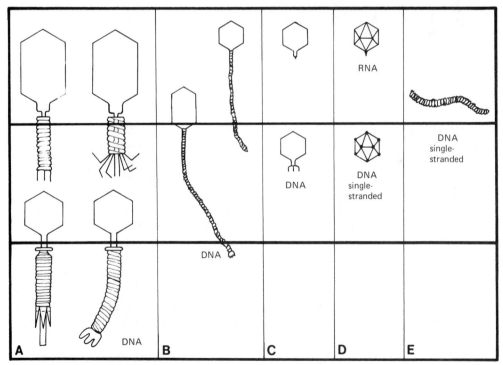

FIG. 9–8. Representative basic morphological features of bacteriophages together with their types of nucleic acid. *A, B,* and *C.* Phages with variations in head shapes and tail structures. *D.* Tailless heads. *E.* A filamentous bacteriophage.

(After Bradley, D. E., "A Comparative Study of the Structure and Biological Properties of Bacteriophages," *Comparative Virology,* Maramorsch, K., and Kurstak, E., eds., pp. 207–253. Academic Press, New York, 1971.)

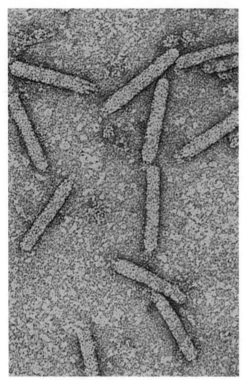

FIG. 9–9. An electron micrograph of purified Mycoplasmatales virus, *laidlawii* 2, negatively stained with uranyl acetate. (From Gourlay, P. N.: *J. Gen. Virol.*, **12**:65–67, 1971.)

cal bacteriophage isolated from mycoplasma (bacteria normally lacking cell walls) is shown in Figure 9–9.

The majority of studies concerning bacteriophages have been carried out with those agents which attack the Gram-negative bacterium *Escherichia coli*. Most of the following discussion will be limited to this group of viruses. In addition, because more is known about the structures involved in the adsorption of bacterial viruses to hosts than is known for other viruses, this topic will also be discussed.

Bacterial viruses are known which contain either DNA or RNA. In the majority of DNA phages the nucleic acid is double-stranded, while in RNA bacteriophages the nucleic acid is single-stranded. The nucleic acid of a typical virion, with the

exception of one phage group, is located within a polyhedral capsid, frequently referred to as the "head" (Figures 9–8 and 9–10). In several cases this capsid is attached to a helical protein structure called a "tail" (Figures 9–8 and 9–10) which aids the phage in adsorbing onto its bacterial host (Figure 9–11).

If a bacterial virus has a receptor adsorption site that is specific for a receptor site on the cell wall of a host bacterium, it is structurally ready for adsorption. The phage's tail and, if present, so-called "tail fibers" serve as "adsorption organs" (Figure 9–10B). After adsorption occurs the nucleic acid of the phage is injected into the bacterium. This process is generally accomplished in the T-even phages of *E. coli* by the tail sheath contracting and the tail core or tube penetrating through the bacterium's cell wall to the cell membrane (Figure 9–12)—a syringe-like operation. (Further details of the cycle of bacterial viruses are discussed in Chapter 14.) The filamentous phages are an exception to the polyhedral form of bacterial viruses.

Filamentous Bacteriophages

The filamentous viruses (FV) are among the smallest viruses known to date. In general, they are described as long deoxyribonucleoproteins measuring approximately 5.5 nm in diameter. Purified preparations of DNA from these microorganisms have been found to have a single-stranded form. Two different length categories of FV have been reported; one is approximately 870 nm, while the second is about 1,300 nm. In 1963 Marvin and Horne utilized these findings as a basis to classify filamentous viruses. According to their proposal, all viruses of the group which measure 870 ± 217.5 nm in length should be designated as belonging to the genus *Inovirus*. All FV with lengths of approximately

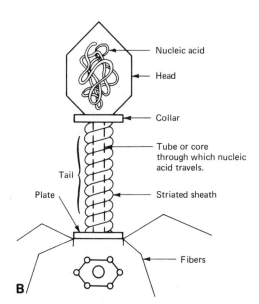

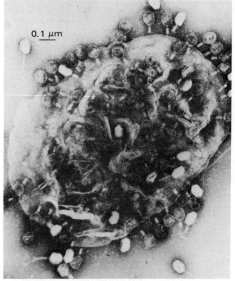

FIG. 9–10. Bacterial viruses. A negatively-stained T$_2$ bacteriophage. Note the head, the striations in the tail, and the fibers which are attached to an end plate. (Courtesy of Siemens, America, Inc.) _B_. A diagram showing the various components of a T$_2$ phage. The plate of this virus is hexagonal and contains a pin at each of its corners, with long, thin tail fibers connected to it.

FIG. 9–11. An electron micrograph showing T$_{4r}$ phages normally adsorbing onto _E. coli._ The cell wall of the organism has been severely damaged. This negatively-stained preparation clearly shows the attachment of the viruses to the bacterium. Note the contracted state of the viral sheaths, and that numerous phage heads are clear, while others are opaque. Which ones still have their nucleic acid? (From Simon, L. D., Swan, J. G., and Flatgaard, J. E.: _Virology,_ **41**:77, 1970.)

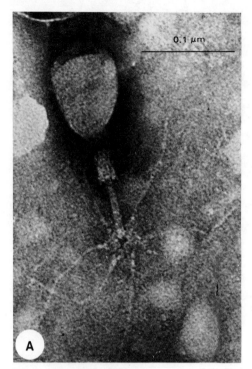

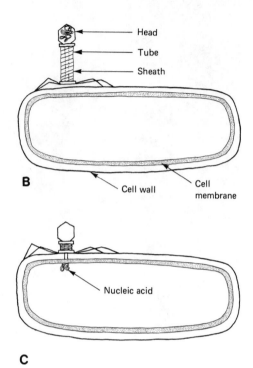

FIG. 9–12. A diagrammatic illustration of the syringe operation which occurs when T-even phage DNA is injected into a bacterial host. _A_. Bacteriophage adsorption. Note the relatively normal appearance of the virus' parts. _B_. The nucleic acid injection stage. Here the sheath contracts and the tail core penetrates through the cell wall. Note also the empty head that results from its release of nucleic acid. _C_. The appearance of T_6 virus showing a contracted sheath, base plate, and tail fibers. (From Anderson, T. F., and Stephens, R.: _Virology_, **23**:113–116, 1964.)

$1,305 \pm 217.5$ nm should be classified as members of the genus _Dolichoinovirus_. These authors have also suggested that the family designation for the entire group of these viral agents be altered from that in the Lwoff-Horne-Tournier system, namely _Inophagoviridae_, to _Inoviridae_.

As their hosts, these viruses utilize Gram-negative bacteria, including _Escherichia coli, Pseudomonas aeruginosa, Salmonella typhimurium, Vibrio parahemolyticus_, and _Xanthomonas oryzae_. Adsorption of bacterial cells takes place at the ends of threadlike bacterial appendages called the _sex pili_ (refer to the section on these structures in Chapter 8 for a more detailed discussion of their functions and to Figure 16–4). At least two viral species can be distinguished on the basis of pili attachment. At the present, two morphologically and serologically distinct sex pili types have been reported, called F and I. The former are characteristically synthesized by Gram-negative organisms possessing the sex (fertility) factor F, while the latter type of pilus is found in association with Gram-negatives with the colicin factor I (see Chapter 16). Filamentous viruses have been isolated which are pili specific; they will adsorb onto only F-pili (Ff) or only I-pili (If), not to both. Marvin and Horne proposed the species designation of _andreios_ for viruses which adsorb to F pili, and the

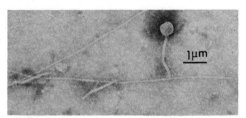

FIG. 9–13. *Pseudomonas aeruginosa* pilus-dependent bacteriophage. Note the long tail of the phage and the additional headless tails attached to the pili. (From Bradley, D. E.: *J. Virol.,* **12**: 1139–1148, 1973.)

designation of *colicinus* for those agents adsorbing to I pili. Recently a binal-shaped pilus-dependent phage was described (Figure 9–13).

Filamentous viruses, discovered in 1963, have brought attention to a form of "symbiotic behavior" previously unrecognized in bacteria. Unlike other types of bacterial viruses whose mode of replication destroys their respective hosts, filamentous viruses are released from dividing and growing bacteria without any apparent marked injury to the host cells. In short, this is a nonlytic form of viral release. Electron microscopic observations with infected bacteria tend to support the nondestructive outcome of infections with filamentous viruses. The findings of several investigators suggest that filamentous viruses are assembled during their extrusion from the host. This resembles the mode of replication found in certain cases of animal viruses. Several investigators believe that FV may serve as excellent models in studies concerned with the development and effects of oncogenic (cancer-inducing) viral agents.

Cyanophages

In 1963, Safferman and Morris reported the discovery of a virus that attacked and lysed several species of blue-green algae. These submicroscopic agents, now known to attack a wide range of blue-green algae, have been referred to as algophages, phycoviruses, and cyanophages. The latter designation appears to be the most appropriate because of their similarity to bacteriophages and the close relationship of blue-green algae to bacteria. It is now clearly evident that cyanophages are ubiquitously distributed in fresh-water bodies.

Several of the cyanophages isolated thus far have been named according to their hosts. Accordingly, phage groups have been designated by the initials of the generic names of the hosts, to which Arabic numerals were added to signify specific subgroups. An example of this system would be LPP phages, which attack three different filamentous blue-green algae genera, *Lyngbya, Phormidium,* and *Plectonema* (Figure 9–14). Because there are difficulties associated with the use of host specificity as a criterion for classification, morphological properties and serological specificities are preferred by several investigators as the major criteria for cyanophage grouping.

Cyanophages are very similar to bacterial viruses both in structure (Figure 9–14) and in infection cycle. LPP phages, one of the most extensively studied cyanophages, exhibit virions of the head-tail type. All the nucleic acids of these viruses isolated prior to 1974 were found to be linear, double-stranded DNAs.

All of the cyanophages isolated until recently demonstrated characteristics of virulent (cell-destroying) phages. However, several of the viruses of blue-green algae have been shown to be temperate (a phage that can become integrated into the host cell DNA).

The hosts of cyanophages, the blue-green algae, are widespread in the aquatic environment and often occur in great numbers in the form of algal blooms (see Chapter 4). The economic effects and

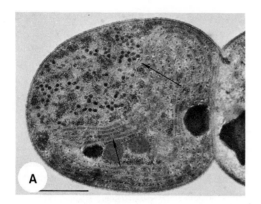

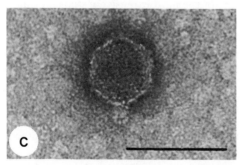

FIG. 9–14. The viruses of blue-green algae (cyanophages). _A_. The blue-green alga _Plectonema_ infected with LPP-1G cyanophage. Note the photosynthetic lamellae (layers) and the numerous viral heads (arrows). _B_. A model of the LPP-1 cyanophage. _C_. A mature virus particle. Is there similarity of this structure to that of bacteriophages? (Courtesy of Padan, E., and Shilo, M.: _Bact Revs._, **37**:343–370, 1973.)

nuisance of blue-green algae on water and environmental quality, including their role in fish poisonings, are well known. The discovery of cyanophages and of their widespread distribution has led several investigators to consider the use of these viruses as possible agents for the biological control of algal blooms.

Viruses of Eucaryotes

In recent years, viruses have increasingly been found in association with eucaryotes, including various algae (Figure 9–15), protozoa, and fungi. Such associations have taken one of two forms. In the first type, the eucaryotic microorganism serves as a vector or transmitter of the virus. This virus-vector relationship appears to be highly specific. At present there is no evidence that any of these viruses multiplies in its eucaryotic microbial vector.

In the second situation the virus infects the eucaryote, which then functions as a host. Since a large number of studies have dealt with the virus-host association in fungi, attention will be given only to the viruses. In 1967 a virus was found in an Ascomycete (see Chapters 4 and 10 for a discussion of fungi). Since that time different viruses have been reported from other species of Ascomycetes and from Basidiomycetes (mushrooms, puffballs, etc.), Deuteromycetes, and Phycomycetes. Thus viruses have now been discovered in all the major fungal groups.

The viruses studied have been found to be primarily non-enveloped, polyhedral particles that contain double-stranded RNA. Recently, an enveloped double-stranded, herpesvirus-type virus particle was discovered. Transmission of fungal viruses can occur through hyphal anastomosis (connections) and through asexual or sexual spores. Effects attributed to

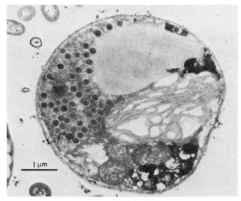

FIG. 9–15. Polyhedral virus-like particles in a spore of the brown alga *Chorda tomentosa*. (From Toth, R., and Wilce, R. T.: *J. Phycol.*, **8**:126–130, 1972.)

these viruses include the death of the host, the formation of abnormal mycelial growth, and a total absence of harmful activities.

Viroids

Presently known viroids consist solely of a short strand of RNA with a molecular weight ranging from 75 to 120,000 daltons. The molecular weight of viroids is only about one-tenth the size of the RNA genome of the smallest known self-replicating plant virus. Introduction of a viroid into a susceptible host leads to apparent replication of the nucleic acid and, in some hosts, to disease (Color photograph 9). Electron micrographs show viroids to have very short structures with an average length of about 500 Å (Figure 9–16).

The Nucleic Acid of the Mature Virion

As indicated earlier, mature virus particles contain only one type of nucleic acid. The specific kind of compound varies according to the virus. While most viruses have either single-stranded RNA or

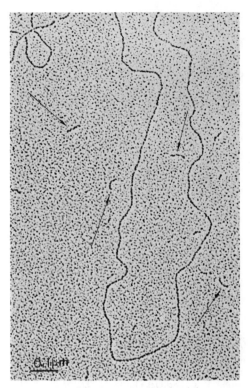

FIG. 9–16. An electron micrograph of the potato spindle tuber viroid (PSTV) in comparison with a conventional viral nucleic acid from bacteriophage T_7 Note the great size difference between the viroids (arrows) and the viral DNA molecule. (Courtesy of T. O. Diener, Research Plant Pathologist, U.S.D.A.)

double-stranded DNA, some of these agents may possess double-stranded RNA or single-stranded DNA. Upon release of the nucleic acid from virions by experimental means which minimize shearing, in most cases the nucleic acid is found to be a single molecule (Figure 9–17). (Some large RNA-containing viruses are exceptions to this finding.) The length of the nucleic acid molecule varies among different viruses, but it is constant for a particular type. The DNA of several viruses is circular or cyclic. In some DNA-containing agents, as well as all RNA viruses, the nucleic acid of the mature virus particle is linear or noncyclic.

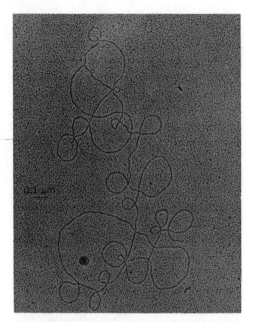

FIG. 9–17. An electron micrograph of the DNA molecule released by osmotic shock of a T₇ bacteriophage. Only one ghost is found near the nucleic acid, thus indicating that the phage contains a single DNA molecule. (From Misra, D. N., Sinha, R. K., and Das Gupta, N. N.: *Virology*, **39**:-183, 1969.)

Viral Classification

Viruses' constant chemical and structural properties lend themselves to precise classification. In 1962 Lwoff and Tournier clearly defined the characteristics of viruses. These and several other investigators have categorized viruses according to properties of their virions, including: (1) type of nucleic acid, (2) capsid organization or architecture, (3) capsid size, (4) number of capsomeres, (5) presence or absence of an envelope, and (6) size of enveloped viruses. Special features, such as those of viral development, intracellular site of viral synthesis, and host-parasite interactions, are used for further subdividing. Representative examples of this system are shown in Table 9–1.

QUESTIONS FOR REVIEW

1. List at least three distinct differences between viruses and bacteria.

Table 9–1   Representative Characteristics Used in the Classification of Viruses

Nucleic Acid (NA)	Double or Single-Stranded	Symmetry of Capsid	Number of Capsomeres	Size of Capsid in Ångstroms	Enveloped or Naked	Host Range of Viruses			
						Animal	Bacterial	Insect	Plant
DNA	Single	Helical		50 × 8,000	Naked		Coliphage fd		
	Double	Helical		90–100	Enveloped	Poxviruses			
	Single	Polyhedral	12	220	Naked		Coliphage φX-174		
	Double	Polyhedral	72	450–550	Naked	Polyoma and Papilloma			
			252	600–900	Naked	Adenoviruses			
			812	1,400	Naked			Tipula iridescent virus	
			162	1,000	Enveloped	Herpesviruses			
		Binal (a combination of polyhedral and helical components)		Polyhedral head 950 × 650 Helical tail 170 × 1,150	Naked		Coliphages T₂ T₄ T₆		
RNA	Single	Helical		175 × 3,000	Naked				Tobacco Mosaic virus
				90	Enveloped	Myxoviruses			
				180	Enveloped	Paramyxoviruses			
		Polyhedral		200–250	Naked		Coliphage f₂		
			32	280	Naked	Picornaviruses			Turnip yellow mosaic virus and Tomato bushy stunt virus
	Double	Polyhedral	92	700	Naked	Reoviruses			Wound tumor virus

2. Explain or define the following terms:
   a. capsomere
   b. virion
   c. capsid
   d. icosahedral
   e. nucleic acid core
   f. envelope
   g. binal arrangement

3. Compare the structural features of:
   a. a typical animal virus
   b. a typical plant virus
   c. a bacteriophage
   d. a cyanophage

4. Do all viruses contain DNA? What is a filamentous virus?

5. What is a viroid?

6. Using the electron micrograph shown in Figure 9–18, what structures of this bacterium would you *not* expect to find in the following?
   a. bacteriophage
   b. typical animal cell
   c. typical plant cell
   d. plant virus

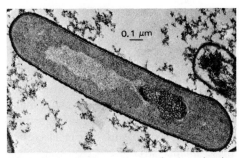

FIG. 9–18. An electron micrograph of an ultrathin section of *Bacillus subtilis*. (Courtesy of W. Van Iterson, University of Amsterdam and the North-Holland Publishing Company, Amsterdam.)

10

The Arrangements
and Anatomy of
Fungi and Protozoa

Fungi

These microorganisms are structurally simple, being composed of irregular plant-like masses lacking an organization into roots, stems, or leaves. Algae also form these *thallus* structures. However, algae differ from fungi in containing chlorophyll and exhibiting an autotrophic form of nutrition. Fungi resemble many bacterial species in possessing a wide range of specialized enzymes and because they can exist in either a saprophytic or a parasitic state, depending on their environment. However, these microorganisms are larger than bacteria, differ in their methods of reproduction, and have a more complicated form of morphologic development.

Most fungi can reproduce both asexually and sexually (Table 10–1 and Figure 10–1). Factors such as genetic make-up, the availability of sufficient numbers of sexually mature cells, and various environmental factors determine whether sexual reproduction will take place. However, organisms such as those grouped into the Deuteromyces or Fungi Imperfecti only reproduce asexually. The vast majority of human pathogens are in these groups. Spores are basic reproductive units for fungi and are of two types—sexual and asexual.

Fungi consist of two morphological types of microorganisms—molds and yeasts. Molds comprise the filamentous form, and have as their basic structure tubular filaments that branch widely and interweave with each other. These are called *hyphae*. Yeasts are unicellular, mononucleated fungi. Certain fungi are known that can alternate between a mold and a yeast phase. Some pathogenic fungi,

Table 10–1   Selected Characteristics of the Major Classes of Fungi

| Class | Type of Mycelium | Spores | | Representative Groups |
		Asexual Site of Formation	Sexual Site of Formation	
Ascomycetes	Septate	At the tips or ends of tryphae (exogenously)	Within sacs	Common antibiotic-producing fungi (e.g., *Pencillium* spp.), yeasts
Basidiomycetes	Septate	At the tips or ends of hyphae (exogenously)	On a surface of a *basidium*	Poisonous mushrooms (*Amanita* spp.), mushrooms, rusts, smuts
Zygomycetes	Almost completely nonseptate (coenocytic)	In sacs (endogenously)	In mycelium	Bread mold (*Rhizopus nigricans*), aquatic species
Deuteromyces (Fungi Imperfecti)	Septate	At the tips or ends of hyphae (exogenously)	None present	Most human pathogens

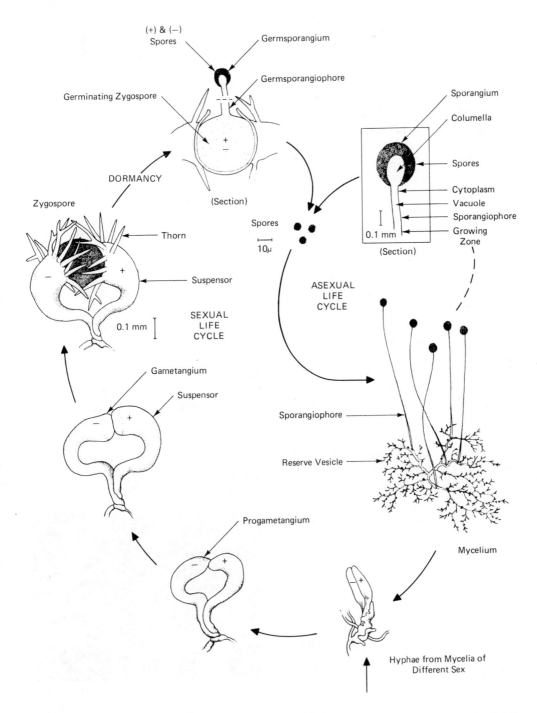

FIG. 10–1. A diagrammatic representation of the asexual and sexual life cycles and the principal structures of fungi belonging to *Phycomyces*. (From Bergman, K., Burke, P. V., Cerda-Olmedo, E., David, C. N., Delbrück, M., Foster, K. W., Goodell, E. W., Heisenberg, M., Meissner, G., Zalokar, M., Dennison, D. S., and Shropsire, W.: *Bact. Rev.,* **33**:99–157, 1969.)

e.g., *Histoplasma capsulatum,* exhibit typical mold structure when grown on artificial media in the laboratory at room temperature, but will assume yeast or yeast-like properties in the body of a host, such as man, or on enriched media at 37°C. Such fungi are called *dimorphic,* as they can exist in two forms. (See Chapter 30 for further discussion.) In their textbook entitled *Medical Mycology,* Emmons, Binford, and Utz suggest the terms "saprophytic form" for the mold phase and "parasitic form" for the yeast phase. The use of these terms would, in general, be more accurate, and would tend to eliminate confusion as to the significance of these two stages. Certain characteristics of selected classes of fungi are shown in Table 10–1.

Molds

Depending upon the species of fungus, the mold filaments may be divided into chains of cells by transverse cross walls called *septa* (singular, *septum*); hyphae exhibiting such divisions are known as *septate.* In species whose hyphae are *nonseptate* the contents of the hyphae can pass freely through the filament. This free movement is called a *coenocytic* state, and is characteristic of the Zygomycetes (Figure 10–7 and Color photograph 33). Hyphae may be uni-, bi, or multinucleated.

As molds continue to grow on suitable substrates, either natural (bread and fruit) or artificial (laboratory media), the hyphae branch, intermingle, and often fuse to eventually form a visible aggregation of these structures called a *mycelium,* analogous to a bacterial colony. The appearance of these hyphal masses is generally dry and powdery (Color photographs 30–34). This is often the result of *sporulation,* the formation of various types of spores. Mycelia in some

instances have two general regions. One of these extends below the surface of the medium in which it is growing for the purpose of food collection. This part of the mycelium is called the *vegetative mycelium.* Certain species possess root-like structures called *rhizoids* which function in this capacity and also serve as anchoring devices. The part of the fungus which is above the substrate and extends into the environment is referred to as the *aerial mycelium.* It is the reproductive portion of the microorganism, with specialized branches that produce the specialized cells called *spores.*

Yeasts

Yeasts form moist, shining colonies (Color photographs 35 and 36). Yeasts exhibit a eucaryotic structure. They are generally oval in shape, though some are rectangular. Characteristically, these organisms have a thick cell wall (Figure 10–12). In certain yeasts, such as *Cryptococcus neoformans,* a capsule may surround the cell wall (Figure 10–2).

Certain yeasts reproduce asexually by a process of division (fission) which results in the formation of a new cell called

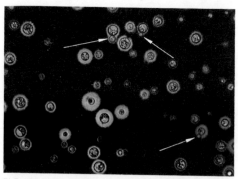

FIG. 10–2. *Cryptococcus neoformans* stained with Nigrosin. The capsular regions surrounding these cells are quite evident. Note also the presence of buds (arrows) on occasional *C. neoformans.* (Courtesy of Dr. M. Silva-Hutner, Columbia University, College of Physicians and Surgeons, N.Y.)

a *bud* or *daughter cell* (Figure 10–2). Later these newly-formed yeasts separate from the *mother cell*. The latter exhibits a bud scar at the region where separation took place, while the bud has a "birth scar" (Figure 10–3). Newly formed cells characteristically do not separate with certain species. These connected yeasts cells are called *pseudohyphae*.

Spores

Asexual Spores

Most fungi produce spores (from the Greek word meaning "seed") during the

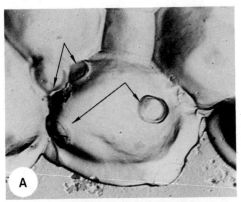

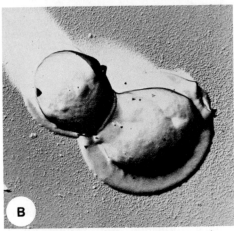

FIG. 10–3. Replicas of the surfaces of yeasts showing bud scars (arrows). These preparations were made by the single-replica technique. *A.* This electron micrograph shows the distribution of birth scars on a single yeast cell. *B.* A side view of a bud scar. Note the depression of the surface.

asexual reproductive process. These structures, which also are called *mitospores* because they result from mitotic division, vary in color, size, and shape (Figure 10–4), and may have one or several nuclei. These properties are the basis for classifying asexual fungi. There are at least five different types of asexual fungal spores. Each of the spore types is briefly described below. In addition, the gross structures of selected common fungal species are shown in Figures 10–5 and 10–7. (Refer to Chapter 30 for additional examples.)

Arthrospores.   These spores generally arise from a fragmentation of hyphae. The structures are cylindrical and are produced as a consequence of double septa forming within the hyphal strand, resulting in joints (Figure 10–4). Arthrospores, or *oidia* as they are sometimes called, do not appear to function as reproductive structures in the same manner as do other fungal spores. However, they are capable of starting new growth in favorable environments. These structures apparently do not exhibit resistance to drying and heat comparable to that of bacterial spores.

Blastospores.   Spores of this type are referred to as *buds*. They are characteristically found in yeast (Figure 10–2) or yeast-like organisms.

Chlamydospores.   These structures are quite similar in several respects to bacterial spores. Chlamydospores are thick-walled, and exhibit an unusually high resistance to drying and heat. Reserve food generally is found in such structures; no doubt the chlamydospore significantly contributes to the survival of the fungus which can produce it.

Conidia.   Spores of this type are referred to as free or unprotected structures, because of the way in which they

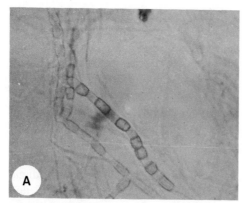

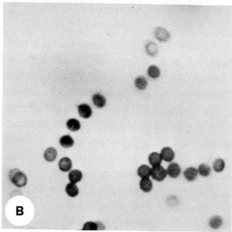

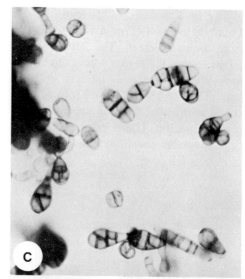

FIG. 10–4. Selected fungal spores. _A._ Arthrospores of *Coccidioides immitis*. Note the pronounced rectangle-like shape. (Courtesy of E. S. Beneki, Department of Botany and Plant Pathology, Michigan State University.) _B._ Conidia of *Aspergillus* spp. Note the dark appearance and apparent rough surface of these spores. _C._ The macroconidia of *Alternaria* sp., a common cause of hay fever. Does the appearance of these spores resemble any object with which you are familiar? _D._ Macroconidia of a ringworm-causing fungus, *Microsporum rivalieri*. Note the difference in size and organization of these structures. (From Zaias, N., Rebel, G., and Taplin, D.: *Sabouraudia*, **4**:201, 1965.)

are formed. In general, conidia arise from a special cell called *sterigma* (Figure 10–5). Such cells are differentiated structures formed at the tips of fertile hyphal strands known as *conidiophores* (Figure 10–5B). Conidia are pinched off from a sterigma and generally form a chain with one spore preceding another. It is not unusual to see long chains of conidia attached to a conidiophore.

These asexual spores are characteristic of the Ascomycetes, several members of the Deuteromycetes (Table 10–1), and even some Basidiomycetes—the mushrooms (Color photograph 6). Conidia which are usually unicellular are referred to as *microconidia*, while those which are large, septated, and multinucleated are called *macroconidia* (Figure 10–4D and Color photographs 79 and 80). The sequence of events that occur in macroconidia formation with certain fungal species is shown in Figure 10–6.

Sporangiospores.   These spores are associated with the Zygomycetes. They

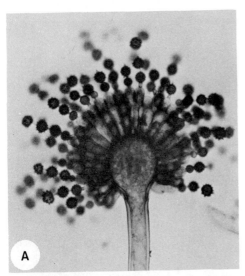

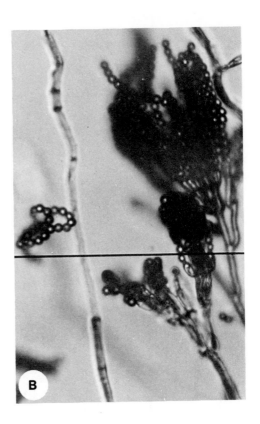

FIG. 10–5. The structures of commonly encountered fungi. The actual typical microscopic appearances of fungus species are shown. *A. Aspergillus niger*. Note the free spores. (Courtesy of CCM: General Biological, Inc., Chicago.) *B. Penicillium notatum*. The characteristic "brush-like" feature of this mold is quite apparent. (Courtesy of S. Stanley Schneierson, M.D., and Abbott Laboratories.)

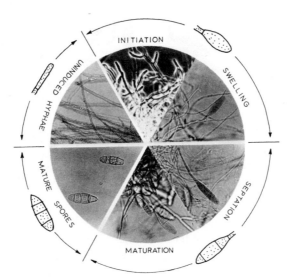

FIG. 10–6. Macroconidia sporulation. The microscopic appearance and diagrammatic representation of macroconidia development are shown. Spore development proceeds from the uninduced hyphae, and spore initiation occurs soon after hyphal-tip swelling. After cross-wall or septum formation eventually divides the hyphal tip into four compartments, the mature spores separate from the remaining portions of the fungal growth (hyphae). (From Page, W. J., and Stock, J. J.: *Appl. Microbiol.,* **24**:650–657, 1972.)

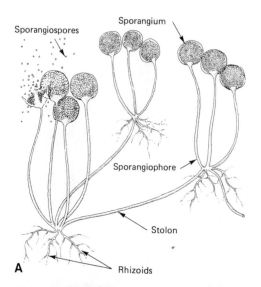

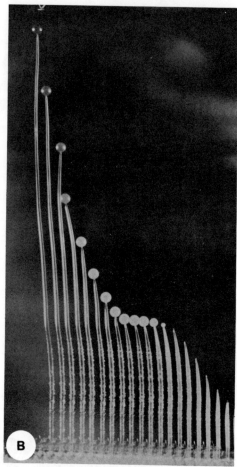

FIG. 10–7. Structural features of the common bread mold *Rhizopus nigricans*. <u>A</u>. A diagrammatic representation of the hyphal differenciation found with *Rhizopus* spp. Note the anchorage system made possible by the root-like rhizoids. <u>B</u>. The stages of sporangiophore development. Twenty photographs of the same sporangiophore, taken at 1-hour intervals, are incorporated into one picture. The sporangiophore will continue to elongate at an approxi-mately constant rate until it has reached a height of 10 cm. (From Bergman, K., Burke, P. V., Cerda-Olmedo, E., David, C. N., Delbrück, M., Foster, K. W., Goodell, E. W., Heisenberg, M., Meissner, G., Zalokar, M., Dennison, D. S., and Shropshire, W.: *Bact. Rev.*, **33**:99–159, 1969.) <u>C</u>. A scanning micrograph showing a collapsed sporangium and numerous sporangiospores. The thin texture of the sac-like structure is obvious.

are formed within a swollen sac-like structure referred to as a *sporangium* (Figure 10–7). The latter arise on the tips of fertile hyphae called *sporangiospores* (Figure 10–7). The tip of a hyphal strand enlarges and becomes club-shaped, thus forming a *columella*. This portion of the hypha serves to support the sporangium which surrounds it. A septum separates the sporangium from the remainder of the sporangiophore from which it arises.

Sporangiospores are released into the environment either through the mechan-

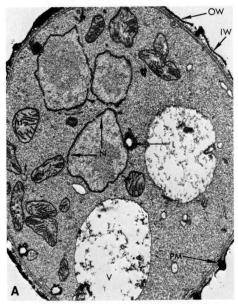

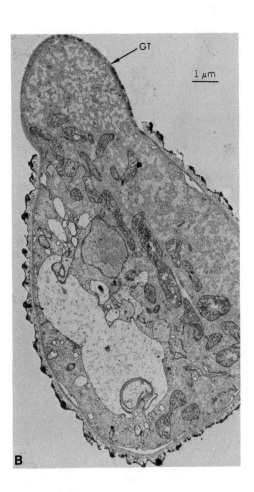

FIG. 10–8. Ultrastructural features of fungal spores. _A_. An ultrathin section of a _Rhizopus stolonifer_ sporangiophore. Several eucaryotic components are evident, including nucleus (N) and mitochondria (m). Other portions shown are vacuoles (V), lipid inclusions (L), plasmalemma (pm), ribosomes (dot-like structures), and both inner (iw) and outer (ow) portions of the cell wall. _B_. An ultrathin section of a sporangiophore showing a protruding germ tube (GT). (From Bussel, J., Buckley, M., Sommer, N. F., and Kosuge, T.: J. Bacteriol., **98**:774–783, 1969.)

ical disruption of a fully developed sporangium, or by other means. Such spores exhibit some resistance to drying.

Germination

Under suitable conditions, e.g., availability of nutrients and moisture, and proper pH and temperature, fungal spores germinate and produce one to several filamentous structures called _germ tubes_ (Figure 10–8). These processes usually penetrate through thinned or weakened portions of the spore (_germ pores_). The fungal germ tubes develop by elongating and branching into the hyphal structures mentioned previously.

Sexual Spores

Reproductive structures of this type are the result of nuclear fusion. Several kinds of sexual spores are found in fungi of medical importance, including ascospores, zygospores, and basidiospores. In general, sexual spores are not observed with great frequency. Certain environmental conditions are necessary before sporulation of this type can be induced.

Ascospores. These are the characteristic sexual spores of the Ascomycetes, formed as the result of the fusion of tubelike structures from two neighboring cells. The two nuclei of these cells, which may or may not be from the same mycelium, unite and form a single nucleus. Daughter nuclei are subsequently produced through meiotic division. As many as eight such structures may be formed. Each nucleus becomes surrounded by a dense protoplasmic layer and a spore coat, or wall, thus forming an *ascospore*. These reproductive structures are in turn contained within the original wall formed during the initial union of the two neighboring cells. This enclosing sac is called an *ascus*.

Zygospores.   Spores of this type are produced by certain species of the Zygomycetes, of which *Rhizopus* spp. are common examples. In this situation, when the hyphae from two apparently identical mycelia join, the tip of each structure is separated from the remainder of the fungal growth by a cross wall or septum. A so-called multinucleated *gametangium* (i.e., a structure which will give rise to cells) is thereby formed. The cell walls between the two fused hyphae are broken

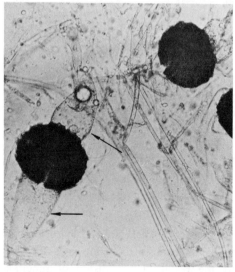

FIG. 10–9. A representative zygospore of *Rhizopus* spp. Note the presence of the two hyphal branches (arrows).

down, thus enabling the two protoplasts to fuse and form a *coenozygote* (a multinucleate fertilized cell or zygote). A thick, black, warty coat is formed which surrounds the coenozygote. The entire structure is called a *zyogospore* (Figure 10–9). Spores of this type are noted for their prolonged dormant state.

Basidiospores.   The common fungi seen in various types of environments, such as the mushrooms, puffballs, and related forms, have septated mycelia and are classified among the Basidiomycetes. Fungi of this group have several properties in common with the Ascomycetes. As indicated earlier, some can produce asexual spores (e.g., conidia). However, many Basidiomycetes have lost their capacity for asexual reproduction and only form characteristic sexual spores called *basidiospores* (Figure 10–10). These structures are formed on the distal end of a club-shaped structure known as a *basidium* (Figure 10–11*A*). Basidia of two kinds are known—unicellular and multicellular or septate. The former type is found in mushrooms and puffballs.

The fruiting body, or the source of basidiospores of a mushroom, begins its development when individual masses of hyphae enlarge to form the well-known young "button" (Figure 10–11*B* and *C*). With an increase in water uptake, this structure forms a mature fruiting body (Figure 10–11*B* and 10–11*C*). The club-shaped basidia line both sides of the undersurfaces of the mushroom's cap. Mature basidiospores are released from this region. Certain mushrooms, e.g., *Amanita* spp., are poisonous. These organisms have characteristic scale-like additions on their caps which give them a distinctive appearance. Such scales are remnants of a "universal veil" or thin membrane that encloses the developing fruiting body.

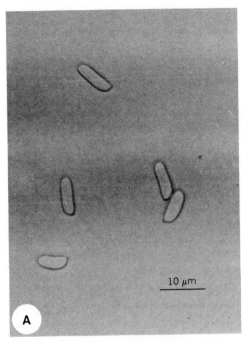

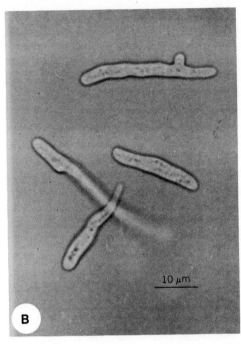

FIG. 10–10. The basidiospores of the fungus *Lenzites saepiaria*, known for its role in the rotting of wood. *A.* Ungerminated basidiospores. *B.* The appearance of basidiospores 4 hours after germination. (From Scheld, H. W., and Perry, J. J.: *J. Bacteriol.*, **102**:271–277, 1970.)

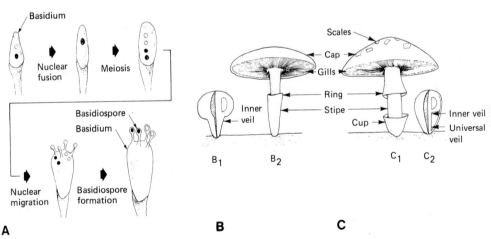

FIG. 10–11. The Basidiomycetes. *A.* A basidium and basidiospores. The development of these spores is shown here. *B.* A diagram of one type of mushroom fruiting body. This is an edible form of basidiomycete. *B*1 shows a cut-away of a button or developing mushroom stage. *B*2 shows the differentiated parts of a mature fruiting body. *C. Amanita*, the poisonous type of mushroom. *C*1 shows a cut-away of the button, and C2 shows the mature fruiting body. (Adapted from Doyle, W. T.: *Nonvascular Plants: Form and Function.* Wadsworth Publishing Company, Inc., Belmont, Calif., 1965.)

The Ultrastructure of Fungi

Both yeasts and molds exhibit eucaryotic cellular organization (Figures 10–8 and 10–12). Their cells generally contain membrane-bound organelles, which include endoplasmic reticula, mitochondria, and well-defined nuclei. The membranes surrounding the nuclear material of the cells contain sterols such as cholesterol-like compounds. Sterols, with the exception of pathogenic mycoplasma, are not found in bacteria and blue-green algae but only in the structures of higher forms of life. Since the fungi resemble higher plants and animals both in their cellular complexity and in their organelles, only the cell wall will be discussed here.

As in bacteria, the cell wall lies immediately external to the fungal cell's cytoplasmic membrane. The hyphal walls

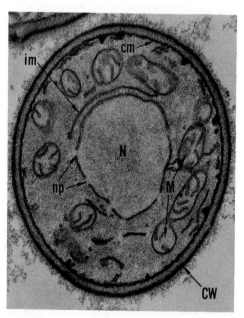

FIG. 10–12. An ultrathin section of the yeast *Hansenula wingei*. The principal structures shown include: cell wall (*CW*); nucleus (*N*); nuclear pores (*np*); mitochondria (*M*); cytoplasmic membrane (*cm*); and internal membranes (*im*). (From Conti, S. F., and Brock, T. D.: *J. Bacteriol.*, **90**:-524–533, 1965.)

of filamentous fungi, as demonstrated by electron microscopy, appear to be composed of thin, thread-like structures called *microfibrils*. These components of the wall measure approximately 15–25 nm in diameter and are arranged in a type of thatchwork. Chemically, the microfibrils in many fungi are composed of *chitin,* a polymer of N-acetylglucosamine (Figure 8–11), which is the principal structural substance in the exoskeletons of crayfish, crabs, and related forms. Cellulose, the major component of plant cell walls, has also been found in the hyphal walls of filamentous fungi.

The chemical composition of yeast cell walls is quite different. It contains approximately equal quantities of the highly-branched, insoluble polysaccharide glucan, and the soluble polysaccharide mannan. Other compounds found in the cell wall include lipid, protein, and the amino sugar glucosamine.

Spheroplasts (semi-gymnoplasts) and protoplasts (gymnoplasts) can be obtained by the careful digestion of yeast cell walls. Helicase, an enzyme preparation obtained from the digestive juices of the snail *Helix pomatia,* can be used for this purpose. Protoplasts can also be produced by growing yeasts in cell-wall-inhibiting media.

Protozoa

Generally speaking, these eucaryotic organisms resemble a typical animal cell in structure. They contain an endoplasmic reticulum, Golgi apparatus, mitochondria, ribosomes, and a nucleus. Several protozoans possess surface envelopes which include plasmalemma and pellicles, and which function to provide protection against drying, toxic chemicals, and mechanical injury. Several flagellated protozoans, some amoeba, and all ciliates have pellicles. The pellicle can be distinguished from the plasmalemma by its greater toughness and thickness.

Protozoan Structure

Organelles of locomotion. As indicated in Chapter 4, protozoa are frequently differentiated on the basis of their means of locomotion: pseudopodia ("false feet"), cilia, and flagella. Several different types of pseudopodia are found in association among amoeba-like organisms (Figure 10–13). These include: (1) finger-shaped, round-tipped *lobopodia*; (2) thin, pointed *filopodia*; (3) branching, slender, pointed *rhizopodia*; and (4) slender *axopodia* (Figure 10–14), which contain several fibers forming an axial filament.

Protozoan cilia and flagella (Figure 10–15) have two centrally located microtubules, surrounded by nine double tubules (Figure 8–8). This so-called "9 + 2" arrangement is characteristic of cilia and flagella associated with all eucaryotic cells, from paramecia to humans. Each of the outer ciliary microtubules has a pair of armlike structures extending toward the neighboring tubule. Chemically, most of the cilium is composed of protein. As the cilium passes from its cytoplasmic site of origin, it is surrounded by the cell's plasma membrane, which contains both lipid and protein.

Cilia are short and usually arranged in longitudinal or diagonal rows. These organelles may cover the surface of the protozoan or may be restricted to the oral or other regions. In some organisms cilia are fused, resulting in stiffened tufts called *cirri* (Figure 10–16). Such cirri are used in locomotion by the creeping ciliates (Figure 10–16*A* and *B*). Ciliary movement also has a motor-coordinating system which lies just beneath the protozoan covering known as the pellicle (Figure 10–16*C* and *D*). Each cilium (as well as

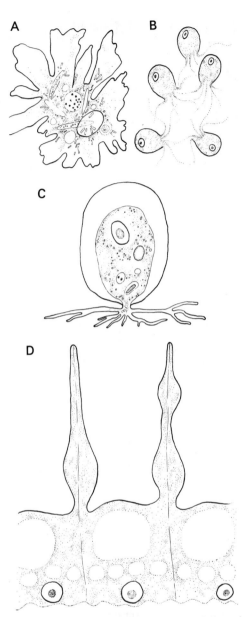

FIG. 10–13. A diagrammatic representation of pseudopodia. *A.* Lobopodia. *B.* Rhizopodia. *C.* Filopodia. *D.* Axopodia. (After Meglitsch, P. A.: *Invertebrate Zoology.* Oxford University Press, London, 1967.)

each flagellum) terminates beneath an organism's surface in a basal granule called a kinetosome. From each kinetosome a kinetodesmal fibril arises and

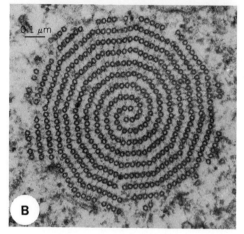

FIG. 10–14. The axopodia of *Echinosphaerium nucleofilum. A.* The living organism, showing numerous protruding axopodia. *B.* A cross-section of an axopodium. (Courtesy of L. E. Roth and Y. Shigesaka, Kansas State University.)

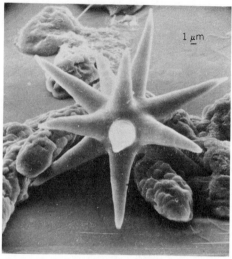

FIG. 10–15. A scanning electron micrograph of *Euglena* sp. Note the flagella in the lower right-hand corner. The star-shaped object is a calcium spicule formed by sponges. Bar marker represents 1 μm.

passes along beneath the row of cilia, connecting the other fibrils of that row. The kinetosomes and fibrils (kinetodesmata) of that row comprise a kinety. All ciliates seem to have these kinety systems.

In addition to serving as a means of locomotion, the cilia and flagella of protozoa appear to respond to stimuli such as chemicals and touch. The only special organelle that functions in the reception of stimuli is the eye-spot or *stigma,* a reddish structure commonly found in photosynthetic flagellates such as *Euglena.*

Contractile vacuole system. The discharge of waste products takes place at the protozoan's surface. In several of these microbes, the processes of excretion and osmoregulation appear to be closely regulated. Studies have demonstrated that these organelles function by separating a dilute solution of water and electrolytes from the cytoplasm and subsequently expelling this solution from the cell. Communication of the vacuole with the external environment at the time of its contraction (systole) takes place through an opening in the cell surface referred to as the contractile vacuole pore (Figure 10–17). In some protozoa, such as amoebas, the pore is a temporary structure formed *de novo* at the onset of each systole. In *Paramecium* (Figure 10–18) and other ciliates, the pore is a permanent opening in the pellicle. A membranous diaphragm keeps the vacuole closed during the expanding (diastole) period.

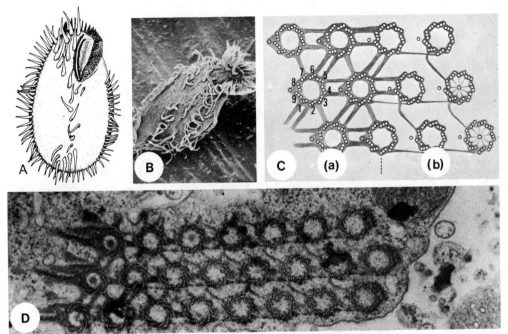

FIG. 10–16. Ciliary structures of the protozoan *Gastrostyla steinii*. *A.* A diagrammatic representation of a cirrus. *B.* A ventral view showing the marginal row of cirri. *C.* Distil network of fibrils (a) and individual fibrils (b) just beneath the network. Numbering of triplet microtubules is shown for one kinetosome in (a) *D.* Kinetosomes and internal fibrils from a left marginal cirrus. (From Grim, J. N.: *J. Protozool.*, **19**(1):113, 1972.)

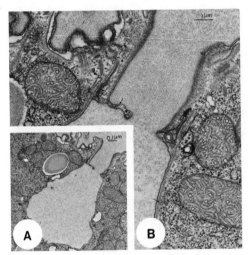

FIG. 10–17. The contractile vacuole. *A.* An electron micrograph showing this organelle attached to the cell surface at the pore. The vacuole appears to be closed. *B.* Another view showing a partially closed, contracting vacuole. (From McKanna, J. A.: *J. Protozool.*, **20**:631–638, 1973.)

Macronuclei and micronuclei. Ciliates are protozoans that are multinucleated. They possess at least one macronucleus and one micronucleus (Figure 10–19). The macronucleus, which varies in shape, regulates metabolic and developmental functions and maintains all visible traits. The micronucleus exerts an overall control over a cell's macronucleus and regulates cellular sexual and reproductive processes.

Methods of Reproduction

Both asexual and sexual reproduction occur among protozoans. Like certain other microbial types, some protozoa are capable of reproducing asexually only. In this process, the parent cell divides, either equally or unequally, resulting in one or more offspring that eventually develop into mature forms of the protozoan. Binary fission is the most common type of asexual reproduction. Division may be nuclear or cytoplasmic. Neither meiosis (reduction division) nor fertilization takes place during binary fission.

Other forms of asexual division among protozoa include budding, multiple fission, and plasmotomy. In the budding process a new individual is formed either exogeneously, at the protozoan's surface, or endogenously, in an internal cavity. Multiple fission involves the formation of a multinucleate organism that undergoes cleavage, resulting in many uninucleated cells. This process is a characteristic feature of sporozoan parasites (Color photographs 115–117). The division of multinucleated protozoa into two or more multinucleated offspring is called *plasmotomy*.

Sexual reproduction also occurs among the protozoa, and may be relatively simple or complex. Although meiosis apparently takes place, the details of this phenomenon are not well understood. Types of sexual reproduction included syngamy, conjugation, and autogamy.

In syngamy, the union of two different mating types of cells (gametes) results in the formation of a fertilized cell or zygote. Such cells may undergo additional development. This type of reproduction is found in sporozoans such as malaria parasites (Figure 41–9).

Conjugation characteristically takes place in ciliated protozoans. Briefly, the process involves the partial union of two ciliates for the transfer of nuclear material from one organism, the donor, to the other, the recipient. Such nuclear matter, which is in the form of a nucleus, unites with a similar structure in the recipient

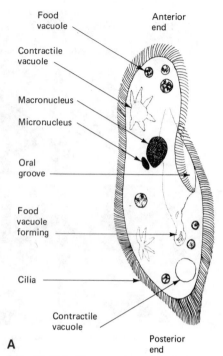

A

FIG. 10–18*A*. The components of the ciliated *Paramecium*. This eucaryotic organism and other protozoa are several thousand times larger than bacteria. Paramecia have a specialized structure, the *oral groove* or *gullet,* which is used for food ingestion. Liquid is excreted through the *contractile vacuole.*

to form a zygote nucleus. Several subsequent divisions take place within the donor cell. Actually, through a series of nuclear divisions, two transferable nuclei are formed in the donor. One remains behind, resulting in new ciliates having the normal structural composition.

Autogamy is a modified version of conjugation. However, it involves only one protozoan, whose nucleus divides into two parts that then reunite to form a zygote.

Trophozoites and Cysts

The actively feeding, growing, and multiplying stage of a protozoan is called the *trophozoite* or *troph* (Figure 10–20).

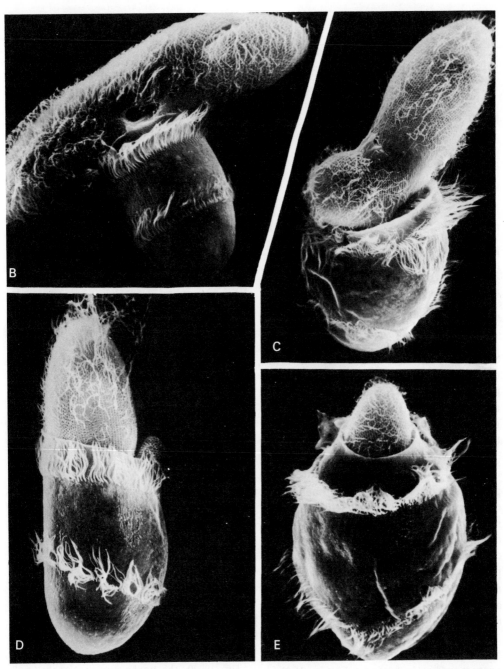

FIG. 10–18*B*, *C*, *D*, and *E*. Scanning micrographs showing various phases of the ingestion of *Paramecium* by another ciliated *Didinium*. The ciliated nature of both organisms is dramatically shown. *B*. Early phase. Compare Figure 10–18*A* with the *Paramecium* shown here. Are there any obvious structures you can recognize? *C*. Here the *Paramecium* is being folded. *D*. The folded protozoan is half-swallowed and is being compressed. *E*. Note the expanded appearance of the engulfing *Didinium*. From Wessenberg, H. and Antipa, G.: *J. Protozool.*, **17**:250–270, 1970.)

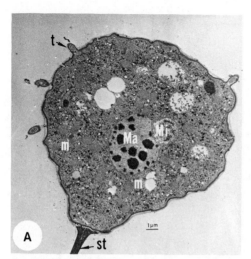

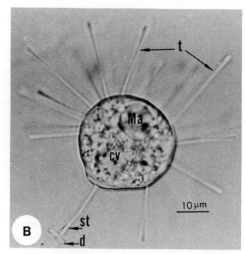

FIG. 10–19. Stalk and tentacles. _A_. An electron micrograph of the adult suctorian, *Tokophyra*, showing eucaryotic organization. Structures particularly evident include the macronucleus (Ma), the micronucleus (Mi), mitochondria (m), tentacles (t), and a rod-like stalk (st). _B_. A young suc-torian observed in a light microscope. The photograph shows a contractile vacuole (cv), the macronucleus (Ma), a disc (d), a stalk (st), and tentacles (t). (From Hascall, G. K., and Rudzinska, M. A.: *J. Protozool.* **17**:311–323, 1970.)

Some ingest solid food particles, a form of nutrition (holozoic nutrition) characteristic of animals. Some pathogens, such as *Entamoeba histolytica* (Color photograph 118), which causes amoebic dysentery, can ingest red blood cells.

Certain protozoans form a cyst (Figure 10–21), a thick-walled structure that provides protection against unfavorable environmental conditions, including drying and some chemicals, and serves as a means for transmission and of multiplication. In the case of certain pathogenic protozoa, such as *E. histolytica* and *Balantidium coli* (Color photograph 114), cysts also provide a means for transmission of the disease agents (see Chapter 41).

Both the trophozoite and cyst stages are important to the life cycles of the protozoa. Certain protozoa have only the trophozoite stage, while others go through both trophozoite and cyst stages. Their

importance in the diagnosis of disease states is discussed in Chapter 41.

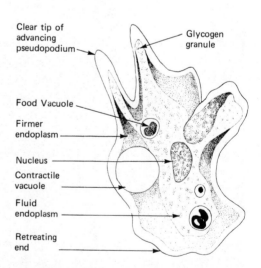

FIG. 10–20. The trophozoite of *Amoeba*. A diagrammatic representation of the components of *Amoeba* spp. Can you note any differences between it and a typical animal cell?

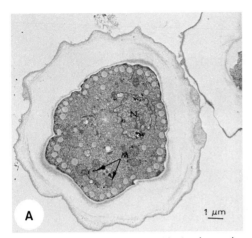

FIG. 10–21. Protozoan cysts of *Acathamoeba castellanii*. <u>A</u>. An ultrathin section of a cyst, showing various organelles, including mitochondria (*M*), a nucleus (*N*), and ribosomes (dot-like structures). The thick cyst wall is quite evident. (Courtesy of Drs. B. Bowers and E. Korn, National Heart and Lung Institute.) <u>B</u>. Mature cysts of *A. castellanii* shown by scanning electron microscopy. (From Pasternak, J. J., Thompson, J. E., Schultz, T. M. G., and Zachariah, K.: *Exptl. Cell Res.*, 60:290–292, 1970.)

QUESTIONS FOR REVIEW

1. With the aid of drawings show the relationships among the following structures.
   a. sporangium
   b. rhizoid
   c. sporangiospore
   d. stolon
   e. sporangiophore

2. Define or explain *coenocytic*.

3. What type of cellular organization do fungi have? Have they any unusual organelles? List at least six organelles found in fungi, and give their functions.

4. What general types of asexual spores do fungi form? Which are characteristically associated with yeasts?

5. Briefly describe zygospore formation. What other types of sexual spores are found with fungi? What is the difference between micro- and macroconidia?

6. Differentiate between a mycelium and hyphae.

7. Define or explain the following:
   a. pellicle
   b. conjugation
   c. contractile vacuole
   d. meiosis

8. Briefly describe the forms of reproduction that occur among the protozoa.

9. What is a trophozoite? How does it differ from a cyst? What is the medical significance of protozoan cysts? In general, what functions do cysts perform?

10. What are the major means of locomotion of protozoa? Describe the different types of pseudopods. What is meant by the 9 + 2 arrangement?

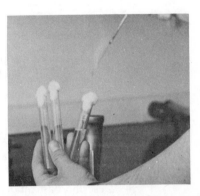
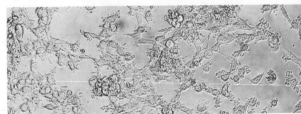

The Cultivation of Microorganisms

DIVISION 3: Behavioral Objectives

After reading the chapters in this division, the individual should be able to:

1. Summarize the properties of major biochemical compounds, including carbo-hydrates, lipids, nucleic acids, and proteins.

2. Describe the growth and incubation requirements of different microbial types.

3. Identify specific procedures and nutrient preparations (*culture media*) used for the cultivation of bacteria, fungi, and viruses.

4. Describe basic inoculation and transfer techniques used with microorganisms and tissue culture systems.

5. Relate the properties of major biochemical compounds to their respective roles in nutrient preparations.

6. Describe standard qualitative and quantitative techniques used in the detection and demonstration of *in vitro* viral activities.

Introduction to Biochemistry

Microbiology is so intimately involved with biochemistry that it is often difficult to separate the two branches of science. Microorganisms are composed of and utilize many of the same compounds that are characteristically used by other life forms. Many aspects of their cellular physiology resemble those of plant and animal cells. For this reason, microorganisms have been used as research tools in many studies of biochemistry, biophysics, genetics, and physiology intended to uncover the secrets of life —including metabolic pathways, DNA replication, genetic fine structure, the mechanisms of viral infection, the nature of metabolic diseases, and the nature of mutation. A glance at the list of Nobel Prizes in medicine (Table 2–1) clearly shows that many Nobel laureates have been associated with microbially-oriented research.

This chapter discusses various biochemical compounds, including carbohydrates, lipids, proteins, and nucleic acids. The role of these and other substances in various aspects of metabolism will be presented in Chapter 15. Pertinent details will be introduced wherever possible in these discussions, but space limitations preclude an extensive discussion of any particular topic. Mastering this subject matter should enable the reader to understand many of the principles and mechanisms discussed in the chapters which follow. For a more thorough treatment of compounds, metabolism, and their relationship to normal functioning and to disease states, the references listed at the end of the text should be consulted.

Functional Chemical Groups

Before presenting basic information regarding biochemical reactions, familiarity with selected aspects of organic chemistry is needed. Therefore, brief characterizations of functional chemical groups (Table 11–1) and selected aspects of their interactions (Table 11–2) are given below. The symbol R in each of the various formulas shown represents a particular organic group which is a component of the compound being discussed.

Lipids

The term *lipid* is usually applied to any substance soluble in organic solvents such as acetone, benzene, carbon tetrachloride, chloroform, and ether. Lipid compounds include fats, fatty acids, oils, phospholipids, steroids, and waxes.

Fatty Acids

Naturally-occurring fatty acids are even-numbered carbon chains (4 to 30 carbons) with an acid group (–COOH), and may be saturated or unsaturated. Saturated fatty acids do not contain double bonds in their chains, whereas unsaturated fatty acids have one or more double bonds. Example of both types are shown in Table 11–3.

Table 11–1   Brief Characterizations of Chemical Functional Groups

Group	Description
Alcohols	Compounds of this type are characterized on the basis of one or more hydroxyl (OH) groups associated with them. Although other formulas are possible, they are generally represented by R—OH. Examples of the R group include CH_3 (methyl) and CH_2CH_3 (ethyl)
Aldehydes	These chemical substances possess a carbonyl group (C=O) and are represented by the general formula R—$\overset{\overset{\textstyle O}{\|}}{C}$—H
Amines	Compounds in this category have a nitrogen-containing group. Several formula arrangements are known. However, a general one such as R—NH_2 may be used to represent amines.
Ketones	A carbonyl group base R—$\overset{\overset{\textstyle O}{\|}}{C}$—H is associated with ketones, but the hydrogen atom is replaced by an organic group (R), e.g., CH_3, CH_2CH_3. The general formula for this group of compounds can be represented by R—$\overset{\overset{\textstyle O}{\|}}{C}$—$R$
Organic acids	Compounds of this nature contain one or more carboxyl groups ($\overset{\overset{\textstyle O}{\|}}{C}$—OH), and are referred to as carboxylic acids. A general classification is possible using the number of carboxyl groups as a basis for the scheme. For example, a monocarboxylic acid has one such group and is represented by R—COOH. An example is formic acid (H—COOH). A dicarboxylic acid has two carboxyl groups and is represented by the formula COOH—R—COOH. Oxalic acid (HOOC—COOH) is a compound of this type. Other forms are also known

Table 11–2   Selected Reactions Involving Functional Group-Containing Compounds

Reaction Type	Reaction
Ester formation	$R - OH + R -\overset{\overset{\textstyle O}{\|}}{C} - OH \longrightarrow R - O - \overset{\overset{\textstyle O}{\|}}{C} - R + H_2O$ alcohol + acid ⟶ ester + water
Anhydride formation	$R-\overset{\overset{\textstyle O}{\|}}{C}-OH + R-\overset{\overset{\textstyle O}{\|}}{C}-OH \longrightarrow R-\overset{\overset{\textstyle O}{\|}}{C}-O-\overset{\overset{\textstyle O}{\|}}{C}-R + H_2O$ acid + acid ⟶ anhydride + water
Amide formation	$R-\overset{\overset{\textstyle O}{\|}}{C}-O-\overset{\overset{\textstyle O}{\|}}{C}-R + 2NH_3 \longrightarrow 2R-\overset{\overset{\textstyle O}{\|}}{C}-NH_2 + H_2O$ anhydride + ammonia ⟶ amide + water

Table 11–3   Representative Examples of Saturated and Unsaturated Fatty Acids

Saturated Fatty Acid		Unsaturated Fatty Acid	
Compound Designation	Chemical Formula	Compound Designation	Chemical Formula
Butyric Acid (found in butter)	$CH_3 (CH_2)_2$ - COOH	Oleic acid (olive oil)	$CH_3 (CH_2)_7$ - CH = CH $(CH_2)_7$ COOH
Caproic Acid (found in butter)	$CH_3 (CH_2)_3$ - COOH	Linoleic acid (linseed oil)	$CH_3 (CH_2)_7$ - CH = CH - CH_2 CH = CH $(CH_2)_4$ COOH
Stearic Acid (found in animal and plant fats)	$CH_3 (CH_2)_{16}$ - COOH		

Fats, Oils, and Waxes

Fats and oils are esters of fatty acids and glycerol. Waxes are esters of fatty acids with long-chained alcohols. The basic difference between fats and oils is that fats are solid at normal room temperature, while oils are liquid. This characteristic is determined by the degree of saturation: the compound containing unsaturated fatty acids is the liquid.

A fat may consist of glycerol esterified with one, two, or three different fatty acids. An example of such a simple triglyceride would be tristearin (Figure 11–1).

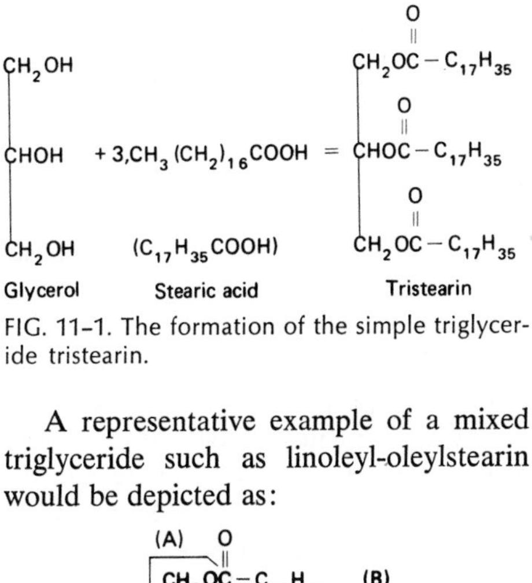

$$CH_2OH \qquad\qquad\qquad \overset{\overset{\displaystyle O}{\|}}{CH_2OC} - C_{17}H_{35}$$
$$CHOH \quad + 3,CH_3(CH_2)_{16}COOH = \overset{\overset{\displaystyle O}{\|}}{CHOC} - C_{17}H_{35}$$
$$CH_2OH \qquad (C_{17}H_{35}COOH) \qquad \overset{\overset{\displaystyle O}{\|}}{CH_2OC} - C_{17}H_{35}$$

Glycerol   Stearic acid   Tristearin

FIG. 11–1. The formation of the simple triglyceride tristearin.

A representative example of a mixed triglyceride such as linoleyl-oleylstearin would be depicted as:

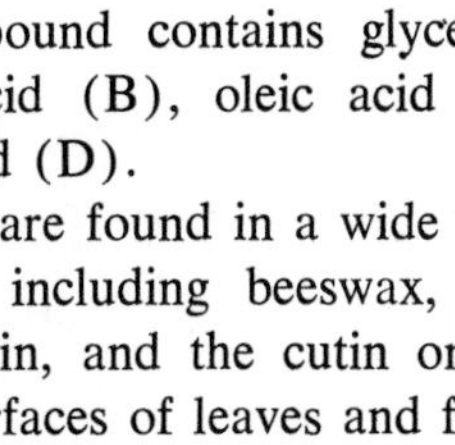

$$\text{(A)} \quad \overset{\overset{\displaystyle O}{\|}}{CH_2OC} - C_{17}H_{35} \quad \text{(B)}$$
$$\overset{\overset{\displaystyle O}{\|}}{CHOC} - C_{17}H_{33} \quad \text{(C)}$$
$$\overset{\overset{\displaystyle O}{\|}}{CH_2OC} - C_{17}H_{31} \quad \text{(D)}$$

The compound contains glycerol (A), linoleic acid (B), oleic acid (C) and stearic acid (D).

Waxes are found in a wide variety of materials, including beeswax, carnauba wax, lanolin, and the cutin on the epidermal surfaces of leaves and fruits. The fatty acids and monohydric (one alcohol group) alcohols commonly found in this class of lipids usually have 16 to 40 carbons in their chains. For example, in beeswax, which is a mixture of esters, the major component is myricyl palmitate, represented by the molecular formula

$$(C_{30}H_{61}\overset{\overset{\displaystyle O}{\|}}{C}OC\ C_{15}H_{31})$$

Phospholipids

There are several different groups of phospholipids, also called *phosphatides*. One group, the *lecithins,* is of particular importance in mammalian physiology. Their composition includes choline, fatty acids, glycerol, and phosphoric acid. Choline,

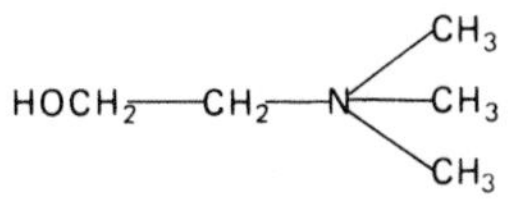

$$HOCH_2-CH_2-N\overset{\displaystyle CH_3}{\underset{\displaystyle CH_3}{-CH_3}}$$

functions as an essential metabolite in mammalian physiology, both as a component of lecithin and as part of the non-lipid acetylcholine. Lecithin is involved in fat metabolism, while acetylcholine is a major factor in nerve activity. The basic structure of lecithin is:

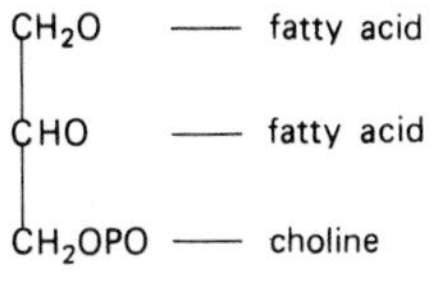

$$CH_2O \quad\rule{1cm}{0.4pt}\quad \text{fatty acid}$$
$$CHO \quad\rule{1cm}{0.4pt}\quad \text{fatty acid}$$
$$CH_2OPO \quad\rule{1cm}{0.4pt}\quad \text{choline}$$

When other compounds are substituted for choline, different phospholipids result. Examples of such substitutions include the cephalins, which contain ethanolamine; phosphatidyl inositol, which contains the carbohydrate inositol; and phosphatidyl serine, which contains the amino acid serine.

Steroids

This group of lipids contains many physiologically important substances, including bile acids, cholesterol, cortisone, ergosterol, and several hormones. The basic structure of steroids is the cyclopentanoperhydro-phenanthrene (CPPP) nucleus:

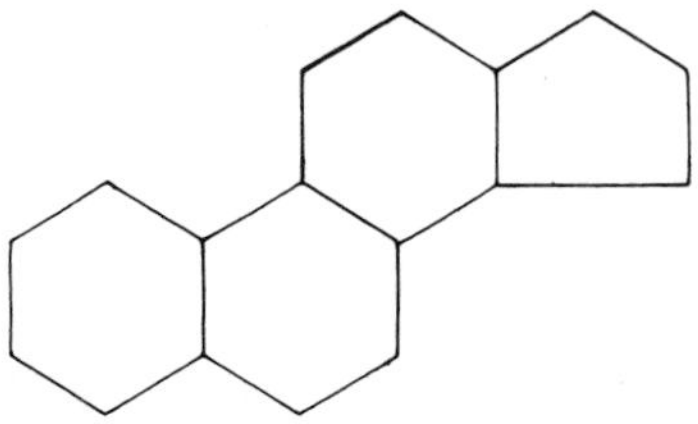

The wide variety of activities ascribed to steroids depends upon the various side groups which may be attached to the CPPP nucleus. This can be seen by examining the structure of cholesterol, an important component of animal cell membranes.

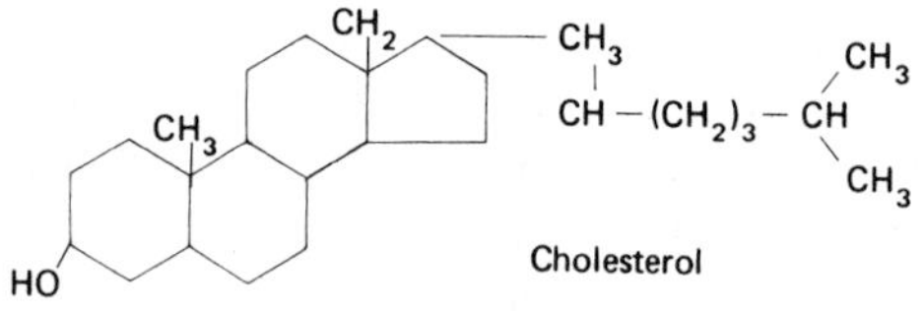

Cholesterol

Carbohydrates

The broad group of organic chemicals known as carbohydrates consists of a wide variety of simple sugars and their derivatives and polymers (high-molecular-weight compounds) such as starch, glycogen, and cellulose. For the sake of brevity, only a limited number of representative carbohydrates will be discussed.

The structure of these compounds will be presented mostly according to the Fischer system. In this system of representation, the molecule is drawn with the aldehyde ($HC=O$) or ketone ($C=O$) group at the top of the carbon skeleton, the primary alcohol (CH_2OH) at the bottom, and hydrogen (H) and hydroxyl (OH) groups at right angles to the carbon backbone of the compound. As examples, four aldo sugars—sugars containing an aldehyde group—are shown in Figure 11–2. These compounds are referred to as triose, tetrose, pentose, and hexose, or as three-, four-, five-, and six-carbon aldo sugars, respectively. The figure also shows fructose, a keto sugar or ketohexose, for purposes of comparison.

Because pentoses and hexoses can exist in cyclic form, different cyclic arrangements are drawn. Figure 11–3 shows the cyclic arrangements of ribose, a five-carbon sugar which is a significant

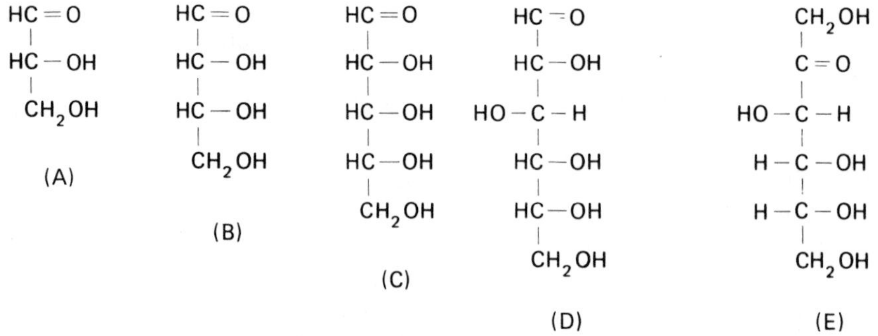

FIG. 11–2. Structural formulas of representative aldo sugars and a keto sugar. _A_. Glyceraldehyde. _B_. Erythrose. _C_. Ribose. _D_. Glucose. _E_. Fructose (a keto sugar).

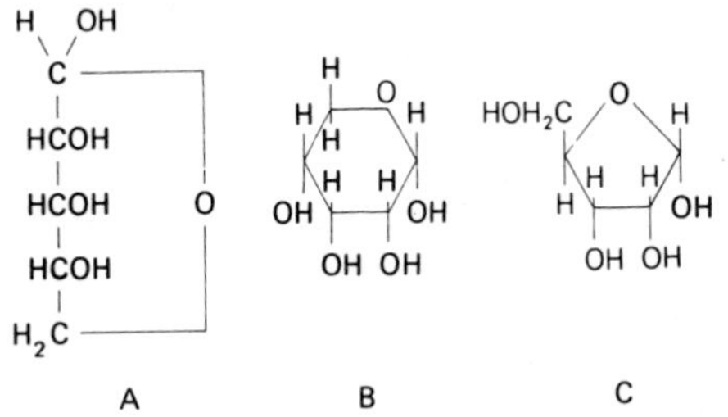

FIG. 11–3. The cyclic arrangements of ribose, a 5-carbon sugar. _A_. The Fischer system representation. _B_. The pyran ring. _C_. The furan ring. B and C are representations of the Haworth system.

structural component of coenzymes, nucleic acids (RNA), and adenosine triphosphate (ATP).

Glycosides

These carbohydrates are formed by the reaction of a sugar with another . compound containing an alcohol group (aglycone). If the sugar happens to be glucose, the compound then is called a _glucoside_. The aglycone component of the glycoside may be methyl alcohol (CH_3OH), glycerol, or a steroid. One medically significant glycoside with a steroid aglycone is digitalis.

A simple glycoside can be compounded by mixing a boiling solution of glucose and methyl alcohol in the presence of hydrogen chloride (HCl). The HCl functions as a catalyst (Figure 11–4).

The glycosidic linkage is an essential feature of carbohydrates composed of more than one sugar unit: disaccharides, trisaccharides, and polysaccharides. In chained polysaccharides, the linkage between the sugar monomers is commonly

expressed as 1, 4 or 1, 6, based upon the attachment points between the sugar units. Thus, using the right-to-left clockwise numbering system of the sugar molecule,

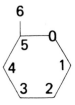

a 1,4 linkage is represented by

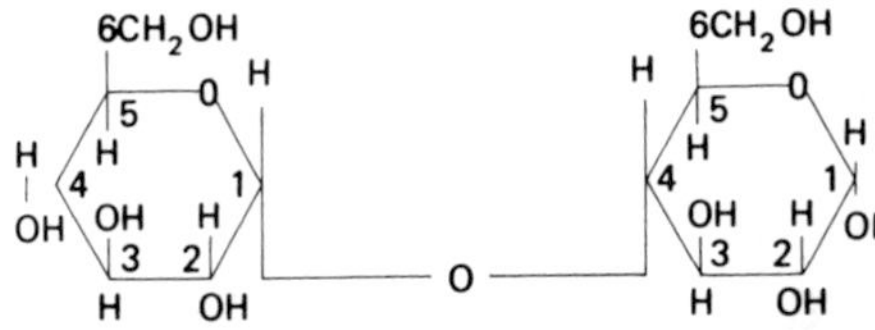

The compound shown here is maltose, a common disaccharide.

Monosaccharides. Probably the most significant monosaccharides are the 6-carbon compound hexoses, which include fructose, galactose, glucose, and mannose. Glucose is the primary energy source for nutrition, but mammals metabolize all four hexoses similarly. Selected aspects of sugar metabolism are presented in Chapter 15.

A significant derivative of the pentose _ribose_ is _deoxyribose,_ found in the genetic material deoxyribonucleic acid (DNA). It is represented by the formula

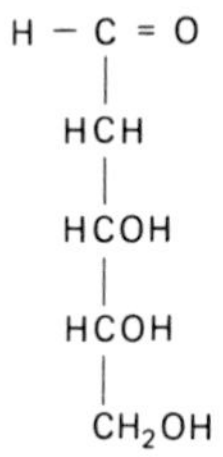

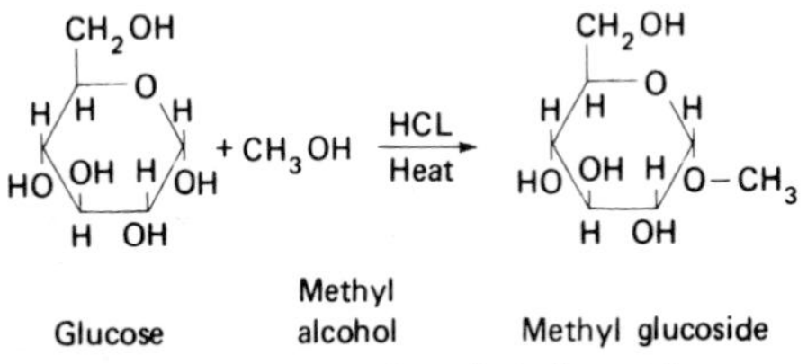

FIG. 11–4. Formation of methyl glucoside.

The sugars discussed earlier contained the same number of oxygen and carbon atoms: glucose $= C_6H_{12}O_6$, and ribose $= C_5H_{10}O_5$. In contrast, deoxyribose is characterized by having fewer atoms of oxygen than of carbon: $C_5H_{10}O_4$.

Other important monosaccharides include amino sugars, sugar acids, and sugar alcohols. The structural formulas of compounds representative of such monosaccharides are shown in Figure 11–5.

The amino sugars are found in mucoproteins, in chitin, and as components of some antibiotics, e.g., erythromycin and streptomycin. Glucuronic acid represents one type of sugar acid found in certain polysaccharides. The sugar alcohols can be found not only in polysaccharides but in phospholipids as well.

Disaccharides.   These compounds are molecules composed of two monosaccharides. Usually they can be split to yield simple sugars. The three most commonly encountered compounds of this type are lactose, maltose, and sucrose. Lactose, a prime component of milk, consists of glucose and galactose molecules. Maltose (refer to the 1,4 linkage discussion) is made up of two glucose molecules and is produced by the degradation of starch. Sucrose is composed of glucose and fructose, and is the natural sugar found in pineapple, sugar beets, and sugar cane.

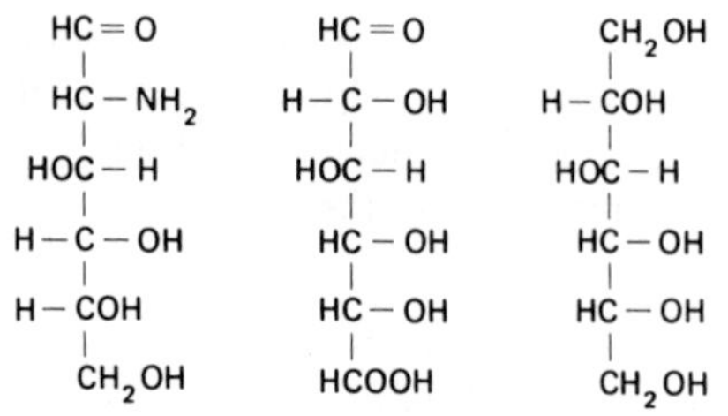

Polysaccharides.   These long-chain polymers of sugar may consist of the same type of sugar molecules or of different ones. *Starch,* which is the main food storage product in plants, is composed entirely of glucose units. It contains two basic structures, amylose and amylopectin. The amylose molecule has a linear arrangement of units, while amylopectin contains some side chains. The linear structures of starch are essentially chains of maltose units with 1,4 linkages. In addition to such 1,4 linkages in the linear structure, amylopectin contains linear chains which are attached by 1,6 linkages to the backbone polymer at intervals throughout the molecule.

The chief animal polysaccharide is *glycogen.* It is structurally related to amylopectin, in that it contains 1,4 linked glucose units cross-connected with 1,6 linkages.

Cellulose is yet another polymer of glucose units connected by 1,4 linkages. This structural component of plants has a different 1,4 linkage from that found in starch, which makes it impossible for mammalian enzymes to hydrolyze. However, various microorganisms present in certain animal digestive systems are able to cleave the molecule into utilizable sugar units. It is because of these microbes that ruminants and termites are able to digest cellulose.

Nucleic Acids

These biological polymers are composed of subunits called *nucleotides.* Smaller components in turn are made up of nitrogenous bases, phosphate, and a 5-carbon sugar (*pentose*). The pentose serves as a basis for the classification of nucleic

FIG. 11–5. Structural formulas of different forms of the monosaccharide glucose. *A.* The amino form, glucosamine. *B.* The uronic acid form, glucuronic acid. *C.* The alcohol form, glucitol or sorbitol.

acids into two main classes: ribonucleic and deoxyribonucleic acids. *Ribonucleic acid (RNA)* contains ribose, while *deoxyribonucleic acid (DNA)* has deoxyribose.

The primary nitrogenous bases found in RNA are adenine, guanine, cytosine, and uracil. Adenine and guanine are examples of purines, while cytosine and uracil are pyrimidines. DNA also contains adenine, guanine, and cytosine, but the pyrimidine thymine replaces uracil. These heterocyclic compounds have the chemical structures shown in Figure 11-6.

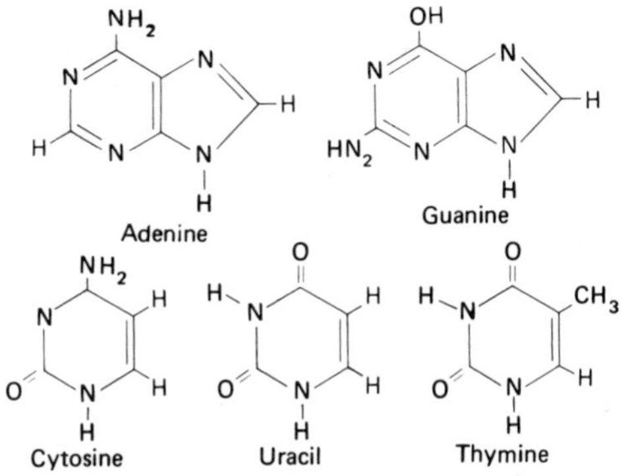

FIG. 11–6. The primary nitrogenous bases of RNA and DNA.

When a purine or pyrimidine is linked with ribose or deoxyribose, the resulting molecule is called a *nucleoside*. With the attachment of a phosphate group, the molecule becomes a *nucleotide*. An example of a ribose *nucleoside* is adenosine (adenine + pentose).

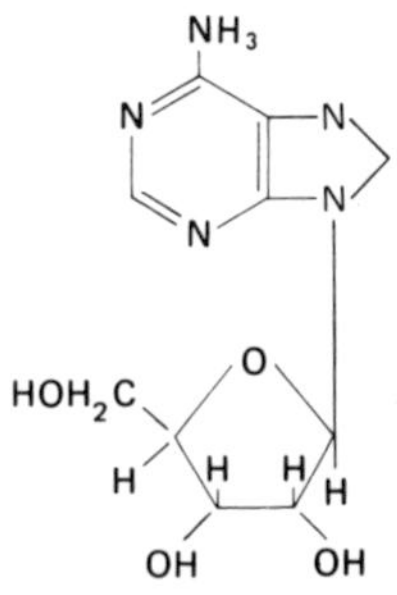

The corresponding nucleotide would be adenylic acid (adenine + pentose + phosphate), also known as adenosine monophosphate (AMP). This compound

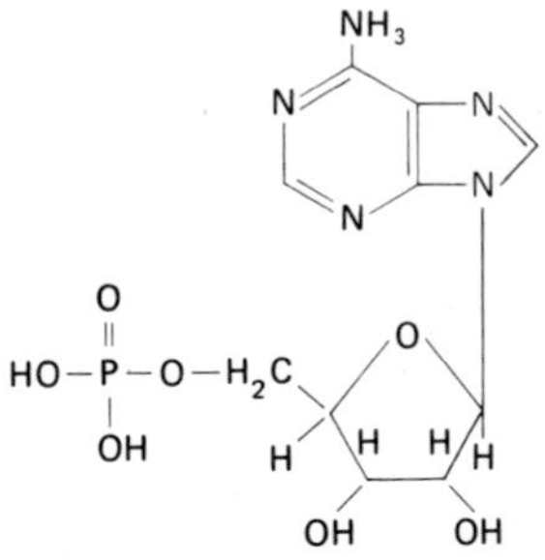

is involved in energy metabolism and protein synthesis. The addition of a second phosphate results in the formation of adenosine diphosphate (ADP), while a third phosphate forms adenosine triphosphate (ATP), which serves as the chemical storehouse for energy in the cell.

The designations of various nucleosides and nucleotides are presented in Table 11–4.

Table 11–4   Common Nomenclature of Nucleosides and Nucleotides

Nitrogen Base	Nucleoside	Nucleotide
Adenine	Adenosine	Adenylic acid
Guanine	Guanosine	Guanylic acid
Cytosine	Cytidine	Cytidylic acid
Uracil	Uridine	Uridylic acid
Thymine	Thymidine	Thymidylic acid

Other nucleoside triphosphates are important in metabolic reactions involving compounds other than nucleic acids. For example, the triphosphates of uridine, cytidine, and guanosine are critical molecules in the synthesis of polysaccharides. Various nucleotides also are involved in other cellular activities. Four coenzymes responsible for oxidation-reduction reactions are nicotinamide adenine dinucleotide (NAD), nicotinamide adenine dinucleotide phosphate (NADP), flavin adenine dinucleotide (FAD), and flavin mononucleotide (FMN). They contain the vitamins niacin and riboflavin in their active forms. Further details concerning the biochemistry of these structures will be found in the reference works listed at the back of this book.

An important coenzyme which contains a nucleotide and a vitamin is coenzyme A (Figure 15–4). This molecule plays a significant role in the catabolism of carbohydrates and lipids. Chemically the compound consists of AMP (nucleotide) and pantothenic acid (vitamin) with mercaptoethylamine. It is interesting to note the reversal of components shown by vitamin B_{12}, which contains a nucleotide as a constituent of the molecule.

Adenosine Triphosphate (ATP)

Adenosine triphosphate is involved in the mobilization of energy. The chemical structure of this critical biochemical compound is shown in Figure 11–7. ATP would not be required if all of the oxidation-reduction reactions and energy-yielding as well as energy-requiring reactions occurred close to one another. However, because these events occur in various regions throughout a cell, it is useful to have a high-energy-containing compound that can be formed in several locations and can easily be made available to cellular areas requiring it, by diffusion or other means. ATP is a versatile compound that can be utilized for various purposes, including amoeboid movement, bioluminescence, cell division, ciliary motion, and muscular activities.

Adenosine triphosphate and other such high-energy phosphate compounds are unique in having one or more so-called high-energy phosphate bonds. The possession of such bonds by ATP enables it to hold much greater quantities of energy than compounds having ordinary linkages. It is customary to indicate high-energy phosphate bonds by a ($\sim$) symbol, and ordinary linkage by ($-$). Thus, the relationship of various components of ATP could be represented by

$$\text{Adenosine} - \text{Phosphate} \sim$$
$$\text{Phosphate} \sim \text{Phosphate}$$

Compare this with adenosine monophosphate, which does not have a high-energy phosphate bond:

$$\text{Adenosine} - \text{Phosphate}$$

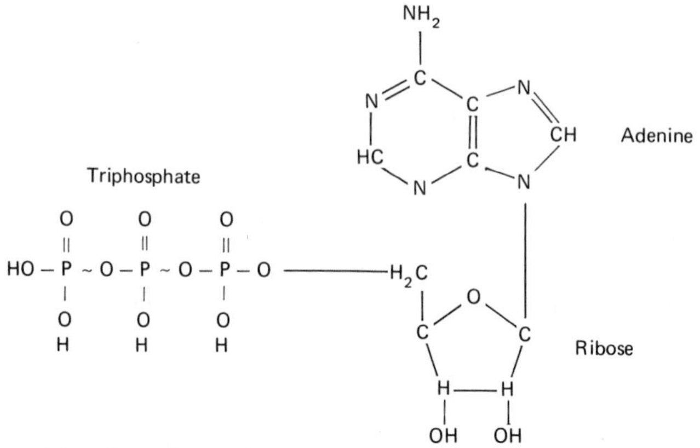

FIG. 11–7. Adenosine triphosphate. Note that the components of this compound, adenine, ribose, and phosphate, also can serve as portions of coenzymes and structural parts of nucleic acids.

When the activities of a cell require an "instantaneous mobilization of energy," a hydrolytic reaction occurs, causing the splitting of a high-energy bond. The event is under the enzymatic control of adenosine triphosphatase (ATP-ase). For each high-energy bond broken, one molecule of inorganic phosphate is produced (Figure 11–8).

ATP + H$_2$O
(Adenosine triphosphate)

$\downarrow$ Adenosine triphosphase (ATP–ase)

ADP + Inorganic phosphate + E
(Adenosine diphosphate)   (PO$_4$) or (Pi)   (Energy)

FIG. 11–8. ATP hydrolysis.

Deoxyribonucleic Acid (DNA)

The DNA molecule usually exists in the form of a double helix formed by the intimate coiling of two DNA strands. Each strand consists of a backbone structure composed of a sugar-phosphate complex bound by phospho-diester linkages —phosphate groups connecting the alcohol groups of two adjacent sugars. The nitrogen bases, such as adenine, thymine, guanine, and cytosine, are attached as small side chains along this backbone structure. Figure 11–9 shows a representation of this DNA molecule and the base pairing exhibited by adenine and thymine, as compared to one involving guanine and cytosine.

J. D. Watson, F. H. C. Crick, and M. Wilkins received the Nobel Prize in Medicine in 1962 for revealing the relationship of the various components in the DNA structure. The structure they proposed is known as the Watson-Crick Model. Based on the x-ray diffraction patterns (Figure 11–10) and the observations that the amount of adenine matched that of thyamine, and the guanine was matched to the cytosine, the helical DNA structure was theorized and reported in 1953.

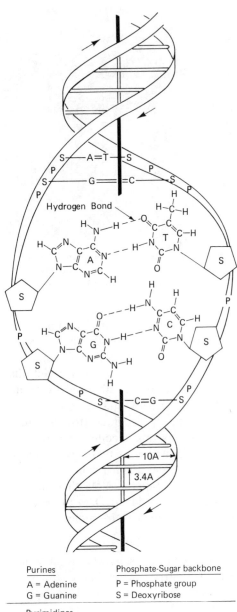

Purines	Phosphate-Sugar backbone
A = Adenine	P = Phosphate group
G = Guanine	S = Deoxyribose

Pyrimidines
C = Cytosine
T = Thymine

FIG. 11–9. A representation of the base pairing found in a DNA molecule. Note that adenine always is paired to thymine, and cytosine to guanine by means of hydrogen bonds. The sugar phosphate backbone component of the DNA molecule also is shown. Note that the distance between base pairs in the DNA chain is 3.4 Angstroms, whereas the width of the molecule is 10 Angstroms.

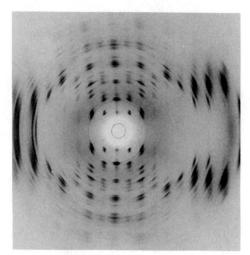

FIG. 11–10. X-ray diffraction pattern of DNA. (Courtesy of Professor M. H. F. Wilkins, Medical Research Council, Biophysics Research Unit, King's College, London.)

Later studies by many scientists, particularly those of A. Kornberg (Nobel Prize 1959) confirmed the Watson-Crick Model of DNA and demonstrated that the nucleic acid is synthesized by an uncoiling of the helix and the formation of complementary daughter strands. Figure 11–11 shows this uncoiling and the subsequent formation of two new strands of DNA using the original components as a template or pattern. Note that the two new strands are identical to those of the original or parent DNA molecule.

Ribonucleic Acid (RNA)

In contrast to the somewhat rigid double-stranded arrangement that characterizes the DNA molecule, free RNA appears to be single-stranded and flexible. This flexibility would appear to be necessary for its function as a protein-synthesizing template in association with ribosomes. The RNA molecule is characterized by the substitution of the pyrimidine uracil for the thymine in DNA, and the incorporation of ribose in place of deoxyribose as the sugar component of its nucleosides.

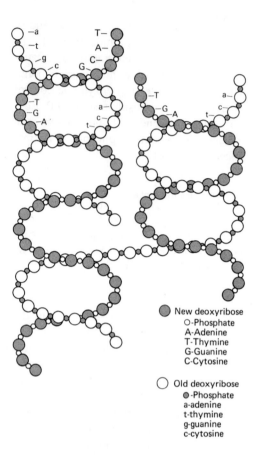

New deoxyribose
O-Phosphate
A-Adenine
T-Thymine
G-Guanine
C-Cytosine

Old deoxyribose
⊙-Phosphate
a-adenine
t-thymine
g-guanine
c-cytosine

FIG. 11–11. DNA synthesis. Note the uncoiling reaction and the subsequent formation of new daughter strands. Do you see the complementary nature of these strands? The separated strands function as templates (patterns) for the growth of new and complementary portions of the DNA molecule (see Figure 11–9).

Proteins

Chemically, proteins consist of carbon, hydrogen, nitrogen, oxygen, and often sulfur. In essence, these compounds are high-molecular-weight polymers of amino acids. The latter are basic units of proteins and have the typical structure:

$$R - \overset{\overset{\displaystyle H}{|}}{\underset{\underset{\displaystyle NH_2}{|}}{C}} - \overset{\overset{\displaystyle O}{\|}}{C} - OH$$

The "R" may be:

1. Hydrogen (H), as in the case of glycine, or a methyl group (CH_3) as in alanine;
2. Larger carbon chains, such as in isoleucine, leucine, and valine;
3. An alcohol group (CH_2OH) (e.g., serine) and threonine;
4. Sulfur (S) (e.g., cysteine, cystine, or methionine);
5. Acid or basic in nature (e.g., glutamic acid and lysine, respectively);
6. Cyclic (e.g., histidine, hydroxyproline, proline, and tryptophan).

The last-named group of amino acids, referred to as *heterocyclic,* are characterized by possessing a side chain with a ring structure in which at least one atom is not a carbon atom. The following structure of tryptophan demonstrates this feature.

Aromatic amino acids, such as phenylalanine and tyrosine, have a benzene ring

in the R group. Structural formulas of ten amino acids mentioned are shown in Table 11–5.

Cystine and cysteine are especially significant amino acids in that their structures permit the formation of disulfide linkages (S=S) between thiol groups (−SH) in proteins. Such bonds contribute to the ultimate shape of the proteins that are important to the activity of enzyme molecules. The disulfide bridge is shown in the cystine molecule (Table 11–5).

Peptide Bond

Proteins are formed by the linking of various amino acids to one another by means of peptide bonds. This type of connection is brought about by an amide bond

$$\overset{\displaystyle O}{\overset{\|}{-C-N}}$$

between the carboxyl (COOH) group of one amino acid and the amino (NH_2) group of another, with the elimination of a water molecule in the process. An example of such peptide linkages is shown in the molecule of glutathione, a tripeptide (Figure 11–12). The specific chemical name of this compound is glutamylcysteinlyglycine.

Two more biologically significant small peptide molecules are the hormones oxytocin and vasopressin. Oxytocin stimulates the contraction of smooth muscle, while vasopressin increases blood pressure and aids in the control of kidney activity.

Protein Structure

As mentioned earlier, thiol groups (−SH) in sulfur-containing amino acids permit the formation of disulfide bonds which can hold peptide chains together in a larger molecule. Additional types of bonding both within and between peptide chains include hydrogen bonds and ionic linkages. All three types of bonds may cause the coiling or the folding of a protein molecule containing them.

Table 11–5   Structural Formulas of Representative Amino Acids

R Group	Typical Base	Amino Acid
$H-$	$\begin{array}{c} H \\ | \\ C - C{\stackrel{\scriptsize O}{=}} OH \\ | \\ NH_2 \end{array}$	Glycine
CH_3-	$\begin{array}{c} H \\ | \\ C - C{\stackrel{\scriptsize O}{=}} OH \\ | \\ NH_2 \end{array}$	Alanine
$\begin{array}{c} CH_3 \\ \diagdown \\ CH- \\ \diagup \\ CH_3 \end{array}$	$\begin{array}{c} H \\ | \\ C - C{\stackrel{\scriptsize O}{=}} OH \\ | \\ NH_2 \end{array}$	Valine
$HO-CH_2-$	$\begin{array}{c} H \\ | \\ C - C{\stackrel{\scriptsize O}{=}} OH \\ | \\ NH_2 \end{array}$	Serine
$HS-$	$\begin{array}{c} H \\ | \\ C - C{\stackrel{\scriptsize O}{=}} OH \\ | \\ NH_2 \end{array}$	Cysteine
$S-CH_2-$ $\big|$ $S-CH_2-$	$\begin{array}{c} H \\ | \\ C - C{\stackrel{\scriptsize O}{=}} OH \\ | \\ NH_2 \end{array}$ $\begin{array}{c} H \\ | \\ C - C{\stackrel{\scriptsize O}{=}} OH \\ | \\ NH_2 \end{array}$	Cystine
$HO-\overset{O}{\underset{}{C}}-CH_2-$	$\begin{array}{c} H \\ | \\ C - C{\stackrel{\scriptsize O}{=}} OH \\ | \\ NH_2 \end{array}$	Glutamic acid
$H_2N-CH_2-CH_2-CH_2-CH_2-$	$\begin{array}{c} H \\ | \\ C - C{\stackrel{\scriptsize O}{=}} OH \\ | \\ NH_2 \end{array}$	Lysine
$\begin{array}{c} HC=C-CH_2- \\ | \quad\quad | \\ N \quad\; NH \\ \diagdown \underset{H}{C} \diagup \end{array}$	$\begin{array}{c} H \\ | \\ C - C{\stackrel{\scriptsize O}{=}} OH \\ | \\ NH_2 \end{array}$	Histidine
CH_2-	$\begin{array}{c} H \\ | \\ C - C{\stackrel{\scriptsize O}{=}} OH \\ | \\ NH_2 \end{array}$	Phenylalanine

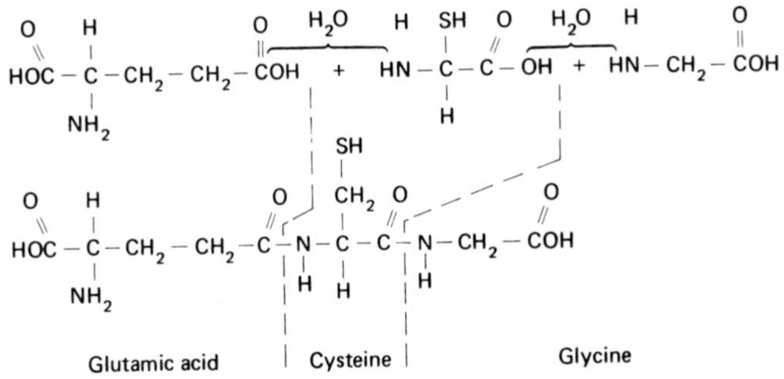

FIG. 11–12. The tripeptide glutathione.

The hydrogen bond occurs when electrons are shared between the hydrogen atoms or closely associated with nitrogen,

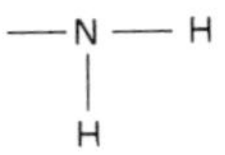

$$-N-H$$
$$|$$
$$H$$

or oxygen,

$$C \overset{O}{\underset{}{=}} O - H$$

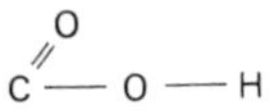

The amino and carboxyl groups of peptide bonds are often involved in hydrogen bonding. Ionic linkage occurs between various positive and negative charges on amino acids.

The structure of protein is usually classified as being primary, secondary, tertiary, or quaternary. The *primary* designation refers to the linear arrangement of amino acids or of the amino acid sequence. The other categories refer to the various types of interactions among the amino acids in the protein that lead to coiling and folding of the molecule.

Enzymes

Reactions between chemical compounds are dependent upon conditions, such as high pressures and temperatures, and/or the presence of an inorganic catalyst, e.g., metal or acid. For example, sugar can react with oxygen to form carbon dioxide, water, and heat energy. This oxidation reaction can be made to occur in three different ways: (1) by the presence of heat energy; (2) through the incorporation of sulfuric acid; and (3) by the introduction of organic catalysts (enzymes).

Heat produces sufficient interactions between sugar and oxygen to bring about the desired reaction. With sulfuric acid the end products are produced as a consequence of the acid acting directly on the sugar. The result in both cases is the same as the products obtained from an essential portion of the metabolism found in animal and plants, yet the high temperature and acid used in the laboratory to convert sugar to carbon dioxide, water, and energy are lethal to plants and animals. In nature, the chemical reactions are caused by enzymes. These protein substances cause energy to be produced in a controlled manner, at favorable temperatures, thus permitting the end products of reaction to be used by the living cells.

Enzymes are either simple or conjugated proteins. The latter group contains, in addition to the protein, a nonprotein portion known as a *prosthetic group, coenzyme,* or *cofactor.* The *coenzyme* designation usually is reserved for organic groups which are known to participate in the enzymatic reaction. Other types of organic or inorganic components of enzymes are referred to as *cofactors.*

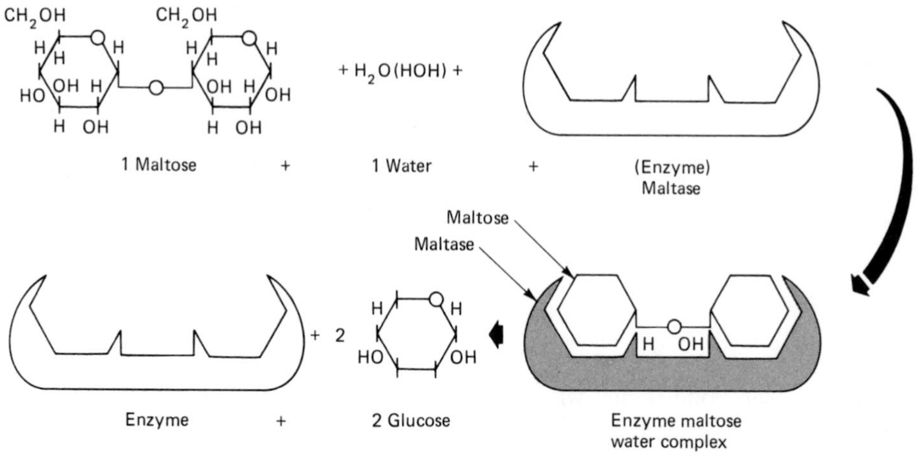

FIG. 11–13. A diagrammatic representation of enzyme substrate interaction.

Table 11–6   Major Classes of Enzymes

Class Designation	Associated Activity	Examples of Enzymes
Oxidoreductases	Transfer of electrons between substrates	Cytochromes, dehydrogenases
Transferases	Transfer of chemical groups between substrates	Transaminase, methyltransferase
Hydrolases	Cleavage of a chemical bond by the addition of water	Peptidase, maltase
Lyases	Removal or addition of a chemical group to a double bond in a substrate	Pyruvate decarboxylase, deaminase
Isomerases	Catalization of the formation of a change of spatial relationships among the atoms within a molecule (steric change)	Racemase, aconitase
Synthetases	Catalization of the coupling of two molecules, requiring energy from a triphosphate compound	Choline acetylase, amino acid-RNA synthetase

The interaction between an enzyme and its substrate—the substance it acts upon—is believed to be due to the complex arrangement of its parts. The folding of the protein molecule produces the environment for the enzyme and substrate molecule to form a proper fit (Figure 11–13), an arrangement that permits the active portion of the enzyme to come into contact with specific sites on the substrate.

One enzyme important in carbohydrate metabolism, *maltase,* converts the disaccharide maltose into two glucose molecules. Figure 11–13 illustrates how a maltose molecule could be held in a position to allow the breaking of the glycosidic bond and the incorporation of water. The enzyme, maltase, reacts with the substrate, maltose, and water (HOH) to produce a complex which results in the formation of glucose and the regenerated enzyme.

Among the most remarkable features of enzymes is their almost absolute specificity. One enzyme usually performs a single reaction with a particular substrate under a certain set of conditions.

On this basis, enzymes can be categorized into broad groups, as shown in Table 11–6. Usually, the suffix *ase* is added to the name of a substrate in order to designate the enzyme which can act upon that substrate.

QUESTIONS FOR REVIEW

1. What are the basic organic chemical groupings associated with lipids, carbohydrates, proteins, and nucleic acids?

2. Differentiate between:
   a. phospholipid and wax
   b. cholesterol and cortisone
   c. glucose and fructose
   d. ribose and deoxyribose
   e. RNA and DNA
   f. nucleotides and nucleosides
   g. starch and cellulose
   h. polypeptide and protein

3. What are the major groups of amino acids?

4. Identify several amino acids which contribute to secondary protein structure.

5. Describe possible mechanisms of enzyme action and protein structure.

6. What is meant by the "complementary nature" of DNA strands?

7. What is meant by "enzyme specificity"?

8. How might enzyme specificity be exploited in clinical medicine?

9. Why is ATP considered to be a critical compound?

Techniques Used in the Cultivation of Bacteria and Fungi

A wide variety of procedures and nutrient preparations are used to induce microorganisms to grow and reproduce. Different microbes require different environments and nutrients, called *culture media* (singular, *medium*). For instance, procedures for culturing fungi are of little value in inducing viruses to grow.

Microorganisms are usually cultivated in containers, including test tubes, flasks, Petri dishes (Figure 12–1), and even huge steel tanks. The tanks are employed commercially to obtain large quantities of the desired organisms or their products, as discussed in the Industrial Applications section of Chapter 5. Whatever the actual container material may be, the procedures are referred to as *in vitro*—literally, "in glass," even though such containers are often made of plastic.

Some microorganisms cannot be grown *in vitro,* but only in living animals. Cultivation methods using live animals are called *in vivo* techniques. When animal tissues are removed and used as a culture medium for microbes, the procedure is an *in vitro* one because a culture vessel is used, not the living (*vivo*) animal. Some microbes can be cultured both *in vivo* and *in vitro.*

Extensive and intensive studies of the particular requirements of different microorganisms have led to the development of many culture media and techniques. Modifications and improvements continually appear, as knowledge increases. This chapter deals with the general requirements for life of microorganisms.

In order for an organism to cause disease, it must be able not only to survive,

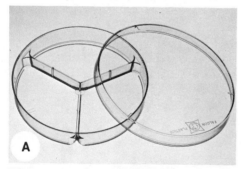

A

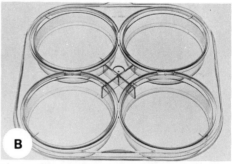

B

FIG. 12–1. A variety of plastic Petri dishes which can be used in the cultivation of bacteria and fungi. _A._ An example of a three compartment Petri dish. Dishes are also available without compartments or with two or four compartments. Different media or specimens can be introduced into each separate area. _B._ A relatively new addition, the Cluster dish. All of these plastic containers are sterile and disposable. (Courtesy of Falcon Plastics, Division of BioQuest, Los Angeles.)

but to grow and reproduce in or on the body of its host. These pathogens—as well as nonpathogenic microbes that populate different body regions—carry on their life processes in environments containing different organic and inorganic substances, oxygen and carbon dioxide concentrations, and alkalinity or acidity (pH). Cultivation techniques and media used to provide suitable conditions for the growth of bacteria and fungi will be discussed from this viewpoint. The cultivation of viruses will be discussed in the next chapter.

Topics will be handled in the following order:

1. Forms of nutrition;
2. Physical requirements for growth;
3. Properties of bacteriological media;
4. Selected media and their ingredients;
5. Preparation of media;
6. Techniques of inoculation and isolation of pure cultures;
7. Conditions of incubation;
8. Use of sterility cabinets; and
9. Media and techniques for the cultivation of fungi.

Forms of Nutrition

Heterotrophy, Autotrophy, and Hypotrophy

Generally speaking, the *heterotrophic* organism requires certain preformed organic compounds for its nutrition. These materials may be sources of carbon (sugars), nitrogen (amino acids), vitamins, or other growth factors. The *autotrophic* microorganism, on the other hand, can synthesize all or nearly all of its essential organic materials from inorganic compounds such as carbon dioxide (CO_2). It usually thrives best in soils and bodies of water, while the heterotroph grows well in any environment with a source of organic and other nutrients.

Both heterotrophic and autotrophic organisms are free-living and can, as a rule, be cultivated on artificial media—assuming, of course, that the particular nutrients and environmental conditions for growth are known.

A third group of microorganisms, the *hypotrophs*, are obligate intracellular parasites. They include the viruses of animals, plants, and bacteria, and most of the group formerly designated as rickettsia. Some larger agents and rickettsia appear to be similar to bacteria in nutritional requirements.

Gaseous Requirements

In addition to their classification by nutritional requirements, microorganisms are also categorized by their response to available gases such as oxygen and carbon dioxide. Oxygen is involved as an electron receptor in metabolism (see Chapter 15) and carbon dioxide can be considered an essential nutrient for some organisms.

The *aerobic* organism requires oxygen, either at atmospheric levels or at some lower concentration.

Microaerophilic organisms require oxygen at less than 20 per cent concentration, and do not grow in the upper portions of liquid (broth) cultures where oxygen is abundant. If this avoidance of oxygen is due to a need for more CO_2 rather than less O_2, the microaerophilic organism would be called *capneic*. The capneic organism requires an atmosphere with a carbon dioxide level of approximately 3 to 10 per cent.

Anaerobes are organisms having no requirement for free oxygen, but possessing varying degrees of oxygen tolerance. *Facultative anaerobes* will grow in either the presence or absence of oxygen. Examples include streptococci (which are primarily oxygen tolerant and utilize anaerobic respiration) and yeasts, which have dual respiration capabilities.

Certain bacteria of medical significance, such as *Neisseria gonorrhoeae,* must be provided with CO_2 for growth purposes. With other pathogens, such as *Brucella* spp., causative agents of brucellosis, CO_2 is used only for primary isolations. As many microorganisms of clinical importance grow better in the presence of CO_2, it is not unlikely that capneic incubation will become the technique of choice in the laboratory. The details of the conditions of incubation are discussed later in the chapter.

Physical Requirements for Growth

Thermal Conditions

As a group, microorganisms have been shown to grow between the temperatures of about freezing and 90°C. Organisms can be classified as *psychrophiles* (cold-loving), *mesophiles* (moderate-temperature-loving), and *thermophiles* (heat-loving), based upon their favorable growth temperature range. The psychrophilic range is approximately 0° to 20°C; that of mesophiles, 20° to 45°C; and that of thermophiles, 45° to 90°C.

The minimum, maximum, and optimum temperatures for an organism are known as its *cardinal temperatures.* The cardinal temperatures for any organism are dependent upon several factors, including the age of the culture and the supply of nutrients. An organism, while not growing at unfavorable temperatures, may still endure them. For example, many organisms can survive in freezing environments; these forms may be called *psychroduric* or *cryoduric.* Organisms that survive at high temperatures are known

as *thermoduric* types. *Bacillus* spp. are good examples of the latter, due to their formation of heat-resistant spores.

Acidity or Alkalinity (pH)

Microorganisms also have certain pH (hydrogen ion concentration) needs, as reflected by their growth responses in various media. An operational definition of pH is simply the negative logarithm of the hydrogen ion [H^+] concentration. The scale of values representing this property of solutions extends from 0 to 14 (Table 12–1). Aqueous solutions also contain hydroxyl ions, [OH^-], which are important in the control of the alkalinity of a solution. A neutral state, in which the concentrations of hydrogen and hydroxyl ions are equal, is represented by the pH value of 7. In general, pure water should have this pH. Solutions with pH values from 0 to 6.9 are *acidic,* while those having values from 7.1 to 14 are *basic* or *alkaline.*

Because of the logarithmic nature of the pH units, a change in one such unit corresponds to a difference of ten times in the hydrogen ion concentration. Consider, for example, a preparation with a pH of 0. The [H^+] here is 10^0 or 1 normal (N). By comparison, a solution having a pH of 1 has a hydrogen concentration represented by 10^{-1} or 1/10 normal, i.e., N/10, of the first preparation (Table 12–1).

Various indicators and electronic pH meters are commonly used to determine the hydrogen concentrations of preparations. Certain pH indicators have particular importance in a bacteriological laboratory, as they are used to demonstrate the decomposition of various carbohydrates and related substances. Common examples of indicators incorporated into bacteriological media include: (1) bromcresol purple; (2) litmus (Color

Table 12–1   pH Values and Corresponding Hydrogen Ion Concentrations

pH Scale	pH Value	Normal Concentrations	Common Examples of Substances Having a Particular pH	
Highly acid	0	10^0N	Human gastric juice	0.9
	1	10^{-1}N		
	2	10^{-2}N	Orange juice	2.0
	3	10^{-3}N		
	4	10^{-4}N	Tomato juice	4.2
	5	10^{-5}N		
	6	10^{-6}N	Media for fungi	5.6
Neutral	7	10^{-7}N	Milk	6.5
			Milk	6.6
			Blood approx.	7.3
			Bile	7.8
	8	10^{-8}N	Some media	8.6
	9	10^{-9}N		
	10	10^{-10}N		
	11	10^{-11}N		
	12	10^{-12}N	Lime water	12.3
	13	10^{-13}N		
Highly alkaline	14	10^{-14}N	A N/1 sodium hydroxide solution	14.0

Figure 50), and (3) phenol red (Color Figure 38). Necessary adjustments to obtain the desired pH usually can be made by the careful addition of standard acids, such as hydrochloric acid (HCl), or bases such as potassium or sodium hydroxide (KOH and NaOH).

Some organisms can be found growing in sulfur springs containing sulfuric acid with a pH of less than 2, others in ammoniated solutions at a pH greater than 8. Fungi, as a rule, grow well at an acid pH range of 5.5 to 6. This property is used in the preparation of selective media for these organisms, since many contaminating bacteria cannot grow under these conditions. (The cultivation of fungi, will be discussed more fully later.) Similarly, the causative agent of Asiatic cholera, *Vibrio cholerae*, can tolerate a pH of 8. This fact is used in the preparation of isolation media for the organism, since it must be separated from other typical organisms comprising the enteric flora found in feces. As a rule, microorganisms appear to prefer a more neutral pH, between 6 and 7.5. Therefore, acidic and alkaline solutions can exert disinfecting effects on various organisms.

Properties of Bacteriological Media

Growth Media

The combining of various substances into nutritive concoctions has long been an integral part of microbiology. Such media are used for the isolation of important organisms from various materials, such as dairy products, foods, soil, water, and clinical specimens. Most organisms found in these situations are heterotrophic in nature, thus simplifying the task of combining the essential nutrient components into a suitable medium. Some of the important ingredients of media are briefly described below.

Nitrogen sources. Nitrogen is a component of cellular proteins, nucleic acids, and vitamins. Microorganisms must therefore be supplied with this element in some form. Many can use ammonium salts, e.g., ammonium chloride (NH_4Cl), while others require the break-down products of proteins, such as peptones (partially hydrolyzed proteins), peptides, and amino acids. Some bacteria (e.g., *Bacillus* spp.) produce extra-cellular protein-digesting enzymes (proteases) which breakdown gelatin and other proteins into smaller components, like peptides and amino acids. These can then be brought into the cells for further metabolic action. Organisms that are able to grow when supplied with ammonium salts usually will grow in the presence of organic nitrogen. A good example is the bacterium *Escherichia coli*.

Carbon and energy sources. Carbon is the most basic structural element of all living forms. It is obtained by organisms from carbohydrates, proteins (peptones, etc.), and lipids, in essence from all organic nutrients and carbon dioxide. The catabolism (metabolic decomposition) of organic compounds results in the production of amino acids, sugar, fatty acids, and other related compounds. Such materials may function in anabolism (constructive metabolism), thus producing the enzymatic and structural proteins, nucleic acids, carbohydrates, and other biochemical compounds peculiar to the organism. The same compounds may be involved in energy metabolism, producing the impetus for growth and reproduction, or as storage products rich in energy-yielding chemical bonds.

Carbohydrate sources of energy and carbon include starch, glycogen, various pentose (5-carbon) monosaccharides such as arabinose, hexose (6-carbon) monosaccharides such as dextrose, and disaccharides such as lactose, sucrose, and maltose. In utilizing the polysaccharides (starch and glycogen) the organism must produce extracellular enzymes to bring about the degradation of the complex compound into smaller molecules which can enter the cell. The enzyme amylase, for example, degrades starch into maltose units, which can then be transported into the cell. Subsequently, the enzyme maltase splits the molecule into two dextrose units for use in further metabolic activi-

ties. This catabolism not only yields the various building blocks for proteins, polysaccharides, lipid, and nucleic acid biosynthesis, but results in the production of energy with which cells can perform anabolic reactions. There usually are exceptions to any rule. Some will be discussed in other chapters in relation to forms of energy metabolism which function solely with amino acids, as with the Stickland reaction found in *Clostridium* species (spp.).

Vitamins and growth factors. Several of the vitamins that have played a significant role in the treatment of human nutritional deficiency diseases are also required by microorganisms. Certain microorganisms are capable of synthesizing their own vitamin requirements, while others must obtain them from their nutrient medium. Vitamin compounds that have been shown to be effective in microbial nutrition include thiamine chloride, riboflavin, nicotinic acid, pantothenic acid, pyridoxine, biotin, para-amino benzoic acid, folic acid, cyanocobolamine, and inositol.

Vitamins can function as portions of coenzymes or as integral components of other biologically active materials. A *coenzyme* may be thought of as the active portion of an enzyme when it is associated with the protein component of that enzyme.

Other growth factors have been observed to be required by various microorganisms. These may be vitamin precursors, such as pimelic acid (the precursor of biotin) and beta-alanine (the precursor of pantothenic acid). Growth factors also may include purines and pyrimidines required for nucleic acid syntheses.

Some microorganisms appear to have peculiar requirements. For example, *Hemophilus influenzae* and certain other bacterial species must have a certain component of hemoglobin for growth, in addition to a complete coenzyme— either nicotine adenine dinucleotide or its triphosphate (NAD or NADP). The interrelationships of the various vitamins and growth factors are more meaningful with a grasp of certain aspects of metabolism presented in Chapter 15.

Essential mineral salts. Various inorganic compounds are essential for microbial nutrition. These substances include phosphates, which are required in nucleic acid synthesis, and sulfates, which may be needed in the formation of certain amino acids. Potassium, magnesium, manganese, iron, and calcium serve as inorganic cofactors for particular enzymes, or may be incorporated into several biochemical reactions. For example, iron is a constituent of cytochromes, which are important in energy metabolism. Calcium comprises a major component of bacterial spores. Inorganic nutrients required in trace amounts include cobalt, copper, zinc, and molybdenum. Such inorganics are components of special enzymes and are considered to be required by most, if not all, life. Some organisms have special mineral requirements. The microscopic algae called diatoms have a cell wall which is partly composed of silicon, and this element must be present if diatoms are to grow.

Water and osmotic pressure. The bacterial cell is composed of approximately 80 per cent water and must be in intimate contact with a water supply for its survival, growth, and reproduction. Such contact may take the form of a mass of cells on a moist, solid surface, or a cell suspension in a liquid medium. When nutrient media are prepared, the various ingredients are dissolved in distilled water, not tap water. Distilled water is used in order to minimize the presence of excess inorganic salts or extraneous organic compounds that may be in tap water. Since tap water may vary in its mineral and dissolved solids composition from day to day, more consistent preparations can be obtained utilizing distilled water. Generally speaking, the osmotic pressure (osmolarity) of a suitably prepared medium is comparable or at least does not vary excessively from that found in the microorganism, a condition referred to as being *isotonic*. Within reasonable limits, changes in osmotic pressure, due to the utilization of a medium's components or because of a partial dehydration of the medium, are not usually sufficient to prevent the growth of the organism.

When cells are taken from an isotonic situation and placed in distilled water at lower osmotic pressure (a *hypotonic* condition), water will enter the cells. This is caused by the greater concentration of dissolved substances within the cell in comparison to the distilled water. Since the dissolved solids cannot distribute themselves because of the microbial membrane, the water is attracted and enters the cells. In most cases the bacterial cell wall is rigid enough to withstand the increased pressure caused by the incoming water molecules. However, some cells will burst, a condition called *plasmoptysis*. Plasmoptysis occurs more readily with animal cells than with plant or microbial cells, because of the absence of a rigid cell wall. Probably the best example of this reaction is the production of red blood cells *stroma*, or ghosts, caused by introducing whole blood into distilled water. The cell membranes are stretched sufficiently to release most of their cytoplasmic components. Apparently little holes are temporarily created during this reaction which subsequently close or heal.

When cells are placed into a solution of greater osmolarity or *hypertonicity*, water molecules escape from them, thus creating a shrinkage known as *plasmolysis*. In this phenomenon, the cytoplasm becomes concentrated and will generally pull away from the cell wall of Gram-negative bacteria but not necessarily of Gram-positive bacteria. With erythrocytes, cells without walls, entire units shrink.

Selected Media and Their Ingredients

Synthetic Media

Preparations used in the cultivation of microorganisms are frequently referred to as *complex media*. This designation draws attention to the wide variety of substances utilized as well as to the procedure used for their incorporation into a medium. In the case of substances such as beef extract, yeast extract, and peptone preparations the general composition is known, but the relative proportions of their individual components and other factors which might be present are uncertain. It is quite possible for different lots of the same substance dispensed into separate containers to vary in the content of amino acids, B complex vitamins, purines, pyrimidines, and other related factors.

The term *synthetic medium* is used to denote preparations having a known composition. These may consist of a few ingredients or many. Two different types of synthetic media are in common use, the organic and inorganic varieties. The latter consist only of inorganic compounds, e.g., calcium chloride ($CaCl_2$), magnesium sulfate ($MgSO_4$), sodium chloride ($NaCl$), etc., and are also referred to as *chemically defined inorganic preparations*. Organic preparations, on the other hand, contain both organic and inorganic ingredients. In general, little

difficulty is experienced in reproducing these preparations.

Certain pathogenic bacteria have nutrient requirements which can pose difficulties in their isolation from clinical specimens or for their maintenance as *stock cultures*. Such organisms are called *fastidious*. This property is demonstrated by the species comprising the genus *Brucella*. Because of the difficulty experienced in isolating these organisms, several investigators set out to determine their exact nutritional requirements, in hopes of developing a superior medium. Such studies resulted in the preparation of a number of synthetic media. One recipe is presented below. The ingredients listed are added to distilled water, and the entire preparation is dispensed into appropriate culture vessels and sterilized (Figure 12–2).

Carbohydrates:	
glycerol	30 mg/1 ml
lactic acid	5 mg/1 ml
Nitrogen source:	
glutamic acid	1.5 mg/1 ml
Vitamins:	
thiamine	0.2 microgram/1 ml
nicotinic acid	0.2 microgram/1 ml
pantothenic acid	0.04 microgram/1 ml
biotin	0.0001 microgram/1 ml
Inorganic Salts:	
sodium chloride	7.5 mg/1 ml
dipotassium phosphate	10.0 mg/1 ml
sodium thiosulfate	100.0 microgram/1 ml
magnesium ion	10.0 microgram/1 ml
ferrous ion	0.10 microgram/1 ml
manganese ion	0.10 microgram/1 ml

Development of Solid Media

Liquid media, while providing an excellent environment for growth, have definite limitations for the isolation and characterization of bacteria. Early approaches to the problem of developing solid media for these purposes were made by Hoffman in 1865 and later extended by Schroeter in 1872. Initially, freshly

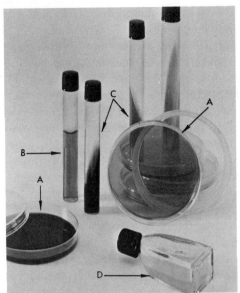

FIG. 12–2. Representative containers for bacteriological media. Media have already been introduced into the vessels. (A) Petri plate. (B) Durham fermentation tube. Note the small inverted vial in the liquid medium. It is used to indicate gas production by a bacterial species. (C) Agar slants. Note the variation in the length of the inclined medium. (D) Bottle or culture flask. Many types of media already dispensed and sterilized are commercially available. (Courtesy of BioQuest, Div. of Becton, Dickinson, Inc. Cockeysville, Md.)

cut surfaces of potato were used to culture bacteria. After a suitable incubation period, bacterial colonies could be observed. This procedure was later extended to include carrot slices, freshly baked bread, meat, and coagulated egg white. Although each of these materials proved satisfactory for the growth of bacteria, they were either difficult to work with, or did not permit the growth of all organisms that were of interest.

In 1881, Robert Koch reported a relatively simple procedure for the surface isolation of bacteria from contaminated materials. An inoculum would either be placed on coagulated blood serum, or be used for slide cultures made with a gelatin-solidified broth. In the latter case, gelatin would be added to a liquid medium which could support the growth of certain organisms. While this preparation was still warm and liquid, it was placed on sterilized glass slides and allowed to harden. Following this step, organisms could be streaked onto the surface of the medium for isolation. The inoculated slide was then covered by a bell jar and left to incubate. Some six years later, an assistant of Koch's, R. J. Petri, introduced the Petri dish (Figure 12–1A) as a simpler, more foolproof medium container than the slide.

Around this time, another associate of Koch's, Walter Hess, learned of a far better solidifying agent than gelatin. As you probably know, gelatin becomes liquid at normal body temperature, 37°C, thus making its use impractical as a solid medium for the isolation of many pathogenic bacteria. Also, certain microorganisms can decompose gelatin—a capability used as an identifying characteristic. The credit for introduction of this new solidifying agent belongs to Hess's wife. Upon learning of her husband's difficulties in attempting to find better ways to grow pathogens, Frau Hess informed him of a substance used by her grandmother in the tropics to keep jams and jellies solid at warm temperatures. This material proved to be the polysaccharide agar-agar, which is extracted from *Gelidium* spp., algae found along the coast of Ceylon, China, Japan, Malaya, and Southern California. Chemically, agar is a sulfate ester of a galactan. It is soluble at temperatures of nearly 100°C, but settles into a firm gel at a temperature of approximately 42°C. In a large number of media for the isolation, characterization, or maintenance of bacteria, approximately 1.5 per cent agar is commonly used. As few bacteria are capable of digesting agar, it has proven to be, together with the Petri dish, an indispensable tool in microbiology.

Preparation of Media

Laboratory media have been devised for the cultivation of specific microorganisms to suit their particular growth requirements. As a rule, media of this type may be obtained in dehydrated form from commercial supply establishments. Reconstitution is a simple matter. The required weight of the powdered medium is usually added to distilled water and heated gently to dissolve and mix the ingredients of the preparation. Adjustment in pH may be necessary before the medium is dispensed into smaller vessels, such as flasks or test tubes. Once this has been done, the medium is sterilized with a high-pressure steam system (autoclaved) according to the directions of the particular supplier.

Certain components of some media—such as serum, plasma, certain carbohydrates, and vitamins—are destroyed or inactivated by heat. Consequently, they are usually sterilized by filtration and then aseptically introduced into the remaining portion of the medium. It is also possible to filter sterilize the entire medium. The technique of filtration and other means of sterilization and asepsis are discussed in Chapter 18.

Media Usage

The cultivation of microorganisms may be necessary for any of the following different purposes: (1) the isolation and identification of organisms; (2) the determination of antibiotic sensitivities of pathogens isolated from patients; (3) sterility testing of products destined for human use; (4) food and water analyses; (5) environmental control; (6) antibiotic and vitamin assays; (7) industrial testing; and (8) the preparation of biological products such as materials used for immunizations. The choice of which medium to use for a specific purpose is important and can be a problem. Literally hundreds of formulations in dehydrated or completed form exist. (Recently, a wide range of sterile, prepackaged and ready-to-use broth and agar media have become commercially available.) The selection of media can be influenced by such factors as availability and cost, personal habit and/or experience, preferences of instructors or of chief laboratory personnel, and reported research findings. It should be noted that the most efficient laboratory is not necessarily the one with the greatest variety of media. Efficient performance and results depend on carefully chosen media. The following sections will present the different categories of media used for the cultivation of microorganisms and representative examples of each.

Differential Media

Several combinations of nutrients and colorimetric (pH) indicators can be used to produce a visual differentiation of several microorganisms growing on the same medium (Color photographs 45 and 46). Classically, differential media permit various species to grow while providing an environment that facilitates discrimination among different organisms. For example, a rich medium such as blood agar can be used to differentiate among numerous bacterial species, especially those belonging to the genus *Streptococcus*. For this group of organisms, differentiation can be accomplished by adding approximately 5 to 10 percent sheep blood to a base medium (e.g., blood-agar base), which is sterilized separately and cooled before the blood is added. Different streptococci produce different enzymes and related compounds that react in different ways with blood cells. Based on these effects, a limited classification can be established, as follows: A green discoloration of areas around bacterial colonies means alpha (α) hemolysis; clear zones surrounding bacterial colonies means beta (β) hemolysis; and no obvious effect means gamma (γ) hemolysis. The typical appearance is shown in Color photograph 45. (These hemolytic reactions are not limited to streptococci. Other organisms are capable of producing similar effects.)

In addition to different sources of mammalian blood, carbohydrates, proteins, and related compounds are used for differentiation purposes. A variety of pH indicators also may be included in media. Examples of those most commonly employed are bromothymol blue, neutral red, and phenol red (Color photographs 40, 44, and 51).

Selective Media

A preparation that can interfere with or prevent the growth of certain microorganisms while permitting the growth of others is a selective medium. Selective media provide a means by which the isolation of a particular species or category of microorganisms can be achieved. Among the substances that can be used as selective agents are dyes such as crystal violet, eosine Y, methylene blue, and brilliant green (these materials inhibit Grampositives); high concentrations of sodium chloride; and bile salts. A medium may also be made selective by adjusting the pH of the preparation to a very high or very low level. Such manipulations will permit the growth of some organisms and inhibit the growth of others. A well-known example of a selective medium is Sabouraud's glucose agar, which has a pH of 5.6. The preparation is used for fungus cultivation (Color photographs 30 to 36). The most recent substances to be employed in culture media to make them selective are antibiotics such as cycloheximide, kanamycin, neomycin, and vancomycin.

Selective and Differential Media

Many media have been developed that are both selective and differential. The properties of both types of media are combined for the purpose of identifying and enumerating organisms in one general procedure. Certain of these media will be described.

MacConkey agar. This medium is used in the selection of Gram-negative bacteria. MacConkey agar (frequently called Mac agar) contains suitable proportions of bile salts and crystal violet dye. Both these ingredients inhibit the growth of Gram-positive organisms. Bile salts function by reducing surface tension, which apparently is inhibitory to these microorganisms. Crystal violet is used in Mac agar because it inhibits a critical step in the synthesis of cell walls of certain Gram-positive bacteria. The carbohydrate lactose serves as the differentiating substance.

Mannitol Salt agar. This medium can be used not only to select for a particular bacterial species, but often to differentiate potentially pathogenic organisms from those of a nonpathogenic nature. Mannitol Salt (MS) agar is employed most commonly for *Staphylococcus aureus,* which can cause a variety of disease states in humans, including blood poisoning (septicemia), boils, food poisoning, osteomyelitis (inflammation of the bone), and pneumonia. In addition to the carbohydrate mannitol, MS agar contains 7.5 percent sodium chloride and the pH indicator phenol red. Potentially pathogenic staphylococci grow on this preparation and ferment mannitol, producing acid. Normally the medium is red; however, in the presence of acid the preparation turns yellow. A typical reaction with a pathogenic *S. aureus* is shown in Color photograph 62.

The ingredients and applications of many differential, selective, and selective and differential media are discussed in the chapters concerned with particular disease-causing agents. Before leaving this topic, it is important to note that the concentrations of the differentiating and selective components can be a critical factor in achieving desired results. Too little of an ingredient may not accomplish the effect, while an overabundance of the compound may inhibit the growth of the microorganism being sought.

Other Media

Certain pathogens are today cultured routinely on modified versions of media employed many years ago. For example, *Corynebacterium diphtheriae,* the etiologic agent of diphtheria, is routinely cultivated on a modification of the original preparation described by Loeffler in 1887. This medium contains beef blood serum, beef extract, tryptose (peptone), dextrose, sodium chloride, and distilled water. Another organism, *Mycobacterium tuberculosis,* is still grown on egg-base media, a 1931 formulation of Lowenstein, modified by Jensen in 1932. The medium contains water, eggs, the amino acid asparagine, potassium phosphate, magnesium sulfate, magnesium citrate, potato flour, and malachite green. The latter compound is used as an inhibitory substance for most bacteria (other than the mycrobacteria) which are usually found in clinical specimens.

Care must be taken in preparing these media to prevent the formation of bubbles. This is especially difficult because both types of media solidify on heating, due to the coagulation of the protein components. Furthermore, if slanted preparations are needed tubes containing the media must be positioned in the proper slant before sterilization. This precaution is unnecessary with agar preparations, which do not solidify when heated. Although the processes of controlled heating for egg-based and serum-based media vary, they are collectively known as *inspissation*. In the case of the Lowenstein-Jensen formulation, the medium must not boil; controlled temperature of 80° to 90°C is maintained for 45 minutes. With Loeffler's medium, coagulation of the serum is achieved below the boiling temperature; however, subsequent to coagulation, the medium is sterilized by means of high-pressure steam at a temperature of 121°C.

Preparation of Media for the Cultivation of Anaerobes

Fortunately, most pathogenic bacteria encountered are heterotrophic and are not particularly fastidious in the sense that they do not require unusual growth factors or incubation conditions. Thus, most of these organisms can be cultivated routinely and identified without the use of complicated equipment or complex media.

Broth media vary in composition. Some contain a beef extract preparation and partially hydrolyzed proteins (peptones). The beef extract, which is obtained by soaking minced ground meat in water, usually contains carbohydrates, minerals, peptones, proteins, and vitamins. The peptones provide peptides and amino acids. In other media, a water extract of autolyzed yeast may be substituted for the beef extract. The yeast extract usually contains more of the B-complex vitamins. Sodium and various phosphates and chlorides are additional ingredients. The sodium is added primarily to assure a suitable osmotic pressure in the medium, while the phosphates are used to provide a buffering action against the acids produced as a result of the metabolic activities of the organisms utilizing the ingredients of the medium. A reducing agent, such as sodium thioglycollate, may also be incorporated into a medium for the cultivation of microaerophilic and certain anaerobic bacteria.

In 1940, Brewer reported an all-purpose liquid medium for the cultivation of both aerobic and anaerobic microorganisms. A modification of this medium by the National Institute of Health (NIH) is currently used in several laboratories. The formula for this fluid thioglycollate medium is:

Yeast extract	5.0	g
Enzymatic digest of casein	15.0	g
Dextrose (glucose)	5.0	g
Sodium chloride	2.5	g
L-cystine	0.75	g
Thioglycollic acid	0.3	ml
Agar	0.75	g
Resazurin (certified)	0.001	g

Distilled water to make a total volume of 1000 ml, or 1 liter. Before the medium is used, of course, it is dispensed into appropriate containers and sterilized.

With this thioglycollate medium, anaerobiosis is maintained by two reducing agents in addition to the thioglycollic acid, L-cystine and agar. Although agar is used as a solidifying agent for several types of media, its 0.75 per cent concentration here is insufficient for this purpose. Agar functions as adjunct to the other reducing agents in the medium.

The resazurin, which is incorporated in a concentration of 0.0001 per cent, serves as an oxidation/reduction indicator. This compound is colorless or nearly colorless while in a reduced state, thereby indicating the existence of anaerobic con-ditions. When oxidized, it turns pink or red, showing the presence of an aerobic state. A sterile tube of this medium, which is suitable for the growth of aerobes, microaerophiles, and anaerobes, will have an upper pink layer and a lower yellow to light brown layer (see Color photograph 28). Aerobic organisms grow well in the upper region, while the lower zone is utilized by anaerobes (Figure 12-3).

FIG. 12-3. *Actinomyces (Arachnia) propionica.* The appearance of anaerobic growth in fluid thioglycollate medium. This organism can grow aerobically as well; however, its growth is best under anaerobic conditions. (From Gerencser, M. A., and Slack, J. M.: *J. Bacteriol.,* **94**:109–115, 1967.)

Prereduced Anaerobically Sterilized Media (PRAS)

Media of this type, when used properly, greatly increase the chances of isolating many fastidious anaerobic bacteria. The media were reported in 1969 by Cato, Cummins, Holdemann, Johnson, Moore, Smibert, and Smith at the Anaerobic Laboratory, Virginia Polytechnic Institute. PRAS media are prepared, dispensed, sterilized, and stoppered in an oxygen-free nitrogen environment; thus no exposure to oxygen occurs. In order to maintain the exclusion of air during inoculations, a stream of nitrogen or carbon dioxide without any free oxygen is directed into the tube being inoculated. Various PRAS media are commercially available.

Media for Chlamydia and Rickettsia

Although the chlamydia and rickettsia are bacteria, the media and methods of inoculation described in this chapter are not applicable to them. These bacteria are obligate, intracellular parasites; they therefore require living cells for their development and reproduction. Chicken embryos may be used for both chlamydia and rickettsia. In addition, tissue culture systems are employed for rickettsia. The specific details of the media and techniques used for their inoculation are described in Chapter 13.

In many instances, rickettsial infection of appropriate tissue culture systems leads to the production of clear areas called *plaques* (Figure 12–4), which represent concentrations of organisms. One rickettsial agent, *Rochalimeae quintana,* can be grown on blood agar. Additional properties of rickettsia and of chlamydia are presented in Chapter 39.

Storage of Media

Most media can be stored under conditions which prevent dehydration. This can be accomplished by refrigeration and by airtight packaging. In either case, the media should first be incubated overnight to determine if sterilization was adequate. Furthermore, all contaminated media should be sterilized and then discarded.

Inoculation and Transfer Techniques

The inoculating loop (Figure 12–5) or its modified form, the inoculating needle, is commonly used by microbiologists in carrying out routine bacteriological tech-

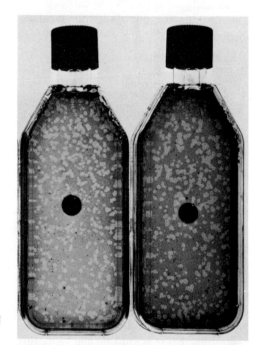

FIG. 12–4. *Rickettsia rickettsii* growing in primary-cell chicken embryo systems. Plaques (clear areas) are quite pronounced. The large, dark discs in the center of the cell systems contain antibiotics, which are being used to determine the antibiotic susceptibility of the rickettsia. (From McDade, J. E.: *Appl. Microbiol.,* **18**:133–135, 1969.)

niques. These procedures include: (1) inoculation of nutrient media with clinical or other types of specimens; (2) subsequent isolation and characterization of pure cultures; (3) transfer of microbial growth from one medium to another; (4) preparation of samples for microscopic examination—smears, hanging-drop, or temporary wet mounts; and (5) maintenance of stock cultures of organisms.

The inoculating or transfer tool basically consists of a thin piece of heat-resistant wire, usually platinum or stainless steel, measuring 2 to 3 inches in length, usually provided with a short handle. Certain inoculating instruments may be manufactured as one piece.

Most states of media, such as broth, agar plates, and slants, may be inoculated with either a transfer loop or a needle. Generally, however, the loop is used with liquid inocula.

Method

Before the inoculating instrument is used it is flamed—heated to redness to incinerate any organisms on its surface. The steps in a normally performed tube inoculation are shown in Figure 12–5. Generally, a tube containing the inoculum and one or more tubes with sterile media are held together in one hand, supported by the three middle fingers. The thumb functions to keep the tubes in proper position. The inoculating tool, which is in the other hand, is flamed. Next, the plugs of the tubes are grasped by the little and ring fingers of the hand which also holds the inoculating tool. The mouths of these tubes are passed through the flame to sterilize them. An inoculum is obtained and introduced into the proper tubes, then the lips of the tubes are again passed

through the flame, and the plugs are inserted into the specific tubes from which they were removed. Once again the inoculating loop is flamed to redness.

This general technique is carried out to prevent the introduction of contaminating organisms, collectively referred to as *sepsis*. Hence, the term *aseptic technique* is used for procedures of this type.

Other means for the transfer of microorganisms include sterile pipettes, cotton applicator swabs, and syringes. The device used is generally determined by the needs of the particular situation.

After inoculation of a particular type and state of medium—agar slant, broth, plate culture—certain cultural characteristics, such as pigmentation, type of growth on agar slants, pellicle formation, and colonial appearance of organisms can be observed (Figures 12–6 and 12–7 and Color photographs 24, 26, and 27). Such properties are often useful in describing a particular bacterial species.

Techniques for the Isolation of Pure Bacterial Cultures

The isolation and the subsequent identification of a bacterial species are both fundamental and important facets of microbiology. Many techniques can be effectively employed to detect and enumerate different microorganisms present in specimens. Among these various procedures, two methods, the pour-plate and the streak-plate techniques (Color photographs 24 and 25), have become indispensable tools of the bacteriologist. The effectiveness of these isolation techniques can be greatly increased by using differential or selective culture media, such as Eosin Methylene Blue Agar (EMB) and Hektoen Enteric (HE) media (Color photographs 88 and 91).

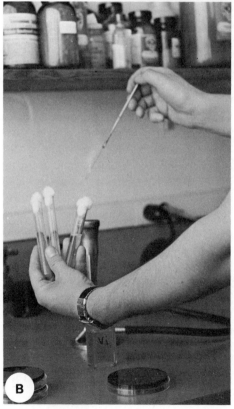

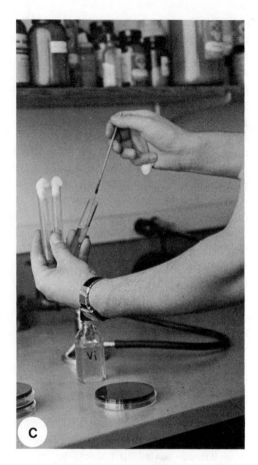

FIG. 12–5. Inoculation and transfer techniques. _A._ Streaking an agar plate. This procedure simply involves spreading an inoculum over the surface of the medium. _B._ Flaming the inoculating tool. Note that the entire wire portion must turn red-hot in order to eliminate undesirable microorganisms. _C._ Transferring the inoculum to two sterile tubes of broth. The mouths of both tubes must be flamed before and after the transfer, as must the inoculating tool. Note how the cotton plug is grasped.

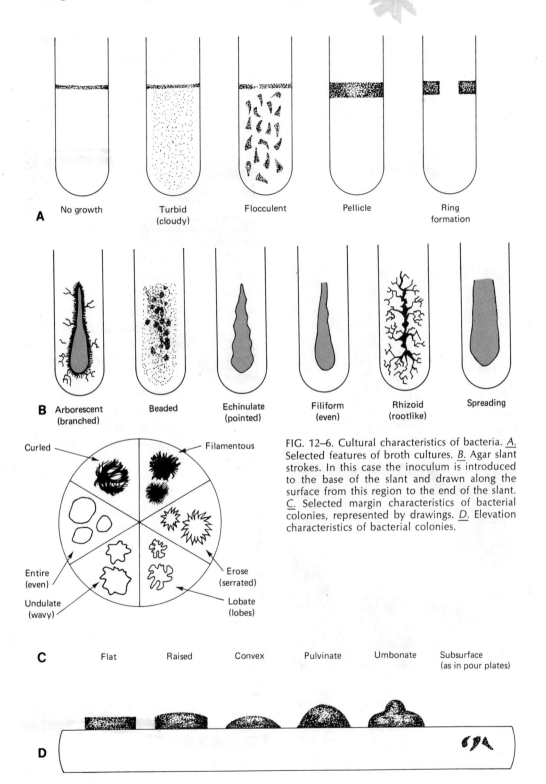

A

No growth | Turbid (cloudy) | Flocculent | Pellicle | Ring formation

B

Arborescent (branched) | Beaded | Echinulate (pointed) | Filiform (even) | Rhizoid (rootlike) | Spreading

Curled — Filamentous

Entire (even)

Undulate (wavy)

Erose (serrated)

Lobate (lobes)

FIG. 12–6. Cultural characteristics of bacteria. _A._ Selected features of broth cultures. _B._ Agar slant strokes. In this case the inoculum is introduced to the base of the slant and drawn along the surface from this region to the end of the slant. _C._ Selected margin characteristics of bacterial colonies, represented by drawings. _D._ Elevation characteristics of bacterial colonies.

C

Flat | Raised | Convex | Pulvinate | Umbonate | Subsurface (as in pour plates)

D

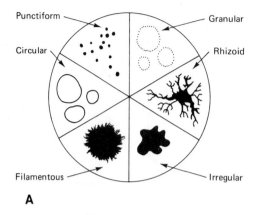

A

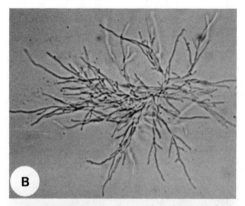

B

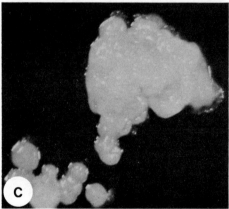

C

FIG. 12–7. Selected characteristics of bacterial colonies. _A_. Diagrammatic representation of colonial forms of growth. _B_. A developing microcolony of *Actinomyces propionicus*. Note the filamentous nature of the organism. _C_. A so-called "molar" tooth colony of the same organism, shown in its mature form. (From Gerencser, M. A., and Slack, J. M.: *J. Bacteriol.*, **94**:109, 1967.)

The pour-plate technique. (Color photograph 25.) The forerunner of the present pour-plate method was developed in the laboratory of the famous bacteriologist Robert Koch. Today this technique consists of cooling melted agar-containing medium (1.5% agar) to approximately 42° to 45°C, inoculating the medium with a specimen and immediately pouring it into a sterile Petri plate, allowing the freshly poured medium to solidify, and incubating the preparation at the desired temperature. In several instances, in which the magnitude of the bacterial population in the specimen to be studied is not known beforehand, suitable dilutions must be created in order to ensure isolated colonies. By means of the pour-plate method, bacteria are distributed throughout the agar and are trapped in position. Although the solidified medium restricts bacterial movement from one area to another, it is soft enough to permit growth, which occurs both on the surface and in the depths of the inoculated medium.

In addition to the qualitative application of this procedure to isolate and detect bacterial species contained within a mixed culture, it is also useful in quantitative measurements of bacterial growth. Unfortunately, however, there are several disadvantages to this technique. Colonies of several species may present a similar appearance in the agar environment, thus making differentiation difficult. Certain species of bacteria may not grow under the cultural conditions of the method and difficulty may be encountered in removing colonies for further study.

The streak-plate technique. (Color photograph 24.) This procedure is also a dilution method. It was originally developed by two bacteriologists, Loeffler and Gaffky, in the laboratory of Robert Koch.

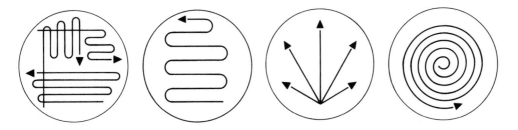

FIG. 12–8. Representative streaking patterns used in the isolation of bacteria.

FIG. 12–9. The "clock-plate" method of streaking.

The modern method for the preparation of a streak-plate involves the spreading of a single loopful of material containing microorganisms over the surface of a solidified agar medium. Figure 12–8 is representative of streaking methods which have been used.

The "clock-plate technique" is one of the more generally used forms of this procedure (Figures 12–9 and 12–10). Here the inoculum is first spread over a small portion of the medium's surface; then the inoculating loop is flamed to destroy any residual bacteria, and the plate containing the medium is rotated approximately one quarter of a turn. The flamed loop is next used to make a second set of streaks, thus diluting (spreading) the bacterial population in the original set of streaks. As the figure shows, the original surface streaks are crossed only once. Further dilutions of the specimen are carried out by repeating this sequence; flaming the loop, rotating the medium, and making additional streaks.

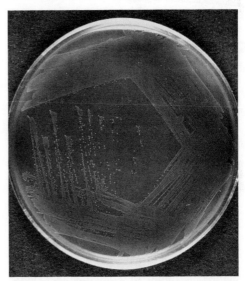

FIG. 12–10. A clear demonstration of the clock-plate technique: Note the isolated colonies of *Moraxella phenylpyruvica*. (From Riley, P. S., Hollis, D. G., and Weaver, R. E.: *Appl. Microbiol.*, **28**:355, 1974.)

If this technique is properly performed, well-isolated colonies should grow after incubation at an appropriate temperature. Supposedly, one colony develops from a single cell, thereby producing a pure culture. It is customary to "pick" (transfer) a small portion of a desired colony to a tube of medium, such as broth or agar slant, and utilize the culture as a source of organisms for additional studies.

Another technique, the "spread-plate" procedure, is used in certain types of investigations. Here a bacterial specimen is placed on an agar medium and spread over its surface with the aid of a sterile bent glass rod. The agar plate can be placed on a rotating wheel device to aid the spreading out of the bacterial specimen.

Because of the high concentration of water in agar preparations, condensation forms in most Petri plates. To avoid such *water of condensation* on media surfaces, which may cause bacterial colonies to run together, plates should be incubated in an inverted position.

Conditions of Incubation

Aerobic Incubation

Microbial growth, as noted previously, can be dependent upon suitable levels of oxygen and carbon dioxide. While aerobic organisms may be able to grow under anaerobic conditions, the obligate aerobes, such as *Acetobacter* spp., must be in intimate contact with air, or approximately 20 per cent oxygen. Many organisms have less stringent oxygen requirements and will grow well in the depths of liquid or solid media. Therefore, cultivation of aerobic or facultative anaerobic bacteria is relatively simple under usual laboratory conditions.

Once an appropriate solid or liquid medium has been inoculated and protected from contamination, all that remains to be controlled is the temperature and occasionally the level of humidity. Standard laboratory incubators usually

are sufficient to maintain such environmental factors.

With any incubator, it is advisable to employ a maximum-minimum thermometer to determine the temperature range provided by the thermostatic control. One type of maximum-minimum recording thermometer consists of a bimetallic coil (in the form of a strip), a dial equipped with a needle indicator to register the temperature, and two hands. The hands are moved by the temperature indicator; one remains set at the highest and one at the lowest temperature value. Periodic recordings of the daily extremes give advance notice of the possibility that the controls may be wearing out, and can provide warning of the instrument's malfunctioning in time to repair it before any serious damage occurs, such as cooking the cultures.

Capneic Incubation

Air enriched with carbon dioxide is required by some bacteria, including *Neisseria gonorrhoeae, N. meningitidis,* and *Brucella* spp., for their primary isolation from clinical specimens. As mentioned earlier, many other microorganisms, such as *Mycobacterium tuberculosis,* appear to grow better if allowed to incubate under these capneic conditions. This form of enriched atmosphere can be supplied in a variety of ways. The candle jar technique is routinely used for *N. gonorrhoeae* cultivation. With this technique, Petri plates and/or tubes with inoculated media are placed in a jar with a candle. The lighted candle will continue to burn after the lid has been placed on the jar, until the CO_2 concentration increases to the point which stops combustion, usually around 3 to 5 percent CO_2. This should not be considered to represent complete combustion of oxygen, as aerobic organisms will grow and strict anaerobes will not grow in such a candle jar.

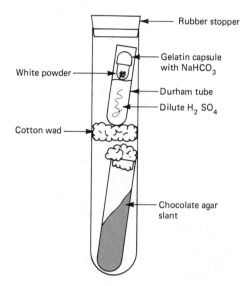

Rubber stopper

Gelatin capsule
with NaHCO$_3$

White powder

Durham tube

Dilute H$_2$SO$_4$

Cotton wad

Chocolate agar
slant

FIG. 12–11. The test tube capneic system. A capsule of sodium bicarbonate is added to a small tube of dilute sulfuric acid and the large tube is immediately stoppered. The reaction is the same as that used in fire extinguishers—acidification of bicarbonate to release CO$_2$. The example shown is a chocolate agar slant culture inoculated with *Neisseria gonorrhoeae*.

For a laboratory which is primarily concerned with the maintenance of *N. gonorrhoeae* on slanted media, the test tube capneic system is worthy of consideration (Figure 12–11).

In this system a capsule of sodium bicarbonate is added to a small tube of dilute sulfuric acid and the large tube is immediately stoppered. The reaction here is the same as that used in fire extinguishers: acidification of bicarbonate to release CO$_2$.

Anaerobic Incubation

Certain anaerobic microorganisms are known to be responsible for a variety of diseases, while others are functional in several industrial fermentation processes. Some of these anaerobes appear to be *aerotolerant;* they can withstand oxygen to a limited degree. Others of them can survive only in an environment without oxygen and are *obligate anaerobes.*

One explanation for their sensitivity to an oxygen environment is related to the role of the oxygen in the formation of hydrogen peroxide (H$_2$O$_2$) during microbial metabolic processes. This product alone can be quite destructive, as shown by the fact that it is commonly used as a disinfectant. Some bacteria produce an enzyme, catalase, which breaks down the peroxide to oxygen (O$_2$) and water (H$_2$O). Strict anaerobic bacteria do not appear to have catalase, and are therefore poisoned by the peroxide.

An additional explanation for the lack of growth by anaerobes in the presence of oxygen concerns the oxidation-reduction potential (Eh) of the media, which may be the more significant mechanism responsible for the anaerobes' oxygen intolerance. The oxidation-reduction potential is an electrical phenomenon that indicates the electron-accepting or electron-yielding potentialities of substances. When the Eh of a medium is lowered by the addition of a reducing or oxygen-absorbing compound, such as cysteine or thioglycollic acid, many anaerobes will grow.

Anaerobic transfer.   The lack of growth of many clinical isolates may not be due to the Eh of the properly prepared anaerobic medium, but in reality to transient exposure to air during the procedure for specimen collection, transportation to the laboratory, or after growth, during the transfer of organisms to subculture media. In order to prevent inactivation of anaerobes when transferring them, the operation should be performed under a flowing stream of nitrogen for cultures on solid media, or by the use of a pipette with liquid media. For example, in the transfer of cultures from thioglycollate broth to a fresh tube of medium, a pipette should be introduced into the bottom of the tube with the finger on the mouthpiece. By carefully lifting the finger, inoculum from the most anaerobic area is allowed into the pipette. Next, with the finger on the mouthpiece, the pipette is removed and inserted into the bottom of a fresh tube of thioglycollate. The finger then is quickly removed, which causes the release of the inoculum into the most anaerobic portion of the medium. Following this step, the pipette is removed and the newly inoculated preparation is incubated at the desired temperature.

Methods of anaerobic incubation. Incubation under anaerobic conditions can be accomplished with vacuum devices. Incubators for this use are usually fitted with gaskets and ports for evacuation and flushing with inert gases. One method commonly used involves flushing a specially equipped incubator with 95 per cent N_2 and 5 per cent CO_2 to remove any oxygen and to introduce CO_2 into the system. The latter gas may enhance growth. Hydrogen also may be used for flushing, but it forms an explosive mixture with oxygen. If for some reason anaerobic hydrogen bacteria are to be grown, hydrogen should be bubbled through water first; an explosion will not occur with wet hydrogen.

Before the advent of the anaerobic incubator, Brewer invented two systems for culturing anaerobic bacteria. In one system thioglycollate agar is inoculated and poured into a Petri dish (Figure 12–12). The cover for this Brewer plate forms a seal with the surface of the agar and with the edge of a slight concave opening, to allow a limited surface for organisms on which to grow. The trapped oxygen is rapidly reduced by the thioglycollate, thus producing anaerobic conditions.

An alternative to the Brewer plate is the Spray dish (Figure 12–12B). This device consists of a deep, double-well dish and cover. The intent is to permit

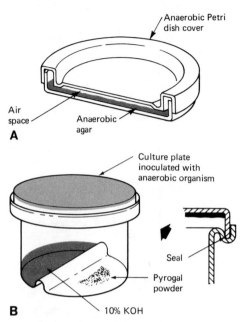

FIG. 12–12A. A cut-away drawing of a Brewer Petri dish. B. Spray dish for anaerobic incubation.

separation of an alkaline solution, such as potassium hydroxide (KOH), and pyrogallic acid. These chemicals when combined absorb oxygen and produce anaerobic conditions. When this system is used, an inoculated Petri plate is inverted over the bottom dish and sealed into place. The dish is then tipped to permit the mixing of the chemicals, thus resulting in anaerobiosis.

The Brewer jar was developed in an attempt to have a larger incubation system for the anaerobic organisms (Figure 12–13). In this system, the inoculated plates and/or tubes are placed in the jar, the cover is sealed into place, the air in the container is immediately evacuated, and the system is flushed with hydrogen. Subsequently, a catalyst, such as platinum, is heated in the lid by an electric current, with the result that the hydrogen combines with residual oxygen to form water. A slight vacuum is created in the chamber due to the combustion reaction.

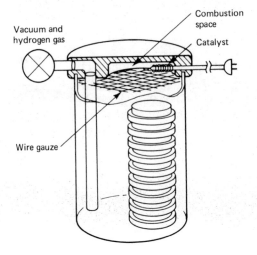

FIG. 12–13. The Brewer anaerobic jar.

A recently developed alternative to the Brewer Jar is the Bio Quest disposable Gas Pak. This enveloped unit is a self-contained hydrogen-generating and catalyst system, much simpler to use than the Brewer Jar. The plates and/or tubes are placed in a jar with a Gas Pak envelope. The envelope is opened, water is added to the reagents, and the jar is sealed immediately (Figure 12–14). The generation of hydrogen in the presence of air and the catalyst causes reduction of the oxygen to water, which condenses on the side of the jar. This system eliminates the need for hydrogen and nitrogen tanks and vacuum pumps, which greatly enhances the ability of a small clinical laboratory to carry out anaerobic cultivation.

Anaerobic indicators and checking the efficiency of anaerobic systems. Anaerobic incubation systems should be checked whenever possible to provide assurance that adequate conditions have been obtained and maintained during incubation. One system used for this purpose incorporates Bacto-OR Indicator Agar (Difco Laboratories). This medium uses methylene blue as an indicator of oxidation-reduction potential. It is usually dispensed into small screw-capped vials and autoclaved (sterilized under pressurized steam). This reduces the methylene blue to a colorless state, leuco-methylene blue. The procedure for testing involves placing an opened vial of medium in the incubator and initiating the anaerobiosis environment. After a suitable incubation period the vial is removed and examined. If anaerobic conditions were maintained during the test period, the methylene blue should still be in the reduced state, i.e., leuco. However, if anaerobiasis was not achieved, the medium will be oxidized and appear blue. (Note that, in the first case, the brief exposure to air many cause a slight oxidation of the leuco-methylene blue at the surface of the medium.)

Another system for checking the efficiency of an anaerobic incubator involves subculturing an obligate anaerobic bacterium in the same incubator as other specimens. If the indicator organism grows, satisfactory conditions were met. Organisms that may be used for this purpose include certain *Clostridium* and *Bacteroides* spp. However, the use of chemical indicators is recommended due to their simplicity and reliability.

Biological or "Sterility Test" Cabinets

A definite need exists to provide protection from airborne contamination. Compact cabinets designed for this purpose are shown in Figure 12–15. Such units have value in laboratories that handle "biohazardous" substances, the preparation of bacteriological media, sterility testing, and the inoculation of a variety of media.

Cabinets of this type are equipped with a double polycarbonate viewscreen which provides a functional visual working angle and contributes to the protection of individuals within the confines of the working area. A recirculating vertical airflow unit creates a "front air barrier" at the opening of the work area (Figure 12–15). This "barrier" protects both the laboratory personnel and materials from contamination by preventing airborne particulates from leaving or entering the cabinets. Air entering and leaving the working area passes through HEPA (High Efficiency Particulate Air) filters which remove particles of 0.3 μm and greater. Although contamination of personnel and

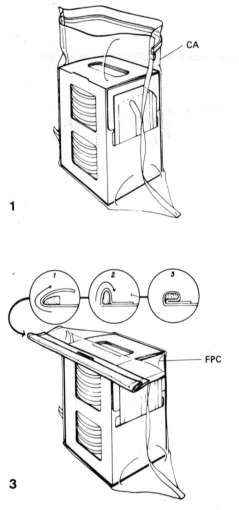

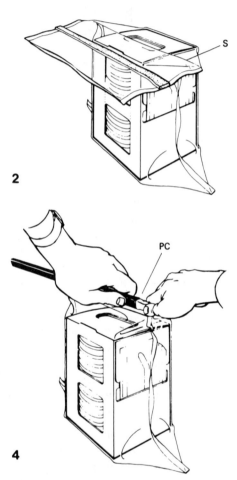

FIG. 12–14. A simple flowchart demonstrating the procedure used for the Gas Pak Disposable Anaerobic System. 1. Tubes or Petri plates are placed into the carrier. The flaps of the carrier assembly (CA) are closed. 2. The foil container of a Gas Pak anaerobic indicator is opened (pulled down halfway) and inserted into the slot (S) provided in the carrier assembly. 3. The incorporation of the hydrogen and carbon dioxide generator envelope and the introduction of water into it is not shown. The entire carrier assembly is placed in the flexible plastic container (FPC), which is folded and pressed flat over the top of the carrier to expel as much air as possible. 4. The edge of the plastic container is folded several times. Finally, a plastic clamp (PC) is slid along its entire length of clamping purposes. (Courtesy of BioQuest, Cockeysville, Md.)

1. Exhaust HEPA filter
2. Exhaust blower
3. Supply blower
4. Supply plenum
5. Supply HEPA filters
6. Polycarbonate view
   screen (air curtain)
7. Front return grill
8. Air velocity control
9. Control switches
10. Air velocity indicator
11. Stainless steel interior sides
12. 115 Volt AC duplex outlet
13. Gas, air/vacuum fixtures
14. Rear return grill
15. Return plenum
16. Solid work surface
17. Base support

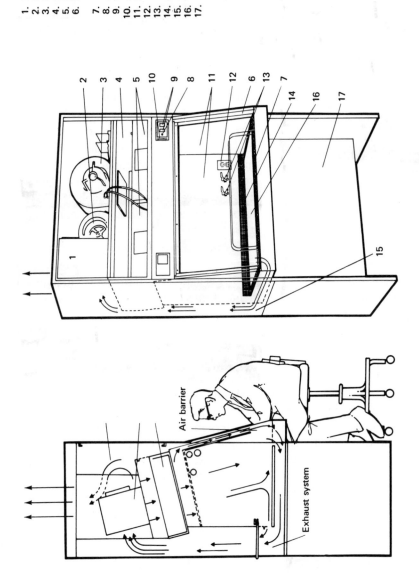

Bioquest biological cabinet
special features

Bioquest biological cabinet
air flow patterns

Air barrier

Exhaust system

FIG. 12–15. Biological Cabinet. At left, a schematic representation of the air flow patterns important in the cabinet's functioning. At right the special features of the basic unit. (Courtesy of BioQuest, Cockeysville, Md.)

materials is prevented in a unit such as the one described, workers must still observe aseptic precautions and techniques. HEPA filtration systems are discussed further in Chapter 18.

Cultivation of Fungi

Molds and yeasts can be grown and studied by cultural methods similar to those used for many bacteria. Most fungi are able to grow and perform their various activities under aerobic conditions. However, many of these microorganisms grow more slowly than bacteria. Consequently, media which can support both bacteria and fungi are apt to become overgrown with bacteria. In working with fungi, therefore, it is advisable to modify the culture media in some fashion to limit the growth of other microbial types. Ingredients that can be added to media for this purpose include antibiotics (such as chloramphenicol, gentamicin, penicillin, and streptomycin), dyes (such as crystal violet), and high concentrations of sugar. Another important property of preparations for fungal cultivation is their acidity, pH 5.6 to 6.

When it is necessary to prevent or suppress the growth of unwanted fungi, such as saprophytes, cyclohexamide (Actidione), another type of antibiotic, may be incorporated into the medium for this purpose.

Nearly all of the culture media used for the isolation and characterization of fungi are obtainable in the dehydrated state from commercial sources. Most can be employed in either the liquid or the solid state. The solid form can be made, in many instances, by simply adding agar to the liquid medium.

Types of Media

In general, three basic types of media can be used in fungus cultivation—natural, dehydrated ("basic"), and synthetic, or chemically-defined preparations. Natural media are not widely used in most laboratories. Examples of such cultivation materials include slices or infusion preparations of animal tissues, fruits, and vegetables. Carrot plugs and potato slices have been commonly employed.

Dehydrated or basic media generally contain, in addition to dextrose (glucose) and/or sodium chloride, a wide assortment of organic ingredients such as peptones, beef extract, and corn meal, which have unknown and variable compositions. One of the most commonly employed of these preparations is Sabouraud (Sab's) dextrose or maltose medium, which also contains peptone, agar, and distilled water. After sterilization, it can be used in the form of slants or plates for the isolation and identification of a wide variety of molds (Color photographs 30–34) and yeasts (Color photograph 36). Other examples of basic media include blood agar, brain agar, corn meal agar, and thioglycollate broth.

Synthetic media—those for which the exact composition is known—are used for the isolation of saprophytic and pathogenic fungi. Examples of this type of medium include Czapek-Dox and Littman Oxgall agar preparations. Most saprophytic fungi grow at room temperature, and are unable to grow at 37°C, but pathogens generally grow readily at 37°C. Recently Vickers, McElligott, Rihs, and Postic reported the incorporation of the dye trypan blue into Sabouraud agar to permit the rapid detection and tentative identification of several species of yeast (Color photograph 36).

Details of the use of several media are given in the chapters concerned with the isolation and identification of pathogenic fungi.

Distinctive Mycelia

The mycelia of several fungi have a characteristic appearance when seen with the naked eye which can serve as the basis for their identification. Coloration, diffusion of pigment, and texture are but a few of the important features. Cultures of these fungi are generally prepared by inoculating the center of a particular medium. After a suitable incubation period at the appropriate temperature, the distinctive mycelium should have developed (Color photographs 30 and 78). It is important to note that the under-surfaces of certain pathogenic fungi also exhibit a characteristic appearance. A trained worker usually has little difficulty in identifying typical fungal species.

QUESTIONS FOR REVIEW

1. Distinguish between *in vivo* and *in vitro* techniques.

2. What is the significance of pH? How can the pH of a medium be altered?

3. Compare the nutritional requirements of autotrophic, heterotrophic, and hypotrophic organisms, and give examples of each organism.

4. Explain the following terms:
   a. aerobe
   b. microaerophilic
   c. anaerobe
   d. facultative anaerobe
   e. capneic
   f. obligate aerobe

5. What is a hypotroph?

6. Discuss the grouping of microorganisms according to their temperature growth requirements.

7. a. What is a growth medium?
   b. What substances serve as sources of carbon, mineral salts, nitrogen, and vitamins?
   c. Distinguish between broth and agar media, and give common examples of each.

8. Discuss anaerobic cultivation methods. Include in your answer a treatment of media and equipment used in general procedures.

9. What appears to be the difference between the Petri and Brewer dishes?

10. Describe the pour-plate and streak-plate techniques. What disadvantages does each procedure possess? What advantages?

11. Distinguish between differential, selective, and selective and differential media.

12. Discuss the classification of bacteria on the basis of their temperature requirements.

13. Does the cultivation of fungi differ from that of bacteria? What general types of media are used for fungus cultivation?

14. What differences in pH requirements exist between fungi and bacteria?

15. What are synthetic media? Can both bacteria and fungi be grown with them?

16. List three cultural characteristics of bacteria which can be noted from broth cultures. Do the same for agar slant and agar plate cultures.

17. What media is often used to culture rickettsia and chlamydia?

13

The Cultivation of Viruses

Although viruses have the ability to direct their own replication, they are totally dependent upon living cells for the machinery and materials to carry out the process. Thus, the routine laboratory cultivation of viruses requires adequate quantities of appropriate cells. Quite often particular viral agents will grow only in a specific type of cell from a certain host, such as monkey kidney or chicken embryo cells.

The early attempts to grow animal viruses were performed in susceptible animals. These included rhesus and other species of monkeys, hamsters, mice, and rats. Although these efforts were quite successful, laboratories were burdened by the need to purchase and maintain susceptible animals. Other means had to be found to meet the needs of viruses and yet keep laboratory expenses within working limits. This chapter will describe some of the procedures currently used for cultivating viruses.

Animal Virus Cultivation in Embryonated Hen Eggs

Embryonated eggs are eggs which have been fertilized by a rooster, have undergone a certain degree of embryonic development in the hen, and usually have been put into an incubator shortly after laying so that development can continue to the desired age, which might be 6 or 8 days. The introduction in 1931 of em-

bryonated eggs as a suitable medium for the growth of viruses provided an invaluable means of obtaining large quantities of viruses for the preparation of vaccines and diagnostic reagents, as well as for viral studies. The first attempt to cultivate viruses by this means was actually made in 1911, but it was not until the reports of Woodruff, Goodpasture, and Buddingh in the United States and Burnet in Australia that the chick embryo came into general usage.

The advantages of using such eggs include: (1) their availability in virtually unlimited quantities, (2) the relative ease of growing and handling them, (3) the presence of a naturally constant environment within the confines of the egg's components—the embryo as it ordinarily comes from the hen is sterile, (4) the general inability of the embryo to produce antibodies against the agents used as inocula, and (5) the availability of eggs with a relatively uniform genetic constitution from flocks which have been imbred for several generations.

The many techniques using chicken embryos in the cultivation of various viruses and rickettsia will not be discussed in great detail. However, brief descriptions of representative methods of inoculation and general precautions associated with these laboratory methods will be presented, primarily to emphasize the value of this simple experimental tool.

Generally, embryonated eggs for the cultivation of viruses are obtained from healthy flocks, free of both bacterial and viral agents. Commercially-reared chickens are routinely inspected for the symptoms of disease, and usually are inoculated against certain bacteria (e.g., *Salmonella pullorum*) and viruses (e.g., Newcastle disease virus—NDV). White-shelled eggs, obtained from white Leghorn chickens, are more suitable than ones with dark or heavily-spotted shells primarily because the eggs' contents are more easily seen during *candling*, the examination of an egg with the aid of a light source of sufficient intensity (Figure 13–1).

Embryonated eggs are collected shortly after laying and are refrigerated at temperatures of approximately 10°C, for not longer than 10 days. Egg fertility decreases substantially after this time. Commercially available incubators generally regulated to maintain a temperature of about 37.5°C and equipped with devices to turn the eggs automatically several times daily are used to incubate eggs until the desired age of the embryo is reached. The relative humidity in such systems is usually 55% to 65%.

When embryonic development has reached the desired point, the eggs are candled. Various types of candlers are available. A hand variety is most advantageous. This process is used to determine if the embryo is alive, and to locate the blood vessels and other parts of the animal. Living embryos usually exhibit spontaneous jerking movements (probably in response to the intensity of the strong light) and well-developed, translucent, floating blood vessels. Dead embryos are immobile and their blood vessels are barely visible.

Before inoculation of the chick embryo, the surface of the eggshell to be used is sterilized with an iodine solution, which may or may not be followed by wiping with an alcohol solution. Sterile precautions are observed in the working area in which the inoculations are to be conducted. Drills, or other devices for boring into the shell, and surgical instruments generally are sterilized beforehand by standard methods such as boiling or autoclaving. In addition, the inocula used usually contain antibiotics to guard against bacterial and fungal contamination.

Several portions of the embryonated egg are utilized for viral cultivation, including the allantoic and amniotic cavities, the yolk sac (Figure 13–2*A*), the chorioallantoic membrane (CAM) (Figure 13–2*B*), and the embryo itself. The particular region utilized depends on the virus to be cultured, as certain viral agents are

FIG. 13–1. The candling process. Eggs are incubated at 37°C until the embryos are 9 days old. They are then removed and checked for fertility and normal development, determined by subjecting them to a concentrated source of light and noting the shadow cast on their shell. Suitable eggs are inoculated. (Courtesy of Chas. Pfizer & Company, Inc., N.Y.)

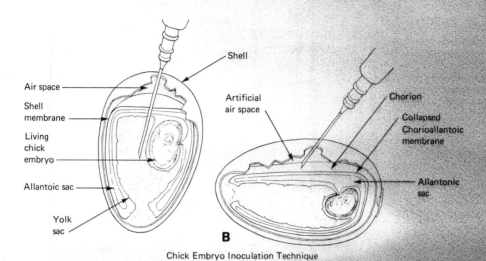

Chick Embryo Inoculation Technique

FIG. 13–2. Diagrammatic representation of the chick embryo's anatomical components, together with selected schematic illustrations of inocula-tion sites. _A_. Yolk sac inoculation. _B_. Chorioal-lantoic membrane (CAM) inoculation.

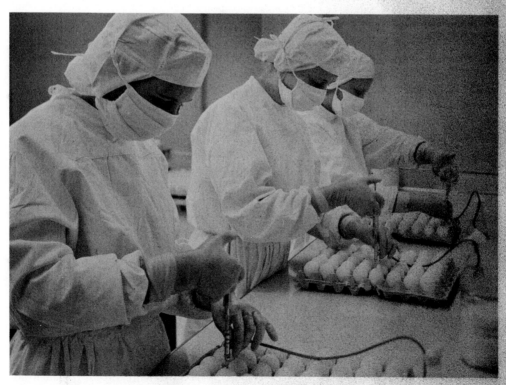

FIG. 13–3. Influenza vaccine production. Eggs which have been incubated, tested for fertility, and prepared for virus inoculation are punctured with a small drill and then seeded with influ-enza virus. Special instruments are used which break the shell but not the inner membrane. The eggs are then sealed with collodion gelatin and returned to the incubator. (Courtesy of Chas. Pfizer & Company, Inc., N.Y.)

capable of proliferating well only in particular portions of the embryo. For instance, the introduction of mumps and Newcastle disease viruses into the allantoic cavity results in the production of large quantities of these agents.

Table 13–1 lists several viruses and the particular region and the age of the chick embryo utilized for the cultivation of each. The age of the chick is important, as particular regions must reach a certain stage of development to provide a suitable environment for virus proliferation. In order to introduce a virus-containing inoculum, a hole is bored in the shell. After the inoculation, this area is sealed with paraffin, transparent tape, or related material. The injected eggs are returned to the incubator until the particular reaction for which they were used occurs. (See Figure 13–3.)

Signs of Virus Infection

Besides proving virus infection, the various embryo inoculation techniques are also used for: (1) studying the morphological features of viruses; (2) isolating viruses from specimens; (3) producing large numbers of viruses for vaccines; (4) determining the effectiveness of drugs on viruses (chemotherapy); and (5) investigating the mechanism of viral infection (Figure 13–4).

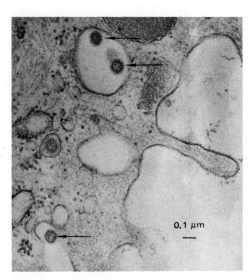

FIG. 13–4. An electron micrograph of a section of the chorioallantoic membrane 20 minutes after the inoculation of type A2 influenza virus. Viral particles (arrows) have penetrated into susceptible cells and are enclosed in phagocytic vacuoles. (From Dales, S., and Choppin, P. W.: *Virology,* **18**:489–493, 1962.)

Proof of virus infection in chick embryos may be exhibited in several ways. Certain viral agents produce local lesions of varying sizes, shapes, and opacities, called *pocks* (See Figure 31–9 and Color photograph 29). However, it is not generally possible to completely identify a particular agent on the basis of this effect alone.

Table 13–1   Anatomical Regions of the Chick Embryo Commonly Used for Virus Cultivation

Site of Inoculation	Age of the Chick Embryos Used	Representative Viruses for which Site is Utilized
Allantoic sac or cavity	12–13 days	Influenza, mumps, and Newcastle disease viruses
Amniotic sac or cavity (involves the amniotic fluid and cell of the amnion)	8–12 days	Eastern, Western, and Venezuelan equine encephalomyelitis viruses, mumps, and Newcastle disease virus
Chorioallantoic membrane (CAM)	9–14 days	Canine distemper virus, *Herpesvirus hominis* (the cause of fever blisters), variola (the causative agent of smallpox), vaccinia or cowpox
	6 days	Viruses of influenza, mumps, rabies, yellow

Additional signs of infection include: (1) the death of the embryo; (2) the demonstration of a hemagglutinating activity (discussed further in Chapters 23 and 34) associated with the allantoic or amniotic fluids; and (3) the demonstration of the virus or related agents by certain techniques of light and electron microscopy. However, it is possible for there to be *no* obvious signs of viral infection.

Tissue Culture Cultivation of Viruses

The technique of tissue culture is almost as old as the specialization of virology itself. The development of modern animal cell culture is based on the contributions of many investigators, including the successful explanting of small tissue fragments in plasma clots by Harrison in 1907, the maintenance of vaccinia virus in explanted corneal tissue by Steinhardt, Israeli, and Lanbert in 1913, the demonstration by Parker and Nye in 1925 of viral replication (multiplication) in cultures of rabbit testis, and the development by Maitland and Maitland in 1928 of a technique causing cells to grow in fluid suspensions of small tissue fragments.

Despite the promising results obtained with tissue culture, many virologists were prevented from using the technique by contamination of preparations with bacteria and fungi, and the tedious, time-consuming procedures to prevent this hazard. Not until the introduction of antibiotics, the use of the enzyme trypsin to free cells from fragments of tissue so they can be grown in single-cell layers, and the formulation of excellent, defined-growth media for cells, did the methods of tissue culture gain routine acceptance by virologists for the cultivation of viruses and other agents requiring a living cell.

Although the tissues of cold-blooded animals and plants can be cultivated, the discussion which follows will be limited to the cultivation of mammalian tissues. According to most authorities, the final impetus which ushered in the era of tissue culture was provided by the *in vitro* cultivation of poliomyelitis virus in tissues other than nerve cells. This was achieved in 1949 by Enders, Weller, and Robbins, who adapted the suspended-fragment technique of the Maitlands and used human embryonic tissue for their investigations. Before then, polio virus was grown only in lower animals and nervous tissue. The destructive action of the virus (Figure 13–5), originally referred to as "cytopathogenic" effect (CPE) but now designated as "cytopathic," was clearly demonstrated. The three scientists received the Nobel Prize for their work.

Preparation of Representative Types of Animal Tissue Cultures

The preparation of animal tissue cultures generally involves both the various procedures by which cells are removed from animals and the procedures used to maintain them under suitable artificial conditions *in vitro,* so that they can serve as hosts for viruses or as sources of DNA, RNA, or other nucleic acids. The animal tissues must be provided with ample nutrients in their growth and maintenance media to keep their metabolic processes functioning in a desirable manner, and they must be kept free from contamination by unwanted microorganisms, such as mycoplasma and latent viruses. An unexpected hazard which confronts individuals working with certain tissue cultures is the presence of viruses other than those that are the subject of a particular investigation. The animals that are used as the source of tissue may be harboring a latent viral infection. When these tissues are grown *in vitro*, the viral agent may use its new environment to unleash some destructive effect, thus producing an extremely confusing picture for the virologist.

Glassware. The success of tissue cultures depends to a large extent upon the glassware (or plastic ware) used. Equipment of this type must be clean, nontoxic to cells, and chemically inert, not reacting with the ingredients of the media used to bathe the cells of the culture. Within the past few years, a variety of disposable glass and plastic culture vessels has become available, including bottles, culture vessels such as tubes and flasks (Figure 13–6*A*), Petri dishes (Figure 13–6*B*), and pipettes. Disposable items are generally clean and sterile and do not require preliminary washing. Nondisposable glassware generally must be presoaked in a mild detergent solution, washed repeatedly, rinsed, first in tap water and finally in glass-distilled water, quickly dried, and sterilized.

Media and solutions. The various media and solutions used in the culture of cells

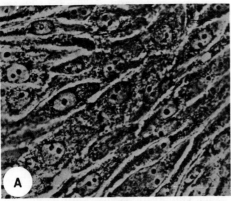

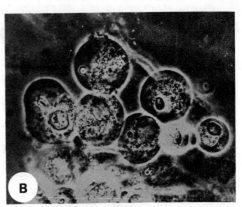

FIG. 13–5. Cytopathic effects following the infection of monkey kidney tissue cultures (MKTCs) with the prototype virus ECHO 23. *A*. Cells of a normal MKTC. *B*. Second day after infection.

(From Wenner, H. A.: *Ann. N.Y. Acad. Sci.*, **101**:347–352, 1962. © The New York Academy of Sciences; 1962; Reprinted by permission.)

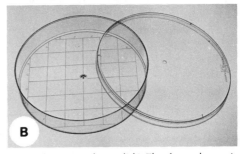

FIG. 13–6. Representative disposable plastic items
~~~~~ tissue cultures. *A*. A tissue culture flask.
~~~~~~~~~~~~~~~~~~~~~~~ The bottom

Type of tissue culture dish. The form shown is equipped with grid markings to assist in counting or locating cells. (Courtesy of Falcon Plastics, Diare commonly designated by the ingredients they contain, such as normal saline, phosphate-buffered saline, and chick embryo extract. Some solutions and media are simple, while others are quite complex. Examples of the former include balanced salt solutions and maintenance media. Synthetic or supplemented growth media are complex. Several types of balanced salt solutions are used in tissue cultures. Alone, these preparations do not support cell growth. They are employed: (1) to rinse the culture, thus freeing it from unwanted components, such as antibodies; (2) to dilute virus suspensions to be used for inoculation of cultures; and (3) as an important component of tissue culture maintenance or growth media. Solutions of this type generally consist of certain essential inorganic and organic compounds (Table 13–2), a component such as sodium bicarbonate ($NaHCO_3$) to buffer the solution (to stabilize the pH of the preparation), and an indicator such as phenol red to show changes in pH. All of these chemicals are dissolved in glass-distilled or deionized water. Many balanced salt solutions (BSS) are in common usage, including Earle's, Gey's and Hanks'.

Maintenance and Growth Media

The selection of a medium is determined by the purpose for which a particular tissue culture is to be used. Cells that are to be transported or stored for a limited period of time are often kept alive in *maintenance media*. A medium of this type contains either small concentrations or no supplements such as serum or chick embryo extract, which are essential for cellular multiplication.

Growth media generally consist of balanced salt solutions with a variety of essential synthetic or natural additives. Examples of the latter include: (1) bovine and chick amniotic fluids; (2) sera from a variety of animals, such as calf, horse, human, ox, and rabbit; (3) embryo tissue extracts; and (4) protein hydrolysates, such as tryptose phosphate broth and yeast extract. Note that the exact composition of these natural ingredients is not known. However, they are essential for the well-being of most established tissue cell cultures.

Synthetic or chemically defined growth media have also been developed. Their exact compositions are known, and can be duplicated as needed. Generally such synthetic media are complex, containing

Table 13–2   Typical Components of Common Balanced Salt Solutions

Component[a]	Chemical Designation
Calcium chloride	$CaCl_2$
Magnesium chloride	$MgCl_2 \cdot 6H_2O$
Magnesium sulfate	$MgSO_4 \cdot 7H_2O$
Potassium and sodium dihydrogen phosphates	$KH_2PO_4; NaH_2PO_4 \cdot H_2O$
Sodium bicarbonate	$NaHCO_3$
Sodium chloride	$NaCl$
Sodium monohydrogen phosphate	$NaHPO_4 \cdot 7H_2O$
Glucose[b]	$C_6H_{12}O_6$

SOURCE: Adapted from Betts, A. O., and York, C. J.: *Viral and Rickettsial Infections of Animals, Vol. I.* Academic Press, New York, 1967.
[a] Note that not all of these components are used in all media.
[b] The only organic component.

a rich variety of organic ingredients including amino acids, carbohydrates, coenzymes, lipids, and vitamins. The particular concentrations and combinations of these substances are determined by extensive studies, the results of which yield an exact and suitable growth medium. It is important to note that not all tissue cultures will grow in such completely defined concoctions.

Aseptic precautions are exercised in preparing the various types of media used in tissue culture procedures. Balanced salt solutions may be sterilized by autoclaving. However, organic components of media, such as sera and amino acids, are sterilized by filtration, passage through asbestos (Seitz) or Millipore filters. Many investigators prefer to filter all solutions and then combine the various media components in desired proportions. In order to keep tissue cultures free from unwanted bacteria and fungi, antibiotics are commonly added.

Representative Techniques for Culturing Cells

The sources of material for the majority of primary cultures can be divided into adult (Figure 13–7A), embryonic, and tumor (Figure 13–7B) tissues. Unfortunately, many varieties of cells derived from such tissues grow poorly or not at all *in vitro*. This obviously limits the type of cell that can be studied and used for the cultivation of viruses. Adult cell cultures most commonly used are derived from the foreskin, the kidney, the lung, and the thyroid. Cultures of adult kidney from every available animal have been quite successfully and widely used. Embryonic cell cultures have been obtained from a variety of animals, including chicks, mice, and humans. Several hu-

sources of many continuous cell lines.

The cells used in most studies are of two general forms: cell sheets (*monolayers,* or single layers of cells), and suspensions of tissue fragments or dispersed cells.

Cell sheets. The initial cultivation of cells from tissue is commonly referred to as the *primary culture,* in contrast to subculture or transfer. Primary cultures have certain disadvantages, including the presence of a variety of cell types and the possible presence of contaminating viruses. The development of pure cultures of cells can pose several problems, but

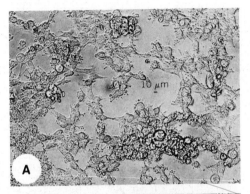

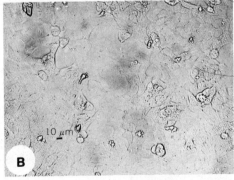

FIG. 13–7. Representative tissue culture types. *A.* Cells from a 17th generation of human bone. *B.* Cells from the 42nd generation of a HeLa culture. Th̲

such preparations are possible to obtain. When the cells of these cultures have been grown under cultural conditions for several generations (usually measurable in years), these systems are called *continuous* or *established cell lines*. It is important to note that pure cultures originally develop from isolated cells. The subsequent cells are descendants of a single cell and constitute a pure culture, called a *clone*.

The U.S. Department of Health, Education, and Welfare issues the publication "Registry of Animal Cell Lines Certified by the Cell Culture Collection Committee" which contains complete descriptions of cell lines used in vaccine production and scientific investigations.

The monolayer procedure includes treating minced tissue enzymatically with trypsin for a period of time. Freed cells are washed, diluted in appropriate quantities, suspended in a suitable growth medium, and seeded, that is, dispensed into any of a variety of tissue culture vessels including Petri dishes, bottles, culture flasks, and screw-capped tubes.

Most primary cells can be subcultured to produce secondary cultures. Morphologically, subcultured cells are similar to primary cells. Cells of this type comprise *cell strains* and apparently can be subcultured indefinitely.

Suspensions of tissue fragments and dispersed cells: suspended cell cultures. Monolayers have largely displaced cell suspensions, but in particular situations the use of dispersed cell cultures has certain advantages. Techniques employing such systems have been used for large-scale production of viruses and of mammalian cells (Figure 13–8).

In tissue fragment procedures, finely chopped pieces of kidney or other tissue are suspended and maintained in an appropriate medium. The original technique

FIG. 13–8. A cell production roller apparatus. These large cylindrical glass vessels are rotated so that their entire horizontal surface is exposed to cell growth. Roller vessel cultures deteriorate less rapidly than stationary systems. (Courtesy of Bellco Glass, Inc., Vineland, N.J.)

using this type of system was that of the Maitlands, mentioned earlier.

Dispersed cell suspensions simply consist of cells submerged in a nutrient fluid. In some cases, the cells are stirred continuously to prevent them from sticking onto the sides of the tissue culture vessel. Preparations of this type are also used to obtain large quantities of cells. Dispersed cell suspensions can also be employed to detect antibody activity against viral pathogens. Normally, in a suitable growth medium cells produce acidic waste products which lower the pH of the system. This change in the pH is shown by an indicator such as phenol red, which in alkaline environments is red, but in acidic states is yellow. When a virus inoculum is added to a dispersed cell suspension, the cells of the system are prevented from metabolizing normally and the color of the medium remains red. However, if specific antibodies against the viral agent (from the serum of a test animal) are introduced into the system at the same time as the virus, in a "serum-virus mixture," the cells metabolize normally. The medium will turn yellow, thus showing the neutralizing capability of the antibodies.

Organ cultures. Fragments of tissue may also be cultured in plasma clots. Preparations of this type were among the earliest tissue cultures. The technique basically consists of placing a piece of tissue in a small drop of sterile plasma which is on a glass surface of some type, such as the inner surface of a test tube or a cover slip within a glass vessel. The preparation coagulates quickly. In some procedures, after coagulation takes place additional nutrients are added in the form of a liquid medium. The container is stoppered, and incubated at approximately 37°C. An outgrowth of cells occurs within a few days.

Several variations of the original procedure developed by Alexis Carrel (Nobel Prize laureate, 1912) are known. One of these is the so-called *organ culture technique.* This procedure has been used in studies concerned with the development and growth of various human respiratory viral pathogens. The original techniques of organ culture were devised by Fells and Robinson. Tissue fragments, *explants,* were implanted onto plasma clots which contained chick embryo extract diluted with BSS and glucose. The tissue was transferred to new clots each day. A raft of rayon, suitably treated so that it would not be toxic, was introduced later to serve as a support for the explants. Modifications of this technique have appeared using a raft in a Petri dish (Figure 13–9), and adding a liquid medium to provide the essential nutrients for the tissue fragments.

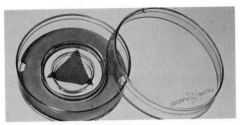

FIG. 13–9. A representative organ culture dish and grid or raft. The triangular grid is sterile and is made of nontoxic stainless steel cloth. (Courtesy of Falcon Plastics, Division of BioQuest, Los Angeles.)

Detection of Viral Multiplication in Tissue Culture Systems

Several tissue culture indications of viral infection have already been described, including cytopathic effects (Figure 13–5) and alterations in cellular metabolism. As this general subject is an important one, certain features of cytopathic changes following cell infection and certain techniques used in the enumeration of viruses will be described here in some detail.

Cytopathic changes. Gross cytopathic changes in virus-infected cultures can be readily observed with the aid of standard light microscopy techniques. Although fixation and staining of infected cells need not be carried out for detecting virus multiplication, this procedure is used for keeping permanent records of its stages.

Characteristic changes brought about by several viruses include cytoplasmic granulation or vacuolation, formation of giant and multinucleated cells, and condensation of chromatin material in the nuclear membrane of cells. The particular type of CPE (cytopathic effect) produced can at times be used as an aid in diagnostic virology, the identification of a particular viral group. Certain viruses, however, characteristically do not cause any observable morphological change in cells.

It should be kept in mind that newly isolated viruses occasionally must be transferred several times before the characteristic CPE are produced. It is also important to note that several changes in the fine structure of cells may be the result of the effects of a temporary lack of essential nutrients, changes in pH, and other related factors. Generally these effects develop within 24 hours and are not neutralized by antiviral substances, such as antibodies.

Plaquing techniques. Dulbecco, in 1952, introduced the plaquing method for viruses. The procedure consists of first inoculating a monolayer tissue culture system with a viral suspension and allowing sufficient time for the virus particles to be adsorbed by the tissue cells. The system then is overlaid with the nutrient agar and incubated at the desired temperature. Viruses that infect the cells multiply within their hosts and produce cellular damage. The presence of the agar overlay limits the spread of these agents to a lateral direction, producing circumscribed areas of cellular degeneration (Figure 13–10). Such sites of destruction, called *plaques,* are detected by staining either the remaining living cells or the dead cells. Neutral red can be used to stain living cells, while trypan blue can be employed for dead cells. The characteristics of the plaques formed (e.g., diameter and margin properties) in a particular type of tissue culture system such as monkey kidney or human kidney or HeLa cell (see Figure 13–7), also helps in the identification of viruses.

The plaque technique can be used for the establishment of pure viral lines. This procedure, called *plaque purification,* is based on the presumption that a single virus particle produces each plaque.

Plaquing methods can be carried out in a variety of bottles, Petri dishes, and

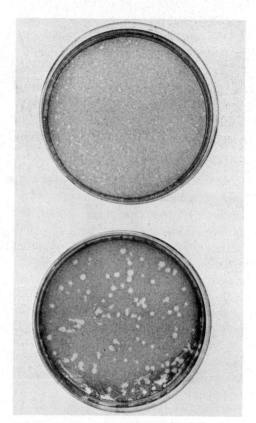

FIG. 13–10. Plaque formation of virulent measles virus in both green monkey kidney (top) and BSC-1 cell (bottom) cultures. (Courtesy of Dr. F. Rapp, Baylor University College of Medicine, Houston.)

related vessels. These procedures are used in *plaque assay* to determine the number of infectious virus particles in a particular specimen. The measurement of infectivity is accomplished by carrying out the plaque technique with given dilutions of virus-containing suspensions. The infectivity of the original virus-containing suspension is computed from the number of resultant plaques, each of which is referred to as a *plaque forming unit* (PFU), together with a correction factor for the dilution of the specimen employed. Modifications of this technique are necessary at times, and are determined by the type of virus being assayed.

The Cultivation and Enumeration of Bacteriophages (Phages)

Numerous types of bacterial viruses are known (Table 13–3), each capable of multiplying within one or more different bacterial species. In general, the cultivation of these parasitic forms is relatively uncomplicated, neither expensive nor overly time-consuming. For these reasons, bacteriophages have been used by many virologists to study the mechanisms of virus infections and related phenomena. Phages are commonly propagated on appropriate, actively growing young bacterial cells. Either broth or agar cultures are used for this purpose. In liquid cultures, the lysis of sufficient numbers of susceptible bacteria will cause the nutrient medium to clear. When agar plates are used, the presence of bacterial

viruses is indicated by the appearance of transparent holes (plaques) against the dense background of bacterial growth on the medium's surface (Figure 13–11).

Various types of bacterial viruses can be isolated from natural sources, such as dairy products, diseased tissues, feces, sewage, soil, and water. The demonstration of such viruses and their bacteriolytic action may be accomplished by passing a sufficient quantity of fluid samples of any of the aforementioned materials through a filter that retains bacteria, but not viruses. Examples of such devices include the Seitz (asbestos) and Berkefeld-N-type filters. (See Chapter 18 for a discussion of filtration and filters.) The next step of the procedure determines whether the resultant filtrate material contains phage. This generally involves introducing a small amount, such as 1 ml,

Table 13–3   A Partial List of Known Bacteriophages

| Bacterial Host | Selected Properties of the Host | | | Phage Designation[a] |
	Shape	Gram Reaction	Habitat and/or Type of Disease Produced	
Bacillus subtilis	Rod	+	Widespread in nature; saprophyte	SP8; SP3; SP10
Escherichia coli	Rod	−	Widespread in nature; found in man's intestines; may be pathogenic under certain conditions	Lambda (λ); Mu-1; P_1; P_2; T-even series (e.g., T_2, T_4); T-odd series (e.g., T_1, T_3, T_5)
Hemophilus influenzae	Rod	−	Human pathogen; can cause ear infections and respiratory involvement	HP_1; R.D. 1
Klebsiella pneumoniae	Rod	−	Human pathogen; causes pneumonia	K.P.
Mycobacterium tuberculosis	Rod	Acid-fast[b]	Human pathogen; causes tuberculosis	D28; D29
Neisseria perflava, strain 7A	Coccus	−	Generally widespread in nature	Phage H
Pseudomonas aeruginosa	Rod	−	Can cause respiratory and urinary infections	PS–7
Salmonella typhimurium	Rod	−	Associated with typhoid fever and food poisoning	P22
Serratia marcescens	Rod	−	May cause respiratory infection	P1
Shigella dysenteriae	Rod	−	Causes bacterial dysentery	F11
Staphylococcus aureus	Coccus	+	Causes many human diseases	Group B ϕ; ϕ 53; 80
Staphylococcus sp.	Coccus	+	Same as S. aureus	3A; S1; S2; S3

[a] It is important to note that new bacteriophages are continually being discovered.

[b] The Gram reaction is not a diagnostic feature of this organism.

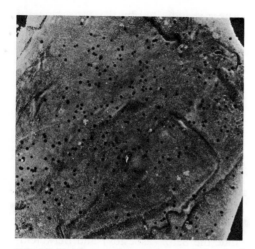

FIG. 13–11. Plaques formed by staphylococcal bacteriophages on growing *Staphylococcus aureus*. The small black spots are colonies of phages. The original sample used for this experiment contained at least 1,905,000,000 bacteriophage particles. (Courtesy of H. E. Morton and E. Lankford, A.S.M. LS-144.)

of the test material into approximately 10 ml of an appropriate fresh culture of a test host organism. Bacteria in the log phase of growth are suitable hosts. Another tube, without the addition of the suspected phage-containing sample, is generally used as a control. Both tubes are then incubated under optimum environmental conditions. If the tube to which the test material was added shows clearing or at least appears to be less turbid than the control, phages were present in the original sample. Unfortunately, the demonstration of bacterial viruses from natural sources is not always so easy. In many studies, additional and more involved procedures are required. Moreover, many samples of natural substances may not yield bacterial viruses.

Once a new phage is found, its characterization is usually undertaken. This involves determining its chemical and physical properties, uncovering its mechanism of bacteriolytic action, and demonstrating its basic differences from and similarities to other bacterial viruses.

Enumeration of Phages

Several methods may be used to estimate the number of virus particles in a sample accurately. One of the most useful and commonly employed procedures is the plaque count assay, which is simple, accurate, and yields highly reproducible results. It was originally introduced by D'Herelle, a French Canadian, around 1917, and was perfected by Gratia in 1937. It was D'Herelle who coined the term *bacteriophage* from the Greek word *phagein*, meaning "to eat."

The procedure can be performed by adding an adequate quantity of a given phage suspension dilution to a tube containing 2.0 ml of melted soft agar (SA) kept at 45°C. One drop of an appropriate fresh bacterial culture is also introduced. The contents of the tube are mixed and quickly poured onto the surface of a dried hard agar (HA) layer contained in a Petri dish. This plate then is rocked gently back and forth in order to equally distribute both the bacteria and the phage over the agar surface before the SA hardens. Viral particles diffuse through the medium, infect, multiply, and lyse susceptible bacteria. Those bacterial cells not infected grow, multiply, and form a "turbid" layer of film over the hard agar surface. Evidence of viral infection is provided by the presence of the previously mentioned plaques. As in the case of the plaque assay for animal viruses, the number of viral particles in the original sample is determined by the number of plaques multiplied by the dilution factor, the reciprocal of the dilution. This value is expressed as the number of plaque-forming units (PFU) per milliliter of the initial sample.

The quantitative determination of virus particles contained in a particular specimen can also be made by electron microscopy.

Phage Typing

Bacterial viruses that are continuously propagated in a specific bacterial species can become adapted to that particular bacterial host. Such viruses exhibit the phenomenon called *host-controlled modification*. They will primarily infect and lyse a specific bacterial species or cells of associated strains. A practical application of this process, namely, phage typing (Color photograph 66), is used to identify strains within certain bacterial species, such as *Salmonella typhi* and *Staphylococcus aureus*. This procedure is an extremely important tool in tracing the sources of epidemics and distinguishing between pathogenic bacterial strains which cannot be differentiated by other means.

Phage typing is performed by growing an unknown bacterial culture—isolated from a patient, for example—on an agar plate. Specific phages are systematically spotted onto the "lawn" of bacteria. After a suitable incubation period, zones of lysis appear if the appropriate phage and bacterial host combination is present. Plastic plates with grid patterns embossed on their bottom surfaces (Figure 13–12) are available to simplify the procedure.

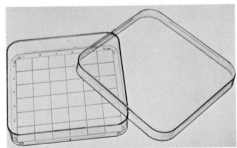

FIG. 13–12. "Integrid" Petri plate, an example of a Petri dish that can be used to systematically conduct phage typing procedures. The grids are used to locate a particular phage or host. The square dish provides maximum space utilization in situations when cultures require larger surfaces. (Courtesy of Falcon Plastics, Division of BioQuest, Los Angeles.)

Cyanophage Cultivation and Enumeration

Techniques for the cultivation and enumeration of viruses that attack blue-green algae have been developed. The cultural conditions, media, and procedures used for the preparation of suitable hosts (and subsequently for cyanophages) differ significantly from those used for bacteria. For example, most bacterial hosts and phages are stable from pH 5 to 8, whereas many blue-green algae and cyanophages are stable within the range of pH 7 to 11. Evidence of infection is provided by plaque formation, or electron microscopy may be used. Many of the studies involving cyanophages are complicated by the fact that their hosts are filamentous.

QUESTIONS FOR REVIEW

1. How are animal viruses grown?

2. What significant contribution has the chick embryo made to virology?

3. Discuss tissue culture. Include in your answer consideration of cell lines, media, tissue fragments, and organ cultures.

4. How is the multiplication of viruses in a tissue culture system detected?

5. a. What are bacteriophages?
   b. How are these agents cultivated?
   c. Explain phage typing.

6. After reviewing the procedures and media used in the cultivation of microorganisms, which of the techniques and media would you employ for the isolation of the following types of organisms?
   a. heterotrophic anaerobe
   b. influenza virus
   c. *Neisseria gonorrhoeae*
   d. bacteriophage of *Staphylococcus aureus*

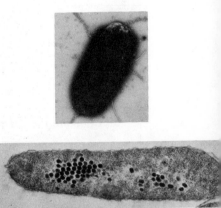

Microbial Growth, Metabolism, and Genetics

DIVISION 4: Behavioral Objectives

After reading the chapters in this division, the individual should be able to:

1. Recognize the significance of specific environmental factors to microbial growth.

2. Describe the events in bacterial sporulation and germination.

3. Compare the replication cycles of different viruses.

4. List and illustrate the general methods used to measure microbial growth.

5. Summarize the processes involved in the production of energy and proteins.

6. Explain the metabolic interrelationship of carbohydrates, fats, and proteins.

7. Describe representative methods used in the measurement of microbial metabolism.

8. Differentiate between autotrophic and heterotrophic metabolism.

9. Summarize the consequences of microbial metabolism.

10. Relate basic genetic principles to microorganisms.

11. Recognize and understand the chemical nature of inheritance and mutation.

12. Describe specific genetic transfer mechanisms in microorganisms.

13. Show the medical and environmental significance of specific genetic transfer mechanisms in microorganisms.

14. List and illustrate general procedures that can be used to confirm the spontaneous nature of mutation in microorganisms.

14

Microbial Growth

The evaluation of how a microorganism responds to its environment, *in vitro* or *in vivo,* is based upon the general kinds of information which are considered in this chapter. Such data provide an insight into the means by which microorganisms cause disease, produce antibitotics, and develop resistance to those antibiotics.

General Bacterial Growth

As a rule, bacteria and many protozoa reproduce by binary fission, the production of two new cells from one parent. Some bacterial species, bacterial variants lacking cell walls, the mycoplasma, and yeasts generally increase their cell numbers asexually by budding. Certain yeasts and molds reproduce both asexually and sexually by the formation of spores. Several protozoa also are capable of sexual reproduction.

Growth can often be differentiated from reproduction in terms of an increase in cell mass rather than in cell numbers. This is not always the case, since the synthesis and accumulation of cellular reserve material may occur without the production of major biologic compounds, such as nucleic acids or proteins. Thus in some situations an increase in mass is not a reflection of growth. In essence, growth is an orderly increase in all of an organism's chemical constituents, which naturally includes nucleic acids and proteins. Growth generally occurs when bacteria are transferred into a growth medium from a different environmental source. The two environments may differ only slightly in their composition, temperature, pH, or osmotic effects.

The phenomenon of growth prior to an increase in actual numbers represents the first phase of the bacterial growth curve, as shown in Figure 14–1.

Batch Culture

The lag phase of growth. The *lag* or *initial stationary phase* of a bacterial culture may last from 4 to 6 hours when sufficient numbers of bacteria are inoculated into a fresh medium to produce an appreciable density. Generally, the fewer organisms used as an inoculum, the longer is this growth phase. During this period, cell protein, dry weight, and size all increase. Moreover, the cells are very active metabolically. The high rate of activity appears to be needed in order to adjust the hydrogen ion concentration and/or oxidation-reduction potential to the level optimum for cell growth and division. The cells here are said to be in a state of "physiological youth." Such cells are exceptionally sensitive to various physical and chemical means of disinfection.

The logarithmic phase. When conditions are suitable, division begins, and after an acceleration in the rate of growth, the cells enter the *logarithmic (log)*

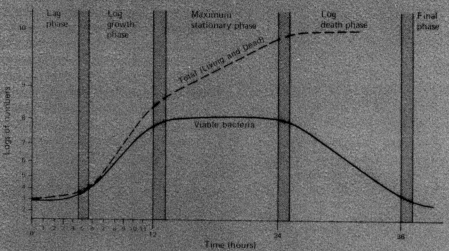

FIG. 14–1. A representation of a generalized bacterial growth curve, showing numbers of bacteria and times of incubation.

phase. During this period cells increase their numbers in a geometrical progression—1 splits to make 2, 2 to make 4, 4 to make 8, etc. Division occurs at a constant and maximum rate. Here the growth rate is constant. The plotting of cell numbers against time on a logarithmic scale (Figure 14–1) produces a straight line. It is during this logarithmic increase in cell numbers that one is able to calculate the average time for a cell to divide, otherwise known as the *generation time* (g). It is usually calculated by mathematical formulae in which g is equal to the period of time required to permit the doubling of cell numbers.

Stationary growth phase. At some point, the growth rate begins to taper off and the *stationary phase* becomes evident. Here the growth and death rates are more nearly identical and a fairly constant population of viable cells is achieved. In 1929, Bail called this stationary or maximum allowable population for a batch culture the *M concentration*. His experiments showed that, no matter how many organisms are used for an inoculum, the same eventual M concentration is achieved. When the growth in a tube

of medium was centrifuged and removed from it, the introduction of a new inoculum into the same medium produced the same M concentration. This procedure could be repeated several times until some essential nutrient was depleted or some by-product toxic for growth accumulated. On the basis of these and other studies, Bail claimed that each living cell required a finite volume or space. He called this property *lebensraum* (from the German, meaning "living room").

Two procedures are available to maximize growth in a liquid medium—a biphasic system and a dialysis bag technique (Figure 14–2).

In the biphasic system, a nutrient broth is placed over an agar medium in an appropriate container. The broth is generally the material inoculated. If the liquid surface is large for its volume, then oxygen will not be a limiting growth factor. In systems of this type, some organisms can produce densities which approach a paste consistency.

With the dialysis bag technique, inoculated broth is placed in dialysis tubing and suspended in aerated broth which

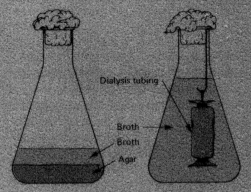

FIG. 14–2. Techniques used to maximize growth in liquid cultures. *Left*, a biphasic system. *Right*, the dialysis bag procedure.

is changed frequently. Very high cell densities are also possible with this method. One advantage of the technique is that the broth surrounding the dialysis tubing need not be sterile, since it is exchanged frequently and contaminating organisms cannot pass through the membrane.

The maximum cell densities of bacterial colonies are also obtainable when organisms are grown on solid media. Here nutrients diffuse to the cells from below, oxygen diffuses into the developing colony, and metabolites released from the cells diffuse into the agar medium.

Logarithmic death rate. In the stationary or batch culture, conditions develop which accelerate the rate of death, and after a short period, a logarithmic death rate can be observed. This situation will continue to the point where a low number of viable cells results. The growth curve then will flatten once more until all of the cells are dead (Figure 14–1).

If one evaluates both viable (living, metabolically active) and total counts of organisms (Figure 14–1), it is evident that the events observed in the growth curve are, indeed, variations in growth rate. The total cell counts will generally increase to some point in the logarithmic

death phase and then decline, due to the lysis of dead cells. This lysis may be caused by enzymes naturally present in cells, called *autolytic enzymes*.

Continuous Culture

The batch processes for growing bacteria are often adequate for use in various biochemical studies, and in antibiotic, antigen, and vaccine production. However, there is usually a considerable variation in the ages of the resulting cells and their metabolic activities. Techniques of continuous culture were developed to a large extent by Noviek and Szilard in 1950 and by others later. In addition to studying various aspects of metabolism, they investigated the mutation rate in a steady-state population of bacteria. Devices similar to that shown in Figure 14–3 have been used for large-scale cell production and the controlled production of many individual biochemical compounds.

In this system the rate of growth is controlled by providing a liquid medium with an essential nutrient at a sub-optimal

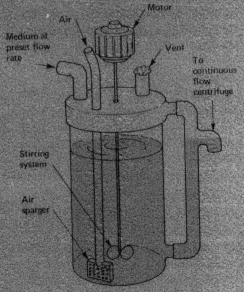

FIG. 14–3. A device for large-scale cell production. Example shown is of continuous culture system utilizing a growth-limiting medium.

level, with a flow rate less than the growth rate. This is called *external control* and results in all cells being in the log phase of growth. For example, in a simple synthetic medium for *Escherichia coli* containing glucose, ammonium chloride, and phosphate, the nitrogen source is usually chosen as the *limiting growth factor* (LGF). By keeping the glucose and phosphate at high levels and determining the growth rate or generation times at varying concentrations of ammonium chloride, one is able to determine the sub-optimal concentration for the LGF. With external control, the system is self-stabilizing, continuously providing cells with whatever growth rate is needed to yield the best product.

Growth on Solid Media

Mass culture techniques and biochemical studies usually use either batch or continuous broth cultures. However, colony and slant growth cultures can be extremely useful in evaluating the purity of cultures and in isolating organisms from a mixture and beginning their identification. Common growth patterns and terminology used for their descriptions are given in Chapter 12. The growth of bacteria into colonies is illustrated by *Microbacterium thermosphactum* in Figure 14–4.

In water analyses conducted by public health agencies, the usual procedure has been to perform viable bacterial counts by specimen dilution and the inoculation of pour plates for total counts, while the inoculation of multiple tubes of selective broth has been utilized for the most probable number (MPN) determination of coliform bacteria. The MPN approach gives a statistical determination of the number of coliform bacteria present in a given volume of water (usually 100 ml).

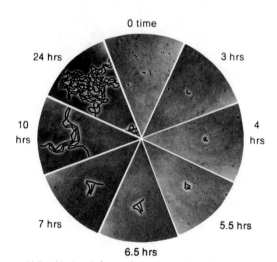

FIG. 14–4. Colony formation in *Microbacterium thermosphactum*. (From Davidson, C. M., Mobbs, P., and Stubbs, J. M.: *J. Appl. Microbiol.,* **31**:551–559, 1968.)

Further details of this procedure are given later in the chapter.

The introduction of membrane filters has greatly improved the reliability of coliform counts, which appear to be replacing the MPN procedure. With such filters, the entire water sample is filtered easily and quickly. The filter then is placed on a selective agar medium or a compressed paper pad impregnated with a selective broth medium. The surface of the membranous material serves as the solid support for growth. Most typical bacterial species are easily recognized and their colonies counted after a suitable incubation period.

The membrane filter approach to the examination of liquids for microorganisms is being applied to the analysis of body fluids to determine if fastidious pathogens are present in low number. Recent indications have shown, for example, that *Mycobacterium tuberculosis* can be obtained more readily from spinal fluids with this technique. With some modifications, blood cultures prepared in this manner have given excellent results.

Bacterial Spores

Bacterial spores were briefly described in Chapter 8. In this chapter we discuss these structures as they appear in members of the genera *Bacillus* and *Clostridium,* and with respect to their relationship to the parent cells.

Dormancy

The dormancy of bacterial spores is well documented. Spores of *Bacillus anthracis,* for example, have been found to survive for 60 years when left in soil at room temperature. Furthermore, meat which had been canned for 118 years was found to contain spores of a thermophilic bacillus. Examination of ancient materials for microorganisms has uncovered the presence of certain sporeformers, such as *Bacillus circulans.* Several species of *Clostridium* were isolated from the abdominal regions of well-preserved mummies in Bohemia, approximately 180 to 250 years old—species not found on the surface of the mummies, on their coffins, or in the ground.

The possibility of recent contamination of uncontrolled specimens cannot be overlooked, and may explain the presence of organisms, including sporeformers, in some materials, but not in others. For a long time one explanation for the existence of spores was to provide a means for survival under unfavorable environmental conditions. If this were the only reason, it would be difficult to explain the presence of organisms capable of forming spores not doing so in dried salt, hot sulphur springs, and in the polar ice cap. In the 1930s, Cook suggested that bacilli which formed spores did so because sporulation is a natural part of an organism's life cycle. Sporulation is a mechanism for survival and may also be a primitive mechanism by which genetic material, obtained as a result of transformation (see Chapter 16), can be recombined and segregated into a separate package, the spore.

Sporulation

Behring, in 1887, viewed sporulation as an intermediate stage in the normal development of the bacterial cell; a process that may be partially or completely inhibited by some physiological injury short of total prevention of growth. This concept can still serve as a good description of sporulation, since it does not attempt to explain the purpose of sporulation beyond defining it as a natural step in the life cycle of certain bacteria. The process as it is known today occurs if the cell is equipped with the proper genetic information, and if it is provided with a proper physiological environment, both internal and external. The following physical factors have been shown to be required for sporulation:

1. *Temperature*—A narrow range that approximates the optimum for vegetative growth.
2. *pH*—Again, a narrow range, about the same optimum level as for vegetative growth.
3. *Oxygen*—Increased oxygen is needed when cells such as those of *Bacillus* spp. begin to sporulate.

Chemically, the following substances appear to be required for sporulation: (1) glucose, (2) particular amino acids, and (3) growth factors such as vitamins and minerals, including folic acid (for *B. coagulans*), phosphate, calcium, manganese, and bicarbonate.

Sporulation research has indicated that the exhaustion of a particular nutrient essential for vegetative growth acts to trigger the entire process. Physiological studies have generally shown that vegetative cells continue to reproduce until

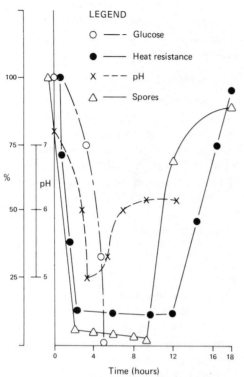

FIG. 14-5. Microcycle sporulation in *Bacillus megaterium*. The figure shows the spore development of this organism and the relationship of certain chemical and physical factors to the process of sporulation. (Adapted from Holmes, P. K., and Levinson, H. S.: *J. Bacteriol.*, **94**:434–440, 1967.)

a particular unknown point is reached and then sporulate in the manner shown in Figure 14–5.

Microcycle sporulation. This is the process by which an initial spore proceeds to germinate into a primary vegetative cell. This cell then sporulates to yield a second-stage spore, without any intervening cell division. A phenomenon of this nature can result from placing the spores in a simple glucose-ammonia containing medium. It is best visualized by referring to Figure 14–6.

Here the original spore coat has not disintegrated, as is usually the case, but still partially envelops the vegetative cell.

The latter is the product of germination. As this cell has sporulated without cell division, the process is called *microcycle sporulation.*

The effects of certain physiological parameters involved in sporulation are evident in Figure 14–5. Note that the glucose concentration drops to a low level within approximately 5 hours, accompanied first by a rapid increase in the acidity of the environment which suddenly ceases, and subsequently by an increase in alkalinity. The particular point at which the pH curve changes in direction from an acid to a basic state is intimately associated with the beginning of sporulation—this is believed to be the case, although obvious forespores and spores are not evident by refractility for nearly 6 hours, or demonstrated by thermal resistance for about 9 hours. At approximately this time, oxygen consumption increases and various sporulation inhibitors no longer function. This particular phase in sporulation is generally called *the point of commitment:* the organism has proceeded to some physiological step from which it has no alternative but to complete the process.

Structurally, five stages in sporulation can be observed, presented diagrammatically in Figure 14–7. Biochemically and physically, a variety of activities are associated with each stage. Brief descriptions of these events are presented in Table 14–1.

Spore Characteristics

After endospore formation, the parent cell disintegrates and the dormant structure becomes an exospore (free spore). A mature spore is shown in Figure 8–25. The central area is the core or spore cytoplasm. The spore wall (CWP) and plasma membrane (PM) become the cell wall and cytoplasmic membrane of the cell that appears upon germination. The

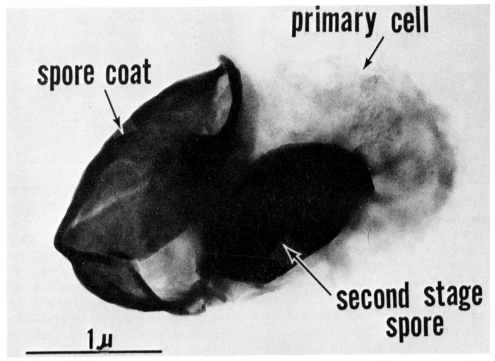

FIG. 14–6. Sporulation in a recently germinated spore, as demonstrated by electron microscopy.

(From Holmes, P. K., and Levinson, H. S.: *J. Bacteriol.*, **94**:434–440, 1967.)

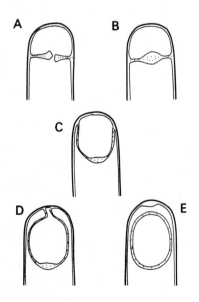

FIG. 14–7. A diagrammatic representation of the five stages of bacterial sporulation. (From Freer, J. H., and Levinson, H. S.: *J. Bacteriol.*, **94**:441–449, 1967.)

refractile and impervious nature of the mature spore is attributed to the cortex and the two spore coats.

Chemically, the spore has very little free water. Calcium dipicolinate comprises approximately 10 per cent of the structure's dry weight. The core region contains a characteristic quantity of DNA. However, with respect to enzymes and various RNA's, relatively low levels are found, and no apparent messenger RNA is present. The spore wall and cortex contain glycopeptides. The coats are mostly proteins with a significant amount of amino acid cystine. This compound permits cross-linkages to form between the other amino acids present and may be in part responsible for the heat-resistance and imperviousness of the spore.

Thermal resistance. This property of bacterial spores can be considered simply

Table 14–1   Brief Descriptions of the Activities Associated with the
Stages of Bacterial Sporulation

Stage	Activity
1	Formation of the initial forespore membranes occurs Enzymes characteristic of spores are produced
2	The heat-resistant catalase of the spore appears The forespore membrane becomes continuous and separate from the plasma membranes of the parent cell
3	The cortex is formed Characteristic refractility of the forespore begins to develop Synthesis of dipicolinic acid (DPA) takes place Increased uptake of calcium is evident
4 and 5	Spore coats are formed The spore matures to a fully refractile, heat-resistant dormant structure

as the ability to germinate and to reproduce after exposure to high temperature. The loss of heat resistance relates to the "inactivation" of any part of the sequence of reactions required for germination and subsequent outgrowth. The food industry has been particularly concerned with bacterial spores and their heat resistance because many clostridia can cause the spoilage of foods which have been canned. Clostridial spores are of primary concern because they can germinate and reproduce in the absence of air. Such anaerobic conditions are present in food products after canning.

Thermal resistance appears to be due to a variety of factors, which include: specific heat-resistant components, such as thermostable enzymes; an absence of free water; a high content of various minerals, particularly calcium; and the presence of dipicolinic acid (DPA). A good but not complete correlation exists between calcium, dipicolinic acid, and heat resistance. If spore-forming bacteria are grown in media deficient in calcium, the level of heat resistance appears to follow the concentration of this element. A similar phenomenon has been observed with spores grown in a manner that produces a dipicolinate deficiency.

Studies have demonstrated that the calcium of *Bacillus megaterium* could be replaced by manganese and other elements. The resulting spores appeared quite normal in morphology, refractility, and resistance to phenol and drying. However, these structures were not thermostable. Only calcium-grown spores were found to be thermostable. Moreover, such spores also contained high levels of dipicolinic acid, which appeared to follow, in equimolar fashion, the concentration of calcium. Dipicolinic acid or pyridine 2,6–dicarboxylic acid may be incorporated within the spore cortex and core through chelate linkages formed with calcium and protein. This chelation may be, in part, an explanation for heat resistance.

Two lines of evidence seem to suggest that dipicolinic acid is not the major factor accounting for heat resistance: (1) germination studies have shown that heat resistance is lost prior to the complete release of calcium dipicolinate in the spore exudate, (2) sporulation at high temperature will result in an increase of the thermoresistance of spores. These spores will either maintain or increase the cation concentration without necessarily increasing dipicolinic acid. Thus, thermoresistance and mineral content may show the better correlation; however, other factors cannot be disregarded as yet.

Germination of Spores

Germination of bacterial spores means the transition of a resting structure to an actively dividing vegetative cell. Some authors reserve the term *germination* for the second of three separate phases of an overall process consisting of activation, germination, and outgrowth.

Phase I. Activation. Dormant structures may fail to develop even though they are placed in an environment which would allow vegetative growth. Under such conditions, a spore will germinate if it is exposed to some triggering or germination agent, either physical or chemical. Physical triggering agents include high temperature and mechanical treatment. Chemical factors include surface wetting agents, inorganic materials such as chloride, cobalt, manganese, phosphate, and zinc, and various normal metabolic compounds, such as adenosine, alanine, calcium dipicolinate, carbon dioxide, glucose, lactic acid, and tyrosine.

Regardless of the agent involved, activation appears to involve: (1) a breaking down of permeability barriers by activation of lytic enzymes, (2) physical disruption of the spore coat and/or cortex material, and (3) a subsequent activation of carbohydrate metabolism. Thus, activation, or Phase I, seems to represent a lag period during which the spore is emerging from its state of dormancy. Emergence may also occur after aging of the spores at refrigeration temperatures, 4°C.

Phase II. Germination. This portion of the process can be considered as the transition of a heat-resistant, refractile, impervious structure into one which has lost these characteristics. Phase II appears to be initiated by the formation of a germination groove in the spore coat, which may serve as the means by which water and nutrients enter the spore. Several events are concomitant with water uptake: (1) a significant increase in oxygen consumption and glucose oxidation, (2) swelling of the spore, and (3) the excretion of approximately 30 per cent of its dry weight. The excreted solids consist about equally of calcium dipicolinate, various proteins, amino acids, and glycopeptide. At this point, the spore is considered to have germinated, on the basis of the following four major criteria: (1) thermal lability, i.e., sensitivity to heat; (2) stainability with simple dyes; (3) a loss of refractility, as determined by its phase contrast appearance; and (4) a decrease in the optical density of the spore suspension.

In 1969, Hashimoto, Frieben, and Conti investigated the germination of individual spores of *Bacillus cereus* and divided the process into two subphases. Specifically, these were (1) the release of calcium dipicolinate and the loss of heat resistance and (2) loss of refractility, attainment of full stainability, and the release of mucopeptide. It was also noted that resistance to heat was lost prior to the complete release of calcium dipicolinate.

Phase III. Outgrowth. Once the spore has been activated and germinated, outgrowth may occur. A complete growth medium is now required, or the germinated cell will not be able to reproduce. The initial stages of outgrowth include growth of the spore wall and membrane into the cell wall and the plasma membrane of the vegetative cell. If an antibiotic such as chloramphenicol, a potent inhibitor of protein synthesis, is added during Phase II, germination will occur without subsequent outgrowth.

Figure 14–8 shows spore germination and outgrowth in *Clostridium bifermentans* as shown by electron microscopy.

Growth of Mycoplasma and L-Forms

Generally speaking, mycoplasma and the L-forms of bacteria are differentiated on

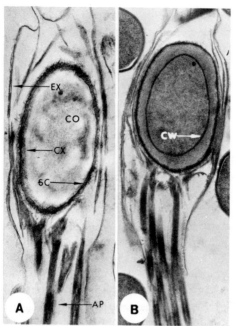
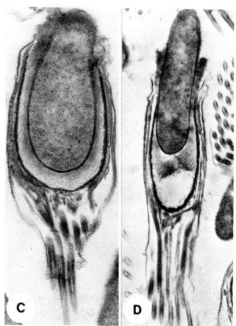

FIG. 14–8. An electron microscopy representation of spore germination and bacterial cell outgrowth. _A._ A thin section of a dormant spore of _Clostridium bifermentans_. The components include appendages (_AP_), the core (_CO_), cortex (_CX_), spore coat layers (_SC_), and exosporium (_EX_). _B._ The early stage of germination. The cortex has been transformed into a region containing amorphous material. The presence of a core wall (_CW_) is evident. _C_ and _D_. The stages of elongation and outgrowth. In _C_ the bacterial cell is constricted by the spore coat as it emerges. In _D_ cortex material (arrows) is extruded. The remains of the spore are left behind. (From Samsonoff, W. A., Hashimoto, T., and Conti, S. F.: _J. Bacteriol._, **101**:1038–1045, 1970.)

the basis of their source and particular nutritional requirements. Mycoplasma have been isolated from both animals and plants. More attention, however, has been given to plant mycoplasma. These microorganisms are stable reproductive units lacking cell walls. Many of them, particularly the animal pathogens, require the addition of steroids in nutrient media used for their isolation and cultivation. L-forms are derived from bacterial cells and also do not have cell walls. However, such organisms, given the appropriate environmental conditions, will usually revert to cell-wall-containing bacteria, and do not generally require steroids.

Exceptions to these microbial variants are known. Some mycoplasma do not require steroids, and L-forms can be found that are stable, i.e., maintained without cell walls. Further differentiation will require more immunochemical studies and genetic analysis.

Since both forms of microorganisms generally lack cell walls and exhibit a great variation in shape and size, their growth patterns have been difficult to observe and study. These organisms are strongly influenced by chemical and physical factors in their environments. Under certain conditions, large, round forms develop, while at other times long filaments or small granules may result.

Recent studies of mycoplasma have shown at least two modes of growth and reproduction. Maniloff and Horowitz reported in 1967 the observation of a simple growth cycle with _Mycoplasma_ *gallisepticum*. These authors found that the *Mycoplasma gallisepticum* reproduced by binary fission in much the same manner as normal cell-wall-containing bacteria.

Studies by Boatman and Kenney in 1970 with another mycoplasma, *M. felis,* indicated that a somewhat more complex growth cycle for these organisms is possible. The results of electron microscopic examinations of specimens taken at various times during growth were used as a basis for a proposed life cycle (see Figure 14–9). In this model, the primary reproductive unit is larger than *Mycoplasma gallisepticum* and it is reasonably uniform in electron density.

The obvious stages involve the for-mation of cells containing small granules. Such cells assume an oval shape prior to the formation of small extensions which elongate into definite lobes. The central areas of low density appear to function as an interconnecting membrane between lobes, thus possibly allowing for the detachment of the lobes without destruction of the remaining portion of the cells. Upon detachment a lobe appears to round up into a primary reproductive unit and thus initiates a reproductive cycle. When all such structures have detached, the central electron dense particle is left behind. Similar granules have been observed in a number of mycoplasma cultures as nonviable units.

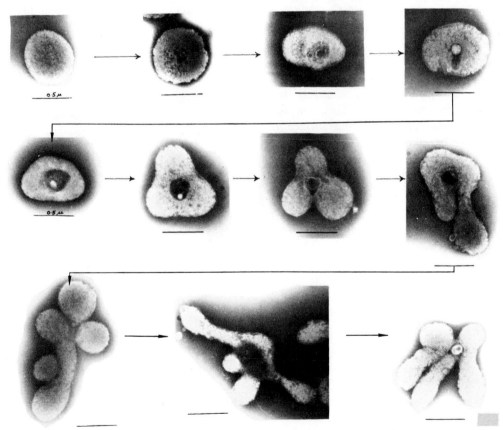

FIG. 14–9. A proposed life cycle for *Mycoplasma felis.* (From Boatman, E. S., and Kenney, G. E.: *J. Bacteriol.,* **101**:263–277, 1969.)

Replication Cycle of Bacteriophages

A general discussion of viral structure and attachment to host cells and the detection of viral activity was presented in Chapters 9 and 13. Here we will discuss the life cycle of bacteriophages in terms of the various events associated with virulent and temperate activities.

Phages that regularly complete their life cycles in bacterial hosts and ultimately cause the lysis of bacterial cells are called *virulent* or *lytic* viruses. Other phages may be maintained in their bacterial hosts without regularly causing the disruption of those cells. When it does not cause disruption the virus is called *temperate*, and the process by which the agent becomes integrated into the bacterial cell is termed *lysogeny*. Lytic and temperate viral activities can usually be differentiated on the basis of the appearance of plaques which develop when bacterial hosts are plated. When relatively few viruses are mixed with many sensitive bacteria and placed on the surface of solid media, plaques will develop after a suitable incubation period. Figure 14–10 compares lytic and temperate viral infec-

tion in terms of the production of clear versus turbid plaques.

A clear plaque represents virulent viral activity in all infected cells, resulting in the death and subsequent lysis of such cells. The turbid plaque indicates that only a portion of the infected bacteria have undergone a lytic cycle and the surviving bacterial cells can and will reproduce, unaffected by the virus under the existing conditions.

Lytic Cycle

The stages of bacteriophage development generally include adsorption, in some cases penetration (viral nucleic acid injection), a "latent" period, viral particle replication, virus maturation, and liberation of mature virus particles (Figure 14–11).

Adsorption and penetration. Adsorption is a specific event, since only certain viruses will be able to infect particular bacterial host cells. As noted in Chapter 9, specific receptor sites for the phage tails must be present for attachment to occur. In addition, sodium or calcium ions may be required. In the cases of phage T_5 (Type 5) and *Escherichia coli,* isolated receptor sites have been found to consist of protein and lipopolysaccharide.

Once the bacteriophage has adsorbed (as a consequence of the formation of a chemical bond between acidic and basic groups), and a limited enzymatic digestion of the cell wall has taken place, the viral DNA enters the host bacterium. This injection of DNA in certain T viruses and *E. coli* appears to be triggered by the contraction of the phage's tail sheath (Figure 9–12B) and the contact which occurs between its central tube or core and the cytoplasmic membrane of the cell. This tube penetrates the cell wall because of enzymes located in the base of

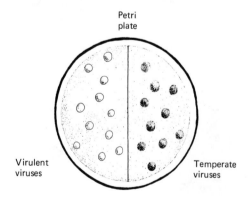

Petri
plate

Virulent
viruses

Temperate
viruses

FIG. 14–10. A comparison of plaques formed by virulent and temperate bacteriophages. The plaques formed by virulent phages are clear; those produced by temperate viruses are cloudy.

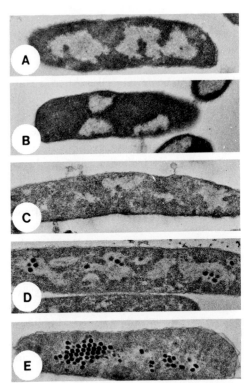

FIG. 14–11. The intracellular development of virus T₂ in *Escherichia coli*. _A._ Time of infection shows *E. coli* with normal DNA (light areas). Adsorbed viruses are not evident. _B._ Two minutes after infection, the appearance of the DNA has changed. _C._ Ten minutes after infection. DNA has become more diffuse. Empty viral heads are evident on cell wall. _D._ Twelve minutes after infection. First phages appear. _E._ Thirty minutes after infection. Cell is nearly ready to burst. (From Jacob, F., and Wollman, E. L.: "Viruses and Genes," *Sci. Amer.*, **204**:93, June, 1961. Micrographs by E. Kellenberger and A. Ryter.)

the tail that can digest the mucopeptide component of the rigid cell wall layer (Chapter 8). In the case of phages such as the T-even viruses, the protein capsid remains on the outside of the host. With filamentous, single-stranded DNA phages, the capsid enters the host. Although a small amount of cytoplasmic leakage can occur after the perforation of the cell wall, the bacterial host does not appear to experience any great difficulty. If however, the *multiplicity of infection* is great, sufficient injury to the cell wall results

to cause lysis. This phenomenon is generally referred to as *lysis from without,* to differentiate it from lysis which would normally occur upon liberation of viruses at the end of the lytic cycle. *Multiplicity of infection* refers to the ratio of viruses to bacterial cells. A multiplicity of 1 indicates equivalent numbers of viruses and hosts. A ratio of 100 or more is usually necessary to cause lysis from without.

Latent period (virus replication and maturation). Following the injection of the DNA, there is a latent period, during which no release of infective viruses can be observed. Once infection begins, the cellular synthesis of bacterium-specific nucleic acids and protein ceases. Certain components of the host cell, such as ribosomes and enzymes, still function, but they are utilized for the replication of virus-specific components.

Two phases of this period are *virus particle replication* and *virus maturation.* During the former phase a portion of the viral DNA, upon reaching the host's cytoplasmic region, is immediately transcribed for the formation of "early" viral messenger RNA (vmRNA). (See Chapter 15 for a description of protein synthesis.) This process specifically involves the host's RNA polymerase. The newly formed vmRNA is translated by the host's ribosomes, resulting in the synthesis of viral enzymes, including those necessary for viral nucleic acid replication. Depending upon the specific virus, the host DNA may or may not be involved with the viral enzymes. In some cases the host DNA is kept intact for this purpose, while with other viruses this DNA is degraded.

During viral maturation viral DNA is utilized in the formation of other essential viral components, including the subunits or capsomeres of the capsid. As these capsid subunits accumulate, viral

DNA molecules combine with a specific protein and become tightly packed into polyhedral units. Subsequently the capsomeres crystallize on the surfaces of the polyhedrons to form mature bacteriophage heads. Significant additional activity is needed to synthesize the remaining subunits of the virus and to assemble them into a complete virus particle, the *virion*. The latter process is under the control of certain viral genes referred to as being *morphopoietic* (from the Greek *morphe*, "form," *poiein*, "to make").

Liberation of virus particles.   As the maturation period of virus particles comes to an end, another viral protein product appears and steadily increases in concentration. This substance, known as *bacteriophage lysozyme,* is capable of destroying the chemical bonds holding together the components of the cell wall's rigid layer. The wall becomes progressively thinner, and eventually ruptures due to an osmotic pressure imbalance (*plasmoptysis*). The virus particles and remaining contents of the cell are thus released into the immediate environment. The lytic cycle is complete and infectious viruses are once more available to begin the cycle. As observed in other phases of the lytic cycle, the liberation process also differs among bacteriophages.

Growth Curve

Utilizing the events of the lytic bacteriophage cycle, it is possible to experimentally carry out a growth curve for bacterial viruses. This type of experiment is generally used to determine the time sequence from injection to the release of mature virus particles and to estimate the approximate number of these agents produced per cell, called the *burst size*. The total procedure is called a *one-step growth curve.*

This experimental procedure is performed by adding a virus suspension at a low multiplicity of approximately 0.1 to 0.01, meaning one viral particle for each 10 or 100 bacterial cells. After a short period of incubation to allow adsorption, non-adsorbed viruses are removed. The low multiplicity of infection is needed to reduce the chance of several viruses infecting a single bacterium and producing abnormal results. Once attachment has occurred, any free or extracellular viruses are removed through the addition of specific antisera and the recovery of infected bacteria by centrifugation. By removing free viruses not only is the opportunity for subsequent infection of additional bacteria substantially reduced, but the skewing of the results is greatly lessened. The bacterial suspension is next diluted in fresh media to a desired concentration. Samples are removed periodically and assayed for the presence of free or extracellular viruses. A typical curve is presented in Figure 14–12.

Generally, the plaque count remains fairly constant for a period of time. This phase of the growth curve is referred to as the *latent stage* or *period*. The designation is misleading in the sense that significant viral activity is going on even though the plaque count does not indicate

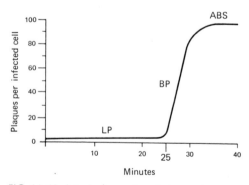

FIG. 14–12. A typical one-step viral growth curve. This representation shows the length of the latent period. (*LP*), burst period (*BP*), and average burst size (*ABS*).

it. The lysis of infected bacteria and the subsequent release of viral particles are evidenced by an abrupt increase in plaque numbers. This stage is called the *burst period*, and it continues until all infected cells have lysed. Again, the plaque count reaches a more or less constant level, even if uninfected bacteria are present. The diluted nature of the bacterial suspension used results in a wide distribution of cells so that newly liberated phages cannot spread to uninfected bacteria. By knowing the number of infected bacteria at time zero, the numbers of plaques obtained at various intervals can be calculated in terms of PFU per infected cell. In Figure 14–12 the burst size was found to be 100 PFU. This is comparable to the burst size which would be found with virus T_2 shown in Figure 14–11*E*.

Lysogeny

When a temperate bacteriophage infects a host cell, two options are possible. The lytic cycle characteristic of virulent virus may occur, or the cell, once infected, may harbor the virus in a noninfectious state. In the latter case the viral agent is referred to as a *prophage*. During this prophage phase, the host cell may undergo significant changes in colonial morphology, antigenicity, and toxin production (Figure 4–13). These effects are called *lysogenic* or *viral conversion* and are discussed in Chapter 16. Lysogenic states have also been found with certain cyanophages.

Occasionally, a prophage can be activated to undergo a lytic cycle. Exposure of a lysogenic culture to ultraviolet light increases the rate of such prophage activation significantly. This is one means of determining if a given culture is lysogenic. The interrelationship of lytic and temperate viral cycles is represented in Figure 14–14.

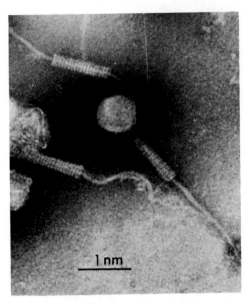

FIG. 14–13. An electron micrograph of *Clostridium botulinum* type ID^{tox+} bacteriophage. This virus has recently been shown to influence the host bacterium's production of botulism toxin. (From Eklund, M. W., and Poysky, F. I.: *Appl. Microbiol.,* **27**:251–258, 1974.)

Resistance to infection. During the lysogenic cycle, the occasional bursting of cells liberates free viruses into the general culture containing lysogenic bacteria. Thus, even though an additional virus is adsorbed and injection occasionally occurs with such lysogenic organisms, a lytic cycle cannot occur. A barrier to infection is established by the first bacteriophage that infected the host. Such bacteria are considered to be *immune*.

Another form of bacterial cell immunity is found when a mutational change occurs altering the chemistry or structure of a receptor site so as to prevent infection by interfering with viral adsorption. This phenomenon is called *resistance*.

Animal and Plant Virus Replication

Studies on viral replication conducted with animal and plant viruses, although

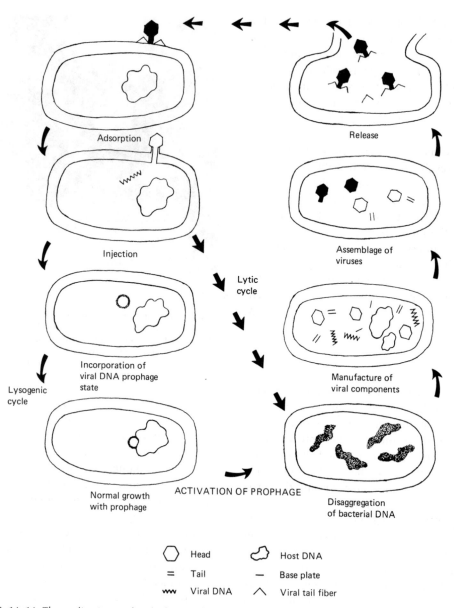

FIG. 14–14. The replication cycle of a bacterial virus.

less extensive than investigations performed with bacteriophages, are sufficient to show that the sequence of events in replication generally is similar for all viruses examined. Some differences in certain details, however, do exist. In the case of animal virions, virus particles adsorb onto specific chemical receptor sites on the host cell (Figure 14–15). The spikes or projections on enveloped virions serve as attachment devices. Because animal viruses lack tail structures, these microorganisms are carried inside the host cell by phagocytic or pinocytic action. Thus virus particles penetrate the cell and remain in a phagocytic vacuole or similar

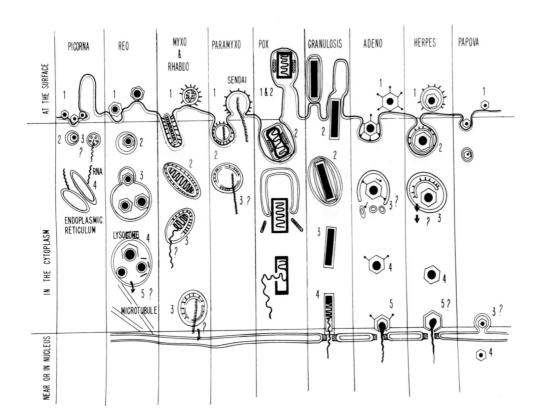

FIG. 14–15. Selected aspects of animal virus replication as demonstrated by several different viruses. Diagrammatic representations of the following aspects are presented: attachment (1), penetration (2), and uncoating (3, 4 and 5). (From Dales, S.: *Bacteriol. Revs.*, **37**:103, 1973.)

structure for a period of time. Once in this situation, a variety of mechanisms come into action to remove viral envelopes and the capsid from the nucleic acid. Such activities are referred to as *uncoating*. Replication of viral nucleic acid and synthesis of other viral components follow. These components are made separately and then assembled into complete virions during the stage of virus maturation. The entire process resembles an assembly-line factory system, in which various parts of a product are made separately and then at some point efficiently assembled.

The replication of enveloped viruses requires the active participation of the host cell. For example, before replication occurs, the viral nucleic acid is surrounded by a protein capsid, which in turn is enclosed by the host cell membrane (the envelope). In certain cases the envelopment occurs through a budding process (Figure 14–16). After envelopment is complete, the release of newly formed viral particles takes place, a process that may continue for several hours or even days. The method of release varies according to the virus involved. Also, host cell death doesn't necessarily occur with viral release.

Plant viruses do not seem to be endowed with any specific mechanisms to ensure their penetration into host cells. Generally, the viruses enter their hosts

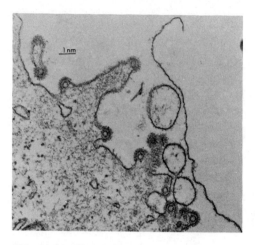

FIG. 14–16. Chimpanzee foamy virus particles budding from the plasma membrane of an infected cell. Note that massive destruction of the cell is not evident. (From Hooks, J. J., Gibbs, C. J., Jr., Cutchins, E. C., Rogers, N. G., Lampert, P., and Gajdusek, D. C.: *Arch. ges. Virus forsch.*, **38**:38–55, 1972.)

through breaks or abrasions in the plant, by insects, or by means of parasitic plants such as dodder.

Measurement of Growth

Microbial growth can be determined by observing an increase in mass or numbers. The selection of techniques for this purpose depends upon the particular organism involved or the requirements of a particular problem. Generally, several different analytical procedures are performed for comparative purposes; these include dry weight, protein or nitrogen concentration, and turbidity.

Cell Mass Determination

Dry weight.   Cell mass can be measured by noting the dry weight of microbial cells in culture. This technique is commonly used to determine the growth of fungi, in which case the mycelial mat is removed from the growth medium, possibly washed briefly to remove extraneous solids, placed in a weighing bottle, and

dried in a heated dessicator. When the microbial remains appear dry, the contents of the bottle are weighed in an analytical balance. Usually this procedure is repeated until a constant weight is obtained. The weight is used to estimate the fungal mass produced under particular growth conditions. Such data may be used to compare the rates of growth of different antibiotic-producing molds or to determine the relative effects of antimycotic (anti-fungal) agents.

With bacteria, cell mass values can be obtained in essentially the same manner. However, to avoid including a major portion of the growth medium along with the bacteria, it is customary to remove the bacteria by centrifugation from a quantity of the medium, and to then determine the weight of solids present. The weight of the medium is then subtracted from the total weight of the bacterial suspension to determine the dry weight of the bacterial cells.

Chemical analysis.   Mass can also be determined by chemical analyses for protein or nitrogen, since the protein or nitrogen concentration in a growing bacterial culture correlates with the increase in cell mass. In this case, samples of the culture are obtained and either analysed immediately, or frozen and stored for some later time. The latter procedure is used when large numbers of specimens are to be analyzed. It is also necessary to prepare cell-free specimens of the medium for control purposes. In this manner the effect of various nutrients or anti-metabolites and related substances upon the protein synthesis of a growing culture can be determined.

Turbidity.   While dry weight and protein or nitrogen concentrations are not difficult to determine, a more rapid measure of cell mass is often necessary. As one observes a growing culture, it is evident that growth is accompanied by an increasing cloudiness of the medium. This *turbidity* can be measured. Changes in turbidity measurements are used in various studies, and can be correlated with some other growth characteristic of a particular organism grown under a particular set of conditions.

Turbidity measurements can be performed with a variety of instruments, including *colorimeters, spectrophotometers,* and *nephelometers*. With the first two instruments, the path of light with a particular wavelength, such as 660 nm or 6600 Å, is interrupted by a suspension of the organisms in a tube of good-quality optical glass or quartz. The amount of light passing through the suspension is monitored by a photoelectric cell and expressed in terms of the percent transmission of light, or the optical density (O.D.) of the material in the light path (Figure 14–17).

Figure 14–17*A* shows the monitoring system adjusted so that the cell-free medium is seen as 100 per cent transmittance. This adjustable system can correct for the effects of different media on the transmission of light. This makes possible a closer estimate of the turbidity pro-

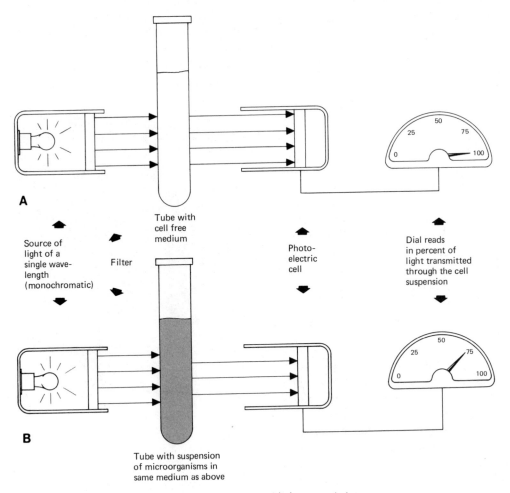

A

Source of light of a single wavelength (monochromatic)

Filter

Tube with cell free medium

Photo-electric cell

Dial reads in percent of light transmitted through the cell suspension

B

Tube with suspension of microorganisms in same medium as above

FIG. 14–17. Measurement of turbidity by monitoring of light transmission.

duced by organisms grown in some particular medium under conditions which may affect the light transmission capacity of the medium.

In part B of Figure 14–17, the suspension of organisms has reduced the percent transmittance as a result of physical absorption and scattering of light rays. The wavelength of 660 nm was chosen here so that the usual brownish color of nutrient media would not interfere with the results. Other wavelengths may be used with equal facility.

With turbidity measurement by light transmission, it is possible to obtain readings for solutions which are at least slightly turbid. The sensitivity is not sufficient to monitor suspensions of organisms that do not show some cloudiness. With nephelometry, on the other hand, the device is most sensitive when microorganisms are in low concentration. Lamanna and Mallette estimate a sensitivity that detects *Escherichia coli* at 10,000 cells per ml, compared with the value on the order of one million cells that is needed in light transmission measurements. In nephelometry the light scattered by the organism is measured, rather than the light transmitted. The mathematics required to prove the greater potential sensitivity of nephelometry are too complex to present here. However, it should be noted that this greater sensitivity is not needed for routine turbidity measurements.

Viable Counts

These determinations are carried out to estimate the numbers of living and/or infective microorganisms in a given material. Cultures of organisms are diluted in a liquid medium and subsequently placed in an environment which allows them to produce some type of visual effect. Agar media or membrane filters are used for certain algae, bacteria, and fungi, while tissue cultures are employed for the chlamydia, rickettsia, and viruses. End results of these procedures include colony counts for bacteria (Figure 14–18) and plaque counts for viruses. Estimates thus obtained are expressed in *colony-forming* or *plaque-forming units, CFU* and *PFU,* respectively. Since details of the procedure for PFU determinations have been described in Chapter 13, only bacterial CFU (Figure 14–19) will be discussed here.

To obtain a colony count for bacteria, 1 ml of a well-mixed bacterial suspension (contaminated drinking water in Figure 14–18) is placed into a 99 ml sterile dilution blank. This 99 ml of sterile fluid may be nutrient broth, physiological saline, or distilled water. A dilution of 1 to 100 is produced when 1 unit of a fluid is added to 99 units of sterile diluent. In the ex-

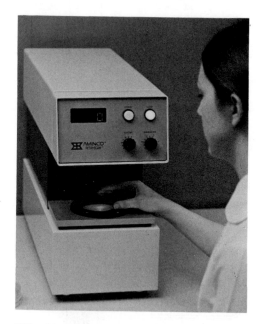

FIG. 14–18. An automatic bacterial colony counter, the Petri-Scan. This device can obtain a colony count from any Petri dish of standard size in one second. The count is flashed on a digital readout visual display (top left-hand corner). (Courtesy of American Instrument Company.)

ample given in Figure 14–18, eventually the water was found to contain 5.5 × 10^5 CFU/ml. The 1 to 100 dilution step, therefore, diluted the original suspension of bacteria from 5.5 × 10^5 to 5.5 × 10^3 CFU/ml, a factor of 100 (10^2). The 1 to 100 dilution may also be expressed as 1/100, or 1 × 10^{-2}. After the dilution step, one or more 1 ml samples are removed and introduced into separate sterile Petri dishes, followed by the addition of melted and cooled nutrient agar. (This step is not shown in the figure, and only one Petri dish per dilution is depicted.) The plates are rotated to ensure proper mixing, and the agar is allowed to solidify. The finished plates are then incubated at a desired temperature. After incubation, it can be observed that confluent growth was obtained with the 1 × 10^{-2} and 1 × 10^{-3} dilutions. This result is represented as being too numerous to count (TNTC). Thus the initial 1/100 dilution was not adequate to obtain the necessary separa-

tion of colonies for counting. Unless some additional information is available to give an indication of the expected numbers of bacteria in the original sample, a series of dilutions must be made. In order to obtain satisfactory results, these dilutions must in turn be plated out in a manner similar to the one described.

The remainder of Figure 14–18 indicates the final aspects of the serial dilution process. A 1 ml sample of the 1/100 dilution is added to a 9 ml dilution blank, which makes a dilution ratio of 1/10 of 1/100, or 1/1000 (10^{-3}). When this procedure is carried still further, 1/10,000 (10^{-4}) and 1/100,000 (10^{-5}) dilutions are produced for plating, incubation, and counting. After incubation, it is evident that only the 1/10,000 dilution has resulted in separating the organisms sufficiently to yield an easily countable plate. This dilution produced a count of 51 CFU/ml.

A good rule of thumb for accuracy is

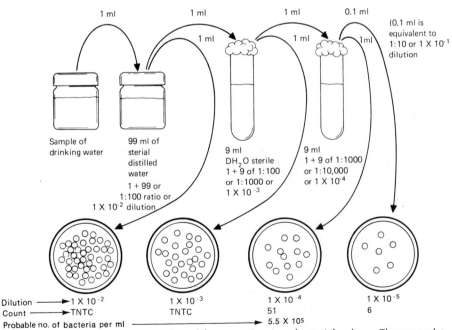

FIG. 14–19. A diagrammatic representation of the procedure used to determine the viable popula- tion in a bacterial culture. The pour-plate tech- nique is used here.

not to count plates with less than 30 or more than 300 colonies. The lower values are affected to a greater extent by the mixing of the dilution blank, and the higher figures may represent a greater proportion of colonies formed by multiple groups of organisms.

To calculate the probable numbers of bacteria per ml in the original sample, it is necessary only to multiply the bacterial colony count by the reciprocals of the dilution and of the volume used. Thus:

$$CFU = \frac{51}{1 \text{ ml} \times 10^{-4}} = 51 \times 1 \times 10,000$$
$$(10,000)$$
$$= 510,000 \text{ or } 5.1 \times 10^{5}$$

The result is the estimated number of bacteria in terms of *colony forming units* (CFU). The latter designation is used rather than absolute numbers, since more than one organism may produce a single colony. This is also true for viral plaques (PFU).

Determining Total Counts of Microorganisms

The method used to obtain total counts of microorganisms in specimens is determined largely by the particular type of microorganism involved. Techniques and equipment which can be used for this purpose include: (1) a direct microscopic count; (2) proportional counting; (3) a counting chamber; and (4) electronic counting.

Direct microscopic count (Breed smear technique). This procedure involves the spreading of 0.01 ml of a well-mixed specimen over a square centimeter (sq cm) area on a glass slide. After drying, substances such as fat from milk, which can affect the accuracy of the determination, can be removed by an appropriate solvent, such as xylene. The average num-ber of microorganisms per field can be determined by using the high dry or oil-immersion objectives. The number obtained is then multiplied by a microscope correction factor (MCF) which takes into account the calibration of this instrument.

This correction factor is calculated according to the following formula:

$$MCF = \frac{\text{area of the smear}}{\text{area of the microscopic field}} \times 100$$

Commercially available ocular micrometers are used to measure the diameter of the microscopic field. Once this value is known, the area can be calculated according to the formula $A = \pi r^2$, where $\pi = 3.142$ and $r =$ the radius of the field. The dilution factor, which takes into account the volume of material used from the sample and adjusts the numbers of microorganisms to that found in 1 ml, is represented by 100 in the MCF calculation. In other words, 100 times the number of organisms found in a 0.01 ml sample will give the number of such microbes expected to be present in 1 ml of the sample studied. This procedure generally involves averaging the counts of microorganisms per field in approximately 50 different fields.

Direct microscopic counts have been used in approximating the quality of various grades of raw and pasteurized milk, and in computing the growth curves of microorganisms. (The latter topic is discussed later in this chapter.)

Unfortunately, direct microscopic counts are not particularly accurate when few microorganisms are present in a specimen—less than 20,000 to 50,000 per ml.

Proportional counting. Since the turn of this century microbiologists have used the technique of proportional counting for estimating microbial populations. This method involves preparing a standardized suspension of yeast cells, or of inert particles such as polystyrene latex spheres, and mixing a definite volume with a definite quantity of an unknown specimen. On examination of the mixture, one can determine the relative numbers of organisms or particles present. If the ratio turns out to be 1:1, then the original unknown sample contained a number of organisms equal to that in the standardized preparation. This method is in use today, especially in situations where the number of virus particles in suspensions must be determined. Ratios are determined with electron microscopy and suitably prepared shadowed specimens.

Counting chamber. In this method, a known volume of a suspension is placed over a calibrated, etched grid contained in a special chamber. With the Petroff-Hauser device (Figure 14–20) the etched lines can be seen on the centrally located surface. This surface is purposely depressed slightly, so that a space of 0.02 mm is formed when the calibrated region is covered with a special cover glass. The counting chamber consists of regular, partitioned, cubical chambers which are of a known volume.

A bacterial suspension to be examined is introduced into this space with the aid of a calibrated pipette, and allowed to settle until the various liquid currents have quieted down. The microorganisms present are counted and their number per unit volume of the suspension is calculated, using an appropriate formula.

Counting chambers can also be used in estimating the total and viable (live) numbers of yeast cells in a suspension. In this case, methylene blue is added to the yeast suspension to act as a *vital dye,* which can distinguish between living and dead cells. Viable yeast cells will be able not only to absorb the dye, but to reduce it to the leuco or colorless form. Thus living cells are colorless, and dead or dying cells are stained blue. As with the Breed smear, it is essential to have large populations in order to obtain a reasonably accurate count.

This method has not proved practical with bacterial cells. Methylene blue or other oxidation-reduction (redox) indicators are limited in this respect.

Electronic counting. This method, used in conjunction with a Coulter Counter (Figure 14–21), involves suspending organisms in a known medium having specific resistance or conductance characteristics. The electronic measure of resistance of the suspending medium is made as it passes through a calibrated opening or orifice. Bacteria or yeasts entering this orifice displace a certain volume of fluid and cause a change in the electrical characteristics, activating the counting device. Counters of this type are used routinely in clinical hematology to count white and red blood cells. Excellent reproducibility and accuracy of results are generally obtained.

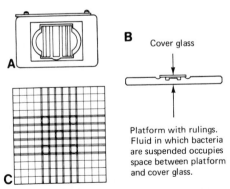

B   Cover glass

Platform with rulings. Fluid in which bacteria are suspended occupies space between platform and cover glass.

FIG. 14–20<u>A</u>. A Petroff-Hauser bacterial counter. <u>B</u>. A vertical section view. <u>C</u>. An enlarged view of the ruled chambers in the center of A. (Courtesy of Arthur H. Thomas Co., Philadelphia.)

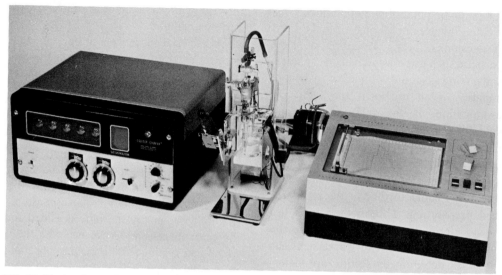

FIG. 14–21. An electronic counting device, the Coulter Counter. (Courtesy of Coulter Electronics, Inc., Hialeah, Florida.)

Most Probable Number

One of the routine functions for any public health department is to examine water supplies for the presence of bacteria indicative of fecal pollution. This is necessary because of the many bacterial, viral, and protozoan diseases which can be transmitted by water. The indicator organisms vary around the world, but the basic principles are the same. In the United States, the presence of *Escherichia coli* in excess of two organisms per 100 ml is indicative of recent fecal pollution and is considered a potential danger. This quantitation can be achieved by a statistical procedure known as the "most probable number" technique (MPN). One means of performing this procedure is to employ 15 lactose fermentation tubes, 5 of which are each inoculated with 10 ml of the water sample. A second set of 5 tubes receieve 1 ml and a third set of 5 tubes are inoculated with 0.1 ml of the sample. The lactose tubes are incubated for 24 to 48 hours at 37°C. The number of coliform organisms per 100 ml of the water is determined by recording the number of fermentation tubes showing the presence of acid and gas for each sample size and comparing these data with a statistical table which was developed by Hoskins in 1934. A representative portion of this table is presented in Table 14–2.

This procedure constitutes a presumptive test for the presence of coliforms in water. Additional tests must be performed to validate results if unsanitary conditions are suspected. Modifications of this procedure have been applied to the estimation of certain viruses in some materials. It also can be used for many different organisms.

Determining the numbers of infective viruses or rickettsia in various types of specimens poses a more difficult problem. In dealing with such parasitic forms a major condition which must be met for their demonstration is the availability of suitable living cells. Detection of viral activity in tissue cultures is discussed more fully in Chapter 13.

Table 14–2   The Application of the
Most Probable Number Technique to
Water Bacteriology

Number of Positive Lactose Broth Tubes			Number of Coliform Organisms per 100 ml of Water
10 ml	1 ml	0.1 ml	
0	0	0	0
0	0	1	2
0	1	0	2
0	1	1	4
1	0	0	2.2
1	0	1	4.4
1	1	0	4.4
1	1	1	6.7

QUESTIONS FOR REVIEW

1. Describe three methods by which you can determine growth in microorganisms.

2. Define:
   a. growth
   b. lag phase of growth
   c. reproduction
   d. $g = \dfrac{t}{n}$
   e. Breed smear technique
   f. lebensraum
   g. MPN
   h. biphasic growth system
   i. proportional counting
   j. continuous cultivation

3. Differentiate between the growth responses of mycoplasma, L-forms, and viruses.

4. What are the stages of the bacteriophage lytic cycle?

5. What is lysogeny?

6. Differentiate between sporulation, dormancy, and germination.

15

Microbial Metabolism

This chapter presents the means by which various forms of life are able to use various biochemicals in the production of energy and as the basic components for growth and reproduction. Selected aspects of carbohydrate metabolism will be discussed to provide a foundation for the interrelationship of carbohydrate, protein, and lipid metabolism. Additional topics to be found in this chapter include: consideration of protein synthesis in the light of recent advances in unraveling the genetic code, brief discussions of methods for measuring metabolism, and various aspects of microbial metabolism. This chapter will emphasize the similarities and differences between metabolic reactions of organisms and show that there is a unity of biochemical activity among life forms.

Processes Involved in Production of the Essential Ingredients for Growth and Reproduction

Glycolysis

The process of *glycolysis* or *dextrose metabolism* is often referred to as the *Embden-Meyerhof-Parnas pathway*. This pathway consists of nine catabolic steps that transform dextrose into energy and organic acids, such as pyruvic and lactic acid, and ethanol. Aerobic glycolysis usually results in more energy production and more extensive breakdown of the sugar, leading to the ultimate oxidation of the dextrose to carbon dioxide and water.

Figure 15–1 shows a simplified version of glycolysis. Dextrose (glucose) may be supplied to the cell of a plant, animal, or microbe by photosynthesis, or in the form of starch, cellulose, or glycogen, or as glucose and maltose. The first step of this pathway is the activation of the sugar molecule by the addition of phosphates. This reaction is accomplished by energy released during the hydrolysis of adenosine triphosphate (ATP). The energy is required for molecular rearrangements; it permits the synthesis of more ATP later, when energy is generated by various oxidation/reduction steps. The molecular rearrangement thus permits the cleavage of a sugar (fructose) diphosphate, resulting in the formation of two 3-carbon compounds—glyceraldehyde phosphate and dihydroxyacetone phosphate. As indicated by the double-headed arrow, these trioses can be changed from one to the other. In the more usual pathway from dextrose to pyruvic acid, two molecules of pyruvic acid are formed for each molecule of dextrose metabolized. With microorganisms, under various conditions differing quantities of glycerol as well as pyruvic acid may be produced.

The process pictured as anaerobic metabolism (Figure 15–1) generates a total of four molecules of ATP during substrate reactions converting dextrose

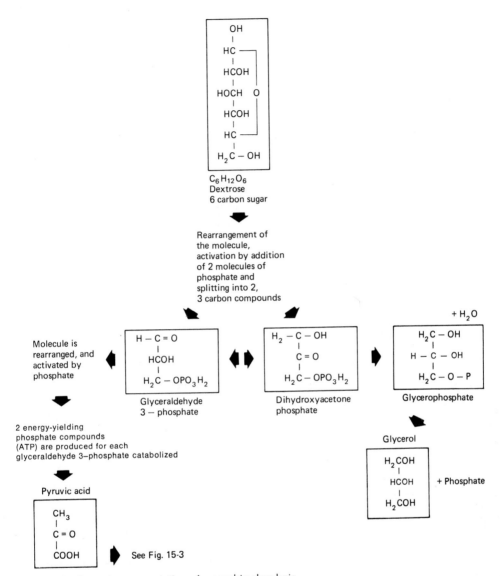

FIG. 15–1. A schematic representation of anaerobic glycolysis.

to pyruvic acid. The ATP molecules are formed subsequent to the formation of the two triose phosphate compounds. Before the entire energy-producing process can begin, two molecules of ATP are required to activate or phosphorylate the dextrose, yielding fructose diphosphate. Thus a net gain of two ATP's results from the anaerobic glycolysis process. These ATP's are then available for various cellular activities, such as nucleic acid synthesis and other energy processes necessary for growth and reproduction.

Anaerobic dextrose catabolism then proceeds, using pyruvic acid as the basic molecule. Some reactions involving pyruvic acid are presented in Figure 15–2. The primary biochemical compounds formed as a result of anaerobic metabolism are lactic acid and ethyl alcohol.

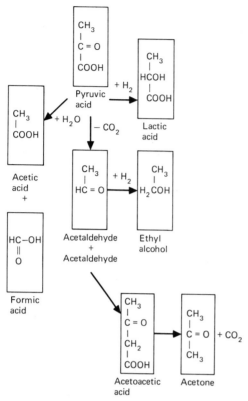

FIG. 15–2. Selected reactions involving pyruvic acid.

During glycolysis, two molecules of nicotine adenine dinucleotide (NAD) were reduced for each molecule of dextrose metabolized.

Lactic acid is utilized in the production of pickles, sauerkraut, and sour cream, while ethyl alcohol constitutes an important part of alcoholic beverages such as beer, whiskey, and wine. (See Chapter 5 for the industrial uses of microorganisms.)

In streptococci and lactobacilli, these reduced coenzymes may then function in the reduction of pyruvic acid to form lactic acid. Yeasts and other microorganisms can use the NADH and pyruvic acid to produce ethyl alcohol. In this case, however, an intermediate decarboxylation (removal of CO_2) from pyruvic acid is

required. The acetaldehyde thus formed can be reduced to alcohol. Under certain conditions two molecules of acetaldehyde combine, producing acetoacetic acid and subsequently acetone.

One other important reaction involving pyruvic acid is the formation of acetic and formic acids. For some time it was thought that this reaction was a simple hydrolysis by the addition of water to pyruvic acid. However, it appears that acetyl CoA (Coenzyme A) and formic acid are produced. The acetyl CoA or "active acetate" is required in aerobic dextrose metabolism (Figure 15–3). The formic acid can be hydrolyzed to yield hydrogen and carbon dioxide.

When organisms can perform the glycolytic reactions under aerobic conditions four times the amount of energy is made available by a more efficient utilization of energy liberated during metabolism. One step following triose phosphate formation is the reduction of a coenzyme, NAD, to NADH. (Reduced forms are identified by a terminal H.) During anaerobic glycolysis, the NADH is used to reduce pyruvic acid to lactic acid. However, in aerobic glycolysis, the NADH is used to reduce the second in a series of coenzymes (flavin adenine dinucleotide), resulting in the progressive reduction of these coenzymes and ultimately oxygen, as pictured in Figure 15–6.

Each pair of electrons going through the electron transport system permits the synthesis of three molecules of ATP. Since two pairs of electrons are generated per dextrose molecule, this adds six ATP's to the two previously formed, thus producing a total of eight.

Krebs (Citric Acid) Cycle

The complete catabolism of dextrose to carbon dioxide and water involves three phases, which have just been described. The initial phase is aerobic glycolysis, and the third is the electron transport system (ETS), which can operate with pairs of electrons produced by either the reactions of glycolysis or those of the second phase of dextrose catabolism, which encompasses the *Krebs cycle.* Hans A. Krebs was the first person to successfully demonstrate the nature and significance of this series of reactions. Krebs and Fritz Lipmann shared the 1953 Nobel Prize for their contributions to the understanding of cellular activities.

Another designation for the series of reactions comprising the Krebs cycle is the *citric acid cycle.* This name is an appropriate one since the 6-carbon compound called citric acid appears at the beginning of each complete "rotation" of the cyclic series reactions. The cycle is called by many authorities "the energy wheel of cellular metabolism."

The Krebs cycle also involves other types of compounds. In addition to the metabolic derivatives of carbohydrates, these include lipids and proteins.

Basically, in the Krebs cycle, citric acid (6-carbon compound) is converted to oxaloacetic acid (4-carbon compound) through a series of oxidation or decarboxylation reactions. The first step or the beginning of a new turn of this cycle involves the addition of acetyl Coenzyme

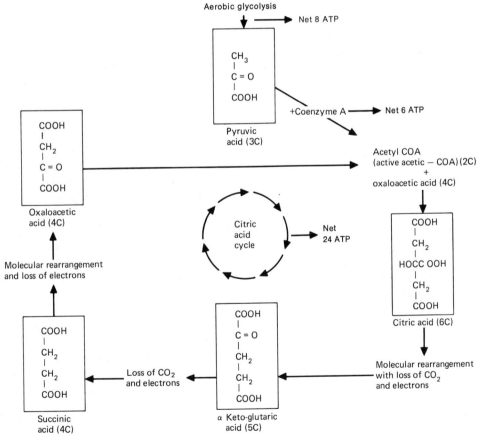

FIG. 15–3. The chain of events in aerobic dextrose metabolism. The major steps in the Krebs or citric acid cycle are also shown. The number of carbons contained in each compound is shown in parentheses, i.e., (5C).

A, an activated 2-carbon derivative obtained through the oxidative decarboxylation of pyruvic acid, to the 4-carbon compound oxaloacetic acid. This reaction results in the formation of citric acid. Coenzyme A (CoA-SH) has a terminal sulfhydryl group, in addition to its other components (Figure 15–4). As a consequence of the transfer of the 2-carbon units by CoA-SH, a high-energy sulfur bond is formed, which stores energy produced from the decarboxylation of pyruvic acid (Figure 15–3). This energy is important in the transfer of activated 2-carbon derivatives into the cycle.

As pictured in Figure 15–3 citric acid is decarboxylated twice, once for each acetyl compound. Each of these reactions yields CO_2 and energized electrons (reduced coenzymes). The citric acid cycle is considered complete and begins again with additional acetyl CoA, when the formation of oxaloacetic acid and four pairs of electrons for the ETS has occurred. These electrons are degraded to a lower energy level in the cytochrome system and three molecules of ATP are generated. This results in a gradual and controlled release of electron energy, rather than a sudden and explosive type of reaction that would be extremely harmful for cells.

In this simplified version of the citric acid cycle there are four electron-yielding reactions. Each pair of electrons which passes through the electron transport sys-

tem yields three ATP molecules. Thus, each pyruvic acid molecule oxidized via this cycle results in the formation of twelve ATP's. Since each molecule of glucose can result in the formation of two pyruvic acid molecules, the production of a total of twenty-four ATP's is possible.

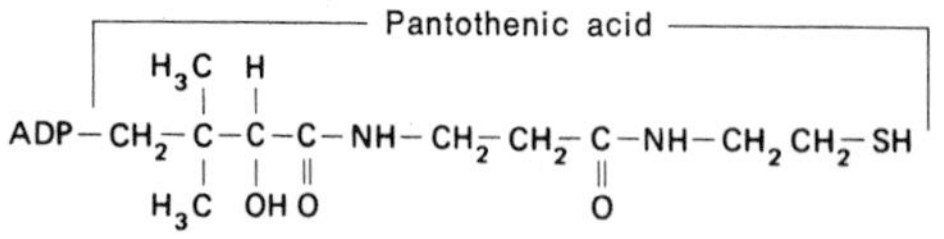

Electron Transport System

This system, which is also known as the *respiratory chain* or *cytochrome system,* is a common pathway for the utilization of electrons formed during a variety of metabolic reactions. It is primarily concerned with aerobic metabolism; however, certain components of the system have been identified with anaerobic organisms.

The component coenzymes, with the one exception of cytochrome oxidase, are termed *anaerobic dehydrogenases,* since they catalyze the reduction of molecules other than oxygen. The reduction of oxygen is carried out by the cytochrome oxidase or cytochrome a_3 molecule.

The cytochrome system consists of three basic biochemical mechanisms for purposes of electron transfer. These are: (1) the reduction of nitrogen-containing cyclic compounds NAD and Flavin Adenine Dinucleotide (FAD); (2) the reduction of the oxygen-containing cyclic compound coenzyme Q; and (3) the reduction of the ferric ion cytochromes. In the case of the first category the active molecule of NAD is the vitamin niacin, while the active molecule in FAD is the vitamin riboflavin. In the second mechanism listed, the active molecule of coenzyme Q is the quinone ring, which is reduced to hydroquinone.

The final category of cytochromes contains a porphyrin structure comparable to chlorophyll, but with iron (Fe) and not magnesium (Mg) as the active component. During electron transfer the

$$\text{ADP}-CH_2-\underset{\underset{H_3C}{|}}{\overset{\overset{H_3C}{|}}{C}}-\underset{\underset{OH}{|}}{\overset{H}{C}}-\underset{\underset{O}{||}}{C}-NH-CH_2-CH_2-\underset{\underset{O}{||}}{C}-NH-CH_2CH_2-SH$$

FIG. 15–4. The structure of coenzyme A. This particular compound is a derivative of adenosine diphosphate (ADP). Attached to ADP is a molecule of pantothenic acid which bears a terminal thiol (-SH) group. Coenzyme A also can be symbolized as CoA-SH.

ferric ion (Fe^{+++}) is converted to ferrous ion (Fe^{++}) for each of the cytochromes through cytochrome oxidase. The term oxidase is used only for those enzymes capable of catalyzing reactions with molecular oxygen. In addition to the iron in cytochrome oxidase, there is evidence that the cuprous ion functions in the final transfer of electrons to oxygen, resulting in the production of water. This flow of electrons creates the consecutive reduction and oxidation cycles (Figure 15–5) that produce sufficient energy to synthesize adenosine triphosphate (ATP).

At least two steps are necessary to yield sufficient energy for converting adenosine diphosphate and inorganic phosphate to ATP [(ADP) + (Pi) = ATP]. This situation can be thought of as a series of dams with hydroelectric power plants, as shown in Figure 15–6.

Running water is necessary to turn the turbines and generate power, but water cannot run until a certain water level is reached behind the dam. As the level rises, sufficient water is available to create power. Since the flow of water proceeds from dam to dam, the distance between them will determine the amount necessary for power. In the electron transport system, three such "dams" are present, and when sufficient "water" (oxidation-reduction reactions) has accumulated, the power can be tapped for ATP synthesis and further progression in the system.

Energy Production During Dextrose (Glucose) Catabolism (A Summary)

The relationship of ATP production (net gain) to the various pathways or portions of pathways concerned with dextrose catabolism can be summed up as follows:

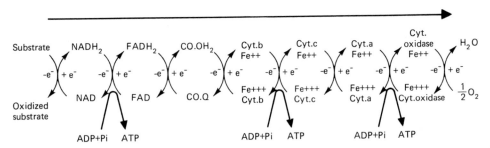

FIG. 15–5. A diagrammatic representation of the electron transport or cytochrome system.

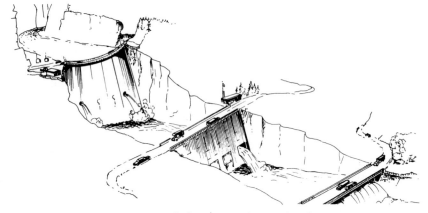

FIG. 15–6. A schematic representation of the electron transport system.

Anaerobic glycolysis

   1 glucose $\longrightarrow$ 2 lactic acids   + 2 ATP

Aerobic glycolysis

   1 glucose $\longrightarrow$ 2 pyruvic acids   + 8 ATP

   2 pyruvic acids $\longrightarrow$ 2 acetyl CoA   + 6 ATP

Citric acid cycle

   2 acetyl CoA $\longrightarrow$ 4 CO_2 + 24 ATP

Thus, anaerobic glycolysis results roughly in a net production of 2 ATPs, whereas the complete aerobic system has a potential of 38 ATPs.

Metabolic Interrelationship of Carbohydrates, Fats, and Proteins

In examining the metabolic pathways of carbohydrates, lipids, proteins, and other significant biochemical compounds, one might conclude that these aspects of metabolism are separate and distinct. Nothing could be further from the truth. A simplified version of the interrelationships between these pathways is given in Figure 15–7.

In the catabolism of dextrose to carbon dioxide, water, and energy, a major intermediate compound, acetyl CoA, can be produced from pyruvic acid (Figure 15–2), as previously discussed. Acetyl CoA is also a catabolic product of fat metabolism. Moreover, it is an important precursor in the synthesis of fatty acids. The interrelationship of fatty acid synthesis and dextrose catabolism is well illustrated by the dependence of this process upon glycerol, which is an alternate product of glycolysis (Figure 15–1).

Acetyl CoA can also be obtained from proteins. For example, the amino acid alanine can be deaminated to yield pyruvic acid and subsequently acetyl CoA (Figure 15–8).

An additional example of the inter-

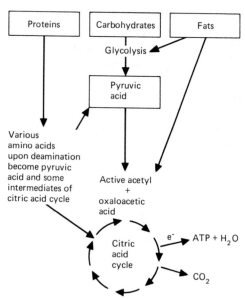

FIG. 15–7. The interrelationship between the metabolic pathways of carbohydrates, lipids, and proteins.

relationship of protein synthesis and dextrose catabolism is the incorporation into amino acids of pyruvic acid and the citric acid cycle intermediates, alpha-keto glutaric and oxaloacetic acids. The addition of an amino (NH_2) group converts these compounds into the building blocks of protein. Conversely, deamination of the amino acids glutamic and aspartic yields the citric acid cycle intermediates, alpha-keto glutaric and oxaloacetric acids. Many of the steps in glycolysis are reversible, so that dextrose units are available for combination into starch, glycogen, or cellulose. Thus metabolic intermediates

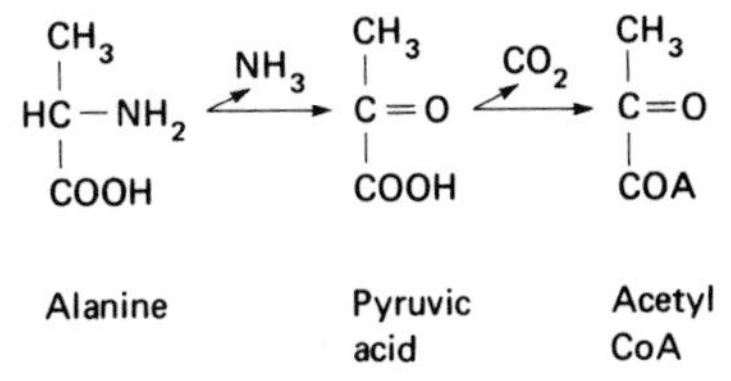

$$
\begin{array}{ccc}
\underset{\text{Alanine}}{\begin{array}{c} CH_3 \\ | \\ HC-NH_2 \\ | \\ COOH \end{array}}
& \xrightarrow[]{NH_3}
\underset{\substack{\text{Pyruvic} \\ \text{acid}}}{\begin{array}{c} CH_3 \\ | \\ C=O \\ | \\ COOH \end{array}}
& \xrightarrow[]{CO_2}
\underset{\substack{\text{Acetyl} \\ \text{CoA}}}{\begin{array}{c} CH_3 \\ | \\ C=O \\ | \\ COA \end{array}}
\end{array}
$$

FIG. 15–8. Deamination of alanine.

or carbohydrates, fats, and proteins are used to create energy and building blocks for more carbohydrates, fats, and proteins. In this manner, the food digested by living beings becomes distinctively part of them.

Protein Synthesis

Probably one of the greatest scientific accomplishments of the decade from 1960 to 1970 was the careful delineation of the steps involved in the process of protein synthesis. Chief among the critical aspects of this work was the initial "breaking" of the genetic code, or nucleotide language, reported by Nirenberg in 1961. The scheme of protein synthesis presented in Figure 15–9 represents the current knowledge in this subject area.

Briefly, messenger RNA (mRNA) carrying the genetic code for a particular protein is produced in the nucleus or in a plastid such as a mitochondrion or chloroplast. This process is known as transcription. It is the synthesis of an mRNA complementary to one strand, the "sense strand," of a DNA molecule in which the DNA functions as a template or pattern (Figure 15–9A). A code word, or codon, consisting of a nucleotide sequence complementary to the sequence of the DNA strand thereby is formed. Transcription is under the control of a DNA-dependent enzyme, RNA polymerase. The enzyme appears to bind particularly to specific nucleotide sequences, called promotor regions, in the DNA molecule. Such

promotors serve as start signals for the transcription of single genes and sometimes groups of genes called operons. (Operons will be discussed later in this chapter.) The mRNA then passes from its site of formation to the ribosomes, which are nucleoprotein particles (see Chapter 8 for a description of these cellular structures).

Decoding the information contained in mRNA is referred to as translation. It consists of two general steps, one of which is ribosome-independent and the other, ribosome-dependent. In the former process, free amino acids are activated through enzymatic reactions involving adenosine triphosphate (ATP) and are coupled to soluble or transfer RNA (tRNA) (Figure 15–9B). For each amino acid there are not only one or more specific activating enzymes but also one and sometimes several different tRNA molecules. Each tRNA molecule contains an anticodon, a sequence of three nucleotide bases that can pair with a complementary codon in an mRNA molecule (Figure 15–9B). Once these reactions have occurred, the amino acids diffuse to the ribosome and enter the ribosome-dependent phase of the translation process.

During the time that a protein molecule is being synthesized, tRNA is continuously released and made available for use by additional amino acids. There seems to be a degree of specificity in the coupling reaction between tRNA and a particular amino acid.

The major function of ribosomes in the second phase of translation is to orient the mRNA and the incoming tRNA complex (tRNA and activated amino acid) so that the information contained in an mRNA molecule can be correctly converted into the amino sequence of a protein molecule (Figure 15–9B). The ribosome-dependent process can be divided into the three

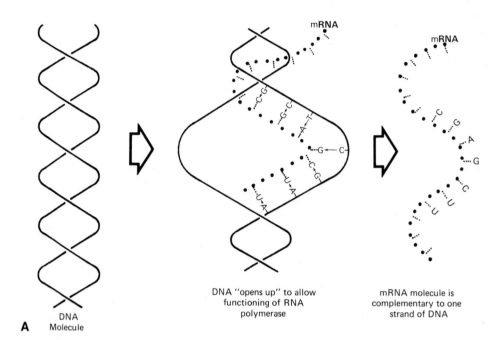

DNA "opens up" to allow
functioning of RNA
polymerase

mRNA molecule is
complementary to one
strand of DNA

A   DNA
Molecule

FIG. 15–9. A diagrammatic representation of protein synthesis. _A_. Transcription, the formation of a messenger RNA molecule. _B₁_. A transfer RNA molecule. _B₂_. Translation. The processes of decoding and tRNA binding are shown.

phases of initiation, elongation, and termination. The initiation phase involves ribosomal attachment to the appropriate portion of the mRNA and ribosomal binding to the initiator tRNA molecule. In the elongation phase, the ribosome travels along the mRNA, catalyzing the translation of the molecule. In the termination phase, the protein product is finished and subsequently released.

The mRNA is labile, and must be replaced fairly often. This lability may be a mechanism to assure that one particular protein is not overproduced. With many mRNA's being synthesized and released to the cytoplasm, the degradation of existing mRNA makes ribosomes available for the synthesis of whatever structural or catalytic (enzyme) type of protein the cell may need.

Genetic Code
When it had been determined that DNA was indeed the magic genetic substance

(see Chapter 16, Transformation), the question was posed as to what sequence of the 4 nucleotides would be necessary to code for each of the 20 amino acids found in proteins. A code using all 4 nucleic acid units would permit 256 combinations. A code using only 3 bases would allow 64 combinations. The doublet code, 2 bases with 16 combinations, would allow for only 16 amino acids. This arrangement then would represent a ratio of 1 base pair to 1 amino acid.

The triplet code with its 64 combinations would permit the 20 needed combinations, with an excess of 44 for alternate combinations to code for certain amino acids. Moreover, a triplet code also would provide some non-coding combinations to act as spacers or regulatory areas. The investigations of Nirenberg and others have demonstrated that the triplet code is indeed the operating genetic system.

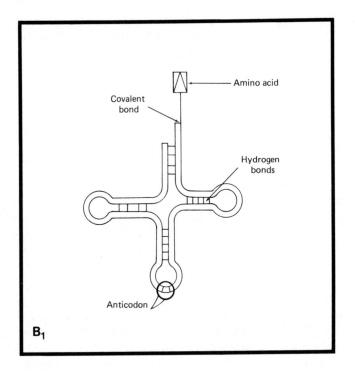

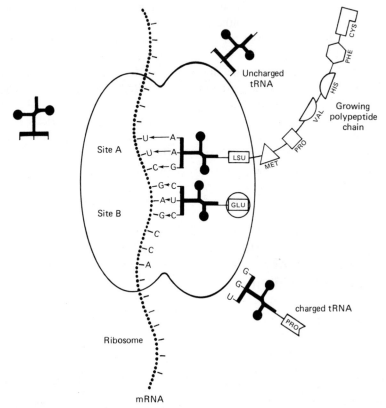

Nirenberg found that synthetic RNA trinucleotides would stimulate the incorporation of specific amino acids onto ribosomes. The first triplets studied, UUU, AAA, and CCC, directed the binding of phenylalanine, lysine, and proline, respectively (see Table 15–1), when experimental protein synthesis was carried out in cell-free systems using combinations of ribosomes and mRNA, sRNA and DNA of *Escherichia coli*. Alternate codes were found for some amino acids.

Examples of representative nucleotide sequences, taken from the 1965 report by Bernfeld and Nirenberg, are shown in Table 15–1. Thus, the code for a single amino acid may be established by as few as one or as many as four arrangements of nucleotides. The 64 possible combinations allows for an average of 3 combinations per amino acid. The data suggest that most amino acids have two sequences. Therefore, approximately 40 of these are utilized in protein synthesis, while the other 24 are available for additional needs of the cell.

The genetic code appears to be universal. Similar code sequences are used in organisms as different as bacteria and mammals. The reason for this universality is not difficult to perceive if one considers that any given form of life must synthesize a large number of protein molecules with similar functions. Enzymes would constitute a good example of such molecules.

Control and Regulation of Metabolism Feedback or End-product Inhibition

Feedback inhibition refers to the control of a series of enzymatic reactions (metabolic pathways) by the end product of the pathway involved. H. E. Umbarger studied the synthesis of the amino acid isoleucine in *Escherichia coli*. The results of

Table 15–1   Selected Amino Acids and the RNA Trinucleotide Sequences which Affect their Binding into Protein

Amino Acid	Alternate Coding[a]
Arginine	CGU, CGC, CGA, AGA
Lysine	AAA
Phenylalanine	UUU, UUC
Proline	CCU, CCC
Serine	UCU, UCC, UCG

[a] A=adenine, C=cytosine, G=guanine, U=uracil.

his investigations demonstrated that when extra quantities of an amino acid are added to a bacterial culture actively synthesizing that particular amino acid, further synthesis of the compound ceases. Thus, by controlling the amount of the isoleucine made available to a culture, the pathway for this compound can be either started or stopped.

Studies of this control mechanism using isolated enzymes showed that the end product, isoleucine, inhibits the activity of the first enzyme involved in the pathway leading to its synthesis (Figure 15–10). As long as the amino acid is required for protein synthesis or for other metabolic reactions, synthesis continues. When the various reactions utilizing isoleucine stop and the compound begins to accumulate, it interferes with the particular enzyme responsible for starting the pathway.

On examining the molecular structure of the end product (isoleucine) and the substrate of the first enzyme (threonine) in the pathway, one might conclude that the configuration of these two compounds

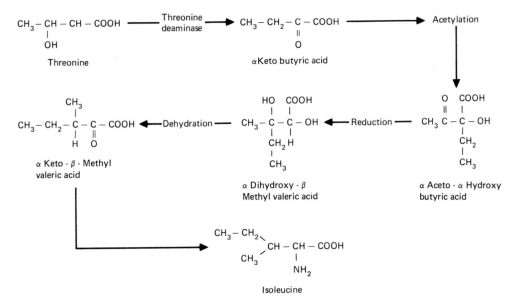

FIG. 15–10. The isoleucine synthetic pathway.

is sufficiently analogous to allow isoleucine to fit into the active site of the enzyme and thus block the activity. However, this does not appear to be the case.

Evidence proposed by Changeaux indicates that the inhibition is "allosteric" or indirect; the isoleucine binds as a site different from the active one. Changeaux showed that the first enzyme, threonine deaminase, could be partially altered by heat denaturation or mutation to desensitize the regulatory site. In this case, the pathway would function continuously and isoleucine would accumulate beyond normal levels.

Isoleucine synthesis is one of many examples of regulatory mechanisms involved in metabolic reactions. The presence of such regulation makes one think of a cell as a finely tuned automatic system for the performance of life processes. Mutations can occur that alter the function of enzymes. The cell in this case often can compensate for this lack or simply rely on the environment to provide a particular compound essential to its nutrition. Mutations or biochemical de-

fects can also cause an accumulation of certain chemicals which may become toxic to the cell. Such metabolic defects occur in humans as well as in other life forms. One example of this type of situation in humans is phenylketonuria (PKU).

The Operon Concept

Feedback or end-product inhibition represents control of metabolism at the enzyme level. A given enzyme beginning a pathway is turned off when a particular metabolite accumulates, then turned on when the concentration decreases. This is a clever system, but apparently it doesn't prevent the synthesis of the enzyme or enzymes involved in the pathway. It would seem reasonable that cells should have a means of regulating the synthesis of enzymes they may need at any particular time. Logically, this control would operate at the level of DNA in protein synthesis. Previously it was mentioned that there were approximately 24 trinucleotide

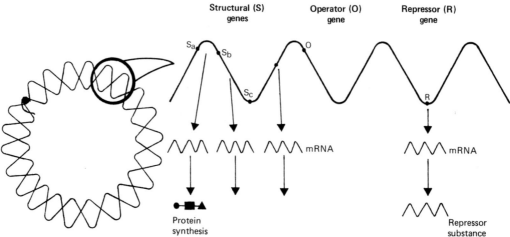

FIG. 15–11. A generalized model of an operon. *Repressible operon:* The end product reacts with a repressor substance which causes the operator gene(s) to stop formation of mRNA for enzyme synthesis. *Inducible operon:* The compound (or related compound) to be metabolized reacts with a repressor substance and causes the operator gene(s) to permit the formation of mRNA for enzyme synthesis.

sequences not available for protein synthesis. These triplets might well serve as regulatory genes used to end a particular message sequence in the DNA. Such regulatory systems have been studied in procaryotes and are known as *operons* (Figure 15–11).

Operons have been shown to be of two types: one in which a cluster of genes controls the synthesis of enzymes normally present and the other in which genes control the synthesis of enzymes normally absent. These operons are known as *repressible* and *inducible* operons, respectively.

A general model for an operon is presented in Figure 15–11. The operon consists of structural genes and the operator gene or genes. The structural genes have the information to cause the synthesis of the enzymes that perform the various steps in the particular metabolic pathway. The operator is a switch that can permit the formulation of mRNA from the structural genes (DNA). In addition, there is a control substance produced from one or more regulator genes. In the repressible operon, the operator or switch is in the "on" position. An end product of the particular pathway can react with the control substance, called regulator, and turn the operator off. No mRNA is produced in this case and the existing mRNA for these enzymes will gradually degrade and stop synthesis of this enzyme. This system is also known as end-product repression. In the inducible operon, the operator is in the "off" position due to the presence of the control substance called repressor. Apparently a compound to be metabolized reacts with repressor, allowing the operator to turn on and permit mRNA to be made for the synthesis of the required enzymes.

Measurement of Metabolism

Metabolic studies have shown how antibiotics may interfere with microbial growth and also how microorganisms can alter their metabolism so as to become resistant to these drugs. They have also

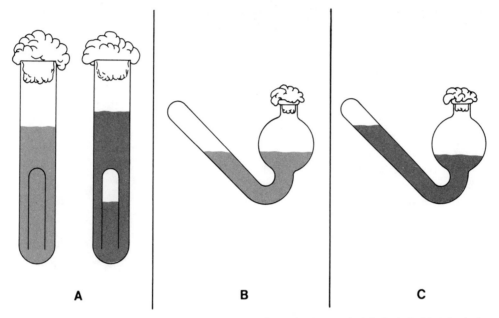

A   B   C

FIG. 15–12. Comparison of gas production from sugar fermentations. _A._ Uninoculated Durham fermentation tube and the results of active fermentation. Note the displacement of the fluid from the inverted vial. _B._ A Smith tube before the addition of an alkali compound. _C._ The results after addition of an alkali compound.

demonstrated some basic differences between pathogenic and non-pathogenic bacteria. The results of such investigations are being used to develop faster methods for the identification of clinically significant microorganisms. The methods which have been chosen for discussion are: (1) simple fermentation test; (2) manometry; (3) oxidation-reduction activity; (4) the use of radioisotopes; and (5) chromatography.

Simple Fermentation Tests

When an organism has the necessary enzymes to ferment a particular sugar, we are generally able to observe this fact by detecting the production of organic acids, with or without gas. This can be accomplished either by incorporating some nontoxic pH indicator into the medium, or by adding it after growth. A decrease in pH indicates the production of organic acids (Color photograph 38). In liquid media, gas production can be observed by the presence of obvious bubbling or by trapping the gas in an inverted small glass tube (Figure 15–12A). This tube, known as a *Durham tube,* is placed upside down in the fermentation medium prior to autoclaving. It becomes filled with the medium due to the vacuum created by heating and subsequent cooling.

Generally, the Durham tube indicates only the presence or absence of gas. The *Smith fermentation tube* (Figure 15–12B) can be used to measure the relative proportions of different gases produced. Since certain microorganisms will often produce more gas than the Durham tube is capable of holding, the Smith tube is used to obtain a reasonably accurate measurement of the volume of gas produced. This can be accomplished by measuring the portion of tube containing gas before (Figure 15–12B) and after (Figure 15–12C) the addition of alkali to absorb CO_2. Thus one can determine the relative amounts of CO_2 produced. The remaining gas consists primarily of H_2 therefore the measurements are compared on the basis of the ratio of H_2 to CO_2.

Manometry

Manometry, or differential gas pressure measurement, can be used in any closed system where gas is either consumed or evolved. The Warburg apparatus (Figure 15–13), which can be used to make such determinations, consist of several manometer-flask systems. A typical flask is shown in Figure 15–14 and a close-up of one type of manometer is shown in Figure 15–15.

The Warburg apparatus consists of a constant-temperature water bath and an agitating device to shake reaction flasks which are immersed in it. Shaking mixes the reactants well and enhances the dif-

FIG. 15–14. A Warburg reaction flask. (Courtesy of Precision Scientific Co.)

FIG. 15–13. A Warburg apparatus for manometric measurement. (Courtesy of Precision Scientific Co.)

FIG. 15–15. A Warburg manometer. (Courtesy of Bronwill Scientific, Inc.)

fusion of gas into and out of the reaction mixture.

To demonstrate how measurements are made, let us assume that the following conditions have been carried out: (1) A resting (non-multiplying) suspension of *Escherichia coli* has been placed into the flask around the raised central well, (2) Alkali has been introduced into the well for the purpose of absorbing CO_2, (3) A solution of some organic acid has been placed into the side arm so that it is not in direct contact with the organisms to be studied.

To examine the rate of hydrogen production under anaerobic conditions, the system is assembled, flushed with sterile nitrogen gas, and allowed to reach temperature and gas pressure equilibrium in the water bath. After a certain period, during which time any changes in pressure have been recorded on the manometer, the flask is tipped to cause the organic acid to mix with the test organisms. Since CO_2 is absorbed in the center well by the alkali, any other gas that has been produced (presumably H_2) will increase the system's pressure, and be evident on the manometer. By regularly recording the increasing pressure, the information necessary to calculate the rate of gas production under these particular conditions is collected.

Similar experiments can be performed with other materials, including cell-free extracts, tissue homogenates, and fractionated extracts of homogenates. Thus one may determine the effect of atmospheric composition, added co-factors, or various metabolites on any biochemical system capable of consuming or producing gas.

Oxidation-Reduction (Redox) Activity

Under anaerobic conditions, the metabolic activity of cells can be monitored in several ways. One such procedure in-

volves adding an electron acceptor such as methylene blue to a resting suspension and then exposing it to a vacuum to remove air from the medium. Under these conditions, metabolic activity is monitored by noting the rate of decolorization of the dye. During the operation of metabolic pathways electrons are transported by various intermediates and dehydrogenases, which can use methylene blue as the electron acceptor, thus causing it to form leuco-methylene blue. A device for performing these tests, the *Thunberg Tube,* is shown in Figure 15–16. T. Thunberg reported his observations concerning the presence of dehydrogenases in various tissues under anaerobic conditions in 1920.

To determine the presence of a particular dehydrogenase, a specific substrate is placed in the side arm. A common source of electrons in biological systems is the Kreb's cycle intermediate, succinic acid. If succinic acid dehydrogenase is present in a particular unknown system, the resting suspension will remove electrons from the substrate to methylene blue with some intermediate steps. The loss of the electron acceptor's color indicates the presence of that particular dehydrogenase. Using properly controlled studies, one can determine:

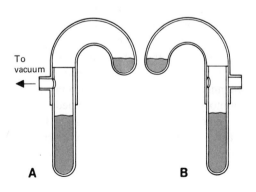

FIG. 15–16. The Thunberg Tube.

(1) possible metabolic pathways; (2) the effect of various respiratory inhibitors; and (3) blocks in metabolic pathways.

Radioisotopes

Some of the elements that make up biochemical compounds, such as carbon, nitrogen, oxygen, and phosphorus, can exist in several forms, called *isotopes*. Isotopes of an element have the same atomic number but different atomic masses. Certain isotopes are stable and can be detected by these differences in mass. Other isotopes are unstable; as they deteriorate, various radioactive particles—alpha, beta, and gamma rays—are released. These can be detected by radiation counters or by their effect on photographic emulsions. Table 15–2 lists some of the common isotopes used in biochemical research and their respective half-lives (the time required to lose half their radioactivity).

Metabolic studies of microbes using radioisotopes.

Melvin Calvin began his studies on the pathway of carbon in photosynthesis in 1946, using $C^{14}O_2$, radioactive carbon dioxide. With algae as the test system, $C^{14}O_2$ was introduced into the atmosphere of the growing microorganisms. Periodically the photosynthetic process was briefly stopped by addition of alcohol to remove small samples of compounds formed. The various carbon compounds of the algae were then isolated, and those containing C^{14} were determined by their radioactivity. In this manner the pathway of carbon in the photosynthesis cycle was mapped.

Another example involved the tritium (H^3) labeled thymidine. John Cairns was able by the use of thymidine to obtain an autoradiograph (photographic record) of what he called the replicating "chromosome" (more accurately termed a *gen-*

Table 15–2   Common Isotopes Used in Biochemistry

Element	Radioisotope	Half-Life
Carbon (C^{12})	C^{14}	5,570 years
Hydrogen (H^1)	H^3	12.2 years
Sulfur (S^{32})	S^{35}	87.1 days
Iron ($Fe^{55.8}$)	Fe^{59}	45 days
Phosphorus ($P^{30.9}$)	P^{32}	14.3 days
Iodine ($I^{126.9}$)	I^{131}	8 days

ome) of *Escherichia coli*. Cairns first fed the nucleic acid precursor to *Escherichia coli,* and later lysed the bacteria cell and very carefully removed the bacterial DNA to photographic plates. After a two-month exposure, the autoradiograph shown in Figure 15–17 was obtained. It shows the circular nature and mode of replication (please refer to Chapter 16) of the organism's genome.

Chromatography

The term *chromatography* refers to procedures that separate various components of a mixture when that mixture is forced to migrate with two or more solvents in a solid matrix, such as filter paper or silicon-coated glass. Under these conditions one solvent is adsorbed to the matrix and the remaining solvents remain mobile. As the solvents seep through the matrix, different conditions for adsorption of the mixture's components occur, and the components separate.

The major initial contribution in this area was made by Michael Tswett in 1906. By running an ether solution of chlorophyll through a column of calcium carbonate he was able to get various colored pigments to separate. When another solvent was passed through the column, the separation was nearly complete.

Chromatography can be performed with various solvent mixtures on filter paper, silica, or cellulose-coated glass, or in columns containing various solid matrices.

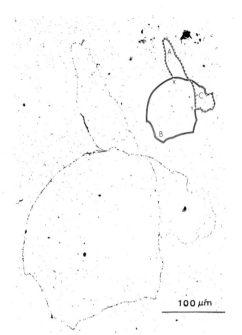

FIG. 15–17. An autoradiograph of *Escherichia coli* DNA. (From Cairns, J.: *Cold Spring Harbor Symp. Quant. Biol.*, **28**:43–46, 1963.)

Gas chromatography is, in essence, a form of column chromatography used for the separation of gases or vaporized chemicals, with some inert carrier gas as the mobile phase. As the carrier gas passes from the column, it enters a detector, which commonly uses the thermal differences of the separated material from the inert gas to give evidence of that particular material. Generally the detector plots this information on a graph. Materials can be identified by their time of detection under particular conditions, as compared to known materials. Gas chromatography has been used in the identification of microorganisms.

Autotrophic and Heterotrophic Metabolism

The differentiation between autotrophic and heterotrophic types of microbial metabolism is based upon the capacity of organisms to use carbon dioxide as the major carbon source for the synthesis of required biochemical compounds. Autotrophs have this ability, while heterotrophs do not. Both groups are further classified into nutritional types according to the means used to obtain energy for growth and metabolism (Table 15–3).

Autotrophic Microorganisms

Photosynthetic autotrophs. The photosynthetic bacteria possess various chlorophylls that are chemically similar to those found in plants. Photosynthetic pigments in bacteria are designated *bacteriochlorophyll-a, -b, -c,* and *-d,* to distinguish them from the plant pigment *chlorophyll-a.* In addition to the bacteriochlorophylls, photosynthetic organisms also have various carotenoid pigments which impart coloration to their colonies; the colors include yellow to orange-brown, red, pink, reddish purple, and violet. Such pigmentation is largely dependent upon the type and concentration of carotenoid present. Green bacteria also contain carotenoids, but these compounds, which are light yellow, do not mask the green bacteriochlorophyll.

In addition to coloring the photosynthetic bacteria, carotenoids absorb light energy, which is then transferred to the bacteriochlorophyll for use in photosynthesis. Unlike the photosynthetic process in green plants, bacterial photosynthesis does not result in the production of oxygen. In algae, the energy absorbed from light by chlorophyll is used to split water molecules, yielding free oxygen and hydrogen ions. The hydrogen serves to reduce nicotinamide adenine dinucleotide phosphate (NADP) and is thereby made available for reducing additional substrates and for the electron transport system, thus bringing about the production of adenosine triphosphate (ATP). Some of the reduced nicotinamide adenine di-

Table 15–3   Classification of Microorganisms by Nutritional Types

Type	Energy Source	Primary Carbon Sources	Selected Electron Sources	Representative Genera
Photosynthetic autotroph	Light	CO_2	H_2S	*Chlorobium* *Chromatium*
Photosynthetic heterotroph	Light	CO_2 and organic substances	Organic substances	*Rhodospirillum* *Rhodopseudomonas*
Chemosynthetic autotroph	Oxidation reactions	CO_2	H_2S	*Beggiatoa*
			S	*Thiobacillus*
			H_2	*Hydrogenomonas*
			Fe^{++}	*Ferrobacillus*
			CH_4	*Pseudomonas*
			CO	*Carboxydomonas*
Chemosynthetic heterotroph	Oxidation reactions	Organic substances	Organic substances	Most microorganisms

nucleotide phosphate (NADPH) and ATP are required for the fixation of carbon dioxide to form carbohydrate and cell material. Thus the energy from light absorption by chlorophyll results in the oxidation of water:

$$2H_2O \rightarrow 4H + O_2 \uparrow$$

and the reduction of CO_2:

$$CO_2 + 2\,NADPH + 3ATP \longrightarrow Cell\ material + H_2O.$$

The initial step in the fixation of CO_2 is the reaction of this compound and ribulose diphosphate to yield two molecules of phosphoglyceric acid. Thus starts the photosynthetic CO_2 fixation cycle. Phosphoglyceric acid is subsequently reduced to glyceraldehyde phosphate, which participates in the reversed glycolysis pathway with the ultimate production of glucose and starch. The newly formed carbohydrate can be utilized for energy and growth materials. The photosynthetic cycle is complete when some glyceraldehyde phosphate condenses to

yield ribulose diphosphate to combine with additional CO_2.

The photosynthetic bacteria do not oxidize water in the preliminary steps of their cycle, and therefore cannot produce oxygen. These organisms must oxidize other electron donor compounds, including hydrogen sulfide (H_2S) and hydrogen (H_2). These two sets of reactions, which result in the fixation of CO_2, can be shown as follows:

$$CO_2 + 2\,H_2S \longrightarrow Cell\ material + H_2O + 2S$$

and

$$CO_2 + 2\,H_2 \longrightarrow Cell\ material + H_2O$$

The sulfide oxidation may result in the accumulation of elemental sulfur (S) within or outside of the cells. When sulfide is depleted, the sulfur is oxidized, resulting in the production of sulfuric acid.

Chemosynthetic autotrophs.   These nonphotosynthetic organisms rely on the oxidation of inorganic compounds for the energy necessary to fix CO_2 as the sole carbon source. Such materials may be hydrogen or hydrogen sulfide, which also are used by photosynthetic bacteria. Other possible sources include ammonia, nitrites, and iron-containing substances. Representative reactions and bacteria capable of performing these reactions are presented in Table 15–4.

Heterotrophic Microorganisms

Photosynthetic heterotrophs. The bacteria comprising this unusual category are facultative in terms of oxygen requirements. Anaerobic conditions must be present when the photosynthetic process is being used to obtain energy. This is also true for photosynthetic autotrophs. However, unlike the autotrophic organisms, the heterotrophs' sources of electrons are alcohols, fatty acids, and other organic acids. When growing aerobically, photosynthetic heterotrophs must be grown in the dark. Under these conditions such organisms are, in essence, the same as chemosynthetic heterotrophs, a class that includes most microorganisms and members of the animal kingdom.

Chemosynthetic heterotrophs. These microorganisms are quite varied in their metabolism. However, they all perform the reactions presented under the headings of the metabolism of carbohydrates, proteins, and lipids in this chapter. The energy-yielding metabolism noted was primarily that of respiration, which was defined as the process utilizing biological oxidation with molecular oxygen as the ultimate electron acceptor. Two other processes are recognized—fermentation and anaerobic respiration.

Fermentation. Fermentation can be defined as the anaerobic decomposition of carbohydrates involving organic compounds as ultimate electron acceptors. Thus a fermentable substance often yields both oxidizable and reducible metabolites. Glucose is an example of such a compound.

During glycolysis, glucose, a 6-carbon sugar, was oxidized to two molecules of pyruvic acid, a 3-carbon compound (Figure 15–1). Fermenting organisms may reduce the pyruvic acid to lactic acid as the sole or primary end product (Figure 15–2). Such organisms are called homofermentative, and include species of Bacillus, Lactobacillus, and Streptococcus. Microorganisms that may produce lactic acid as well as acetic, formic, and other acids, possibly ethanol, other alcohols, and acetone are referred to as being heterofermentative. This group includes yeasts, other fungi, and bacterial species belonging to the Enterobacteriaceae family, and the genera of Clostridium and Streptococcus.

Two metabolic pathways peculiar to microorganisms which are intimately in-

Table 15–4   Energy Production by the Oxidation of Inorganic Compounds

Representative Bacterial Genera	Energy-Yielding Reactions
Ferrobacillus	$4 Fe^{++} + 4 H^+ + O_2 \longrightarrow 4 Fe^{+++} + 2 H_2O$
Hydrogenomonas	$2 H_2 + O_2 \longrightarrow 2 H_2O$
Nitrobacter	$2 NO_2^- + O_2 \longrightarrow 2 NO_3^=$
Nitrosomonas	$2 NH_3 + 3 O_2 \longrightarrow 2 NO_2^- + 2 H^+ + 2 H_2O$
Thiobacillus	$2 H_2S + O_2 \longrightarrow 2 S + 2 H_2O$
	$2 S + 3 O_2 + 2 H_2O \longrightarrow 2 SO_4^= + 4 H^+$

volved with glycolysis are the *hexose monophosphate shunt (HMP)* and the *Entner-Doudoroff (ED) pathway.* The HMP is associated with some heterofermentative organisms, e.g., *Bacillus subtilis, Escherichia coli, Leuconostoc mesenteroides,* and *Streptococcus faecalis.* Slight variations of the HMP occur in conjunction with, or instead of, portions of the glycolytic pathway. For example, with *L. mesenteroides,* glucose phosphate is oxidized to phosphogluconic acid. This latter compound is decarboxylated, dephosphorylated, and ultimately used in the production of lactic acid and ethanol. In contrast to glycolysis, this pathway yields approximately one third the growth obtained when glucose phosphate is metabolized in glycolysis. However, when the HMP pathway is used in conjunction with glycolysis, it can serve as a source of ribose phosphate and other pentoses used for cell growth. In addition, the pathway permits catabolism of these 5-carbon sugars.

In the second deviation from classical glycolysis, the Entner-Doudoroff pathway, phosphogluconic acid loses a molecule of water to form keto-deoxyphosphogluconic acid. This compound then is cleaved to yield pyruvic acid and triose phosphate. *Pseudomonas lindneri* utilizes this pathway to produce two molecules of ethanol by decarboxylation and dephosphorylation of the triose phosphate, with reduction and decarboxylation of the pyruvic acid.

The fermentation of non-carbohydrate compounds can be illustrated by the action of *Clostridium* spp. on amino acids. In one kind of amino acid fermentation, the *Stickland reaction,* two different amino acids participate. One is oxidized, while the other is reduced. The overall reaction can be represented as follows:

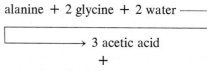

alanine + 2 glycine + 2 water ⟶

⟶ 3 acetic acid
+
carbon dioxide + 3 ammonia

The alanine is oxidized and deaminated to yield pyruvic acid and ammonia. The pyruvic acid is further oxidized and decarboxylated to yield acetic acid and carbon dioxide. During this time, glycine is reduced and deaminated to produce acetic acid and ammonia.

Anaerobic respiration. Anaerobic respiration is defined as the process utilizing biological oxidations in which an inorganic compound other than oxygen serves as the ultimate electron acceptor. Such compounds include carbonates, nitrates, and sulfates. Many facultative anaerobic bacteria can reduce nitrate to nitrite under anaerobic conditions. This type of reaction permits some continued growth when free oxygen is absent, but the accumulation of nitrite is eventually toxic to the organism. Certain species of *Bacillus* and *Pseudomonas* are able to continue the reduction to gaseous nitrogen. This process is called *denitrification,* and can only occur when these aerobic organisms are grown under anaerobic conditions. In contrast, the organisms that reduce sulfate and carbonate are strictly anaerobic. *Desulfovibrio desulfuricans* reduces sulfate to hydrogen sulfide as a consequence of the oxidation of carbohydrate to acetic acid. *Methanobacterium omelianskii* is able to reduce carbon dioxide to methane as the result of a similar oxidation of carbohydrate to acetic acid. The accumulation of acetic acid by these organisms indicates the lack of a mechanism to further oxidize acetic acid which may be produced from pyruvic acid by oxidative decarboxylation.

The reduction of "bound oxygen" in anaerobic respiration with nitrate, sulfate, and carbonate involves cytochrome-containing electron transport systems comparable to that illustrated for respiration.

Consequences of Microbial Metabolism

In addition to various industrial applications utilizing microorganisms, a major consequence of microbial growth and metabolism is the participation of these forms of life in the natural cycles associated with animals and plants. Representative cycles are described below.

The Natural Metabolic Cycles

The earth's supplies of carbon, oxygen, nitrogen, phosphorus, and sulfur are in a constant state of dynamic interaction. These elements undergo natural cycles of oxidized and reduced, inorganic and organic forms. The carbon and oxygen cycle (Figure 15–18) and the nitrogen cycle (Figure 15–19) have been selected for discussion here.

Carbon and oxygen cycle. These two elements are intimately involved in a single cycle. In the earlier discussion of plant and algal photosynthesis, it was noted that light energy is used to split water for the production of oxygen and the concomitant release of hydrogen for the ultimate reduction of carbon dioxide. Various plants and algae are digested and assimilated by animals and certain microorganisms for utilization in their processes of growth and metabolism. This plant and algae organic material are converted into useful compounds in animals and microorganisms. Not only do all of these forms of life respire and/or ferment the various biochemical compounds with the release of CO_2 and H_2O, but they in turn die

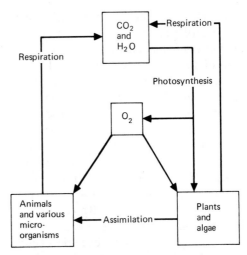

FIG. 15–18. The carbon and oxygen cycle.

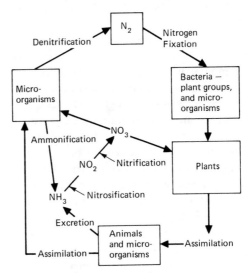

FIG. 15–19. The nitrogen cycle.

and decay, thus yielding compounds which serve as nutrients for other animals and microorganisms.

Nitrogen cycle. Most microorganisms and all higher forms of life are not able to use atmospheric nitrogen (N_2). This capability to fix nitrogen with the production of intracellular ammonia for protein synthesis is limited to blue-green algae and two groups of bacteria. These algae and various species of the bacterial genera *Azotobacter* and *Clostridium* engage in *non-symbiotic nitrogen fixation*. This type of fixation occurs in the soil independently of plants. Species of the bacterial genus *Rhizobium* perform *symbiotic nitrogen fixation*. The latter process is dependent upon an intimate association with the roots of legume plants—alfalfa, clover, and soy bean—in bacteria-plant groups. This association is truly *synergistic,* since neither organism alone can fix atmospheric nitrogen. Rhizobia grow in root cells and produce nodules which may contain millions of bacteria. These organisms obtain most of their nutrients from the plant host while supplying it with nitrogen.

Nitrogen fixation has been shown to proceed by reduction of the nitrogen to ammonia, which is then utilized for the amination of a Kreb's cycle intermediate compound, alpha-ketoglutaric acid, to form the amino acid glutamic acid. Thus, by transamination and other reactions, the amino acids required for protein synthesis are produced. The microbial excretions of nitrogenous compounds, as well as dead organisms, serves to make nitrogen available to other microorganisms, animals, and plants through assimilation.

The excretion of nitrogenous compounds by animals and microorganisms and the decay of dead animals, plants, and microorganisms is a major source of available nitrogen. In Figure 15–19 this cycle is represented by the excretion of ammonia and by microbial *ammonification*. In the latter process, microorganisms degrade proteins and other nitrogenous compounds, producing ammonia. For example, urea, which is a major excretory

product of animals, may be hydrolyzed abiologically or ammonified to ammonia. Many microorganisms are capable of performing the ammonification of urea. A test is available for the detection of the essential enzyme urease in this reaction and is an important aspect in the identification of clinically significant organisms, including *Proteus* spp. and *Klebsiella pneuomoniae*. The capability to oxidize NH_3 to nitrite, called *nitrosification,* is limited to species of *Nitrosomas*. The oxidation of nitrite to nitrate, *nitrification,* is limited to species of *Nitrobacter*. If soil is depleted of these two groups of bacteria, its fertility decreases rapidly, since plants cannot utilize NH_3 as a source of nitrogen.

The final stage in the nitrogen cycle is the return of gaseous nitrogen to the atmosphere. Our discussion of anaerobic respiration noted that nitrate can serve as an ultimate electron acceptor and can be reduced to nitrite. Nitrate reduction can be performed by many organisms; however, nitrite reduction to ammonia and nitrogen is limited to only a few species of *Bacillus* and *Pseudomonas*. This stepwise conversion of nitrate to N_2 is called *denitrification*. Tests for nitrate reduction are also valuable in the identification of microorganisms.

Perspective. All of the various aspects of heterotrophic and autotrophic metabolism described may appear to be quite diverse. However, in nature they are intimately interrelated. The discussion presented was meant to provide a general basis for the various microbial activities contained within the confines of this textbook.

QUESTIONS FOR REVIEW

1. Briefly outline glucose catabolism and differentiate major functions of the three phases.

2. How are various metabolic activities in the cell closely related?

3. Why is ATP considered to be a critical biochemical?

4. Briefly describe protein synthesis, starting with a discussion of the genetic code.

5. Distinguish between end-product inhibition and end-product repression.

6. Why should it be reasonable that cells can turn on and turn off the production of mRNA?

7. Describe and discuss a relatively simple versus a more difficult method for measuring metabolic activity.

8. What are the essential differences among the four nutritional types of microorganisms discussed in this chapter?

9. Differentiate between respiration, anaerobic respiration, and fermentation.

10. Discuss the relationship of various ecological problems to natural metabolic cycles.

Microbial Genetics

Genetics is essentially a product of the twentieth century, beginning in earnest in 1900 with the rediscovery of Mendel's extensive studies of inheritance in pea plants. Earlier, of course, people had had ideas about the inheritance of characteristics. Montaigne and Da Vinci were among those who discussed how offspring come to resemble parents. One among the many points of contention between early scientists and philosophers concerned the inheritance of acquired characteristics—whether changes produced by the environment were passed on to future generations.

Evolution and the Inheritance of Acquired Characteristics

Today, belief in the inheritance of acquired characteristics is associated with the name of Jean Baptiste de Lamarck (1744-1829). Lamarck, who coined the terms *biology* and *invertebrate,* also introduced the concept of *evolution,* a continual process of gradual modification of plant and animal species in response to environmental conditions. Thus, exposure to the sun accounted for the difference between the white and black races. The protective coloration of birds and animals, especially insects, was attributed to their prolonged exposure to the natural conditions that they came to resemble. Giraffes became long-necked by continually stretching to reach the leaves on high branches of trees.

Charles Darwin, in the nineteenth century, subscribed in part to the inheritance of acquired characteristics as a force in what he called *natural selection.* In 1831-1836, as a naturalist on a British ship voyaging around South America and the Galapagos Islands, Darwin made detailed observations of the flora and fauna he encountered (including people). The captain, a religious fundamentalist, had invited a naturalist hoping that he would find positive proof that the world had been created in six days in final form. The captain could not have been pleased with the results, for Darwin emerged with a detailed theory of evolution. He believed there was natural variation among the individuals of a species, and the struggle for existence determined which individuals would survive to pass on their characteristics. In this view, when the long-necked giraffe emerged among his short-necked relatives, he was better able to survive because more food was within his reach. Short-necked giraffes gradually died out, so that now all giraffes have long necks.

Carrying Darwin's thinking a little further, a dark-colored bird had a greater chance of survival than his lighter relatives because he was better able to hide from hawks. Any creature which could fight better, run faster, take better care of its young, or utilize more sources of food, had a survival advantage and its characteristics would tend to continue by natural selection. In 1859 Darwin published his theory in *The Origin of Species by Means of Natural Selection, or the Preservation of Favoured Races in the Struggle for Life.* In 1868, he proposed that the *germ cells* that carry inheritance are composed of tiny reproductions of all the organs and other body characteristics.

Inheritance of acquired characteristics still had its supporters. In 1879 Butler used the earlier thoughts of Maupertuis to argue that the germ cells, or *gametes,* had a memory for all the characteristics of the body, but that this memory could be altered by the environment. (Pierre de Maupertuis, 1698-1759, a leading astronomer, was also one of the first scholars to take a serious interest in human genetics.)

Few of the so-called philosophical scientists, or natural philosophers, paused to conduct experiments with which to confirm their theories. However, two scientists did put their genetic hypotheses to the test of experiment. In 1875, Galton performed transfusions between white and black rabbits, expecting to produce spotted offspring because the blood supposedly transported the "gemmules," or miniatures of the body characteristics, to the sex glands. This did not occur.

Probably the most classic experiment disproving the inheritance of acquired characteristics was reported in 1892 by Weismann, the founder of the germ plasm theory. He cut off the tails of successive generations of mice, to see if he could induce taillessness in the offspring. It never happened.

This chapter will present selected aspects of classical genetic studies of plants and animals that have provided a basis for microbial genetics. In recent years, much of the molecular nature of heredity has been learned with the aid of fungi, bacteria, and bacterial viruses.

Classical Genetics

Mendel's Genetic Principles

For hundreds of years man had observed that his offspring and those of plants and other animals might resemble either parent, both, or neither one. No attempts at a reasonably thorough study of these variations were recorded until the work of the Austrian monk Gregor Mendel, published in 1868. A century earlier, the botonist Kölreuter did cross tobacco plants and observe hybrids with characteristics intermediate between the parents.

Mendel, working in his monastery garden, became intrigued with the evaluation of hereditable characteristics of pea plants. He observed pod color and shape, pea color and texture, flower color and stem length of parental and offspring plants. As data mounted, he was able to discern two particular patterns in heredity.

1. Whatever determines a characteristic in the resultant offspring must exist in pairs and separate into different structures so that each such unit will have one set of characteristics. This pattern became obvious when Mendel observed that when pollen from a plant with one set of characteristics was placed on a plant of different characteristics, the resulting seeds produced an offspring possessing characteristics belonging to both parents. For example, if parent A had smooth peas in a long, slender pod and parent B had wrinkled peas in a short pod, the offspring might show smooth peas in a short pod. Thus some mechanism was involved in incorporating representative characteristics into the second generation.

2. The separation of characteristics into hereditable structures must occur independently of any other

characteristic. In essence, this meant that each characteristic was passed to the offspring by itself, with no readily observable pattern of one characteristic consistently appearing with any other. This observation was later found to be partly true. It should be noted, however, that all of the features of the pea plant studied by Mendel were independent and unlinked. Thus, for example, wrinkled peas were not always found in long, slender pods.

Mendel's writings went largely unnoticed for 35 years, until they were discovered in 1900 independently by three scientists—de Vries in Holland, Correns in Germany, and Tschermak in Austria. These concurrent discoveries intensified the interest in heredity and resulted in the establishment of the Mendelian laws just described: *The Law of Segregation* and *The Law of Independent Assortment.* De Vries added the mutation theory, which he published in 1901-1903; it is often mistakenly attributed to Darwin.

Units of Inheritance

With the discovery of Mendel's writings in 1900 and the intense research which followed, a chromosome theory of heredity gradually developed. Earlier cytological studies had shown that distinctly staining structures (*chromo,* colored; *some,* body) in the nucleus segregated in various cells. In 1902, three scientists, one of whom again was Correns, compared the chromosomal property with Mendel's findings and hypothesized that chromosomes were the independent segregants mentioned by Mendel.

Between 1902 and 1905 this concept was strengthened by the findings of McClung, Stevens, and Wilson in relation to the determination of the sex of individuals by the X and Y chromosomes. These are called *sex chromosomes,* in contrast to the other human chromosomes, which are referred to as *autosomes.* During this same period, 1902 to 1905, the results of several studies seemed to show the existence of more pairs of segregating genetic units or genes than of observable chromosomes. Some scientists interpreted this to mean that chromosomes were unrelated to heredity. However, other scientists were able to prove that more than one characteristic was located on each chromosome.

Utilizing these findings, Janssens hypothesized that the reason genetic characteristics outnumbered chromosomes was an exchange of genetic material between chromosomes. In 1901, he published the results of studies which demonstrated the physical crossing-over process (*chiasmata*) between chromosomal strands during meiosis. The actual proof that more than one gene resided on one chromosome was reported by Thomas Hunt Morgan in the years 1910, 1911, and 1912.

Morgan studied heredity in the fruit fly, *Drosophila melanogaster,* and discovered that certain characteristics were always found associated with the sex chromosome. He received the Nobel Prize for this work.

By correlating the results of his studies with those of Janssens, Morgan was able to establish the linkage of traits and the exchange of traits between chromosomes as the basis for the development of chromosome mapping (mapping the arrangement of genes along a chromosome). Subsequently, Sturtevant in 1913 reported the establishment of a linear map for certain traits in *Drosophila.* The construction of a linear map is based upon the rate at which the crossing over between chromosomes will separate certain traits.

Meiosis, discussed in more detail later, is the process by which a cell destined to become a sex cell or gamete can reduce or halve its normal chromosome complement—a necessary preliminary to sexual reproduction. During meiosis, the partners of homologous chromosome pairs —two chromosomes which are involved in the determination of the same hereditary traits, such as hair texture and color, eye color, etc.—will separate. Thus, newly formed sex cells contain half of the chromosomes typically found in other body cells. This means that the genetic content, or genotype, in the gametes is also reduced. The individual expressions or physical representation of the genotype, which is called the *phenotype*, is determined to a large extent by the combinations of genes received by offspring from their parents. For example, if an individual receives one gene for pure brown eyes from one parent and one gene for pure blue eyes from the other parent, the resulting eye color will be brown, because the brown eye color gene is dominant over the recessive blue eye color gene. As Mendel discovered, recessive traits can only show themselves in the absence of dominant genes. The term *allele* is used to designate alternate genes determining one particular trait, such as blue and brown eye color. Alleles can alternate in occupying the same location or locus on the chromosome.

Mitosis

The reproduction of cells is extremely important for the normal development and growth of the majority of animals, plants, and microorganisms. This process must occur in a way that insures that newly formed cells are essentially identical to parent cells so that the characteristic components of cells, tissues, organs, and systems of individual forms of life can be maintained from one generation to the next.

Mitosis is the process in which, generally speaking, genetic material is duplicated and equally distributed to new cells. This orderly nuclear division occurs regularly in animals, plants, and eucaryotic microorganisms. With protocaryotes, however, it has been difficult to observe the sequence of events involved in the division of nuclear material.

Mitosis consists of five distinct stages, described in relation to the distinctive changes which the involved cells exhibit. These stages—*interphase, prophase, metaphase, anaphase,* and *telophase*—are shown in Figure 16–1.

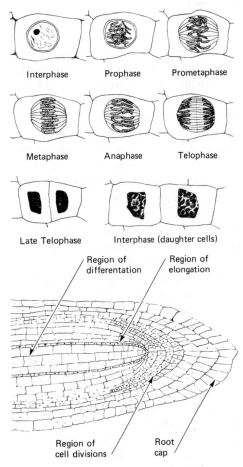

FIG. 16–1. Typical mitotic figures from plant root tip preparations.

The significant features of the mitotic process include: (1) its role in the growth and reproduction of cells, (2) the replacement of damaged or aging and dying cells, and (3) the replication of chromosomes and their accurate transfer from mother to daughter cells, thus maintaining the genotype (the numbers and kinds of genes) of a particular organism. This last aspect resembles the reproduction of bacteria, which also split to produce offspring identical to the so-called mother cells. Under normal conditions, the new generation of daughter cells continues to transmit the genotype characteristic of the species.

Meiosis

In most cases, if it were not for mutations, little variation would occur in the species, and environmental pressures could conceivably cause elimination of a particular species and its associated branch of the evolutionary tree. Rather than relying solely on mutation as the means of producing changes, the phenomenon of sexual reproduction has evolved which is, in reality, gene recombination. In animals, plants, and a large number of microorganisms this process occurs through the fusion of nuclear material from two different reproductive cells, male and female, within a species. When fertilization involves two different individuals the process is called *cross-fertilization*. *Self-fertilization* can also occur in protozoa and some parasitic worms. As a consequence of sexual reproduction, the hereditary composition of new individuals becomes mixed, providing a basis for genetic variation and hence for evolution. While sexual reproduction in plants and animals is important to the propagation of a species, in certain microorganisms the process is concerned with the transfer of genetic material for purposes of recom-

bination and not for increasing microbial numbers. This particular point will be considered in more detail later in this chapter.

One of the hereditary characteristics of a species is the number of chromosomes found in the *somatic* or body cells of that species. For example, man has 46. If the gametes or reproductive cells in man—sperm and egg—arose by mitosis, then each fertilization or fusion of these cells would result in twice the normal number of chromosomes, or 92 for the first generation. Thus some process other than mitosis must be in effect to maintain constancy in chromosomal numbers. This process is known as *meiosis* or *reduction division*. All sex cells are produced through this process, whether in man or other types of animals.

Meiosis involves two cell divisions, one immediately following the other. The final result is the halving of the number of chromosomes. The original cell contains the *diploid* quantity of chromosomes, while the gamete is reduced through meiosis to the *haploid* state. By means of this chromosomal reduction, the characteristic number of chromosomes for a given species is maintained from generation to generation. Thus, when an ovum or egg cell is fertilized by a sperm cell, the diploid stage or the *characteristic diploid number* of the species is reestablished.

The Chemistry of Genetics

DNA and Chromosomes

An elaborate series of experiments were performed during the years 1928 to 1948 to prove conclusively that the genetic substance was in reality deoxyribonucleic acid (DNA). Until then, the relative roles of protein and DNA in heredity were hotly disputed.

In 1868, Frederick Miescher undertook an experimental approach that led to his discovery of DNA one year later, in 1869. Working with purulent (pus-containing) material, which he obtained from the University of Tubingen's medical clinic, Miescher removed cells from bandages by washing and subsequently exposed them to a variety of extraction procedures with acids, alkalis, and salt solutions. This resulted in the formation of a highly viscous substance which he called *nuclein* because it came from the nuclei of white blood cells. The interesting chemical composition of this material—14 per cent nitrogen and 2.5 per cent phosphorous—convinced Miescher that he had found a hitherto unknown compound. Upon returning to his home in Switzerland, he began a similar series of experiments with salmon sperm. Miescher found that his nuclein comprised approximately 50 per cent of the animal's sperm and was combined with a highly basic protein which he called *protamine*. Although Miescher never isolated pure DNA, he did discover that nuclein was composed of large molecules which did not pass through a certain size filter.

In 1881, E. Zacharias, a botanist, showed that nuclein was associated in some manner with chromosomes. The results of his investigations, and those of others, led Oskar Hertwig in 1883 and 1884 to conclude that nuclein was responsible for the transmission of hereditary characteristics.

In the 1890s and through nearly half of the twentieth century, evidence pointed to the protein of the nucleus as being the material responsible for heredity. Strasburger in 1909 reported that nuclein or chromatin could not be the genetic substance because the quantity appeared to vary throughout the process of mitosis, while protein appeared to be more constant. These results were confirmed by many other investigators using staining techniques. This view of nuclear protein as the basis of heredity was widely held by eminent cytologists, including E. B. Wilson. It was not until 1949 that quantitative chemical analyses of DNA from cell nuclei proved that DNA and not protein remained constant throughout the mitotic cycle, and that it was a fluctuation in the cellular protein content which had masked the staining of the DNA.

The Chemistry of Mutations

DNA consists of a linear chain of nitrogen bases known as the purines (adenine and guanine) and the pyrimidines (thymine and cytosine). These compounds are linked together by means of sugar-phosphate components. The DNA of most forms of life is double-stranded and complementary: adenine is always opposite thymine and guanine is always linked to cytosine. (Refer to Chapter 11 for a discussion of DNA and protein characteristics, and Chapter 15 for more information concerning protein synthesis and the genetic code.)

This apparent simplicity of the DNA caused many scientists earlier to disregard it as the genetic substance. Since then, however, its purines and pyramidines have been shown to form various combinations which allow for a sufficiently complex formulation. Three bases are normally necessary to code for a particular amino acid; a specific protein is formed in association with a certain sequence of such triplets. Permanent hereditary changes—mutations—result from alterations of a triplet's components or of the sequence.

Such mutations develop as a consequence of natural or spontaneous events, or are induced by various physical or chemical agents. The consequences of a mutation will depend upon the effect of the resulting change on the transcription of the DNA code into a form of ribonucleic acid (RNA), messenger RNA, which subsequently is translated into protein (Figure 16–2). The change in one base could cause the substitution of one amino acid for another in the final product.

The effect of this change would depend upon the location of that amino acid. It is well known that a large portion of the amino acids comprising a particular enzyme serve to form its structural framework while other amino acids in a specific sequence function in determining its active sites—the particular areas of the enzyme which are involved in enzymatic activity. Most changes in the genetic code associated with the structural aspects of enzymes probably would not affect activity. However, certain amino acids that are involved in determining shape could cause the enzyme to bind with a substrate in a manner that would permit maximum activity. Still other

amino acids in a specific sequence function to determine the active portion of the protein. A change here obviously could eliminate activity. Research on *Escherichia coli* demonstrated that certain mutations, which eliminated the activity of a particular enzyme, did permit the synthesis of a protein which was practically identical in all other characteristics.

Alterations of one or several amino acids in hemoglobin have been shown to be responsible for sickle cell anemia and other blood dyscrasias (abnormalities). A mutation resulting in the deletion of one or more purine or pyrimidine bases or their abnormal placement in a DNA molecule will result in a complete misreading of the genetic code. These events are called "reading-frame shifts." A mutation of this type will cause the synthesis of a nonfunctional protein. Mutations can also be caused by the rearrangement of chromosome pieces on the same or separate chromosomes. Situations of this nature are referred to as being a *translocation* form of chromosomal aberration.

Mutagenic agents.   Early work on mutations with *Drosophila* was performed with x-irradiation primarily because x-rays cause chromosomal breakage. One of the first chemical mutagens studied, mustard gas, was chosen because its mode of action was quite similar to that of x-rays. Mustard gas represents a group of mutagenic chemicals known as *alkylating agents*, which attach other chemical groups in place of guanine in DNA. The substituted guanine appears to cause defects by pairing with a thymine molecule rather than with cytosine. Thus, when the DNA strand replicates, the original guanine is replaced by adenine, which will pair with the incorrect thymine. Alkylating agents also produce de-

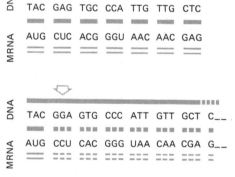

FIG. 16–2. Representation of the effects of alterations in the genetic code. A normal triple sequence in a DNA molecule is shown at the top and underlined. The corresponding messenger RNA (mRNA) molecule is located directly underneath and doubly underlined. With the hypothetical insertion of a new base (arrow) a change in the reading of the genetic code occurs beyond this site of mutation. This effect is shown in the bottom portion of the diagram. The altered DNA and mRNA molecules are respectively underlined with broken single and double lines.

letions and chromosome rearrangements.

Many other chemical and physical agents have tested for mutagenic activity. Ultraviolet rays appear to act as a mutagen because UV wavelengths are strongly absorbed by DNA. Some of the chemicals studied include base analogs, acridines, and nitrous acid. Base analogs are purines and pyrimidines not normally found in DNA. Their incorporation into DNA, during nucleic acid synthesis, results in incorrect pairing during the replication process. For example, 5-bromouracil appears to be incorporated into DNA in place of thymine. Due to stereochemical differences, 5-bromouracil will pair with thymine rather than adenine, thus introducing a change in the code.

The acridine group of chemicals appears to penetrate or intercalate the DNA and consequently separate the bases. This separation might lead to the unnatural insertion or deletion of a base which causes "reading-frame shifts." Nitrous acid was originally tested as a mutagen due to its known interaction with proteins, which were thought to be the genetic material. However, experiments have shown that nitrous acid does cause mutations by removing an amino group (NH_2) common to adenine, guanine, and cytosine. When these bases are deaminated by removal of the amino group, they are converted to hypoxanthine, xanthine, and uracil, respectively. The new compounds will not pair with the appropriate purine or pyrimidine, thus creating spot changes in the genetic code.

Special Genetic Transfer Mechanisms in Microorganisms

The generally accepted view that hybridization is important to the survival of a species (hybrid vigor) apparently does not apply to bacteria because of their haploid nature. It is important to stress the point that while plant and animal species are classified according to their ability to combine gametes with a resultant diploid cell, microbial species are classified primarily by common morphological and biochemical characteristics independent of genetic homology. Bacteria have exchanged genetic material between genera and between species. A more fruitful discussion of these phenomena will be presented after the problems of the interactions of microbial genetics with the pathogenesis and epidemiology of disease agents have been discussed.

Transformation

The apparent genetic problem of the haploid bacterial cell was dispelled in 1928, when F. J. Griffith observed some startling results while investigating the destructive effects of pneumococci in mice. The virulence of a pneumococcus is largely dependent upon the presence of a polysaccharide capsule that prevents its destruction by phagocytes in the host animal. These encapsulated organisms can mutate to nonencapsulted forms which are *avirulent*—unable to produce disease. The many types of pneumococci are differentiated by their chemically and immunologically distinguishable capsular material. Griffith mixed live, uncapsulated, avirulent bacteria from a culture of one type of pneumococcus with heat-killed capsulated pneumococci of a virulent type, and inoculated a number of mice with this preparation. To his surprise, some of the mice died. Analyzing his results, Griffith concluded that neither the avirulent live bacteria nor the the heat-killed virulent ones could have killed the mice, since neither had that effect when injected alone. He isolated living pneumococci from the dead mice and identified them as capsulated organisms belonging to the type represented by the heat-killed bacteria. It would therefore appear that either the dead bacteria were rejuvenated by the living avirulent ones, or the dead bacteria somehow transformed the avirulent organisms into virulent ones.

In 1933, J. L. Alloway reported the next significant step in the elucidation of this transformation phenomenon. He performed *in vitro* the same type of experiment that Griffith had performed *in vivo*. In place of the killed cells, these studies utilized a sterile, cell-free extract of the virulent pneumococci. This extract did not cause the death of mice when injected alone, but when mixed with avirulent bacteria of a different type, the result was the production of virulent pneumococci, indistinguishable from the ones that were used to make the extract. A *transforming principle (TP)* had been prepared in crude form. The 1940s yielded significant reports proving absolutely that Alloway's TP was deoxyribonucleic acid (DNA).

Thus began the era of intensive investigations into the molecular basis of genetics and of life itself. Avery, McLeod, and McCarty, in 1944, separated the crude extracts of TP into protein, lipid, polysaccarides, ribonucleic acid (RNA), and DNA. In 1946, McCarty and Avery reported that only the fraction containing DNA was active in transformation. The identity of DNA was proved by a wide variety of established chemical and physical analytical techniques. Then, in 1948, it was shown that the active DNA had to be highly polymerized and that only certain of the avirulent pneumococci were "competent" to be transformed by the DNA. A recipient cell that is able to absorb donor DNA and subsequently undergo transformation is a competent cell. Competence appears to develop as a function of population density: when the cell concentration of a culture reaches a critical level, most cells exhibit competence. (However, loss of this property can occur abruptly.) With the appearance of competence in a culture, a protein is produced that can change incompetent cells into competent ones. Although the exact mechanism involved is not known, it is believed that this "competence factor" influences some change in cell surfaces so as to bring about the development of receptor sites and/or increased permeability to large DNA molecules.

Pneumococci have complex nutritional requirements and therefore do not lend themselves to relatively simple studies concerning the DNA transfer of types of information other than pathogenicity. More recent work in this area by W. R. Romig and others has used *Bacillus subtilis*. Because this organism can be grown on a simple, defined medium, nutritional mutants of several kinds can be studied. Probably the most significant work with *B. subtilis* has been the determination that the DNA used for transformation experiments need not be obtained from a related bacterial culture. For a long time, it was thought that viruses must be intact to be infective; however, in the case of certain bacteriophages, extracted viral DNA can be used as TP and cause infection of bacterial cells, resulting in the ultimate lysis of the cells and the production of intact viruses.

A more exciting study in transformation with *B. subtilis* showed that the infective DNA could be obtained from an animal virus such as vaccinia (cowpox). One may therefore speculate that potentially pathogenic viruses in man may use the indigenous bacteria as a reservoir; these bacteria may serve as "carriers" until some later time when the virus becomes active and causes the disease for no readily apparent reason.

While transformation experiments can yield a significant amount of information concerning transfer of genetic information per se, little can be learned about the mapping of genes on the bacterial "chromosome" or genome, beyond the fact that bacteria, like plants and animals, have linear arrangements of their genetic information. Two other mechanisms of genetic transfer were discovered by Joshua Lederberg: sexual recombination or conjugation in 1946 by Lederberg and E. L. Tatum, and transduction, or bacterial virus mediated transfer, by Lederberg and N. Zinder in 1952.

Bacterial Recombination

Recombination, or *conjugation,* refers to the transfer of genetic material between two living bacteria. Recombination, being the major means of genetic exchange and variability in sexually reproducing higher organisms, had been investigated with bacteria as a means of confirming the presence of chromosomes by C. H. Browning in 1908. However, the proof of conjugation in bacteria did not become available until Tatum and Lederberg obtained multiple mutants (*polyauxotrophs*) of *Escherichia coli.*

The bacterial strains used had two or more differing genetic defects. One parent organism had defects which caused it to require the vitamin biotin (B) and the amino acid methionine (M) for survival, while the other parent strain required the amino acids threonine (T) and leucine (L). These parent strains were symbolized as $B^-M^-T^+L^+$ and B^+M^+ T^-L^-. The minus sign represented a requirement for the particular biochemical substance for growth on minimal medium, and the positive signs indicated no deficiency requirement. Neither strain was able to grow on minimal medium and only a transfer of B^+M^+ to one parent or T^+L^+ to the other would permit growth under the test conditions.

When the two strains were mixed and placed on minimal medium, recombinants were obtained, symbolized by B^+M^+ T^+L^+. These organisms represented the natural type of genetic makeup. The statistical probability of the double spontaneous mutations yielding the same result would be of the order of one chance out of 10^{14}. The numbers of resulting colonies obtained were far greater than expected by double mutation. It certainly appeared that recombination by crossing-over was occurring, indicating that a linear arrangement of genes (*linkage*) was present in bacteria, as in higher organisms. This crossing-over phenomenon can be represented as follows:

$$\frac{B^+\ M^+\ T^-\ L^-}{B^-\ M^-\ T^+\ L^+} = \overline{B^+\ M^+\ T^+\ L^+}$$

Thus sexuality in bacteria was discovered. Subsequent research in this area has shown that certain strains are donors; they have been classified as F^+ (F refers to "fertility"). The recipient strain, or F^-, receives the DNA from F^+ in a linear fashion known as unilateral transfer. It would appear that the only function of the F^+ (male) is to transfer DNA to the F^- (female), and the F^+ need not be viable.

To eliminate the possibility that transformation might be taking place, B. Davis in 1950 carried out a series of experiments using a U-tube device (Figure 16–3). The U-tube was constructed with two arms, (A) and (B), separated by a porous glass filter (C) which would prevent passage of bacteria between the arms. When F^+ and F^- strains were placed in the same arm, recombinants were obtained at expected frequencies. However, if F^+ were placed in (A) and F^- were placed in (B), and the medium flushed between the arms, no recombinants were obtained. Thus transformation

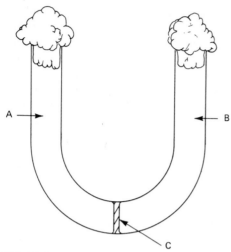

FIG. 16–3. A representation of the U-tube used by Davis. Refer to the text for an explanation of the device.

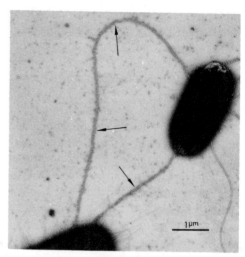

FIG. 16–4. An electron micrograph of a presumed specific pairing between an Hfr cell (bottom) and an F cell. The sex pili can be clearly differentiated from other pili by the massive attachment of male-specific, spherical RNA-containing bacteriophages (arrows). (From Curtiss, R., III, Caro, L. G., Allison, D. P., and Stallions, D. R.: *J. Bacteriol.*, **100**:1091–1104, 1969.)

was eliminated as an explanation of this phenomenon, and the need for intimate contact was firmly established.

The F factor has been characterized as an extrachromosomal genetic complex composed of circular DNA that possesses genes for the following: (1) the regulation of its own replication; (2) the synthesis of sex or F pili conduits (See Chapter 8) through which donor DNA passes to a recipient cell and to which male-specific, spherical RNA-containing bacteriophages (Figure 16–4) and filamentous DNA-containing bacteriophages absorb; and (3) the formation of a particular surface component that may serve to lower negative electrical surface charges of donor cells, so that intimate contact with recipient cells can occur after random collision.

Plasmids

Various small, extrachromosomal DNA factors capable of autonomous (independent) replication have often been demonstrated in bacteria. These genetic elements, which were originally catego-

rized as *episomes,* included the F factor, R factors (transfer resistance to antibiotics), and bacteriocinogenic factors (associated with the synthesis of bacterial killing substances, the bacteriocins). Recently the terminology has been revised. Those extrachromosomal units that can replicate either autonomously or as part of the host (usually a bacterial cell) chromosome and are capable of shifting between these two modes of replication are referred to as *episomes.* All others are called plasmids.

Mapping of the Bacterial Genome

Linear transfer of genetic material (DNA) between the F+ and F− bacteria allowed investigations into genetic mapping in *E. coli.* Before extensive work was begun, it was learned that with a particular F+ strain, rates of recombination of the order of one in a million occurred. Unfortunately, this was not sufficient to permit large-scale studies into the conjugation phenomenon. However, during these studies, mutants of F+ strains were obtained which allowed recombination to occur at a rate of approximately one in a hundred. This strain is called Hfr for "high frequency recombinants" (super males). Investigations with this mutant strain have shown that fertility in *E. coli* is dependent upon the presence of the F or sex factor in the bacterium. With F+ cells, the sex factor was present as an individual cytoplasmic unit (a plasmid); when mated with F− cells, this F factor was transferred at a high rate without the bacterial genome. Only in the case of Hfr, where this F factor was integrated with the genome, could other genes be transferred to the recipient or female. Thus, it was found that the recombination observed in F+ populations was in reality due to the presence of a small number of Hfr mutants.

E. L. Wollman and F. Jacob reported in 1955 that they had developed a relatively simple procedure for genetic mapping analyses in *E. coli*. They found that after mixing Hfr and F− strains conjugation could be interrupted by whirling the bacteria in a kitchen blender. Analysis of recombinants in the F− bacteria indicated that the genome was indeed linear. This was demonstrated by breaking the mating pairs at different times and observing that after certain intervals additional genetic characteristics would be expressed by the original F− bacteria.

Figure 16–5 represents a simplified view of the conjugation process in *E. coli*. In the hypothetical experiment presented, Hfr and F− strains of *E. coli* and samples of the mixture were removed to a blender after selected time intervals. After blending to rupture the conjugation tube, the recombinants were analyzed on suitable media for nutritional character-

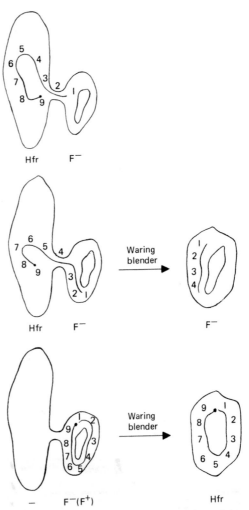

FIG. 16–5. A diagrammatic representation of the conjugation process in *Escherichia coli*.

istics and characteristics of antibiotic and bacterial virus resistance. These characteristics or *markers* (genetic traits) are indicated by numbers 1 through 9. The sexuality factor of F is always the last marker transferred and thereupon the former F− becomes either an Hfr if the F factor is integrated with the F− genome, or F+ if it behaves as an episome or cytoplasmic unit of inheritance. If more frequent samples were taken, each separate marker would be determined by recombination analyses and then the entire bacterial chromosome would be mapped. This and other types of analysis have proved that the bacterial chromosome is truly one linkage group and is circular. This circular strand of genetic information which controls the destiny of *E. coli* always breaks at the point of F factor integration, and the F factor is always the last marker to be transferred.

Conjugation has been shown to take place between *E. coli* and other enteric bacteria such as *Salmonella* and *Shigella* species. One wonders, therefore, whether or not bacterial recombination could take place in the human intestine to the extent that an organism wrongly identified as *E. coli* would be isolated from a patient infected with the etiological agent of typhoid fever, *Salmonella typhi.*

Sexduction (F-duction)

The process whereby a restricted number of markers is transferred at a high frequency to F⁻ cells is called sexduction or F-duction. This phenomenon occurs when an F particle becomes separated (excised) from the bacterial chromosome and takes with it an adjacent segment of the bacterial chromosomal DNA. The resulting F particle carrying bacterial genes is referred to as an F prime (F') particle. It behaves in a manner similar to an F⁺ particle. As a consequence of an F' × F⁻ mating, the recipient bacterial cell acquires the additional genes carried by the F' particle upon integration into the recipient's chromosomes.

Transduction

When Lederberg extended his studies on recombination or conjugation to *Salmonella* species, the unidirectional transfer of genetic material occurred. In essence this phenomenon resembled conjugation as observed with *E. coli.* However, when performing these studies in a Davis U-tube, it was observed that physical con-

tact was not required. This, then, appeared to be related to transformation as shown in studies with pneumococci, *Hemophilus* spp. and *B. subtilis.* In order to confirm the presence of transformation in *Salmonella,* DNAase was added to the culture to prevent the genetic transfer of free DNA (this enzyme will inactivate the TP). Rather than confirming the presence of transformation in this genus, the absence of inactivation by DNAase initiated research into the transduction phenomenon.

Zinder and Lederberg reported in 1952 that bacterial genetic transfer was possible via a filterable agent identified as a bacterial virus or bacteriophage. As described in Chapters 13 and 14, such viruses are able to infect a bacterial cell and, through the process of lysogeny, become an integral part of the bacterial genome. At this time virus is undetectable in the cell and is called a *prophage.* However, either spontaneously or after induction by ultraviolet light, the virus is activated, replicates at the expense of the cell, and eventually causes the lysis of the host cell. Thus many viruses can be released into the culture to infect other bacteria, as a consequence of the infectious process. Further details of viral activities are discussed in Chapters 13 and 14.

Compared with bacterial conjugation, transduction permits the transfer of relatively small segments of DNA, due to the limitation of space within the virus. Usually this transfer consists of the virus DNA (prophage) and one bacterial marker. However, occasionally the prophage and two markers may be transduced. This phenomenon has been used to study the fine structure of the bacterial DNA according to short linkage patterns. Figure 16–6 presents a hypothetical experiment comparing genetic mapping by conjugation and by transduction. Part I of the illustration indicates, by time of

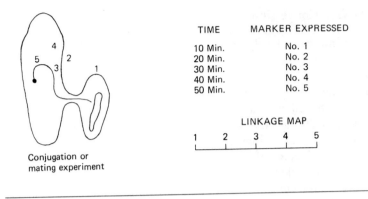

TIME   MARKER EXPRESSED

10 Min.   No. 1
20 Min.   No. 2
30 Min.   No. 3
40 Min.   No. 4
50 Min.   No. 5

LINKAGE MAP

Conjugation or
mating experiment

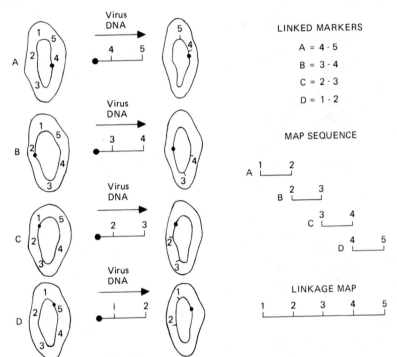

FIG. 16–6. A hypothetical experiment comparing the genetic mapping procedure by conjugation and transduction.

transfer, the linkage map to be 1-2-3-4-5. This is quite simple and straightforward; however, it does not permit evaluation of small segments of the bacterial DNA. In part II, we have a more complicated situation. It can be seen that the linked markers were transferred with the phage DNA, and the probable genetic map would be the same as that obtained by conjugation experiments. Fine structure of the genetic material is not obvious from this illustration. However, transduction analysis has provided the means to evaluate defects within a gene and has led to observations concerning the physical characteristics of the unit of inheritance which, until recently, was only a hypothetical entity.

Lysogenic or Viral Conversion

During the 1950s a more medically significant event was being discovered,
namely, *lysogenic* or *viral conversion*.
Here, unlike transduction, a particular
phenotypic change in the microorganism
occurs in all infected cells, as a consequence of lysogeny. Such conversions as
the development of smooth colonial types
in mycobacteria and alterations of the
serological types of salmonellae, are of
clinical significance.

Probably the most significant alteration of a microbial characteristic by lysogeny was reported by Freeman in
1951. This investigation showed that the
etiological agent of diphtheria, *Corynebacterium diphtheriae*, could produce its
toxin only when infected by a specific
bacteriophage. There are other requirements, primarily the presence of a certain
concentration of iron, but if the phage
is not present, lysogenic state toxin production will not occur.

Toxin production as a consequence of
lysogeny can be demonstrated by a relatively simple procedure. Prior to 1948,
the detection of toxin production by *C.
diphtheriae* required either inoculation
of guinea pigs for virulence testing or test
tube serological tests using culture filtrates
and antitoxin. In 1948, Elek reported a
technique whereby the presence or absence of toxin could be observed in a
Petri plate containing serum agar. A
strip of filter paper impregnated with
antitoxin was placed on the surface of
the sterile serum agar medium. Cultures
of *C. diphtheriae* exposed to bacteriophage or suspected of being toxigenic
were then streaked across the plate as
shown in Figure 16–7. When the streak
cultures had grown to a reasonable size,
the presence of toxin was indicated by
zones of precipitation in the agar where

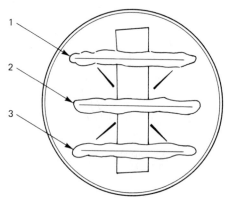

FIG. 16–7. Demonstration of toxin production by
a lysogenic culture of *Corynebacterium diphtheriae*. (1) and (3) are nonlysogenic; (2) is lysogenic. Note the lines of precipitation that have
formed where the optimum concentrations from
the bacterial culture have reacted with the optimum concentrations of antitoxin from the filter
paper.

the streaks crossed the impregnated filter
paper strip.

These zones of precipitation are
formed when the optimum concentrations
of toxin have diffused from the bacterial
cultures and reacted with the optimum
concentration of antitoxin diffusing out
from the filter paper. This phenomenon
is a form of *immunodiffusion* (see Chapter
23). It is used widely as a standard serological or immunological technique and is
described in more detail in a later chapter.

Cytoplasmic Inheritance

The genetic characteristics of microorganism, animal, and plant cells are not
entirely regulated from within a nucleus
or nucleus-type organelle. Several observations have indicated that certain
hereditary characteristics are under cytoplasmic control. This refers to the self-
duplication or apparent autonomous nature of the chloroplasts and mitochondria
of certain animal, plant, and microbial
cells. These plastids contain DNA in

addition to the biochemical materials, such as enzymes, required for their particular functions within the cells. An example of such regulatory influences is the "petite colony" mutant of yeast, which appears to be a genetic defect in the mitochondria resulting in both a respiratory deficiency and small cell size. The phenotypic expression produced by these cytoplasmic or extranuclear elements may be due to autonomous units without strict chromosomal control, may be self-duplicating and yet under chromosomal direction (semi-autonomous), or may be due to episomes.

The elements of cytoplasmic inheritance may be lost with treatment by the chemical acriflavine, or by some other means. When existing in the autonomous state, episomes are inactivated by such compounds. This characteristic is used for determining whether or not a cytoplasmic inheritance unit (element) is episomal.

Autonomous Cytoplasmic Inheritance

Probably the best example of this type of cytoplasmic inheritance is the apparent complete autonomy of sigma particles found in the fruit fly, *Drosophila*. These particles give the fly an extreme sensitivity to carbon dioxide. It has been shown that the virus-like or "infectious" sigma particles are passed to the young flies via the cytoplasm of the egg, independently of the chromosomes. This can be demonstrated by analysis of matings using both CO_2-sensitive and resistant female and male flies. In the first mating, a sensitive female is crossed with a resistant male. All of the resulting offspring are CO_2-sensitive and therefore carry the sigma particles. The reverse mating of a resistant female and a sensitive male results in all or nearly all resis-

tant offspring. These data are difficult to explain in classic genetic terms as other than an example of autonomous cytoplasmic inheritance.

Semi-Autonomous Cytoplasmic Inheritance

Certain strains of *Paramecium aurelia* have been observed to excrete substances called *kappa particles,* which cause the death of sensitive strains. Kappa particles present in the cytoplasm of the "killer" strains are 0.2 to 0.8 μm in diameter and contain DNA. These self-duplicating particles are under the control of a nuclear-located dominant gene, K. As in the case of CO_2 sensitivity with *Drosophila*, genetic analyses are necessary to determine the relationship between the self-duplicating cytoplasmic element and the nucleus.

In Figure 16–8 a mating is shown between a "killer" paramecium KK, with kappa particles, and a sensitive paramecium KK, in which no cytoplasmic exchange took place. The killer characteristic cannot manifest itself without the release of kappa particles into the sensitive mate. Therefore, only those cells produced by the killer parent having both particles and KK will be "killers." Both nuclear and cytoplasmic units are required. This can also be demonstrated by observing the mating of the same parents with cytoplasmic exchange occurring (Figure 16–9). Again, only those cells which have both elements can become killer paramecia.

Plasmid Cytoplasmic Inheritance

Plasmids have been well studied in a variety of bacteria, including the members of the bacterial genera *Vibrio, Pasteurella, Staphylococcus,* and *Bacillus.* These DNA-containing structures are

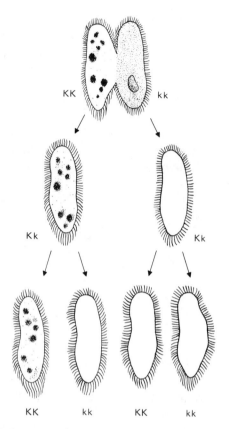

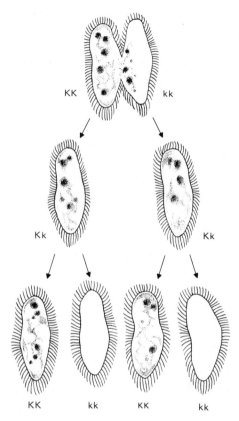

FIG. 16–8. A diagrammatic representation of the mating between a "killer" paramecium (KK with kappa particles) and a sensitive organism (kk), without cytoplasmic exchange.

FIG. 16–9. A diagrammatic representation of the mating between a "killer" paramecium (KK with kappa particles) and a sensitive organism (kk), with cytoplasmic exchange.

categorized as non-requisite genetic factors. They concern dispensable properties which may be transferred between bacteria by conjugation, transduction, and possibly transformation. By a variety of means, the following have been found to be plasmid in nature: the sex factor, bacteriocins, resistance transfer factors (RTF), and those factors that apparently are not transferred by conjugation, but can be transferred by bacteriophages.

Bacteriocins.   The temperate bacteriophage and sex or F factor have been described previously. We shall now discuss the bacteriocins and RTF. The bac-

teriocins were first described by Gratia in 1932 as a *colicin* or antibiotic-like material from *Escherichia coli,* a polypeptide material which can kill sensitive members of strains closely related to the one that produced the material. The ability to form bacteriocins is related to possession of a bacteriocinogenic factor (plasmid).

Colicins are produced by and act on other members of the family Enterobacteriaceae. Bacteria that carry the *col+* determinant, which is necessary for colicin production, are said to be colicinogenic. Colicins act by adsorbing to specific receptors on the surfaces of sensitive organisms, so that modification or loss of these receptor sites renders bacteria resistant to the specific colicin.

Antibiotic-like substances similar to those from *E. coli* (colicin) have been found with *Pseudomonas* (pyocin) and *Bacillus megaterium* (megacin). Collectively, these substances are categorized as bacteriocins. Chemically, bacteriocins may be simple proteins, proteins and carbohydrates, or comparable to incomplete bacteriophage particles (phage tails). The mode of action differs among bacteriocins: some appear to damage the cell membrane of susceptible hosts, whereas others disrupt or interfere with the synthesis of nucleic acid or protein synthesis.

RTF. The resistance transfer factor (RTF) was described by Mitsuhashi in 1965 as an episomal element in *Staphylococcus aureus,* which serves as the basis for bacterial resistance to a variety of antibiotics. Studies have indicated that as many as six different antibiotic-resistance characteristics may be associated with episomes in this organism. This point is particularly significant in that it confers the characteristic of vulnerability due to treatment with the antiseptic chemical acriflavine. Loss of resistance to these antibiotics can be demonstrated by acriflavine treatment *in vitro*. We may speculate on the potential use for it in the treatment of patients with severe staphylococcal infections. Such *in vivo* utilization could combine one or more of the antibiotics in question with acriflavine.

Transfer of multiple drug resistance requires cell contact and generally involves conjugation, although RTFs can also be transferred from cell to cell by transduction. The agents responsible for the drug resistance are called R factors. These factors consist of two distinguishable parts, the basic resistance transfer factor (RTF) and a variable genetic determinant for antibiotic resistance (r determinant), which contains the genes for drug resistance (R genes). The genetic (r) determinants can not be transferred unless they fuse with a transfer factor.

Mutation

The controversy between proponents of Lamarck and Darwin, discussed in the introduction to this chapter, has carried over into microbiology. The concept that changes are due to adaptation to conditions is certainly very logical. An excellent example involves the development of resistance to antibiotics by microorganisms.

Consider the case of a penicillin-sensitive *S. aureus* culture obtained from a patient. Upon the administration of this antibiotic, the condition should respond favorably to the treatment. However, the patient may subsequently return to the hospital with a fulminating infection, and the staphylococcus culture obtained this time is found to be penicillin-resistant. According to the adaptation theory, some of the bacteria that were in contact with the antibiotic managed to survive by adaptation. On the other hand, proponents of modern Darwinism would theorize that those bacteria that happened to be resistant to the antibiotic were the only survivors. In either case, the time between apparent recovery and relapse is the time required for the resistant bacteria to increase to sufficient numbers. The question that now remains is to differentiate between adaptation and random variation.

In 1943, S. E. Luria and M. Delbrück reported an indirect approach to the problem of the nature of microbial mutation. The procedure used was their "fluctuation test," based upon a statistical analysis of the probability of mutation to bacterial virus resistance in *E. coli* being random or directed in different populations. Their data presented strong evidence for the spontaneous and random nature of mutation. Simpler and more direct experiments were subsequently reported by H. B. Newcombe in 1949 and J. Lederberg and E. M. Lederberg in 1952.

Newcombe Spreading Technique

Investigators who had worked with *E. coli* bacteriophages (T phages) had observed that when a sensitive culture of *E. coli* was exposed to the virus, certain proportions of bacteria would survive and demonstrate resistance to infection. The Luria and Delbrück fluctuation test had shown that this change from sensitivity to resistance was a random event and probably was not directed by the presence of the virus.

Newcombe consequently conducted experiments in which he could differentiate the numbers of resistant cells originating in discrete bacterial colonies, and correlate these to exposure to the virus. In his procedure, equal numbers of bacteria were placed onto an agar medium in duplicate and allowed to grow long enough for each cell to undergo a small number of divisions. At this point, the cells on one plate would be redistributed by spreading while the other plate would be undistributed. If both plates now were exposed to virus and if adaptation was the basis for change, the same number of resistant colonies should appear on both plates after additional incubation.

The adaptation theory assumes that all bacteria present at the end of the first period of growth would be susceptible to the virus and the redistribution would not greatly affect the final number of resistant colonies produced by exposure to the virus. If, however, a mutation to resistance had occurred prior to the spreading step, then the colonies which had been redistributed would yield a higher percentage of virus-resistant forms. In a micro-colony in which the mutation took place, the number of resistant cells would depend upon the generation time (GT) and the incubation time. If the mutation had occurred in the single cell which initiated the growth of the colony, assuming a GT of 30 minutes and an incubation time of 2 hours, then there would be 4 generations with 16 resistant bacteria. On the other hand, if the mutation took place during final division, there might only be 1 resistant bacterium out of the 16 cells. The data obtained by Newcombe verified the hypothesis that mutations in bacteria were random and undirected. One example of the results obtained showed that if 51,000 bacteria were plated originally, the numbers of resistant colonies were 46 and 2,254 for non-redistributed and redistributed colonies, respectively.

Lederbergs' Indirect Selection Procedure

Subsequent to Newcombe's confirmation of the spontaneous nature of mutation in microorganisms, the Lederbergs developed a relatively simple method by which virus-resistant mutants could be isolated without any exposure to the bacterial virus. In this replica-plating technique (Figure 16–10) a velveteen nap was utilized as an inoculation surface to transfer bacteria from colonies on one plate to several other plates containing fresh media. When this is properly done, the transferred bacteria will develop into colonies at locations on the new plates that correspond to those colonies used from the inoculum (Figure 16–11). The relative locations of such colonies on all

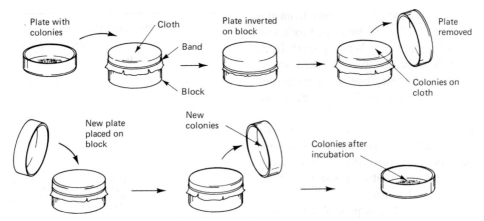

FIG. 16–10. General aspects of the replica-plating technique.

plates inoculated with the same velveteen pad should be the same. Using the bacterial colonies on one nutrient agar plate (1) as their inoculum sources, the Lederbergs introduced these organisms onto one with nutrient agar and one plate with nutrient agar plus a bacterial virus (2)

that could infect and kill the bacteria, thus preventing colonies from developing.

The sequence diagrammed in Figure 16–11 has been greatly simplified for clarity and brevity. Three colonies of the original 12—numbers 2, 7, and 12—were resistant to virus. Colony number 2 was

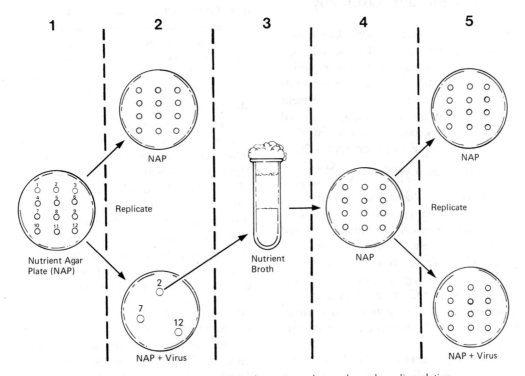

FIG. 16–11. Spontaneous nature of mutation in bacteria as shown through replica plating.

picked by an inoculating needle from the nutrient agar plate to nutrient broth and allowed to grow (3). When growth from the nutrient broth was streaked on a nutrient agar plate, twelve colonies developed (4). The replication technique was then repeated as before. This time, the resultant 12 colonies appeared on both media, indicating that isolation of a pure colony of virus-resistant bacteria from the nutrient agar plate is possible without any exposure to virus.

The various techniques of Luria and Delbrück, Newcombe, and the Lederbergs have been utilized to examine mutations of a wide variety of characteristics with many different microorganisms, including antibiotic resistance in *Staphylococcus aureus*, *Escherichia coli*, *Pseudomonas aeruginosa*, *Shigella* spp., and *Salmonella typhi*.

Genetics and Taxonomy

Percent G + C comparison. One means of studying the relationship between genetics and taxonomy involves determining the percent of the nitrogenous compounds guanine and cytosine % (G + C) present in the DNA of an organism, as compared to the total base composition, of adenine, thymine, guanine, and cytosine. Organisms with similar values in $\dfrac{G+C}{A+T+G+C}$ or % (G+C) have been shown to be related genetically, and very similar in terms of numerical taxonomy. Selected bacteria and their % (G+C) values are presented in Table 16–1.

In many cases, genera are well grouped by their %(G+C) value. However, certain significant discrepancies exist, either as the result of incomplete data or true unrelatedness.

By using a combination of numerical taxonomy, genetic relatedness, and anti-

Table 16–1   Selected Bacterial Genera and their per cent Guanine and Cytosine (G + C) Ratios

Percent (G + C)	Representative Genera
30–36	*Bacillus, Clostridium, Fusobacterium, Staphylococcus, Streptococcus*
38–44	*Bacillus, Coxiella, Hemophilus, Lactobacillus, Neisseria, Proteus, Streptococcus*
46–52	*Clostridium, Corynebacterium, Enterobacter, Escherichia, Klebsiella, Neisseria, Pasteurella, Proteus, Salmonella, Vibrio*
54–60	*Alcaligenes, Corynebacterium, Enterobacter, Klebsiella, Lactobacillus, Pseudomonas, Serratia, Spirillum*
62–68	*Bacillus, Micrococcus, Mycobacterium, Pseudomonas, Rhizobium, Vibrio*
70–80	*Mycobacterium, Nocardia, Sarcina, Streptomyces*

genic analysis, Sneath reported in 1964 that Gram-negative bacteria appear to belong to three clusters of genera. The first of these consisted primarily of the Enterobacteriaceae together with two species of *Pasteurella* and *Vibrio cholerae*. The second cluster included species of *Achromobacter, Alcaligenes, Brucella, Moraxella, Neisseria,* and *Pasteurella multocida. Pseudomonas* spp. and closely related organisms formed the third group. Gram-positive genera, with the exception of those in the order Actinomycetales, comprised one group. Organisms in the order actinomycetales formed a second group. One interesting point noted here was that the genus *Bacillus* appeared to be more closely related to Gram-negative than to Gram-positive bacteria.

DNA hybridization. When the DNA double-stranded helix is heated, the bonds holding the base pairs together are weakened, resulting in the separation of strands. Upon cooling, the strands re-associate and the DNA appears to be identical to the original. As would be expected, when DNA from *Escherichia coli,* for example, is studied in this manner there is complete re-association with more DNA from *E. coli.* Similarly, when two different strains, species, etc., are studied, the degree of relatedness of the two organisms can be measured by determining the ability of their respective DNAs to re-associate to form a "hybrid" DNA molecule. These measurements can be performed in a variety of ways, including enzymatic cleavage of single-stranded DNA and radioisotope tagging of one source of DNA. When such studies were done by comparing *E. coli* with *Salmonella typhimurium* and *Pseudomonas aeruginosa,* relationships of 71% and 1%, respectively, were obtained.

QUESTIONS FOR REVIEW

1. What are the Mendelian laws of heredity? Evaluate them with linked and unlinked characteristics.

2. Why did *Drosophila* become so important to the understanding of genetic principles and the basic chemistry of genetics?

3. Define or explain the following terms:
   a. alleles
   b. homozygous
   c. heterozygous
   d. sex-linked characteristics
   e. genotype
   f. phenotype

4. Compare the processes of mitosis and meiosis. Indicate specific similarities and differences.

5. Define or explain:
   a. transformation
   b. transduction
   c. recombination
   d. lysogenic conversion
   e. F-duction

6. Why has transformation played such an important role in genetics?

7. Describe one experiment to show that bacterial mutations are not directed.

8. How do chemical mutagenic agents cause mutations?

9. What contributions to the development of modern genetics are associated with the following individuals?
   a. Darwin and Lamarck
   b. Luria and Delbrück
   c. Avery, McLeod, and McCarty
   d. Morgan and Sturtevant
   e. Lederberg and Tatum
   f. Miescher and Strasburger

10. Distinguish among the following:
    a. F^+ and F^-
    b. F^+ and F'
    c. F^- and Hfr
    d. F^+ and Hfr

11. What are RTFs? Do they have medical significance?

The
Control
of
Microorganisms

DIVISION 5: Behavioral Objectives

After reading the chapters in this division, the individual should be able to:

1. Relate effective disinfectants, sterilizing chemicals, and physical methods of sterilization to specific applications.

2. Recognize the advantages and disadvantages of disinfectants and physical control methods.

3. Describe the general features of antiseptic and drug testing methods.

4. Describe the methods used in monitoring sterilization equipment.

5. Recognize the importance and basis of antibiotic resistance.

6. Relate the properties of antibiotics to their effectiveness in the control of microbial pathogens.

7. Describe the procedures used in evaluating the effectiveness of antibiotics and anti-microbial agents in general.

8. Recognize the problems associated with the development of effective anti-microbial agents.

The Use of Chemicals in Disinfection and Sterilization

Antisepsis and *disinfection* are general terms that describe procedures used for the reduction of microbial populations by killing and by physical removal. Antisepsis is the term used for application of chemicals to the skin and mucous membranes, whereas disinfection is the term used for application of chemical or physical agents to inanimate materials. Sanitization refers primarily to removal, but the term should not be used to infer an appreciable degree of disinfection.

Historical Background

The Arabs learned several hundred years ago that cauterization of a wound with hot metal prevented infection. This was a common procedure despite the fact that the patient would be scarred for life. Even though cauterization was traumatic, it gave victims more of a fighting chance to overcome the effects of disease agents. The French surgeon Paré in 1537 treated gunshot wounds with bandages soaked in egg yolk, turpentine, and other materials. The turpentine served as a chemical cautery and the egg material contained the antibacterial enzyme lysozyme.

The concept of antisepsis was introduced largely by Semmelweis (1816–1865) and Lister (1827–1912).

Semmelweis

Ignatz Semmelweis, a Hungarian physician working in Vienna, observed that the incidence of childbed fever, otherwise known as puerperal fever, was very much higher in the obstetrical ward in the Vienna General Hospital, which was operated by physicians, than in a similar ward run by midwives. By comparing the procedures in both locations, Semmelweis observed that the midwives washed their hands frequently, whereas the physicians, after performing autopsies, treated patients without changing their blood-splattered clothes or washing their hands. Semmelweis felt that these procedures were important factors accounting for the difference in infection rates between the two wards. In order to lower the occurrence of infections in his maternity clinics, he required the attendants to wash their hands with chlorinated lime. The infection rate dropped significantly.

Unfortunately, Semmelweis' efforts to persuade other physicians of the necessity for cleanliness and disinfection ended in failure, and he was dismissed from the hospital staff. Ridicule drove him from Vienna in 1854, and eventually led him to insanity.

Holmes

Oliver Wendell Holmes, already well known as an author, was one of the first to call attention to the problem in the United States. His article "On the Contagiousness of Puerperal Fever" was published in 1843. Unlike Semmelweis, he was accepted and went on to become dean of Harvard Medical School.

During the early 1800s microorganisms were considered to be biological nonentities. Infections were believed to be caused by some magical power in air, or by an imbalance of body fluids. Certainly contaminated hands were not involved. It took the incredible tenacity of Pasteur to show the world that microorganisms could not only ferment fruit juice to wine, but could also cause spoilage of the wine, before the idea of the possible role of microorganisms in disease could evolve.

Surgical Antisepsis

Aware of the numerous studies by Pasteur, Lister in England undertook the challenge of preventing surgical infections. His efforts with carbolic acid clearly established modern surgical procedures, described in Chapter 2.

In 1881 Koch and his associates evaluated 70 different chemicals for use in disinfection and antisepsis. Among these chemicals were various phenols and mercuric chloride ($HgCl_2$). In 1886 Neuber applied the latter compound as a surgical antiseptic as well as for the disinfection of operating rooms. He also insisted upon the use of clean gowns on patients, and the wearing of clean apparel by surgeons in operating rooms.

Probably the last and certainly one of the more significant reports of the nineteenth century with regard to disinfection was made by Krönig and Paul in 1897. These scientists published standardized and well-controlled procedures for the evaluation and comparison of chemicals. Their reports included the concentrations of chemical compounds, specific test bacteria used, viable plate counts, the temperatures at which the tests were performed, and the culture media used. Kill curves were reported in terms of surviving bacteria as related to the period of exposure.

The General Use of Antiseptics and Disinfectants

Today there are an almost limitless number of chemical agents for controlling microorganisms, and new ones appear on the market regularly. A common problem confronting all personnel who must utilize disinfectants or antiseptics is which one to select and how to use it. Since there is no "ideal" or "all-purpose" agent, the compound to choose is the one that will kill the organisms present in the shortest time, without any damage to the contaminated material.

General Directions for Using Any Chemical Method for Controlling Disease

1. All surfaces of the contaminated material that are to be treated must be exposed to the chemical agent. Therefore, before chemical treatment is begun the material must be scrubbed and thoroughly rinsed to rid it of all soil and organic matter. Furthermore, there must be enough space left between items so that all surfaces of each item are fully exposed to the solution.

2. The time at which a particular article was immersed in solution and the time for its removal should be marked. This prevents others from interrupting the process before it is completed.

3. As solutions used to kill spores are highly volatile, the room in which they are used should be well ventilated.

4. Certain chemicals alter the composition of the materials to be treated. Usually the labels of containers with such compounds indicate the materials to be avoided. Never use a chemical without first checking the label to find out if it is safe for a particular use.

5. It is always best to dilute each solution in the proportions suggested by the manufacturer.

6. Solutions should be changed often. This is especially true if cloudiness or sedimentation appears.

7. It is generally a good practice to have hand lotions in the vicinity for proper hand care after using disinfectants.

Antiseptic solutions are primarily applied externally. However, Zephiran at a 1:10,000 dilution can be used for irrigation of catheterized bladders due to its relatively low toxicity. This antiseptic does not kill *Mycobacterium tuberculosis* and must never be used in cases where urinary tract infections are caused by that organism. Generally, the external antiseptics are applied and allowed to evaporate, as in the case of alcohol; or rinsed off with alcohol after drying, as in the case of Iodine-Alcohol; or rinsed off with water (sterile water for surgical preparations) as in the case of idophors; or rinsed with water leaving an active residue, as with hexachlorophene preparations. In general, 70 to 90 per cent isopropyl alcohol is the least expensive and a very effective antiseptic. The addition of iodine to this alcohol greatly increases its disinfecting properties. While these statements are true, they must be qualified to indicate these solutions' lack of activity against spores. The least expensive and best sporicidal formulation appears to be the combination of formaldehyde and alcohol, but this solution is too toxic for antiseptic use.

Since disinfectant solutions or gases do not have to come into contact with human skin or mucous membranes, greater toxicity is permitted, making them more generally applicable as antimicrobial agents.

The choice of disinfectant depends largely upon the needs of the particular operation and the desires of the individuals performing the procedure. Consideration should be given to the observations which show that some compounds can be extremely irritating, and that some people have more sensitive skin than others.

Selected Disinfecting and Sterilizing Chemicals

Chemical disinfectants and sterilants are used in what are generally termed "cold sterilization" methods. Since there are so many varied individual and compounded agents it is necessary to first consider the particular use, and under what conditions it will be employed. Then that product or formulation which best suits the particular requirements should be selected. Table 17–1 should help to clarify some of the confusion on this question.

The Halogens

This group is made up of the compounds of chlorine and iodine, both organic and inorganic. Most of the inorganic halogen compounds are deadly to living cells.

Iodine.   Iodine solution, either in water or alcohol, is highly antiseptic and has been used for years as a preoperative preparation of the skin, generally applied to the skin's surface directly before any surgical procedure. It is also extremely effective against many protozoans, such as the amoeba that causes dysentery. In proper concentration, iodine does not drastically harm human tissues. However, the clinical use of tincture of iodine stains tissue and may cause local skin irritation and occasional allergic reactions. Preparations of iodine compounded with non-ionic detergents and polymers such as polyvinylpyrolidone have been developed for disinfection and antiseptic uses, respectively. The iodine binds loosely with the organic compound and is released

Table 17–1   Selected Compounds for Chemical Control of Microorganisms

Procedure	Effectiveness	Advantages	Disadvantages	Preferred Use	Recommended Exposure Time
Halogens 1. Chlorine	Kills most vegative cells, some viruses and fungi; spores usually resistant	Excellent deodorant	Activity reduced by organic material and some metallic catalysts; irritating odor and residue; solutions are somewhat unstable	Purification of drinking water	Immediate effect (from seconds to minutes, depending upon compound and concentration)
2. Iodine	Vegetative cells; some spores and viruses when used in high concentration	Extremely useful as a skin disinfectant; can be used over wide pH range	Irritating odor and residue, except with iodofors	Wound dressing, pre-operative preparation	At least 60 seconds to kill vegetative bacterial cells
Alcohols	Vegetative cells and many viruses killed, spores unaffected	Unaffected by organic compounds. No residue left; stable and easily handled	No outstanding disadvantages as a disinfectant	Skin and surfaces	10 to 15 minutes in 70% to 80% solutions
Phenols and related compounds	Vegetative cells and some fungi killed; only moderately effective against spores	Stable to heating and drying; unaffected by organic compounds	Pure phenol is harmful to tissues and has disagreeable odor	In combination with halogens and detergents, they make excellent disinfectants	Effect is immediate
Detergents quaternary ammonium compounds	Kills bacteria (including staphylococcus and some viruses; TB and spores unaffected	Stable in the presence of organic compounds, easy to handle. No irritating residue left	Hard water, detergents, and fibrous materials interfere with activity; can rust metals	Small metal instruments	Depends upon type and concentration, generally 10 to 30 minutes
Heavy metals	Some vegetative cells and viruses killed; TB and spores unaffected	Fast and inexpensive, no special equipment required	Inactivated by organic compounds and chemical antagonists	Little used except as preservatives and in fungal and protozoan infections	Effective as long as in contact
Aldehydes	Staphylococcus, TB, and viruses killed readily; spores killed only upon prolonged exposure	Glutaraldehyde is nontoxic and non-irritating to tissue	Prolonged exposure required	Instrument disinfection	A 2% solution for 3 to 18 hours
Ethylene oxide	100% effective if properly managed	Can treat critical items which would be destroyed by other techniques	Slow; equipment is expensive; leaves irritating residue; materials must be aired before use	Plastics, rubber, and instruments which are sensitive to heat or chemicals	1 to 2 hours at 60° C for small loads; 10 to 12 hours necessary for large loads

slowly to produce an effective disinfection. Antiseptic idophors are used routinely for preoperative skin cleansing and disinfection.

Chlorine. Free chlorine, like free iodine, has a characteristic color and odor. Chlorine in any of its various forms has long been recognized as an excellent deodorant and later as a disinfecting agent. It is a standard treatment for drinking water in all communities. Unfortunately, most compounds of chlorine are inactivated in the presence of organic material and some metallic catalysts.

Hypochlorite solutions are those most generally used in disinfecting and deodorizing procedures as they are relatively harmless to human tissues, easy to handle, colorless, and do not stain, although they bleach. They are widely employed in hospitals to disinfect rooms, surfaces, and nonsurgical instruments. They all tend to leave a residue that can be irritating to skin and tissues.

Several organic chlorine derivatives are also used for the disinfection of water. This is particularly true for campers and others who must use water that is likely to be contaminated. The most common of the compounds employed is halazone, or parasulfone dichloramidobenzoic acid.

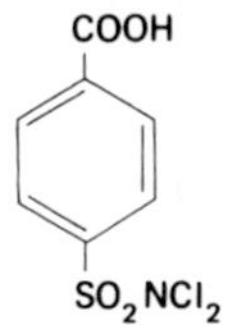

A halazone concentration of 4 to 8 milligrams per liter will safely disinfect water containing typhoid bacilli, even in fairly hard waters, in approximately 30 minutes. Another compound used for the same purpose is succinchlorimide.

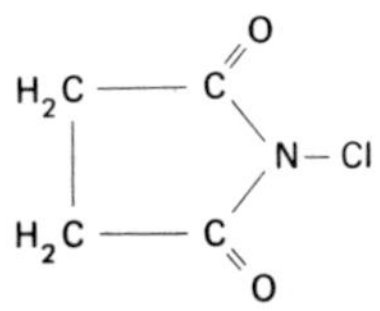

A concentration of 11.6 mg will disinfect a liter of water in 20 minutes. These organic chlorides are quite stable in tablet form, becoming active when placed in the water.

The Alcohols

These are among the most effective and heavily relied upon chemicals for sterilization and disinfection. Three types are used: ethanol, methanol, and isopropanol. As a general rule, the bactericidal value increases as the molecular weight increases. In practice, a solution of 70 to 80 per cent is employed. Percentages above 90 and below 50 generally are not as effective, except for isopropyl, which is effective up to 99 per cent.

Although alcohols are somewhat affected by organic material, they leave no residue on surfaces. It is a common practice to wipe large pieces of equipment and furniture in an office with alcohol. A 10-minute exposure is sufficient to kill vegetative cells, but not spores.

The alcohols, alone or in combination, are often used as skin disinfectants. A quick wipe is not really enough to sterilize, but only to cut down the population and thus reduce the chance of infection. It has been common practice to dip instruments into alcohol and then flame them. The effectiveness of this procedure is questionable, and it should not be substituted for better sterilization methods. Isopropyl alcohol is often easier to obtain than ethanol, which is under close government supervision. It has proved to be somewhat more toxic to microorganisms.

The Phenols

Phenol (carbolic acid) can probably be called the oldest recognized disinfectant. It was used by Lister in the late 1800s as a germicide in the operating room. In low concentration, its deadly effect is due to the fact that it precipitates proteins actively. It has been chosen as the standard for the comparison of the activities of other disinfectants in terms of phenol coefficients. Phenol and cresol (methylated phenol) (Figure 17–1) have

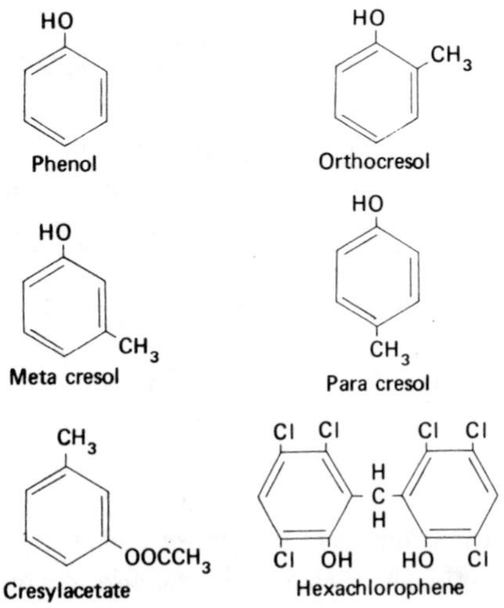

FIG. 17–1. Phenol and various cresol and hexachlorophene structures.

a typical odor and are harmful to tissues. However, they are very stable to heating and drying and retain their activity in the presence of organic material. Unfortunately, they are only moderately effective against bacterial spores. The addition of a halogen, chlorine for example, or a short chain organic compound enhances the activity of the phenols.

Hexachlorophene (Figure 17–1) is one of the most useful of the phenol derivatives. Combined with a soap, it is a commonly used, highly effective skin disinfectant, although slow-acting. Unlike most phenolic compounds, hexachlorophene has no irritating odor and has a high residual action. It is also a good deodorant, a property which has been put to extensive use by commercial deodorant and soap makers.

An interesting feature of phenol and the cresols is their anesthetic and/or analgesic pain-killing properties. They can only be used externally because they are highly toxic. A slight modification of cresol has resulted in cresylacetate (Figure 17–1), which has been used in spray form for antisepsis and as an analgesic on the mucous membranes of the ear, nose, and throat.

The Peroxides

Hydrogen peroxide (H_2O_2) is an effective and nontoxic topical antiseptic rarely used for general disinfection. The molecule is unstable and when warmed degrades into water and oxygen, as shown.

$$2H_2O_2 \longrightarrow 2H_2O + O_2 \uparrow$$

The evolved oxygen is chemically active, reacts with negatively charged groups in proteins, and may lead to inactivation of vital enzyme systems. A 3 per cent solution is often used to cleanse and disinfect wounds, since anaerobic bacteria are particularly sensitive to oxygen. Sodium

peroxide (Na_2O_2) has been employed in the form of a paste for the treatment of acne. Zinc peroxide (ZnO_2) is used medically in a creamy suspension with zinc oxide (ZnO) and zinc hydroxide [$Zn(OH)_2$], for skin infections caused by microaerophilic and anaerobic organisms.

The Antiseptic Dyes

Of the variety of dyes which have a growth inhibiting or *bacteriostatic* activity we shall present two, namely, *acridine* derivatives and *rosaniline* dyes. *Acriflavine* is a mixture of two compounds (Figure 17–2). It was evaluated by Ehrlich and shown to have trypanosomicidal activity—effectiveness against the causative agents of African sleeping sickness.

Acriflavine has low toxicity and is relatively free from skin-sensitizing properties. It has a broad spectrum of activity and has been used for treatment of urinary tract infections. The mechanism of action appears to be due to the ability of acridines to react with DNA.

One methyl derivative of a rosaniline dye, *crystal violet,* is a potent bacteriostatic agent for Gram-positive bacteria, besides being the primary stain in the Gram reaction (Figure 17–3).

Crystal violet has been used for the treatment of candidiasis and *Trichomonas*-caused vaginitis. *Candida albicans*

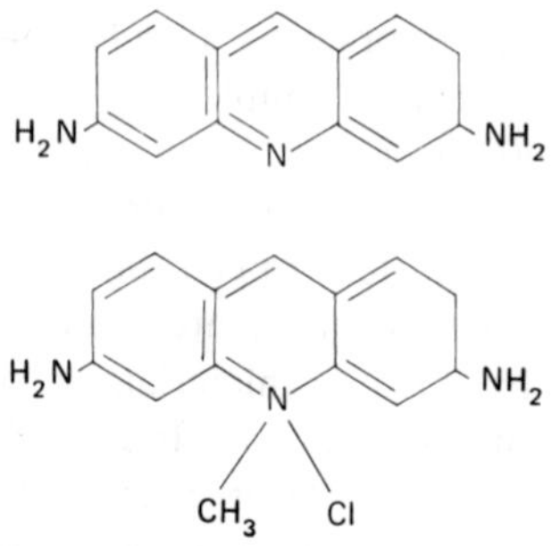

FIG. 17–2. Diaminoacridine (top) and diaminomethyl-acridinium-chloride (bottom).

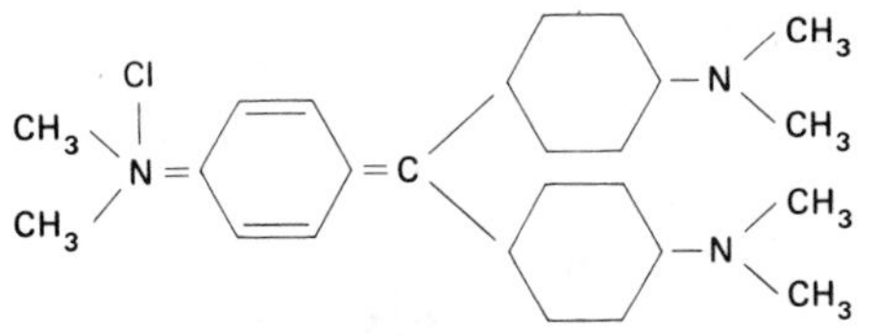

FIG. 17-3. Crystal violet (hexamethylpararo-saniline).

is particularly sensitive to the dye. The mechanism of action of this compound against Gram-positive bacteria appears to be very similar to that of penicillin, blockage of a final step in the synthesis of cell wall material.

The Detergents

These are organic compounds which, because of their structure have one, *hydrophilic,* end of their molecule which mixes well with water, and one, *hydrophobic,* which does not. Therefore, the detergent molecules orient themselves on the surfaces of objects with their hydrophilic ends toward the water.

Detergents may or may not be ionic (electrically charged) (Figure 17–4). Generally, the non-ionic ones do not qualify as good disinfectants and may in some cases even support the growth of bacteria and fungi.

There are two types of ionic surface active agents: *anionic* or negatively charged and *cationic* or positively charged. The anionic detergents are only mildly *bactericidal* (bacteria killing). The cationic, of which the most effective and widely used are the quaternary ammonium compounds, are extremely bactericidal, especially for *Staphylococcus* and some viruses. However, they do not affect spores. It is thought that they act by dissolving the fat-like substances or lipids on or in cell walls or membranes. They are absorbed by porous or fibrous materials, which may lessen their efficiency in the presence of this type of substance. Hard water, containing Ca or Mg ions, will interfere with their action. Also, they will rust metal objects unless an anti-rust agent, such as nitrite, is added. Even with these drawbacks, cationic detergents are among the most widely used disinfecting chemicals, as they are easily handled and are not irritating to tissues in the concentrations ordinarily used.

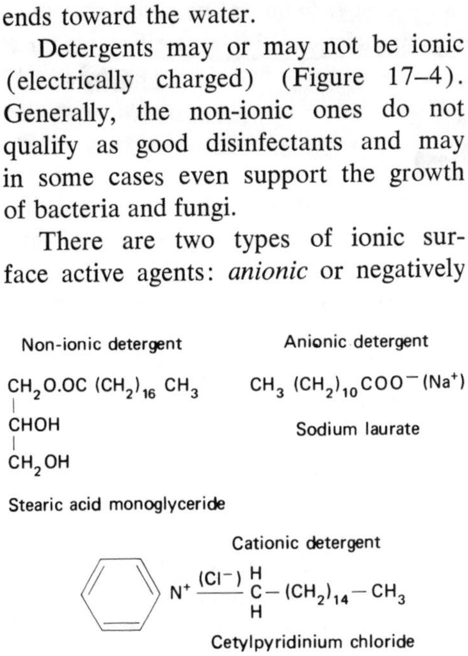

Heavy Metals

Heavy metals usually exhibit their deadly effect by precipitating proteins or reacting with enzymes or other essential cellular components. Those in common use are mercury, silver, arsenic, zinc, and copper.

Mercury. Mercuric bichloride ($HgCl_2$), formerly very popular, has its action greatly reduced in the presence of organic material, and is now considered obsolete. Also, the effect of mercury on organisms may be reversed by the antagonistic action of added material rich in thiol groups (–SH) for which the mercury is specific. Organic mercury compounds are effective for use in the treatment of minor wounds and as a preservative in serums and vaccines.

Silver nitrate (Argyrol). It was once useful—before penicillin—in preventing gonococcal infections in the eyes of children whose mothers were infected.

Non-ionic detergent

$CH_2O.OC\ (CH_2)_{16}\ CH_3$

CHOH

CH_2OH

Stearic acid monoglyceride

Anionic detergent

$CH_3\ (CH_2)_{10}COO^-(Na^+)$

Sodium laurate

Cationic detergent

Cetylpyridinium chloride

FIG. 17–4. Structures of various detergent-disinfectant molecules.

Arsenic. It achieved fame as the first known treatment for syphylis and still finds some use in the treatment of protozoan infections.

Zinc. A mixture of a long-chained fatty acid and the zinc salt of the acid is commonly used as an antifungal powder or ointment. It is particularly effective for the treatment of athlete's foot. The zinc salt also acts as an astringent and aids in healing any superficial lesions, as does zinc oxide paste, which is commonly recommended for treatment of diaper rash and concurrent bacterial or fungal infections.

The Aldehydes

A 20 per cent solution of formaldehyde (Figure 17–5) in 65 to 70 per cent alcohol makes an excellent sterilizing bath if instruments are suspended in it for 18 hours. However, because of the residue it leaves, the instruments must be rinsed before being used, thereby recontaminating them. A related compound, glutaraldehyde (Figure 17–5), in solution is as effective as formaldehyde, especially if the pH is 7.5 or more. Staphylococci and other vegetative cells are killed within 5 minutes, *Mycobacterium tuberculosis* and viruses in 10 minutes, and spores sometimes in 3 hours, although as much as 12 hours may be required. The 2 per cent solution is nontoxic and practically nonirritating to patients.

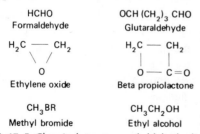

FIG. 17–5. Chemical structures of aldehyde disinfectants and several gaseous sterilants.

Gaseous Methods

Ethylene oxide (EtO). Perhaps the best-known and most often used sterilizing gas is ethylene oxide (Figure 17–5). Introduced in 1940, EtO is a highly explosive gas which is soluble in water. A special autoclave-type sterilizer and a table model are available for use with EtO (Figure 17–6). The chamber should be humidified for at least one hour before the actual sterilizing for highest EtO activity. To insure sterility of critical objects, an overnight exposure to 12 percent EtO at 60°C is recommended. Because the gas is explosive in air, it must be used with caution. EtO often is diluted with carbon dioxide, freon (another inert gas), or, more rarely, methyl bromide.

Unfortunately, EtO leaves a residue that is irritating to tissue, and all exposed items must be well aired before use. The procedure is slow and time consuming and the equipment is expensive. The true advantage of EtO lies in the ease with which it penetrates plastic to sterilize contents of wrapped or sealed packages. Materials that are heat- or moisture-sensitive and *not damaged by EtO* are readily sterilized. These materials include optical equipment, catheters, heart-lung machine components, artificial heart valves, respiratory therapy equipment, and often difficult-to-decontaminate items such as pillows, mattresses, and shoes.

Special sterilizers have been designed for use with ethylene oxides. The components of one such device are shown in Figure 17–7. A mixture of pressurized ethylene oxide and carbon dioxide is metered into the sterilizing chamber, which is heated by flowing steam through a coiled heat exchanger. When properly used, these devices are very effective for sterilization.

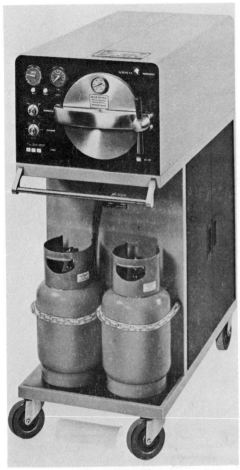

FIG. 17–6. An example of an instrument used in ethylene oxide sterilization. (Courtesy of American Sterilizer Company, Erie, Pennsylvania.)

Formaldehyde vapor. Other chemicals that have been used in gaseous disinfection and sterilization include formaldehyde, beta-propiolactone, methyl bromide, and ethyl alcohol. We have discussed the usefulness of formaldehyde in liquid disinfection. It can be very useful as a gas, as well. When formalin (37 per cent aqueous formaldehyde) or paraformaldehyde (polymerized HCHO) are warmed, they release formaldehyde, which has proved to be extremely effective for disinfection of instruments and various materials that have been contaminated with spores of *Mycobacterium tuberculosis*. Disadvantages: the vapor has poor penetration, reacts with extraneous organic materials, and has a tendency to polymerize as a thin white film on the surface of the objects being treated.

Beta-propiolactone. BPL (Figure 17–5) is stable at temperatures below freezing, but when vaporized in a humid environment at ambient temperature, it becomes a powerful sterilant. As a liquid it has been applied to the sterilization of vaccines, tissues, sera, and surgical ligatures. BPL decomposes very rapidly on exposure to moisture and within a few hours, none is left. When used properly it can be relatively nontoxic. However, liquid BPL has been shown to be carcinogenic.

Methyl bromide vapor. It requires humidity for activity. Although it penetrates well, its microbicidal activity is weak. It has been used primarily as a disinfectant for fungi and non-spore-forming bacteria.

Ethyl alcohol. It is primarily a liquid disinfectant, since it works best within certain concentrations in water and is not sporicidal. Under conditions where a wide variety of interconnected materials are used in intimate contact with man, it is often advisable to disinfect gently so long as there is no apparent danger to the individual. In one such case, aerosolized warmed 70 per cent ethyl alcohol was used to disinfect the hoses and filter traps used in physiological testing of exhaled air in a manned space suit testing program. Additional items, such as the heat exchanger for condensation of moisture from the air, were sterilized by filling with 6 per cent hydrogen peroxide. This combination

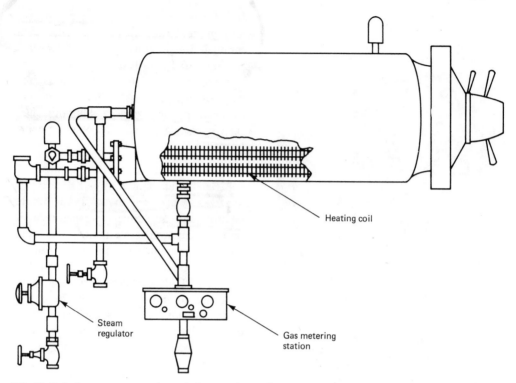

FIG. 17–7. Basic components of an ethylene oxide sterilizer.

of disinfectants was used primarily because both left no residues that might have interfered with the testing program.

Antiseptic and Disinfectant Testing Methods

Generally speaking the distinction between antiseptic and disinfectant is not made when a given product is evaluated for its antimicrobial activity. Until the early 1950s, the only procedure accepted by the United States Department of Agriculture for proving sterilizing power was the phenol coefficient test.

Phenol Coefficient Test

This procedure was first proposed by Rideal and Walker in 1903 and later standardized by Ruehle and Brewer in 1931. The test compares the relative ac-

tivity of a given product with the killing power of phenol under the same test conditions. Various dilutions of phenol and of the test product are made and mixed with a specified volume of a broth culture of *Staphylococcus aureus* or of a certain species of *Salmonella*. At intervals of 5, 10, and 15 minutes a specified volume of each diluent tube is removed, added to a nutrient broth medium, and incubated for at least 2 days. If the product is bacteriostatic rather than bactericidal, it may be necessary to incubate the system for as long as 10 to 14 days to determine the agent's effectiveness. The broth medium is selected to suit the product being tested. For example, oxidizing chemicals or mercurials must be tested with fluid thioglycollate medium, while a broth made up of nutrient ingredients plus lecithin and sorbitan monooleate ("Tween 80") is necessary for testing phenolics and quaternary ammonium compounds.

After the incubation period, the broth subcultures from the disinfectant dilutions are examined for the visible evidence of growth or no growth. The *phenol coefficient* is defined at the ratio of the highest dilution of a test germicide showing kill in 10 but not in 5 minutes to the comparable dilution of phenol. However, this value does not indicate the relative effectiveness of the product for use in disinfection of floors or walls.

Floor and Wall Disinfection

Certain questions are often raised concerning the use of products for floor and wall disinfection, including: (1) What concentration should be used for disinfecting surfaces? (2) Is this product compatible with soaps and detergents? (3) Is this product active in hard water or at low or high pH levels? and (4) What is the spectrum of activity against various microorganisms? Until the development of standard "Use-Dilution" methods by the Association of Official Analytical Chemists (A.O.A.C.), the "appropriate" dilution of a germicide was computed by multiplying the phenol coefficient by 20. While this practice appeared reasonable for some products, its applicability was not universal.

The Use-Dilution Test

The A.O.A.C. Use-Dilution Method has now been adopted for purposes of establishing appropriate dilutions of the germicide for actual conditions. In this procedure, three bacterial species are tested against the product. They are *Staphylococcus aureus* (ATCC 6538), *Salmonella cholerasuis* (ATCC 10708), and *Pseudomonas aeruginosa* (ATCC 15442). The ATCC designation refers to the catalogue number for the particular organism at the American Type Culture Collection, Rockville, Maryland. Cultures of these bacterial species may be obtained from this agency. The cultures and dilutions of disinfectant are prepared according to the specific instructions of the A.O.A.C. The bacterial species are used to contaminate small stainless steel cylinders which are dried briefly and then placed in specified volumes of the test product. Such cylinders are exposed for 10 minutes, allowed to drain on the side of the tube, transferred to appropriate subculture media, and incubated for 2 days. The results are read simply as growth or no growth, using at least ten replicates of each organism at the test dilution of the product. A satisfactory "use dilution" is one which kills all test organisms, producing at least a 95 per cent level of confidence. Occasionally it may be necessary to perform a 30- or even 60-cylinder test per organism in order to achieve this level of effectiveness.

The A.O.A.C. Use-Dilution Method, although superior to the phenol coefficient procedure, must not be considered the ultimate in tests. It is therefore essential that each institution perform some modification of this A.O.A.C. procedure under their own use conditions and with pathogens from their particular locale. In addition to the A.O.A.C. Use-Dilution Method, two other common test methods are the A.O.A.C. Germicidal Spray and A.O.A.C. Tuberculocidal Test Methods.

The previous discussion indicated that these tests represented the bactericidal activity of disinfectants. Generally this statement is true, and is based upon either the selection of particular disinfectants known to be bactericidal, or the use of particular dilutions of disinfectants which are usually bactericidal.

Bacteriostatic-Bactericidal Test

Many compounds may be either bacteriostatic or bactericidal, depending on the concentration employed. This point can be tested by inoculating serially diluted disinfectant solutions in growth media. After a two-day incubation period, the dilutions which show no growth are subcultured to fresh media. If the growth was prevented by bacteriostatic action, the organisms will grow on subculture. In this manner, the concentration of a particular product that is bacteriostatic can be compared with results of the bactericidal tests discussed previously.

Tissue Toxicity Test

One approach to the comparison of products used as antiseptics has been the Tissue Toxicity Test. In this procedure, as developed by A. J. Salle and others between 1935 and 1947, germicides were tested for their killing effect with bacteria and their toxicity for chick-heart tissue cells. A *toxicity index* was formulated, defined as the ratio of the greatest dilution of the product that can kill the animal cells in 10 minutes to the dilution that can kill the bacterial cells in the same period of time and under identical conditions. For example, a tincture of iodine solution was found to be toxic for chick-heart tissue at a 1:4,000 dilution and bactericidal for *Staphylococcus aureus* at a 1:20,000 dilution, giving a toxicity index of 1/5 or 0.2. In contrast, a tincture of merthiolate solutions was found to have a toxicity index of 3.3, and tincture of metaphen, an index of 10.0. Theoretically, an antiseptic should have an index less than 1.0, indicating a greater toxicity to bacteria than to tissue cells; but the exact relationship of an index based upon toxicity to chick heart *in vitro* to human skin *in vivo* is difficult to assess.

Reminders

It is important that proper cleaning be performed before disinfection. If possible, the cleaning agent should be germicidal, so that microorganisms will not remain in the solution and perhaps contaminate floors or attendants by splashing.

Virus Disinfection

Disinfection of objects contaminated with viruses poses a difficult problem. While some viruses, such as influenza, are as sensitive as vegetative bacteria, others, such as enteroviruses (e.g., polio, ECHO, and coxackie), are more resistant and therefore comparable to *Mycobacterium tuberculosis*. The resistances of hepatitis viruses are as yet unknown. If hepatitis viruses are suspected, heat sterilization is the method of choice, even if it degrades the contaminated material. Known cases of hepatitis virus infections have resulted because chemicals, rather than heat, were used to "disinfect" dental tools.

QUESTIONS FOR REVIEW

1. What are some perferred uses for each of the following?
   a. chlorine
   b. alcohol
   c. phenol
   d. formaldehyde
   e. ethylene oxide

2. List the contributions to aseptic technique ascribed to:
   a. Semmelweis
   b. Lister
   c. Koch
   d. Krönig and Paul

3. What benefits do the iodophors offer versus tincture of iodine?

4. Which halogen molecule is a disinfectant component of halozone?

5. What chemical change in the toxic cresol molecule yields an active anesthetic-antiseptic for use on mucous membranes?

6. Why might cationic detergents be more effective disinfectants than the anionic or neutral molecules?

7. What are some similarities and differences between formaldehyde, ethylene oxide, and beta-propiolactone when used for gaseous sterilization?

8. What is the basic difference between the phenol coefficient and use-dilution disinfectant testing methods?

9. Which disinfectant and/or particular method might be considered in each of the following cases?
   a. oral thermometer for use with TB patients
   b. blood pressure cuff
   c. inhalation therapy equipment
   d. disposable needles and syringes
   e. kitchen floor

Physical Methods of Microbial Control

Table 18–1 summarizes the important, commonly used methods of physical control with the advantages, disadvantages, and applications of each. These are described in more detail in the text.

In addition to the presentation of heat as a major physical control agent, this chapter discusses: (1) preparation of selected materials for sterilization, (2) methods used in the monitoring of sterilization equipment, (3) various irradiations for general applicability to disinfection and sterilization, and (4) filtration with various porous materials.

Preparation of Materials for Sterilization

With any and all procedures, it is absolutely essential that everything to be sterilized be scrupulously clean. This means the complete removal of all debris, particularly organic material such as blood or serum. This is especially important when using chemical disinfectants, as many of them are inactivated in the presence of organic material. Moreover, some substances are capable of acting as protective agents, in that they

Table 18–1   Selected Physical Control Methods

Procedure	Effectiveness	Disadvantages	Preferred Use	Recommended Exposure Time
Autoclaving	Liquids can be sterilized, good penetration, 100% effective	Equipment is expensive; dampens fabrics; corrodes metals; new high-pressure autoclaves improved but costly	All critical materials that can withstand temperature and pressure	Generally 15 to 30 min at 250°F (121°C) and 15 pounds pressure
Dry heat, oven	Easily handled, 100% effective	May char fabric and melt rubber; poor penetration so procedure is slow	Glassware, wax, oils, powders	1 to 2 hr at 160-180°C
Dry heat, heat transfer	Can disinfect complex mechanical equipment which cannot be handled by other methods	Items must be dried after treatment; residue left; effective only with small items	Dental hand-pieces and small instruments	Oils and beads: 125°C for 20 to 30 min; spores: 160°C for 1 hr
Ultraviolet radiation	Kills bacteria, some viruses, and some fungi. Leaves no residue	Poor penetration (surface disinfection only); effects may be reversible; may cause burns to human tissue	Air and surface disinfectant	Prolonged exposure
Filtration	100% effective for bacteria and larger organisms. May be used for removal of viruses (ultrafiltration)	Some filter media are adsorptive, fragile, or electrically charged	For thermolabile liquids, e.g., enzymes, some sugars, and certain antibiotics	Not applicable

keep the sterilizing agent from reaching the organism. Cutting down a bacterial population through the physical action of wiping organisms off surfaces and the killing (bactericidal) effect of a good detergent are other ways of enhancing the effect of any sterilizing technique. Instruments and other metal objects should be placed in hot sodium triphosphate solution to remove organic debris before being disinfected or sterilized.

The cleansing of needles and syringes involves special problems, since they must be absolutely clean before being sterilized. Immediately after use, all syringes should be rinsed thoroughly by pulling a cleaning solution up through the needle into the syringe several times before dropping it into the solution. This procedure makes cleaning much easier as it eliminates the drying of serum and blood on the glass or inside the needle. The syringe then should be scrubbed with a brush and a good cleansing detergent or disinfectant. A small wire can be passed through the bore of the needle to ream out any debris that may have adhered to the inside. After washing, both items must be thoroughly rinsed in several changes of clean water, and completely dried. They are then ready for wrapping.

Syringes may be wrapped in paper in such a manner that the plunger can be removed from the paper and placed in the barrel of the syringe aseptically. Special types of envelopes are available for sterilizing these items. Needles, once they are cleaned, are placed in a glass tube with a constricted neck or with cotton in the closed end to prevent dulling the point. The tube is then plugged, usually with cotton, and the whole assembly sterilized in this manner. The needle can be joined to the syringe by removing the plug and tipping the needle out of the tube so that it can be held at the sides of the lock. Once it has been attached to the syringe, it can be completely removed from the tube and used immediately. Syringes and needles prepared in this manner should not be set up until they are to be used.

For other items which require wrapping before sterilization, either paper or muslin is recommended. A loosely woven material such as muslin allows for better penetration and circulation of heat than the more tightly woven fabrics. Items should be wrapped with several thicknesses and then sealed with a heat-sensitive tape, commercially available. Instruments which are hinged should be wrapped in open position to insure proper sterilization. It is essential to write the date on wrapped packs when they are sterilized, since they must be resterilized if not used within four weeks.

Danger of Hepatitis Infection

In the office, excluding obvious disease, the greatest potential danger to the patient lies in the use of contaminated needles and the transmittance of serum hepatitis. An infected patient often carries the living virus in his bloodstream for several weeks before symptoms arise, and several years after recovery from the disease. In either case, the organism is highly infective and can cause severe illness and even death. Its transmission has been traced directly to the injection of the virus by the use of contaminated needles and syringes. Hepatitis virus is extremely stable and resists considerable heating, drying, and most chemicals. This is one of the main reasons that any items which come into contact with serum or blood must be processed rigorously to ensure sterilization. Perhaps the easiest and surest way to protect a patient is to utilize the many disposable presterilized products which are available commercially.

Heat Killing of Microorganisms

Thermal procedures are usually simple, reliable, and relatively inexpensive. Much of the knowledge concerning the heat destruction ("thermal kill") of microorganisms has come from the studies conducted by the food-processing industry.

Terminology of Thermal Kill

Although this chapter does not compare various procedures in depth, four terms concerning the thermal kill of microorganisms are necessary for general information:

1. *Thermal death point*: That temperature at which a suspension of organisms is sterilized after a 10-minute exposure.
2. *Thermal death time*: The length of time required for a particular temperature to sterilize a suspension of organisms.
3. *D value*: The time required to kill 90 per cent of the organisms in a suspension at a specified temperature. The temperature is generally expressed as a subscript, as in $D_{100°C}$ or $D_{59°F}$.
4. *Z value*: The number of degrees of temperature needed to effect a tenfold change in the D value.

In essence, the thermal death point and the thermal death time take into consideration the interaction of time and temperature without any particular guidelines, while the D value is the actual number of minutes required to reduce the viable count of microbes, according to certain established guidelines. Lastly, the Z value relates D values. The following example shows the relationship between these terms.

Bacillus megaterium spores have a reported $D_{100°C} = 1$ min. If the same spores had $D_{95°C} = 10$ min, then the Z value could be calculated according to the formula.

$$Z = \frac{T_1 - T_2}{\log D_2 - \log D_1}$$

where

$$T_1 = 100 \quad D_1 = 1 \quad \log D_1 = 0$$
$$T_2 = 95 \quad D_2 = 10 \quad \log D_2 = 1$$

Therefore

$$Z = \frac{100 - 95}{1 - 0} = \frac{5}{1} = 5.$$

In essence, this hypothetical experiment shows that for *B. megaterium* a change of 5°C can cause a tenfold change in D, or the time required to kill 90 per cent of the organisms. With this information, we could then predict that $D_{105°C}$ would be 6 seconds and $D_{110°C}$, 600 milliseconds. Assuming that a suspension of these spores contained one billion per ml at 110°C, it would take approximately 7 seconds to reduce the viable count to less than one per ml. Thus, by knowing a few simple concepts and the heat stability of the material to be disinfected or sterilized, we can calculate the appropriate temperature and time for sterilization.

How Heat Disinfection Works

Moist heat appears to exert its killing effect by the denaturation of proteins, chiefly enzymes. Another theory of the killing action of moist heat involves a change in the physical state of cell lipid. Support of this view is provided by the observation that *Clostridium botulinum* spores are more heat-resistant when grown in the presence of higher-molecular-weight fatty acids. When grown in lipid-free media, the spores exhibited less heat resistance. There are probably several factors involved in the effects of moist heat.

Bacterial death caused by dry heat appears to be due largely to the oxidation of the cell components. Studies have shown that the drier the preparation, the greater the heat resistance. If dried organisms are heated *in vacuo* or under nitrogen, the killing effect is slower and the organisms appear to be more resistant. Lyophilized pellets of *Escherichia coli* have shown levels of resistance to dry heat almost comparable to that of some spore-forming bacteria. If, however, pellets are dropped in boiling water, the *E. coli* cells are killed rapidly. Thus, the rapid denaturation of proteins and possibly the physical change in lipids appear to be more rapid in sterilization than are oxidative effects alone.

Moist Heat

Autoclaving. The surest and most preferred technique for sterilization is the application of steam under pressure, or *autoclaving*. The autoclave (Figure 18–1) consists of a steel chamber capable of withstanding more than one atmosphere (15 lbs. per square inch—psi) of pressure. Items to be sterilized are placed in the autoclave. As steam vapors enter the chamber, the air inside is forced out a vent. When the temperature inside the chamber reaches 212°F (100°C), or boiling, and all the air is removed, the vents are closed, but the steam continues to enter. This causes an increase in the internal pressure to 15 psi. Most autoclaves have a control valve which may be set for any desired pressure. A temperature of 250°F (121.5°C) at a pressure of 15 psi must be maintained for 15 minutes. All living material, including bacteria, fungi, spores, and viruses, is theoretically destroyed in 10 to 12 minutes. The extra time is a margin of safety. Thick packs or large liquid volumes may be held for a longer time, up to 30 minutes, to insure that adequate sterilizing temperatures have been reached at their centers. The various components of an autoclave and the path of proper gas flow for sterilization are shown in Figure 18–2.

FIG. 18–1. A modern automatic autoclave. (Courtesy of Barnstead Still and Sterilizer Company, Boston.)

Key points to remember when using the autoclave. The moist heat does the sterilizing, *not* the pressure. It is imperative that *all of the air in the autoclave be forced out* by the steam in order to achieve the appropriate temperature. Residual air will contribute to the pressure in the system, but it will effectively lower the maximum temperature attainable. Adequate *circulation of steam* within the chamber is also essential. Improper loading of items will result in "dead spaces" that are not heated to temperature. This,

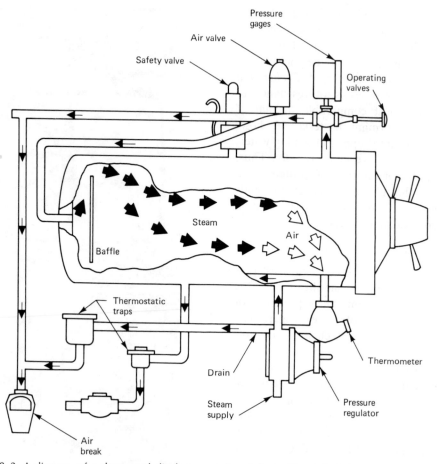

FIG. 18–2. A diagram of a downward displacement (gravity) sterilizer, showing various components and the path of proper air and steam flow.

of course, may cause conditions within the chamber which will prevent sterilization. When loading, vessels or beakers must be oriented to each other so that all the air may be freely replaced with steam. Packs or wrapped goods must be positioned so that the steam can reach the center of each. This usually means that these items must be tipped or laid on their sides and dry goods set far enough apart so that steam can circulate.

The condensation of the steam upon cooler items causes the release of the latent heat from the water to that item's surface, raising its temperature to a level incompatible with life. Unfortunately, the collection of water upon cooler surfaces during autoclaving dampens fibrous materials, dulls the edges of instruments, and causes metals to rust. It is recommended that a *corrosion inhibitor* such as sodium benzoate or other commercially available products be used to protect metallic items before autoclaving.

Materials may be dried in the autoclave by turning off the steam to the chamber and opening the evacuation valve. The excess pressure dissipates immediately and, as the chamber cools, moisture is removed by evaporation from the sterilized equipment. The items can be removed, dry and sterile, and used or stored for future use.

If operating instructions are followed accurately, and the loading of the chamber is done correctly, the use of the autoclave for sterilization is foolproof. Unfortunately, the equipment is expensive and requires special installation.

Faster autoclaves are commercially available, and others are in development. These instruments rely upon operation at higher temperatures, produced by use of steam at higher pressures. Table 18–2 presents steam pressures, temperatures, and suggested sterilization times that are possible with various kinds of autoclaves. It is essential to repeat that *the temperature is the critical variable and is dependent upon the proper displacement of the air.*

Sterilizing soft items. Surgical packs, dressings, linen, and various cloth, paper, and other materials usually require drying after exposure to the steam condensate during autoclaving. This may be accomplished by evacuation of the chamber. For applications of this type, the standard gravity autoclave is being replaced by high-vacuum systems. Reasons for this change include shortening of overall exposure to heat, more complete drying, and shortening of the overall process time.

In a high-vacuum system, the load is subjected to a pre-vacuum of 15 mm Hg absolute pressure for a few minutes prior to the entrance of steam. This allows the steam to penetrate all parts of the load more rapidly than would be possible otherwise. The load then is processed at 121.5°C for 15 minutes, or at 135°C for 3 minutes. The steam is removed until the pressure comes down to about 40 mm Hg absolute pressure to remove excess heat and moisture. Then sterile air is let in to bring the internal pressure to the normal 15 psi. This procedure produces a dry, sterile load.

Boiling. The least expensive and most readily available sterilizing technique is boiling. The recommended time for this procedure is 15 minutes once the water has reached a rolling boil. Vegetative cells are killed with 5 to 10 minutes exposure. However, most spores and viruses can survive many hours of this treatment. The addition of certain substances and chemicals to the boiling bath may add to the killing power of this method. However, for all critical items a better and more reliable technique is advised.

Pasteurization. Pasteurization is a method of heat disinfection commonly applied to milk, wine, and cider. The

Table 18–2 Autoclaving Pressure-Temperature-Time Relationships

| Steam Pressure in pounds per square inch (psi) | Temperature | | Sterilization Time (minutes) |
	Degrees C	Degrees F	
15	121	250	15
20	126	259	10
30	135	273	3
50[a]	146	298	1

[a] For experimental autoclave.

process prolongs the shelf life of such products by decreasing the number of organisms that may cause spoilage. While this was the original intent of pasteurization, the process has attained greater significance as a means of preventing milk-borne diseases such as tuberculosis, brucellosis (undulant fever), Q fever, certain streptococcal infections, staphylococcal food poisoning, salmonellosis, shigellosis, and diphtheria. Pathogens gain access to milk from infected cows, from infected handlers, or by contamination of the product prior to pasteurization. Adequate sanitation is uppermost in preventing contamination after pasteurization.

The microorganisms that cause these diseases are killed by exposure to 62.9°C (145°F) for 30 minutes or 71.6°C (161°F) for 15 seconds. The causative agents of tuberculosis, *Mycobacterium tuberculosis* and *M. bovis*, were once thought to be the most heat-resistant of the pathogenic microorganisms encountered in milk. Consequently, they were used to test the pasteurization method for its general applicability in controlling milk-borne disease. However, as improved techniques for studying rickettsia were developed, it was found that *Coxiella burnetti,* the causative agent of Q fever, could survive pasteurization under certain conditions which the TB organisms could not. During the batch process, milk is placed in kettles and heated at 62.9°C for 30 minutes for pasteurization, with some mixing (Figure 18–3). This method does not produce the desired temperature at the surface of the dairy product—an inadequacy that became apparent only after the development of several Q fever cases traced to pasteurized milk. With the subsequent improvement in mixing, the danger of contracting Q fever was eliminated.

FIG. 18–3. Batch pasteurization of milk. (Courtesy of Borden, Inc., N.Y.)

The *high temperature short time* (HTST) or *flash pasteurization method* (71.6°C for 15 seconds) is conducted in coiled tubing or with thin sheets of milk flowing between metal plates (Figure 18–4), and proper mixing is not a problem. However, adequate disinfection is dependent upon the cleanliness of the milk, as dirt and debris protect organisms, resulting in failure of the pasteurization process.

Milk that has been properly pasteurized has good flavor and sufficient food value. However, excessive heating causes a flavor change objectionable to some people. Moreover, the vitamin content may be substantially reduced. The temperatures used are adequate to control what appears to be the significant disease agents, but cannot inactivate staphylococcal enterotoxin, a bacterial product that causes severe gastroenteritis. The organisms present in milk from cows with

FIG. 18–4. Flash pasteurization of milk. Control panel and related equipment. (Courtesy of Borden, Inc., N.Y.)

infected udders (mastitis), are killed by pasteurization; however, their toxic product is not inactivated. Infected cows should be detected by inspecting the dairy herds.

Dry Heat Methods

Direct flaming or incineration. One of the simplest of sterilization procedures is direct flaming. No special equipment, other than a hot flame, is needed, and the method is 100 per cent effective. It merely requires that the material to be sterilized be heated to a red glow. No known living organism can withstand such treatment. As a practical means of sterilization, however, direct flaming has little application. Obviously, it cannot be used on flammable materials such as cloth, rubber, and plastic, nor on liquids. Moreover, instruments and other metal objects cannot withstand repeated exposure to the high temperature. Nevertheless, the bacteriologist finds this technique of great value in the flaming of wire transfer loops for the inoculation of sterile tubes and flasks.

Hot air sterilization. Items to be sterilized by this method are placed in an oven-like apparatus capable of temperatures 160°C to 180°C (320–356°F). Materials are placed well inside the oven so as to allow good circulation. Hot air sterilization procedures require a 2-hour exposure at 160°C or 1 hour at 180°C. Because dry heat has less power of penetration than moist heat, a longer exposure time is necessary to kill all forms of life.

This method offers two definite advantages over autoclaving. First, there is no water present to dampen materials or to corrode instruments, and second, the hot-air equipment is relatively economical. Little installation is necessary and hot-air ovens are easy to use.

There are, however, several disadvantages. Many smaller offices cannot afford to have equipment tied up with procedures of washing, sterilizing in dry heat, and cooling. The cooling process may require a total of several hours. Another limitation is that not all items can be sterilized by this method. Fibrous materials are often scorched or charred at the prolonged high temperatures necessary for sterilization. Plastics and rubber, unless they are the more expensive heat-resistant varieties, do not fare well in dry heat. Even solder of some types will melt at 170°C.

But, for the sterilization of glassware such as Petri dishes and pipettes, dry heat is the method of choice. After Petri plates have been sterilized by this means, the oven often is used as a convenient storage facility. Dry heat sterilization also is the method of choice for powders, waxes, mineral oil, vaseline, and other materials which must be kept dry, or which will not allow moisture to penetrate.

Heat transfer. A newer technique for dry heat sterilization of instruments using 200°C has been proposed. Stainless steel and metal items have been sterilized in 38 minutes, including a 10-minute cooling time. Because of the higher heat necessary, this type of procedure may be of only limited use.

Heating in oil or silicone fluid. One method of "dry"—nonsteam—heat sterilization uses hot oils or silicone fluids. Items to be sterilized are thoroughly cleaned and dried. They are then placed in an oil or silicone bath and heated at 150°C for 15 minutes, or 125°C for 20 to 30 minutes. Obviously this procedure is useful only on nonfibrous materials. It has been used primarily for the sterilization of dental handpieces and small instruments but must never be used on syringes or needles because of the danger of introducing an oil embolism.

The technique has other limitations. For example, oil has poor penetrating powers. Bacterial spores are unaffected unless the bath is heated to at least 160°C and the instruments treated for an hour. After sterilization, the instruments must be dried and the residual oils wiped off, usually with carbon tetrachloride. This type of action may cause recontamination, thus making this type of sterilization procedure unacceptable for critical items.

Heating in low-fusion solder. Low-fusion solder can be substituted for the oil, but higher temperatures (218° to 280°C for 10 seconds) are necessary. This procedure lacks the disadvantage of a residue, but it cannot be used on handpieces. Also, after a time the solder will oxidize at the surface. The resulting "scum" tends to stick to metals as they are withdrawn from the bath. Further, the heating may not be even throughout the bath.

Granular heating media. Sand, glass beads, and stainless steel beads of small diameter have been tried as a replacement for liquids in sterilizing systems. These materials have the advantage of allowing other, nonmetallic materials to be sterilized. The steps in these procedures are about the same as described above. They also have the same major disadvantage, namely, that the temperature may vary considerably from the center to the edges of the "bath." Moreover, large instruments should not be placed in this type of sterilizing unit, because they will cause a drastic drop in the temperature, and sterilization will not occur.

Some present application of dry heat sterilization will probably be replaced by the use of high-vacuum steam sterilization, which incorporates exposure of the items to low moisture levels for shorter periods of time at lower temperatures.

Radiation

Ultraviolet Radiation

Microorganisms present in the air are subject to the killing action of ultraviolet light (UVL), a component of sunlight. Ultraviolet wavelengths are found just beyond the blue portion of the visible light spectrum, in the range of approximately 4000 to 2000 Å (400 to 200 nm). The wavelengths for killing microorganisms are found in the narrower range of 2800 to 2500 Å (280 to 250 nm); the most effective radiation is at least 2537 Å. Compounds such as purines and pyrimidines absorb UVL at approximately 2600 Å, while the aromatic amino acids, such as tryptophan, phenylalanine, and tyrosine, absorb at 2800 Å.

It would appear that this absorption of UV radiation produces chemical modifications of the nucleoproteins, creating cross-linkages between pairs of nitrogenous bases. Such abnormal linkages may then cause a misreading of the genetic code, resulting in mutations. A significant number of mutations can produce severe impairment of vital functions and consequently cause the organism's death.

Ultraviolet radiation has been applied with some success to air and water sterilization. However, the poor penetration of the rays is a limiting factor. Material to be sterilized, such as liquid, gas, or aerosol, must be passed over and/or under the surface of a suitable lamp in thin layers if the treatment is to be effective. Persons working at or near a source of UVL must wear glasses to protect their corneas from severe irritation or possible permanent damage.

The potential of ultraviolet radiation as a relatively inexpensive treatment of raw water is receiving considerable study. Hill and associates in 1970 investigated the survival of eight enteric viruses after exposure of UV irradiation. Pathogens including coxsackie, echo, polio, and reoviruses were treated in estuarine water. The results of this study showed that the mean half-lives of these viral agents ranged from 27 to 40 seconds. The findings suggest that UV irradiation may be an effective tool in the disinfection of sewage effluent in estuaries. Moreover, such treatment may protect shellfish and their consumers from contamination and infection.

Reactivation of ultraviolet-treated organisms. During a series of experiments concerning ultraviolet killing of *Escherichia coli,* certain suspensions, although treated in the same manner as others, were observed to exhibit a lower incidence of mutation or death. Further investigation showed that the length of exposure to visible light to which the suspensions were subjected prior to their placement in the dark incubators correlated well with the decrease in mutation or kill efficiency. This *photoreactivation* was found to be caused by an enzyme active in the presence of light (5400 to 4200 Å) but not in a dark environment. One consequence of ultraviolet treatment is the linkage of adjacent thymine molecules present in deoxyribonucleic acid (DNA). The enzyme involved in photoreactivation is capable of breaking a linkage of this type, thus repairing the defect.

Dark reactivation may also occur. Here, the irradiated suspension must be stored cold or in an inadequate growth medium prior to the completion of the experiment and the placement of treated organisms into ideal conditions. The mechanism of dark reactivation appears to be quite different from photoreactivation. The thymine-thymine linkage is not simply broken, but removed. The defect is then corrected by a DNA polymerase which replaces the thymines, using the complementary DNA strand for the necessary information.

Ionizing Radiation

These electromagnetic radiations include alpha, beta, gamma, and x-rays, cathode rays, and high-energy protons and neutrons. On absorbing such radiation, an atom emits high-energy electrons, thus ionizing its molecule. The ejected electron is absorbed by another atom, creating a chain of ionizations, or an ionization path, in the irradiated substance. This activity excites chemical groups in DNA, causing the production of highly reactive, short-lived chemicals called *radicals*. Such radicals may alter chemical groups in DNA or actually break DNA strands, causing mutations.

According to the "Target Theory," a cell will be killed when an ionization path occurs in a significant portion of its "sensitive volume." It is safe to assume that the target or sensitive volume is none other than DNA. When one wades through the complicated mathematics of the Target Theory concerning the relative sensitivities of different organisms to ionizing radiation, it becomes evident that such cells are sensitive inversely to the size of their DNA volume. Thus the smallest cells with the smallest targets are the most resistant.

Organisms can be protected to some degree against ionizing radiation by reducing agents such as sulfhydryl-containing compounds and various chelators (chemicals that bind metal ions).

Ionizing rays have been considered

for disinfection and sterilization procedures. However, expense has been a limiting factor. High levels of radiation have been used to prevent spoilage in packaged meats, without causing significant changes in the appearance, taste, texture or nutritive value of the product. Ionizing radiation has also been used for the "radiopasteurization" of strawberries, citrus fruits, and peaches as an adjunct to refrigeration, thus increasing the market life of these fruits, and to sterilize insect pests in stored grain. Since 1963 the U.S. Food and Drug Administration (FDA) has permitted unrestricted public consumption of fresh bacon "radiosterilized" with cobalt 60.

Radiation sterilization can be used to produce vaccines. A 1970 report of Reitman and his associates indicates that gamma irradiation was used to produce an effective vaccine against Venezuelan Equine Encephalitis virus infection. This vaccine appeared to be superior to both the live and the formalin-inactivated vaccines.

Filtration

This useful process of sterilization simply involves the passage of a liquid or gas through a screen-like material having a pore size small enough to retain microorganisms of a certain size. The screen or filter medium becomes contaminated while the liquid or gas that passes through is sterilized. Certain filters also utilize materials that adsorb microorganisms. Most commonly-used filters do not remove viruses.

Filtration is used for sterilizing substances that are sensitive to heat. Included in this group are enzyme solutions, bacterial toxins, cell extracts, some sugars, and various other heat-labile materials.

Liquids can be filtered through any

of a variety of materials including clay, paper, asbestos, glass, diatomaceous earth, and cellulose acetate. The earliest filters of the type, developed by Chamberland in Pasteur's laboratory, were made of unglazed porcelain. A cylinder of unglazed porcelain, closed at one end, was fashioned out of hydrous aluminum silicate or kaolin (china clay) and quartz. This was heated enough to bind the particles in the mixture but not to glaze the porcelain formed. By varying the proportions of the ingredients, cylinders of varying porosities could be made. A filter arrangement with the Chamberland device is shown in Figure 18–5.

Diatomaceous Earth Filters

Berkefield and Mandler filters are cylinder types made of a white powder composed primarily of silicon residues from diatoms (diatomaceous earth),

water, asbestos, and organic matter or plaster of paris. The cylinders are made of the wet clay-like material, dried, formed, and baked to bind the constituents. With this type of filter, the candle is held in a mantle or funnel connected by means of a clamp or nut (Figure 18–6).

Fritted Glass Filters

Fritted glass filters are made by placing finely ground glass particles in a suitable disk mold and heating them enough to cause some melting and cohesion of the particles. The porosity of this filter disk can be controlled by the fineness of the ground particles and the fusion temperature used. Once formed, the disk is

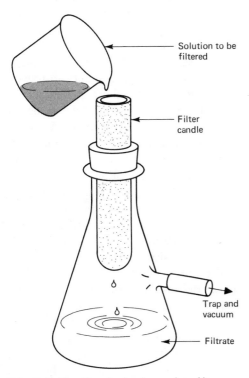

FIG. 18–5. The Chamberland porcelain filter.

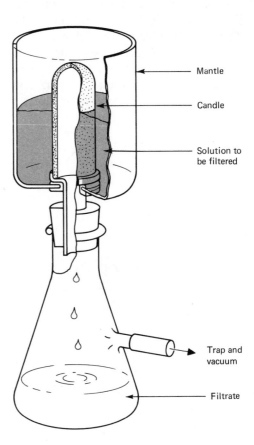

FIG. 18–6. Diatomaceous earth filtration.

usually fused into a funnel (Figure 18–7). The device can be used with negative or positive pressure in a suitable flask.

Asbestos and Paper

Pads of compressed paper and/or asbestos can be used in disk form when held firmly in a two-part funnel holder. A commonly employed filter, the Seitz filter, uses asbestos pads. The two compartments of the filter are clamped together to hold the pad in place between them. This is, in essence, comparable to the fritted glass disk arrangement, described above.

Cellulose Acetate Membrane

Membrane filters of cellulose acetate are also made in disk form. However, the filter pad is usually much thinner than those mentioned previously. Membrane filters are 0.1 mm thick, in contrast to approximately 5 mm for the Seitz and fritted glass types. The membrane is held in place on a supporting screen by a suitable holder (Figure 18–8).

Previously mentioned filters combined sieving with adsorption based on opposite charge effects. Thus, filtration of various organic compounds through porcelain, diatomaceous earth, glass, or asbestos devices may result in lower concentrations. In addition to charge effects, the adsorptive nature of such filters will cause the removal of certain components from solutions. The cellulose acetate filter truly works by sieve action alone. This disposable membrane filter is being utilized with greater frequency because of its uncharged and non-adsorptive nature. Applications include the processing of various pharmaceutical products and certain alcoholic beverages, such as beer and wine.

Air Filtration

Filtering air to reduce microbial contaminants has found significant application in hospital operating rooms and in assembly rooms for space vehicles, among other uses. It has been used by microbiologists for nearly a century to prevent contamination of culture media. Sterile non-absorptive cotton is probably one of the oldest known materials used for this purpose. When it is properly placed to plug a test tube or flask of media (Figure 18–9), after sterilization of the plugged containers the contents will remain sterile unless the cotton becomes charred or moistened. A wet cotton plug allows bacteria to penetrate.

This is also true for surgical masks which are made of cloth, paper, or fiberglass. Because bacteria penetrate through wet masks, they must not be worn longer than 20 to 30 minutes and should be changed more often if necessary.

The access of bacteria to culture media can also be prevented by the use of plastic or stainless steel sleeves which fit

FIG. 18–7. A fritted glass filter.

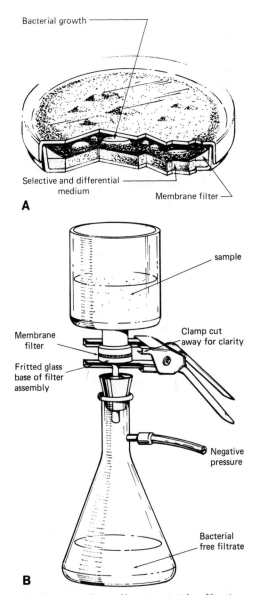

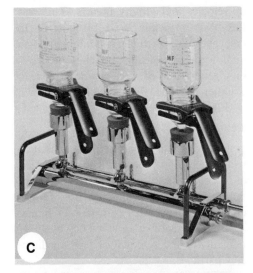

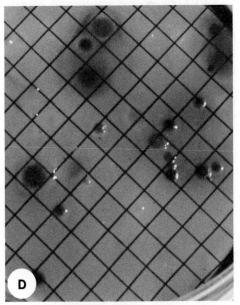

FIG. 18–8. Membrane filtration. <u>A</u>. After filtration of a sample such as water, the membrane can be placed directly onto a selective and differential medium. After incubation, distinct colonial types, which can be counted and identified, from on the membrane filter's surface. <u>B</u>. A diagrammatic representation of the basic features of a membrane filter apparatus. The sample is pulled through the membrane filter by negative pressure. Bacteria and related organisms unable to pass through the membrane's pores remain on its surface. <u>C</u>. A system for membrane filtration of water or dilute fluids. <u>D</u>. The appearance of bacterial colonies on a membrane filter. (Photographs courtesy of Millipore Corporation, Bedford, Massachusetts.)

over the mouth of the tube or flask (Figure 18–9). While the cotton prevents penetration by actual filtration, the enclosure forces the air stream to reverse its direction to enter the tube. Solid particles continue in the original direction, because of velocity and gravity factors. This was the basic principle used by Pasteur to disprove the idea that air contained some vital force responsible for the spontaneous generation of life, as described in Chapter 2. The Pasteur flask is shown in Figure 2–5.

HEPA filters. Commercial air filtration systems for air conditioning exhibit a wide range of efficiency. The application of such devices to the extensive decontamination of air requires the use of high-efficiency particulate air (HEPA) filters. These systems have an efficiency of 99.97 percent for the removal of 0.3 μm diameter particles.

HEPA filters are constructed of cellulose acetate pleated around aluminum foil, and are manufactured in various sizes for different applications. One such application is the formation of non-turbulent or laminar air flow for maximum contamination control in a given area. This use of HEPA filters is shown in Figure 18–10.

One problem commonly encountered when pouring media into culture vessels is contamination by airborne microorganisms. To prevent such contamination, some HEPA filter systems have been designed with one entire wall consisting of banks of filters. The opposite wall is used for the air exhaust. In this system, any particles in the room that might be aerosolized by some movement are scavenged by the average air velocity of 50 to 100 feet per minute.

QUESTIONS FOR REVIEW

1. What are the essential differences between downward-displacement and high-vacuum autoclaves?

2. Compare the time and temperature relationships for sterilization by: (1) dry heat at 160°C, and (2) pressurized steam at 121°C and 134°C.

3. Discuss at least one physical control procedure for the sterilization of the following items:

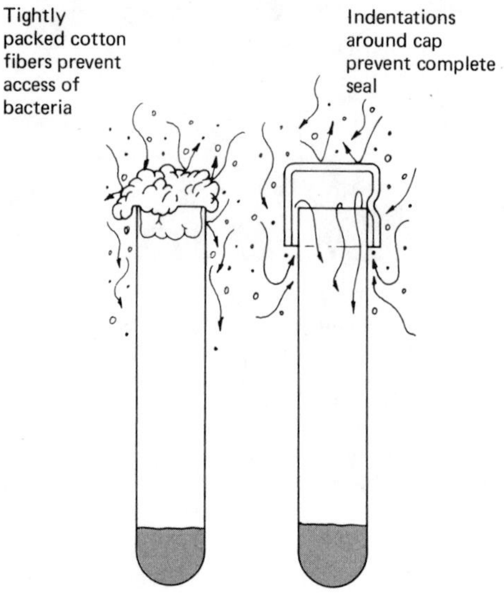

Tightly packed cotton fibers prevent access of bacteria

Indentations around cap prevent complete seal

FIG. 18–9. Air filtration by means of a cotton plug and metal cap.

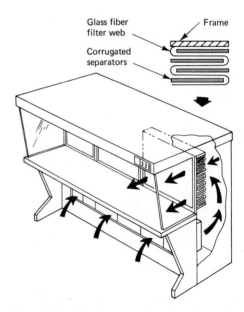

Glass fiber filter web

Frame

Corrugated separators

FIG. 18–10. A laminar air flow bench for the prevention of sterile media contamination.

a. milk
b. antibiotics
c. vaseline
d. syringes
e. contaminated swabs

4. Ultraviolet radiation is most effective at a wavelength of _____Å, which is absorbed by _____ and _____, two components of the bacterial _____.

5. Ionizing radiation is given this name because of the formation of _____ _____ within biological materials. This is due to the absorption of _____, _____, or _____ rays and the activation of _____.

6. Describe the essential differences between filtration through asbestos pads and through cellulose acetate membranes.

7. Describe the disadvantages of each method given in this chapter for the physical control of microorganisms.

8. What methods of sterilization would individuals in the following occupations employ?
a. respiratory therapist
b. surgical nurse
c. dental hygienist
d. dietician
e. dentist
f. medical technologist
g. medical record librarian
h. radiological technician
i. physician
j. pharmacist

9. Differentiate between sterilization and pasteurization.

19

Chemotherapy

Historical Background

The discoveries of Salvarsan in 1909, sulfa drugs in 1936, and penicillin in 1929 ushered in the modern era of chemotherapy. However, chemotherapeutic agents have been in clinical use since ancient times, in the form of extracts of herbs, leaves, and roots. During the sixteenth century, for example, extracts of cinchona bark (quinine) were used to treat malaria, and extracts of ipecacuanha roots (emetine) were used in the treatment of amebiasis.

The selection and study of synthetic compounds or natural extracts for therapeutic purposes was largely haphazard until the brilliant work of Paul Ehrlich (1854-1916) in developing his "magic bullet," Salvarsan, for the treatment of syphilis.

Ehrlich

Ehrlich knew that various stains had affinity for different types of tissues. Therefore, he thought, if compounds could be found with affinity for bacteria, then diseases could be cured with little or no harm to the patient. In 1891, Ehrlich observed that methylene blue showed an attraction for nerve cells and also had some effect on the course of malaria. In 1894, he learned that the arsenical compound atoxyl was effective against protozoans, such as the trypanosomes (Color photograph 11). Unfortunately,

the drug was toxic for the patient. Ehrlich then thought that perhaps if the molecule of atoxyl were changed slightly, it would still kill protozoa, but cause little harm to the patient. The organic chemists in his laboratory synthesized different chemicals and tested them against trypanosomes in mice.

Compound number 606 became Ehrlich's "magic bullet." Atoxyl, which has the structure:

was converted to Salvarsan in the period

of 12 years. Although Salvarsan was effective in mice, it was not quite as useful against trypanosomes in horses, in which these organisms caused a severe disease. Further research showed Salvarsan to be effective against experimental syphilis infections in rabbits and in chickens. In 1910 a less toxic compound, number 914, Neosalvarsan, was created.

Ehrlich believed that, for a drug to be effective, an interaction must occur between it and the host, producing an altered substance. This erroneous theory interfered with the recognition of some antimicrobial agents, but did contribute to the discovery of sulfa drugs.

Fleming and Penicillin

In 1929, Alexander Fleming, known for his discovery of the antibacterial enzyme lysozyme, reported unusual antibacterial activity of an extract obtained from the fungus *Penicillium notatum*. After observing a lack of growth by the bacterium *Staphylococcus aureus* in the area surrounding a contaminate mold colony, Fleming decided to isolate the substance responsible for this reaction and determine its spectrum of activity. The isolated material, which he named penicillin, was effective *in vitro* against a variety of bacteria, including species of *Corynebacteria*, *Neisseria*, *Staphylococcus*, and *Streptococcus*. No activity was reported with *Escherichia coli* or *Hemophilus influenzae*.

For lack of time and money, Fleming did not pursue this investigation further. He simply placed his discovery on the shelf in hopes that someday it would be carried on. A decade later his hopes were realized, when two other Englishmen, Chain and Florey, expanded Fleming's investigations and developed an antibiotic preparation for human use. Thus the antibiotic era of medicine came into being.

Meanwhile, in 1935, Domagk also was looking for antimicrobial compounds. Despite the relative success which was possible with silver and gold salts, he turned his attention to stains. One such compound of interest at the time was prontosil. This stain appeared to be ineffective against streptococci *in vitro,* but was apparently active *in vivo*. Mice would recover from experimentally induced streptococcal infections if given prontosil. Several investigators proved that this compound was metabolized in the body to sulfanilamide, and that it was an effective antimicrobial both *in vitro* and *in vivo*. Within five years after these discoveries, Woods reported that prontosil's activity was due to its competition with a vitamin needed by certain bacteria for growth.

After Fleming's discovery that microorganisms can produce substances which can either prevent growth or kill other microorganisms, the search for antibiotics blossomed. Table 19–1 lists the microbial sources of over 20 antibiotics. Several of these drugs are bacteriostatic, bactericidal, antifungal, antiprotozoan, and antiviral in nature. The organisms producing them are largely soil and water species which must constantly compete for food and room to live. Thus, the production of antibiotics—which is a natural means of controlling microbe populations *in situ*—has been put to use to save human lives.

The search for new and better antimicrobial agents is particularly evident in the case of virus diseases. One area of great significance in this regard is the study of interferons and their induction. Closely associated with the desire for antiviral agents is the search for anticancer drugs. In some hosts, cancer cells appear to react as if they were foreign invaders, almost to the extent of the immunological reactions found with microorganisms.

One peculiarity of certain cancer cells is a difference in amino acid metabolism from "normal cells." In particular, such cancer cells appear to require pre-formed asparagine whereas the other cells are able to synthesize it. The administration of the enzyme asparaginase, produced by the bacterium *Escherichia coli,* is able to deplete the blood plasma of asparagine, thus causing the cancer cells to starve. Treatment has been effective in various malignant states including mouse lymphoma, canine lymphosarcoma, and especially for children with acute lymphatic leukemia.

Today the search for synthetic antimicrobial agents continues, in conjunction with efforts to isolate new natural antibiotics from microorganisms. Antimicrobial activity is occasionally discovered under rather unusual circumstances, such as a case reported by Schmidt and Rosenkranz in 1970. They found that local anesthetics which were being used prior to obtaining specimens from the lungs of patients for culture were in some cases preventing the growth of the pathogens being tested. They discovered that these anesthetics were antibacterial and antifungal for several organisms.

Principles of Chemotherapy

When a microorganism has been isolated from a patient, it is advisable to determine its sensitivity to a variety of antimicrobial agents. With the results of such tests an attending physician can choose that drug which may be best for the patient. The final choice of an antibiotic depends upon the patient's allergies, his general physical condition, and the site of the infection. The latter factor is particularly important. For example, certain orally administered drugs may reach high levels in urine and fair levels in blood. However, they may fail to cross the blood-brain barrier, or not penetrate well into tissues, and thereby not reach the organisms causing the particular problem.

When the laboratory performs drug susceptibility tests and reports that a certain organism is sensitive to a particular antibiotic, the result should mean that the organism will be sensitive to that level of drug which can be achieved in the body. Unfortunately, it is not always possible to correlate *in vitro* tests with *in vivo* results. A part of the problem is due to the selective concentration of the chemotherapeutic agents in certain tissues, thereby producing drug concentrations either greater or lower than those used in laboratory testing. It is important, therefore, that the achievable levels of the drug in the various parts of the body be known, as well as the relative sensitivities of the pathogen. This relative sensitivity is called the *minimum inhibitory concentration* (MIC), meaning the lowest concentration of a drug which will prevent growth of a standardized suspension of the organism. Additional discussion is presented later, in the section on antibiotic testing methods.

Chemotherapy of Selected Bacterial Diseases

The perfect antimicrobial agent would have maximum toxicity for the parasite and no toxicity for the host. It was just this very requirement that Ehrlich was investigating when he developed arsphenamine for the treatment for syphilis. Few, if any, drugs have no toxicity for the patient. Physicians frequently are faced with the problem of balancing the usefulness of a chemotherapeutic agent for a particular pathogen against its potential side effects, which may include such things as the depression of blood cell formation or the production of hypersensitivity.

Tables 19–1 and 19–2 list a broad range of antibiotics and other preparations employed in the treatment of various infectious diseases. The vast majority of the drugs listed are in routine use. The association of a single drug with a particular microorganism should not be considered as an endorsement. Furthermore, it should be noted that under certain conditions some medications may not work.

Table 19–1   Common Microbial Sources of Some Antimicrobial Drugs

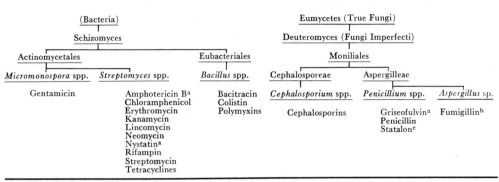

NOTE: Drugs are primarily antibacterial unless otherwise designated.
[a] Antifungal drugs; have also been used against certain protozoan pathogens.
[b] Antiamebic drug.
[c] Antiviral drug.

Table 19–2   Chemotherapy of Selected Bacteria

Microorganism	Disease	Drug of Choice or Multiple Therapy	Primary Effects	Possible Side Effects
GRAM-POSITIVE				
Bacillus anthracis	Anthrax	Penicillin	Bactericidal	Allergy, hemolytic anemia
Clostridium tetani	Tetanus	Penicillin	Bactericidal	Allergy, hemolytic anemia
Streptococcus (Diplococcus) pneumoniae	Pneumonia, meningitis, etc.	Penicillin	Bactericidal	Allergy, hemolytic anemia
		Clindamycin	Bactericidal	Diarrhea, nausea
Staphylococcus aureus	Wound infection, boils, pneumonia, meningitis, etc.	Methicillin	Bactericidal	Allergy, renal toxicity neutropenia
		Clindamycin	Bactericidal	Diarrhea, nausea
		Rifampin	Bactericidal	Some disturbance of liver activity
Streptococcus hemolyticus	Strep throat, skin infections, meningitis, etc.	Penicillin	Bactericidal	Allergy, hemolytic anemia
GRAM-NEGATIVE				
Bacteroides fragilis	Wound infections, lung abscesses, etc.	Tetracyclines	Bacteriostatic	Nausea, vomiting, diarrhea, dermatitis, vaginitis, allergy
Bordetella pertussis	Whooping cough	Clindamycin	Bacteriostatic	Diarrhea, nausea
		Ampicillin	Bactericidal	Allergy, bone marrow depression, diarrhea, candidiasis
Brucella abortus	Brucellosis	Tetracyclines	Bacteriostatic	Nausea, vomiting, diarrhea, dermatitis, vaginitis, allergy
Escherichia coli	Urinary tract and wound infections	Ampicillin	Bactericidal	Allergy, bone marrow depression, diarrhea, candidiasis
Hemophilus influenzae	Pneumonia, meningitis	Tetracyclines	Bacteriostatic	Nausea, vomiting, diarrhea, dermatitis, vaginitis, allergy
		Rifampin	Bacteriostatic	

Table 19–2—*Continued*

Microorganism	Disease	Drug of Choice or Multiple Therapy	Primary Effects	Possible Side Effects
Neisseria gonorrhoeae	Gonorrhea	Penicillin	Bactericidal	Allergy, hemolytic anemia
		Rifampin	Bactericidal	
Yersinia pestis	Plague	Streptomycin	Bacteriostatic	Dermatitis, fever, nephrotoxicity, neurotoxicity, hearing loss
		Tetracyclines	Bacteriostatic	Nausea, vomiting, diarrhea, dermatitis, vaginitis, allergy
Proteus mirabilis	Urinary tract and wound infections	Kanamycin	Bacteriostatic	Nephrotoxic, hearing loss
Pseudomonas aeruginosa	Urinary tract infection, infected burns, pneumonia	Gentamicin, Carbenicillin (alone or in combination with Gentamicin)	Bacteriostatic	Nephrotoxic, hearing loss
Salmonella typhi	Food poisoning, gastroenteritis	Chloramphenicol	Bacteriostatic	Drug fever, bone marrow depression
Shigella dysenteriae	Dysentery	Ampicillin	Bactericidal	Allergy, bone marrow depression, diarrhea, candidiasis

ACID-FAST OR PARTIALLY ACID-FAST MICROORGANISMS

Microorganism	Disease	Drug of Choice or Multiple Therapy	Primary Effects	Possible Side Effects
Actinomyces israeli	Actinomycosis	Sulfonamides	Bacteriostatic	Vertigo, malaise, headaches, fever, dermatitis, hematuria
Mycobacterium leprae	Leprosy	Diamino diphenyl sulphone (**DDS** or Dapsone)	Probably bacteriostatic	Vertigo, malaise, headache, fever, leukopenia, hematuria
Mycobacterium tuberculosis	Tuberculosis	Isonicotinic hydrazide	Bacteriostatic	Renal toxicity, constipation, gastritis, neurotoxicity, drowsiness
		Para-amino-salicylate	Bacteriostatic	
		Streptomycin	Bactericidal	Dermatitis, fever, nephrotoxicity, neurotoxicity
		Rifampin	Bactericidal	Some disturbance of liver function
Nocardia asteroides	Nocardiosis	Sulfonamides	Bacteriostatic	Vertigo, malaise, headaches, fever, dermatitis, hematuria

OTHER BACTERIAL SPECIES

Microorganism	Disease	Drug of Choice or Multiple Therapy	Primary Effects	Possible Side Effects
Chlamydia trachomatis	Trachoma	Tetracyclines	Bacteriostatic	Nausea, vomiting, diarrhea, dermatitis, vaginitis, allergy
Coxiella burnetti	Q fever	Tetracyclines	Bacteriostatic	Nausea, vomiting, diarrhea, dermatitis, vaginitis, allergy
Miyawaganella psittasi	Psittocosis	Tetracyclines	Bacteriostatic	Nausea, vomiting, diarrhea, dermatitis, vaginitis, allergy
Mycoplasma pneumoniae	Primary atypical pneumonia	Tetracyclines	Bacteriostatic	Nausea, vomiting, diarrhea, dermatitis, vaginitis, allergy
Rickettsia rickettsii	Rocky Mountain spotted fever	Tetracyclines	Bacteriostatic	Nausea, vomiting, diarrhea, dermatitis, vaginitis, allergy
Treponema pallidum	Syphilis	Penicillin	Bactericidal	Allergy, hemolytic anemia

The decision as to which drug to administer rests with the physician. In making his choice, he must consider the general state of a patient's health, the presence of liver or kidney ailments, the existence of allergies, and the particular body portion or systems involved in the disease process. Moreover, since many bacterial pathogens vary in their drug sensitivities, the identification of the pathogen and its antibiogram must be known before the proper selection of chemotherapeutic agent can be made. An *antibiogram* is the evaluation of an organism's resistance or sensitivity to a series of antibiotics and chemotherapeutic agents. Antibiotic testing methods are discussed later in this chapter.

Since the pioneering efforts of Ehrlich and Domagk with synthetic drugs, and of Fleming, Chain, Florey, and Waksman with antibiotics, many extremely useful antimicrobial agents have been developed. One of the most active fields in pharmaceutical research involves determining the action of naturally formed drugs and studying the effects on antimicrobial activity of slight chemical changes in these and related preparations. The development of penicillinase-resistant penicillins for the treatment of staphylococcal infections is a good example of this type of investigation.

The basic structures of penicillin G and several modified penicillins are presented in Figure 19–1. The enzyme, penicillinase, breaks the beta lactam ring, as shown in the figure. Modifications of the compound's basic structure produced other antibiotics having a resistance to the enzyme's action. Two such examples, methicillin and oxacillin, are shown in Figure 19–1. In methicillin, the addition of two ether linkages ($-OCH_3$) to the

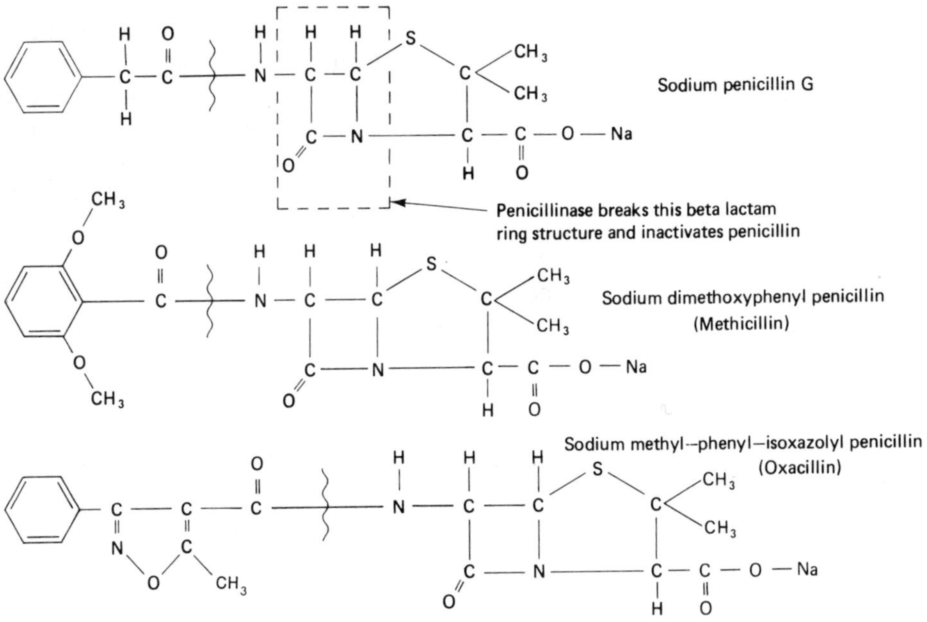

FIG. 19–1. A comparison of penicillin G and several penicillinase-resistant penicillins.

benzene ring appears to have changed the molecule's steric configuration so that the active portion of the enzyme cannot come into intimate contact with the beta lactam ring. With oxacillin, on the other hand, a ringed structure

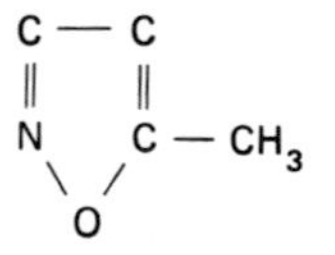

$$
\begin{array}{ccc}
C & — & C \\
\parallel & & \parallel \\
N & & C — CH_3 \\
\diagdown & & \diagup \\
& O &
\end{array}
$$

was attached to the benzene ring, and added to that portion of the antibiotic molecule which is common to all three drugs. This addition appears to inhibit the enzyme's activity. Both methicillin and oxacillin are very similar to penicillin in activity against various Gram-positive and Gram-negative bacteria.

Another chemical substitution in the basic penicillin structure produced the compound ampicillin.

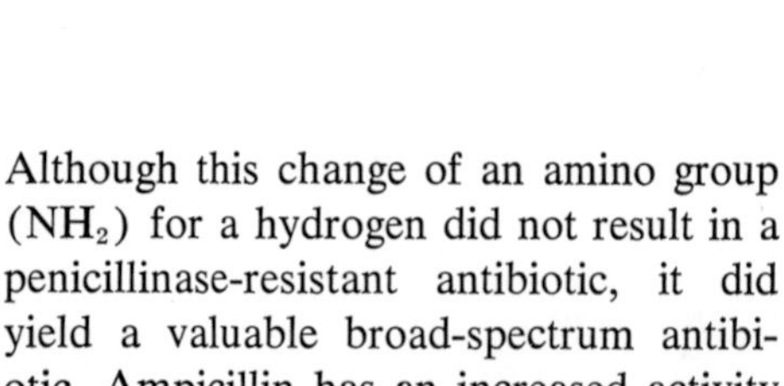

Although this change of an amino group (NH_2) for a hydrogen did not result in a penicillinase-resistant antibiotic, it did yield a valuable broad-spectrum antibiotic. Ampicillin has an increased activity against Gram-negative bacteria, particularly *Escherichia coli* and other enteric bacteria which commonly cause urinary tract infections.

Some Commonly Used Antimicrobial Drugs

Sulfa Drugs

Domagk reported in 1935 that a red dye compound, prontosil (Figure 19–2), was chemotherapeutic for streptococcal infections in mice; the chemical substance had been used clinically two years previously by Foerster. This drug was not active *in vitro* and fulfilled Ehrlich's assumption that a chemotherapeutic agent must be modified in the body in order to be effective. By 1936, scientists at the Pasteur Institute in Paris had discovered that prontosil was converted to sulfanilamide (Figure 19–2), which was active both *in vitro* and *in vivo*.

Sulfanilamide and sulfadiazine (Figure 19–2) are but two of many types of sulfa drugs. Each of these compounds has certain peculiarities related to their solubilities and relative toxicities.

Range of activity. Sulfa drugs are used for treatment of *Escherichia coli* urinary tract infections, meningococcal infections, certain protozoan diseases, chancroid, trachoma, and infections caused by *Nocardia* spp. They are not particularly

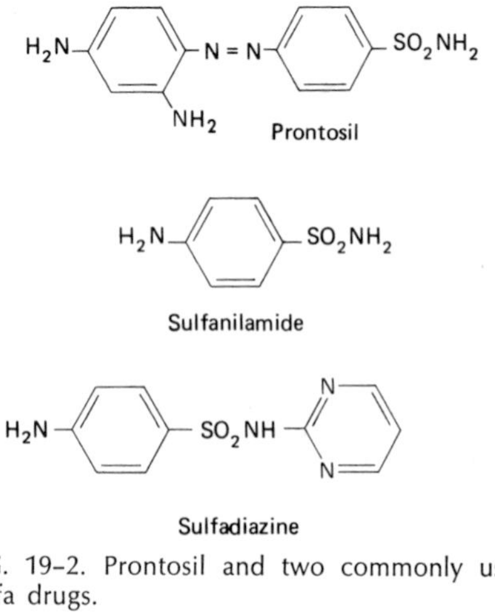

FIG. 19-2. Prontosil and two commonly used sulfa drugs.

effective in the presence of necrotic tissue or pus and therefore are used only for mild to moderate infections.

Mechanism of action. Sulfa drugs are bacteriostatic, acting upon bacteria which are growing and actively metabolizing. The mechanism of action is associated with the similarity of their structures to the vitamin para-aminobenzoic acid (PABA).

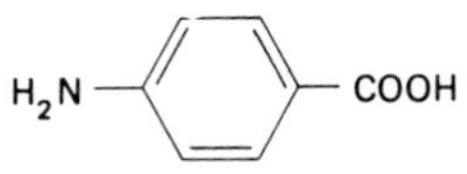

$$H_2N - \text{(benzene ring)} - COOH$$

This vitamin is required for the synthesis of the vitamin and coenzyme folic acid. Man and some bacteria are able to synthesize PABA and are therefore not sensitive to sulfa drugs, *per se*. However, those organisms which cannot synthesize the PABA, and consequently must obtain it in a preformed state, cannot differentiate between the structures of the sulfa drugs and PABA. Therefore, such bacteria incorporate the drug into the larger molecule of folic acid, producing inactive coenzymes.

Penicillins

The clinical value of penicillin was proved during the period of 1941 to 1945, as a result of the concentrated efforts by the United States and England to develop large-scale commercial production for military use in World War II. Not until 1945 did this first "antibiotic" come into clinical prominence for application to the population at large. Figure 19–3 shows the basic structure of penicillin as it appears in: (1) the natural product, Penicillin G; (2) a semi-synthetic penicillin, ampicillin; (3)

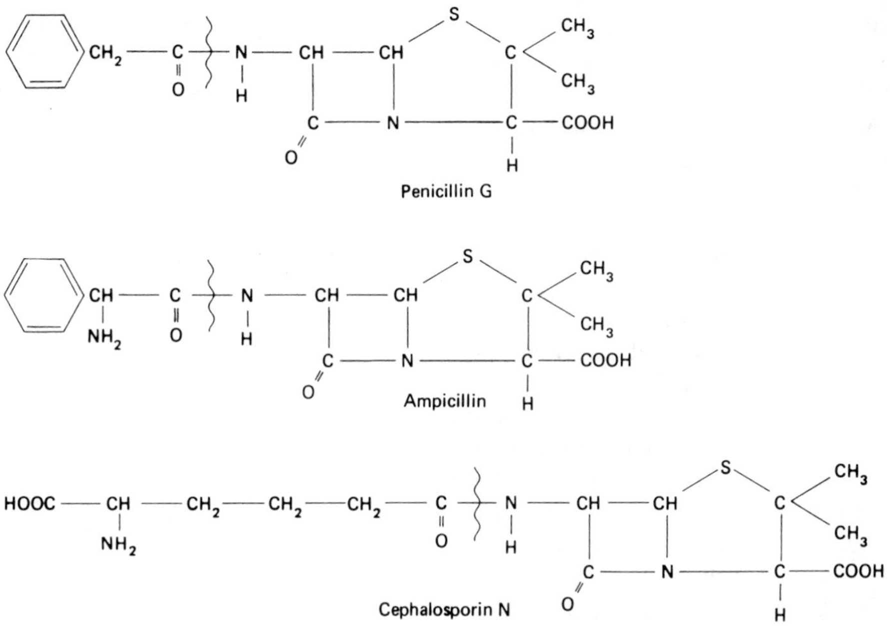

FIG. 19–3. Three antibiotics of the penicillin family.

another semi-synthetic penicillin, carben-icillin; and (4) cephalosporin N, one of a new group of natural and semi-synthetic "penicillins," called cephalosporins.

The cephalosporin antibiotics are included with penicillin because of the extreme similarities in basic structure. The portions of the molecules shown in Figure 19–3 to the left of the wavy line differ, while those portions to the right are identical.

Ampicillin resulted from an effort to obtain improved drugs. The slight modifications of the molecule by the addition of an amino (NH_2) group converted penicillin into a broader-spectrum chemotherapeutic agent.

Disodium carbenicillin is the first semisynthetic penicillin to attain extensive clinical usage specifically because of its pronounced activity against selected Gram-negative organisms, primarily *Pseudomonas* and certain strains of *Proteus*. The primary application of this antibiotic, either alone or in combination with gentamicin, has been for serious *Pseudomonas* infections such as severe burns, and infections of the pulmonary and urinary systems. Microbial resistance to carbenicillin appears to develop primarily through inappropriate use of the drug.

The original cephalosporin-producing molds, *Cephalosporium* spp., were isolated from salt water by Brotzu in 1945. Florey, in 1948, then set out to repeat with this antibiotic what he had previously so successfully achieved with penicillin. Additional work showed that other antibiotics obtained from these molds were more effective. By making chemical changes in their basic formula, several new broad-spectrum antibiotics were developed, and are currently available for use. Examples of these include cephalothin, cephalexin, cefazolin, and cephaloridine.

Range of activity.   Penicillin G and closely related drugs are highly active against sensitive strains of Gram-positive cocci, Gram-negative cocci, Gram-positive bacilli, and Gram-positive and -negative anaerobic bacteria. At high concentrations, which can be produced in the urinary tract, penicillin is known to be effective against *Escherichia coli* and *Proteus mirabilis*. However, ampicillin is the drug of choice because it can be used in smaller concentrations against *Escherichia coli, Hemophilus influenzae, Proteus mirabilis, Salmonella,* and *Shigella* spp., as well as the other organisms which respond to penicillin. The spectrum of the cephalosporins is similar to ampicillin, but they are active against pneumococci, *H. influenzae,* and most anaerobic bacteria. In contrast to penicillin and ampicillin, cephalosporins are not inactivated by penicillinase, an enzyme produced by penicillin-resistant staphylococci.

Mechanism of action.   All four of these chemotherapeutic agents are bactericidal and act by interfering with the microbes' cell wall synthesis. The portion of their structure associated with the four-member lactam ring,

is comparable to a region of the dipeptide

alanylalanine. It appears that the penicillins are incorporated into cell walls in place of this compound. Penicillin is effective only during the growth stages of sensitive organisms, since fully-formed cell walls are not sensitive to its action.

Clindamycin: A Useful Alternative to Penicillin-Cephalosporin Antibiotics

Clindamycin is a semi-synthetic antibiotic that is essentially an anti-Gram-positive agent with one or two significant exceptions. The antibiotic inhibits pneumococci, streptococci, and most *Staphylococcus aureus* isolates. It is not active against the commonly encountered Gram-negative rods. Clindamycin is an inhibitor of protein synthesis in the bacterial cell.

Chloramphenicol and the Tetracyclines

Chloramphenicol and one naturally occurring tetracycline, chlortetracycline (Figure 19–4), are both produced by species of *Streptomyces*. These compounds are bacteriostatic, broad-spectrum antimicrobials having the same mechanism of action. Chloramphenicol was isolated by Burkholder, Bartz, and others from *Streptomyces venezuelae* in 1948. It became available in 1949 after its successful synthesis was accomplished. Chlortetracycline was isolated from *Streptomyces aureofaciens* and became available in 1949 due to the work of Duggar, Subba, Row, and others. Two new synthetic tetracyclines, doxycycline and minocycline, have become available in recent years. They differ only in very minor degrees from other tetracyclines.

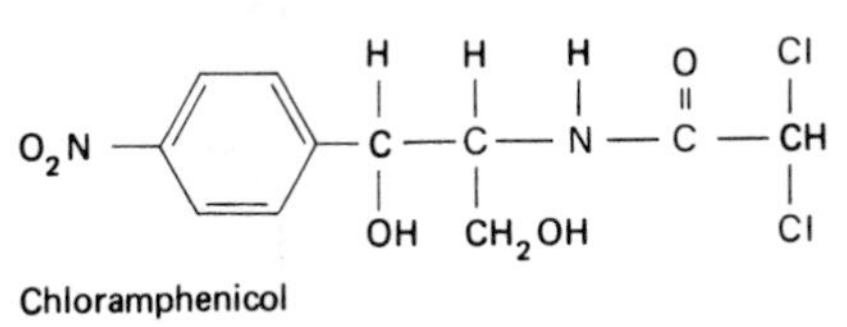

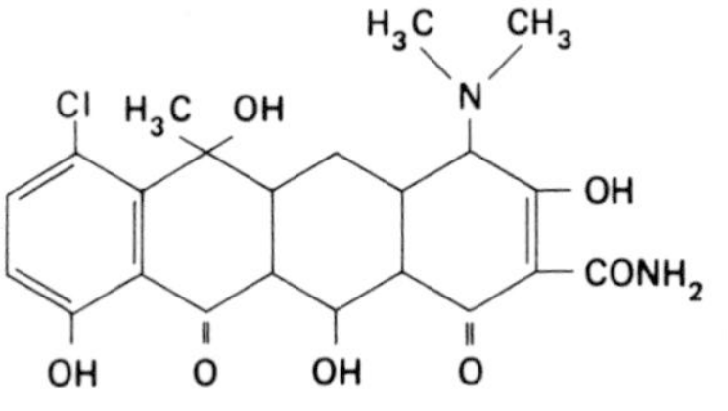

Range of activity. Chloramphenicol is particularly useful for infections by many Gram-positive and Gram-negative bacteria, rickettsia, and chlamydia. It is the drug of choice for typhoid fever. However, because of its highly toxic effect on blood-cell-forming tissues, Chloramphenicol must be reserved for cases resistant to other forms of treatment.

Chlortetracycline is also active against a variety of Gram-positive and -negative bacteria, rickettsia, and chlamydia. It is much less toxic than Chloramphenicol and can be used more freely. However, it is inferior to Chloramphenicol for *Salmonella* infections.

Mechanism of action. These two antibiotics are thought to exert their effects at the level of protein synthesis. The drugs interfere with the transfer of activated amino acids from transfer RNA to the growing polypeptide chain (see Chapter 15 for a discussion of protein synthesis). Studies with animal cells *in vitro* have shown little effect of these antimicrobial agents on protein synthesis; however, some effects have been observed *in vivo*.

Aminoglycosides (Streptomycins)

This group of chemotherapeutic drugs includes streptomycin, kanamycin, and gentamicin, as shown in Figure 19–5. The R and R^1 substituents on the gentamycin molecule refer to slight varia-

Chloramphenicol

Chlortetracycline

FIG. 19–4. Chloramphenicol and chlortetracycline.

tions which comprise the three components of gentamycin, a mixture of gentamycin C_1 (R and R^1 = CH_3), gentamycin C_2 (R = CH_3 and R^1 = H), and gentamycin C_{1a} (R and R^1 = H).

The name for the group of antibiotics is derived from the complex structure, which includes an amino sugar. Streptomycin was discovered by Waksman and Schatz in 1944 as a product of *Streptomyces griseus*. Kanamycin was isolated from *Streptomyces kanamyceticus*. Gentamycin is produced by species of *Micromonospora*, which are closely related to the streptomyces.

Range of activity. Streptomycin's primary activity is against Gram-negative bacteria, enterococci, and *M. tuberculosis*. Since organisms rapidly develop resistance to this drug, it must be used in combined therapy. When combined with penicillin or ampicillin it is particularly effective against enterococcus infections, especially endocarditis. In the treatment of tuberculosis, it can be combined with isonicotinic hydrazide (INH) and para-aminosalycilic acid (PAS).

Kanamycin is active against a wide variety of Gram-positive and Gram-negative bacteria and *Mycobacterium tuber-*

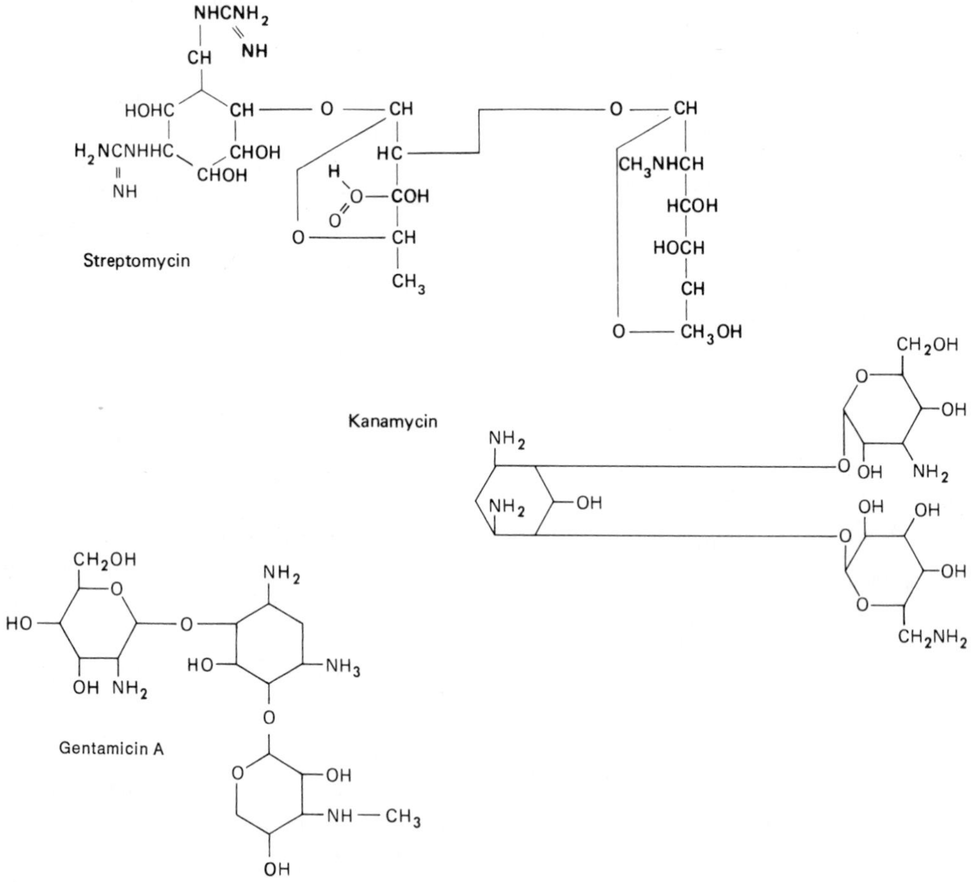

FIG. 19-5. Three representative antibiotics of the aminoglycoside group.

culosis. It is not particularly effective with *Pseudomonas* spp., various streptococci, and anaerobes.

Gentamicin is primarily active against infections with Gram-negative bacteria and is a drug of choice for *Pseudomonas* infections. While it is effective against most *Proteus* spp., kanamycin is usually the more effective drug.

All three aminoglycosides may be toxic to kidneys and auditory nerves.

Mechanism of action. These aminoglycosides, although somewhat different in spectrum, are all bactericidal and interfere with protein synthesis. The mechanism of action appears to be their combination with a sub-unit of the ribosome, causing a misreading of the genetic code.

Polypeptides

Two of the more common drugs in this group are Polymyxin B and Colistin (Polymyxin E). The various members of this group can be isolated from *Bacillus polymyxa*. Colistin or Polymyxin E was also found in a *Bacillus colistinus* culture from Japanese soil.

Range of activity. These drugs are effective against most Gram-negative bacteria, with the exception of *Proteus* spp. They are used for *Pseudomonas* infections, in addition to gentamycin.

Mechanism of action. These antimicrobial agents act as detergents on the microbial membranes and cause a leakage of essential cytoplasmic components. They may be bacteriostatic or bactericidal, depending upon the dosage used and the relative numbers of organisms to be treated. Both compounds are somewhat toxic: however, kidney damage and neurotoxicity are usually reversible.

Antimycobacterial Drugs

Two drugs commonly used in combination with streptomycin are isonicotinic hydrazide (INH)

and para-aminosalicylic acid (PAS).

Range of activity. After the discovery that sulfa drugs were active by competing with PABA in microbial metabolism, investigators set out to apply this type of mechanism to other organisms. Bernheim in 1941 found that salicylic acid would stimulate the metabolism of *Mycobacterium tuberculosis*. On the basis of this information, Lehman was able to show in 1946 that para-aminosalicylic acid was active against bovine tuberculosis.

The first description of the anti-tuberculosis activity of INH was by Fox, Grunberg, and Schnitzer in 1951. This drug penetrates into the tissues so well, that it can act against bacilli located in tubercles and inside phagocytes—unlike streptomycin and PAS. Isonicotinic hydrazide is relatively non-toxic, but it may cause renal (kidney) complications, particularly in patients with renal tuberculosis.

Mechanism of action. Isonicotinic hydrazide is bacteriostatic initially, and becomes bactericidal later. The activity appears to be due to its incorporation into nicotinamide adenine dinucleotide (NAD) or nicotinamide adenine dinucleotide phosphate (NADP), both of which are coenzymes. Isonicotinic hydrazide also resembles vitamin B and probably interferes with those enzymes which require B_6 as a coenzyme. Thus, blocking of essential enzyme activity due to its incorporation into coenzymes appears to be the mechanism involved.

At one time it was thought that the mechanism of action for PAS was an interference with salicylate metabolism. However, the drug has since been shown to act as sulfa drugs do, namely, by interference with PABA metabolism. PAS is a relatively ineffective bacteriostatic drug. The prime value of this anti-tubercular agent is its activity in delaying the emergence of resistance to streptomycin and INH. The usual side effects of PAS are nausea and vomiting, which are commonly prevented by the simultaneous administration of an antacid compound.

Rifampin

Rifampin is a relatively new semisynthetic derivation of rifamycin B produced by *Streptomyces mediterranei*. The anti-bacterial spectrum of the drug is broad. It is active against Gram-positive and Gram-negative organisms and is highly effective in the treatment of tuberculosis. In fact, the development of rifampin may be considered a major advance in anti-tuberculosis chemotherapy since it is of great value in patients with drug-resistant organisms. Microbial resistance to rifampin also can develop, however. Therefore, in anti-tuberculosis therapy it is used in combination with other drugs. Rifampin interferes with nucleic acid synthesis.

Mechanisms of Drug Resistance

When the bulk of antimicrobial agents began to become available for chemotherapy in the early 1950s, these "Wonder Drugs" were thought to be the final answer to the control of infections. Penicillin, in particular, was added to items such as chewing gum, mouthwash, and toothpaste. In addition to this indiscriminate use of drugs, many physicians routinely prescribed them for minor infections. Partly as a result of drug misuse, microorganisms such as *Staphylococcus aureus* became resistant to these agents, and consequently became more difficult to eliminate. Even with the development of more and more specific and broad-spectrum drugs, resistance remains a problem that requires constant consideration.

Some mechanisms by which organisms develop resistance to antimicrobial agents include: (1) an enzymatic alteration of the drug, (2) a change in the selective permeability of their cell walls and membranes, (3) a change in the sensitivity of affected enzymes, and (4) an increased production of a competitive substrate. One example of antibiotic inactivation is the production of the enzyme penicillinase by *Staphylococcus aureus*. Since the sensitive portion of the penicillin molecule is a beta lactam ring, the enzyme is more correctly known as *penicillin-beta lactamase*. The pharmaceutical industry has attacked this particular problem of penicillin resistance by modifying the structure of the drug. As a result, the drugs methicillin, oxacillin (Figure 19-1), and nafcillin have been produced. These compounds are effective against penicillinase-producing staphylococci. Another antibiotic related structurally to oxacillin is ampicillin. This compound lacks a resistance to penicillinase, but has a broad spectrum of activity against many Gram-positive and Gram-negative organisms, as discussed earlier.

One example of drug resistance due to changes in cellular permeability and sensitivity involves streptomycin. It appears that this antibiotic exerts its primary activity against a cell's protein-manufacturing process, specifically at the level of the translation of genetic information involving messenger RNA (mRNA) and ribosomes. Resistance here can occur by the development of a decreased sensitivity of the enzymes concerned with attaching mRNA to ribosomes. Streptomycin also appears to affect cell membrane permeability. Resistance, therefore, can occur due to changes in the selective permeability of the cell.

Sulfonamides also appear to act both at an enzymic level (the pathway from para-aminobenzoic acid, PABA, to folic acid) and at membrane sites. Resistance to sulfonamides may therefore be due to changes in enzyme sensitivity and/or selective permeability. With sulfonamides, the bacterium can also develop resistance by overproducing PABA, as occurs with S. aureus.

The Ominous Nature of Antibiotics

As more antibiotics become known, both medical and nonmedical uses increase. Very few of these compounds have become obsolete or have been withdrawn from the market. Currently, however, it appears that several of these antibiotics are overused and overprescribed by appropriate medical personnel. For example, market research data show that almost two-thirds of the prescriptions given to patients for the common cold are anti-biotics, yet most colds and sore throats are caused by viruses, microorganisms that are not affected by the majority of currently available antibiotics or antimicrobials. Furthermore, as many as 1.5 million people are hospitalized annually in the United States for adverse drug reactions and approximately 130,000 die from reactions associated with antibiotics and antimicrobials. With such increased unnecessary exposure to these drugs, a significant increase has occurred in antibiotic-resistant organisms. Several health care institutions and personnel are monitoring their usage in order to improve this serious problem.

Future Antibiotic Strategy Against the Drug Resistance Problem

Since the discovery of transferable antibiotic resistance in 1959, a fairly clear picture of the process as it occurs in the laboratory has emerged (see Chapter 16 for a discussion of resistance transfer factors). Furthermore, it is well known that in most cases the introduction of a new antibiotic, which is initially effective against bacteria such as Staphylococcus aureus, for example, has been followed by the appearance of strains resistant to that antibiotic. During the 1940s and 1950s, antibiotic resistance in bacteria was generally thought to arise by mutation and selection (see Chapter 16). However, since 1960, evidence has accrued to show that most antibiotic resistance in organisms belonging to the Enterobacteriaceae, such as Escherichia coli, Citrobacter freundii, and S. aureus, is determined and controlled by extrachromosonal particles called plasmids (see Chapter 16). At times such plasmids are physically distinct from a bacterium's chromosome, and depending on the bacterium, can be transferred from one organism to another by several means, including bacterial viruses. It should be noted that certain cases of antibiotic resistance are chromosome-mediated.

The overall impact of the plasmid on a population of bacterial cells is that it provides a means for greater flexibility to survive under a variety of environmental factors. Take, for example, penicillinase production (penicillinase is an enzyme that inactivates penicillin) and staphylococcal resistance against penicillin. Several studies have shown that penicillinase production is plasmid-determined in the great majority of penicillin-resistant strains. Thus under natural or laboratory conditions this antibiotic resistance could be imparted to antibiotic-sensitive organisms through cell transfer mechanisms. With such transfer the usefulness of an antibiotic can be greatly decreased. Although this may be a valuable evolutionary weapon for organisms, it obviously poses a serious threat to the effectiveness of antibiotic therapy and to the control of infectious diseases. The use of antibiotics has undoubtedly increased the number of plasmid-containing bacteria. Future application of chemotherapeutic agents must be directed toward reducing the incidence of such plasmid carriers if the usefulness of antibiotics is to be not only retained but also improved.

Antibiotic Sensitivity Testing Methods

Minimum Inhibitory Concentration Determination

The best methods for determining the antibiotic susceptibility of microorganisms involve a careful estimation of an antimicrobial agent's minimum inhibitory concentrations (M.I.C.s). The determinations can be performed in either liquid or solid media. The procedure re-

quires a mixing of two-fold serial dilutions of the antimicrobial agent to be tested with growth media. A standardized microbial suspension is then used to inoculate these prepared tubes or plates. After a suitable incubation period, one can readily determine the minimum inhibitory concentration of a drug which can prevent growth.

The *tube dilution test* utilizes liquid media, and the M.I.C. is reported as the lowest concentration of antibiotic which totally inhibits the growth of the organisms.

With the *agar dilution* system, multiple organisms can be tested on each dilution plate. The agar dilution procedure is presented in Figure 19–6. The test organism may be applied to the plates individually with an inoculating loop, or a number of organisms may be tested by means of a replicating device. This may be a wooden block with nails. Since wood usually will not take autoclaving, the nails that will be used for inoculation purposes are first surface sterilized by dipping in 70 per cent ethanol, and then flamed. This is adequate for all organisms with the exception of spore-forming bacteria.

The test organisms are suspended in sterile medium or physiological saline and placed into test tubes or vials, so that when the nails of the replicating device are placed into these tubes the ends of the nails will pick up the organisms. Following this step, each plate is touched with the replicating device and each organism is inoculated onto the equivalent spot on each respective plate. Using the conditions shown in Figure 19–6 as an example, after incubation examination of the plates shows that organism #1 has an M.I.C. of 5 μg/1 ml, organism #4 has an M.I.C. of 2.5 μg/1 ml, and so forth. The same results could be expected

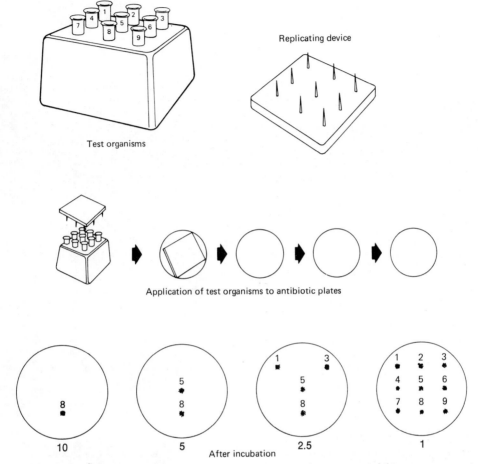

FIG. 19–6. The agar dilution technique for the determination of minimum inhibitory concentrations (M.I.C.) of antimicrobial agents.

if the tube dilution test were used. Growth in that case would be evidenced by turbidity.

Although the inhibitory concentrations of a drug can be determined by this procedure, the nature of the reaction still remains to be determined. In other words, was the antimicrobial agent bacteriostatic or was it bactericidal? Such determinations are generally not performed in clinical laboratories, but are left to the manufacturer of the particular preparation. It should be noted, however, that whether a drug is bacteriostatic or

bactericidal may depend on the concentration used.

Both of the above dilution methods are tedious and are not usually performed in the routine clinical laboratory. One approach to making the tube dilution method easier, and also using less reagent, has been the use of the *microtiter technique*. With this procedure, rapid dilution is accomplished through the use of small calibrated loops (25 to 50 microliters). The total volume of the test reagents employed is approximately 0.2 ml. The dilutions for a number of antibiotics and several organisms can be carried out in an inexpensive plastic tray having multiple shallow wells. After incubation, the M.I.C.s are determined as described earlier.

One approach to simplifying the agar dilution technique has been to use a gradient plate procedure.

Gradient plates are prepared so that particular regions of an agar medium contain a gradually increasing or decreasing concentration of the antibiotic or other material being tested. The antibiotic-containing agar is poured into a plate placed at an appoximate 45° angle. After the agar solidifies, an additional quantity of medium, without the antibiotic, is poured into the plate, which is now held flat. A relatively uniform gradient of antibiotic concentration is established by this type of preparation. The antibiotic concentration corresponds to the height of antibiotic-containing agar. Organisms are streaked on this type of plate and after incubation the approximate M.I.C. can be determined.

Drug Diffusion Methods

Cylinder and well methods. The screening of large numbers of organisms with various antibiotics requires simpler approaches than those described above. For example, small cylinders can be placed into the agar plates or wells can be cut into the agar for the purpose of holding a specified quantity of a particular antimicrobial agent. This type of procedure is shown in Figure 19–7A. The Petri dish here contains an agar medium seeded with a test organism. The three wells have been cut out and filled with solutions of a drug. If the antimicrobial agent is effective against the test organism, three zones of inhibition will develop (Figure 19–7B). However, if the drug is ineffective, then the results shown in Figure 19–7C are found.

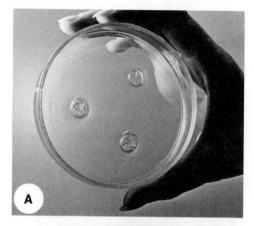

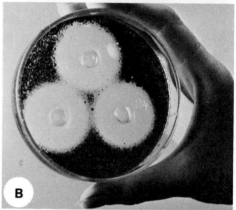

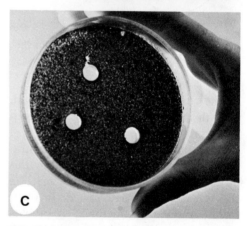

FIG. 19–7. Another method of antibiotic testing. _A._ A Petri dish containing a medium seeded with a test organism. Three wells have been cut for the placement of an experimental drug. _B._ The results of a test in which the test organisms are sensitive to the drug. _C._ Drug resistance on the part of the test organisms. (Courtesy of Lederle Laboratories, Pearl River, N.Y.)

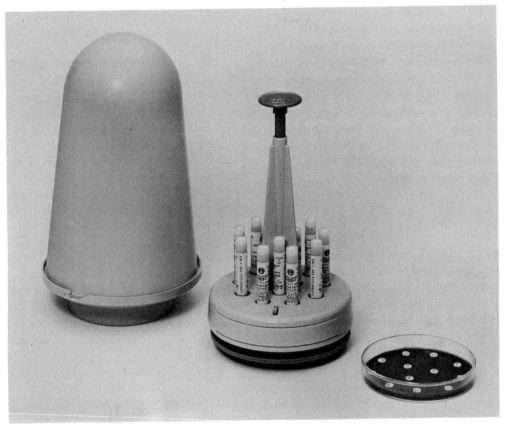

FIG. 19–8. Commercially available paper disks can be obtained in cartridges and applied to the medium in a Petri plate. This is usually done with a multiple applicator device. (Courtesy of Bio-Quest, Division of Becton, Dickinson and Company, Cockeysville, Md.)

Filter paper disk. Because the well method is still a bit awkward to perform as a routine laboratory procedure, *impregnated paper disks* have received wide acceptance (Figure 19–8). A. Bondi in 1947 reported the use of filter paper disks containing specified concentrations of antibiotics. The standardization of variables to minimize difficulties in interpretation was a critical aspect of this work.

It must be realized that several factors can affect the size of the zone of antibacterial activity. These include: (1) the depth of the medium used, (2) the choice of medium, (3) the size of inoculum, and (4) the diffusion rate of a particular antibiotic. The last factor, in particular, has resulted in unfortunate misinterpretations of results.

Until recently, most laboratories have used single- or double-disk methods with little consideration of the important variables. Such techniques are being replaced by the standardized procedure of Kirby and Bauer. In brief, the single-disk methods utilize one disk of either a high or a low antibiotic concentration. To determine the relative sensitivity of the organism to the drug requires interpretation of zone sizes. With a double-disk method the interpretation is simpler. Here both high- and low-strength disks are applied for each antibiotic to be tested. The organism is reported as being sensitive if a clear zone of no growth appears around both disks. If a zone appears around the high-concentration disk alone, the organism is called *moderately susceptible*. If zones are lacking in either disk, the organism is considered to be resistant to the drug. Although interpretation is simpler here, the accuracy of the double-disk method does not approach that of the Kirby-Bauer procedure.

Kirby-Bauer (K-B) standardized single-disk method. This procedure was first reported in 1966. The Kirby-Bauer method uses a single high-strength antibiotic disk with Mueller-Hinton agar dispensed in 150 × 15 millimeter (mm) Petri plates. The depth of the medium is 5 to 6 mm (approximately 80 ml of medium). Standardization of the test organisms is accomplished by: (1) introducing the growth from 5 isolated colonies into 4 ml of Brain-Heart Infusion Broth; (2) incubating the preparation for 2 to 5 hours in a water bath or thermal block, or until adequate turbidity is evident; and (3) adjusting the turbidity of the bacterial suspension according to a standard made from barium sulfate (McFarland Standard 0.5).

A sample is taken by means of a sterile cotton swab. Excess fluid is removed by rolling the swab against the side of the tube containing the bacterial suspension. Then it is used to spread the organisms onto the surface of the agar medium. After a few minutes wait for the surface moisture to be absorbed by the agar, disks are applied. This procedure may be done with the large size applicator comparable to the one shown in Figure 19–8. After incubation, the sizes of zones can be measured with the aid of calipers, or they can be compared against a template consisting of various

zones, the sizes of which are based on the data published by Ryan and his associates in 1970.

Selected drugs and zone sizes are presented in Table 19–3. These were evaluated according to M.I.C.s for pathogens, and obtainable levels of antimicrobial agents in the human body. With this system, when an organism is reported to be sensitive (S) or resistant (R), the level of confidence in such a report is very high. An intermediate (I) classification indicates that the organism is probably resistant to obtainable body levels of the drug in question. The drug should not be used without first performing a tube dilution test confirming the M.I.C. obtained. In practice the I designation is considered the same as a R rating. The drug is not used if the microorganism has been found to be sensitive to several other drugs.

The K-B method and the agar-overlay modification techniques to be presented next are suitable only for rapidly growing pathogenic bacteria, e.g., enterobacteriaceae, staphylococci, and *Pseudomonas* spp. Fortunately, the vast majority of pathogens are in this category. The other single- or double-disk procedures can be used with most bacterial species. However, without some form of standardization, the accuracy of the results is questionable.

The agar-overlay method. The agar-overlay modification of Barry, Garcia, and Thrupp (1970) has greatly simplified performing the Kirby-Bauer procedure without affecting the interpretation of zone sizes. Figure 19–9 shows the series of steps involved in this test.

In this procedure, 0.5 ml of Brain-Heart Infusion Broth is inoculated with the test colonies to make the solution slightly turbid (Figure 19–9A). The tube then is placed into a constant temperature

Table 19–3   Zone Size Comparison of Selected Chemotherapeutic Drugs

Chemotherapeutic Drug	Concentration in Disk	Inhibition Zone Diameter (mm)		
		R[a] less than	I between	S more than
Ampicillin[b]	10 μgm	21	21–28	28
Chloramphenicol	30 μgm	13	13–17	17
Colistin	10 μgm	9	9–10	10
Kanamycin	30 μgm	14	14–17	17
Penicillin[b]	10 units	21	21–28	28
Sulfonamides	300 μgm	13	13–16	16
Tetracyclines	30 μgm	15	15–18	18

[a] R = resistant, I = intermediate resistance, S = sensitivity. See text for additional information concerning the differences between R and I and reasons for the various zone sizes for different drugs.
[b] Interpretation of zone sizes with ampicillin and penicillin varies with different organisms. These values are primarily for staphylococci.

bath or block held at 37°C for 4 to 8 hours (Figure 19–9*B*). During this incubation period, tubes containing 8 ml of melted 1.5 per cent agar are placed into a constant temperature bath or block maintained at approximately 52°C.

After the incubation period mentioned earlier, 0.001 ml of the broth culture is introduced by means of a calibrated loop into a tube of melted agar (Figure 19–9*C*). The contents of the tube are mixed (Figure 19–9*D*) and then poured onto the surface of 70 ml of solidified Mueller-Hinton agar in 150 mm × 15 mm plastic Petri plates (Figure 19–9*E*). It is imperative that the plates be warmed to at least room temperature before attempting the latter step. Tilting and/or rotating the plate generally is necessary in order to produce a uniform layer of the seeded agar. The colder the plate, the more difficult this step is to perform.

The required antibiotic disks are applied 3 to 5 minutes after the agar layer has solidified (Figure 19–9*F*). These disks are placed firmly on the agar surface (Figure 19–9*G*). Following this step, the Petri plate cover is replaced (Figure 19–9*H*) and the entire system is incubated at 35°C overnight (Figure 19–9*I*). The zones of inhibition which develop are compared with standards to determine relative sensitivities (Figure 19–9*J*).

Antimycotic Agents

Mycotic or fungal infections have generally been highly resistant to chemotherapeutic drugs. In fact, the changes of the normal bacterial population (flora) resulting from antibiotic treatment tend to contribute to superinfection with fungi, such as the yeast *Candida albicans*. The characteristics of several antimycotic agents are shown in Table 19–4.

Antiviral Agents

Until quite recently chemotherapy of true virus diseases had been virtually nonexistent. Considerable prophylactic and therapeutic success had been achieved with a large number of viral agents through the use of vaccines, but no success had been obtained with chemotherapeutic drugs. During the last few years several developments have taken place that have provided some promising antiviral drugs. Examples of these include amantadine, 5 - iodo - 2' - deoxyuridine (IDU), methisazone, interferon inducers, and cytosine arabinoside (cytarabin).

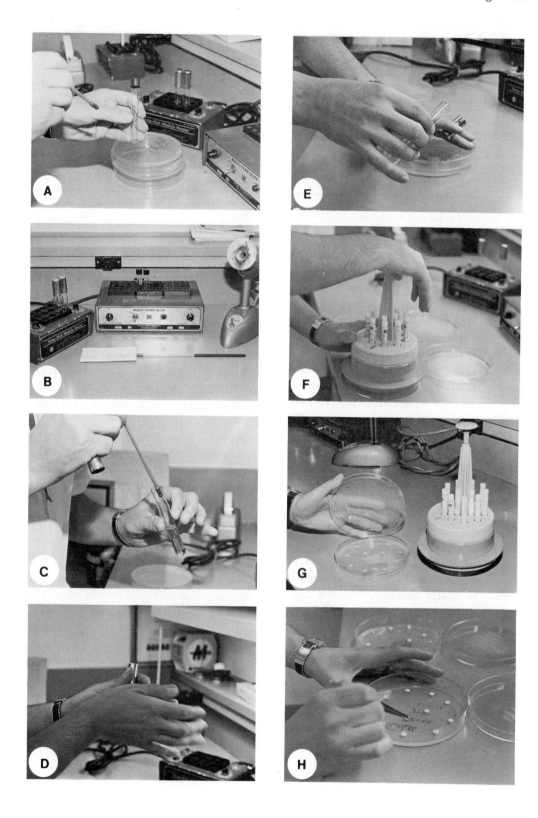

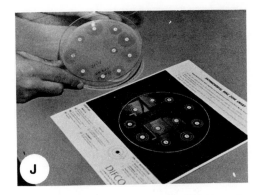

FIG. 19–9. Agar-overlay modification of the Kirby-Bauer standardized antibiotic disk sensi- tivity test. (Courtesy of St. Mary's Long Beach Hospital, Long Beach Calif.)

Table 19–5 provides a comparative summary of these antiviral agents, and Figure 19–10 shows their chemical structures.

Antiviral Agent Sensitivity Testing

With the recent unraveling of many of the biochemical, biological, and biophysical properties of viruses that can cause human infections, an impressive amount of enthusiasm has erupted in anticipation of an era of effective viral chemotherapy. Despite the wealth of knowledge that has been gathered, there remain a number of serious problems that are peculiar to the field of viral chemotherapy. Among these obstacles are the following: (1) the ac- companying toxicity to mammalian cells by chemotherapeutic agents effective against viruses; (2) a multiplicity effect, which refers to a situation in which an antiviral agent is effective against viruses in low concentration but ineffective against high concentrations of viruses; (3) the difficulty in demonstrating the clinical effectiveness of antiviral agents; and (4) the possible emergence of drug-resistant viral strains.

All of these problem areas are important. The evaluation of clinical effectiveness is especially critical, because this obstacle must be overcome before a drug can be made available for general use. The

Table 19–4   Characteristics of Antimycotic Drugs

Drug	Fungus Diseases Affected	Side Effects
Amphotericin B (Fungizone)	Superficial candidiasis	Essentially none
	Systemic candidiasis, not involving the heart (endocarditis)	Kidney damage, convulsions, hypotension, nausea, vomiting, abdominal pain, metallic taste, cardiac arrest, and anemia[a]
	Deep-seated fungous infections including aspergillosis, coccioidomycosis, histomycosis, systemic sporothricosis, blastomycosis, and cryptococcosis	Same as for systemic candidiasis
Flucytosine (Ancobon)	Systemic candidiasis, not involving the heart, and cryptococcosis	Gastrointestinal distress and reduction of white blood cells (leukopenia)
Griseofulvin (Fulvicin, Grifulvin, Grisactin)	Dermatophytoses (ringworm of the hair, nails, and/or skin)	Fatigue, skin eruptions, nausea, vomiting, and diarrhea
Nystatin (Mycostatin)	Intestinal candidiasis	Basically none

[a] The side effects listed occur more readily with the rapid introduction of the drug.

Table 19-5   A Comparative Summary of Antiviral Drugs

Drug	Representative Viral Disease(s) Affected	Possible Side Effects	Mechanism of Action
Amantadine	Influenza A₂ (Asia)	General irritability, insomnia, confusion, hallucinations, inability to concentrate	Prevents penetration of certain viruses into host cells
5-Iodo-2'-deoxyuridine	Severe *Herpesvirus hominis* (herpes simplex) infection	Nausea, vomiting, hair and fingernail loss, lowering of white blood cells (leukopenia) and platelets (thrombocytopenia)	Blocks synthesis of nucleic acids
Cytosine arabinoside	Progressive varicella (chickenpox) and zoster (shingles) infections	Nausea, vomiting, loss of appetite, chromosomal changes, lowering of white blood cells and platelets, anemia	Inhibits DNA synthesis
Methisazone	Progressive vaccinia	Nausea, vomiting, loss of appetite, liver toxicity (hepatotoxicity)	Interferes with protein synthesis at the level of translation

Table 19-6   Current Clinical Status of Antiviral Agents

Agent	Type of Application			
	Topical		Systemic	
	Prophylaxis (preventative measure)	Therapy	Prophylaxis	Therapy
Amantadine	—	+	+	—
Cytosine arabinoside (AraC)	—	—	—	—
Idoxuridine (IDU)	.	—	+	—
Interferon	+ᵃ	—	—	—
Methisazone	—	—	+	—

ᵃ Has not been tested adequately in cases of natural infection. Refer to Chapter 20 for a discussion of interferon.

clinical value of a few antiviral agents has been established (Table 19–6). Before the clinical effectiveness of an antiviral agent can be determined, certain requirements must be satisfied. First, the drug in question must be evaluated both in cell culture and in animal models for antiviral activity and toxicity. This aspect of the evaluation is the first phase of drug evaluation. In the second phase, human experimentation is performed with the objective of determining tolerable dosages and general effects of the antiviral agent on the body. The third phase is the formal therapeutic trial, which is directed toward determining the true clinical effect of the drug on actual cases of virus infections. Certain preparations satisfy some of these drug-evaluation requirements but for various reasons fall short of satisfying all of them. It is obvious that the problems peculiar to the area of viral chemotherapy must be overcome before a proven treatment for viral diseases will be at hand.

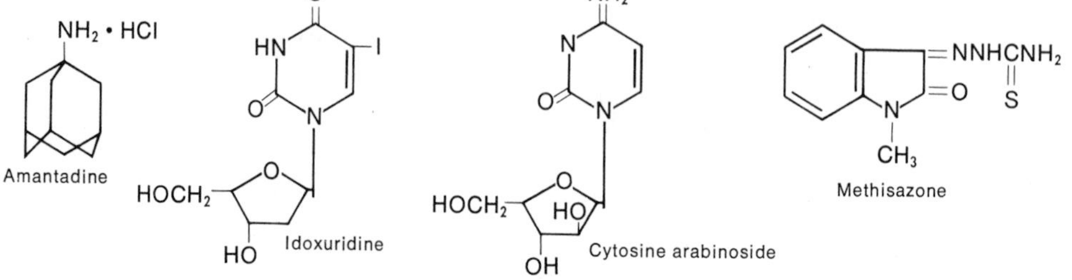

FIG. 19–10. The chemical structures of promising antiviral agents.

QUESTIONS FOR REVIEW

1. Discuss the basic philosophy which resulted in the discovery of prontosil.

2. List the contributions of the following scientists to the field of chemotherapy.
   a. Ehrlich
   b. Domagk
   c. Fleming
   d. Waksman
   e. Bondi
   f. Kirby and Bauer

3. List antibacterial, antifungal, antiviral, and antiprotozoan drugs which are derived from *Streptomyces* spp.

4. What is the value of a semi-synthetic antibiotic?

5. What value has rifampin in antituberculosis therapy?

6. Define, describe, or discuss each of the following:
   a. M.I.C.
   b. side effects
   c. drug allergy
   d. antibiogram
   e. drug resistance

7. Compare the tube dilution, agar dilution, and Kirby-Bauer methods of antibiotic sensitivity testing in terms of ease of performance and relative quality of results obtained.

8. Describe the procedure used in sensitivity testing of an antiviral agent.

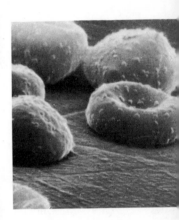

Principles
of
Immunology

DIVISION 6: Behavioral Objectives

After reading the chapters in this division, the individual should be able to:

1. Identify the significant factors that contribute to host resistance and microbial virulence.

2. Relate the properties of microorganisms to the causation of disease processes.

3. Describe the properties of antigens and immunoglobulins (antibodies).

4. Understand the basis of generally employed *in vitro* antigen and antigen and antibody reactions.

5. Recognize the nature of human blood groups and related physiological problems.

6. Understand the immunological basis and extent of hypersensitivity.

7. Relate immunological principles to the causation of disease and diagnosis.

8. Recognize the importance and limitations of immunizations in the prevention and control of disease states.

9. Identify the nature of some complications associated with immunizations.

Host Resistance

Humans and other animal species are protected in varying degrees from infectious diseases by certain physiologic defense mechanisms, referred to as *immunity*. Collectively, the various factors provide protection either by posing barriers to microorganisms attempting to gain entrance into the body, or by preventing damage from occurring once such organisms or their toxic products find their way into the body.

Certain defense mechanisms are utilized in efforts to combat any and all disease-causing agents. This form of immunity is called *nonspecific resistance,* and includes inflammation, mechanical barriers, species or racial factors, phagocytosis, and various chemical products of the body. The defense mechanisms that provide *specific immunity* against particular microorganisms and/or their products are discussed in later chapters. Chapter 21, *Factors Involved in Microbial Virulence,* approaches the general topic of host resistance from the opposite viewpoint—that of the invading microorganism.

Species or Racial Resistance

It is well known that some animal species are apparently nonsusceptible to certain diseases which can have rather disastrous effects on other animals. Humans exhibit such *nonsusceptibility* toward a variety of infectious diseases of other animals, including canine distemper, cattle plague, chicken cholera, and hog cholera. On the other hand, lower animal species are similarly resistant to human-associated bacterial infections such as dysentery, gonorrhea, typhoid fever, whooping cough, and viral diseases such as measles and mumps.

Generally speaking, nonsusceptibility is determined by physiologic and anatomic properties of the particular animal species and is inheritable. Demonstrable antibodies are not associated with this state of resistance. The term *natural immunity* is used to denote states in which antibodies are present without any known prior stimulation of their production. Changes in body temperature, diet, and stress can affect species resistance, as shown by several classic experiments. Chickens and frogs normally are not susceptible to the bacterial disease anthrax. However, the cold-blooded frog will succumb to inoculation with the infectious agent, if its temperature is artificially raised to approximately 35°C, and the warm-blooded chicken will succumb if its body temperature is lowered to that level. The multiplication of various pathogens is dependent upon the availability of growth factors in a readily utilizable form. Some disease agents depend on the food of their host. Dogs normally are resistant to anthrax. However, when meat is omitted from their diets, they become susceptible to the infection.

Species or racial resistance depends on the interplay of many factors, not all of which are known.

Mechanical and Chemical Barriers, "The Body's First Line of Defense"

Several portions of the body pose formidable barriers to many potential disease-causing agents. Their effectiveness depends greatly on the physiologic or pathologic state of the host. Conditions such as alcoholism, poor nutrition, and the debilitating effects of aging, fatigue, and prolonged exposure to extreme temperatures and to immunosuppressive therapy are conducive to the establishment of a disease process. Some pathogenic agents seem to initiate their particular infectious process only when they gain access through a particular portal of entry, each of which has its own defense barriers. Chapters in Division 7 contain general descriptions of the various body systems.

Intact Skin

Unbroken skin serves as an excellent mechanical barrier through which most microorganisms cannot penetrate. In addition to the several layers comprising this body covering, certain bactericidal secretions are formed by associated glands. Injuries to the skin, such as abrasion, laceration, or burns, provide the opportunity for microorganisms to pass beyond this first line of defense. However, the mere penetration of the skin does not establish an infection. Once organisms enter the body by this means they may or may not encounter favorable conditions for their growth and multiplication. Several other defense mechanisms which we shall discuss can interfere with the activities of pathogens. Nevertheless, accidental injuries, regardless of how minor they appear to be, should not be neglected. Given the right set of circumstances, any type of wound can result in a serious infection.

Mucous Membranes

The respiratory system is protected by several mechanisms. In addition to the presence of nasal hairs, the mucous membranes of this region are covered with a thick, slimy secretion which serves to entrap dust, foreign particles, and various microorganisms. Similarly, parts of the respiratory passages are lined with cilia. These barriers, plus the coughing and sneezing reflexes, help to eliminate accumulations of foreign particles. If microorganisms evade such defense barriers, leukocytes operating in the body are called forth to stop them.

Genito-Urinary System

The mucous membranes of the female genito-urinary tract are afforded protection against several pathogens by a thick secretion which tends to trap certain invading organisms. In addition, the acid nature of the vaginal environment discourages the establishment of some infectious agents. The outward flow of urine and its acidity contribute to the defense of the urinary tract. However, various pathogens, including those causing gonorrhea and syphilis, are still able to invade the body by this portal of entry.

Eyes

Several factors function to prevent disease agents from entering and attacking the inner lining of the eyelid (the conjunctivae). These include the washing effect of tears and the mechanical motion of the eye lids, eyelashes, and eyebrows. Tears contain a bactericidal substance called *lysozyme,* discussed later.

Gastro-Intestinal System

The composition and acidity of gastric juice provides a definite degree of protection to the stomach. However, some organisms are shielded by the presence of food.

In the small intestine, mucous, certain enzymes, bile, and the process of phagocytosis are important factors contributing to the body's defense. The large intestine contains numerous microorganisms (indigenous flora) that are important in maintaining a "normal" balance. The contributions of this group of organisms are discussed later in the chapter.

The Components of Normal Blood and Their Roles in Health and Disease

Blood is the transportation system and means of intercommunication between the various tissue cells of the body. It transports food and hormones, removes cellular waste products, assists in the regulation of body temperature, and aids in the removal and, in certain situations, the destruction of foreign substances and invading microorganisms. As several of the following chapters will show, blood can play an important role in the transmission, production, diagnosis, cure, and prevention of the numerous effects caused by microorganisms.

An adult male weighing about 150 pounds generally has 5 to 6 quarts of blood circulating through his arteries, veins, and capillaries. As a liquid, blood is a somewhat atypical form of connective tissue. It consists of cellular elements in a fluid substance called *plasma* (Figure 20–1). As the structural components of mammalian blood are not all thought to be "true cells", they may be referred to as the *formed elements;* these include *erythrocytes* (red cells), *leukocytes* (white cells), and *platelets. Chylomicrons,* which are visible minute fat globules, are also suspended in the plasma portion of blood. The cellular elements comprise approximately 45 per cent of the blood, and plasma constitutes the remaining portion. A special type of calibrated tube called a *hematocrit* can

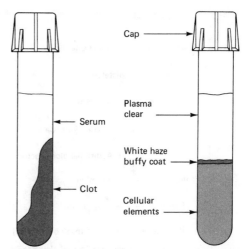

FIG. 20–1. The distinction between serum (left) and plasma (right).

be used to determine the proportions of cells and plasma in a blood sample.

Plasma and serum. When blood is removed from the body by means of a sterile syringe and needle and introduced into a test tube, clotting of the specimen normally takes place within 2 to 6 minutes. The complex mechanism of clotting is shown in Figure 20–2. The soluble protein substance *fibrinogen,* which normally circulates in the plasma, is converted into the insoluble protein called *fibrin* to form the fiber framework of the clot. The majority of the blood cells in the specimen become enmeshed in the fibrin. Within a few hours the clot shrinks and expels a clear, yellow fluid called *serum* (Figure 20–1). The serum contains several types of proteins, including albumin and normal and immune globulins. *Normal globulins* are important to the maintenance of adequate cellular nutrition and a normal osmotic pressure. *Immune globulins* are the so-called antibodies which are produced by the body in response to: (1) infectious agents, (2) various vaccine preparations of killed microorganisms, weakened or attenuated organisms, or their products; or (3)

Stage   Reactions

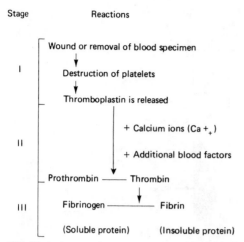

FIG. 20–2. A general representation of the blood clotting mechanism. Thromboplastin is an important enzyme which is released from platelets and so-called tissue juice. This enzyme is believed to react with antiprothrombin, which prevents the conversion of prothrombin to thrombin. All of the other reactants are found in blood plasma.

other foreign protein substances, such as pollens.

Plasma is formed in a blood specimen by the introduction of an anticoagulant such as potassium, sodium oxalate, or heparin. These substances interfere with the formation of *thrombin* (Figure 20–2). Consequently, the cellular elements will settle to the bottom of the tube containing the specimen, either on standing or centrifugation. The clear fluid left above is called *plasma*. Thus, plasma is blood without cells but with fibrinogen, and serum is *defibrinated* plasma.

Plasma is a complex mixture of substances including carbohydrates, lipids, proteins, gases, inorganic salts, hormones, and water. The pH of plasma normally is slightly alkaline, approximately 7.4.

Red cells are formed in the bone marrow and measure about 7.5 to 7.7 μm and 1.9 to 2 μm in thickness. In mammals, these cells are not nucleated when mature, and appear as biconcave disks (Color photo-

graph 10). The red cells are composed of a membrane which is in close association with the protein iron-containing compound, *hemoglobin*. Hemoglobin has great attraction for oxygen and the red cell is highly specialized for the transport of this gas. In addition, these cells possess the major, minor, and Rh blood factors. An erythrocyte's life span generally ranges from 100 to 120 days. When insufficient numbers of these cells are produced by the body, the condition is known as *anemia*.

White cells or leukocytes are classified into two groups based upon: (1) the presence and type of cytoplasmic granules, (2) the shape of the nucleus, (3) the appearance of the cytoplasm, and (4) size. The groups are called *granulocytes* and *agranulocytes*. The former category is made up of cells which contain distinct cytoplasmic granules. Upon staining (as in the case of blood smear preparations) these cytoplasmic components react with dyes to yield characteristic colors. Based upon the resulting chemical reaction, three types of granulocytes may be noted (Color photograph 10): (1) the *eosinophile* (the granules react with acid dyes and become red); (2) the *basophile* (the granules react with basic dyes and become blue); and (3) the *neutrophile* or *polymorphonuclear leukocyte* (the granules react with neutral dyes or acid and basic dye mixtures, and become neutral or orange-colored). Granulocytes possess irregular and multilobed nuclei. The term "polymorphonuclear leukocyte" refers to a white cell with a "many-lobed nucleus." These cells also are designated as "polys" and PMNLs. Like erythrocytes, they are formed in the bone marrow. The life span of these cells is no longer than two weeks.

Granulocytes, principally the eosinophiles and the neutrophiles, are associated with phagocytosis. These cells are capable of engulfing various foreign particles, such as bacteria, and eventually digesting them. The details of this important defense mechanism will be discussed more fully in a later section.

The *agranulocytes* can be distinguished from the granulocytes in that they do not possess granules, and their nuclei are rounded rather than lobed. The two general cell types of this group are the *lymphocyte* and the *monocyte* (Color photograph 10). Lymphocytes possess individual rounded nuclei which occupy the major portion of the cell. Monocytes are larger than lymphocytes and their nuclei are generally kidney-shaped. Certain lymphocytes may survive for as long as 200 days. Lymphocytes are principally produced in the appendix, lymph nodes, spleen, thymus, and other lymphoid tissues. Monocytes are formed in the bone marrow. As to function, certain small lymphocytes and certain monocytes are involved with specific antibody formation. Monocytes also participate in phagocytosis.

Disease states can cause changes in the proportions of the different types of leukocytes. Also, certain pathogens produce an increase of white cells, called *leukocytosis*. These include *Streptococcus* (*Diplococcus*) *pneumoniae* (the etiologic agent of lobar pneumonia), *Neisseria gonorrhoeae* (the etiologic agent of gonorrhea), and *Staphylococcus aureus* (the etiologic agent of boils, carbuncles, pneumonia, etc.). Other microorganisms cause a reduction in the number of leukocytes, called *leukopenia*. The etiologic agents of influenza, measles, tuberculosis, and typhoid fever are included in this group.

Differential count. The procedure known as the *differential count* is performed to determine the respective numbers of the various white cells. This count is made from a stained blood smear. The normal values, based on an approximate total of 100 cells, are as follows:

Granulocytes		
Basophiles	0 -	1
Eosinophiles	1 -	4
Neutrophiles	60 -	70
Agranulocytes		
Large lymphocytes	0 -	3
Small lymphocytes	25 -	30
Monocytes	4 -	8
	90 -	116

Phagocytosis

Phagocytosis is one of the most important lines of defense after the mechanical barriers have failed. It is a process by which certain types of cells engulf foreign particles. This is usually accomplished by an extension of the cell surrounding the foreign matter. In 1882, Metchnikoff (Figure 20–3) observed "ameboid cells"

FIG. 20–3. Elie Metchnikoff (1845–1916). He shared the Nobel Prize for Physiology and Medicine with Paul Ehrlich in 1908. (Courtesy of the National Library of Medicine, Bethesda, Md.)

(leukocytes) ingest cells of the yeast *Monospora bicuspidata* within the water flea *Daphnia*. Apparently he was among the first investigators to recognize the important role played by leukocytic ingestion in protecting a host from disease.

Phagocytosis is quite complex. At least three variables influence this defense mechanism—the type of particle ingested, the phagocytic cell, and the environment or menstruum in which the process takes place. In addition, noncellular components of blood have been shown to be important in phagocytic ingestion. Between 1895 and 1900, Denys and Leclef demonstrated the enhancing effect of immune serum on active phagocytosis. In 1903, Wright and Douglas showed that this increased activity was caused by a serum component which affected bacteria, and not by the ingesting leukocyte alone. They named this substance *opsonin*. Today the most important forms of opsonin are those that are heat-stable and are actually antibodies against the surface antigens of bacteria or against other antigens that are subject to phagocytic action. The terms *immune opsonins* and *bacteriotropins* are used for these antibodies. They combine with the surface antigen of a cell and prepare it for ingestion by the phagocyte. It is important to note that ingestion of bacteria can occur in the absence of detectable antibody. In this phenomenon, called *nonimmune* or *surface phagocytosis,* the pathogen is trapped against tissue surfaces.

If the phagocytic process and the digestion of the invading organism are complete, the disease state is either averted or cured. However, in the event that pathogens manage to escape the processes of ingestion and intracellular destruction, they can reproduce and cause serious infections. This tends to happen with *Mycobacterium tuberculosis, Neisseria gonorrhoeae, N. meningitidis,* and coag-ulase-positive staphylococci. Certain anesthetics, increasing or lowering body temperature, and various drugs can depress phagocytic activity, thus seriously lowering an individual's resistance.

Phagocytic Cell Types

It was Metchnikoff who first distinguished two major kinds of cells having phagocytic capabilities and named them *microphages* and *macrophages*. The microphage category includes polymorphonuclear leukocytes (PMNLs), of which neutrophiles appear to have the most pronounced phagocytic activity. PMNLs are the principal cells involved in the inflammatory response to invading microorganisms. Eosinophiles are also believed to have some phagocytic capabilities. It is doubtful, however, if basophiles do.

Macrophages form the cells of the reticuloendothial system (RES) and are of either the "fixed" or "wandering" types. The reticular or supporting cells found in several organs, including the liver, also have phagocytic features. *Fixed macrophages* generally are found lining the capillaries and sinuses of body structures and regions such as the spleen, bone marrow, and lymph nodes. Cells of this type normally function in disposing of old and fragmented red blood cells. The *wandering* type of macrophage, which includes monocytes, also aids in the disposal of various blood cells. This is especially true of macrophages that have passed through and out of blood cells. In addition, these macrophages assist in the repair of tissue damage by destroying and absorbing cellular debris.

Stages in Phagocytosis

The destruction of various types of microorganisms by phagocytosis occurs in three stages: (1) contact between the phagocyte and the particle (or the cell to be ingested); (2) ingestion; and (3) intra-

cellular killing and destruction (digestion).

Phagocyte contact with particle or cell.
This stage may be either random or
specifically directed. Random contact depends upon chance collision between ingesting cells and particles to be ingested.
A more specific response also is known
in which phagocytic cells migrate toward
bacteria or particulate matter, drawn by
chemotaxis, reaction to chemical stimuli.
Several bacterial extracts or whole organisms have been reported to attract leukocytes (*positive chemotaxis*). Other
materials are known to repel leukocytes
(*negative chemotaxis*). The exact mechanism of chemotactic responses is not
known.

Ingestion. This stage of phagocytosis is
explained in part from observations of
food intake by amoeba. Various studies
have shown that ingestion of bacteria
takes place through an invagination of a
leukocyte's cytoplasmic membrane. In
general, bacteria or particles coated or
opsonized with antibody molecules are
more readily and efficiently ingested. In
the ingestion process, a phagocytic vacuole (Figure 20–4) forms, engulfing the
bacterial cell. This activity requires the
expenditure of energy by the leukocyte;
such energy for the most part is derived
from glucose metabolism. The vacuole
migrates into the cytoplasm, where it col-
lides with lysosome-like granules, which
explosively discharge their contents into
the bacterium-containing vacuole. The
membranes of both the vacuole and granule fuse, resulting in a digestive vacuole, or
phagolysosome.

The granules of phagocytic cells appear to decrease in number upon the
ingestion of organisms or particles. This
event is called the *degranulation phenomenon* and is directly related to the number

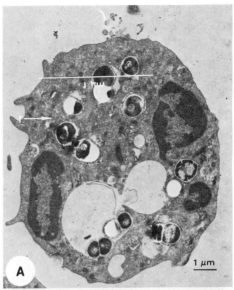

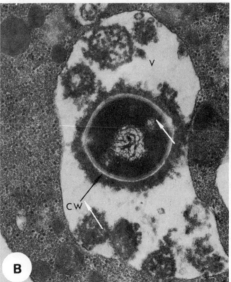

FIG. 20–4. Intraphagocytic degradation of group
A streptococci as shown by electron microscopy.
A. Streptococci contained within polymorphonuclear leukocytes (PMNLs) 45 minutes after *in vitro*
phagocytosis. Early evidence of degradation can
be seen with certain bacteria (arrows). *B.* A streptococcal cell undergoing the initial process of
intraphagocytic degradation. Note the presence
of lysozomes (*L*) surrounding the vacuole (*V*),
the lysozomal fusion occuring with the vacuolar
wall, and the intravacuolar discharge of lysozomal contents. Changes in the cell wall (*CW*) and
internal regions are evident at this point. (From
Ayoub, E. M., and White, J. G.: *J. Bacteriol.,*
98:728–736, 1969.)

of particles ingested. Chemical analysis has shown such granules to contain *phago-cytin,* as well as a large number of degradative enzymes. Both lysosomal components and metabolic products contribute to the bactericidal activity in the phagocyte.

Intracellular destruction. As a result of the burst of metabolic activity following ingestion, both lactic acid (which lowers the pH in the vacuole) and hydrogen peroxide are produced. In addition, a number of the lysosome granules are potent antibacterial agents. This group of destructive agents includes histones, lysozyme, phagocytin, and various enzymes capable of digesting the carbohydrates, lipids, and nucleic acids of ingested and subsequently killed microorganisms. Several of these antimicrobial agents are discussed in more detail elsewhere in this chapter. The enzymes include lipases, oxidases, phosphatases, proteases, etc.

During the maturation of neutrophilic leukocytes, two types of granules are formed: primary and secondary granules (Figure 20–5). Both of these cellular structures can discharge their contents into phagocytic vacuoles. The primary granule is the earliest visible granule and contains typical lysosomal enzymes. The secondary granule is the predominant granule in a mature cell and contains various bactericidal substances.

Failure of intracellular destruction. Once ingested by phagocytes, several Gram-positive cocci are killed and degraded. This set of events is well documented for pneumococci and streptococci. However, when toxin-producing staphylococci are ingested, such organisms are apparently not killed. Tubercle bacilli are readily ingested, but they remain intact inside the phagocyte because of their resistance to digestion. Unfortunately for the host, the bacilli produce a substance toxic to the ingesting polymorphonuclear leukocyte. This product, known as the *cord factor,* damages the cell, which in turn is ingested and digested by monocytes. Thus tubercle bacilli are provided not only with an environment in which to multiply, but a means by which they can be spread to other regions and establish new infections.

Host-associated phagocytic immunodeficiencies (dysophagocytosis) are also recognized. They include several genetic disease states. One form of phagocytic dysfunction currently under study is the rare genetic disease Chediak-Higashi syndrome (C-HS). This condition has been found to occur in cattle, humans, mice, and killer whales. Its characteristics include an increased susceptibility to bacterial infections and the presence of large abnormal granules (C-HS granules) in a number of different cell types. Large primary granules that fail to degranulate after phagocytic ingestion appear to be a major factor in the increased susceptibility to infection (Figure 20–5). In humans this change in granule activity is accompanied by an impaired capacity to kill certain Gram-negative and Gram-positive bacteria (Figure 20–5). The ingestion of organisms generally is normal; however, the killing capacity is diminished. This is interpreted as an alteration in the rate and not as the absence of killing.

Inflammation

This body response is considered to be the second line of defense against infection. In addition to infectious disease agents, inflammation can be produced by irritants including chemicals, heat, and mechanical injuries.

Signs of Inflammation

The characteristic features, or so-called *cardinal signs,* of the inflammatory re-

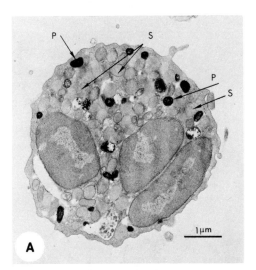

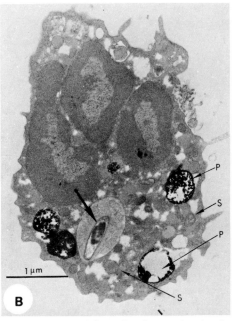

FIG. 20–5. Leukocyte dysfunction in Chediak-Higashi syndrome (C-HS). <u>A</u>. An electron micrograph of a normal polymorphonuclear leukocyte (PMNL) incubated without bacteria. The cell contains primary (P) and secondary (S) granules characteristic of mature cells of this type. <u>B</u>. A C-HS polymorphonuclear leukocyte incubated in the presence of *Bacillus subtilis*. Phagocytic vacuole formation has occurred with an intact, apparently undigested bacterium (arrow). However, the appearance of the cell indicates that the degranulation of primary granules (P) was delayed. (From Renshaw, H. W., Davis, W. C., Fudenberg, H. H., and Padgett, G. A.: *Infect Imm.*, **10**:928–937, 1974.)

sponse are heat (*calor*), pain (*dolor*), redness (*rubor*) and swelling (*tumor*). The first of these signs, redness, is the result of an increased amount of blood in the involved area. The dilation of local blood vessels causes a slowing of blood flow. Such inflamed areas are said to be *hyperemic*. This reaction of blood vessels is accompanied by an increased permeability which causes a swelling, *edema*. Tissue fluid accumulates in the spaces surrounding tissue cells. Another aspect of the decrease in blood flow can be the generation of clots in small vessels in the general area of injury. These formations may serve to stop the further penetration of infectious agents and/or their products into the general circulation. The pain experienced in an inflammatory reaction is believed to be caused by damaging effects on the sensory nerves in the involved tissue.

Pus formation may also be associated with inflammation. Pus formation involves the passage of phagocytes from the blood between the cells of the vessel walls (Figure 20–6) into the extravascular areas of tissue injury. This process of ameboid movement is called *diapedesis*. Such phagocytic cells generally leave the blood stream, attach themselves to the endothelial lining of the blood vessel by *unilateral sticking*, and trap microbes before they pass in between the cells of the vessel. The attachment of phagocytes may depend on the presence of fibrin, the substance formed from the conversion of fibrinogen.

Mechanism of Inflammation

Inflammation is a complex mechanism. Several substances believed to be released from damaged cells have been implicated as causes for its characteristic symptoms.

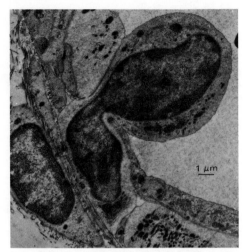

FIG. 20–6. A monocyte passing across the endothelium of a venule. The advancing edge of the cell is flattened against the surrounding endothelial sheath. (From Marchesi, V. T.: *Ann. N.Y. Acad. Sci.*, **116**:774–778, 1964. © The New York Academy of Sciences; 1964; Reprinted by permission.)

Included in this group of factors are histamine and serotonin, i.e., 5-hydroxytryptamine (Figure 20–7).

Inflammatory Exudate

The process of inflammation arouses and brings into play several mechanisms of the host's defense. With the increased blood flow to the injured area, the concentration of white blood cells and various antimicrobial factors in the *inflammatory exudate* are greatly increased. The injuries and the increasing number of dead host cells cause the release of still more antimicrobial substances, which render the involved area unfavorable for the growth of several types of microorganisms.

The exudate associated with inflammation also contains the various elements needed for blood coagulation. Many of these substances function to wall off the site of activity and prevent its spreading to other areas. A closed region or sac of this type, containing pus and micro-

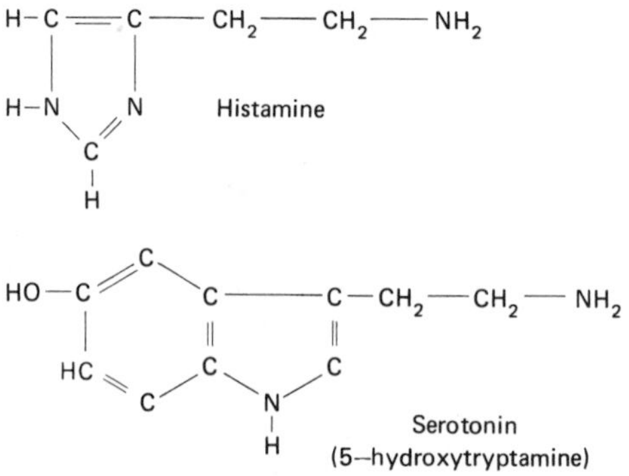

FIG. 20–7. The general structural formulas of histamine and serotonin.

organisms, is referred to as an *abscess*. Pimples, boils, and furuncles are commonly used terms for this kind of lesion. Intercommunicating abscesses are known as *carbuncles* (Color photograph 60).

Antimicrobial Substances

Chemical substances capable of *in vitro* antimicrobial activity have been obtained from various animal fluids and tissues. The full extent of the *in vivo* effectiveness of these compounds is not totally known. Several antimicrobial substances and the types of microorganisms which can be affected by them are listed in Table 20–1, and the better-known of these are discussed more fully.

Complement

The bactericidal property of serum, as well as of whole blood, has been recognized since approximately 1888. Buchner originally referred to such protective substances as *alexines*. On further study, these substances were found to be inactivated by heating to 56°C for 30 minutes. In order to produce a bactericidal effect, specific antibody was found to be necessary. Ehrlich discovered that such antibody also was required for other activities, such as the lysis of red blood cells (hemolysis) by this thermolabile

Table 20–1   Representative Antibacterial Substances in Animal Tissues and/or Fluids

Substance	Common Sources	General Chemical Composition	Types of Microorganisms Affected
Complement	Sera of most warmblooded animals	Believed to be a protein-carbohydrate-lipoprotein complex	Gram-negatives
Histone	Components of the lymphatic system	Protein	Gram-positives
Interferon	Virus infected cells	Protein	Various viruses and certain protozoa
Leukin	Leukocytes	Basic peptides (protein-like)	Gram-positives
Lysozyme	Include leukocytes, saliva, perspiration, tears, egg whites	Protein	Mainly Gram-positives
Phagocytin	Leukocytes	Protein	Gram-negatives
Properdin	Serum	Protein	Gram-negatives and certain viruses
Protamine	Spermatozoa	Protein	Gram-positives
Spermidine, spermine	Prostate and pancreas	Basic polyamines	Gram-positives
Tissue polypeptides	Components of the lymphatic system	Basic peptides	Gram-positives

SOURCE: Adapted from Carpenter, P. L.: *Immunology and Serology*. W. B. Saunders Company, Philadelphia, 1965.

(heat-sensitive) component of serum. He applied the term *complement* to the thermolabile substance.

Complement, which is commonly designated by C′, is a complex group of at least 9 major proteins normally present in the sera of most vertebrates. Some of these proteins are themselves complexes. For example, the first component of complement, C′1, is a large molecule (macromolecule) that consists of three subunits, C′1q, C′1r, and C′1s. A method of shorthand has been developed to identify complement components based on the classic pathway of complement activation. When complement participates in a serologic reaction these protein components activate one another sequentially. Thus the sequence of reactions proceeds as follows: C′1, C′2, C′3, C′4, C′5, and so on to C′9 (see Chapter 23 for further details). For technical reasons, complement reactions are studied most easily when they take place at cell surfaces. While all components (C′1–9) are necessary to produce a lytic antigen-antibody reaction, other immunobiologic activities involving complement require the sequential participation of a more limited number of these protein fractions.

Complement has several properties that distinguish it from the immunoglobulins and other serum factors so important in immunology (Table 20–1). For example, complement concentrations are not increased by immunization.

A limited amount of information exists on the synthesis of complement components. Macrophages have been shown to manufacture C′4 and C′2. C′1 synthesis has been associated with epithelial cells of the gastrointestinal mucosa and the liver has been suggested as the site for the formation of other protein components.

Complement is well known for its ability to react with a wide variety of antigen-antibody combinations. Such reactions appear to have important physiological consequences. Included in this group of reactions are: (1) the destruction of erythrocytes as well as other tissue cells; (2) the initiation of inflammatory changes; (3) the lysis of certain bacterial cells; and (4) enhancing of the phagocytosis involving some "antibody-coated particles." The cytotoxic effect of complement has been put to use in the diagnosis of several infectious diseases as in the complement-fixation test (Chapter 23).

The complement system is not only of significance in the diagnosis of disease (Color photograph 56), but it now is clearly of great importance in understanding the pathophysiology of several human disease states. Defects in the components of the system as well as defects in some of the protein substances that regulate complement activity have been reported. Patients with defects have disorders associated with the synthesis, activation, or stabilization of complement. Simple defects in which a component is absent or reduced in concentration appear to follow the usual patterns of Mendelian inheritance (see Chapter 16). Many individuals with complement deficiencies also have connective tissue diseases such as systemic lupus erythematosus (SLE), rheumatoid arthritis (RA), and post-streptococcal glomerulonephritis.

Leukins

In 1891, Hankin obtained an extract from the lymph nodes of both cats and dogs which had bactericidal activity against *Bacillus anthracis,* the etiologic agent of anthrax. Some years later, in 1909, Schneider obtained active substances from leukocytes, which he named *leukins.* Other studies yielded leukins and leukin-like compounds from the leukocytes of dogs, guinea pigs, man, rabbits, and rats. The substance from rabbit white blood cells was found to be heat-stable, and to contain a large quantity of the basic amino acid arginine.

Lysozyme

This thermostable enzyme was discovered by Alexander Fleming in 1922. The protein is present in several body fluids and tissues, including leukocytes, perspiration, saliva, and tears. Lysozyme is capable of acting against Gram-positive bacteria, and under certain conditions against several Gram-negative species. Its bactericidal action is associated with the hydrolysis of bacterial cell walls, especially where repeating units of N-acetylglucosamine and N-acetylmuramic acid are exposed. Recent studies have shown lysozyme's effectiveness against several microorganisms to be increased by the presence of minimal antibody concentrations.

Phagocytin

In 1894, Buchner in Germany and Denys and Havet in France simultaneously reported the extraction of bactericidal substances from leukocytes. The effectiveness of these extracts against Gram-negative organisms was later confirmed by Hiss in 1908, and by Zinsser in 1910. Subsequent studies in the late 1950s and 1960s characterized the active ingredient as being: (1) effective in slightly acid environments; (2) minimally inactivated by heating at 65°C for 2 hours under acid conditions; (3) not dependent on divalent ions such as calcium and magnesium for activity; (4) bactericidal for Gram-negative organisms; and (5) active against straphylococci and group A streptococci. Hirst named this substance *phagocytin.* Approximately 70 to 80 per cent of the phagocytin of man, rabbits, and guinea pigs is contained in the granules of polymorphonuclear leukocytes. The substance is believed to function in conjunction with other tissue and fluid products, such as lysozyme and histones.

Properdin

Pillemer and his associates in 1954 reported the existence of a relatively heat-sensitive protein in normal serum. The substance was described as having bactericidal activity against Gram-negative bacteria in the presence of magnesium ions (Mg^{++}), and complement. Recent studies indicate that properdin is a system consisting of at least four protein factors. These factors unite to activate certain complement components.

In addition to its bactericidal action, properdin has been reported to cause the inactivation of various viruses, produce hemolysis, provide protection against total body irradiation, and to participate in activities such as opsonization that promote phagocytosis.

Spermine

In 1953, Dubos and Hirsh isolated a basic peptide which was found to be active *in vitro* against tubercle bacilli. This substance, called *spermine*, is known to be present in the tissues of man and various other animal species. The effectiveness of the peptide in these tissues is unknown. Chemically, spermine is low in the amino acid lysine, but high in arginine. *In vitro* activity against tubercle bacilli is dependent upon activation by spermine oxidase. Dubos found that tissue containing this enzyme (e.g., guinea pig kidney) was more resistant to tubercle bacilli than those tissues (e.g., rabbit kidney) apparently lacking spermine oxidase.

Interferon

Several studies have demonstrated the production by certain virus-infected cells of a protein called *interferon*. This substance is excreted into the extracellular environment and exerts an antiviral action before specific antibody levels can reach effective titers. Interferons can be synthesized by cells of different animal species. In general, the product produced by a given species is the same regardless of the viral agent which caused its formation. Interferons, however, are known to differ among animal species with respect to antigenicity and molecular weight. Thus it appears that a host specificity exists in the production of interferon.

While viruses are potent inducers of interferon, many other microorganisms, particularly those with an intracellular phase to their growth cycle, also bring about the synthesis of this substance. Included in this group are the causative agents of malaria, the rickettsia, and other bacteria such as *Brucella abortus* and *Francisella tularensis*. Many pure chemical substances will also induce interferon. These include bacterial endotoxins, double-stranded ribonucleic acid, synthetic ribonucleic acid, and complex polysaccharides.

Numerous reports have provided indirect evidence to support the view that interferon constitutes an important antiviral factor in host resistance. This can be demonstrated by removing interferon from virus-infected tissue culture preparations producing the substance, and introducing it into other systems to protect or prevent uninfected cells from viral challenge (Figure 20–8).

Properties.   Interferons generally are difficult to obtain in large quantities for a variety of reasons. Current studies show that for large-scale production of human interferon, human embryonic fibroblasts are among the best producers. The main difficulty with the use of these cells for human consumption is the problem of ex-

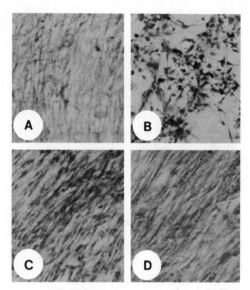

FIG. 20–8. Interferon and cytopathology. The photographs shown represent the appearance of chick embryo tissue culture cells 72 hours after infection with vaccinia virus. A. Control cells. B. Infected chick embryo cells. C. Control cells in the presence of interferon. D. Virus infected cells in the presence of the same quantity of interferon. (From Magee, W. E., and Levine, S: Ann. N.Y. Acad. Sci., **173**:362–378, 1970. © The New York Academy of Sciences; 1970; Reprinted by permission.)

cluding cancer-producing viruses that may be present in the cells.

Several studies have been carried out to characterize interferons. In addition to the properties mentioned earlier, these protein substances exhibit (1) unusual stability at low pH; (2) a general resistance to temperatures at 50° C, and slightly greater in certain instances; (3) susceptibility to various protein-digesting enzymes; (4) a low toxicity on host cells; and (5) a capability of acting on several viruses.

Action. Interferons are produced by cells infected with either completely infectious inactivated viral particles or other inducers. In the case of viruses the quantity of interferon formed by cells varies

considerably and usually depends on their concentration. It can be altered by inactivation of the virus with heat or ultraviolet light. Interferon is dependent on viral nucleic acid; studies have shown that empty virus cores do not induce its formation. Additional investigations have further demonstrated the capability of other sources of nucleic acids (e.g., laboratory synthesized) to bring about the synthesis of interferon. Thus it appears likely that the cells producing these protein substances are reacting to the presence of foreign nucleic acids.

The importance of interferon in host resistance lies in its potential as an inhibitor of viral synthesis. Experimental studies have shown that, depending on interferon concentrations, various cellular activities involved in viral replication can be inhibited. As inhibition becomes more complete, the quantities of viral DNA and viruses synthesized are greatly reduced (Figure 20–9).

Interferon does not inhibit all viruses equally. Several viruses, including arboviruses, influenza, and vaccinia, are quite sensitive, while adenoviruses and Newcastle disease virus are relatively resistant. In cellular terms, interferon does not prevent virus attachment and penetration of host cells. One of the currently held concepts of interferon action is that it interferes with the translation of viral messenger RNA (mRNA) by ribosomes. No inhibition of normal-cell mRNA translation occurs. Thus interferon interferes with the synthesis of viral proteins.

Therapeutic value. Because of its range of activity and its low toxicity for host cells, interferon appears to have great potential as a therapeutic agent against viruses. Progress in this direction is hindered by difficulty in obtaining large quantities of interferon, the lack of an effect on viral synthesis already in prog-

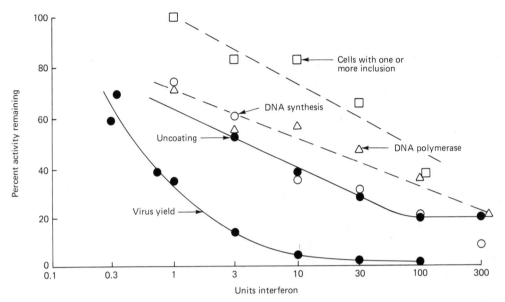

FIG. 20–9. Results of studies showing the effect of interferon concentrations on various activities in vaccinia-infected chick embryo cells in a tissue culture system. Such studies show the dramatic effects of interferon on viral DNA and virus particle yields. (From Magee, W. L., and Levine, S.: *Ann. N.Y. Acad. Sci.,* **173**:362–378, 1970. © The New York Academy of Sciences; 1970; Reprinted by permission.)

ress, and the short duration of activity. If a means can be found to maintain high and effective levels of interferon, the control of several virus-caused diseases can be achieved.

The Indigenous Microorganisms of Man

The flora and fauna indigenous to man are often referred to simply as *normal flora*. In this context, "flora" denotes all microscopic life forms and "normal" becomes a statistical term. The reader must not equate normal with nonpathogenic, for many organisms found on and in the body can pose problems under conditions such as the following:

1. Deterioration of the host's defense mechanisms.
2. Relocation of microorganisms, when an organism finds its way to another area of the body previously uninhabited by it.
3. A disturbance of the "normal flora."

Normal flora are commonly referred to as *amphibionts,* ranging from commensals to pathogens. The amphibionts are obligately parasitic on man or other animals but are not obligately pathogenic. They are encountered at least as often in the absence of disease as in its presence. The indigenous microorganisms may flourish in the general region of tissue damage and contribute to the disease state as *opportunists,* rather than primary etiological agents. Thus, these organisms may be implicated although Koch's postulates would not necessarily hold true (refer to Chapter 2).

Amphibiont Sites

As a rule, few or no microorganisms are found in the following anatomical locations: blood, larynx, trachea, nasal sinuses, bronchi, esophogus, stomach, upper intestinal tract, upper urinary tract (including the posterior urethra), and posterior genital tract (passage above cervix included). However, in studies with animals, notably dogs and rabbits, microorganisms from the mouth and throat regions and from the lower intestine were found in the blood and other tissues after these animals were subjected to various types of physical or mental stress and trauma. In particular, *Clostridium perfringens* (one of the causative agents of gas gangrene) has been isolated from the "healthy" tissues of these animals.

The regions of the body that constitute the major habitats for indigenous microorganisms include the skin and contiguous mucous membranes, conjunctivae, upper respiratory tract (oropharynx included), mouth, lower intestine, external genitalia, anterior urethra, and vagina. It will become apparent later that each habitat has certain characteristics which allow a different overall range of microorganisms to thrive. These differences can be categorized into the following three types of environment:

1. Extremely high levels of both moisture and nutrients, as in the lower intestines and the mouth.
2. A high level of moisture and a low level of nutrients, as with mucous membranes.
3. A low level of moisture and a moderate level of nutrients, as on the skin.

Other variables include availability of oxygen, pH, temperature, and relative exposures to contaminants and ventilation.

Numbers of total aerobic and anaerobic bacteria in certain anatomical regions:

Lower intestine—approximately 100 billion microorganisms per gram of fecal matter.

Mouth—approximately 1 billion microorganisms per ml of saliva.

Nose—approximately 20,000 microorganisms per ml of a nasal washing.

Skin—approximately 1 million microorganisms per cm^2; this value is dependent upon the skin surface tested.

Development of the Indigenous Flora

Development of the indigenous flora begins with the normal birth process, since the infant has been bathed during the gestation period in a sterile amniotic fluid. As the baby passes through the birth canal it begins to pick up organisms, many of which may remain with it for its lifetime. Additional microorganisms are acquired by the infant as a consequence of coming into contact with the air of the environment and with hospital personnel. Such organisms may be transient in nature, or may become permanent members of the flora.

Appreciable numbers of bacteria have been cultured from the mouths of infants within 6 to 10 hours of birth and in the feces within 10 to 20 hours.

As mentioned earlier, each anatomical area varies in relation to pH, oxygen content, nutrients, and moisture as well as bactericidal factors, thus different organisms will predominate. While the amphibionts persist in their respective locations, saprophytic as well as many parasitic microorganisms are destroyed or excreted. These locations can change as a consequence of changes brought about by the maturation process of the individual, e.g., hormonal regulation, alteration in dietary habits, and chemotherapy. Thus microorganisms may be of a temporary or permanent nature, depending upon the conditions which exist in the body.

The Variety of the Indigenous Microorganisms

The microorganisms presented below are considered representative of the "normal flora" of the human adult; they appear to exist in at least 5 per cent of the adult population. This figure is arbitrarily determined by findings of the literature surveyed. It should be evident that many potential pathogens are present in various habitats in the absence of disease. A slight imbalance of the host's defense mechanisms or ecological shifts as a consequence of chemotherapy could result in disease.

Bacteria. The Gram-positive and Gram-negative cocci include aerobic and anaerobic streptococci, anaerobic micrococci, *Neisseria* spp., staphylococci, and *Veillonella* spp. The Gram-positive rods include *Actinomyces* spp., clostridia, aerobic and anaerobic corynebacteria, and *Leptotrichia* spp. Aerobic Gram-negative rods are represented by *Hemophilus, Moraxella* spp., pseudomonads, vibrios, and various members of the Enterobacteriaceae family. The anaerobic Gram-negative rods include *Bacteroides* spp., fusobacteria, spirilla, and vibrios. Among the organisms which generally are not Gram-stained, but nevertheless should be included here, are the mycobacteria and spirochetes.

Fungi. The indigenous fungi are primarily saprophytes of soil which show preference for a parasitic habitat. Because of their primary saprophytic role, it may appear questionable to call them amphibionts. However, according to Rosebury, an amphibiont may be considered to be any organism which is ". . . encountered in one or more typical indigenous locations frequently, and distinctly more frequently, than in the adjacent environment." On this basis, and according to the proposition that an organism routinely isolated from the body in the absence of disease may be indigenous, fungi are included.

The two most common genera found are *Candida* and *Pityrosporum*. In addition, the dermatophytes, *Trichophyton* spp., and *Epidermophyton floccosum* and the yeast *Torulopsis glabrata* often are encountered. The habitats for fungi include the urogenital tract, lower intestinal tract, mouth, skin, and upper respiratory tract.

Protozoa. Indigenous protozoa or normal "fauna" can be found in the mouth and in the lower intestinal and urogenital tracts. The most generally encountered Mastigophora, or flagellated protozoa, are *Chilomastix mesnili, Giardia intestinalis,* and *Trichomonas* spp. *Enteromonas hominis* and *Retortomonas intestinalis* are found much less commonly. The only other protozoan class reported to occur is the Sarcodina. Members of this group that have been found include *Dientamoeba fragilis, Endolimax nana, Entamoeba* spp., and *Iodmoeba butschlii.*

Mycoplasma and L forms. These microorganisms can be found in all body habitats of humans and other animals. They appear routinely in the mouth, upper respiratory, intestinal, and genito-urinary tracts.

Benefits Due to Indigenous Microorganisms

Probably one of the main benefits derived by humans from his microbial inhabitants is protection from disease. This may seem incongruous, since it has been stated previously that the amphibionts can cause disease under certain circumstances. The key phrase is *under certain circumstances.* As a rule, the "normal flora" occupy their particular niche and thus inhibit organisms invading from other portions of the body or from the external environment. Such inhibition is brought about by competition for food, by the production of antibiotics or antibiotic-like substances, or by changes in environmental conditions, such as oxygen content, pH, etc.

This ecological balance apparently prevents indigenous pathogens such as the yeast Candida albicans and the bacteria Streptococcus (Diplococcus) pneumoniae, Hemophilus influenzae, and Staphylococcus aureus from causing severe disease. When the balance is upset because of chemotherapy, for example, one or more pathogens may grow unchecked. A frequent sequel of antibiotic therapy in children is the appearance of Candida albicans infections. These infections may occur in the mouth or in the perianal region. Untreated candidiasis can result in serious involvement of the lungs, meningitis, and septicemia. Indigenous microorganisms that have been shown to inhibit the growth of C. albicans include Enterobacter aerogenes, Escherichia coli, Pseudomonas aeruginosa, and streptococci.

Another significant role for indigenous organisms is their involvement in helping to maintain mechanisms for antibody production. Studies with germ-free animals have shown that such animals generally have low or inapparent levels of immunoglobulins. Because an indigenous flora is lacking and a weakened type of immunological response exists, these animals are particularly susceptible to infection. It would appear from the information available that the amphibionts act as a constant source of antigens or irritants to the antibody-producing systems of the body, and thereby permit a more rapid immunological response when necessary.

In this regard concern has evolved as to the effects of prolonged space travel. Investigations have shown that under isolation man develops a condition of reduced "normal flora," which might lead to some deterioration of his antibody-producing systems. In the lower animals studied, deterioration of this nature has occurred. Because of this potential danger, some space scientists have advocated incorporation of Lactobacillus pills into the diet of astronauts. Lactobacilli are noted for their ability to stabilize the intestinal flora. Some pediatricians prescribe the use of these organisms in certain cases of diarrhea for a similar purpose.

The role of amphibionts in nutrition has been an area of considerable interest. It has been shown that some of these organisms synthesize a variety of vitamins in excess of their own needs, which are thus made available for man. These vitamins include biotin, pyridoxin, pantothenic acid, and vitamins K and B_{12}. This function of the amphibionts must evidently be of a supplementary rather than indispensable nature. If such were not the case, certain vitamin deficiency diseases would not have been so readily discovered. However, it is quite probable that some individuals without a proper diet are benefited by this function. An interesting observation is that symptoms of vitamin B deficiency have been found in patients undergoing chemotherapy.

Conditions that Lower Host Resistance to Disease Agents

Several of the preceding sections of this chapter have emphasized the importance of various factors and mechanisms to host resistance. Some consideration should be given to selected circumstances that can influence these factors and lower host resistance to infectious disease agents. A representative number of conditions are listed in Table 20–2. In the majority of cases of infection, multiple circumstances or conditions are involved. The frequency of these conditions as direct or indirect causes varies with different segments of the population and with the nature of health care services provided. Developmental and/or genetic defects also are important.

Table 20–2   Conditions or Factors that Lower Host Resistance to
Infectious Disease Agents

Condition or Factor	Selected Effects	Condition or Factor	Selected Effects
Acute radiation injury	Alteration of the cellular defenses of the host	Excessive or indiscriminate use of antibiotics	Elimination of natural flora that provide protection; overgrowth of resistant microbial forms; interference with digestive process and vitamin utilization
Age	Decreased efficiency of antibody synthesis and cell-mediated immunity at extremes of age; decreased levels of certain complement components during first 3 months of gestation	Immunological deficiency	Interference with immunoglobulin production and/or cell-mediated immunity
Agranulocytosis	Reduction or absence of phagocytosis by neutrophiles	Immunosuppression	Impairment of cell-mediated immunity mechanisms
Alcoholism	Nutritional deficiencies; possible depression of the inflammatory response to bacterial infection	Mechanical obstruction of body drainage systems (urinary, tear, and respiratory mechanisms or systems)	Interference with the mobilization and functioning of phagocytic cells
Altered lysosomes	Extensive or limited inability of macrophages and neutrophiles to destroy ingested microorganisms		
Circulatory disturbances	Localized destruction of tissues; congestion; accumulation of fluid in tissue	Traumatic injury	Direct access to body tissues for opportunists and pathogens; possible interference with immunity mechanisms; possible obstruction of body drainage systems
Complement deficiencies and/or defects	Limited or extensive inability to inactivate and/or destroy certain infectious disease agents		

QUESTIONS FOR REVIEW

1. a. What significant role do the normal body flora play in the control of infectious disease agents?
   b. Are pathogens encountered as normal flora? If so, list several representative microorganisms in this category.
   c. Are all types of microorganisms found as normal flora members? Explain.

2. What parts or regions of the human body act as mechanical barriers to microorganisms? Explain how each functions in this capacity.

3. Compare the composition of whole blood to plasma. Do the same for plasma and serum.

4. Differentiate among the various types of formed elements in blood with regard to their morphological features and functions.

5. Explain the roles played by the following cells and processes in maintaining the defense mechanisms of the body.
   a. lymphocyte
   b. interferon
   c. monocyte
   d. phagocytosis
   e. eosinophile
   f. neutrophile
   g. complement
   h. inflammation
   i. properdin
   j. lysozyme

6. What is a differential count? What is its significance?

7. Describe the stages of phagocytosis.

8. What is phagocytic dysfunction?

9. What are interferon inducers?

10. List and describe at least six factors that lower host resistance to pathogens.

Factors Involved in Microbial Virulence

It is generally agreed that only a small percentage of the tens of thousands of known microorganisms are capable of overcoming the defense mechanisms of a host, thus causing disease. Moreover, it appears that a large number of these disease-producing agents can maintain themselves only within the systems of the animals and plants they invade. In short, their existence is dependent on the availability of a suitable host, a type of *obligatory parasitism*.

An *infectious disease* may be described as an interference with the normal functioning of a host's physiochemical process, caused by the activities of another organism living within its tissues or on its surfaces. A relatively small fraction of the organisms harbored by most forms of animal and plant life can directly invade and cause obvious infections. However, several of these agents have the potential to produce infections if they accidentally gain access to the tissues of the host. Such organisms are called *opportunists*. Opportunities of this type occur in cases of wounds, burns, or times of lowered host resistance when the normal defense mechanisms are not operating effectively. The distinction between an opportunist and a true pathogen can be difficult to make. As research continues, it appears that the majority of microorganisms have disease-producing potential, given the suitable environmental conditions and a particular host. Table 21–1 lists representative mechanisms of action exhibited by several pathogens. Portions of this chapter and the following one contain details of these mechanisms and of the pathogens exhibiting them.

The capacity of a given pathogen to produce disease is called *virulence*. Some microbiologists also use this term to refer to the killing power of organisms. This property generally is dependent on features of the organism including its invasiveness, ability to survive and to reproduce in the face of the host's defensive mechanisms, and its production of poisonous substances (*toxins*) antagonistic to the host. Experimentally, the virulence of a particular disease agent is measured by the numbers of such organisms required to kill a particular host under standardized conditions within a specified time. Naturally, the resistance of the host is an important factor. The relationship of virulence (V), numbers of pathogens or dosage (D), and the resistant state (RS) of the host to the establishment of an infectious disease can be shown by the frequently quoted formula:

$$\text{Infectious Disease} = \frac{V \times D}{RS}$$

Invasiveness

Unfortunately, the terms used to express the invasiveness of disease agents with respect to the bloodstream are applied

Table 21–1   Representative Mechanisms of Action Exhibited by
Infectious Disease Agents[a]

Mechanism	Selected Disease State and/or Pathogen
Allergic reactions (e.g., delayed hypersensitivity)	Deep-seated fungous infections[b], dermatomycosis (fungous skin diseases)[c], helminthic diseases[d], leprosy[e], protozoan infections[f], syphilis[g], and tuberculosis[h]
Blood loss and/or utilization of vitamin B$_{12}$	Hookworm and fish tapeworm[d]
Fusion of cellular and viral membranes; includes the formation of giant cells known as syncytia	Viruses including *Herpesvirus hominis*, measles, parainfluenza, respiratory syncytial disease, and varicella-zoster agent[e]
Genetic integration (incorporation of nucleic acid of a pathogen into that of the host)	Botulism[j], diphtheria[k], and cancerous states induced by oncogenic viruses[l]
Immunodepression (interference with a host's immune responses)	Lepromatous leprosy[e], measles[i], syphilis[g], tuberculosis[h], and virus-induced cancer
Interference with essential body functions	Anthrax[e], botulism[j], cholera[m], diphtheria[h], plague[h], rickettsial infections[n], salmonellosis[m], and shigellosis[m]
Interference with phagocytosis	Infections with bacterial pathogens such as anthrax bacilli[e], menigococci[j], pneumococci[h], and Group A streptococci[e], yeasts such as cryptococci[k], and influenza viruses[k]
Interference with phagocytic killing	Bacterial diseases including brucellosis[m], gonorrhea[g], leprosy[e], meningococcal meningitis[j], tuberculosis[h], and typhoid fever[m]; fungous diseases including histoplasmosis[k]; and protozoan infections such as leishmaniasis, pneumocystis pneumonia, and trypanosomiasis[f]
Intracellular growth and cellular destruction	Bacterial diseases such as brucellosis[m], leprosy[e], salmonellosis[m], shigellosis[m], tuberculosis[h], and rickettsial infections[n]; most viral infections
Mechanical blockage of organs and/or associated vessels	Helminth diseases including ascariasis, filariasis, and schistosomiasis[d]; fungous diseases such as aspergillosis and candidiasis[k]; the bacterial disease lymphogranuloma venereum (LGV)[g]; and the protozoan disease malaria[f]
Migration through body tissues and/or organs	Helminth diseases including ascariasis, fasciolopsiasis, hookworm, strongyloidiasis, and trichinosis[d]

[a] These include microorganisms as well as helminths (worms). The helminths are discussed in Chapter 42.
[b] Refer to Chapters 32 and 34.
[c] Refer to Chapter 30.
[d] Refer to Chapter 42.
[e] Refer to Chapter 29.
[f] Refer to Chapter 41.
[g] Refer to Chapter 37.
[h] Refer to Chapter 33.
[i] Refer to Chapters 31 and 34.
[j] Refer to Chapter 38.
[k] Refer to Chapter 34.
[l] Refer to Chapter 40.
[m] Refer to Chapter 35.
[n] Refer to Chapter 39.

loosely at times, and thus misinterpretations can easily arise. To avoid unnecessary confusion, the following pertinent terms are defined. The demonstration of bacteria in blood either by means of bacteriological culture or microscopic examination is referred to as *bacteremia*. This type of finding does not imply that such organisms are pathogenic, since blood may, from time to time, contain temporary invaders. Some microorganisms could gain entrance to the blood stream via the intestines or tonsils. The presence of organisms in the blood and their association with the toxic or septic symptoms of a host is referred to as *septicemia*. A disease state involving such pathogens with the production of localized collections of pus in the tissues of the host (abscess) is called *pyemia*.

Relatively Nontoxic Bacterial Structures and Products Contributing to Invasiveness

According to Talmage and Cann, *invasiveness* refers to the ability of a parasite not only to survive, but to establish itself in the tissues of the host. Thus from a microorganism's point of view, several obstacles must be overcome as it penetrates deeper into the tissues of the host. This group of barriers includes phagocytosis, the lytic action of serum in the case of Gram-negative organisms, and the difficulty of spreading through tissues.

Capsules.   Since phagocytic and other antimicrobial activities of the host involve the surfaces of invading organisms, it is not unusual to find bacterial and yeast pathogens equipped with certain protective substances.   Early studies clearly described the presence of a halo-like area surrounding various pathogenic bacteria (Color photograph 20). These regions later came to be known as *capsules* and are an extremely important class of surface components. Representative bacterial species with capsules include the anthrax bacillus, *Hemophilus influenzae, Klebsiella pneumoniae,* meningococci of groups A and C, the pneumococci, and certain strains of staphylococci (Figure 21–1). Loss of the capability to form capsules lowers the organism's virulence and resistance to phagocytosis.

Other types of surface components can provide protection to bacterial pathogens. Such protective substances are associated with the cell wall and include the "M" protein and hyaluronic acid (polysaccharide) of group A hemolytic streptococci, and the kappa (κ) substance of group B meningococci. Endotoxins of Gram-negatives also function in this manner.

Coagulase.   Most, if not all, pathogenic staphylococci are noted for their production of the extracellular enzyme *coagulase* or *staphylocoagulase*. This substance causes citrated or oxalated rabbit or human plasma to clot (Color photograph

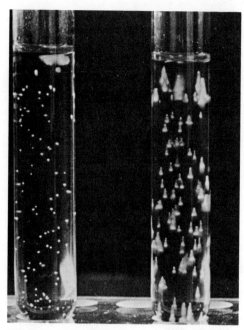

FIG. 21–1. The appearance of capsule-producing bacteria in semi-soft agar. The *Staphylococcus* culture on the left (Giorgio strain) is not a capsule producer; the one on the right (Smith diffuse strain) is. Note the somewhat comet-shaped growth with the agar exhibited by the Smith diffuse strain. The capacity to produce capsules frequently is lost during *in vitro* growth. (From Melly, M. A., Duke, L. J., Liau, D. F., and Hash, J. H.: *Infect. Immun.,* **10**:389–397, 1974.)

64). In order for the reaction to occur an accessory factor, "coagulase-reacting factor" or CRF, must be present in the host's plasma. This serum substance is heat-labile, inactivated by heating to 56°, and reacts slowly with the inactive coagulase to form the active enzyme. The CRF is believed to be protein in nature. Once activated, coagulase converts fibrinogen to fibrin and a clot results.

Staphylocoagulase has antigenic properties. At least seven immunologically distinct varieties have been reported. Mention should be made also of a form of coagulase other than the extracellular or free variety. A bound coagulase is recognized which causes the clumping of staphylococci when they are incubated in appropriate serum preparations. The coagulase-reacting factor is apparently not required for this reaction to occur.

The details of procedures used to demonstrate coagulase production are given elsewhere in the text.

Hyaluronidase. The ability of pathogens to spread among the tissues of its host has long been a subject for study. The existence of so-called "spreading factors" was suggested early in such investigations. One of the substances implicated was the enzyme *hyaluronidase* which is produced by various organisms, including clostridia, pneumococci, and streptococci. This microbial product hydrolyzes hyaluronic acid, a thick, high-molecular weight polysaccharide that is an essential component of the intracellular ground substances of several tissues. There is little doubt of the role hyaluronidase plays in promoting the diffusion and penetration of bacteria and their toxic products. Several helminths also produce this substance.

Streptokinase. Several Gram-positive bacteria produce this enzyme, which causes fibrin clots to dissolve. Included in this group of organisms are gas gangrene bacteria, hemolytic streptococci, and staphylococci. Streptokinases have a marked specificity. For example, the kinases produced by human strains of streptococci dissolve only human fibrin, and dog associated strains of the organisms liquefy only the fibrin of dogs.

Purified streptokinase can be applied therapeutically in cases requiring the dissolving of clots.

Bacterial Toxins

Several normal components or products associated with bacterial cells at one time or another are known to be toxic for higher forms of life. The toxins of bacteria are categorized as either *endotoxins* or *exotoxins*. The former are substances which are liberated only after an organism disintegrates by *autolysis*. Exotoxins are products released either during the lifetime of an organism or on autolysis into the medium in which it is growing. Occasionally, enzymes that are released from cells also are placed into the latter category. Examples of such substances and their respective types of action include: (1) coagulases—cause fibrin clots, (2) fibrinolysins—dissolve fibrin clots, (3) hyaluronidases—increase tissue permeability, (4) proteinases—decompose proteins, and (5) lecithinase—decompose lipids. Representative toxins, and substances which are not truly toxic but aid microorganisms in their invasion of a host, are discussed in the following sections.

Endotoxins

These poisonous substances are derived from the cell walls of Gram-negative bacteria. Chemically, endotoxins are lipopolysaccharide-protein complexes. Studies in which these components were separated demonstrated that the lipopolysaccharide fraction was toxic and pyrogenic (*fever causing*), while the protein portion imparted antigenic properties to the entire complex identical to the somatic (O) antigens of the intact bacterium.

Endotoxins from several pathogenic and nonpathogenic Gram-negative organisms have been isolated and studied, including species of *Escherichia, Neisseria,* rickettsiae, *Salmonella, Serratia, Shigella,* and *Veillonella.* Several of the characteristics which distinguish endotoxins from exotoxins are listed in Table 21–2.

Modes of endotoxin action. Various studies have shown the effects of these toxic substances to be nonspecific. No

Table 21–2   A Comparison of Selected Characteristics of Endotoxins and Exotoxins

Characteristic	Endotoxin	Exotoxin
Chemical composition	Lipopolysaccharide-protein complex	Protein
Source	Cell walls of Gram-negative bacteria; released only on autolysis or artificial disruption of cells	Mostly from Gram-positive bacteria; excretion products of growing cells, or in some cases, substances released upon autolysis and death
Effects on host	Nonspecific	Generally specific
Thermostability	Relatively heat-stable (may resist 120°C for 1 hour)	Heat-labile most are inactivated at 60° to 80°C
Toxid[a] preparation possible	No	Yes

[a] Modified protein toxin which is not toxic, but still remains antigenic.

doubt exists as to their involvement in disease states caused by Gram-negative bacteria; however, the exact role played by endotoxins is not clearly defined. Regarding fever production endotoxins apparently cause the release of a fever-inducing substance from polymorphonuclear leukocytes, which in turn interferes with the temperature regulatory centers in the brain. The Limulus test (which is described in Chapter 23) can be utilized for the detection of minute concentrations of endotoxin.

Exotoxins

The potential importance of toxins to infectious diseases was suggested by the classic experiments of Loeffler, in 1884, with diphtheria bacilli. He concluded that organisms injected into guinea pigs, as a consequence of their growth and development, produced a poisonous substance which spread by way of the circulatory system and caused death. Loeffler's concept was substantiated by the experiments of Roux and Yersin in 1889. Thus the property of toxigenicity was established. Since this time several bacterial species have been found to elaborate a wide variety of exotoxins (Table 21–3).

Exotoxins may be excreted during the growth of bacteria, or, as certain recent studies have shown, they may be released on the death and autolysis of cells. These poisonous substances have several properties which distinguish them from endotoxins (Table 21–2). The chief features include their protein nature and specificity of action.

An interesting aspect of exotoxin production is its association in certain cases with bacterial viruses. For example, diphtheria bacilli produce an exotoxin only when they are harboring a particular lysogenic bacteriophage. Only those bacteria infected by such specific viruses elaborate the toxin. (See Chapter 16 for additional details of this phenomenon.) A similar situation exists with cells of *Clostridium botulinum* and *Streptococcus pyogenes* and the erythrogenic toxin associated with scarlet fever.

Modes of exotoxin action.   Several of the classic exotoxins, including botulism, diphtheria, and tetanus, have been studied with respect to their specific mechanism and site of action. In general, exotoxins function by destroying specific components of cells, or by inhibiting certain cellular activities. Some of these substances work only on specific cell types. Further details can be found in the specific chapters dealing with these toxin-producing agents.

Table 21–3   Selected Representative Exotoxins Produced by Bacterial Pathogens

Bacterial Species	Gram Reaction[a]	Disease	Toxin Designation	Type of Toxin Action
Bordetella pertussis	−	Whooping cough	Pertussis (whooping cough toxin)	Necrotizing
Clostridium botulinum	+	Botulism	Six type-specific toxins[b]	Paralytic (blocks acetylcholine release)
Clostridium novyi[c]	+	Gas gangrene	Alpha (α) toxin Beta (β) toxin	Necrotizing Hemolytic lecithinase, necrotizing
			Delta (δ) toxin	Hemolytic
Clostridium perfringens[c]	+	Gas gangrene	Alpha toxin	Hemolytic lecithinase, necrotizing
			Theta (θ) toxin	Hemolytic cardiotoxin
			Lambda (λ) toxin	Proteolytic
Clostridium tetani	+	Tetanus	Tetanolysin	Hemolytic cardiotoxin
			Tetanospasmin	Spasm-causing
Corynebacterium diphtheriae	+	Diphtheria	Diphtheritic toxin	Necrotizing
Yersinia pestis	−	Plague	Plague toxin	Probably necrotizing
Shigella dysenteriae	−	Bacillary dysentery	Neurotoxin	Hemorrhagic, paralytic
Staphylococcus aureus	+	Food poisoning	Enterotoxin	Vomiting
		Pyogenic infections	Alpha toxin	Hemolytic, leucodic, necrotizing
			Beta toxin	Hemolytic
			Delta toxin	Dermonecrotic, hemolytic, leucolytic
			Leucocidin	Leucocidic
Streptococcus pyogenes	+	Pyogenic infections and scarlet fever	Alpha toxin	Hemolytic
			Erythrogenic toxin	Scarlet fever rash
			Streptolysin O	Cytotoxin, hemolytic
			Streptolysin S	Smooth muscle contraction, hemolysin

SOURCE: Modified from Davis, B., Dulbecco, R., Eisen, H., Ginsberg, H., and Wood, W.: *Microbiology.* Harper & Row Publishers, Inc., New York, 1968.
[a] − = Gram-negative, + = Gram-positive.
[b] Two of these toxins, C and D, affect lower animals.
[c] Only a few of the several toxins produced by this species are given.

Exotoxins of major clinical importance.

Botulism. The exotoxin of *Clostridium botulinum,* the causative agent of fatal food poisoning, affects only nerve tissues, that is, it is a *neurotoxin.* This poisonous substance interferes with the mechanisms involved with the nerve transmission of stimuli to muscles, by blocking the release of acetylcholine.

Diphtheria. This exotoxin appears to inhibit protein synthesis. It is also noted for general destructive effects on various types of tissues (Figure 21–2).

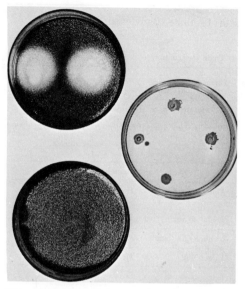

FIG. 21–2. The colony overlay test (COT), a method for detecting toxin production (toxicogenicity) by *Corynebacterium diphtheriae* strains in tissue culture. The plate on the right shows growth of bacterial cultures after 18 hours of inoculation. The cultures located at 3 and 9 o'clock are toxin producers, whereas the remaining two are not. This is evident from the top tissue-culture plate inoculated with the toxicogenic strains. Note the two areas where toxin has destroyed the monolayer of tissue-culture cells. The lower plate is a control. (From Laird, W., and Groman, N.: *Appl. Microbiol.*, **25**:709, 1973.)

Gas gangrene. Several members of the genus *Clostridium* may be associated with this disease state. One of them, *C. perfringens,* is known to produce an alpha (α) toxin which can destroy cell membranes.

Tetanus. The exotoxin elaborated by *Clostridium tetani,* the causative agent of lockjaw, is also a neurotoxin. It primarily exerts its destructive effects on the anterior horn cells of the central nervous system.

Exotoxins of minor clinical significance. Several exotoxins produced by various bacterial species are considered to play a lesser role in clinical disease states than others. This view is taken largely because such substances, under normal conditions, are either elaborated in small quantities, or are not extremely toxic. Examples of these exotoxins included dysentery bacillus neurotoxin, scarlet fever erythrogenic toxin, staphylococcal enterotoxin, and streptolysins O and S.

The erythrogenic toxin of scarlet fever. In general, a small number of the strains belonging to group A streptococci are capable of producing this "minor" toxin. Three toxins are recognized, labeled A, B, and C. The first of these toxins occurs with the greatest frequency. Erythrogenic toxins have a selective action on the skin and are neutralized by scarlet fever antitoxin. No effects are suffered by the streptococci multiplying at the time.

Staphylococcal enterotoxins. Numerous coagulase-positive strains of *Staphylococcus aureus* produce enterotoxins. These substances are: (1) protein in nature, (2) poor antigens, (3) resistant to boiling temperatures for approximately 30 minutes, and (4) not neutralized by antitoxins prepared against other toxins produced by staphylococci.

Man and monkeys appear to be the only naturally susceptible victims for this enterotoxin. Affected individuals generally experience nausea and vomiting within a few hours after the toxin's ingestion. Fatalities are rare.

Streptolysin O. The presence of two distinct soluble hemolysins in broth cultures of certain streptococci was demonstrated by Todd and his associates in approximately 1938. One of these bacterial products was called *O lysin,* because of its sensitivity to oxygen. The other hemolysin, designated *S lysin,* in addition to other properties, was noted for its extreme sensitivity to heat. The activity of both streptococcal products

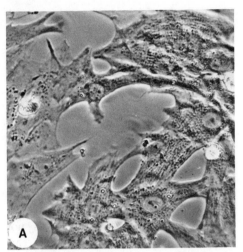

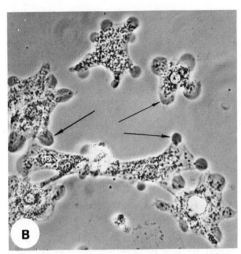

FIG. 21–3. The toxicity of streptolysin O for beating mammalian heart cells in tissue culture as observed by phase contrast microscopy. _A_. The appearance of normal rat heart ventricle cells after 2 days of growth. Before exposure the myocardial cells on the right exhibited striations and were beating vigorously. _B_. The same cells 3 minutes after exposure to group C streptolysin O. Note the granulation and numerous plasma membrane blebs (arrows) associated with killed myocardial cells. (From Thompson, A., Halbert, S. P., and Smith, U.: _J. Exp. Med.,_ **131**:745–763, 1970.)

on red blood cells is enzymatic in nature. Certain streptococci produce only O lysin, while others secrete only S lysin. Most members of Group A produce both hemolysins.

Streptolysin O is elaborated by most streptococci in Group A, those organisms of human habitation in Group C, and certain members of Group G. This streptolysin can be inactivated by heating at 37° C for 2 hours. It is a protein, and is antigenic, a property which is evident during the course of infections caused by streptococci. Streptolysin O is noted for its toxic action on red blood cells as well as various other types of cells, including frog heart and mammalian kidney and heart (Figure 21–3). Several studies by Halbert support the view that this streptococcal product may play a significant "etiological" role in rheumatic heart disease.

Streptolysin S. This exotoxin is produced by most strains of group A streptococci, and probably members of other groups. Because purification of streptolysin S has met with limited success, its chemical makeup remains in doubt. However, it is believed that this bacterial product may be either polysaccharide or protein in nature.

The toxin is not antigenic in the generally accepted sense upon injection into laboratory animals. It is, however, noted for a pronounced toxicity on the tissues of laboratory animals. The hemolysis which develops around surface-located colonies on blood agar plates is caused by streptolysin S.

Shigella dysenteriae exotoxin. This simple protein substance is noted for the neurologic effects it can produce in man and various laboratory animals. The toxin is comparable in toxicity to those found with the neurotoxins associated with tetanus and botulism. Fortunately the quantities produced per cell in cultures of _S. dysenteriae_ are quite low.

Algal Toxins

Algal toxins comprise a wide variety of naturally occurring poisonous substances in aquatic environments. Their widespread occurrence and significance to various species of life have been more fully recognized in recent years. Thus far, many algal toxins, which become poisonous to mussels and clams and subsequently to humans who eat shellfish, have been studied in crude form only. Nevertheless, a few toxins have been isolated in pure form and characterized. One of these is produced by the blue-green alga *Microcytis aeruginosa*. The toxin is a highly potent poison: it causes death in experimental animals in less than 30 minutes, and it is responsible for the production of paralysis and death in humans.

Toxin-producing algae pose an acute as well as a potentially serious threat to human well-being. This is especially true because many algal species that may represent a potential food supply produce toxins and because the poisonous substances produced by marine algae threaten the existence of edible marine organisms. The problem could become more acute as the world becomes more dependent upon food from aquatic sources.

Mycotoxins

Mycotoxicoses represent a situation specifically associated with fungous-toxin contamination of foodstuffs and feed. This disease state differs from another fungous disease category, the mycosis, which involves a generalized invasion of living tissue by actively growing fungi. Mold-induced deterioration of foods and feeds results in economic losses associated with deterioration of the quality of commod-

ities and with the health hazard involved. Although there have been some isolated reports of a variety of mycotoxicoses in animals, including the toxicity syndrome ergotism, which has been recognized for centuries, only recently has there been an increasing awareness of the potential health significance of mycotoxins as natural chemical environmental contaminants.

In 1966 Feuell summarized the distinctive characteristics of a mycotoxicosis. His definition of these criteria included the following: (1) the disease is not transmissible; (2) drug or antibiotic treatments have little or no effect on the disease; (3) in the field outbreaks, the trouble is often seasonal, because certain climatic conditions affect mold development; (4) the outbreak is usually associated with a specific feed or foodstuff; and (5) examination of the suspected food or feed reveals signs of fungal activity.

Of the mycotoxins studied, those produced by species of *Aspergillus,* the aflatoxins, are the best known. These poisons comprise a unique group of low-molecular-weight, naturally occurring compounds. Aflatoxins have been found in a wide array of edible commodities, including beans, cereals, coconuts, milk, peanuts, sweet potatoes, and commercially prepared animal feeds.

In addition to their intoxication effects, aflatoxins have been found to have carcinogenic properties. This finding has reinforced but has not confirmed the concept that naturally occurring mycotoxins may be a causative factor in human cancerous states on a broad basis. Studies with aflatoxins during the 1960s demonstrated the involvement of the fungal product with liver damage in several birds, fish, and mammals. During this same time period, these mycotoxins were shown to initiate tumors only in ducklings, ferrets, rats, and trout. Specific toxicological and biochemical studies with experimental animals have shown that mycotoxins cause such effects as ultrastructural alterations; changes in the synthesis of DNA, RNA, and protein; and mitochondrial activity. Despite the vast number of these studies the precise mode of action of aflatoxin is not known. Like many carcinogens, aflatoxins act as nonspecific cell poisons that exert multiple effects on the structures and biochemistry of susceptible cells. Since most of these changes may be secondary to carcinogenic activity, they must be identified as such if the primary mode of action is to be defined.

It should be noted here that while a great amount of data has been accumulated, few studies have been conducted on the *in vivo* effects of aflatoxin on plants. In these hosts aflatoxin has been found to inhibit seed germination, growth, and chlorophyll development, and to induce chromosomal abnormalities and changes in cellular structures (Figure 21–4).

Selected Mechanisms and Effects of Viral Pathogenicity

Many microbial pathogens are intracellular parasites. The virulence factors that are produced extracellularly enter and act within host cells. Some viruses enter the tissues of a host directly through some injury (trauma) or insect bite (see Chapter 39). Most viral infections, however, start on the mucous membranes of the respiratory and gastrointestinal tracts. To start an infectious process, virus particles must first survive on these mucous membranes in the presence of other microorganisms (including normal flora). In order for such viruses to replicate, they must enter susceptible host cells, either in the mucous membrane itself or in tissues distant to the point of entry. Replication of the virus

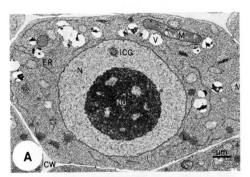

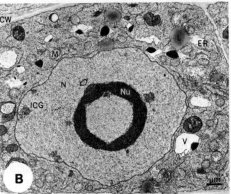

FIG. 21–4. The effects of a fungal toxin (specifically, aflatoxin) on plants. Cellular changes after exposure to aflatoxin are obvious in the electronmicrographs of root cells. *A.* Control. *B.* The effects of treatment with aflatoxin. Abbreviations: *CW*, cell wall; *ER*, endoplasmic reticulum; *ICG*, interchromatin granules; *L*, lipid bodies; *M*, mitochondria; *N*, nucleus; *Nu*, nucleolus; *V*, vacuole; and arrow, light nucleolar cap. (From Crisan, E. V.: *Appl. Microbiol.*, **12**:991–1000, 1973.)

that invades the mucous membrane can produce disease effects directly, as in the case of respiratory infections (Chapter 34). However, sometimes it sets the stage for subsequent damaging replication in another part of the host. Poliovirus is a good example of this situation. The virus first replicates in alimentary-tract cells and ultimately in specific sites in the central nervous system (Chapter 38). Extensive knowledge of the factors that affect the early stages of viral infections is almost completely lacking.

Viruses break through host defenses to

cause disease. As with bacteria, this process depends not only on the strength of the defenses and on the microorganism's capacity to counteract them, but also on the number of invaders. A sufficiently large infecting dose can overwhelm the initial defenses of a susceptible host and cause irreparable injury before adequate defenses can be brought into action.

In natural disease states, and in most laboratory experiments, small infecting doses of viruses are involved. Viral numbers, however, must be built up to a population large enough to be able to damage the activities of host defense mechanisms (Chapter 20).

The pathological effects of viruses. In the numerous studies that deal with the effects and mechanisms of viral pathogenicity, two important questions arise: Which pathological effects are specific to virus attack, rather than the host's nonspecific responses to general injury? How are the pathological effects produced? Our discussion will concern itself with selected aspects of the second question.

Cellular damage of animal tissues by virus attack has been recognized for many years by the classical methods of histopathology; for example, brain cells are damaged by Newcastle disease virus, and respiratory epithelium is changed and injured by a variety of respiratory viruses (Figure 21–5). Electron microscopy and immunofluorescent techniques have demonstrated additional interesting reactions, namely, that viral replication can occur in cells without significant damage.

Latent infections. It appears that not all viral infections result in the death of the host cell. A good example of this type of situation is given by the *Herpesvirus* that causes cold sores or fever blisters. This

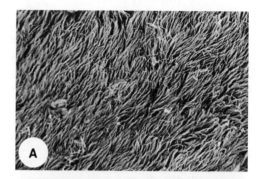

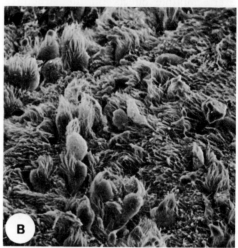

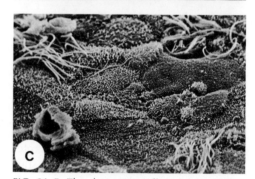

FIG. 21–5. The destructive effects of respiratory viruses. *A.* A scanning electron micrograph showing the appearance of normal tracheal-tissue-culture cells taken from a calf. Note the pronounced number of cilia. *B.* The rapid destructive effects of the ciliated epithelium by a rhinovirus, 6 days after inoculation of the tissue culture system. *C.* Similar destruction by a parainfluenza virus, 11 days after inoculation. (From Reed, S. E., and Boyde, A.: *Infect. Immun.,* **6**: 68–76, 1972.)

virus can remain dormant or silent for months, years, or even decades. The virus lies latent within nerve cells of ganglia, producing no disease symptoms until stresses such as fever, exposure to extreme cold, emotional problems, or sunburn trigger the virus, causing small skin eruptions to develop. Yet between outbreaks the herpesvirus apparently does not destroy the nerve cells in which it continues to exist.

Slow virus infections. In recent years it also has become apparent that some slowly developing, persistent diseases that do not superficially appear to be infectious diseases can be caused or triggered by unusual "slow" viruses. Strong evidence has accumulated that several severe neurological diseases are caused by these agents. There is also preliminary evidence, as yet inconclusive, that a number of common degenerative diseases, such as diabetes, leukemia, multiple sclerosis, and rheumatoid arthritis, may actually be the result of slowly developing, unapparent viral infection.

Cytopathic effect. Ginsberg in 1961 suggested that virus-induced cell damage may result from a passive role of the virus; excessive production of virus or viral components may have repercussions for the replication process, such as depletion of cellular components essential for cell life or for the repair of mechanical injury. There is increasing evidence that more positive processes of cell damage occur. One of these is virus cytotoxic activity. There are two levels at which pathologically important cytotoxic activity can operate, namely, biochemical damage without morphological damage and biochemical damage such as cell lysis, fusion, or death, in which morphological damage does occur. Morphological damage is usually referred to as a cytopathic effect (see Chapter 13).

Further research will undoubtedly uncover other mechanisms by which viruses can establish infections. Such information will add to the understanding of microbial virulence and may provide the basis for the development of effective means of treatment and control.

QUESTIONS FOR REVIEW

1. Distinguish between the following:
   a. virulence and pathogenicity
   b. opportunist and pathogen
   c. endotoxins and exotoxins
   d. symbiosis and parasitism
   e. aflatoxin and carcinogen

2. What microbial factors can influence the course of infection?

3. List any microbial structures or activities that contribute to virulence.

4. List at least four bacterial species that can produce powerful exotoxins, together with the diseases each causes.

5. a. What factor or factors may cause a decrease in a pathogen's virulence?
   b. How might virulence be increased?

6. What mechanisms are involved in viral pathogenicity?

Antigens, Antibodies, and Acquired States of Immunity

As a general rule, most persons successfully recovering from an infectious disease acquire a definite degree of resistance toward the inciting cause. The resistance acquired may be toward a specific microorganism, or toward certain microbial products. This resistance is due to the formation of *antibodies* or *immunoglobulins* within the infected host.

The substances which provoke the formation of antibodies and visibly react with them are called *antigens*. Since many microorganisms and various cells have effective antigens on their surfaces, microbial antigens can be detected serologically and thus they can serve as aids to the identification of microorganisms. Antigenic substances play a most important role in the prevention of disease. They are utilized in the preparation of vaccines and bacterins, which in turn are used to produce active states of resistance. Antigens also have immunogenetic significance, as in the case of blood types discussed in Chapter 24.

The antibody response of different animal species to the same specific protein antigens has been found to vary. Definite structural differences have been discovered between antibodies produced upon antigenic stimulation. It appears that differences exist among components of antigens of specific substances from different sources. For example, insulin from different sources functions similarly physiologically but will differ antigenically.

The nature of antigens and antibodies and selected theories concerning antibody formation are considered in this chapter.

Antigens

The macromolecules of most but not all substances are antigenic. Included in the group of antigens are: (1) most free proteins; (2) combinations of proteins and other substances, including nucleo-proteins (nucleic acid plus protein), lipoproteins (lipid and protein), and glycoproteins (carbohydrate and protein); and (3) certain polysaccharides. The majority of lipids are not considered to be antigenic.

Examples of antigens are the various bacterial components, including flagella, capsules, cell walls, fimbriae (pili)—and, of course, the entire microorganism. Besides the naturally occurring antigenic substances, synthetic ones are also possible. These antigens result from chemical modifications of non-antigenic substances. Reactions of this sort can occur both *in vitro* and *in vivo*. Several drugs and small reactive molecules which by themselves are not antigens can be chemically bonded (*coupled*) to proteins, and thus become antigenic.

Antigens provoke their particular effects because antibody-forming (*immunopoietic*) tissues of an animal recognize them as foreign matter. The greater the incompatibility between the antigen and the recipient's tissues, the greater the *immune response*. This is generally true, except when the toxicity of the foreign substance overwhelms the animal's recognition mechanism.

Factors That Determine Antigenicity and Immune Responses

Antigens generally have molecular weights of 10,000 or greater, and a large molecular surface, which has room for many *determinant antigenic sites.* These determinants are believed to be molecular in nature and located on the surfaces of the antigens. They are responsible for the formation of active antibody sites that will react with them. Antibody molecules are produced against these selected sites and not against the entire surface area of the antigen. The number of determinant antigenic sites on the surface of an antigen is known as the *valence.* In general, an antigen's valence is proportional to its molecular weight.

Other factors that affect the antigenic response include the species of animal receiving the substance, the animal's degree of *immunological maturity* (the degree to which its immune mechanisms are functioning), the route of inoculation, and the use of an *adjuvant.* An adjuvant is a preparation that consists of material, such as mineral oil, mixed with an antigen to prolong and intensify the antigenic stimulus. Freund's complete adjuvant is an example. It is prepared by mixing antigen with killed tubercle bacilli (*Mycobacterium tuberculosis*) and mineral oil.

Classes of Antigens

Haptenes

In 1921 Landsteiner suggested the term *haptene* for substances that did not cause the production of antibodies in animals, but were "serologically active" *in vitro.* These properties were found to be characteristic of certain lipids and polysaccharides of animal and bacterial cells.

Two types of haptenes are now generally recognized: the *simple* and *complex* forms. Simple haptenes do not provoke an antibody response, nor do they visibly react with homologous antibodies *in vitro.* However, simple haptenes can combine with such antibodies and thereby prevent the reaction between the antibody and its corresponding antigen. The name comes from the Greek term *haptein,* meaning "to grasp."

Complex haptenes are substances which also do not cause antibody production, but when combined with homologous antibody, they produce a visible reaction, such as precipitation.

Autoantigens ("Self vs. Not-Self")

Generally, antibodies are not produced in an animal against its own body substances, or cells from which they can be derived. In other words, the immunopoietic tissues recognize the individual's cells as belonging to the "self," and not as foreign matter, "not-self."

In exceptional situations, however, antibodies are produced against body components. These substances are referred to as *auto (self)-antibodies,* and the antigens as *autoantigens.* The resulting state represents the process known as *autoimmunization,* or *autoallergy.*

Under normal conditions, autoantibody-producing antigens are limited to the confines of particular cells and tissues and do not gain access to immuno-

Table 22–1   Some Autoimmune Disease States with the Incriminated Antigenic Substances

Autoimmune Disease	Antigenic Substance
Acquired hemolytic anemia	Red blood cells
Allergic encephalomyelitis	Myelin from the central nervous system
Aspermatogenesis	Spermatozoa
Idiopathic thrombocytopenic purpura[a]	Blood platelets
Rheumatoid arthritis	Immunoglobulins[b] (IgG)
Systemic lupus erythematosus (LE)	Deoxyribonucleic acid
Thyroiditis (Hashimoto's disease)	Thyroglobulin

[a] This disease state is characterized by bleeding in various tissues, and the presence of a rash and purpura (little areas of hemorrhaging) in the skin. It is also called purpura hemorrhagica.
[b] Other causes are believed to be operative in this disease condition.

poietic tissues. However, under certain conditions disease states associated with the production of antibodies toward various normal cellular components are possible.

Representative autoimmune diseases and the antigenic substances believed to be responsible for each are shown in Table 22–1. The exact mechanism or mechanisms underlying the cause of these states remain undetermined in the majority of cases. Reactions caused by serum antibodies are believed to be involved in some of these states, while cell-mediated (delayed hypersensitive) reactions are associated with others.

Isoantigens

The erythrocytes of certain individuals are known to have antigens that differ from those of other persons. In addition, antibodies capable of specifically reacting with these blood cell antigens also differ among individuals. When the same animal species is involved, these two factors are referred to as *isoantigens* and *isoantibodies,* respectively.

The agglutination (clumping reaction) which results from mixing antigenically different red blood cells—such as blood types A, B, or AB from one person with the normal serum of another

individual—is called *isohemagglutination.* Blood typing procedures are based on this phenomenon. Serious complications can occur if transfusions are carried out with blood cells from a donor having different isoantigens from the cells of the recipient. This subject is discussed more fully in Chapter 24.

Heterophile Antigens

These substances are present in various cells and tissues, and cause the production of antibodies which react with the tissues of some mammals, fish, and even plants. Forssmann, in 1911, reported that the injection of emulsions containing guinea pig tissues into rabbits produced antibodies which caused the lysis of sheep erythrocytes in the presence of complement. The antigenic substance involved here was subsequently named the *Forssmann antigen*. It has been found in other animals including birds, cats, dogs, mice, and tortoises. Forssmann antigen has been associated with certain bacterial species, e.g., *Bacillus anthracis, Streptococcus (Diplococcus) pneumoniae, Salmonella* spp., and *Shigella dysenteriae*. In these situations, however, the antigen might have become "implanted" in some microorganisms because of the intimate contact between pathogens and their respective hosts.

To avoid confusion, it is advisable to refer to the antigens obtained from guinea pigs as being of the Forssmann variety, and to designate all other sources of antigenic material as *heterophile antigens.*

Forssmann antibodies—those which will react with sheep red cells—are present in the sera of individuals with infectious mononucleosis (IM), a fact that has been used for diagnostic purposes. Two types of reactions can be observed, namely, agglutination and lysis. The former is generally utilized in routine testing.

Antibodies

Blood serum contains many types of proteins, some of which can be distinguished from one another on the basis of their physicochemical and antigenic features. (Antibodies behave similarly to other proteins in that they too can be antigenic upon their injection into a foreign animal. See Chapter 25 for a discussion of serum sickness.) Physicochemical properties include: (1) chemical composition, (2) chromatographic features, (3) electrophoretic characteristics, (4) molecular weight, (5) relative solubilities in alcohol, electrolytes, and water, and (6) sedimentation coefficients.

Antibodies are proteins which belong to a group known as *globulins.* Their presence in the blood of an immune animal was demonstrated by von Behring and Kitasato in 1890. These investigators showed that serum obtained from a laboratory animal that had been injected with several small doses of diphtheria toxin had protective powers. Two preparations were used. One of these consisted of the anti-serum (antitoxin) plus a lethal dose of the toxin. The other preparation contained only toxin. Different animals were injected with these ma-

terials. Only the recipient of the antiserum-toxin mixture survived. Additional experiments showed the reaction to be specific: serum from animals receiving diphtheria toxin produced antibodies specific only for this poison; serum from animals given another toxin did not produce a protective effect against diphtheria. The results obtained by von Behring and Kitasato also clearly demonstrated the phenomenon of *passive immunization,* the transfer of antibodies from an immunized individual to a nonimmune recipient (discussed more fully in Chapters 25 and 26).

Methods of Studying Antibodies and Antigens

Electrophoresis

The migration of protein particles in an electrical field is determined by several factors including their net electric charge, positive or negative, the voltage applied, and the nature of the medium in which the procedure is performed. This technique is called *electrophoresis.* Early electrophoretic studies showed that the globulins of vertebrates could be divided into three broad categories or classes, called alpha (α), beta (β), and gamma (γ). It has been common practice to group all antibodies into the gamma category.

With more sensitive procedures, antibodies have been shown to be more complex and to exhibit a wider range of properties than was previously thought. Such techniques include *ultracentrifugation* and *immunoelectrophoresis.*

Ultracentrifugation

This technique involves the use of special centrifuges (Figure 22–1) driven by air, electric motors, or oil turbines. Some of

FIG. 22–1. A high-speed, refrigerated centrifuge. This instrument can be used for the harvesting of various microorganisms or their components. (Courtesy of Ivan Sorvall, Inc., Norwalk, Conn.)

these instruments are fast enough to exert sedimentation forces greater than 750,000 times the force of gravity (*g*). Protein solutions are placed in appropriate quartz or lucite containers and spun at a desired speed. The reason for such transparent containers is to allow a beam of light to pass through the solution, enabling an observer to periodically measure the migration of the protein per unit time. Information of this type is used to determine a substance's *sedimentation constant*. Such values for sedimentation are determined at 20°C, or corrected for this temperature, and given in Svedberg (S) units. The faster the rate of sedimentation, the larger is the sedimentation constant. The importance of ultracentrifugation studies is to provide data concerning the shape and molecular weight of molecules.

Immunoelectrophoresis (IEP)

This technique is an extremely valuable tool which enables the immunologist to uncover and identify antibodies or antigens contained within a mixture. The technique combines the elements of electrophoresis and double gel diffusion (see

Chapter 23). Various types of gel or gel-like materials are used in performing immunoelectrophoresis (IEP). In general, the first step involves the separation of the components of a protein mixture which migrate in an electrical field, that is, electrophoretically. Such constituents form bands or spots. Next, thin troughs are hollowed out in the agar, parallel to the migration lines formed by the individual protein components. The appearance of a typical immunoelectrophoretic system is shown in Figure 22–2. Anti-sera against one or several proteins in the original mixtures are placed in these troughs. In areas where homologous antigen (proteins from the original mixture) and antibody (anti-sera) have met as a result of their diffusion through the gel, precipitation lines develop, usually in the form of arcs. IEP can be applied to a variety of body fluids, including amniotic fluid, cerebrospinal fluid, human plasma and serum, respiratory secretions, saliva, animal and plant tissue antigens, and microbial antigens.

The Classes of Immunoglobulins

The early studies of Tiselius demonstrated that antibodies are primarily contained in the slowest moving electrophoretic fraction. Such substances were designated as γ globulin. The peak of this serum fraction was observed to have a somewhat broader boundary than does albumin, another component of this type of preparation (Figure 22–3 and 22–7). The current view is that the broad γ globulin peak contains a variety of different antibodies, and that the electrophoretic appearance represents a composite of these globulins. In general, any proteins exhibiting antibody activity or having antigenic determinants in common with antibody molecules are referred to as *immunoglobulins* (Ig).

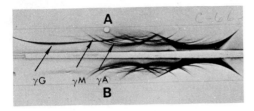

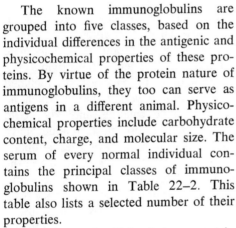

FIG. 22–2. Immunoelectrophoretic patterns of: _A._ Normal serum. _B._ Agammaglobulinemic serum. Although numerous serum fractions are shown, only a select few are specifically indicated. (Courtesy of Dr. M. D. Poulik, Wayne State University School of Medicine, and The Child Research Center of Michigan.)

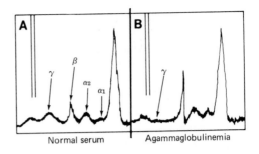

Normal serum　　　　Agammaglobulinemia

FIG. 22–3_A_. A diagrammatic representation of the electrophoretic pattern associated with the serum of a normal individual. _B._ The pattern of an agammaglobulinemic serum. Note the absence of the gamma globulin peak (arrow).

The known immunoglobulins are grouped into five classes, based on the individual differences in the antigenic and physicochemical properties of these proteins. By virtue of the protein nature of immunoglobulins, they too can serve as antigens in a different animal. Physicochemical properties include carbohydrate content, charge, and molecular size. The serum of every normal individual contains the principal classes of immunoglobulins shown in Table 22–2. This table also lists a selected number of their properties.

The most plentiful of these protein substances in man is IgG or γ (gamma) G. The IgM is next in the order of abundance. These immunoglobulins originally were called macroglobulins because of their large size, hence the M designation. Both IgD and IgE are usually present in low concentrations.

Subclasses.　On the basis of antigenic reactivity and subsequent immunochemical analysis, several different subclasses of certain immunoglobulins have been found. The four subclasses of IgG (IgG1 to IgG4) and the two subclasses each for IgA (IgA1 and IgA2) and IgM (IgM1 and IgM2) possess important biological distinctions.

Table 22–2　The Immunoglobulins and Selected Properties

Immunoglobulin Class	Former Designation	Molecular Weight	Carbohydrate	Approximate Sedimentation Coefficients in Svedberg (S) units	Associated Activity
IgA (or γ A)	γ, A, or B$_2$A	170,000	5% to 10%	7, 9, 11, and 13 S	Skin-sensitizing, toxin neutralization
IgD (or γ D)	—	150,000	—	7 S	Not well defined
IgE (or γ E)	—	200,000	10.5%	8 S	Allergic reactions in humans
IgG (or γ G)	gamma globulin or γ ss	150,000	2.5%	7 S	Classic antibody, placental transfer, toxin neutralization
IgM (or γ M)	γ$_7$M, or B$_2$M 19Sγ	900,000	5% to 10%	19 S (ranges from 18 to 32 S)	Frequently the first globulin with antibody activity after immunization, high bactericidal activity

General Immunoglobulin Structure

Thousands of individual antibody molecules, differing in their primary structure, can be found circulating in serum. There is great diversity in the sequence of amino acids in the molecule, but all normal immunoglobulins share the same basic molecular arrangement, which consists of a unit of four polypeptide chains —two identical H (heavy) chains and two identical L (light) chains. These components are covalently linked to one another by disulfide bonds (S-S) as shown in Figure 22–4. These linkages also occur within the individual chains and are called *intra-chain disulfide bonds*. The formula $(L_2H_2)_n$ can be used to represent the general composition of immunoglobulins.

Two different types of light chains, designated kappa (κ) and lambda (λ) occur in all immunoglobulins. A given antibody molecule contains either two κ or two λ chains (or multiples of two), but never one of each. Each class of immunoglobulin has a different type of heavy chain structure. These chains are designated by a Greek letter corresponding to the Roman capital letters used for the immunoglobulin classes. Thus the H chain designation for IgA is α (alpha); for IgD, δ (delta); for IgE, ε (epsilon); for IgG, γ (gamma); and for IgM, μ (mu). Figure 22–4B shows a hypothetical comparison of the five classes of immunoglobulins.

The different subregions of the immunoglobulin are generally referred to as the "F_c domain" and the "F_{ab} domains." The F_{ab} domains contain the antigen-binding sites. These are composed of both H and L chains. The F_c domain contains the greater constant portion of the H chain. This region participates in various biologic activities or reactions, including complement fixation and skin sensitization.

Antibody Production (Responses to Antigenic Stimuli)

Antibodies for a particular antigenic substance are not detectable in the serum of an individual until exposure to the antigen has occurred. This antibody response is known to be affected by various factors, including: (1) the nature of the antigenic material, (2) the dosage received, (3) the number and frequency of exposures, i.e., injections, (4) the particular animal species, and (5) the individual involved.

Primary Response

The effects of antigenic stimulation on the body can be best studied by observing the response produced with a single injection of antigen. The original description of the primary response included a *latent* or *lag period* during which no increase in circulating antibody could be detected. Improved techniques have shown that in some instances antibody synthesis does occur shortly after the initial introduction of the antigenic stimulus. After a period which may vary from a few hours to several days, the antibody titer reaches a peak or plateau (Figure 22–5). A peak is formed when the rates of antibody production and antibody breakdown are approximately the same. Such antibody levels may remain for several months or longer and then slowly begin to decline, as antibody degradation exceeds production. The details depend in part upon the animal species and antigenic material used.

Secondary Response

A sudden secondary rise in antibody titer can be produced by a second injection of antigenic material at some time after the first exposure to antigen. (This is not true of some antigens.) This effect is frequently called a *specific anamnestic* response, from the Greek term *anamne-*

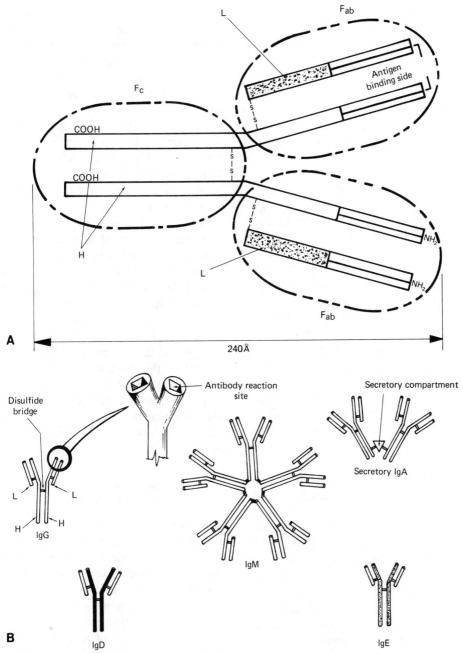

FIG. 22–4 <u>A</u>. A diagrammatic representation of the basic immunoglobulin structure (IgG). An immunoglobulin molecule contains four polypeptide chains, two heavy (H) and two light (L) chains. These components are joined by disulfide bonds (-S-S-). The N-terminal (NH$_2$) portions of a light chain and the adjacent heavy chain form an antigen binding site. These sites are variable and are contained within the F$_{ab}$ region of the molecule. Such immunoglobulin molecules are divalent; that is, they possess two antigen binding sites per molecule. The F$_c$ portion of the molecule, which also is shown, contains the greater constant portion of the H chains. <u>B</u>. A hypothetical comparison of immunoglobulins showing their heavy- and light-chain components. The antigen binding sites of the IgG structure also are indicated.

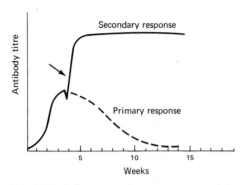

FIG. 22–5. A diagrammatic representation of the primary response to an antigenic stimulus. The secondary response is also shown (arrow). (After Gray, D. F.: *Immunology*. Elsevier Publishing Company, Inc., New York, 1970.)

sis, meaning recall. Nonspecific responses also are possible; however, they are also caused by various other stimuli. The antibody titers associated with a specific anamnestic response generally are higher than those produced by the primary reaction, occur with little or no lag period, and remain for long periods.

Anamnestic reactions are produced by reimmunization with vaccines. The effectiveness of "booster shots" can be explained on this basis.

The Sources or Occurrences of Normal Immunoglobulins

Generally, after exposure to an antigenic stimulus, a temporary increase in IgM occurs, which is followed by a more permanent and greater IgG response. Upon a second injection of the same antigen, or reimmunization, the secondary response usually produces IgG, although exceptions to this are known.

The immunoglobulins of the IgA class are the predominant type found in various body secretions including colostrum (the early form of breast milk), gastro-intestinal fluids, saliva, tears, and substances associated with the respiratory tract. Differences exist between IgA molecules

associated with these external secretions and those found in serum. IgA immunoglobulins have been reported to increase in certain pathologic states such as chronic liver disease.

The remaining two classes of immunoglobulins, IgD and IgE, are not well characterized. Both types of molecules are present in human serum in low concentrations. The IgE globulins are associated with skin-sensitizing effects caused by certain allergens (antigens that produce allergies).

In newborn infants, the levels of IgG approach those found in adults. Most of these immunoglobulins are of maternal origin. Such IgG molecules decrease sharply in quantity by approximately the fourth month after birth. It is about this time that the child's own IgG synthesizing machinery comes into play.

IgA and IgM immunoglobulins do not appear in the newborn's serum because they cannot pass through the human placenta. Synthesis of IgM occurs at about the same time as IgG. IgA levels increase later, generally between the ages of 4 and 10 years.

Immunoglobulin Abnormalities (Gammopathies)

Immunoglobulin abnormalities are classified into one of three categories according to the following criteria: (1) increases in the concentration of several or all immunoglobulins, (2) abnormally large increases in the concentration of a single immunoglobulin type, and (3) decreases in the concentration of several or all immunoglobulin classes as seen in immunologic deficiency disease states.

As mentioned, antibodies are formed exclusively by cells of lymphoid origin. In certain pathologic states a single cell undergoes a *neoplastic* (cancerous) transformation: rapid and unregulated multi-

Atlas of Color Plates

Plate 1—A Survey of the Microbial World

Figures 1 and 2. Photomicrographs of representative algae commonly encountered in natural bodies of water. Note the characteristic symmetry exhibited by many of these microorganisms. (Courtesy of Clay-Adams, Division of Becton, Dickinson and Company, New York.)

Figure 1. The blue-green alga *Oscillatoria* sp.

Figure 2. Desmids—specialized members of the chlorophyta. Note the characteristic bilateral symmetrical appearance.

Figure 3. An algal bloom in a recreational park near Salem, Oregon. Note the massive accumulation of algae.

Figure 4. <u>A</u>. The curled colonies of *Mycobacterium smegmatis,* a rapidly growing bacterial species. (From Vestal, A. L.: *Procedures for the Isolation and Identification of Mycobacteria,* DHEW No. (HSM) 73-8230, 1973.) <u>B</u>. Seven-day-old colonies of *Mycoplasma fermentans.* Note the individual depressed centers surrounded by thin films of growth on the agar surface. The actual diameter of stained colonies measured 1–3 mm. (Courtesy of Dr. M. G. Gabridge, University of Illinois at Urbana.)

Figure 5. The spoilage effect caused by fungi. On the uppermost Tokay grape the black, dry fungal growth is obvious. Note the rather healthy appearance of the other grape.

Figure 6. *Mycena* sp., a common mushroom in areas of rotting and decaying wood and leaves. This genus contains over 200 species in North America.

Plate 2—Lichens, Viroids, and Cells of Animals and Plants

Figure 7. A close-up view of a crustose lichen on a tree trunk found near New Orleans, Louisiana.

Figure 8. An example of a fruticose lichen found in California.

Figure 9. The stunting of tomato plants that occurs as a consequence of potato spindle tuber viroid (PSTV) infection. (Courtesy of T. O. Diener, Research Plant Pathologist, U.S.D.A.)

Figure 10. A photomicrograph of a stained smear made from human blood. The circular, non-nucleated cells are erythrocytes. Lymphocytes and a polymorphonuclear leukocyte (PMNL) are also shown.

Figure 11. A stained section of epithelial cells found in the mucosal lining of the human trachea. The ciliated nature of the surface epithelial cells and the cylindrical features of the columnar epithelial cells are readily apparent. Note the appearance of the stained nuclei. Can nucleoli be seen?

Figure 12. A photomicrograph taken of a stained transverse section of a corn stem *(Zea mays).* The major area shown is that of a vascular bundle. The cell types included here are *xylem* (large and red), involved in the transportation of water and minerals needed by the plant, and the *phloem* (smaller and green), involved in conducting the products produced by the plant. The large, green, thin-walled cells surrounding the vascular bundle are called *parenchymal* cells. Depending upon their location and their contents, these parenchymal cells can function in several capacities, including storage and photosynthesis. Compare the cell wall thicknesses of the respective cell types shown.

Figure 13. This photomicrograph shows a portion of a cross-section of a woody stem. Note the wall thickness of the sclerenchymal cells (red). The clear area in the center of these cells is a *lumen*.

Figure 14. A simple stain preparation. This photomicrograph shows the appearance of the rod *Bacillus subtilis* stained with crystal violet as observed under the oil immersion objective. The clear areas within the rods are spores.

Plate 3—Differential Staining and Bacterial Anatomy

Figure 15. A typical Gram-positive reaction. The bacteria shown are *Streptococcus* sp. These organisms characteristically retain the primary dye, usually crystal violet, and appear dark purple in color. This photomicrograph also demonstrates the possible variations in the arrangement of cells (e.g., diplococci, single cocci) which may be observed during the examination of a microscope field.

Figure 16. The appearance of a Gram-negative bacterial species. In this case, the primary dye was not retained following the decolorization step. Consequently, the organisms take the counterstain (usually safranin).

Figure 17. A typical acid-fast reaction. Microorganisms exhibiting this type of result show a red coloration.

Figure 18. Bacterial cells exhibiting a non-acid-fast (blue) reaction.

Figure 19. A photomicrograph of the flagellar arrangement of *Spirillum volutans*. In addition to showing the spiral morphology of this organism, the lophotrichous flagella arrangement (two or more flagella at one or both ends of a cell) is evident. Note that special staining procedures are needed to demonstrate these organelles.

Figure 20. The capsules of *Enterobacter aerogenes*. In the procedure used to demonstrate this bacterial structure a combination of India ink and safranin was employed. The capsules (clear areas) are seen against the dark background. Individual organisms are red.

Figure 21. A specially stained sputum specimen from a patient with *Streptococcus (Diplococcus)*

pneumoniae. Note the clear areas surrounding the individual red diplococci.

Figure 22. The spores and vegetative cells of *Bacillus megaterium*. The preparation shown was stained by the Schaeffer-Fulton technique. Spores appear green, while vegetative portions of cells are red. Note the presence of spores (endospores) inside their respective vegetative cells.

Figure 23. A photomicrograph of the anaerobic sporeformer *Clostridium tetani*. This preparation was stained by a combination of carbol fuchsin and methylene blue. In this case spores are red, while the vegetative cells are blue. Note the end position taken by these structures. This type of appearance is referred to as a "drumstick." (Courtesy of CCM: General Biological, Inc., Chicago.)

Plate 4—Cultivation Techniques

Figure 24. Streak plate preparation with *Micrococcus (Sarcina) lutea*. Note the well-separated bacterial colonies.

Figure 25. Pour plate preparation also with *Micrococcus (Sarcina) lutea*. Observe the random distribution as well as the varied shapes of the bacterial colonies. Compare the appearance of *S. lutea* in this preparation to that found with the streak plate in Figure 24.

Figure 26. Selected characteristics of bacteria grown on agar slants. Most of the species shown are highly pigmented, however other cultural features are also obvious. Specific properties will be indicated in parentheses after each organism. Tube A, *Serratia marcescens* (nondiffusable red pigment, smooth growth); Tube B, *Bacillus* species (nonpigmented, opaque growth); Tube C, *Pseudomonas aeruginosa* (a greenish pigment diffusing into the agar); Tube D, *Micrococcus (Sarcina) lutea* (a yellow, smooth, glistening type of growth); Tube E, *Micrococcus roseus* (a coral-colored, smooth growth); Tube F, *Chromobacterium violaceum* (a purple, smooth growth); and Tube G, *Mycobacterium phlei* (an orange, coarse, granular type of growth).

Figure 27. Selected broth culture characteristics of bacteria. Tube A, control, uninoculated; Tube B, a typical example of turbidity; Tube C, sediment formation. Certain organisms have a tendency to form a surface film or pellicle. Quite often such structures may become dislodged as a result of shaking, and fall to the bottom of the tube. This property of pellicle formation is not shown here.

Figure 28. Representative growth characteristics of bacteria in Fluid Thioglycollate Broth. Tube A, uninoculated. Note the presence of the upper pink and lower yellow zones. Tube B, the growth of a typical anaerobic organism; Tube C, the growth of a typical aerobic organism.

Figure 29. Pock formation on the chorioallantoic membrane (CAM) of a chick embryo. Pocks can be recognized as small, whitish, dense areas. (Courtesy of S. Stanley Schneierson, M.D., and Abbott Laboratories, Chicago.)

Plate 5—Common Fungi

All fungi shown here have been cultured on Sabouraud's Glucose Agar.

Figure 30. The fungus *Penicillium notatum*. This microorganism is a frequent inhabitant of laboratory environments. Note the organism's coloration and pattern of growth.

Figure 31. The mycelium of the fungus *Alternaria* sp. This organism has been implicated in the causation of certain allergic states.

Figure 32. *Aspergillus niger*, a common laboratory contaminant.

Figure 33. The common bread mold, *Rhizopus nigricans*. Notice its different pattern of growth. The black, dotlike structures are sporangia.

Figure 34. The cottony mycelium of *Fusarium* species. A slight tinge of pink, purple, or yellow often is found in the mycelium or in the medium. This genus contains species that are parasitic on higher plants or saprophytic on decaying plant matter. (Photo by C. Righter.)

Figure 35. The glistening colonies of brewer's yeast, *Saccharomyces cerevisiae*.

Figure 36. The colonies of two additional yeasts, *Cryptococcus neoformans* (dark blue) and *Candida albicans* (light blue) on Sabouraud Glucose Agar containing trypan blue. This agar is a new selective and differential medium for yeasts. (From Vickers, R. M., McElligott, J. J., Jr., Rihs, J. D., and Postic, B.: *Appl. Microbiol.*, **27**:38, 1974.)

Plate 6—Selected Aspects of Microbial Metabolism

Figure 37. Urease activity with two bacterial species. Tube A, negative reaction (yellow) of *Escherichia coli;* Tube B, positive reaction (red) with *Proteus vulgaris.*

Figure 38. Carbohydrate fermentation employing Durham fermentation tubes. The indicator used is phenol red. Tube A, uninoculated; Tube B, acid production; Tube C, acid and gas production (note the collection of gas in the inverted vial).

Figure 39. The demonstration of lipid hydrolysis using Bacto-Spirit Blue Agar containing Bacto-Lipase Reagent. The organisms employed here are the red-pigmented *Serratia marcescens, Escherichia coli,* and *Staphylococcus aureus.* The lipolytic activity of a bacterial species is recognized by the deep blue color or clearing that develops in the medium surrounding the test organism. A comparable color change is not observed with non-lipolytic microorganisms.

Figure 40. Carbohydrate fermentation reactions as demonstrated by fermentation discs on a seeded phenol red agar pour plate. The area around the dextrose (glucose) disc (D) shows acid production, while the reactions surrounding the lactose (L) and mannitol (M) discs are negative.

Figure 41. Starch hydrolysis. A typical positive starch hydrolytic reaction is produced by the organism (*Bacillus subtilis*) on the right of the starch agar plate. The complete absence of starch upon the addition of an iodine reagent is indicated by the lack of a purple background surrounding the bacterial growth. A negative reaction is indicated by a purple background surrounding bacterial colonies.

Figure 42. Motility agar. The ability of organisms to spread in semi-solid agar provides a method that can be used as a substitute for microscopic examination of cultures for motility. Approximately 0.3% agar is used to produce a soft gel without hindering motility. The medium is inoculated by a single stab straight down the center of the tube. During incubation motile cells swarm out from the line of inoculation. Tetrazolium salts, which are colorless when introduced, may be used to aid in the visualization of organisms. As a consequence of microbial metabolism the salts are reduced, turn a particular color, and change the appearance of the medium in the areas in which the organisms are present. Note the difference in the motility agars shown.

Figure 43. Bacto-Citrate Malonate Agar. This medium is used in the differentiation of enteric bacterial pathogens. The medium before inoculation is green throughout. If citrate and mannitol are not utilized the medium remains unchanged (tube A). Fermentation of mannitol with no utilization of citrate results in a yellow coloration in the slant region and in the butt (tube B). The utilization of citrate alone is indicated by a blue slant and no color change in the butt (tube C), although the blue coloration may diffuse into the butt region. Some of the reactions are indicated in the table below. Brom-thymol blue is the indicator used in this medium.

	Tube A	Tube B	Tube C
Slant	No change (citrate not utilized)	Yellow (citrate not utilized)	Blue (citrate utilized)
Butt	No change (mannitol not utilized)	Yellow (mannitol fermented)	No change (mannitol not utilized)

Figure 44. The Snyder colorimetric test for caries activity diagnosis. This medium contains dextrose (glucose) as the fermentable carbohydrate, and brom-cresol green as the indicator. The indication of acid production is represented by the presence of a yellow coloration in the medium. Tube A, uninoculated (blue); Tubes B and C, acid production, indicating caries activity by the inoculated organisms.

Plate 7—Differential Plate Reactions

Figure 45. Representative hemolytic reactions on blood agar media. _A_. Alpha (α) hemolysis. Note the greenish discoloration of the medium surrounding the bacterial colonies. _B_. Beta (β) hemolysis. Here clear zones surround the individual bacterial colonies. _C_. Gamma (γ) hemolysis. Discoloration, or clear zones, is not present.

Figure 46. _A_. The appearance of _Streptococcus salivarius_ grown on Bacto-Mitis-Salivarius medium. _B. S. mitis_ on the same medium.

Figure 47. Differentiation of _Pseudomonas_ sp. on Bacto-Pseudomonas agar F medium. Left side, _Serratia marcescens;_ right side, _Pseudomonas fluorescens_. Note the apparent elaboration and diffusion of fluorescein (yellow fluorescent pig-

ment) by the culture on the right-hand side of the plate.

Figure 48. Differentiation of _Pseudomonas_ sp. on Bacto-Pseudomonas agar P medium. This medium enhances the production of pyocyanin (a bluish colored pigment) and _inhibits_ the elaboration of fluorescein. Note the blue coloration of the medium surrounding the bacterial growth.

Figure 49. The typical black colonies of _Corynebacterium xerosis_ on Mueller-Hinton-Tellurite medium.

Plate 8—Multiple Test System Reactions

Figure 50. Selected litmus milk reactions. Tube A, uninoculated; Tube B, an alkaline reaction (blue to purple), indicating utilization by the inoculated organism of the milk proteins as a source of carbon and nitrogen; Tube C, an acid result (pink to red), demonstrating the production of a considerable quantity of acid; Tube D, the beginning of litmus reduction (white portion of the medium). The reaction is caused by the oxidation-reduction activities of the inoculated bacteria. This reaction begins at the bottom of the tube and spreads upward. Tubes E and F, casein curd formation and peptonization. With peptonization, a reduction in curd size occurs and a brownish supernatant called _whey_ is formed.

Figure 51. Selected Triple Sugar Iron Agar medium (TSIA) reactions. This medium is an example of a preparation used in the identification of Gram-negative enteric pathogenic bacteria. TSIA is especially valuable when it is used with additional media, such as Endo, EMB, or MacConkey Agar. The ability of an organism to ferment dextrose (glucose), lactose, and saccharose (sucrose) with the production of acid and gas can be determined with TSIA. The indicator here is phenol red. In addition, the medium can be used to detect hydrogen sulfide (H_2S) formation.

Alkaline reactions (Alk) are indicated by a red coloration, acid (A) production by a yellowing of the medium, gas formation by the presence of air pockets in the preparation, and the presence of hydrogen sulfide (H_2S) by a blackening of the medium. (Courtesy of S. Stanley Schneierson, M.D., and Abbott Laboratories, Chicago.)

Figure 52. Analytab Products, Inc. (API), 20 Enteric ready-to-use system. The combination of substrates in this system allows the performance of 22 standard biochemical tests. The tests in the top row show the appearance of uninoculated systems. The tests in the bottom row demonstrate examples of color changes and hence positive reactions. What each compartment determines and what the appearance of a positive reaction should be are indicated in the accompanying table.

Test Symbol	Test Determines	Appearance with Positive Reaction
ONPG	beta-Galactosidase	Yellow
ADH	Arginine dehydrolase	Red
LDC	Lysine decarboxylase	Red or orange
ODC	Ornithine decarboxylase	Red
CIT	Citrate (Simmons) utilization	Blue/green
H_2S	H_2S production	Black deposit
URE	Urease (Ferguson)	Red
TDA	Tryptophan deaminase	Brown
IND	Indole	Red ring
VP	Acetoin	Red
GEL	Gelatin	Diffusion of black material
GLU	Glucose	Yellow-gray
MAN	Mannitol	Yellow
INO	Inositol	Yellow
SOR	Sorbitol	Yellow
RHA	Rhamnose	Yellow
SAC	Sucrose	Yellow
MEL	Melibiose	Yellow
AMY	Amygdalin	Yellow
ARA	Arabinose	Yellow

Figure 53. Roche Diagnostics' Entero-Tube (EN-CISE™) Identification System. This photograph shows another multiple test system, which allows for the performance of 11 standard biochemical tests. The top system shows the appearance of an uninoculated set of tests. The bottom system demonstrates examples of color changes that are associated with positive reactions. Refer to the table on the following page for details as to the contents of each compartment and the appearance of positive tests.

Plate 9—Representative Immunologic Reactions

Figure 54. Typical slide blood agglutination reactions. The left-hand side of each slide contains anti-A blood typing serum, and the right-hand portion contains anti-B blood typing serum. Samples of the different blood types have been added to these reagents in order to produce the typical reaction known for each. Slide 1 shows the characteristic reaction for blood type A; Slide 2 represents blood type B; Slide 3 shows blood type AB; and Slide 4 demonstrates the reaction for blood type O.

Figure 55. The tube precipitin reaction. Tube A represents a positive result. Note the ring of precipitation which is present at the interface. Tubes B and C are antigen controls, and Tubes D and E antibody controls.

Figure 56. A complement fixation titration. Tubes A through D exhibit a strongly positive result (4+). Tube E is weakly positive. (2+). Tubes F and G represent negative reactions. Note that in a positive complement fixation reaction no hemolysis occurs, while in a negative reaction hemolysis is evident. (Courtesy of S. Stanley Schneierson, M.D., and Abbott Laboratories, Chicago.)

Figure 57. An indirect immunofluorescent test for antinuclear antibody. The Antinuclear Antibody (ANA) test for the detection of the autoimmune condition of systemic lupus erythematosus (LE). The upper section shows a negative reaction, while the lower one demonstrates a positive result. In the latter, anti-DNA antibodies from an LE patient are bound to the DNA in human tissue-culture cell nuclei. (Courtesy of Smith Kline Instruments, Inc., a subsidiary of Smith Kline & French Laboratories.)

Figure 58. The direct fluorescent antibody technique showing the presence of bacterial flagella. Cells as well as the wavy flagella are quite evident. (From Elliot, J. G., Carpenter, J. A., and Hamdy, M. K.: *Appl. Microbiol.*, **28**:1063–1065, 1974.)

Figure 59. Positive human skin test. Reactions of 5 mm or more induration are considered positive. (Courtesy of Mycology Section, Laboratory Division, Center for Disease Control, U.S.P.H.S.)

Entero-Tube reactions for Figure 53

Compartment Number	Test Determines	Appearance with Positive Reaction	Positive Reaction Shows
1	Dextrose	Yellow coloration	Fermentation resulting in acid production
1	Gas production	Separation of wax overlay from the dextrose agar surface	Gas produced from dextrose
2	Lysine decarboxylase	Purple coloration	Formation of alkaline end-product cadaverine by the removal of CO_2 (decarboxylation) from lysine
3	Ornithine decarboxylase	Purple coloration	Formation of alkaline end-product putrescine by removal of CO_2 from ornithine
4	H_2S production	Black coloration	Reduction of sulfur-containing protein-related compounds
4	Indole	Pink to red coloration after Kovac's reagent addition	Production of indole from tryptophan (tryptophanase activity)
5	Lactose	Yellow coloration	Fermentation of lactose resulting in acid production
6*	Phenylalanine deaminase (PA)	Brown coloration	Formation of pyruvic acid from phenylalanine by removal of an amino group (deamination)
6	Dulcitol	Yellow coloration	Fermentation of dulcitol resulting in acid end-products
7	Urea	Pink to red coloration	Hydrolysis of urea resulting in formation of ammonia
8	Citrate	Blue coloration	The organisms are capable of using sodium citrate as their sole source of carbon

*Note: Because all organisms that are phenylalanine-deaminase-positive are dulcitol-negative, it is not possible to have both the PA and the dulcitol tests positive at the same time.

Plate 10—Selected Manifestations of *Staphylococcus aureus* Together with a Representation of Procedures Used in the Organism's Identification and the Determination of Its Antibiotic Sensitivity

Figure 60. One form of staphylococcal manifestation, the carbuncle. (Courtesy of Wyeth Laboratories, Philadelphia, Pa.)

Figure 61. A case of staphylococcal osteomyelitis. The severity of the infection necessitated the amputation of the individual's large toe. The amputation of the foot also was scheduled, as the tarsal and metatarsal bones were destroyed. Fortunately, antibiotic treatment was successful. Note the appearance of the lesion shown here. (Courtesy of Wyeth Laboratories, Philadelphia, Pa.)

Figure 62. The appearance of *Staphylococcus aureus* on Bacto-Mannitol Salt Agar. The presence of yellow zones around the bacterial colonies indicates the formation of acid from mannitol. This medium does not differentiate between coagulase-positive and coagulase-negative staphylococci.

Figure 63. A photomicrograph showing the typical Gram-stain reaction of *S. aureus*. Note the clustering of the cocci.

Figure 64. The coagulase test. A positive reaction is generally considered to be the best single criterion of potential pathogenicity. The upper tube shows a coagulated plasma clot (positive result), while in the lower tube coagulation of the plasma is absent.

Figure 65. Antibiotic sensitivity testing. In order to determine the antibiotic or antibiotics which may be effective in the treatment of bacterial infections, the procedure of antibiotic sensitivity testing is performed. The results obtained from this type of test generally provide some insight into the specific chemotherapy to be used. In some cases, however, the *in vitro* effectiveness of antibiotics may not be evident in the patient. The results of the test shown indicate by the presence of large, clear areas surrounding the individual antibiotic-containing discs that the organism tested is sensitive to several chemotherapeutic agents. The green disc contains penicillin.

Figure 66. An example of phage typing. (Courtesy of the National Medical Audiovisual Center, Atlanta, Georgia.)

Plate 11—Bacterial and Mycotic Skin Infections

Figure 67. Multiple streptococcal skin ulcers on the leg. The sharply punched-out appearance is typical of freshly debrided ulcers. (From Allen, A. M., Taplin, D., Lowy, J. A., and Twigg, L.: *Mil. Med.*, **137**:295, 1972.)

Figure 68. *Trigonosoma decorum* flies feeding on the seropurulent exudate from streptococcal lesions on the foot. These wound-feeding flies can spread virulent streptococci from one person to another. (From Allen, A. M., Taplin, D., and Twigg, L.: *Arch. Derm.*, **104**:271, 1971.)

Figure 69. The multiple lesions of impetigo on the face of a young child. (From Allen, A. M., *Inf. Dis.*, **1**:31, 1971.)

Figure 70. Inflammatory *Trichophyton mentagrophytes* infection on the waist. The presence of discrete foci of infection suggests that the spreading of the lesions occurred by the seeding of spores. (From Allen, A. M., and Taplin, D: *JAMA*, **226**:864, 1973.)

Figure 71. Disabling *Trichophyton mentagrophytes* infection in areas of the feet formerly covered by wet boots and socks. (From Allen, A. M., and Taplin, D.: *JAMA*, **226**:864, 1973.)

Figure 72. Confluent rings of an inflammatory *T. mentagrophytes* dermatophytosis involving the lower abdomen, groin, and hip areas. (From Allen, A. M., Taplin, D., Lowy, J. A., and Twigg, L.: *Mil. Med.*, **137**:295, 1972.)

Plate 12—Dermatophytes and Selected Manifestations

Figure 73. The mycelium of *Microsporum canis*. (Courtesy of Dr. E. S. Beneke, Department of Botany and Plant Pathology, Michigan State University.)

Figure 74. The mycelium of another *Microsporum* species, *M. gypseum*. (Courtesy of Dr. E. S. Beneke, Department of Botany and Plant Pathology, Michigan State University.)

Figure 75. Tinea capitis, or ringworm of the head. This manifestation may be caused by several fungal agents, including *M. canis* and *M. gypseum*. (Courtesy of Dr. Vincent Derbes, New Orleans, Louisiana and Schering Laboratories, Division of Schering Corporation, Union, New Jersey.)

Figure 76. Another dermatophyte infection, tinea pedis. (Courtesy of Dr. M. Murray Nierman, Calumet City, Illinois, and Schering Laboratories, Division of Schering Corporation, Union, New Jersey.)

Figure 77. *Piedraia hortai*, an involvement of the hair. (Courtesy of Dr. E. S. Beneke, Department of Botany and Plant Pathology, Michigan State University.)

Figure 78. The mycelium of *Trichophyton rubrum*. This fungus is a common etiologic agent of athlete's foot. (Courtesy of Dr. E. S. Beneke, Department of Botany and Plant Pathology, Michigan State University.)

Figure 79. The microscopic appearance of *T. rubrum* macroconidia. Note the long, cylindrical nature of these structures. (Courtesy of Dr. E. S. Beneke, Department of Botany and Plant Pathology, Michigan State University.)

Figure 80. A photomicrograph showing the typical club-shaped macroconidia of *Epidermophyton floccosum*. These structures vary in size ranging from 6 to 10 μm(μ) in diameter by 8 to 40 μm(μ) in length. *E. floccosum* does not form microconidia. A characteristic feature of this agent is that it does not invade hair. (Courtesy of Dr. E. S. Beneke, Department of Botany and Plant Pathology, Michigan State University.)

Plate 13—Selected Clinical and Laboratory Diagnostic Features of Microbial Diseases Associated with the Skin and Central Nervous System

Figure 81. Cutaneus anthrax. (Courtesy of Drs. M. H. Matz and H. G. Brugsch: *JAMA,* **188**:115, 1964.)

Figure 82. Clinical manifestations of scarlet fever. A closeup of the rash on the forearm. (Courtesy of Dr. A. Nahmias, Emory University School of Medicine, Atlanta, Georgia.)

Figure 83. Measles rash on Caucasian skin. (Courtesy of Dr. L. Conrad, Immunization Branch, State and Community Services Division, Center for Disease Control, U.S.P.H.S.)

Figure 84. Measles rash on Negroid skin. (Courtesy of Dr. L. Conrad, Immunization Branch, State and Community Services Division, Center for Disease Control, U.S.P.H.S.)

Figure 85. Coccidioidomycosis. *A.* Disseminated lesions on the buttocks and back. (Courtesy of Dr. Robert W. Huntington, Jr.) *B.* Involvement of the finger. (Courtesy of the Mycology Section, Laboratory Division, Center for Disease Control, U.S.P.H.S.)

Figure 86. The colony of *Coccidioides immitis.* (Courtesy of the Mycology Section, Laboratory Division, Center for Disease Control, U.S.P.H.S.)

Figure 87. *C. immitis* arthrospores. (1,200 ×). (Courtesy of the Mycology Section, Laboratory Division, Center for Disease Control, U.S.P.H.S.)

Plate 14—Selected Examples of Enteric Differential Media

Figure 88. Eosin-Methylene Blue Agar (EMB). This medium is utilized for the detection and the isolation of Gram-negative intestinal pathogens. The preparation contains two sugars, lactose and saccharose (sucrose), and two indicator dyes, Eosin Y and Methylene Blue. The dyes differentiate between lactose-fermenting and non-lactose-fermenting organisms. *A* shows the appearance of non-lactose-fermenting bacteria (uncolored colonies). *B* shows lactose-fermenting bacteria (dark colonies, and some with dark centers surrounded by light peripheries).

Figure 89. S. S. Agar. This preparation is a highly selective medium. It is utilized for the isolation of *Shigella* and *Salmonella* spp. Use is made of the lactose-fermenting properties of organisms. Neutral Red is the indicator. *A* shows the colonial appearance of non-lactose-fermenting organisms (transparent or translucent colorless colonies). *B* depicts the lactose fermenters, which generally exhibit colonies ranging from pink to red colonies.

Figure 90. The incorporation of the selective and differential medium MacConkey Agar into urine dip-slides. Colonies of lactose fermenters appear red on the medium. Low colony and high colony results are shown. (From Pazin, G. J., Wolinsky, A., and Lee, W. S.: *Amer. Fam. Phys.,* **11**:85–96, 1975.)

Figure 91. The colonial characteristics of common human pathogens grown on Pfizer Hektoen Enteric (HE) Agar. (Courtesy of Dr. F. C. Fink, and Pfizer Diagnostics, Department of Chas. Pfizer & Co., Inc., New York, N.Y.) The medium is a modification of the formula reported by King and Metzger in 1967, while working at the Hektoen Institute for Medical Research in Chicago, Illinois. The medium incorporates several ingredients, among which are the three carbohydrates, lactose, salicin, and sucrose. HE Agar favors the detection and the isolation of enteric pathogens, and can inhibit many nonpathogenic bacteria. In addition to demonstrating sugar fermentation, the medium also serves as an H_2S production indicator. The colonial characteristics of several bacterial species are as follows. *A.* The salmon-colored colonies of *Escherichia coli.* *B.* The appearance of the *Klebsiella-Enterobacter-Serratia* Group, designated as Strain #1. *C.* The blue-green to blue colonies of *Proteus* Strain #2. Note the black centers. This coloration represents H_2S production. Non-hydrogen sulfide producers also can be detected. *D.* Colonies similar in appearance to *Proteus* are formed by *Salmonella* strain #1. The black center also is an indication of H_2S production. Non-hydrogen sulfide producing *Salmonella* spp. can be detected as well. Are there any distinguishing features between the *Salmonella* and *Proteus* colonies shown? *E.* The green, moist, raised colonies of *Shigella.* Members of the genus *Providencia* also produce this type of appearance.

Plate 15—Selected Characteristics of Venereal Disease Agents

Figure 92. A Gram stain preparation of a clinical smear from a patient suspected of having gonorrhea. The organisms are located intracellularly within a leukocyte and exhibit the characteristic "coffee bean" appearance (paired cocci with their adjacent sides flattened). During early stages of gonorrhea, or in longstanding cases of infection, *Neisseria gonorrhoeae* can be found extracellularly. (Courtesy of Dr. D. S. Kellogg Jr., and the Venereal Disease Research Laboratory, National Communicable Disease Center, Atlanta, Georgia.)

Figure 93. A Gram stain preparation of a pure culture of *N. gonorrhoeae*. The typical Gramnegative nature of this organism is quite evident.

Figure 94. The oxidase test. Members of the genus *Neisseria* produce a positive oxidase reaction upon the application of tetramethyl-p-phenylenediamine (oxidase reagent) to their colonies. Colonies demonstrating a positive result are first pink and later dark red. Negative reactions are indicated by colorless colonies. It is important to note that this test does not differentiate one *Neisseria* species from another member of the genus. (Courtesy of S. Stanley Schneierson, M.D., and Abbott Laboratories, Chicago.)

Figure 95. The causative agent of syphilis, *Treponema pallidum* (arrows), as it appears in tissue. Note the characteristic spirochete morphology.

Figure 96. Differentiation among the pathogenic *Neisseria* species. _A_. The carbohydrate oxidation reactions of *N. gonorrhoeae* are shown. This organism produces acid only from glucose (Tube A). Maltose and sucrose, Tubes B and C, respectively, are not attacked. _B_. The carbohydrate oxidation reactions of *N. meningitidis*. This organism is capable of producing acid from glucose and maltose (Tubes A and B respectively). Sucrose is not attacked. The presence of acid is determined with the aid of an appropriate indicator in the semisolid media containing the respective sugars.

Plate 16—Selected Clinical Features of Syphilis and Chancroid

(All photographs are from *Syphilis, a Synopsis,* Public Health Service Publication No. 1660, 1968. Reproduced with permission of Technical Information Services, Bureau of State Services, Center for Disease Control, Department of Health, Education, and Welfare.)

Figure 97. Primary syphilis: Typical Huntarian chancre on the lower lip.

Figure 98. Primary syphilis: Note chancre on the vulva (left) and the presence of condylomata acuminata (genital tumors).

Figure 99. Secondary syphilis: Extensive papulosquamous rash on the body.

Figure 100. Late congenital syphilis: moon's molar, shown at the lower right.

Figure 101. The gumma is the hallmark of the lesions of late benign syphilis and a classic example of granulomatous inflammation. The gumma, from an anatomic viewpoint, is a firm, white lesion that may vary from microscopic size to 10 centimeters or more in diameter. This photograph shows two of these lesions in a liver specimen. At the lower periphery, one gumma is seen as a firm, white, somewhat irregular nodule. The other is hemorrhagic and largely necrotic.

Figure 102. Chancroid. The lesions here differ from those found in syphilis. They are usually multiple soft, tender ulcerations.

Plate 17—Selected Manifestations of *Pseudomonas aeruginosa* and Human Helminth Parasites

Figure 103. The appearance of a patient with a generalized cutaneous *Pseudomonas* infection. Toxemia and a septic clinical course of infection were noted here in the absence of positive blood cultures. (From Hall, J. H., Calloway, J. L., Tindall, J. P., and Smith, J. G., Jr.: *Arch. Derm.,* 93:312–324, 1968. Copyright 1968, Amer. Med. Assoc.)

Figure 104. The green nail syndrome as exhibited by a housewife. This manifestation is caused by the pigments elaborated by *Pseudomonas*. (From Hall, J. H., Calloway, J. L., Tindall, J. P., and Smith, J. G. Jr.: *Arch. Derm.,* 93:312–324, 1968. Copyright 1968, Amer. Med. Assoc.)

Figure 105. The Schwartzman phenomenon. A patient with pyoderma gangrenosum receiving an intradermal injection of 0.1 ml of a heat-killed *Pseudomonas* extract produced this reaction. (From Hall, J. H., Calloway, J. L., Tindall, J. P., and Smith, J. G., Jr.: *Arch. Derm.,* 93:312–324, 1968. Copyright 1968, Amer. Med. Assoc.)

Figure 106. Another *Pseudomonas* manifestation, the infected toeweb of a mill worker employed in a humid, warm type of environment. (From Hall, J. H., Calloway, J. L., Tindall, J. P., and Smith, J. G., Jr.: *Arch. Derm.,* 93:312–324, 1968. Copyright 1968, Amer. Med. Assoc.)

Figure 107. A photomicrograph of a blood smear showing the presence of the microfiliarian parasite *Wuchereria bancrofti*. This helminth is the causative agent of filiariasis. *Culex* spp. are commonly involved as the mosquito vectors for the disease agent.

Figure 108. A stained biopsy specimen section is shown in this photomicrograph showing the deposition of a *Schistosoma japonicum* ovum in intestinal tissue. Note the presence of the egg's spine (arrow) buried deep in the tissue.

Figure 109. The contents of a hydatid cyst, primarily showing a free scolex of *Echinococcus granulosis*. The scolices (frequently referred to as hydatid sand) of this helminth exhibit characteristic invaginated hooklets.

Plate 18—Pathogenic Protozoa and Selected Vectors

Figure 110. Cone-nosed bugs of the family Reduviidae. Species of the genus *Panstrongylus* are vectors of *Trypanosoma cruzi,* the etiologic agent of Chagas' disease. (Courtesy of the Bureau of Vector Control, Berkeley, California.)

Figure 111. Nonencysted extracellular *Toxoplasma gondii* in a bone marrow smear. *A*. The preparation was stained by the Giemsa method. Compare the appearance of these protozoa with that shown in Figure 87. *B*. Acridine orange stain and fluorescence microscopy were used here. Note the pronounced differences in nuclear and cytoplasmic regions. (From Abell, C., and Holland, P.: *Amer. J. Dis. Child.,* **118**:782–787, 1969.)

Figure 112. Photomicrograph of a blood smear containing the causative flagellate of African sleeping sickness, *Trypanosoma gambiense*. The common arthropod vector for this agent is *Glossina* spp. (tsetse flies).

Figure 113. A blood smear showing *Trypanosoma cruzi*. Note the pronounced curving of the organism.

Figure 114. Photomicrograph of the ciliate *Balantidium coli*. This protozoan has both trophozoite and cyst stages. *B. coli* can cause enteritis in humans.

Plate 19—Representative Stages in the Asexual Life Cycles of Four Species of the Genus *Plasmodium* and Other Protozoa

The descriptions given are adapted from the 1960 U. S. Department of Health, Education and Welfare publication of the *Manual for the Microscopical Diagnosis of Malaria in Man.*

Figure 115. *Plasmodium falciparum. A*. A single erythrocyte showing a double infection with young trophozoites. The parasite close to the center of the red cell is called a "signet ring" form, while the other organism located at the periphery is referred to as a "marginal form." *B*. One red blood cell with 3 somewhat more developed trophozoites. *C*. The parasites shown are called aestivo-autumnal "tenue forms." *D*. The parasite is undergoing initial chromatin (red area) division. *E*. A mature schizont with merozoites. Note the number of the latter forms. *F, G,* and *H*. These stages are representative of the successive events which take place in gametocyte (sex cell) development. Such forms generally are not found in the peripheral circulation. *I*. A mature macrogametocyte (female sex cell). *J*. A mature microgametocyte (male sex cell).

Figure 116. *Plasmodium malariae. A*. An erythrocyte with an early ring form (trophozoite) of the parasite. *B*. A developing trophozoite. *C*. One of several forms which trophozoites may exhibit during their development. *D*. A mature trophozoite. The parasite is exhibiting a band form. *E* and *F*. Representative stage found during schizont development. *G*. A mature schizont. Note the number of merozoites present. *H*. An immature microgametocyte. *I* and *J*. The appearance of mature micro- and macrogametocytes.

Figure 117. *Plasmodium vivax. A*. A typical "signet ring" stage. *B*. An enlarged erythrocyte with a ring form of trophozoite. The cell also contains Schüffner's stippling. It should be noted that such stippling may not always be present in infected red blood cells. *C*. Another trophozoite form. *D*. The presence of two ameboid-shaped trophozoites. *E* and *F*. Erythrocytes showing progressive stages in schizont division. *G*. A mature schizont. Note the number of merozoites. *H*. A developing gametocyte. *I* and *J*. Mature micro- and macrogametocytes.

Figure 118. A trophozoite of the etiologic agent of amoebic dysentery, *Entamoebic histolytica*. Note the distinct nucleus.

Figure 119. A cyst of *Pneumocystis carinii,* showing eight elongated sporozoites. The other structures shown are red blood cells. The specimen used was a pulmonary aspirate. It was stained with polychrome methylene blue. (From Kim, H. K., and Hughes, W. T.: *Amer. J. Clin. Path.,* **60**:462–466, 1973.)

Figure 120. *Trichomonas (vaginalis) hominis* stained with acridine orange. The specimen used was a vaginal smear. Note the presence of the dot-like bacteria. (Courtesy of Dr. H. J. Clitheroe.)

Plate 20—Color Photographic Quiz

Examine each of the photographs shown and answer the question listed for each one. The respective answers are given at the bottom of the page.

1. Figure 121. Give the Gram reaction and morphology of the organism shown.

2. Figure 122. A blood smear revealed the presence of the following microorganisms. Identify.

3. Figure 123. This photomicrograph shows bacterial colonies growing on Eosin Methylene Blue (EMB) agar. Are these microorganisms lactose fermenters?

4. Figure 124. Identify.

5. Figure 125A and B. Two blood samples needed to be typed in a laboratory. The left-hand side of each slide contains anti-B blood-typing serum, and the right-hand portion contains anti-A blood-typing serum. Give the major blood type for slide A and for slide B.

6. Figure 126A and B. Two bacterial structures are shown in these two micrographs. For Figure 126A give the major function and distinguishing chemical composition associated with the structure. For Figure 126B list at least three bacterial pathogens known to produce the structure shown.

Color Photographic Quiz Answers

1. Gram-negative rod.
2. *Plasmodium falciparum.*
3. No. Lactose fermenters produce dark, usually purple colonies on this medium.
4. The mycelia of *Penicillium notatum.*
5. The blood type shown in Figure 125A is O; for Figure 125B it is AB.
6. The structure shown in Figure 126A is the bacterial spore. This particular structure functions to protect the microorganism against extreme temperatures, chemicals, and the effects of drying. The structure shown in Figure 126B is the bacterial capsule. Three bacterial pathogenic species known to produce capsules are *Hemophilus influenzae, Neisseria meningitidis,* and *Streptococcus pneumoniae.*

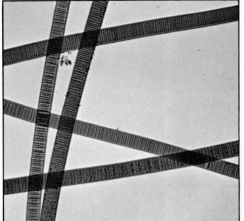

Figure 1. *Oscillatoria* sp.

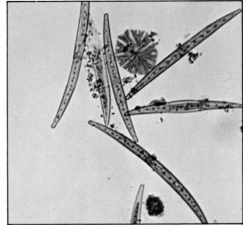

Figure 2. Desmids.

Figure 3. Algal bloom.

Figure 4. Bacterial colonies.

Figure 5. Microbial spoilage.

Figure 6. Common mushroom.

Figure 7. Crustose lichen.

Figure 8. Fruticose lichen.

Figure 9. Viroid effects.

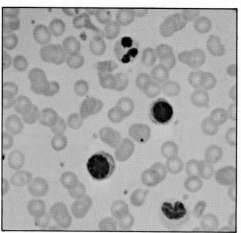

Figure 10. Stained smear of human blood.

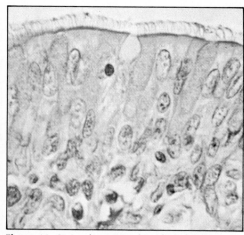

Figure 11. Stained section of epithelial cells.

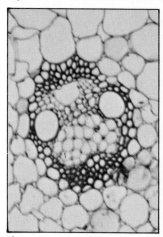

Figure 12. *Zea mays.*

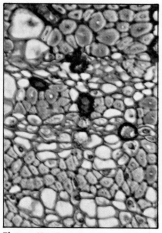

Figure 13. Cross section of a woody stem.

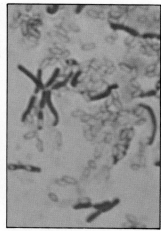

Figure 14. Simple staining.

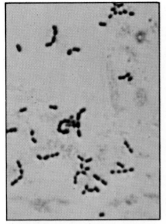

Figure 15. Typical Gram-positive reaction.

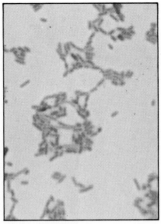

Figure 16. Typical Gram-negative reaction.

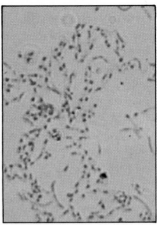

Figure 17. Typical acid-fast reaction.

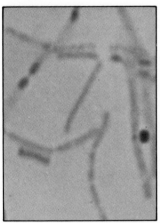

Figure 18. Typical non-acid-fast reaction.

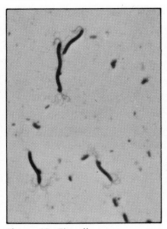

Figure 19. Flagella.

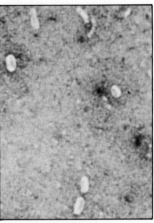

Figure 20. Capsules.

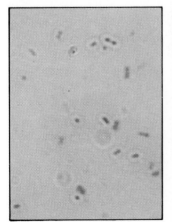

Figure 21. Diplococci with capsules.

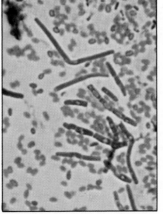

Figure 22. Spores and vegetative cells.

Figure 23. Spores and vegetative cells.

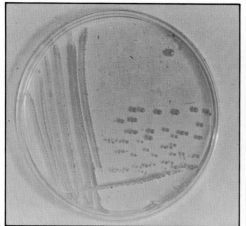

Figure 24. Streak plate.

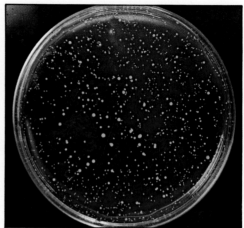

Figure 25. Pour plate.

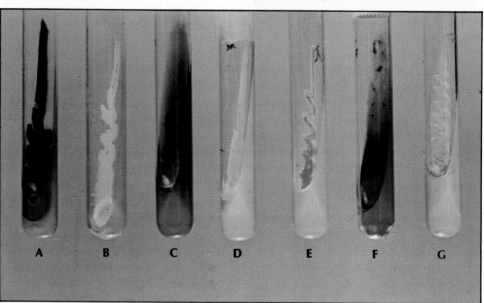

Figure 26. Agar slants.

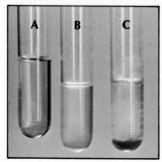

Figure 27. Broth cultures.

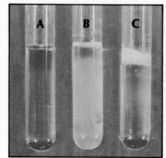

Figure 28. Fluid Thioglycollate Broth.

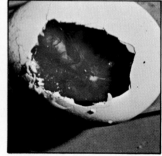

Figure 29. Pock formation on chorioallantoic membrane.

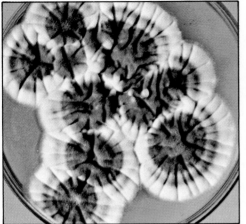

Figure 30. *Penicillium notatum.*

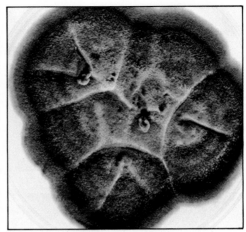

Figure 31. *Alternaria* sp.

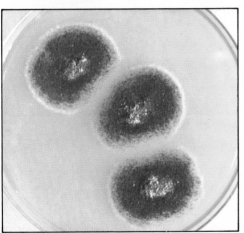

Figure 32. *Aspergillus niger.*

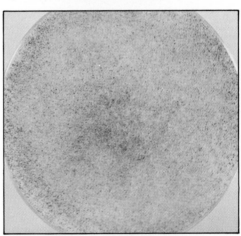

Figure 33. *Rhizopus nigricans.*

Figure 34. *Fusarium* spp.

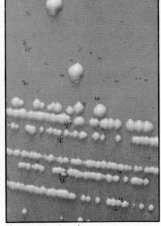

Figure 35. *Saccharomyces cerevisiae.*

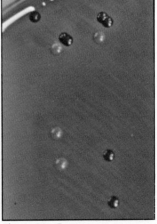

Figure 36. *Cryptococcus neoformans* and *Candida albicans.*

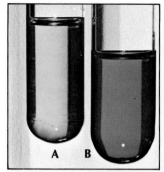
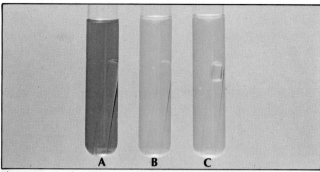

Figure 37. Urease activity.

Figure 38. Durham fermentation tubes.

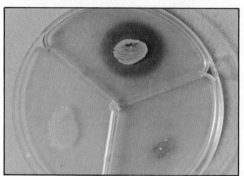
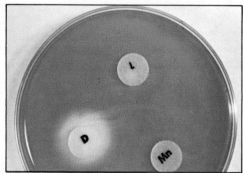

Figure 39. Lipid hydrolysis.

Figure 40. Fermentation discs

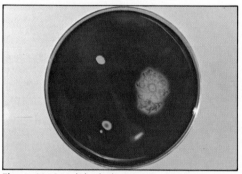

Figure 41. Starch hydrolysis.

Figure 42. Motility agar.

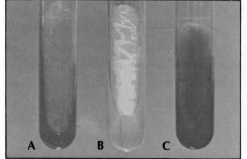
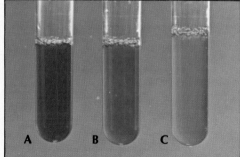

Figure 43. Bacto-Citrate Malonate Agar.

Figure 44. The Snyder colorimetric test for caries activity diagnosis.

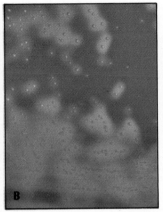

Figure 45. Hemolytic reactions on blood agar media.

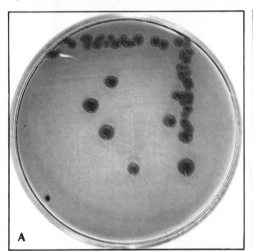
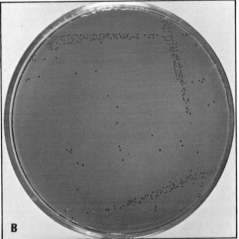

Figure 46. *Streptococcus* spp. on Bacto-Mitis-Salivarius medium.

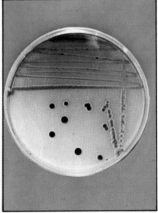
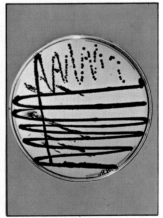

Figure 47. *Pseudomonas* sp. on Bacto-Pseudomonas agar F medium.

Figure 48. *Pseudomonas* sp. on Bacto-Pseudomonas agar P medium.

Figure 49. *Corynebacterium xerosis* on Mueller-Hinton-Tellurite medium.

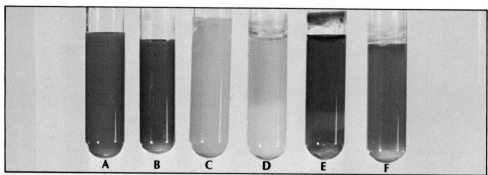

Figure 50. Selected litmus milk reactions.

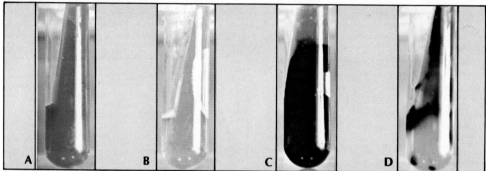

Figure 51. Selected Triple Sugar Iron Agar reactions.

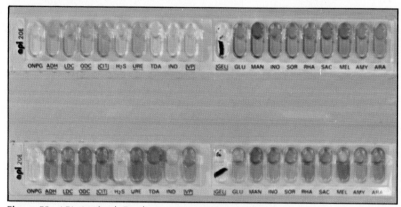

Figure 52. API, Analytab Products, Inc., reactions.

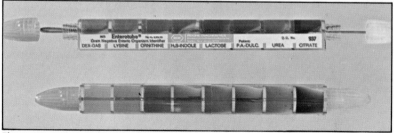

Figure 53. Entero-Tube, Roche Diagnostics.

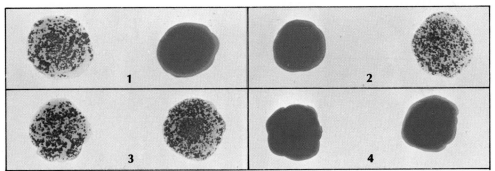

Figure 54. Typical slide blood-agglutination reactions.

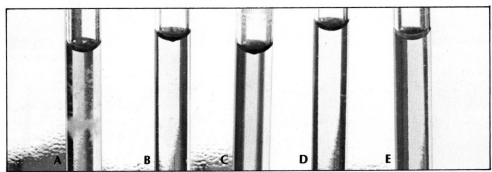

Figure 55. The tube precipitin reaction.

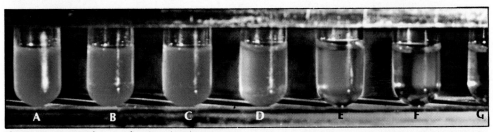

Figure 56. A complement-fixation titration.

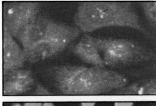
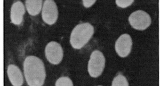

Figure 57. An indirect immunofluorescent test.

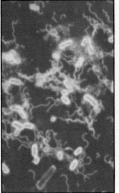

Figure 58. A direct fluorescent antibody procedure.

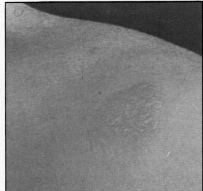

Figure 59. Positive human skin test.

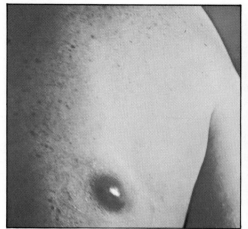

Figure 60. Carbuncle.

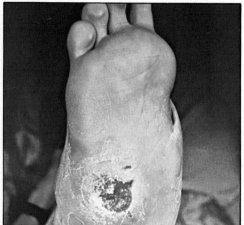

Figure 61. Staphylococcal osteomyelitis.

Figure 62. *Staphylococcus aureus* on Bacto-Mannitol Salt Agar.

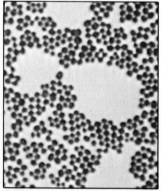

Figure 63. Gram-stain reaction of *S. aureus*.

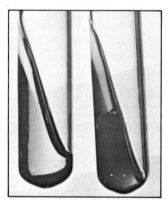

Figure 64. The Coagulase test.

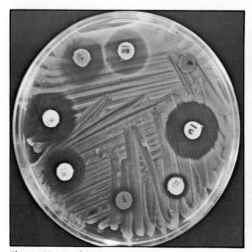

Figure 65. Antibiotic sensitivity testing.

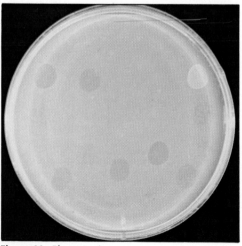

Figure 66. Phage typing.

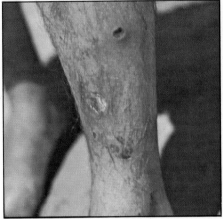

Figure 67. Streptococcal skin ulcers.

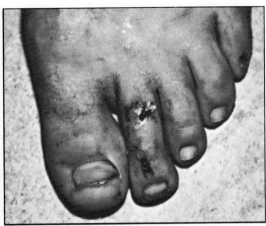

Figure 68. Wound-feeding flies.

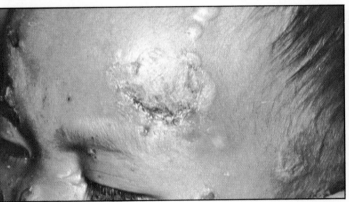

Figure 69. Impetigo.

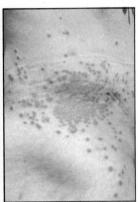

Figure 70. Fungus infection on the waist.

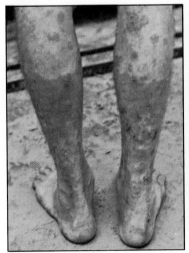

Figure 71. Disabling *T. mentagrophytes* infection.

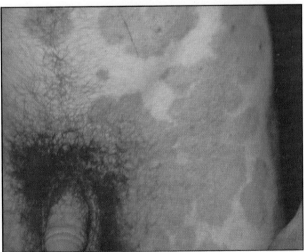

Figure 72. Ringworm of the lower abdomen, groin, and hip areas.

Figure 73. Mycelium of *Microsporum canis.*

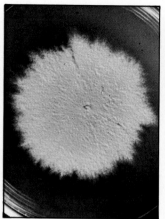

Figure 74. Mycelium of *Microsporum gypseum.*

Figure 75. Tinea capitis.

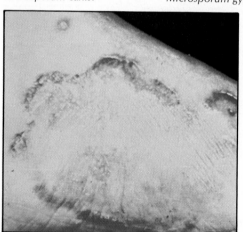

Figure 76. Tinea pedis.

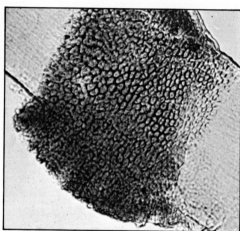

Figure 77. *Piedraia hortai.*

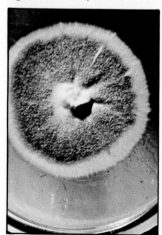

Figure 78. Mycelium of *Trichophyton rubrum.*

Figure 79. *Trichophyton rubrum* macroconidia.

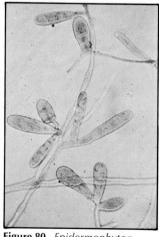

Figure 80. *Epidermophyton floccosum* macroconidia.

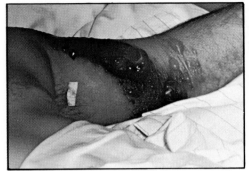

Figure 81. Cutaneous anthrax.

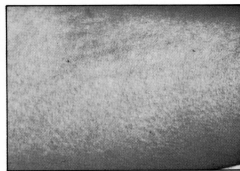

Figure 82. Scarlet fever rash.

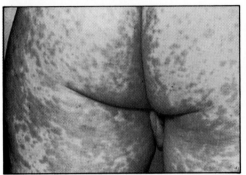

Figure 83. Measles rash on Caucasian skin.

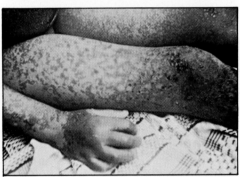

Figure 84. Measles rash on black skin.

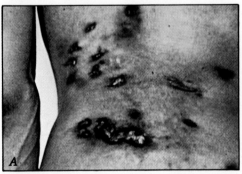

Figure 85. Lesions of coccidioidomycosis.

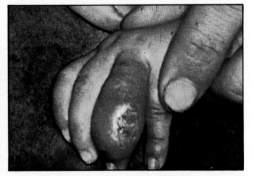

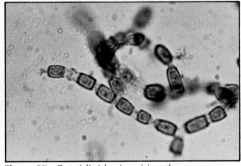

Figure 86. *Coccidioides immitis* colony.

Figure 87. *Coccidioides immitis* arthrospores.

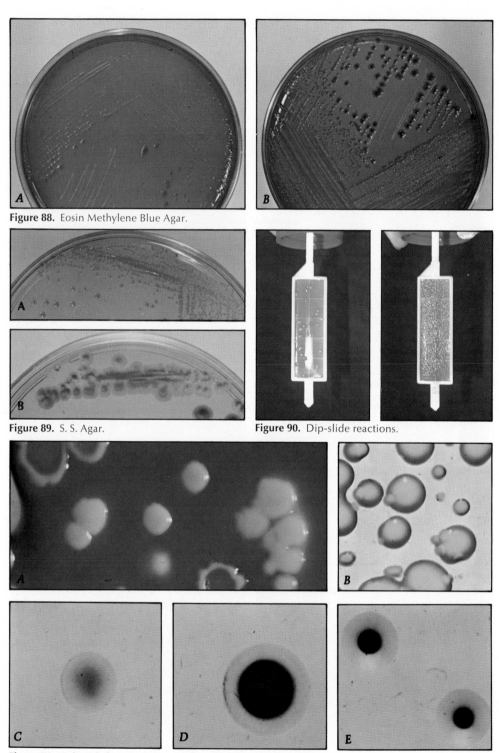

Figure 88. Eosin Methylene Blue Agar.

Figure 89. S. S. Agar.

Figure 90. Dip-slide reactions.

Figure 91. Colonial characteristics on Pfizer Hektoen Enteric (HE) Agar.

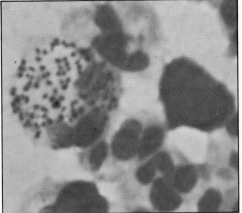

Figure 92. Gram-stained smear of gonorrhea.

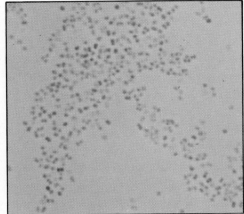

Figure 93. Gram stain of a pure culture of *N. gonorrhoeae*.

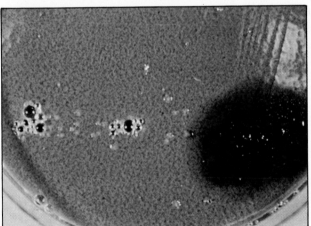

Figure 94. Oxidase test.

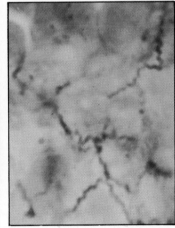

Figure 95. *Treponema pallidum*.

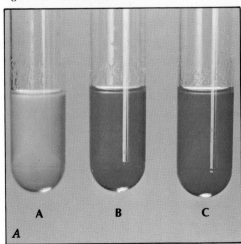

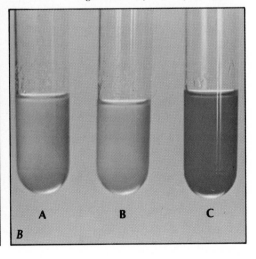

Figure 96. Pathogenic *Neisseria* spp.

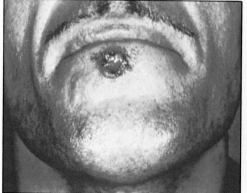

Figure 97. Huntarian chancre on the lip.

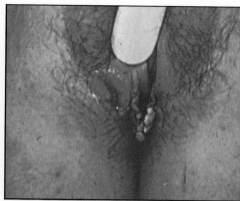

Figure 98. Primary syphilis on the vulva.

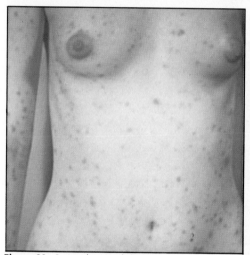

Figure 99. Secondary syphilis.

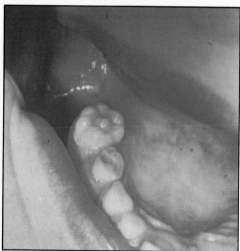

Figure 100. Moon's molar.

Figure 101. The gumma.

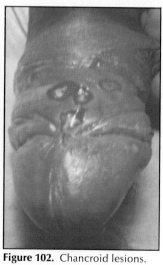

Figure 102. Chancroid lesions.

Figure 103. Cutaneous *Pseudomonas* infection.

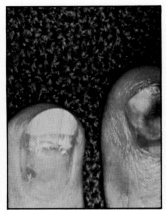

Figure 104. Green nail syndrome.

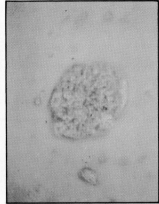

Figure 105. Shwartzman phenomenon.

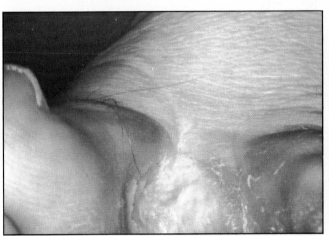

Figure 106. Infected toeweb.

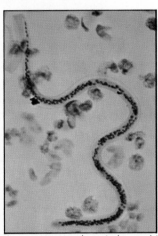

Figure 107. *Wuchereria bancrofti.*

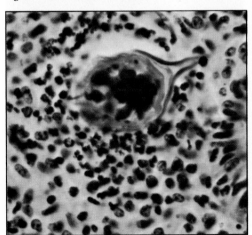

Figure 108. *Schistosoma japonicum* ovum in intestinal tissue.

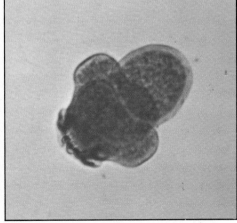

Figure 109. Scolex of *Echinococcus granulosis* in a hydatid cyst.

Figure 110. Cone-nosed bugs of the family Reduviidae.

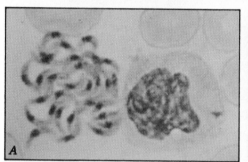
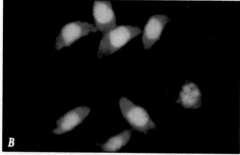

Figure 111. Non-encysted extracellular *Toxoplasma gondii* in a bone marrow smear.

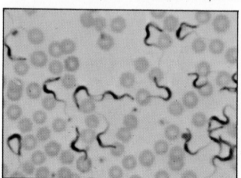
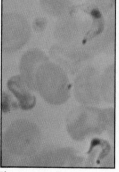
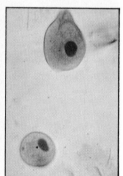

Figure 112. Blood smear of *Trypanosom gambiense.*

Figure 113. *Trypanosoma cruzi.*

Figure 114. *Balantidium coli.*

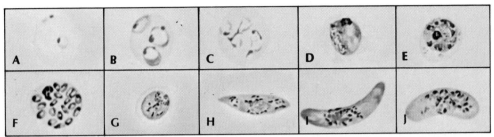

Figure 115. *Plasmodium falciparum.*

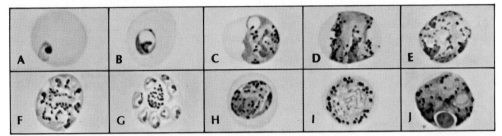

Figure 116. *Plasmodium malariae.*

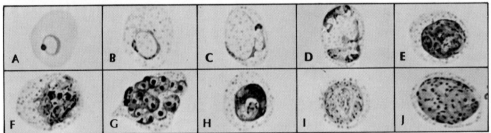

Figure 117. *Plasmodium vivax.*

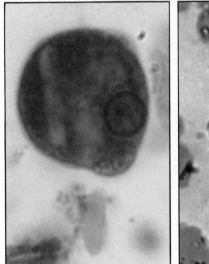

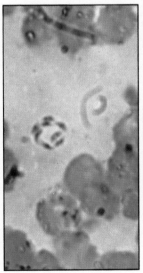

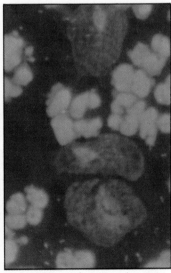

Figure 118. *Entamoeba histolytica.*   **Figure 119.** *Pneumocystis carinii.*   **Figure 120.** *Trichomonas hominis.*

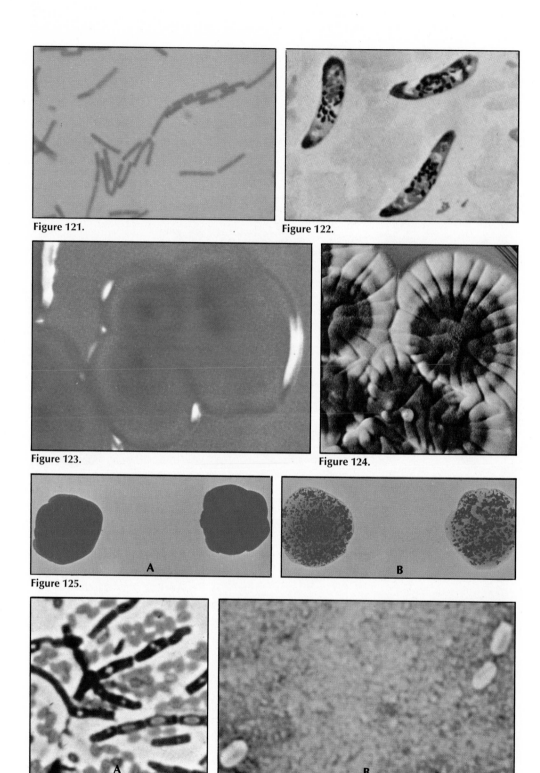

Figure 121.

Figure 122.

Figure 123.

Figure 124.

Figure 125.

Figure 126.

plication, resulting in a large family of *monoclonal* (daughter) cells, that produces a single type of homogenous immunoglobulin. The clinical state is referred to as *monoclonal gammopathy.* These proteins are found in patients suffering from *multiple myeloma* and other malignancies that involve lymphoid tissue. The particular cellular products are referred to as *M-components, myeloma,* or *monoclonal immunoglobulins.* These abnormal immunoglobulins are in the 7 S category. In addition to the usual types of immunoglobulins, the serum of a multiple myeloma victim contains a large excess of one normal immunoglobulin, as a consequence of the neoplastic transformation of one type of lymphoid cell. The urine of such an individual contains massive concentrations of a light-chain subunit of the myeloma cellular product called *Bence-Jones protein,* named after the physician who first studied it.

The different myeloma proteins can be grouped into classes on the basis of the antigenic specificity of the H and L chains comprising them. It appears at this time that the most common type of myeloma is of the IgG category. Bence-Jones and IgA myelomas are less frequent in occurrence.

The general signs of a myelomatous condition include skeletal lesions, plasma cell infiltration of bone marrow, and the production of myeloma protein. Apparently there is no consistent correlation between clinical features and a particular class of myeloma. Diagnosis of these neoplastic states includes bone marrow examination and immunoelectrophoretic analysis of serum and urine (Figure 22–6).

Studies involving the characterization of the different abnormal immunoglobulins have shed considerable light on the structure of normal immunoglobulins. Myeloma protein, and the 19 S macroglobulin associated with another malig-

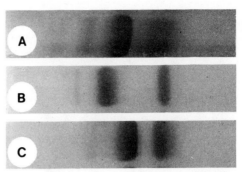

FIG. 22–6. Urea starch gel electrophoretic patterns of pure normal IgG and reductively cleaved myeloma proteins. _A_. Normal IgG. _B_. IgA myeloma globulin. _C_. IgG myeloma globulin. (Courtesy of Dr. M. D. Poulik, Wayne State University School of Medicine, and The Child Research Center of Michigan.)

nancy of lymphoid tissue known as *Waldenström's macroglobulinemia,* have been most helpful in this regard.

Polyclonal Gammopathies

The term *polyclonal gammopathies* refers to many different immunoglobulins being produced by many different clones of plasma cells. This situation results from the proliferation of plasma cells that are making several different classes of immunoglobulins in response to antigenic stimulation. Such general immunoglobulin increase is commonly found with chronic infections (leprosy, malaria, and tuberculosis), collagen diseases, liver disease, sarcoidosis, and various malignancies (Figure 22–7). Diagnosis of these immunoglobulin abnormalities is similar to that for the monoclonal gammopathies.

The Thymus Gland and its Role in the Immune Mechanism

The thymus is located in the chest region, between the lungs and behind the sternum or breastbone. This gland normally consists of two lobes, each of which is divided into smaller regions called *lobules.* A lobule is made up of a *medulla* (center) that is composed of epithelial cells, lym-

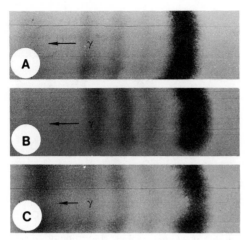

FIG. 22–7. Filter paper electrophoretic patterns of: *A.* Normal serum. *B.* Agammaglobulinemic serum. *C.* The appearance of serum from a hypergammaglobulinemic individual. Note the intensity of the IgG (γ) portion shown here. How does it compare with the normal and agammaglobulinemic states? (Courtesy of Dr. M. D. Poulik, Wayne State University School of Medicine, and The Child Research Center of Michigan.)

phocytes, and Hassall's corpuscles, and a cortex (surrounding area consisting primarily of lymphocytes).

At birth the thymus is the most fully developed of the peripheral lymphoid tissues, with the exception of the bone marrow (the marrow is considered the central lymphoid tissue in mammals). At the time of birth the human thymus generally ranges in weight from 15 to 20 grams. The structure increases in size until at puberty its weight approaches 40 grams. Subsequently the gland atrophies and decreases in size, until at middle-age the thymus is a relatively insignificant tissue both physiologically and structurally.

The thymus gland is believed to be the central reservoir for the multiplication of *lymphocytes* (thymocytes) during embryonic development. It is from this region that certain lymphocytes acquire a surface antigen, the theta (θ) antigen, and spread peripherally to seed (populate) the lymph nodes, the spleen, and related structures.

The importance of the thymus is indicated by the obvious defects that occur on its removal from a newborn or very young individual. When the thymus is removed from an experimental animal, such as a newborn mouse, the following effects can be noted: (1) no maturation of peripheral lymph nodes occurs; (2) the number of lymphocytes in the peripheral blood decreases; (3) the antibody response is extremely poor, i.e., no antibodies are produced toward several antigenic substances; and (4) such thymectomized animals accept foreign tissue grafts. These various defects can be corrected by grafting thymus tissue from a donor of the same inbred animal species to the thymectomized recipient.

The Immune Response in the Developing Individual

From conception to the time of birth, the human fetus develops in a highly protective environment. For a long period of time it was thought that the immune system of the newborn was immature rather than naïve and that the system matured and developed fully only sometime after birth, during the postnatal period. Currently available evidence suggests that this is not the case. It appears that the maturation of the human immune system begins *in utero* sometime during the second to third month of the pregnancy period. The differentiation of cells destined to carry out both specific and nonspecific immunologic activities appears to have a common ancestral origin (Figure 22–8). These cells appear to arise from a population of stem cells or hemocytoblasts that are located with the bood-forming (hematopoietic) tissues of the developing embryo (bone marrow, fetal liver, etc.). Depending upon the type of environment into which differentiated cells enter, their development will proceed along one of

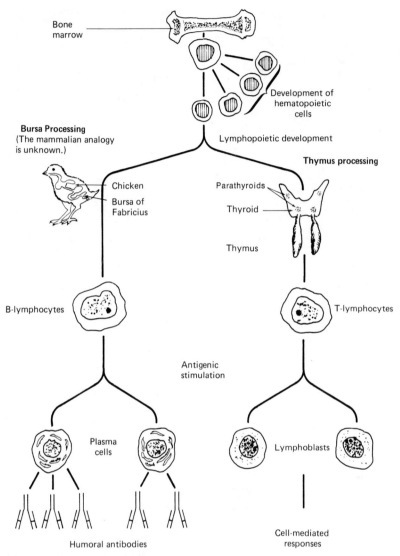

FIG. 22–8. A schematic representation of the development (ontogeny) of the principal cells involved in the immune response. Parent (progenitor) cells are differentiated into hematopoietic (blood-forming) and immunocompetent T- and B-lymphocytes. Note that the proliferation and transformation of these cells to those of the lymphoblast and plasma-cell series occurs upon antigenic stimulation.

two avenues: the hematopoietic and the lymphopoietic. The former will result in production of the elements of peripheral blood, such as erythrocytes, granulocytes, monocytes, and platelets. The lymphopoietic pathway can result in still further differentiation. One type of differentiation occurs under the influence of the thymus and includes a population of small lymphocytes, which participate in the tuberculin reaction, in the rejection or acceptance of certain tissue grafts, and in an individual's defense against various microorganisms. Such situations are collectively

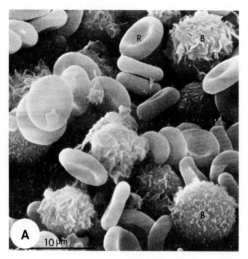 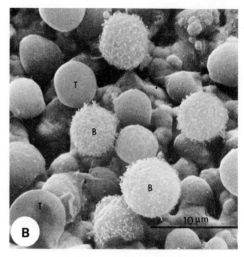

FIG. 22–9. B- and T-lymphocytes. _A_. A scanning electron micrograph showing the characteristics of B-type lymphocytes and red blood cells (R). _B_. A scanning electron micrograph showing both B- and T-type cells. (From Polliack, A., Lampen, N., Clarkson, B. D., De Harven, E., Bentwick, Z., Siegal, F. P., and Kunkel, H. G.: _J. Exp. Med._, **138**:607–622, 1973. Courtesy of Dr. Aaron Polliack, Department of Hematology, Hadassah University Hospital and Hebrew University Hadassah Medical School, Jerusalem, Israel; work performed at Memorial Sloan-Kettering Institute for Cancer Research, New York, in Dr. de Harven's laboratory.) Currently the validity of B and T surface characteristics detected by electron microscopy have been questioned.

grouped under cell-mediated immunity (see Chapter 25). The resulting cells that form this type of differentiation are referred to as thymus-derived, thymus-dependent, or T-lymphocytes. Current studies also have shown them to participate in antibody production. A second type of differentiation produces a population of lymphocytes that acquire specific surface antigens known as B-antigens. Correspondingly, the cells are called B-cells and plasma cells. These cells are the major ones associated with antibody synthesis, or humoral immunity. The B- and plasma cells come under the influence of and are increased in number within a second anatomic site in the body; they are referred to as being thymus-independent. The identity of this location is known with certainty in birds, in which the Bursa of Fabricius serves in the aforementioned capacities.

The B- and T-cells (Figure 22–9) occupy different areas within the same lymphoid tissues. Both cell types are intimately associated with another form of white blood cell, the macrophage (see Chapter 20). These cells comprise the important responsive elements of an individual's immune system. From a morphological standpoint, there is little to separate B- and T-cells examined by conventional light microscopy. However, startling differences have been revealed by scanning electron microscopy. T-cells exhibit a bland, flat surface, whereas B-lymphocytes demonstrate a rather agitated appearance with numerous surface projections (Figure 22–9). Selected properties of these two cell types will be described.

B-cells. The B-lymphocyte is not so named because it originates in the bone tissue but because it was first described as originating from the Bursa of Fabricius of chickens (Figure 22–8). B-cells tend

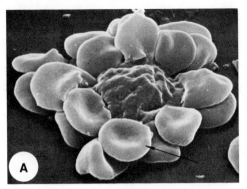

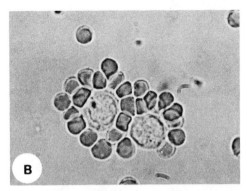

FIG. 22–10. Rosette formation. _A_. A scanning electron micrograph showing a large rosette-forming cell (center) with spot-like contacts between cytoplasmic folds and erythrocytes (arrow). (From Gudat, F. G., and Villiger, W.: _J. Exper. Med._, **137**:483–493, 1973.) _B_. Spontaneous binding of sheep red blood cells demonstrating E rosette formation, as shown by light microscopy. (From Aiuti, F., Ciarla, M. V., D'Asero, C., D'Amelio, R., and Garofalo, J. A.: _Infect. Immunity_, **10**:110, 1974.)

to carry immunoglobulins on their surfaces. Although this occurs even in animals not stimulated with antigen, the response is heightened by antigenic stimulation. Antibody is produced and excreted, with a proportion of the antibody molecules remaining attached to the cell surface. This property can be demonstrated _in vitro_. When a B-cell bearing antibody contacts erythrocyte antigens, an immune adherence occurs. Upon repetition of this exposure the B-cell becomes surrounded by red blood cells, forming a rosette. The B-cell is located in the center of the rosette (Figure 22–10).

T-cells. As indicated previously, T-type lymphocytes (Figure 22–9) acquire a surface antigen, θ (theta), which serves to distinguish them from the B-type lymphocytes. T-cells may also be distinguished from other lymphocytes on the basis of such properties as the absence of the high level of immunoglobulins found on the B-type cell and the _in vitro_ formation of rosettes that occurs with sheep red blood cells (Figure 22–10). The T- or E-rosette develops when T-lymphocytes from non-immune animals are incubated with sheep red blood cells.

T-cells have several properties and participate in several activities: (1) they react with one or several antigens; (2) they acquire the capacity to regulate B-lymphocyte responses to antigens; and (3) they become specific effector cells that produce cell-mediated reactions such as the tuberculin response, the rejection of foreign tissue grafts or malignant cells, and the differentiation of resting macrophages (phagocytic cells) into a form capable of destroying microbial pathogens.

The roles of B- and T-cells and of macrophages in antibody production are shown in Figure 22–11.

Mechanism of Antibody Formation

During the 1890s the attention of many investigators was directed toward uncovering the mechanism or mechanisms responsible for antibody formation. As yet, no hypothesis for antibody synthesis is universally accepted. Because of space limitations the development of current hypotheses cannot be presented. However, since most of these concepts can be grouped into two general categories, brief consideration will be given to the cur-

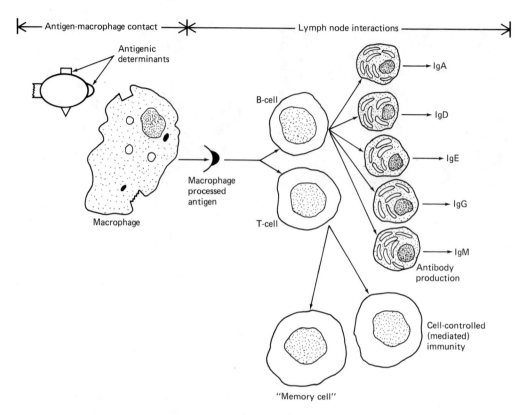

FIG. 22–11. The steps in the present concept of antibody production. When an antigen enters the body, it comes into contact with a macrophage, is processed, and is then transported through lymphatic channels to a neighboring lymph node. There, the macrophage (with processed antigen) interacts with T- and B-cells.

The T-cells differentiate into memory cells and cells that control subsequent antigen recognition, whereas the B-cells differentiate and proliferate into a clone of cells rich in ribosomes (the plasma cells). Plasma cells produce the release antibody with receptor sites specific for the antigen that caused their production.

rently recognized principal mechanisms believed to be involved in antibody formation, the *template and selective hypotheses.*

Template hypotheses.   There are two types of template hypotheses, the *direct* and the *indirect.* The direct template concept, which was first proposed by Breinl and Haurowitz in 1930 and by Mudd in 1932, suggests that the antigen acts directly as a pattern for the molding or forming of an antibody's active or determinative site. This modified portion of the antibody then would have a struc-

tural image that is the reverse of the site on the antigen which caused its formation.

The first of the indirect template mechanisms was proposed in 1949 by Burnet and Fenner. According to this hypothesis, it is assumed that protein synthesis (which includes antibody production) is under genetic control and that the specific pattern is thereby set by the antibody-forming cell. The antigen functions indirectly by causing the genetic mechanism to alter its antibody pattern or template. This modification will be carried by the cells descending from the first one altered by the antigen. While the template hypotheses can account for antibody specificity, they don't satisfactorily explain certain other known immunologic phenomena, including the primary and secondary responses to antigens and the nonantigenic nature of "self" components.

Selective hypotheses. Selective hypotheses postulate that certain cells, present in the body prior to the exposure to antigens, are endowed with the necessary information to synthesize a particular antibody. Such cells are capable of producing one or a few antibodies. The numbers of cells necessary to meet the immunologic needs of the individual would be in the thousands, since one cell or its descendents could produce only one or a few types of antibody molecules. The term *clone* is used for the cell line generated by a genetically stable cell. An important aspect of the selection hypotheses is that during embryonic development, normal (self) components of the body react with and destroy those cells which could produce antibodies against them. Thus only those cells which survive this period and are available after maturation of the immunologic mechanism of the individual occurs constitute the antibody-producing force of the adult. Antigens here function by combining with such cells and stimulating their antibody-producing capability. The selective hypotheses appear to be more applicable to explanations of various observed immunologic phenomena.

Immunosuppression and Immunosuppressive Agents

The suppression of the immune response can be of considerable importance in various situations, such as in the survival of foreign tissue grafts (kidney and heart transplants) and in the control of auto-

immune phenomena (Chapter 25). Although application of immunosuppressive agents such as x-rays or various drugs can serve a useful function, prolonged exposure to these agents can increase an individual's susceptibility to a variety of microbial pathogens. Moreover, serious infections with opportunistic microorganisms are not uncommon among patients receiving intensive treatment with x-rays or chemical immunosuppressants.

The production of immunoglobulins can be suppressed in any of several ways, such as by the incorporation of chemical drugs, by the application of physical agents such as x-rays, or by the control of the antibody response by biological means. Examples of the biological control of the antibody response include the inhibition of the immune response to one antigen by the introduction of a second antigen (antigen competition); immunoglobulin deficiency diseases in which there are pronounced losses in immunoglobulin levels due to deficits in B-cells or in T-cells, or a decrease in B- and T-cell functions; and a state of specific non-reactivity to a normally effective antigenic challenge created by a prior exposure to the antigen concerned. The latter condition is referred to as immunologic unresponsiveness, or *immunologic paralysis*.

States of Immunity

Previous chapters in this division have called attention to various properties of the host and of pathogens that are concerned with the defense against, as well as the causation of disease. The resistance displayed by individuals varies considerably, since it is greatly affected by many factors which may be innate or native to the person, or acquired by either natural or artificial means, as shown in Figure 22–12. Brief attention is also given at the

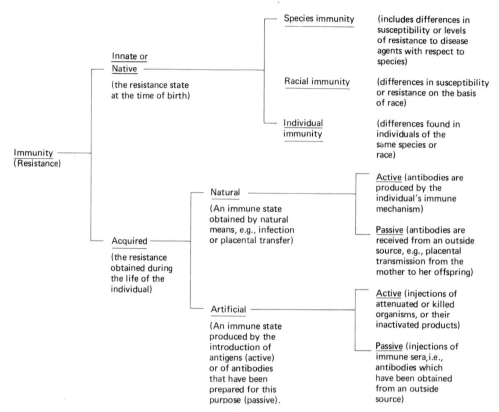

FIG. 22–12. A brief characterization of different states of immunity.

end of this chapter to a congenital abnormality, called *agammaglobulinemia,* that affects the state of an individual's immunity.

Generally speaking, two major categories are recognized, *innate* or *native* and *acquired immunities.* Innate immunity was described in Chapter 20, and includes species, race, and individual resistance to infection.

Acquired immunity is further subdivided into *natural* and *artificial,* depending on the processes involved in producing the immunity. For example, immunization by the injection of a bacterial vaccine would be considered an artificially produced contact with the organism, in contrast to a natural infection.

Both of these categories are further subdivided into active and passive types.

In the *active state,* an individual makes his own antibody in response to an antigenic stimulus, while in the *passive state* the antibody is acquired through transfer from an immunized individual. The acquired states of immunity are described in more detail below.

Acquired Immunity

Naturally Acquired Active Immunity

An individual who recovers successfully from an infection acquires in most instances a specific resistance to the causative agent. This immunity is produced by the antibody-synthesizing mechanism of the person, which was stimulated into action by the infecting organism. Depending on the antigenic nature and dosage of such pathogens, and related factors, a relatively long-lasting immunity may be produced. It generally ranges from a few months to several years. Although immunity is never absolute, individuals having a naturally acquired active immunity are protected against ordinary attacks by infectious agents to which they have been previously exposed. Such resistance, however, is generally not substantial enough to overcome massive infections. Diseases to which an individual can develop sufficient protection as a consequence of infection include chickenpox, classic and German measles, mumps, smallpox, and typhoid fever. It should be noted that immunity to reinfection by certain pathogens is either minimal or nonexistent. This group of diseases includes gonorrhea, pneumonia, and syphilis.

Sub-clinical or inapparent infection. Many persons experience mild attacks by pathogens which result in disease states that are seldom diagnosed. Symptoms of such infections are either lacking or extremely mild. Nevertheless, the individual acquires a strong immunity through such repeated attacks. Diseases associated with this type of phenomenon include diphtheria, poliomyelitis, and scarlet fever.

Naturally Acquired Passive Immunity

This form of immunity is derived through the natural transfer of antibodies from an immunized donor to a nonimmune recipient. The duration of such immunity ranges from a few weeks to a few months.

In man, as in apes and rodents, many newborns during their first months after birth demonstrate resistance toward several infectious diseases. This immunity is attributed to certain immunoglobulins acquired from the mother during uterine life by passage through the placenta. Thus, in the case of the human species, an expectant mother having antibodies against diseases such as diphtheria, German measles, poliomyelitis, and possibly salmonellosis, imparts a share of these protective substances to her unborn child. These immunoglobulins are of the IgG class. To be sure of conferring protection on the newborn, all women should be immunized with available vaccines before pregnancy.

In humans, immunoglobulins pass easily from the maternal circulation through the placenta into the fetal circulation because of the single layer of cells separating these two systems. In lower animals, however, the placenta has several cell layers separating the two circulatory systems. Thus antibodies are prevented from passing into the fetal blood. Immunogobulins in these cases are secreted in the first milk produced after birth, called *colostrum*. When the young ingest this secretion, they obtain temporary resistance. The immunoglobulins are absorbed, undigested, through the wall of the small intestine. In general, milk-borne antibody appears to be of little importance in man. However, it should be noted that breast milk does contain antimicrobial factors of various kinds.

Artificially Acquired Active Immunity

This form of immunity is induced by imitating nature's means of producing a mild infection. A carefully chosen antigenic stimulus is provided, without the severe effects of the actual disease. Preparations used to induce artificial active immunity include: (1) killed or inactivated microorganisms; (2) inactivated bacterial toxins, known as *toxoids;* (3) living but attenuated (weakened) microbes; and (4) living virulent organisms administered in association with homologous antiserum, employed in certain situations. The specific types of vaccines and related preparations, immunization schedules, and descriptions of the procedures used in their preparation are presented in Chapter 26. Any vaccine to be used against an infectious disease should possess the following five general properties listed by G. S. Wilson at the 1961 International Conference on Measles:

1. The vaccination should not be harmful to the individual receiving it.

2. The effects of the vaccine should not be greater than that associated with the disease itself.

3. The vaccine must be easy to administer.

4. The benefit from vaccination should serve the community, as well as the individual.

5. The immunity conferred by the vaccine should be sufficient to eliminate the need for frequent revaccination.

In general, artificially active immune states required approximately one to two weeks to develop and are relatively long-lasting.

Artificially Acquired Passive Immunity

When exposure has occurred to any one of various disease agents or their products, such as those associated with botulism, diphtheria, gas gangrene, German measles (especially in pregnant women), infectious hepatitis, rabies, and tetanus, an ample supply of immunoglobulins must be provided to the individual if serious consequences are to be prevented. In short, such persons must be given artificial passive immunization. Standardized doses (determined by the patient's body weight) of purified serum preparations, originally obtained from immunized individuals, are administered as soon as possible after exposure. The passive state of immunity which results is immediate but only temporary, since no active production of antibody toward the disease agent or its product occurs. If the immune serum

used is obtained from the same animal species as the recipient, the half-life of the injected immunoglobulin is approximately the same as that of normal globulins. However, if the immunoglobulins received come from another animal species, then their introduction into the individual will provoke antibody production that results in their rapid elimination. Subsequent injections of the same preparation may cause severe allergic reactions, including anaphylactic shock and serum sickness, as discussed in Chapter 25.

Adoptive immunity. This immune state is primarily an experimental phenomenon. It has at this time no practical significance as a means of inducing antimicrobial protection. Adoptive immunity is a form of artificially acquired passive immune state produced by the transfer of cells capable of synthesizing immunoglobulins, or of directly reacting with a specific antigen, from an immunized donor to a nonimmune recipient. Such cells are referred to as being "immunologically competent."

Agammaglobulinemia, A Congential Immunological Abnormality

The absence of gamma globulin in the serum or tissues of an individual is the characteristic feature of this clinical state. The congenital form of agammaglobulinemia was first described by Bruton in 1952. (The condition is known as Bruton's sex-linked agammaglobulinemia.) One of the curious findings in patients was the existence of specific immunity against certain but not all viruses. The disease, as indicated earlier, may be congenital in nature. This inborn error in metabolism is transmitted as a sex-linked recessive trait, and therefore, is primarily found in males. Individuals having this disease formerly died as a consequence of infection. However, now the majority of cases are recognized during the first or second year of life. In cases of severe bacterial infections, the patients are saved with the aid of antibiotic therapy and injections of purified immunoglobulin preparations.

Electrophoretic examination of the sera from agammaglobulinemic persons shows that, in addition to the almost complete absence of IgG, IgA and IgM also are lacking (Figure 22–2). It appears that proteins different from those found in normal sera replace these globulins.

The basic defect in persons having this condition may be either an inability to synthesize the necessary globulins, or the activation of an abnormal mechanism which destroys these protein substances shortly after they are formed. Other features of agammaglobulinemia include a deficiency of B-type lymphocytes in lymph nodes, as well as in the general circulation; a low level of polymorphonuclear leukocytes (Color photograph 10);

and a pronounced lack of plasma cells in the bone marrow and lymphatic tissue. The latter is particularly obvious after the injection of an antigenic substance.

Most agammaglobulinemic individuals have some IgG, although it is present in low levels. Such persons may have 75 to 100 mg per 100 ml of blood, in contrast to the normal levels of 600 to 1200 mg in the same volume of blood. The term *hypogammaglobulinemia* is used to designate individuals having some but not normal amounts of immunoglobulins.

The mechanism involved in protecting both agammaglobulinemic and hypogammaglobulinemic patients appears to be cellular in nature. Supporting evidence for this view is provided by producing cell-mediated (delayed-hypersensitivity) reactions to certain substances in normal recipients of leukocytes obtained from agammaglobulinemic individuals. The injection of large doses of agammaglobulinemic sera fail to accomplish the same effect. This type of cellular transfer is referred to as adoptive immunity and has been discussed earlier.

QUESTIONS FOR REVIEW

1. Define or explain the following terms:
    a. immunoglobulins
    b. adjuvant
    c. vaccine
    d. autoantigens
    e. antigen
    f. isohemagglutination
    g. immunopoietic
    h. immunoelectrophoresis
    i. thymus gland
    j. immunoglobulin abnormalities
    k. B- and T-cells

2. Which components of a bacterial cell are antigenic?

3. Discuss haptenes.

4. Discuss autoimmunization. List at least four autoimmune diseases, together with the antigenic substances believed to be their cause.

5. What are heterophile antigens?

6. What are the classes of immunoglobulins? How are they differentiated from one another? Draw a representative figure of an immunoglobulin, and indicate the region involved

in biologic activities, such as skin sensitization.

7. Describe the responses involved in antibody production. How do they differ?

8. Briefly describe one hypothesis for antibody production.

9. What are the sources of normal immunoglobulins?

10. Differentiate between native and naturally acquired immune states.

11. What host factors contribute to an individual's immunity? What accounts for differences in the immunity of individuals?

12. a. Distinguish between active and passive states of immunity. Which of these is longer lasting?
    b. Discuss congenital natural immunity. What types of immunoglobulins are involved?

13. a. What types of preparations are used in producing artificially acquired active immune states?
    b. What types of preparations are used in producing artificially acquired passive immune states?

14. What are subclinical infections? What role do they play in immunity?

15. What is the thymus gland? How important is it to an individual's immune status?

23

In Vitro Antigen and Antibody Reactions

During the past two decades, immunologic research has blossomed forth and yielded an overwhelming body of knowledge concerning humoral antibodies. The branch of immunology concerned with the nature and behavior of humoral antibodies is called *serology*. Because of space limitations, detailed descriptions of immunologic and serological reactions will not be given. The references listed in the bibliography section can serve as sources for detailed descriptions of procedures, or mechanisms concerned with specific antigen and antibody reactions.

This chapter will provide a survey of a representative number of currently available, functional methods used for the detection and measurement of antibodies in human serum. Many of these serological procedures, or so-called antibody detection systems, are powerful tools not only in the diagnosis of disease states, but in the identification of microorganisms. These tests are based on antibodies produced *in vivo* in response to the antigenic components of microorganisms. Such microorganisms contain a wide variety of different antigens. Some of these are *type specific,* limited to a particular species, while others are *common group antigens,* antigenic to related groups of microorganisms. Certain important procedures, such as viral hemagglutination and serological tests for syphilis, have been placed in other chapters concerned with

specific disease agents. Immune hemagglutination and associated problems are included in a separate chapter on blood groups.

Production of Antisera

In order to obtain potent antisera for use in diagnostic tests, some type of experimental animal is inoculated with suspensions of a particular antigen. Animals utilized for this purpose include chickens, mice, horses, rabbits, sheep, and even humans. In most laboratory situations, the course of immunization involves a series of inoculations. The introduction of antigen may be done by one of several routes, including intraperitoneal, intravenous, and subcutaneous.

Determinations of the antibody level (*trial titrations*) are performed periodically by taking a blood sample from the laboratory animal. The blood is allowed to clot, and the serum is removed for testing. Once the antibody concentration reaches the desired level, the animal is bled. Depending upon the purpose of the procedure, the animal may be completely freed of blood. The immune serum obtained in this manner should contain the antibodies produced in response to the antigenic stimulus. These antibodies are capable of binding in some manner with the antigen which caused their formation.

The Diagnostic Significance of Rising Antibody Titers

Generally speaking, the titer, or concentration of antibody in a patient's serum, will fluctuate as a consequence of immunizations and of subclinical as well as full-blown current infectious states. (An individual with a subclinical state of a disease generally doesn't experience all of the characteristic symptoms, or such effects are less severe. Quite often nonspecific symptoms such as headache, nausea, fever, etc., are mainly evident.)

In order to distinguish the antibody production associated with an actual ongoing infection from the effects of vaccination, or from antibodies associated with a past infection, at least two specimens of a patient's serum are necessary. One of these samples is obtained soon after the onset of the disease in question, and the other approximately 12 to 14 days later. The sera from both specimens are used in a particular serological test-of-choice, and the results are compared to determine if a rise in antibody has occurred. If such is the case, as indicated by a greater degree of antibody activity in the later specimen, identification of the causative agent is possible.

If little or no antibody is detected in either specimen, it can be assumed, barring any abnormalities, that an organism other than the one being tested is the cause of the infection. Abnormalities that could cause a lack of antibody response include: (1) the administration of immunosuppressing drugs, (2) an exposure to excessive radiation, or (3) the presence of a congenital defect such as agammaglobulinemia.

If antibody is present in both samples, with no appreciable change noted in the titers, it can be assumed that the antibody levels were present before the onset of the current infection, and bear no relationship to the disease state.

The Agglutination Reaction

This classic serologic reaction was formally described by Gruber and Durham in 1896. Agglutination involves the clumping of cellular or particulate (particle-like) (Figure 23-1) antigens by homologous antibodies. This phenomenon

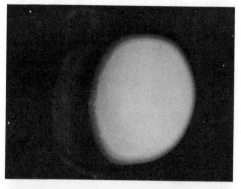
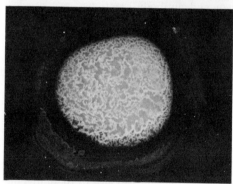

FIG. 23–1. The agglutination test for the diagnosis of brucellosis in dairy cattle. This test is based on the presence of agglutinins in the blood of infected animals. When the antigen, a suspension of *Brucella* spp. cells, is added to serum, the agglutinins clump with the antigen. In the plate or rapid test such mixtures are spread into thin, somewhat even layers over a glass plate. Within a few minutes clumping can be seen with the naked eye (bottom). A negative result (absence of agglutinin) is shown at the top. (Courtesy of United States Department of Agriculture.)

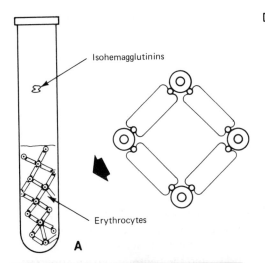

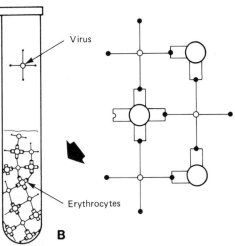

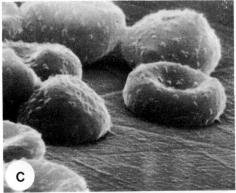

FIG. 23–2. Hemagglutination reactions. _A_. Diagrammatic representation of the agglutination of erythrocytes by isohemagglutinins. _B_. Viral hemagglutination. _C_. A scanning micrograph showing the agglutination of human erythrocytes by influenza viruses. The little dot-like structures on the blood cells are the viruses. (Courtesy of Dr. L. F. Baker, Department of Microbiology, U.S.C. School of Medicine.)

is widely used for the rapid diagnosis of several infectious diseases, and for the determination of blood types (Color photograph 54). Because blood typing procedures involve reactions between erythrocytes and corresponding _hemagglutinins_ (specifically _isohemagglutinins_) the phenomenon may be referred to as _hemagglutination_ (Color photograph 54 and Figure 23–2_A_).

Examples of Agglutination and Related Reactions

Cold hemagglutination.   The sera of patients with atypical primary pneumonia of mycoplasmal origin (Chapters 24 and 33), and protozoan infections, such as trypanosomiasis, contain antibodies capable of agglutinating erythrocytes from these patients at 2°C, but not at 37°C. Such antibodies are called _cold agglutinins,_ and the phenomenon is referred to as _cold hemagglutination._ There is diagnostic significance to these unusual antibodies in that they generally appear in association with very few diseases.

Hemagglutination.   Other forms of this biological process exist, including the agglutination of red cells by viruses and mycoplasma. Several viruses, including influenza (Figure 23–2_B_ and _C_), mumps, vaccinia, and variola (smallpox) are capable of binding to particular receptor sites of erythrocytes from suitable animal species. The reaction was first reported by G. K. Hirst in 1941. The phenomena occurred with chicken red cells and influenza virus. This activity results in the formation of a bridge between individual red cells, causing them to agglutinate. Additional features of these reactions are discussed in later chapters.

Weil-Felix test. In 1916, E. Weil and A. Felix reported that a strain of the bacterium *Proteus,* originally isolated from the urine of a typhus fever victim, was agglutinated by the sera of patients suffering from this disease. Serum from normal persons did not produce a similar result. Later studies showed that *Proteus* spp. were not the cause of typhus fever, and that antibodies against *Proteus* spp. normally occur quite commonly in man. However, these organisms can serve as an important diagnostic tool, if at least two serum specimens are taken at different times during the course of disease.

The Weil-Felix reaction incorporates the somatic antigens (O) of *Proteus.* It is important to use nonmotile organisms, because motile strains have flagellar antigens which could interfere with the test. Three strains are used in the diagnosis of various rickettsial infections: OX2, OX19, and OX-K.

Widal test. The original Widal test was a microscopic procedure used for the laboratory diagnosis of typhoid fever. This method consisted of mixing drops of the patient's blood with a loopful of a 24-hour *Salmonella typhi* culture on a glass slide or other appropriate surface. After a 30- to 60-minute incubation period, the mixture was observed microscopically for the presence of clumping, which represented a positive test. A saline control was always included, which consisted of saline and *S. typhi.* The Widal test has largely been modified to eliminate the objection to the use of only one dilution of a patient's blood.

Passive agglutination. In recent years it has been possible to extend the agglutination reaction to a variety of soluble (non-particulate) antigens by attaching them to the surface of insoluble particles. In passive agglutination reactions the types of particles used include bentonite (a mineral colloid), polystyrene latex spheres, and red blood cells. Adsorption of the soluble antigens usually is achieved by simply mixing them with the insoluble particles. Diagnostic tests employing this technique are in widespread use for the detection and identification of a variety of disease states. Examples of procedures include latex agglutination (LA) tests, which are valuable in the diagnosis of several mycotic (fungal) and other infections, and the bentonite flocculation (BF) test, which is employed for the diagnosis of several helminth diseases.

Hemagglutination Inhibition (HI)

In 1941 G. K. Hirst reported the phenomenon of viral hemagglutination, and thereby provided a new picture and greater understanding of the relationship between viruses and host cells. His finding quickly led to the development of a new *in vitro* method, the hemagglutination-inhibition (HI) test, for the detection and titration of viral antibodies in a patient's sera and for the identification of specific viruses. In recent years the hemagglutination-inhibition test has become the method of choice for determining the immune status of an individual against rubella (German measles) and the serological diagnosis of rubella virus infections.

The accurate determination of rubella HI antibodies is especially pertinent because current recommendations suggest that if a woman of childbearing age is contemplating vaccination, she should be tested for rubella HI antibody. If such antibodies are present, nothing can be

FIG. 23–3. The equipment used in reading the results of an HI test. A microtiter plastic plate contains the components of the test. (Photo by C. Righter.)

gained by immunization. If the test is performed by competent personnel, the presence of any level of HI antibody may be considered indicative of previous infection.

The HI test can be used only in situations involving viruses that agglutinate, or clump, erythrocytes of particular birds or mammals. Examples of such viruses include influenza, mumps, vaccinia, smallpox, Newcastle disease, and rubella (German measles). Viral hemagglutination can be inhibited by specific antibodies against the virus in a reaction called hemagglutination inhibition. The mechanism involved in this reaction is quite simple. The antibody molecules attach to the viral particles and subsequently hinder the adsorption of viral particles to erythrocytes. Failure of hemagglutination to occur constitutes a positive test for antibody. Unagglutinated red blood cells slide down the sides of the container that holds the reaction materials and settle directly to its bottom, forming a compact circular red "button" or "doughnut." Agglutinated cells stick to the sides and rounded portion of the chamber's bottom, forming a ragged-edged, film-like deposit. Hemagglutination-inhibition tests can be performed in test tubes of specific diameters or in commercially available plastic trays or plates, such as microtiter plates (Figure 23–3).

Because the HI procedure frequently is used to show the antibody response of individuals during and after suspected illness, two serum specimens (*paired sera*) are taken and tested. One sample is collected shortly after the onset of symptoms (*acute phase*), and the other is taken two to three weeks later (*convalescent phase*). Serial dilutions of the two specimens (e.g., 1:8, 1:16, 1:32, etc.) are prepared and then used to determine each specimen's titer, which is the reciprocal of the highest serum dilution that completely prevents hemagglutination. Table 23–1 shows HI titers of a paired sera procedure. The titers are 8 and 256 for the acute and convalescent samples, respectively. The "O" indicates hemagglutination inhibition, and the "+" represents hemagglutination.

In order to determine if the procedure was done correctly, several types of controls are used. These include antigen control, serum control, positive and negative sera controls, and red blood cell control.

Table 23–1   Hemagglutination-Inhibition Titers of a Paired Sera Procedure

Serum Sample	Serum Dilution Used								HI Titers
	1:8	1:16	1:32	1:64	1:128	1:256	1:512	1:1024	
Acute	0	+	+	+	+	+	+	+	8
Convalescent	0	0	0	0	0	0	+	+	256

Hemadsorption (HAD) and Related Reactions

Hemadsorption has been observed with various microorganisms, including viruses and the nonpathogenic mycoplasmas. Briefly, the procedure to demonstrate HAD involves the introduction of a red blood cell suspension into the system in which the organisms are growing. In the case of mycoplasma, the erythrocytes are simply poured over colonies of the organism. The tests are then incubated, usually at 37°C, for 5 to 15 minutes, and examined for hemadsorption—the sticking of red blood cells to the mycoplasma colonies after rinsing (Figure 23–4). The mechanism of attachment is not the same here as in hemagglutination, which involves adsorption to neuramic acid receptors.

The Precipitin Reaction

Serological precipitation or *precipitin* reactions refer to the interaction of a functional class of antibodies called precipitins with soluble (colloidal) antigens referred to as *precipitinogens*. In experimental systems a visible "floc" or precipitate generally appears at the point where optimal proportions of antibody and antigen, as well as electrolytes exist (Color photograph 55).

The major difference between precipitin and agglutination reactions is the state of dispersion of the antigenic material used. In precipitin reactions the molecules of precipitinogens are free in solution and the solutions appear clear, while the molecules of agglutinogens are bound to a surface in some manner.

The precipitin test was first described by Kraus in 1897, and his terms are still used. In Kraus' original experiment, bacteria-free culture filtrates of *Yersinia pestis* (the causative agent of plague), and *Vibrio cholerae* (the causative agent of

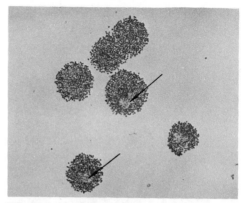

FIG. 23–4. The hemadsorption of guinea pig red blood cells on colonies (arrows) of *Mycoplasma gallisepticum*. Note how the colonial borders are sharply defined by this phenomenon. (From Manchee, R. S., and Taylor-Robinson, D.: *J. Bacteriol.*, **100**:78–85, 1969.)

Asiatic cholera) were mixed with their respective homologous antisera, and a flocculent precipitate formed in each. This did not occur when the bacterial antigens and antisera were interchanged.

Ring or Interface Test

During the normal sequence of events in an infection, precipitating antibody is often produced. This is usually in response to soluble microbial substances released as a consequence of a disintegrative process. The presence of these antibodies can be demonstrated by means of the *ring* or *interface test* based on a useful form of the precipitin reactions. This procedure, first introduced by Ascoli in 1902 for diagnosing anthrax in cattle, involves the use of antigenic material carefully layered over an equal quantity of antisera in a narrow tube, in order to form a sharp liquid interface. If the reactants are homologous, a ring of precipitation develops at this point. In this test, the reactants diffuse into one another until the optimal, or immunologically equivalent, or serologically equivalent proportions of each for precipitation is achieved. The general form of this test still is functional today. However, in modern practice agar gel bases (gel matrix) are incorporated to stabilize the precipitates which result. Examples of such gel diffusion tests include the *Oudin* and *Ouchterlony techniques* (Figures 23–5, 23–6, 23–7, and 23–8).

Oudin test. The Oudin (single diffusion) technique is performed by introducing antiserum into a tube of melted agar, the temperature of which is approximately 45°C. This mixture, filling a narrow tube to one third of its height, is allowed to solidify. An antigen-containing solution then is layered on top of the agar preparation, and the entire system is refrigerated for a period of time. Diffusion of the antigen into the agar gel takes place during this refrigeration. Depending on the number of antigenic components in the test material, a preparation of this type may contain one or more bands or discs of precipitation formed with homologous antibodies (Figure 23–6*B*). One distinct band will develop for each homologous soluble antigen-antibody system present. This feature of the Oudin method is a pronounced advantage.

Double diffusion procedure. A variation of the single diffusion technique of Oudin is the double diffusion procedure. One new ingredient is added: a layer of clear agar is placed between the two zones containing antigen and antibody. Once the tube system is prepared, the molecules of both antigen and antibody diffuse into the clear agar or so-called neutral zone (Figure 23–7). Precipitation bands will form at the sites where there is serological equivalence—where both reactants are present in equivalent proportions. This technique can be a valuable tool to determine the number of antigen-antibody combinations present in a specimen under investigation.

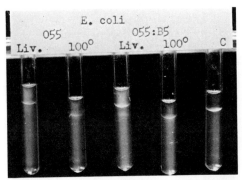

FIG. 23–5. The simple diffusion (Oudin) precipitin test using a homologous *Escherichia coli* antigen-antibody system. The control is labeled C. (Courtesy of the National Medical Audiovisual Center, Atlanta, Georgia.)

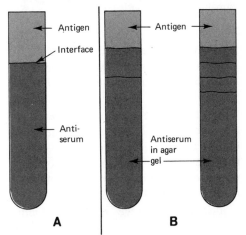

FIG. 23–6. Diagrammatic representations of the precipitin test and its variations. *A*. The ring test. *B*. The Oudin techinque. The left tube contains a simple system, with one type of antigen and homologous antibody. The right tube contains a complex system of multiple antigens as indicated by the multiple precipitin bands.

Ouchterlony test. The Ouchterlony test also incorporates gel diffusion. In this case an agar pour plate is made without the addition of antiserum. After the agar solidifies, circular or square holes or wells are made in the surface. Solutions containing antigens are added to certain wells, while another well receives the antibody preparation (Figure 23–8). The plate is incubated to allow the various reactants to diffuse. Lines or bands of

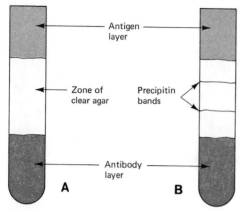

FIG. 23–7. The gel double diffusion technique.
_A._ The system before reactions occur. _B._ The
formation of precipitin bands.

precipitation develop when different antigenic components react with homologous antibodies contained within the antibody preparation. The results obtained by this technique are dependent upon several factors, including the relative concentrations of the reactants, the incubation period, the rate of diffusion, and the molecular weight of the antigens used. The arrangement shown in Figure 23–8C possesses a distinct advantage over the Oudin method in that several different antigen solutions may be tested at one time. The Oudin test is limited to the investigation of one such preparation.

The double diffusion procedure of Ouchterlony can produce several different geometrical patterns between the separate wells containing antigen and antibody solutions. These patterns are formed as a consequence of the reacting substances diffusing from their reservoirs. Precipitation lines or bands develop where serologic equivalence exists. Lines generally occur where the distance between the two reactants is at a minimum.

Much useful information can be obtained from this technique, including the detection of identical or cross-reacting components of various antigen or antibody preparations (gel diffusion analysis). Examples of three patterns representing possible reactions are shown in Figure 23–8. The precipitin band pattern of the _reaction of identity_ develops when pure antigen preparations are placed into two wells adjacent to a centrally located well containing a homologous antibody solution (Figure 23–8A and D). Note that the bands fuse.

The pattern of Figure 23–8B represents a situation of two unrelated antigens and an antiserum preparation containing antibodies for each of the antigens. The arrangement of precipitin bands here is referred to as the _reaction of nonidentity_. The antigens and antibodies diffuse toward one another from their wells, forming two precipitin bands which also cross.

Antiserum preparations usually will react with their homologous antigen counterparts. However, due to certain similarities of other antigen preparations to the homologous antigen substance, reactions between similar or different heterologous antigens and an antiserum can occur. These events are referred to as _cross-reactions_. Such reactions may be due to several factors, including: (1) the presence of several different antigenic molecules as contaminants in an antigen preparation; (2) a preparation used as an antigen, may actually consist of numerous types of antigenic molecules; and (3) the limited specificity of the antiserum preparation.

The Ouchterlony _reaction of partial identity_ or _cross-reaction_ is shown in Figure 23–8C. In this situation one of the antigens and the antiserum used form a homologous system. However, the second antigen employed is a cross-reacting one. The precipitin bands which develop fuse, but one of them continues toward the cross-reacting antigen preparation. This _spur,_ as it is sometimes called, is formed by those antibody molecules which have

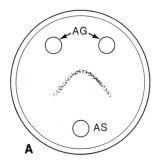 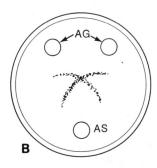 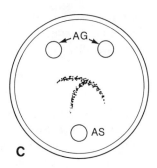

Double diffusion precipitin Rxs

FIG. 23–8. Selected geometrical patterns representing possible double diffusion precipitin reactions. _A. Reaction of antigen identity:_ both upper wells contain the same antigen, while the lower well contains homologous anti-serum. _B. Reaction of antigen nonidentity:_ each of the upper wells contains a different antigen and the central well holds anti-sera to both antigens. _C. Reaction of partial identity or cross-reaction:_ the upper left well contains a cross-reacting antigen, while the upper right well is filled with an antigen that is homologous for the anti-serum preparation in the lower well. _D._ The actual appearance of an antigen identity reaction. (From Stickle, D., Kaufman, L., Blumer, S. O., and McLaughlin, D. W.: _Appl. Microbiol.,_ **23**:490–499, 1972.)

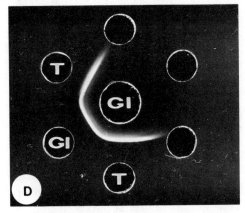

not combined with the cross-reacting antigen and have gone beyond the precipitation band facing it.

Toxin Neutralization
(Testing Antitoxins)

The exotoxins of various microorganisms are known to be neutralized by small quantities of homologous antibodies, commonly called _antitoxins._ Although the exact mechanism by which this is accomplished remains unknown, this phenomenon can still be used to determine the effectiveness of commercially or otherwise produced antitoxic serum, usually by comparison with one of known potency.

Because toxins can readily lose their toxicity, before any evaluation procedure

is carried out it is necessary to standardize a quantity (batch) of toxin against an antitoxin preparation of known strength. Varying dilutions of toxin are mixed with constant amounts of standard antitoxin. The mixtures are incubated for a short time to allow the substances to react. Then specific doses of the mixtures are injected into groups of laboratory animals, which are then observed for death or pronounced tissue damage. The results of this titration show the concentration of toxin needed to produce a particular effect, as well as the amount of standard antitoxin which nullified it. Using this information, the unknown antitoxin serum is tested to determine its capability in neutralizing the toxin. Thus the quantity of the unknown antitoxin which nullifies the particular toxin concentration used in the case of the standardized preparation should contain the same number of so-called *protective units*.

The Danysz Phenomenon

In 1902, J. Danysz observed that the manner in which toxin and antitoxin are mixed before injection into an animal determines not only the toxicity of the mixture for the animal, but also the relative concentrations of each reagent. For example, it is possible to determine what concentration of antitoxin is necessary to just completely neutralize a given amount of corresponding toxin if added in a single dose. However, an entirely different situation results if, during the preparation of the mixture, the quantity of toxin is divided into several portions and added to the given concentration of antitoxin at different times. In this case, the final preparation after the last portion of the toxin has been added is highly toxic. This is due to the fact that the initial amount of toxin added to the antitoxin combines with more antitoxin than it would if it were all introduced as a single dose. Therefore not enough antitoxin is left to combine with and neutralize the second and following doses of toxin. The result is a toxic mixture.

Endotoxin Detection

The *Limulus* endotoxin assay.   In 1968, Levin and Bang described the ability of an aqueous extract of amoebocytes (lysate) from the blood of the horseshoe crab (Figures 23–9*A* and 9*B*) to form a gel in the presence of minute amounts of endotoxin. These endotoxins are lipopolysaccharide components of the outer cell-wall layer of Gram-negative bacteria (Chapter 8). Since the initial description

of it in 1968, the lysate procedure for the detection of endotoxins has already been used for the detection of bacteriuria (bacteria in the urine), for the diagnosis of Gram-negative spinal meningitis (Chapter 38), and for the detection of pyrogens (fever-causing agents) in radiopharmaceuticals and biologicals by pharmaceutical companies. It is quite possible that the test can be used routinely to determine pollution in natural bodies of water such as lakes, streams, etc., and to detect Gram-negative bacterial contamination in various food products. The assay is quite unique in that it can be used to detect endotoxin in concentrations as little as 5×10^{-4} $\mu g/ml$.

The gel formation reaction is comparable to blood clotting in mammals. In 1972, Young, Levin, and Prendergast showed this result to be enzymatic, consisting of a high-molecular-weight enzyme followed by its conversion of a low-molecular-weight clottable protein to a gel (Figure 23–9*C*). The *Limulus* assay is not affected by the presence of antibiotics. It can therefore be used to monitor the effectiveness of certain treatments for bacterial infections.

The *Limulus* assay is performed by adding dilutions of specimen samples to equal volumes of *Limulus* lysate in glass test tubes. The reaction mixtures are incubated for 60 minutes at 37°C. After incubation, the presence of a solid gel or a marked increase in viscosity (Figure 23–9*C*) represents a positive test. Known positive and negative controls are included in general procedures to facilitate the reading of test results.

The *Limulus* test has certain disadvantages. It appears that Gram-positive bacteria and yeast are undetectable. This problem is due to the fact that these organisms do not contain endotoxin-like substances in their cells. Another disadvan-

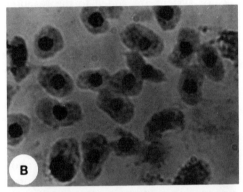

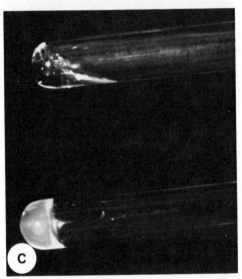

FIG. 23–9. The *Limulus* test. *A*. The horseshoe crab. *B*. A microscopic view of the cells of the horseshoe crab, amoebocytes, involved with the test. *C*. A close-up view of a negative result (top tube) and a strongly positive result (bottom tube). (Photographs courtesy of Dr. James H. Jorgensen, University of Texas Health Science Center at San Antonio, Texas. From Jorgensen, J. H., and Smith, R. F.: *Appl. Microbiol.*, **26**:43, 1973.)

tage is that the procedure does not provide information regarding the identity of causative agents, or the presence of mixed bacterial infections. Despite these deficiencies, the *Limulus* assay is a sensitive, simple, and rapid test for detecting bacterial endotoxins. However, the assay procedure is still in the process of being standardized for general use.

In Vitro Hemolysis Tests

Complement Fixation

As mentioned earlier, complement is a normal serum component found in a variety of animals. It is known for its thermo- or heat-lability. Heating serum for 30 minutes at 56°C inactivates the complement.

Historically, the contribution of complement to the destruction of invading cells was first noted by Pfeiffer in 1896. His studies compared the fates of cholera-causing organisms (*Vibrio cholerae*) upon their intraperitoneal injection into normal and immunized guinea pigs. The vibrios taken from normal animals at various intervals appeared quite normal. However, those organisms sampled within a short time after their initial injection into the immunized guinea pigs swelled, stained unevenly, and eventually burst. The immunized animals showed no sign of infection, and apparently the vibrios underwent *cytolysis*, cellular disruption.

The fact that serum components participated in the phenomenon was shown *in vitro* by exposing the cholera-causing organisms, using the hanging-drop technique (Chapter 6) to: (1) normal serum; (2) untreated immune serum; and (3) immune serum which was heated at 56°C for 30 minutes. Only the untreated immune serum caused the lytic effect. Pfeiffer's experiments demonstrated the presence in immune serum of a thermolabile substance which contributed to the destruction of bacteria.

The reaction was one of *immune cytolysis*. Normal sera had no effect. This type of reaction apparently was not limited to bacteria. In 1895 Bordet reported a somewhat similar phenomenon with antisera prepared against red blood cells. This observation led to the development of the complement-fixation test (Color photograph 56).

The complement-fixation (comp-fix) procedure. The recognition of the fact that various antigen-antibody combinations have the ability to fix, or combine with, complement has provided a means for the detection of either antibodies or antigenic substances in unknown specimens. Two systems are incorporated into the performance of this technique, the test and indicator systems. In a typical laboratory diagnostic situation the *test system* consists of the patient's serum, an antigen preparation that may be commercially made or laboratory-produced, and complement, or *alexin*, commonly obtained from guinea pig serum, and commercially available. The components of the *indicator system* are sheep red blood cells, and serum containing homologous antibodies against them. This antibody preparation is referred to as *hemolysin* or *amboceptor*.

All sera used in complement-fixation tests are heated before use to 56°C for 30 minutes to inactivate any complement present in the respective sources of antibodies. In order to insure the success of the comp-fix procedure, all reagents must be freshly and carefully prepared, and must be added in proper proportion to one another, so that a suitable balance between components is achieved. For example, sufficient hemolysin must be added to the indicator system to render the sheep erythrocytes susceptible to lysis by complement (sensitized). The concentrations needed are determined before the complement-fixation is performed.

A positive test. If a particular heated serum specimen is suspected of having specific antibodies, dilutions of it are made and incorporated, together with antigen and complement, into the test system. Subsequently, the components of the indicator system are added to the reaction mixture. If the serum sample contains antibody, the antibody will combine with antigen, and fix the complement in the system, so that no free complement remains (Figure 23–10). Fixation is shown when the indicator system is added and lysis of the sensitized sheep red blood cells does not occur. Thus a positive complement-fixation test is represented by a cloudy red suspension (Color photograph 56). This result indicates the presence of antibody toward the antigen used in the test system.

The negative test. If a serum sample lacks antibody against the particular antigen used in the test system, complement fixation cannot occur. Thus complement is present in solution and is free to react with the components of the indicator system. The antigen-antibody complex formed by the sheep erythrocytes and hemolysin thereby fix complement and lysis of the red blood cells occurs, producing a clear red solution (Color photograph 56 and Figure 23–10). In a negative test, i.e., hemolysis, antibodies are not present toward the antigen used in the test system.

Controls. Certain controls must be incorporated during the preparation and performance of the complement-fixation test, largely because of the labile nature of both the complement and the erythrocytes. Antigen and patient's serum controls are employed to determine

COMPONENTS IN COMPLEMENT FIXATION

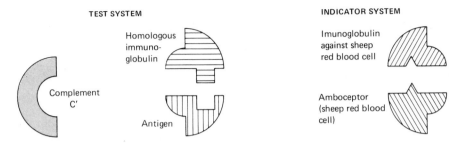

TEST SYSTEM

Homologous
immuno-
globulin

Complement
C′

Antigen

INDICATOR SYSTEM

Imunoglobulin
against sheep
red blood cell

Amboceptor
(sheep red blood
cell)

FINAL COMBINATIONS OF COMPONENTS

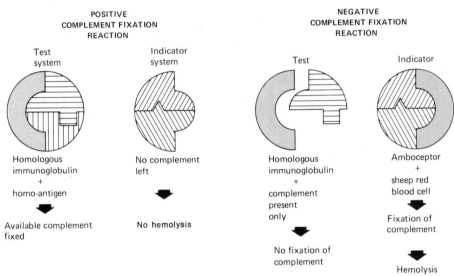

POSITIVE
COMPLEMENT FIXATION
REACTION

Test
system

Indicator
system

Homologous
immunoglobulin
+
homo-antigen

Available complement
fixed

No complement
left

No hemolysis

NEGATIVE
COMPLEMENT FIXATION
REACTION

Test

Indicator

Homologous
immunoglobulin
+
complement
present
only

No fixation of
complement

Amboceptor
+
sheep red
blood cell

Fixation of
complement

Hemolysis

FIG. 23–10. A diagrammatic representation of the complement-fixation reaction. The upper portion shows the reagents used. The remaining sections indicate the combinations which occur or do not occur. *Left,* a positive complement-fixation test. *Right,* a negative reaction.

their possible anticomplementary activity, which could produce misleading test results. The fragility of the red blood cells and the functioning of the indicator system of sheep erythrocytes and hemolysin also are separately determined.

The mechanism of complement fixation. As mentioned in an earlier chapter, at least nine components of the complement system are recognized. Much detailed study has been given to the reaction of complement with sensitized erythrocytes having bound antibodies directed against their surface. Early investigations demonstrated that the basic reaction occurs in several stages, and that the components of complement combine with sensitized cells in a precise manner. A general summary of these event follows.

Once antibody (principally IgM and IgG) has been bound to an erythrocyte's surface, the stage is set for the subsequent events. It is important to note that this combination of antigen (antigenic site) and antibody is not a visible reaction. The first component, C′1, is bound by the antigen-antibody combination, and subsequently undergoes an alteration that enables it to react with the active component C′4b. C′1 is a trimolecular complex held together by calcium ions. Its three subunits are designated C′1q, C′1r, and C′1s. Through a series of reactions C′1q attaches to antibody (A), which in turn is attached to the erythrocyte's surface. The next component to interact is C′1r, which also is essential for the activation of C′1s. By means of these and additional interactions C′1 is converted into an enzymatically active substance that reacts with C′4. The activated form of C′1 is designated C′$\overline{1}$ and is called C′1 esterase. Thus the reactions that have taken place can be generally represented by antigen AC′$\overline{1,4b}$.

Next in the sequence of reactions (complement cascade) the formed complex (antigen AC′$\overline{1,4b}$) combines with one fragment of C′2, namely C′2a. This new fragment is created by the enzymatic action of C′1s in the presence of a magnesium ion (Mg^{++}). The resulting complex, then, is antigen AC′$\overline{1,4b,2a}$. The C′$\overline{4b,2a}$ portion, which is called C′3 convertase, attacks the next component, C′3, and converts it into C′3a and C′3b fragments. Only the C′3b fragment attaches to the complex, thus forming antigen AC′, $\overline{1,4b,-2\,a,3b}$.

The next component to be activated is C′5. In this step the C′$\overline{4b,2a,3b}$ portion of the complex cleaves C′5 into C′5a and C′5b fragments. The C′5b fragment then combines with C′6. This combination in turn binds C′7. The final combination of C′5b,6,7 takes place near the position occupied by C′1,4b,2a,-3b and establishes the conditions necessary for hemolysis to occur. C′8 is bound next by the complex, followed by C′9. The entire sequence of reactions leading to the formation of antigen AC′$\overline{1,4b,2a,-3b,5b,6,7,8,9}$ (antigen AC′$\overline{1\text{-}9}$) results

in the appearance of actual holes in the cell's membrane. Such circular lesions can have dimensions of 10 nm. Through these holes small intracellular molecules escape and extracellular water enters rapidly, thus causing the cell to expand and to rupture.

Application of complement fixation.
Complement-fixation procedures have been employed more or less successfully in the laboratory diagnosis of a wide variety of microbial infections as well as certain helminthic diseases (Table 23–2). Historically, the most widely recognized application of this phenomenon has been incorporated into the Wasserman test and its modifications for the diagnosis of syphilis. The antibody-like material reagin, associated with this disease is the same as that involved with other flocculation tests discussed later, such as VDRL and Kahn.

Antistreptolysin Test

The thermolabile hemolysin of streptococci, known as streptolysin O, is antigenic in man and most laboratory animals. In cases of various human streptococcal diseases, antistreptolysin O titers increase during the times of infection and convalescence. In many diagnostic laboratories, the antistreptolysin test is routinely used to measure the levels of antibodies against this bacterial product, and its hemolytic effect.

In Vitro Immunological Procedures Incorporating Differential Staining

Fluorescent Antibody Techniques

Fluorescent antibody methodology has been described as a combination of "the test-tube techniques of immunology with the microscopic methods of cytology." In a broad sense the procedure involves

Table 23–2   Representative Diseases for which Diagnostic Complement-Fixation Tests Can Be Used

Type of Disease				
Bacterial	Mycotic	Protozoan	Viral	Helminthic[a]
Gonorrhea	Aspergillosis Blastomycosis	Amebic dysentery	ARD[b]	Echinococcosis
Syphilis	Coccidioidomycosis	Chagas' disease Leishmaniasis	Enteroviruses Influenza	Paragonimiasis Schistosomiasis
Rickettsial infections	Histoplasmosis	Malaria	Measles	Trichinosis
Tuberculosis	Sporotrichosis		Mumps	
Whooping cough				

[a] In several instances these tests are in an experimental stage.
[b] Acute respiratory diseases caused by adenoviruses.

bringing a fluorescent dye (marker) into contact and chemical bonding with serum proteins (Figure 23–11). This process is referred to as *labeling* or *conjugation,* and the resulting preparations generally exhibit good biological activity. Typically, such fluorescent serum-protein conjugates, containing specific antibodies, can be used for the detection of homologous antigens in smears or tissue sections. The fluorescent antibody techniques reported by Coons, Creech, and Jones in 1941 and their variations have received wide application in microbiology and pathol-

ogy. The most commonly used of these are called *direct* and *indirect* methods (Figures 23–12 and 23–13 and Color Photographs 57 and 58).

The direct fluorescent method. This procedure is generally considered to be the simplest one because of the use of a single staining reagent, and because the manipulations involved are not complex. Basically, the staining technique consists of applying a few drops of a standardized labeled antibody preparation to an antigen-containing specimen. The specimen is

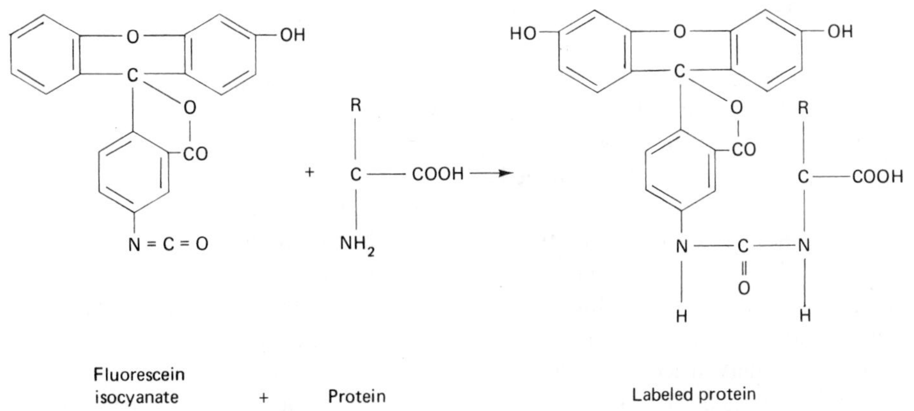

FIG. 23–11. A representation of the labeling of a serum protein with a fluorescein derivative process. The linkage here is an isocyanateamine one.

(Based on Goldman, M.: *Fluorescent Antibody Methods.* Academic Press, 1968.)

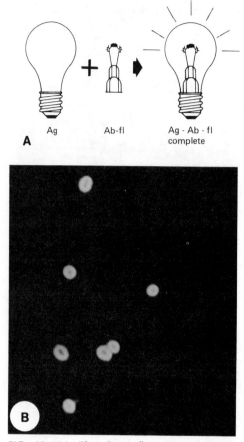

A

| Ag | Ab-fl | Ag - Ab - fl complete |

B

FIG. 23–12_A_. The direct fluorescent antibody technique schematically represented. _B_. The appearance of noncapsulated _Haemophilus influenzae_ by immunofluorescence. (Courtesy of Catlin, B. W.: _Amer. J. Dis. Child._, **120**:203–210, 1970.)

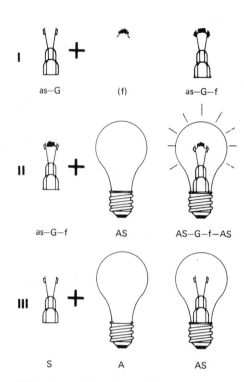

I   as–G   (f)   as–G–f

II   as–G–f   AS   AS–G–f–AS

III   S   A   AS

FIG. 23–13. The indirect fluorescent antibody technique. A hypothetical application of this technique is: I. Antibodies (as) which have been prepared against sheep globulin (G) in the rabbit are coupled (labeled) with a fluorescein (f) marker producing as-G-f. II. This preparation is then applied to an antigen-containing (A) specimen which has been treated with sheep globulin (S) to form an antigen-antibody (AS) complex. The labeled anti-sheep globulin reacts with the antibody in this complex and causes the entire "immunologic sandwich" to fluoresce upon examination (as-AS-G-f). III. Note that the combination of sheep globulin and antigen-containing specimen does not fluoresce, and therefore there is no indication of a reaction.

fixed to a slide with the aid of acetone, ethanol, methanol, or heat. This test system (the specimen and the labeled antibody) is incubated at a specific temperature for a designated length of time. Following incubation, the specimen is freed of excess antibody by washing with saline and distilled water. The resulting preparation is usually dried, mounted in glycerol, and examined with the aid of a fluorescence microscope. If the homologous antigen is present in the specimen, the labeled antibody will unite with it, and thus pinpoint its location.

Controls.   In order to substantiate the immunologic specificity of the fluorescence observed with the unknown antigen-containing specimen, certain appropriate controls must be carried out, which typically include:

1. Exposure of the antigen-containing specimen to labeled normal serum—serum which does not contain antibody against the antigen in question. Fluorescence should not be observed.

2. Exposure of the antigen-containing specimen to homologous unlabeled antibody preparation. Here, fluorescence should be absent also.

Purpose. Staining antigens by the direct method serves as a means of identifying unknown microbial agents (see Figure 23–12). This technique can also be used in determining the distribution of antigens in tissue.

The indirect fluorescent antibody method.

The indirect (antiglobulin) method, first described in detail by Weller and Coons in 1954, basically results in the formation of an immunologic sandwich, in that non-fluorescent antibody (globulin) bound to primary antigen is in turn bound by fluorescent antiglobulin. It is not the antigen that is directly rendered fluorescent, but rather the intermediate substance, or more specifically, the non-fluorescent antibody bound to the antigen. This indirect method utilizes both the antigen-binding capability of antibodies and also their protein nature, which enables the globulins to serve as antigens. The results of this method—the microscopic appearance of the stained antigen—are generally indistinguishable from those obtained with the direct fluorescent antibody technique. A schematic example of this method is shown in Figure 23–13.

Procedure. Standardized reagents are used. Briefly, the method can be described as follows. After the specimen is fixed in a manner similar to that described for the direct test, unlabeled spe-

cific antiserum (G) is applied to it. These reactants are incubated together for 15 to 60 minutes. The preparation is washed in saline, then in distilled water, and subsequently dried. Following this step, labeled antiglobulin (AG) is layered over the specimen and the preparation is incubated again for a period of 15 to 60 minutes. Rinsing and washing steps are carried out as in the direct test. The resulting antigen-globulin-antiglobulin complex is dried, mounted, and examined with the aid of a fluorescent microscope (Color photographs 57 and 58).

Controls. This technique exhibits a distinct increase in sensitivity. Because of this fact, as well as the more involved nature of the procedure, adequate controls are even more important to establish the specificity of the staining reaction. In other words, the possibility of non-specific fluorescence in the test system must be ruled out. Suggested controls generally include incubating homologous antigen with combinations of the following reagents: (1) saline and labeled antiglobulin (AG); (2) normal serum and labeled antiglobulin (AG); (3) specific antiserum (G) and labeled normal serum. An additional control incubating heterologous antigen with a specific antiserum (G) and labeled antiglobulin (AG) also could be incorporated. If the fluorescence in the case of the indirect test is specific, then fluorescence should not be observed with the various controls.

Applications. The indirect fluorescent antibody technique has been used to demonstrate antibodies against various microbial pathogens, including *Treponema pallidum* and *Herpesvirus hominis* (the causative agent of fever blisters).

Variations of this basic technique exist. Testing for the presence of antibody in serum, referred to as "fluorescent antibody serology," has been used in the diagnosis of syphilis and the detection of malaria antibodies.

Applications of Diagnostic and Investigative Electron Microscopy

Immune electron microscopy. In recent years, a number of techniques have been developed that have significantly extended the potential of electron microscopy and have increased its versatility. One such technique, known as immune electron microscopy (IEM), was first used by Anderson and Stanley to observe the presence of tobacco mosaic virus in the presence of specific antibody. Immune electron microscopy has since been used to detect the presence of small amounts of antibodies (Figure 23–14), to show antigenic similarities and differences among viruses, and to identify viral particles extracted directly from human tissues and feces. Recently Feinstone, Kapikian, and Purcell found a virus-like particle in the feces of patients with hepatitis A (infectious hepatitis) using IEM. The discovery of the virus-like antigen by means of immune electron microscopy not only emphasizes the value of the technique, but also provides for the first time a means for diagnosis and for studying hepatitis A infections.

Ferritin-Conjugated Antibodies

Ferritin is a protein having a molecular weight of 700,000 and containing about 23 per cent iron, largely in the form of ferric hydroxide and phosphate. The iron is concentrated within the ferritin molecule in four particles or *micelles*. These units form a central core measuring 5.5 to 6.0 nm (55 to 60 Å) in diameter. Because of its composition and molecular

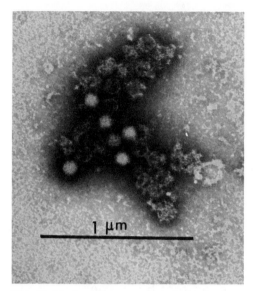

FIG. 23–14. Aggregates resulting from the incubation of adenoviruses with specific antibodies against them. Visualization was achieved by using immune electron microscopy (IEM), a technique that permits visualization of reactions between viruses and antibodies (specific protein substances). (From Vassall, J. H., II, and Ray, C. G.: *Appl. Microbiol.*, **28**:632, 1974.)

arrangement, the ferritin molecule is electron dense and has a characteristic appearance in electron micrographs.

Techniques are in use by which ferritin can be coupled (attached) to specific antibody molecules. Such preparations are used in various types of investigations including locating bacterial, fungal, and viral antigens in tissue and studying antigen-antibody interactions.

Virus Neutralization

Serologic reactions of various kinds are used for purposes of: (1) viral identification and classification, (2) detecting antibodies against certain viral agents in the normal population, and (3) studying the responses of individuals to prophylactic immunization. Examples of procedures used include animal protection, complement-fixation, hemagglutination inhibition, and neutralization tests. Since the *in vitro* methods are less expensive and more rapid to perform, they are more commonly used than *in vivo* tests.

Procedures

Viral neutralization tests can employ either tissue culture systems or laboratory animals such as chick embryos, mice, or rats. The details of the procedure vary with the viral agent, the host used, and related factors. However, two general procedures are employed. In one of these, dilutions of a virus suspension are mixed with constant volumes of undiluted serum, incubated for 1 to 2 hours, and then a specific quantity of each mixture is injected into separate groups of animals. For example, dilution mixtures ranging from $1/100$ (10^{-2}) to $1/1,000,000$ (10^{-6}) are each injected into 4 animals. The animals are observed for a specified length of time to determine the effects caused by the virus which were not inhibited by the antibodies present in the serum. Naturally controls are also used; these include viral dilutions with and without serum lacking specific antibodies. In the other method, the viral concentration is kept constant and the serum is diluted. When tissue culture systems are employed, cells are examined for any evidence of a specific inhibition or neutralization of cytopathic effects.

For general diagnostic purposes, two blood specimens should be obtained from the patient suspected of having a viral infection. One such sample should be taken during the acute phase of the disease, and the second during the convalescent period. The presence of an infection generally is indicated by a fourfold increase in antibody titer in the second blood specimen.

The Quellung Reaction

This is a diagnostic test for infections caused by various encapsulated bacteria, including *Diplococcus pneumoniae, Hemophilus influenzae,* and *Klebsiella* spp. The procedure involves treating encapsulated cells with specific antisera which combine with the capsular polysaccharide, thus rendering the structure visible. From electron microscopic studies it appears that the capsule actually swells. "Quellung" is the German word for swelling. The quellung reaction is not used very often. As mentioned in an earlier chapter, capsules can be demonstrated with the aid of India ink.

QUESTIONS FOR REVIEW

1. Differentiate between the following combinations:
   a. antigen and antibody
   b. serum and plasma
   c. toxin and antitoxin
   d. antitoxin and antibody
   e. agglutination and precipitation
   f. reagin and complement
   g. serology and immunology
   h. Ascoli test and blood typing

2. What significance do serological tests have in the diagnosis of infectious diseases?

3. Construct a table listing:
   a. representative serological tests
   b. the types of reagents used
   c. the appearance of both positive negative reactions

4. a. What is viral neutralization?
   b. What is toxin neutralization?

5. a. What is complement? Where can this substance be found normally?
   b. Discuss the complement-fixation test. Include in your answer the components of the test and indica-cation system, and the appearance of a typical positive and negative test.

6. Differentiate between the indirect and direct fluorescent antibody tech-niques.

7. What value does the *Limulus* test have?

8. Explain how electron microscopy can be used for diagnostic purposes.

The Human Blood Groups

The ABO System

In 1900, Karl Landsteiner observed that the mixing of erythrocytes and sera from two different human donors, followed by incubation at body temperature, resulted in the agglutination of the red cells. This phenomenon is known as *isohemagglutination* because it involves reactions between agglutinogens and agglutinins from the same species (*iso-*). It enabled Landsteiner to demonstrate the existence of the A and B blood types. In addition, he found certain situations in which no visible reactions occurred between the reactants. Blood cells exhibiting this negative result were at first classified as belonging to a C blood type, but later the designation was changed to O. The fourth and last of the major blood types, AB, was discovered by von Decastello and Sturli in 1902. The major blood types are referred to as the A-B-O or ABO system.

In addition to having specific blood group antigens, certain humans possess antibodies which react with the erythrocytes from individuals of other blood types, causing them either to agglutinate or to lyse. These immunoglobulins are called *isohemagglutinins* and *isohemolysins,* respectively. The lysis occurs as a consequence of antibody molecules (isohemolysins) sensitizing the blood cells, thus making them vulnerable to the hemolytic activity of complement. Usually,

the antibodies encountered in the blood serum or plasma of an individual are not directed against the blood factors normally present. However, most individuals have antibodies against blood factors which are absent from their blood cells. For instance, a person of blood type O has antibodies against type A (anti-A) and type B (anti-B). Antibody concentrations can be increased as a result of transfusions, or in the case of women who have borne children possessing different blood characteristics. Although an individual's blood type is determined by the genes obtained from both parents, these genetic determinants do not necessarily represent the same blood factors. The genetic implications of blood groups will be discussed more fully later.

From the findings of Landsteiner and other investigators, the presence of specific blood group antigens, and their clinical importance, were firmly established. The International System of Nomenclature proposed by Landsteiner and Von Dungern and Hirschfeld, together with the agglutinogens and agglutinins of the respective major blood groups, are shown in Table 24–1.

The Universal Donor and Recipient

A transfusion reaction can occur in an individual recipient if the concentration of agglutinins in his plasma is sufficient to bring about the agglutination or hemolysis of erythrocytes from a donor.

Table 24–1   Selected Characteristics of the
Major Human Blood Groups

International Designation	Agglutinogen Associated with Cells	Presence or Absence of Agglutinins within Normal Sera	
		anti-A or α (alpha)	anti-B or β (beta)
A	A	−	+
B	B	+	−
AB	AB	−	−
O	O	+	+

It is obviously advisable to transfuse a patient with blood of his particular type. However, there may be circumstances in which this is impossible, because blood of the recipient's type is unavailable. Type O blood is used in such situations, because antibodies against type O blood are not normally encountered. While the plasma portion of O blood contains agglutinins against both the A and B antigens (Table 24–1), these antibodies would be sufficiently neutralized or diluted in the recipient's circulation.

Individuals with O type blood have been and still are commonly referred to as "universal donors." Unfortunately, this designation can mislead persons into thinking that transfusions using their blood can be performed safely in all cases. Serious transfusion reactions can occur as a consequence of the presence in these individuals of antigen-antibody systems other than the ABO system, such as minor blood group and Rh factors. In general, transfusion reactions are prevented by performing the direct and indirect cross-matching procedures to determine the blood compatibilities of prospective donors and recipients.

Table 24–1 shows that persons with an AB blood type do not have agglutinins against the A or B factors. Consequently such individuals could receive blood from donors belonging to any of the four major blood groups. The desig-

nation of "universal recipient" therefore is given to persons with an AB blood type.

Laboratory Determination of Blood Groups (Blood Typing)

Two diagnostic procedures, the tube and slide tests, are commonly employed to determine blood types. The determination of an individual's blood group can be made either by testing his red cells with standardized anti-A and anti-B sera, or by testing the patient's serum with standard, sensitive, known A and B red cells. For reliable results, both test systems should be employed. However, in usual classroom and laboratory situations, only the first combination is employed.

The tube technique usually incorporates erythrocytes from the individual being tested with standard test sera (individual preparations of anti-A and anti-B reagents). Specific proportions of the individual anti-sera and the erythrocyte suspension are mixed, incubated at 37°C for 30 to 60 minutes, and observed for the presence or absence of agglutination. Table 24–2 shows the pattern of reactions that are used for blood type determinations.

The slide test utilizes the same type of ingredients. It is performed by first placing one or two drops of each test antiserum on opposite portions of a glass slide, then adding a drop of the patient's cells to each of them. The combinations are mixed separately with the aid of ap-

Table 24–2   Reaction Patterns Used in
Blood Type Determinations

Blood Type	Isoagglutinins	
	anti-A	anti-B
A	+	−
B	−	+
AB	+	+
O	−	−

plicator sticks, and observed for agglu-- tination. Color photograph 54 depicts the actual reactions characteristic of the major blood types. Reactions should develop within 5 to 10 minutes.

Hemolysis of erythrocytes may occasionally occur during these procedures. Usually this is the result of mixing incompatible blood cells with unknown or improperly prepared test sera. The reaction probably is caused by isohemolysins rather than isoagglutinins. The problem is usually solved by heating the serum at 56°C for 30 minutes, or by serial dilutions of the serum.

Mention should also be made of the possible occurrences of *false positive* and *false negative* results during testing. For example, *rouleaux formation,* a phenomenon characterized by red cells aggregating together much like a pile of coins, should be differentiated from true agglutination.

Suitable controls include: (1) the pretesting of sera for activity, (2) dilution of cells and sera in physiological saline if a reaction has not occurred after a sufficient length of time, and (3) the incorporation of tests with known cells and anti-sera. The incubation temperature should also be checked, as variations in temperature can affect results. These procedures are discussed later in the chapter.

The ABO Subgroups

Antigenic variations of the ABO system have been reported since 1935. Their frequencies vary; A_1 and A_2 are more commonly encountered than others such as A_3, B_3, B_V, etc. The blood group A has been divided into the major subdivisions A_1 and A_2. The AB group is subdivided into A_1B and A_2B.

Subgroups also have been reported in relation to the B group, including B_V, B_3, B_K, B_W, and B_X. However, major divisions comparable to the A determi-

nants have not been formulated. These B subgroups are primarily subjects for continued investigation.

Inheritance of the ABO Blood Groups

The ABO blood factors of man constitute one example of genetic characteristics determined by a multiple allelic series. An *allele* is a gene belonging to a group of alternate genes that occupy a specific area on a chromosome. Inheritance of the A and B characteristics follows normal Mendelian principles. An individual's blood type is determined by receiving, from each parent, one of four allelic genes: A_1, A_2, B, or O. The specific blood group agglutinogens become permanently established, a finding which can be readily demonstrated in fetuses and newborns. Blood group-associated isohemagglutinins, however, are not normally detectable at birth, but become so within 3 to 6 months.

The genotype and phenotype of offspring can be determined by the "Punnett Square Technique," commonly referred to as the checkerboard system. The possible types of genes of one parent appear across the top of the checkerboard square, and the genetic contributions of the other parent along the side. It is important to remember that each parent generally contributes one gene for each characteristic.

Parent 1 (genotype AB)

		A	B
Parent 2 (genotype AO)	A	AA	AB
	O	AO	BO

Table 24–3 shows the possible genotypic (assortment of genes) and phenotypic (demonstrable expression of the individual's genotype) combinations from selected parental matings. It can be seen from this table that the A and B alleles

Table 24–3   Genotypes and Phenotypes Resulting from Selected Parental Matings
(Checkerboard System)

Parental		Offspring's Possible	
Genotypes	Corresponding Phenotypes	Genotypes	Phenotypes
AA × AO	A × A	AA, AO	A
AO × AO	A × A	AA, AO, OO	A or O
BB × BO	B × B	BB, BO	B
BO × BO	B × B	BB, BO, OO	B or O
AA × BB	A × B	AB	AB
AO × BO	A × B	AO, BO, AB, OO	A, B, AB, or O
AB × AO	AB × A	AA, AO, BO	A or B
AB × BO	AB × B	AO, AB, BB, BO	A, AB, or B
AB × OO	AB × O	AO, BO	A or B

exert a dominance over the O gene. Generally speaking, the O blood type manifests itself only in persons lacking either the A or B genes. It other words, a homozygous O state must be present. In AB individuals neither allele is dominant over the other; a state of *co-dominance* exists.

Secretors and Nonsecretors

The blood group substances (BGS) A and B are not limited to red cells, but can be demonstrated in various other tissue cells and body fluids. Examples of tissue cells found to contain BGS include kidney, liver, lung, and muscle. These A and B factors have been detected in amniotic fluid, gastric juices, ovarian cyst fluid, perspiration, saliva, semen, tears, and urine of approximately 80 per cent of the population. Such individuals are referred to as "secretors." Conversely, persons lacking the blood substances in their tissues and body fluids are called "nonsecretors."

The secretion of these water-soluble body substances is under the control of a Mendelian dominant gene, *Se*. Non-secretors possess the homozygous recessive *se se* state.

Other Blood Group Substances

Chemically, purified substances with A, B, H, and Le^a activity (the latter two factors are discussed later in this chapter) have been characterized as large mucopeptides. By weight, they consist of 85 per cent carbohydrate and 15 per cent peptide. The two chemical components are linked in a covalent manner. The molecular weight of these substances was found to range from 200,000 to 1,000,000.

H substance (antigen). It is well known that the A and B genes control the A and B factors, respectively. However in the case of the O gene, a particular antigen is not specified. Nevertheless, many investigations have demonstrated a distinctive isoantigen in association with blood type O cells. Moreover, almost all humans, as well as a variety of other animal species, have been found to have this factor in varying quantities. Because of its wide distribution, the antigen has been designated as the H or *heterogenetic* substance. It should be stressed at this point that this H substance does not appear to be an O gene product, as it has been found in association with blood cells of persons lacking the O gene.

Based on studies utilizing monospecific H anti-sera, a definite pattern of reactivity was shown to occur with the various groups of the ABO system. The results demonstrated the following decreasing order of relative reactivity:

$$O > A_2 > A_2B > B > A_1 > A_1B$$

Judging from the chemical characteristics of the A, B, and H substances, the gene controlling the production of the H factor (H gene) is independent of the ABO allelic genes.

In addition, as with the A and B blood group substances, the H substance also is found in a water-soluble form in various body fluids. Its secretion is controlled by the pair of allelic "secretor" genes discussed earlier.

The Rh System

With the discovery of the ABO system, it was believed that transfusion problems could not develop if the donor and recipient belonged to the same blood group. Unfortunately, between the years 1921 and 1939, some hemolytic transfusion reactions were reported even when blood typing tests apparently showed donor and recipient compatibility. No explanation for these reactions was offered. Moreover, prior to 1940, several reports appeared of newborns exhibiting a clinical state called erythroblastosis fetalis. Such infants were swollen and markedly anemic.

In 1937, Landsteiner and Wiener, immunizing guinea pigs and rabbits with rhesus monkey blood, discovered antisera which not only agglutinated the red cells from the monkey but also the cells from approximately 85 per cent of their human blood samples. A hitherto unknown human blood agglutinogen was obviously uncovered. The new factor was designated "Rh," primarily to indicate the source of the antigen (the rhesus monkey). Upon further investigation, it was found to occur with all blood groups.

The importance of the Rh factor was realized when the antibody response of sensitized Rh-negative individuals to the administration of Rh-positive antigens was demonstrated. One of the several investigations which clearly provided a basis for this realization had been reported by Levine and Stetson in 1939. These investigators observed a transfusion reaction in a woman shortly after the delivery of her stillborn fetus. Apparently in need of a transfusion, the woman received blood from her husband, which resulted in a pronounced hemolytic reaction. The mother's serum was found to contain an agglutinin against the Rh factor. Levine and Stetson postulated that the presence of this agglutinin was the direct result of an *in utero* immunization of the mother by a fetal antigen inherited from the father. Later studies by Levine and his colleagues proved this to be the cause, and showed that the resulting antibody could pass through the placenta and bring about the condition of erythroblastosis fetalis, commonly called "the Rh baby."

Other Rh and Hr Factors

Since the original report of the Rh factor in human blood was made by Landsteiner and Wiener, more than 25 other blood factors have been discovered which evidently belong to the Rh-Hr blood group system. These blood factors have proved to be of great clinical significance, second only to the ABO system.

The Rh-Hr system is a complex one, and controversies have arisen over the nomenclature for the Rh agglutinogens. Two principal methods are currently being used: the Wiener scheme (the original Rh-Hr nomenclature designations)

Table 24–4   A Comparison of the Nomenclature used as Designations for the Rh Blood Factors (Wiener) and Rh Agglutinogens (Fisher-Race)

Wiener System	Fisher-Race System
Rh_0	D
rh′	C
rh″	E
hr′	c
hr″	e
hr	d

Designations for the more recently discovered Rh factors are symbolized by various combinations of subscript or superscript letters and numerals, e.g. D_u, C_w.

and the Fisher-Race system (combinations of the letters C, D, and E). Table 24–4 shows the comparison between these two systems of notation.

Designations for the more recently discovered Rh factors are symbolized by various combinations of subscript or superscript letters and numerals, e.g., D_u, C_w.

The Fisher-Race designations are simpler than those of Wiener, and are consequently widely used by persons doing blood analyses. Commercially prepared Rh blood-typing sera generally are labeled with the designations of both systems. The controversies over terminology go beyond the simple labeling of sera preparations, to fundamental differences as to the nature and genetic control of the "Rh antigenic specificities."

Rh typing.   The determination of the Rh factors of an individual's red cells is obtained by agglutination tests employing the appropriate anti-sera, anti-Rh_0, -rh′ and -rh″. The classic and clinically most important of the factors is Rh_0 (D).

Hemolytic Disease of the Newborn (the Rh Baby)

Erythroblastosis fetalis is the blood incompatibility normally encountered when differences in Rh factors exist between the mother and her child. In the usual case this condition develops with babies born to mothers negative for the Rh_0 (D) factor and Rh_0 (D) positive fathers (this specific Rh terminology is explained below). The red cells of the child may inherit the paternal blood factor, which is foreign to the mother. If this antigen is carried across the placental barrier, it serves to immunize the mother to the Rh factor. The resulting maternal isoantibodies pass from the mother's circulation into the fetal system and attack the baby's red cells. The most common clinical manifestations of the disease are anemia and jaundice of the newborn.

Once a mother has been actively immunized against the Rh_0 factor and has given birth to one child with erythroblastosis fetalis, the disease manifestations will be more severe with future offspring, especially if the father is homozygous for the blood factor ($Rh_0^+Rh_0^+$). However, if the father is heterozygous ($Rh_0^+Rh_0^-$), they may produce normal children lacking the Rh_0 factor. Almost all Rh_0 negative women without previous exposure to the Rh_0 factors via transfusions have given birth to one or more normal Rh_0 positive children before sufficient maternal antibodies were produced to cause trouble.

Generally speaking, the Rh_0 (D) antigen has been the major factor involved in the hemolytic disease of the newborn. However, all of the other blood antigens should be regarded as capable of causing the condition.

Prevention of Rh Isoimmunization

Fetal erythrocytes are commonly observed in the maternal circulation near term, and their numbers generally increase after childbirth. Much clinical evidence indicates that the processes of labor and delivery cause fetal red cells to enter the maternal circulation. Other investigators hold that there is a continual leakage of the fetal cells into the mother's system throughout pregnancy. Probably both play significant roles in the isoimmunization of certain Rh-negative female patients. The major threat of isoimmunization occurs at the end of the third trimester of pregnancy and immediately after childbirth.

Two groups of investigators (Finn, Clarke, Donohoe, McConnell, Shippard, Lehane, and Kulkle on one hand, and Freda, Gorman, and Pollach on the other) reported a procedure which has the potential of eradicating the maternal Rh problem. The basic approach is to prevent a new mother from developing antibodies that might endanger a later child—in other words, to suppress the antigenic stimulus by the fetal cells during the postpartum period, with the aid of passive immunization. This is done by administering an immunoglobulin G (γ G) preparation which contains high titers of anti-D (anti-Rh$_o$) antibody. Rh negative unsensitized mothers receive this material within 72 hours after delivery. The immunoglobulin preparation also must be administered in cases of abortion and miscarriages involving the Rh problem. The passive nature of this immunization is apparent from the general observation that the antibody disappears after approximately 6 months. Thus, a short-lived passive immunity is used to prevent a long-lasting active immunity.

Blood Testing Techniques

Compatibility Testing
or Crossmatching

The primary purpose of this type of testing is to prevent a transfusion reaction, as a consequence of blood incompatibilities between the recipient and donor or donors. Specifically, the crossmatching technique is designed to detect any incompatibility between the recipient's serum and the donor's cells (this is known as the *major crossmatch*), or between the recipient's cells and the donor's serum (this is referred to as the *minor crossmatch*). The crossmatch procedure is done after the respective blood specimens have been typed as to the ABO and Rh factors and any other factor that appears to be indicated.

Agglutination or lysis of the red cells from either the donor or recipient in their tests is considered to be indicative of an incompatible situation. However, it should be stressed that occasionally an incompatible crossmatch may be due to an error in blood typing of the specimens used, or to the presence of atypical antibodies in the blood of either the donor or recipient. Therefore, when situations of this nature are suspected it is customary to investigate the possibility of error.

The methods used in crossmatching should involve at least four different phases or approaches. These include detection of: (1) "saline-acting" antibodies at 22° and 37°C; (2) "high protein medium-acting" antibodies; and (3) antiglobulin activity (see the section concerned with the Coombs test). A general description of the saline and protein crossmatch procedure follows.

Saline crossmatching. The saline crossmatch procedure is carried out by combining the recipient's serum with a 2 per cent saline suspension of the donor's red cells in one test tube, and the donor's serum with the recipient's cells in another tube (Figure 24–1A). The presence of either macro- or microscopic hemagglutination or hemolysis shows incompatibility. This particular technique is carried out, as mentioned previously, at 22° and at 37°C.

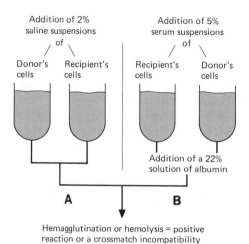

Addition of 2%
saline suspensions
of

Donor's   Recipient's
cells   cells

Addition of 5%
serum suspensions
of

Recipient's   Donor's
cells   cells

Addition of a 22%
solution of albumin

A   B

Hemagglutination or hemolysis = positive
reaction or a crossmatch incompatibility

FIG. 24–1. _A_. The saline procedure. _B_. The protein crossmatch procedure.

Protein crossmatching.

The protein crossmatch technique combines the recipient's serum with a 5 per cent serum suspension of donor cells in one system, and the donor's serum with a similar concentration of the cells of the recipient in another. A 22 per cent solution of albumin is added to both combinations (Figure 24–1*B*). Again, as in the saline procedure, observation of the two systems is made for the presence of hemagglutination or hemolysis. The presence of either result constitutes an incompatible state. If no reaction develops, both systems are incubated at 37°C for 30 minutes and examined once more.

Saline RT Test

Several different types of antibody may be present in the sera of individuals isoimmunized against various blood factors. Antibodies which are capable of causing the agglutination of saline suspension of homologous erythrocytes generally are called *complete* or *bivalent* antibodies, or *saline agglutinins*.

Saline RT (room temperature) procedure for the detection of agglutinins is carried out by mixing and subsequently incubating the patient's serum with a 2 per cent saline suspension of test blood cells. The latter specifically contain the antigens capable of reacting with the blood group antibodies for which the test is being conducted. Agglutination or hemolysis constitutes a positive test.

Coombs Tests

Those antibodies which are unable to bring about agglutination in saline are referred to as *incomplete*. Certain incomplete antibodies can be detected on the basis of their agglutination of erythrocytes suspended in protein solutions, such as human AB serum and bovine serum albumin. These antibodies are referred to as *conglutinating* antibodies or *albumin agglutinins*. Two tests for the detection of incomplete antibodies, the direct and indirect Coombs tests, have great clinical importance in cases of hemolytic anemia and hemolytic disease of the newborn.

Direct Coombs test.

The direct Coombs test is used to determine whether or not the erythrocytes of patients have been sensitized (coated) by antibodies *in vivo*. In this test, saline-washed blood cells which are suspected of being sensitized are mixed with anti-human globulin serum (Coombs reagent) and observed for the presence of agglutination. A control of the patient's cells and saline is also included. The presence of clumping in the erythrocyte-Coombs reagent system is considered a positive test. While this test demonstrates the presence of incomplete antibodies, it does not identify them specifically.

Indirect Coombs test.

The indirect Coombs test is a modification of the direct procedure, used for detecting either complete or incomplete antibodies in the serum of sensitized individuals. The procedure employed consists of the following three stages: (1) sensitization of erythrocytes (Rh positive) with Rh anti-serum (patient's serum); (2) washing the sensitized cells in order to remove excess antibody; and (3) mixing the resulting preparation with the Coombs reagent. Agglutination of the Rh antibody-coated red cells by the anti-human serum (Coombs reagent) constitutes a positive test.

The difference between this test and the direct test is that in the latter procedure red cells are examined for the presence of antibody on cells (sensitization *in vivo*), while in the indirect test, Rh positive cells sensitized *in vitro* by the antibodies present in the patient's serum are used to detect the Rh antibodies.

Some Problems Encountered In Blood Typing and Crossmatching

Rouleaux formation. Occasionally certain false reactions occur during the performance of blood typing or crossmatching procedures, which can cause considerable difficulties in the interpretation of these tests. One of these results is *rouleaux formation*. This phenomenon can be described as the pseudoagglutination of red cells, giving a stack-of-coins appearance to a blood preparation. This type of reaction has been commonly observed to occur with patients having: (1) hyperglobulinemic state, (2) excess fibrinogen, (3) severe infections, or (4) transfusions with dextran prior to the testing procedure. Rouleaux formation can be eliminated by diluting serum specimens accordingly.

Cold agglutinin disease. Cold agglutinins are IgM autoantibodies that usually have specificity for an I antigen present on the red blood cells of most adults (Table 24–6). The autoantibodies (anti-I) occur in two general clinical conditions. First, they develop transiently following certain infectious diseases, particularly pneumonia caused by mycoplasma (see Chapter 33). Clinically significant hemolysis is present in 5 percent of the patients with the condition. The second situation is noted in the cold agglutinin syndrome, which is characterized by mild to moderate anemia, chronicity, and occurrence in older individuals. Complement (C′) activation is responsible for the anemia observed in these individuals. If sufficient numbers of complement components attach to the blood cells, intravascular hemolysis (within blood vessels) will develop. Components of complement are routinely found on the erythrocytes of patients with cold agglutinin disease in the absence of the autoantibodies. Cold agglutinins do not bind to red blood cells at normal body temperatures. They are thought to become attached at the lower temperatures of blood in the peripheral blood vessels (especially with exposure to low environmental temperatures). Cold agglutinins will agglutinate I antigen containing erythrocytes of individuals at temperatures ranging from 0° to 20°C and occasionally at room temperature (25°C). The reaction, however, is reversible and disappears at body temperature (37°C).

Other Blood Group Systems

In recent years several blood group systems have been discovered in addition to the ABO and Rh systems (Table 24–5). Some of these systems have little clinical significance, possibly because of low antigenic potency or limited occurrence. Some, however, are clinically important, as they appear to be antigenically potent. These systems are by no means as far-reaching as the ABO and Rh groups.

Table 24–5   Additional Major Blood
Group Systems

Blood Group	Agglutinin Designation(s)	Technique Used for Detection
Duffy	anti-Fy[a]	anti-human globulin[a]
	anti-Fy[b]	anti-human globulin
Kell	anti-K	anti-human globulin
	anti-k	anti-human globulin
	anti-Kp[a]	anti-human globulin
	anti-Kp[b]	anti-human globulin
Kidd	anti-Jk[a]	anti-human globulin
	anti-Jk[b]	anti-human globulin
Lewis	anti-Le[a]	Saline RT; ficin[b]
	anti-Le[b]	Saline RT
Lutheran	anti-Lu[a]	Saline RT
	anti-Lu[b]	Saline RT
P	anti-P P_1	Saline RT
	anti-P_1	Saline RT
	anti-Pk	Saline RT
MNS	anti-M	Saline RT
	anti-N	Saline RT
	anti-S	Saline 37° C or RT
	anti-s	Saline RT

[a] Consult section on the Coombs test.
[b] A protein-digesting enzyme.

Table 24–6   Representative Minor
Blood Groups

Blood Group	Agglutinin Designation	Technique Used For Detection
Batty	anti-By	Anti-human globulin
Char	anti-Chr[a]	Anti-human globulin
I	anti-I	Saline, ficin
	anti-i	
Swann	anti-Sw[a]	Saline (RT)
Wright	anti-Wr[a]	Several techniques

Detection of new blood group systems can occur accidentally or as a consequence of deliberate animal immunizations for the express purpose of finding previously unrecorded antibodies. The rapid development of newer techniques and improvements in older procedures have made it possible to discover additional, previously unknown systems.

Table 24–5 lists the so-called "additional major" blood group systems, together with the procedure used for their detection, while Table 24–6 shows certain representative minor blood groups which have been discovered relatively recently. Systems representative of the first group will be discussed briefly below.

The Lewis System

Mourant in 1946 first discovered antibodies of the Lewis blood group in blood samples from two different individuals. The system was named after one of them. The antigens of the Lewis group, Le[a] and Le[b], are chemically related to, but genetically independent of, the ABH anti-

gens. Moreover, while the Lewis blood factors are inherited characteristics, the genetic aspects do not follow the usual Mendelian pattern. The antigens are found in saliva and serum and occur in association with red cells as a consequence of absorption from body fluids.

The presence of Lewis antigens on erythrocytes results from the combined effect of the genes controlling secretion of the Lewis factors (L, 1) and the genes which regulate ABH substance secretion (Se, se).

When an individual's genotype is made up of the dominant Se and L genes (which control the secretion of ABH and Lewis substances), a priority is given to the production of the ABH material. Any remaining uncommitted substrate is used to produce the Lewis factor for the saliva. If the individual is a non-secretor, meaning that he lacks the dominant gene Se, but possesses the L gene, all the available substrate is converted into the Lewis substance. This material saturates the saliva and often enters the plasma. Thereupon, erythrocytes absorb the Lewis factor (Le[a]), and the individual becomes positive for the antigen of the blood system.

The MN System

The MN antigens were discovered and subsequently reported by Landsteiner and Levine in 1927 and 1928. With the use of two antibodies, anti-M and anti-N, produced in rabbits, all human erythrocytes tested were found to contain either the M, N, or both agglutinogens. Consequently, individuals could be categorized into groups M, N, or MN.

Genetically, the two antigens of the system are the products of a pair of genes which are both allelomorphic and codominant. Transfusion reactions implicating the MN group have been rare. However, this blood system has gained major significance in medicolegal situations involving disputed parentage (Table 24–7).

The Ss System

The Ss antigens, which comprise another blood system, are known to be commonly associated with the MN group. Walsh and Montgomery discovered the S agglutinogen in 1947, while Levine and his associates reported the existence of the related factor(s) in 1951. Genetically, the genes controlling the Ss antigens are not allelic to the MN system, but, rather, are believed to occupy a closely associated chromosome site. In contrast to

Table 24–7   Possible MN Blood Groups of Offspring Resulting from Mating

Blood Groups of Parents	Possible MN Groups of Offspring
M × M	M
N × N	N
MN × MN	M or MN or N
M × N	M or MN or N
M × MN	M or MN
N × MN	MN or N

the MN group, the Ss system has been clinically implicated in cases of transfusion reactions and hemolytic disease of the newborn.

Other Systems

In addition to the blood group systems discussed or listed in Table 24–6 several other blood group antigens and antibodies have been discovered. Although only a few case reports have been made, it is known that some of these systems, such as the Kidd blood group and others, can be responsible for transfusion reactions and hemolytic disease of the newborn.

QUESTIONS FOR REVIEW

1. Discuss the major blood types.

2. Who was Karl Landsteiner?

3. Distinguish between a universal recipient and universal donor.

4. Differentiate between isoagglutinins and isohemolysins.

5. Describe the procedure used to detect ABO subgroups.

6. Give the possible genotypes and phenotypes of offspring from the following parental genotypes:
   a. AO × AB
   b. OO × AA
   c. AO × BO
   d. AO × BB
   e. AB × OO
   f. AB × BO

7. Explain or define "secretors," in this context.

8. What is the "H" substance?

9. Discuss the major features and possible complications of the Rh system.

10. Diagrammatically differentiate between the following testing procedures:
    a. direct and indirect Coombs tests
    b. major and minor crossmatch
    c. saline and protein crossmatch procedures

11. What significance do minor blood groups possess?

Hypersensitivity States (Allergy)

In 1906 von Pirquet introduced the term *hypersensitivity* to denote the increased reactivity upon subsequent exposures of persons previously vaccinated with vaccinia virus. Later, he extended the limits of hypersensitivity to include any altered activity, or *allergy,* caused by contact with animate or inanimate substances. This state is generally described as an acquired "exaggerated responsiveness" of the individual toward a specific substance that normally does not produce similar reactions in the majority of previously unexposed members of the same species. The "inciting or inducing agents" are generally referred to as *allergens.*

Initial exposure to an allergen immunologically primes, or sensitizes, the individual to subsequent contact with the same allergen. Further contact with the antigen can lead not only to a secondary boosting of the immune response but can also cause tissue-damaging reactions. Several factors influence the pathophysiological expressions of hypersensitive responses, including the portal of entry, the cellular and tissue responses to the allergen, and the genetic makeup of the individual.

Classification of the Hypersensitivities

Historically, hypersensitivity reactions were divided into two classes on the basis of the time required for a sensitized individual to exhibit an obvious physiological response upon re-exposure to the sensitizing allergen. Reactions that developed within a few seconds to 24 hours following allergen exposure and that involved circulating antibodies were usually classified as immediate, and those that developed after 24 but within 48 hours and that involved the direct participation of sensitized lymphocytes were considered to be of the delayed type of hypersensitivity. Although these designations are still used today, they are now endowed with a different meaning. In 1968, Coombs and Gell defined four types of hypersensitivity (Table 25–1): Type I (classical immediate hypersensitivity), Type II (cytotoxic), Type III (immune-complex-mediated), and Type IV (cell-mediated, or delayed, hypersensitivity). Types I through III are immunoglobulin-dependent hypersensitivities, whereas Type IV reactions are mediated by antigen-sensitized T-lymphocytes rather than by freely diffusible antibody molecules. In addition, specific interactions of sensitized T-cells with antigens form the basis of several situations such as rejection of transplanted tissues and organs and protection against cancer.

The immunoglobulin-dependent (immediate) hypersensitivities can be subdivided into two categories depending upon whether the classic, heat-stable im-

Table 25–1   A Comparison of Different Types of Hypersensitivity[a]

Characteristic	Hypersensitivity Type Reactions			
	I (Classic Immediate)	II (Cytotoxic)	III (Immune-Complex-Mediated)	IV (Cell-Mediated)
Maximum reaction time for clinical manifestation (response)	30 min	Variable	3–8 hr.	24–48 hr.
Reaction mediators (regulators)	IgE, IgG, complement (C′), and pharmacological substances including histamine, SRS-A, ECF-A, kinins, and prostaglandins[b]	IgG, IgM, and complement	IgE, IgG, IgM, complement, eosinophiles, neutrophiles, and lysosomal enzymes	T-lymphocytes, macrophages, and soluble mediators such as MIF and TF[c]
Appearance of response to intra-dermal antigens	Wheal-and-flare		Erythema and edema	Erythema and induration
Inhibition by anti-histaminic drugs	Yes, in certain situations	No	No	No
Inhibition by cortisone	No, with normal dosages	No	No	Yes
Passive transfer with serum from sensitive donor	Generally yes	Yes	Yes	No
Examples of allergic states	Anaphylaxis, asthma, serum sickness, and drug, food, and insect allergies	Transfusion reaction, hemolytic disease of the newborn, and drug-induced allergies	Arthus reaction, serum sickness, and certain auto-immune diseases	Infection allergies, auto-immune disease, graft rejection, contact dermatitis to drugs, and tumor immunity

[a]Source: Gell, P. G. H., Coombs, R. A., and Lachman, P. (eds.): *Clinical Aspects of Immunology,* 3rd ed., Section IV. Blackwell Scientific Publications, Oxford, 1974.
[b]SRS-A is a slow-reacting substance of anaphylaxis; ECF-A is an eosinophilic chemotactic factor of anaphylaxis.
[c]MIF is a migration inhibitory factor; TF is a transfer factor.

munoglobulins, IgA, IgD, IgG, and IgM, or the heat labile antibodies, IgE, are *primarily* responsible for the immune response. Heat-stable antibodies resist destruction by heat at 56 to 60°C for periods of 30 minutes to 4 hours. It should be noted that both immunoglobulin categories may be present simultaneously.

From the characteristics listed in Table 25–1 and this discussion it is obvious that we are dealing with several different types of physiological response of immunized cells or tissues. Nevertheless, the induction of a hypersensitivity state requires one or more exposures to the inciting allergenic substance, followed by a so-called latent period with no obvious symptoms or effects. The particular hypersensitive state is then initiated by still another exposure to the allergen.

The particular type of hypersensitivity

acquired is determined by several factors, including: (1) the chemical nature of the allergen; (2) the route involved in the sensitization, e.g., inhalation, ingestion, injection, etc., and (3) the physiological state of the individual. The form of the response produced is dependent upon the specific type of contact with the precipitating allergenic dose, and the acquired hypersensitive state.

There are other differences among the types of hypersensitivities. These are listed in Table 25–1 and will be discussed later.

Type I (Classical Immediate Hypersensitivity)

Examples of this type of allergic response include certain forms of asthma, anaphylactic shock, hay fever (*allergic rhinitis*), and hives (*urticaria*). One of the distinguishing features of this hypersensitive state is the rapid liberation of physiologically active chemicals, such as histamine and serotonin, from affected cells. Substances of this kind are normally released from cells as a consequence of antigen and antibody interaction. Initially homocytotropic (reactive with cells of the same species) or heterotropic (reactive with cells of other species) immunoglobulins produced by plasma cells (Chapter 22) attach by means of their F_c portions (Figure 22–4A) to basophils and mast cells. Mast cells contain heparin and histamine in numerous intracytoplasmic granules and are found in connective tissue. The F_{ab} regions of the attached immunoglobulins (Figure 22–4A) protrude from the cellular surfaces and, when combined with antigen, alter the permeability of the mast cells. This reaction leads to the degranulation of mast cells and the release of the physiologically active substances mentioned earlier. It is known that the maintenance of intracellular cyclic adenosine monophosphate (cAMP) concentrations is required for the stability of mast-cell granules. The antigen-immunoglobulin interaction described probably interferes with the stable cellular state. The human homocytotropic antibody has been identified as IgE and the heterotropic immunoglobulin as IgG. In humans the overwhelming majority of Type I reactions are associated with IgE. Because of their pharmacologic properties, the liberated substances produce secondary involvement and responses in other cells.

Examples of these effects can include hemolysis, increase in muscle activity, increased capillary permeability, and excessive mucus production. Another important characteristic of the immediate reaction is that the sensitivity response can be conferred on a normal, nonsensitive person simply by the injection of serum from a sensitive individual.

Representative Type I Allergic States

Anaphylaxis

Before 1837 or so, certain protein solutions, such as egg albumin, which were used for the primary inoculation of laboratory animals, were considered to be largely harmless. The report of Magendie in 1839, however, changed this view, as he found that repeated injections of such material often produced severe symptoms and even the sudden death of dogs. Several other investigators observed a similar reaction during the nineteenth century, but no systematic study of it was initiated until Portier and Richet rediscovered the phenomenon in 1902.

Richet and his colleagues attempted to immunize dogs to certain substances known to be toxic for these animals. Such materials included eel serum and an extract of sea anemone tentacles. Unfortunately, they found that reinjection of sublethal dosages of these substances some three weeks after primary injection produced reactions similar to those reported by Magendie. Thus, instead of becoming immune to such foreign matter, the experimental animals became unusually sensitive to them. Moreover, death was caused by reinjection with dosages too small to affect normal laboratory animals. In essence, the effect was the opposite of protection (*prophylaxis*). Richet designated this unfavorable phenomenon as *anaphylaxis*. The reaction has come to be known as *anaphylactic shock*.

Two general types of anaphylactic responses are recognized—*systemic* or *generalized anaphylaxis* and *cutaneous anaphylaxis*. Both states are temporary. Usually recovery occurs within an hour's time, unless death occurs rapidly. The anaphylactic phenomenon resembles antibody-antigen reactions in several ways, as will be shown.

Generalized anaphylaxis. This form of anaphylactic response is produced by the intravenous injection of specific soluble antigenic substances, such as horse serum, egg albumen, etc., to which an animal has been previously immunized. Within the context of the allergic response, the allergens or sensitizers that originally cause the hypersensitive state are called *inducers*. The anaphylactic response is brought about by similar substances, but they are designated as *elicitors*. Generalized anaphylaxis is characterized by asphyxia (suffocation), bronchial constriction, shock, vascular engorgement, and other respiratory changes. It is important to note that the features of anaphylactic shock will vary depending on the species of animal involved.

Cutaneous anaphylaxis in humans. This condition results from the intradermal injection of an elicitor into a previously sensitized individual. The reaction begins with an intense itching at the injection site. This response is shortly followed by the development of an elevated, pale, irregular wheal (a flat, elevated, swollen area), surrounded by a region of erythema (redness). The response, which usually subsides within approximately 30 minutes, is referred to as the *wheal-and-flare reaction*.

Production of active anaphylaxis. Three definite steps are required to bring about anaphylactic responses. These are: (1) injection of the inducer substance; (2) the passage of time, referred to as the *incubation* or *latent period,* which leads to the sensitized state in the individual; and (3) exposure to the elicitor, gener-

ally by injection or inhalation. The elicitor is frequently called the *shocking* or *injection dose.* An anaphylactic reaction exhibits the same order of specificity as that found with *in vitro* serologic tests: the inducer and elicitor are closely related.

Anaphylactic responses are dependent on both the number of antibody-antigen complexes formed, and the rate at which they are formed. The more rapidly such complexes develop, the stronger the response. The release and rapid degradation of certain pharmacologically active substances play a vital role in anaphylaxis and related responses.

Several active participants or mediators have been identified with their roles in anaphylaxis. These include cell-associated substances, histamine and serotonin (5-hydroxytryptamine), and basic peptides called *kinins*. The latter are formed by several enzymes called *kallikreins*. The kinin group includes bradykinin, lysyl-bradykinin, and a slowly reactive substance—anaphylaxis ("SRS-A"). The last-named material is found only in the tissues of animals experiencing anaphylaxis. SRS-A is noted for causing a slow contraction of smooth muscle and for its insensitivity to antihistamine drugs in normal dosages. The concentration of kinins in general is found to increase in some animal species undergoing anaphylaxis. They apparently cause an increased permeability of capillaries, contraction of smooth muscle, and vasodilation (dilation of small arteries).

Other pharmacological mediators of anaphylaxis that have been found include eosinophilic chemotactic factor (ECF-A) and prostaglandins (PG). ECF-A is probably responsible for the marked increase in eosinophils (eosinophilia) found in many hypersensitivity reactions. Numerous prostaglandins have been identified in tissues; however, their precise role in anaphylaxis remains vague.

The temporary nature of anaphylactic reactions is accounted for by the rapid degradation and excretion of histamine, serotonin, and the kinins. Thus, large concentrations of such active substances cannot accumulate. Anaphylaxis can be produced in various laboratory animals, many of which exhibit differences in symptomatology. Such variations are partly explained by the varying amounts of these pharmacologically active substances in their tissues, and the differences in the responses of tissues such as smooth muscle and blood vessels.

Anaphylaxis in humans. Systemic or generalized anaphylactic shock can occur in situations involving serum therapy and the administration of penicillin. Individuals with this condition may exhibit abdominal cramps, diarrhea, diffuse erythema, hives, intense itching, nausea, respiratory difficulties, and vomiting. Death may occur rapidly. The prompt administration of epinephrine (adrenalin) intravenously or intracardially usually will abort an attack of anaphylaxis.

Certain precautionary measures should be taken to guard against the fatal complication. These include: (1) skin testing individuals with minute amounts of substances known for their possible elicitor roles, e.g., serum, penicillin, etc., before full doses of such substances are administered; and (2) keeping a container of epinephrine close at hand to administer as needed.

Passive transfer of atopy (Prausnitz-Küstner or P-K reaction). The presence of antibodies in the serum of atopic individuals was discovered in 1921 by Prausnitz and Küstner. This discovery came about as a consequence of Küstner's pronounced sensitivity to fish. A small quantity of his serum was injected into Prausnitz's skin. After 24 hours, an extract of fish was introduced into this site as well as into an untreated region. The latter served as a control. Within 20 minutes following the injection of the fish extract, a typical wheal-and-flare response developed at the site that received the serum. The control region showed no reaction. The P-K procedure can be used for patients who are extremely sensitive to specific allergens and cannot undergo direct testing.

In performing this test, several hours should lapse between injections of serum from a sensitive individual and of the suspected allergen. Mixtures of these two substances should not be employed, as no reaction will develop.

Cytotropic antibodies. The specific circulating antibodies associated with the wheal-and-flare (P-K) response have been referred to by several names, including atopic reagins, reaginic antibodies, skin-sensitizing antibodies, or simply reagins. Unfortunately, the term reagin is also used for the antibody associated with the Wasserman test used in the diagnosis of syphilis. Nevertheless, human skin-sensitizing or homocytotropic antibodies belong to the IgE class of immunoglobulins. Based on studies involving sera from atopic individuals, antibodies to these antigens are: (1) destroyed by heating at temperatures of 60°C for 30 to 60 minutes are heat-labile; (2) unable to pass the placental barrier; (3) present in low concentrations in sensitive persons; (4) remain fixed to tissue cells long after their passive transfer, as in the P-K reactions; (5) do not fix complement; and (6) do not produce detectable reactions *in vitro* with allergens, except with recently developed highly sensitive techniques.

Atopy

About 10 per cent of the population in the United States is believed to have a rather unusual type of allergy. Such individuals possess a natural hypersensitivity, in the absence of a deliberate exposure, to a large number of environmental allergenic substances such as airborne pollens of grasses, ragweeds, and trees, animal danders, foods, certain fungi, and house dust components. Upon inhalation or ingestion of an appropriate allergen, various kinds of clinical syndromes can develop, the most frequent of which are asthma, eczema, certain gastro-intestinal disorders, hay fever, hives, and rhinitis. Coca applied the term *atopy* to these allergic disease states, from the Greek word meaning "out of place."

It appears likely that the hypersensitive state develops in susceptible persons as a consequence of their repeated accidental absorption of the allergenic substances mentioned earlier. Such absorption could involve the mucous membranes of the gastro-intestinal or respiratory tracts, or the skin. The various atopic allergic disease states are precipitated by subsequent exposure to these allergens. The tendency to develop diseases of this type shows a familial distribution, and it is believed to be inheritable. Persons exhibiting atopic reactions are referred to as *atopics*. Such individuals have the genetic capacity to produce blood plasma concentrations of IgE that are ten times greater than those of non-atopics.

Skin testing for atopic states. An interesting characteristic of atopic individuals is their ability to exhibit, upon injection of an appropriate allergen, a *wheal-and-flare (erythema) response*. Itching usually occurs first at the site of inoculation and is followed by the development of a wheal, which is surrounded by a reddened area. The effect may persist for approximately 20 minutes. This type of response can be used to determine the substances to which individuals may be sensitive. Sterile dilutions of allergens are introduced into the skin of individuals either by intradermal injection or by scarification (i.e., making a small number of superficial scratches). Sensitivity to a particular allergenic substance will be indicated by the development of the wheal-and-flare response in the area of its inoculation. Intense reactions usually are considered to be associated with allergens responsible for the immediate difficulties of the person being tested.

Type II
(Cytotoxic Hypersensitivity)

Examples of type II responses in humans include: (1) blood transfusion reactions in which blood group antigens in red blood cell membranes are the inciting factors, (2) erythroblastosis fetalis (the Rh baby), in which Rh antigens on fetal or newborn red blood cells are the targets of maternally formed antibodies, and (3) drug-induced anemias in which a drug forms an antigenic complex with the surfaces of erythrocytes and evokes the production of antibodies that are cytotoxic for the cell-drug complex. Detailed descriptions of the first two responses may be found in Chapter 24.

Formed elements of blood erythrocytes, leukocytes, and platelets are especially prone to these reactions. Allergens create situations that will induce cytolysis (disruption of cells) or cytotoxicity (death of cells without disruption). The antibodies primarily involved in type II hypersensitivity responses are IgG and IgM, which can fix complement.

Type III (Immune-Complex-Mediated Hypersensitivity)

Examples of type III responses include the Arthus reaction, serum sickness, and certain auto-immune reactions. In immune-complex-mediated hypersensitivity the union of soluble antigen and immunoglobulins takes place within the body and may give rise to an acute inflammatory reaction. If complement (C′) is fixed, biological molecules called anaphylatoxins are produced, which ultimately will cause the release of histamine with permeability changes in blood vessels. Other pharmacological substances (chemotactic factors) are produced that set in motion a chain reaction of events that will damage tissues and intensify the inflammatory response. Such events include the influx of polymorphonuclear leukocytes, the phagocytosis of immune complexes by these cells, and the release of proteolytic (protein-digesting) enzymes from the phagocytes. Extensive damage activates all the components of complement and, under appropriate conditions, leads to the aggregation of platelets. Such an accumulation of platelets can result in the release of additional pharmacological substances and in the formation of microthombi, which can lead to localized obstruction of circulation (ischemia).

The effects of immune complexes *in vivo* depend on the absolute concentrations of antigen and antibody, which determine the reaction's intensity, and on the relative proportions of these reactants, which govern the distribution of the complex within the body. In cases of antibody excess the immune complexes are rapidly precipitated and tend to settle around the site of antigen introduction. In situations with antigen excess, soluble complexes are produced which may result in systemic reactions and may be widely distributed in

the body and deposited in such sites as the kidneys, joints, and skin. Many cases of glomerulonephritis are due to immune complexes.

The Arthus Reaction (Antibody Excess)

In 1903, soon after the discovery of anaphylaxis, M. Arthus, a French physiologist, described this *in vivo* antibody-dependent allergic reaction. Originally this state was recognized in rabbits, and later in humans and other animals. When rabbits were given weekly subcutaneous injections of horse serum, no reaction was apparent. However, after several weeks, inoculation with the same type of material produced a localized inflammatory response.

Arthus reactions are not restricted to the skin. The phenomenon can involve most tissues in individuals having sufficiently high antibody levels. A so-called "pure" reaction is seldom seen, according to Quinn, because of other immediate hypersensitivity states and the massive infiltration of polymorphonuclear leukocytes into the involved area.

The regions exhibiting the Arthus response show the following tissue changes: (1) a marked reduction in blood flow, (2) the formation within small blood vessels of thrombi "rich" in platelets and leukocytes, (3) escape of erythrocytes into neighboring connective tissue, (4) development of edema, and (5) as mentioned earlier, the massive infiltration of of the area by polymorphonuclear leukocytes. Tissue destruction also occurs in the later stages of the reaction. In short, the changes which take place are those of classic inflamation. Certain of the components of complement are believed to play a role in the Arthus reaction.

The passive and reverse passive Arthus reactions. It is possible to create the Arthus response passively by intravenously injecting antibodies (anti-serum) into a nonsensitive animal. The corresponding antigenic material is then introduced subcutaneously.

The reverse passive Arthus reaction is performed by first subcutaneously injecting the anti-serum into the animal, and then introducing the antigen either intravenously or into the same area receiving the anti-serum. The development of tissue changes is influenced by several factors, including the nature and quantity of antibody involved.

Serum sickness (antigen excess). The original description of this anaphylactic condition was made by von Pirquet and Schick in 1905. Approximately 8 to 12 days after receiving an injection of large volumes of foreign protein, such as antitoxin, individuals have been known to develop the distressing condition known as serum sickness. The likelihood of this sensitivity state occurring increases with the dose of foreign protein introduced.

Persons with serum sickness generally may experience fever, generalized swelling of lymph nodes, itching, polyarthritis, hives or erythematous eruption, and edema of the ankles, eyelids, and face. The severity of these symptoms is determined by the severity of the attack. In general, however, they may subside in two days, although in certain cases persistence of symptoms has been noted to last for two weeks.

The various effects observed in serum sickness are associated with antibodies which are produced by their reacting with injected foreign soluble protein. Together these substances form toxic complexes which not only cause injury to blood vessels, but bring about the various symptoms described earlier. The production of antibodies and the formation of toxic combinations with the foreign protein generally take place prior to the appearance of symptoms.

As the level of antibody increases, the level of foreign protein decreases. This sequence of events ultimately leads to the disappearence of the effects of serum sickness. In time, antibody levels generally subside. If at this time a second injection is given of the same foreign protein initially introduced, another attack of serum sickness will develop within 3 to 5 days.

Severe and even fatal reactions can be provoked in individuals having a high level of antibody. Reinjection of foreign protein in such persons produces an immediate local response as well as a later, generalized reaction, within 12 hours. Individuals sensitive to horses or their products—horse hair, dander, and serum—exhibit this type of condition. The reaction is of a typical anaphylactic type and should be specifically called *serum allergy*. The testing of persons with such "sensitivity" to foreign serum proteins is extremely important from a clinical standpoint. The procedure used here involves the intracutaneous injection of a diluted preparation of the foreign serum in question. A positive reaction is indicated by the presence of a wheal and erythema surrounding the site of injection. A result of this type should be regarded as strong evidence for the existence of a serum-sensitive state in the person tested.

The Shwartzman Reaction

In 1927 G. Shwartzman observed local hemorrhagic and necrotic inflammations which developed from intradermal injections of bacterial culture filtrates. The reaction could be made to occur quickly if 30 minutes after the intradermal injection a second so-called "provocative" intravenous injection was given. Some time later Shwartzman proved that systemic reactions involving internal organs also were possible when both the initial and provocative injections were given intravenously. The reaction is evoked by the endotoxins of Gram-negative bacteria in the initial injection. The provocative injection can be either endotoxin or a variety of "immunologically unrelated" substances, including agar and starch.

The endotoxin causes reduction of phospholipids from blood platelets. This reaction initiates and contributes to blood coagulation. Typically, the features of the localized phenomenon are swelling and reddening in the area of injection, fever, and reduction of white cells (leukopenia). The Shwartzman reaction was shown not to be induced by an immune mechanism.

Type IV (Cell-Mediated or Delayed Hypersensitivity)

During the 80 years or so which followed the initial discovery of anaphylaxis by Magendie, a variety of additional allergic reactions were observed. Such responses appeared to be in a category which was fundamentally different from those associated with types I through III (Table 25–1). For example, these reactions took longer to develop, 24 to 28 hours after the injection of allergenic material into a sensitized individual. Neither circulating antibody nor the passive serum transfer of the reaction could be demonstrated. These responses came to be known as the delayed type of hypersensitivity. Considerable attention has been given to their use in the diagnosis of several infectious diseases (Table 25–2).

Type IV responses are characterized by several properties. These include: (1) no release of histamine or chemically related substances occurs, (2) cortisone is helpful in inhibiting the reaction, (3) the sensitivity associated with this state

cannot be transferred by the injection of serum from a sensitive individual to a non-sensitive one, (4) passive transfer of the response to non-sensitive recipients can be accomplished by means of living (viable) lymphoid cells from sensitized donors and a non-antibody active "transfer factor," (5) responses are not inhibited by antihistamines, but are inhibited by steroid compounds such as cortisone and hydrocortisone, and (6) *in vitro* migration of cells from sensitized animals is inhibited by the presence of antigen-specific migration inhibition factor (MIF).

Type IV hypersensitivity is typified by several conditions, including diagnostic skin test reactions for leprosy, tuberculosis, and histoplasmosis (Color photograph 59); contact dermatitis caused by chemicals, drugs, or poison ivy; certain auto-immune diseases; and tissue graft rejection reactions. Some of these states will be discussed later.

Cell-mediated or delayed hypersensitivity is dependent upon the interaction of T-type lymphocytes with antigen. Thymic-derived lymphocytes bearing specific receptors on their surface are stimulated by contact with antigen to release factors termed *lymphokines* by Dumonde. Whenever such receptors react with appropriate antigenic determinants, the T-cell will become sensitized. Subsequently, when the sensitized T-lymphocyte interacts with the specific antigenic determinant, a cell-mediated response will be initiated. The T-cell undergoes blastogenesis and cellular division, which results in the production of specifically sensitized cells and a corresponding increase in the number of reactive T-cells. This activity takes place in blastogenetic centers such as lymph nodes. From such areas sensitized T-cells can enter the circulation, seed other lymphatic tissues, or accumulate at sites where the antigen is introduced.

Table 25–2   Representative Examples of Delayed Skin Reactions Employed as Diagnostic Tests

Disease State	Type of Infectious Disease Agent Involved (If Applicable)	Nature of Preparation Used[a]
Brucellosis	Bacterium	Brucellergin (extract of *Brucella* spp.)
Leprosy	Bacterium	Lepromin (extract of lepromatous tissue)
Lymphogranuloma venereum	Bacterium	Chorioallantoic membrane (extract from infected chick embryo)
Psittacosis	Bacterium	Heat-killed organisms
Tuberculosis	Bacterium	Purified Protein Derivative (PPD), or Old Tuberculin (OT)
Blastomycosis	Fungus	Concentrated culture filtrate
Coccidioidomycosis	Fungus	Coccidioidin (concentrated culture filtrate)
Histoplasmosis	Fungus	Histoplasmin (concentrated culture filtrate)
Leishmaniasis	Protozoan	Extract of cultured organisms
Echinococcosis (sheep tapeworm)	Helminth	Hydatid fluid extract
Trichinosis (pork roundworm)	Helminth	Extract of the causative agent
Contact dermatitis	Simple chemical compounds	Small quantities of suspected chemicals

NOTE: The information obtained from such tests also can be used in epidemiologic surveys.
[a] Refer to the individual chapters in which these disease states are discussed for further details.

It has become increasingly apparent from several studies that cell-mediated responses are vitally important to recovery from several infectious diseases, such as those caused by fungi, certain protozoa, viruses, and various species of bacterial genera, including *Brucella, Mycobacterium,* and *Salmonella.* Recovery from infection is delayed or fails to occur if there is a substantial reduction or absence of T-lymphocytes, even if immunoglobulin synthesis is unaffected. Under the influence of antigen-stimulated release of lymphokines (Table 25–3) from sensitized T-cells, activated macrophages demonstrate increased phagocytic, biosynthetic, and microbial destructive properties. Such macrophages are far more effective than normal macrophages in eliminating microorganisms.

Table 25–3   Representative Lymphokines and Associated Function(s)

Lymphokine	Designation (if appropriate)	Function(s) or Activities
Chemotactic factor	CF	Causes chemotaxis (chemical attraction) of macrophages
Cloning-inhibition factor	CLIF	Blocks *in vitro* multiplication of certain cell types
Dialyzable transfer factors	TF	Converts normal lymphocytes *in vivo* and *in vitro* to antigen-sensitized lymphocytes
Inhibitor RNA synthesis	IDS	Reversibly inhibits mitosis of lymphocytes
Lymphotoxin	LT	Causes cytotoxicity
Macrophage-activation factor	MAF	Partly responsible for increased lysosomal activity of macrophage
Macrophage-aggregation factor	MAF	Restricts macrophage movement and induces formation of giant cells
Macrophage inhibition factor	MIF	Inhibits migration of macrophages
Proliferation-inhibition factor	PIF	Blocks *in vitro* multiplication of certain cell types

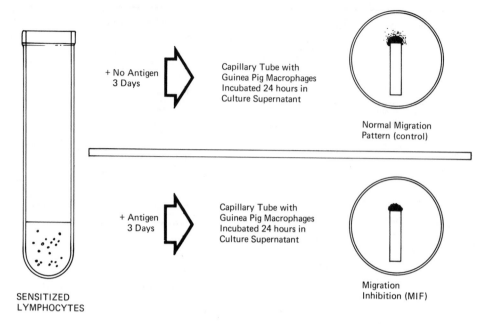

FIG. 25–1. MIF *in vitro* assay. A patient's lymphocytes are cultured with and without antigen. The supernatant fluids from these cultures are tested for their ability to inhibit the migration of macrophages obtained from a normal guinea pig. (After Maddison, S. E., *Clin. Peds.*, **12**:529–537, 1973.)

Lymphokines: Indicators of Cellular Immunity

Both specific antigens and non-specific substances stimulate lymphocytes to produce a number of hypersensitivity mediators (regulators). These products have been grouped under the term *lymphokines* (Table 25–3). One of these mediators, the macrophage-migration-inhibition factor (MIF), is used in an assay that is generally considered to be a reliable indicator of the cellular immune status of an individual. The technique most frequently used for the MIF assay involves setting up tissue culture systems that consist of a patient's leukocytes with and without a specific antigen. The supernatant fluids (the materials bathing the cells) are harvested and replaced on three successive days, after which they are concentrated by freeze-drying (lyophilization). The concentrate is tested for its ability to inhibit the migration of macrophages which have been obtained from a normal guinea pig and which have either been packed into capillary tubes or placed in agar. The area of macrophage migration in the presence of culture supernatants with antigen is compared with the area of migration in culture supernatants without antigen (Figure 25–1). Individuals having cell-mediated defects do not make MIF. Therefore, for these individuals the test should show no inhibition of macrophage migration in either case. Normal individuals, on the other hand, do produce MIF. Additional *in vitro* tests with which to determine the cell-mediated immune status of an individual have been developed. These tests are of particular importance to patients who are having an organ transplant, or those who have immune deficiencies, cancer, or an infectious disease, since it may be hazardous to inject such individuals with specific antigen. *In vitro* assays to determine the immune status of such patients obviates the danger of additional exposure to antigen, as in the case of skin testing.

Representative Type IV Allergic States

Allergy of Infection

Type IV (delayed hypersensitivity) may develop during the course of infections caused by certain bacteria, fungi, viruses, and animal parasites, such as worms. When present, the allergic state brings about an accelerated as well as pronounced tissue reaction to the infectious agent. The classic and the most thoroughly studied example of this type of hypersensitive reaction is associated with tuberculosis. The phenomenon is commonly referred to as the *tuberculin type of allergy.*

Hypersensitivity of this type was first demonstrated in 1891 by Robert Koch during his experiments with tuberculosis. He showed that guinea pigs infected with *Mycobacterium tuberculosis* some 2 or more weeks earlier reacted differently from uninfected (normal) guinea pigs to the subcutaneous reinjection of virulent living tubercle bacilli. At the site of inoculation the tuberculous animals developed within 2 days massive inflammatory reactions which increased in intensity and became necrotic, with areas of cellular death. Extension of the infectious processes to regional lymph nodes either was delayed or did not occur. In other words, the tissues of infected animals reacted violently to the tubercle bacilli, and tended to localize the infection by walling off the area of involvement. This sequence of events is known as the *Koch phenomenon.* Uninfected guinea pigs injected with similar material normally developed progressive tuberculosis.

Koch also demonstrated that the specific inflammatory reaction and associated tissue changes could be caused by dead, as well as living, tubercle bacilli. Furthermore, a bacteria-free protein fraction extract prepared from these organisms, known as *tuberculin,* produced the same response. Larger dosages of tuberculin given subcutaneously to infected animals could result in severe delayed responses, and even a systemic shock reaction.

The various observations of Koch and his colleagues prompted von Pirquet to suggest that this reaction to tuberculin was indeed another example of sensitization. In 1907 he proposed the use of tuberculin for the detection of tuberculous individuals. The tuberculin skin test, and variations of it, are widely used today for this purpose, as well as for the standardization of skin testing material.

Tuberculin injected subcutaneously into a tuberculous guinea pig produces no obvious response for a few hours. However, local inflammation appears and gradually increases in intensity. The area around the site of inoculation becomes reddened, firm, and swollen, or *indurated,* in 24 to 48 hours. The reaction can reach 5 mm in diameter. This response, known as the *tuberculin reaction,* is associated with type IV hypersensitivity.

In actual cases of tuberculosis infection, the allergic state becomes established early, generally before the obvious signs of the infection are apparent. The relationship between clinical symptomatology and hypersensitivity is not clearly defined. Several additional factors are associated with the infectious process, as discussed further in Chapter 33.

The tuberculin type of reaction in a sensitized animal is brought about by protein or certain protein degradation products referred to as *purified protein derivative* (PPD). PPD was isolated in 1934 by Seibert, Aronson, Reichel, Clark, and Long. Similar reactivity is not evoked by lipids or carbohydrates.

Type IV hypersensitivity can develop in a variety of infections of humans and lower animals (Table 25–2). And, as indicated earlier, the presence of this allergic state can be helpful in diagnosis and epidemiological surveys. However, it should be noted at this point that the significance of a positive delayed-type skin test (Color photograph 59) to an infectious disease varies with the infection. *Reactions of this sort do not necessarily indicate current infection.* The relationships of particular skin tests to actual disease states are discussed in several of the chapters concerned with pertinent disease agents.

Contact Dermatitis

This particular form of hypersensitivity includes certain types of drug allergy. Contact dermatitis is perhaps one of the most commonly encountered human allergic diseases. The sensitization and the production of symptoms result simply from contact with various chemical causative compounds. Included in the group of *incitants* are: (1) simple chemicals, e.g., formaldehyde and picric acid; (2) metals, e.g., mercury and nickel; (3) various drugs and dyes; (4) certain cosmetics; (5) insecticides; and (6) the active components associated with poison ivy, poison oak, poison sumac, and other plants.

Two types of responses are generally recognized, namely, *contact skin sensitivity* and *allergic contact dermatitis*. The former refers to the individual's capacity to react to a dermal application of a sensitizing substance, or *sensitizer*. Allergic contact dermatitis is an allergic response to a sensitizer. In this case both human and various laboratory animal sensitization occurs as a result of skin contact with the incitant, or the intrader-

mal injection of this material. Approximately 5 to 20 days are needed for the development of the hypersensitivity reaction. Filter paper patches treated with the sensitizer in question are used to determine if this state exists. Such treated material is held in place on the skin by adhesive tape for approximately 24 hours. The test is generally read twice, once a few hours after the removal of the patch and 24 hours later. In diagnosing certain cases of contact dermatitis it may be necessary to continue examinations for two or more weeks. A positive reaction is characterized by an erythematous region containing various-sized vesicles (blisters) (Figure 25–2).

Treatment of contact dermatitis requires the identification of the causative agent. Attempts to desensitize individuals have met with limited success. When the chemical involved has an oily nature, the possibilities are better. Avoiding the incitant is of course advisable, but it is not always practical.

Penicillin allergy. Penicillin is considered to be among the least toxic drugs in current clinical use. Apparently, however, the antibiotic molecule combines in some manner with certain protein derivatives to form stable inducers. These newly formed complexes or conjugates can induce antibody production and bring about generally either type of hypersensitive state,

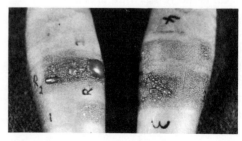

FIG. 25–2. A positive patch test for contact dermatitis. (Courtesy of Armed Forces Institute of Pathology, Washington, D.C., Neg. No. AFIP 57–15160–2.)

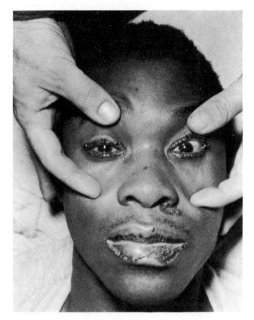

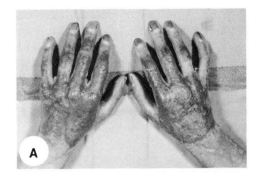

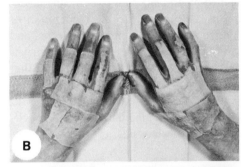

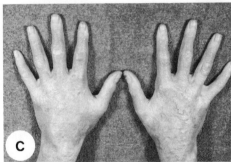

FIG. 25–3. Penicillin sensitivity. This individual is exhibiting a hemorrhagic reaction involving his eyelids, and nasal and oral mucosa. (Courtesy of Armed Forces Institute of Pathology, Washington, D.C., Neg. No. AFIP 54–1548–3.)

immediate or delayed (Figure 25–3). Approximately 10 percent of the people who have had repeated doses of penicillin fall victim to this condition. The injection of 1 mg of the antibiotic can result in a fatal anaphylactic shock reaction.

The type IV hypersensitivity to penicillin can also develop in persons who are repeatedly exposed to the antibiotic in some form. Hospital personnel and individuals involved in the preparation and packaging of penicillin fall into this category. The sensitivity develops as a drug contact dermatitis.

Tissue Transplantation Reactions

Experiments in the transplantation of animal kidneys began a chain of events that has led to an entirely new medical era, one in which a variety of tissues and organs can be surgically replaced and transferred

FIG. 25–4. An example of the successful transplantation of skin in cases of severe burns. _A_. Deep dermal burns affecting both hands. _B_. The application of homograft. _C_. The result after three homografts. The healing is obvious. (From Shuck, J. M., Pruitt, B. A., and Moncrief, J. A.: _Arch. Surg., **98**:472, 1969, © AMA.)

between different sites on the same individual or from one body to another. The transplanting of skin from one region to another in an individual is a fairly common and usually successful operation. This particular type of procedure has been used for victims of fires (Figure 25–4) and other situations in which extensive skin destruction has occurred.

Other types of transplants, such as those involving the heart, liver, or lung, have proved to be more difficult. The transplantation of tissues involves a complex collection of cells, each of which has a large variety of antigens controlled by deoxyribonucleic acid (DNA). Except for identical twins, each individual's chromosomal DNA is unique. This uniqueness of "self" (see Chapter 22) is accompanied by a highly sensitive sensing mechanism of the host for the recognition of foreign substances from both external and internal sources. The recognition mechanism evokes the complex responses that comprise an individual's immunity. Following actual tissue transplantation, both humoral (circulating antibodies) and cell-mediated mechanisms of immunity are activated.

Transplant categories. The survival of transplanted tissues may be defined in terms of genetic relationships (identity). For example, where only the tissue of one individual is involved, the transplant is called an *autograft*. If a graft (the tissue to be transplanted) is taken from one animal and given to another of the same species (genetically dissimilar members of the same species), the tissue is referred to as an *allograft*. When both individuals are genetically identical—identical twins or mice from the same highly inbred line— the tissue is an *isograft*. Finally, a transplant involving two different species, such as the transplantation of kidneys from a chimpanzee into a human, is referred to as a *xenograft*.

Genetic control. The basic goal of transplantation is the long-term survival of the grafted tissue. The success of the procedure (survival of the graft) depends on several factors, including the degree of antigenic similarity between donor and recipient, and the nature of the transplanted tissue itself.

One basic approach used to prevent immune rejection of transplants is to carefully select donor tissues and cells so that they closely match those of the recipient. Finding the best match involves histocompatibility antigen. Each individual inherits four genes—two from each parent— that control the human leukocyte-antigen (HL-A) system. Each of these genes seems to bring about the synthesis of a distinctive histocompatibility antigen. These antigens are lipoprotein substances that are associated with the plasma membranes of white blood cells, platelets, and most of the fixed tissues of the body. To date, at least 31 different HL-A antigens have been identified. In combinations of four each, these antigens produce thousands of different tissue types. The best tissue matches are between close relatives. In the general population there is little chance of a perfect HL-A match. It is for this reason that a general rating scale is applied in the selection of donor tissues and organs. In comparing two individuals (donor and recipient) for histocompatibility, if they share all of the same antigens the match is designated as an "A." In the event the antigens are almost identical the match is termed a "B." With one antigen markedly different the match is assigned to a "C" category, and with more than one antigen clearly different the match is rated as a "D." Finally, if the antigens are completely incompatible, an "F" designation is made.

Determination of the suitability of tissue for grafting purposes (histocompatibility testing) is made by using the lymphocyte toxicity test or the mixed leukocyte (lymphocyte) reaction (MLR). The lymphocyte toxicity test is a widely applied method and is designed to measure the histocompatibility antigenic composition of donor and recipient. This is accomplished by performing the test on lymphocytes of both donor and recipient with a battery of antisera. The mixed lymphocyte reaction test determines only the compatibility of donor and recipient and reflects incompatibilities of the major transplantation antigen.

Graft rejection.   When tissue is transplanted from one individual to another there are actually two rejection (tissue deterioration and ultimate destruction) processes to be considered. The first and traditionally most studied is the host rejection of grafted tissue (host-versus-graft reaction). The second is the reverse of this reaction, the graft-versus-host response, which develops when immunocompetent tissues are transferred to an immunologically handicapped host.

In the case of the host-versus-graft reaction, following the surgical implantation of a skin allograft a characteristic sequential process takes place, during which the T-lymphocytes of the recipient become sensitized to the transplantation antigens in the graft. In addition, as the process continues, inflammation becomes evident, and there is an extensive invasion of the graft by macrophages and T-cells. A battery of lymphokines is released from antigen-stimulated T-cells, which leads to substantial cellular destruction and tissue damage (necrosis). In response to the extensive damage to the grafted tissue, a scab-like graft appears; it is subsequently sloughed from the recipient. Collectively, the entire process is referred to as the *first-set rejection,* and it usually is completed before immunoglobulin production against the transplantation antigens reaches a peak. In the event that a second skin allograft from the same donor is implanted into the recipient after rejection of the first allograft, a more rapid destruction of the graft occurs. This is because of an expanded population of antigen-sensitized T-lymphocytes, a situation created by exposure to the transplantation anti-

gens of the first graft. The process of rejection of a second skin allograft is referred to as *second-set rejection.*

Although immunoglobulins are not essential for graft rejection, they may become involved at any stage in the process. Both IgG and IgM immunoglobulins can participate in allograft rejection. Their destructive effects are mediated by complement. *White graft rejection,* which involves rapid tissue destruction, occurs in recipients with high concentrations of immunoglobulins against transplantation antigens.

Homograft rejection can be curtailed or totally inhibited in certain situations by several means, including the injection of corticosteroids or anti-lymphocytic drugs, and whole body irradiation. In several instances, a combination of such agents has been employed. It is important to note that, while this type of procedure can promote the survival of allografts, it does lower the individual's ability to produce antibodies against pathogenic disease agents. Thus antibiotics also must be used to prevent infection of persons receiving grafts.

Auto-allergy (Auto-immune) Diseases

Normally in the body of an immunocompetent individual there exist appropriate mechanisms to prevent the recognition of "self" components (see Chapter 22) as antigens by the lymphoid system. Such unresponsiveness, referred to as *immunological tolerance,* is essential for human survival. Unfortunately, as with all types of machinery, there is always a possibility that tolerance mechanisms might falter and break down, thus creating auto-allergic (auto-immune) disease states. In these disorders self-antigens, or auto-antigens, stimulate the production of circulating immunoglobulins (humoral response) or of specially sensitized lymphocytes (cell-mediated response), either of which will react with the auto-antigen.

Causes of auto-allergy. There are several etiological agents that may evoke an auto-allergic response. These include: antigens that normally do not circulate in the blood; an altered antigen (such alterations could develop through exposure to chemicals, physical agents, or microorganisms); a foreign antigen that is similar to an auto-antigen; and a mutation in immunocompetent cells that results in a responsiveness to normal auto-antigens. These agents may precipitate an auto-allergy following events such as tissue injury, administration of drugs, or certain microbial infections. Several human viruses are enveloped (see Chapter 9) with membranes which are partly derived from nuclear, intracytoplasmic or plasma membranes of the host, but which also may include virus-specific antigens. Several of these viruses have been associated with auto-allergic reactions.

Even though direct supporting evidence is lacking, many authorities believe that auto-allergic diseases largely represent type IV or cell-mediated responses. Although immunoglobulins are frequently present, there appears to be little or no correlation with the disorder. Auto-allergic or auto-immune diseases represent a broad range of disorders and a confusing spectrum of overlapping clinical manifestations, pathological lesions, and immunological properties. Some diseases, such as Hashimoto's thyroiditis, are organ-specific; others, such as the auto-immune hemolytic anemias, are localized but are not organ-specific; and still others are non-organ-specific. Systemic lupus erythematosis (SLE) is an example of an auto-allergic disorder in which both lesions and auto-antibodies are not limited to any one organ or tissue. Characteristi-

cally, in SLE the formed elements of the blood are affected, and an unusual collection of auto-antibodies is encountered, some of which react with DNA and other nuclear components of all body cells.

Witebsky's postulates. Numerous auto-allergic and auto-antibody-associated diseases have been reported. However, determination of the relationship of immunologic phenomena to the cause of the illness is not always a simple matter. Much the same problem confronted microbiologists in their initial efforts to accurately demonstrate which microorganisms isolated from diseased individuals were actually responsible for the disease. Robert Koch established a set of postulates to enable microbiologists to assign specific microbes as the agents of specific infectious diseases (see Chapter 2). In a similar type of effort, Witebsky proposed the following postulates to provide guidelines in determining the relationship of immunologic phenomena to auto-allergic disease: (1) the auto-allergic response must be regularly associated with the disease state; (2) immunization of an experimental animal with the antigen from the appropriate tissue should result in a replication (duplication) of the disease; (3) the immunopathologic changes that develop in the experimental animal should parallel those that occur in the human disease; and (4) transfer of the auto-allergic illness in the experimental animal should be possible by transfer of serum or lymphoid cells from the diseased individual to a normal recipient.

Apart from the large number of auto-allergic disease states that are currently recognized and the rather confusing overlapping of clinical manifestations, certain characteristics have become apparent. First, the incidence of auto-allergic diseases and associated immunoglobulins tends to increase with age. Second, such diseases occur most commonly among persons with generalized immunological deficiencies. Third, a greater proportion of females have auto-allergic diseases. In addition, it has been observed that any given auto-immune disease may produce lesions that resemble those associated with the other types of hypersensitivities.

Therapy for auto-allergic diseases varies widely and is influenced by several factors, such as the particular disease, the severity of the clinical manifestations, and the associated hazards of prolonged therapy with corticosteroids and other immunosuppressive agents and procedures (see Chapter 22).

QUESTIONS FOR REVIEW

1. Differentiate between inducers and elicitors.

2. List at least two differences among types of hypersensitivity. List and briefly describe two examples of the different states of sensitivity.

3. From what standpoint can type IV be of diagnostic importance? To which diseases is the reaction applicable?

4. What is auto-allergic disease?

5. What is the difference between systemic and cutaneous anaphylaxis? What accounts for the temporary nature of anaphylactic reactions? What symptoms do humans exhibit in cases of anaphylactic shock?

6. Distinguish between passive and reverse Arthus reaction.

7. a. What is atopy?
   b. Describe the wheal-and-flare response.
   c. Discuss the Prausnitz-Küstner reaction. Does it have any clinical importance?
   d. What are lymphokines?

8. Does the Shwartzman reaction involve an immune mechanism of the host? Explain.

9. Describe the Koch phenomenon.

10. What is contact dermatitis? What types of substances act as incitants here? How can an incitant be identified?

11. Define or explain and give examples of:
    a. xenograft
    b. rejection
    c. allograft
    d. second set reaction
    e. histocompatibility
    f. HL-A system

12. List the causes of auto-allergy.

13. Of what value are Witebsky's postulates? State them.

14. Differentiate between a humoral response and a cell-mediated one.

15. Describe the MIF *in vitro* assay.

26

Immunization and Public Health

The objectives of this chapter are primarily to: (1) describe methods used to administer vaccines and related preparations; (2) discuss in general terms the methods employed for the preparation of agents used for immunization; (3) describe the vaccines currently available to provide protection against bacterial, rickettsial, and viral infections; (4) present a flexible schedule for immunization; and (5) discuss certain consequences and problems associated with vaccinations.

Administration of Vaccines

Generally speaking, the biological preparations utilized for the purposes of immunization or diagnosis can be divided into three basic categories. These divisions are: (1) prophylactic agents for active immunization, including bacterial, rickettsial, and viral vaccines, toxins, and toxoids; (2) prophylactic preparations for passive immunization, e.g., immune serum globulins (gamma globulins); and (3) diagnostic reagents for the demonstration of hyperimmune states or detection of susceptibility to disease agents, including purified protein derivative (PPD) and diluted diphtheria toxin. The applications of this last category are discussed mainly in several other chapters dealing with bacterial and mycotic infections.

Preparing for Administration

Aseptic precautions must be practiced during any type of inoculation procedure,

including the proper cleaning and sterilizing of all nondisposable equipment used and the washing and drying of the inoculator's hands. The various containers of the different preparations also should be adequately disinfected. This can be accomplished by wiping the cap or other part which is to be used with 70 per cent alcohol or other appropriate agent.

Before injecting any type of biological preparation, the site to be used must be adequately prepared. In general, wiping the area with a cotton swab or gauze soaked with a 70 to 75 per cent alcohol solution is a common procedure. This procedure may be followed by swabbing with a tincture of iodine solution. Regardless of the technique employed, it is good practice to wipe the area to be disinfected only once in one direction, instead of rubbing the region several times. Rewiping the area with one alcohol-soaked swab quite often simply redistributes the dirt and microorganisms over the site to be used. In addition, vigorous rubbing may damage the epidermal tissue. The skin should be allowed to dry before the injection is made, to provide more exposure time of the microorganisms present on the skin to the antiseptic. Another point worthy of note is that the penetration of alcohol into an injection site can be quite painful.

Routes of Administration

Injection. In order for antibody production to occur, the antigenic material must be introduced beneath the epithelial tissues of the individual. Several injection routes can be utilized for the immunization of man, including intradermal (intracutaneous), intramuscular, and subcutaneous. Other routes of injection, such as intraperitoneal, intrathecal, and intravenous, have been utilized in certain situations requiring the administration of anti-sera and related materials, but such applications are rare. In the case of experimental animals used for the production of antibodies, the intraperitoneal and intravenous routes are generally employed. Both of these methods give excellent anti-sera. For the primary immunization of humans, the intramuscular route of injection is most commonly used. The intradermal procedure is often used in the revaccination of previously inoculated individuals. Brief descriptions of commonly employed injection routes together with selected immunization procedures will be presented.

Intradermal (ID). The introduction of biological material in this technique is made approximately in the middle of the front surface of the forearm. A short needle with a short bevel is used. With the bevel up, the needle is inserted approximately 2 mm into the dermis, almost parallel with the skin's surface. It is necessary for the individual giving the injection to stretch the area to be used during the procedure. This can be done simply by gently pulling the forearm of the patient with the free hand of the administering individual. A raised area (bleb), usually demonstrating some blanching, results if the injection was not made too deeply.

Intramuscular (IM). Small quantities of biological preparations are injected by this route into the deltoid or triceps. Larger volumes, and occasionally small quantities, are administered into the mid-

dle third of the antero-lateral aspect of the thigh.

Subcutaneous. This type of injection procedure is commonly performed utilizing the outer surface of the arm or thigh, generally where the blood vessels are few and the skin is loose. The skin surface of the abdomen also has been used as an injection site. Biologic preparations are injected into the middle region of a skin fold formed by pinching the surface of the skin.

The effectiveness of subcutaneous injections of vaccines often is enhanced by the incorporation of adjuvants into the preparation. Subcutaneous injections quite often induce slow antibody responses, which consequently necessitate the use of several injections in order to produce sufficient antibody titers. Adjuvants such as mineral oil and certain aluminum compounds eliminate the necessity of repeated inoculations as they slowly but continuously release antigenic material for prolonged periods of time. This type of adjuvant action provides a level of antigenic stimulus sufficient to induce antibody formation without additional inoculations.

Oral administration. With the development of the Sabin live poliomyelitis vaccine, another type of procedure for the mass immunization of whole community populations has been widely practiced, namely, oral administration. In this technique the vaccine is usually given to the recipient in a small disposable cup or with a calibrated dropper.

Intranasal administration. It has been suggested that immunization procedures, to be effective, should simulate the immune responses induced by natural infection. In the case of upper viral respiratory disease, natural infection leads to the appearance of specific antibodies both in the serum and in the secretions at the local site of infection. This finding has given rise to one new mode of vaccine delivery, namely, the nose spray. In certain parts of the world, preparations for diseases such as German measles and influenza are currently being administered intranasally.

Smallpox vaccination administration. A relatively painless immunization is the one involving smallpox vaccine. (The preparation of smallpox vaccine is discussed later in this chapter.) Techniques for smallpox inoculation differ somewhat from those used with other vaccine preparations. The principal procedures to be considered include the *multiple pressure method,* the *multiple puncture,* and the *scratch technique.* A hyposprayjet injector (Figure 26–1), which utilizes a high velocity jet of air, is also employed for mass immunization. It is important to note that alcohol solutions, especially medicated ones, inactivate the virus vaccine. Either acetone or ether is suitable for disinfecting the site to be used for vaccination.

Multiple pressure method. In the multiple pressure method a small drop of the vaccine is placed onto a suitably prepared surface of the skin, generally the upper arm or the thigh. With the use of a sterile Hagedorn needle (a somewhat thicker and heavier type of needle than the one used in sewing) a series of pressure movements (ten are considered ample) are made to introduce the vaccine into the deeper layers of the epidermis. These pressure movements are made with force only sufficient to demonstrate the elastic nature of the skin, and not to draw blood. Drawing blood would probably inactivate the vaccine, and revaccination would be warranted. The multiple pressure technique is considered to be the method of choice in the United States, and also is used in Great Britain.

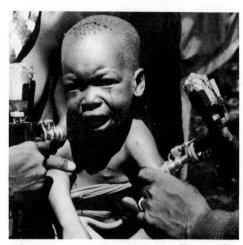

FIG. 26–1. Vaccination against smallpox with a jet injector. (Courtesy of World Health Organization, Geneva. Photo by Chevalier.)

Multiple puncture method. This technique incorporates a Heaf device or gun to introduce the vaccine. The Heaf device is commonly used in tuberculin sensitivity testing procedures. In general this procedure is not widely practiced or recommended for smallpox vaccination. Reasons include difficulties in sterilizing the device, and the potential danger of transmitting other infectious disease agents.

The scratch method. The scratch method is performed by making a slight linear ¼ ″ scratch, through a drop of vaccine preparation which has been applied to the arm. The drawing of blood must be avoided here also. This procedure is perhaps a little more painful than the multiple pressure procedure, but it has proved to be effective. Claims have been made that this method may reduce the possibility of vaccination failures. In Great Britain the scratch technique is used as an alternative procedure.

Results of smallpox vaccination. The typical results of smallpox vaccination are produced equally well by the multiple

Table 26–1   Smallpox Vaccination Reactions

Stage	Reactions		
	Primary	Vaccinoid	Immediate
Papule	3– 5 days	3–4 days	1–3 days
Vesicle	5– 8 days	5 days	None
Pustule	9 days	6–7 days	None
Scab Formation	12–14 days	8 days	None

NOTE: The descriptions of these reactions vary widely among standard references. However, the times listed are within reasonable ranges.

pressure and scratch procedures. Such results should be read, if possible, on the second, fourth, and seventh days following the primary vaccination (Table 26–1). Complications also may occur during this time period and may require treatment. In the case of revaccination, the site should be examined between the fourth and seventh days after vaccination.

Three general reactions are distinguished: the primary type, the vaccinoid or accelerated, and the immediate "no take" or immune reaction. The World Health Organization (WHO) Expert Committee on Smallpox recommends the use of the terms *major* and *equivocal* for the vaccinoid and immediate reactions, respectively.

The primary reaction. The primary reaction is characterized by the appearance of a papule (a circumscribed elevated area of the skin) developing on the third to fifth day, followed by vesicle (blister) formation anywhere from the fifth to the eighth day. The vesicle eventually fills with pus (becoming a pustule) on the ninth day, and begins to dry up shortly thereafter. Scab formation occurs approximately two weeks after the vaccination (Figure 26–2). The vaccination site should be kept dry until the scab falls off, within about three weeks. This primary reaction is seen with persons who have never been immunized against small-

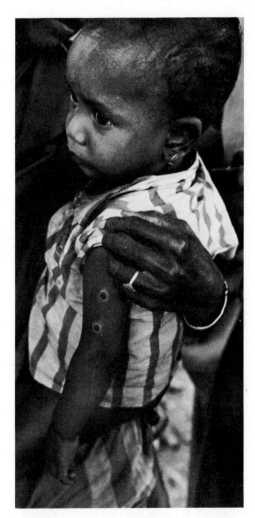

FIG. 26–2. A positive reaction with smallpox vaccination showing scab formation. This child was revaccinated. (Courtesy of World Health Organization, Geneva. Photo by J. Mohr.)

pox, or with individuals whose immunity has completely disappeared.

The vaccinoid reaction. The vaccinoid state develops in persons with a partial immunity to the vaccine, resulting either from a previous vaccination, or from a previous smallpox infection. In this type of reaction the various stages develop at an accelerated rate (Table 26–1), and the manifestations of the different stages are much milder.

The immediate reaction. In the last reaction type, the immediate, papule formation occurs within three days. Usually no vesicle or scar develops. This reaction may be due to several factors, including a high level of immunity, an allergic response to the virus preparation, faulty administration, or inactive vaccine. The possibility of an inactive vaccine can be easily determined by noting the response of individuals vaccinated with the preparation.

A situation in which no reaction occurs definitely should be considered due either to faulty administration, or to an inactive vaccine preparation. Revaccination is warranted.

The smallpox vaccination controversy. Arguments against continuing smallpox vaccination have been raised in the United States and in western Europe. The effectiveness of the procedure is not in question. Rather the financial costs of administration and the possibility of medical risks or hazards are of concern. An estimated 150 million dollars per year is spent to control smallpox in the United States. This figure is based on the expenditures associated with vaccine production, lost time from work to obtain vaccinations, surveillance procedures at international ports, and other related factors. In addition to this rather large expense, smallpox vaccination can cause several

medical complications (Table 26–5). Among the more serious forms of reactions that pose medical risks to any individual about to receive the vaccine for the first time are post-vaccinal encephalitis, generalized vaccinia, and eczema vaccinatum. If vaccination with current preparations is to be terminated, the public's health must still be preserved. Alternatives to vaccination are therefore needed. Several possibilities have been advanced, including the early administration of vaccinia immune globulin (VIG) to the exposed; the vaccination only of exposed individuals, travelers, or medical personnel working in high-risk areas; and the development of other vaccine preparations that pose less severe health hazards.

Preparation of Representative Vaccines

Vaccines are preparations of either disease-causing microorganisms or certain of their component parts or products, such as toxins, which have been altered to the point where they are unable to produce disease, but are still antigenic. These various products are used to produce an artificially acquired active state of immunity.

Logically, the term *vaccine* (meaning "from cows") should be reserved for the smallpox immunizing preparation, and the term *bacterin* should be used for bacterial immunizing suspensions. However, common usage has extended the former term to include all microbial suspensions. Moreover, *vaccination,* a word coined in relation to smallpox immunization, is now applied to all active immunization procedures.

Bacterial Vaccines

Preparations of this type are generally suspensions of killed bacteria in isotonic (physiologic) salt solution. (One exception to this is BCG (Bacille Calmette-Guérin) vaccine, which is an attenuated preparation for immunization against tuberculosis.) The use of such dead cell preparations is the most commonly employed means for inducing an active state of immunity. Bacterial vaccines are prepared by culturing the organisms, harvesting them after a suitable incubation period, and then killing them with the use of heat or chemical agents.

The use of heat has the disadvantage of reducing the immunizing potency of preparations even if the lethal temperature and the time of exposure are kept at the lowest limits possible to obtain sterilization. Chemical killing agents used for vaccine production include acetone, formalin, merthiolate, phenol, and tricresol. The concentrations of these chemicals are adjusted appropriately to insure the antigenic effectiveness of the bacterial preparations.

Before killed vaccines are released for human use, they are thoroughly tested for safety and potency. Two general types of bacterial preparations are utilized—*stock* and *autogenous vaccines*. The former is prepared from laboratory stock cultures, while the latter vaccine is specially made from organisms freshly isolated from a patient. Autogenous vaccines are of significant value in certain staphyloccal infections.

Microbial components. Several preparations consisting of different parts of microorganisms are being tested for their immunizing properties. Examples of these include the pili of *Neisseria gonorrhoeae* and the ribosomes of *Escherichia coli* and *Vibrio cholerae*. At the time of writing no commercial preparation has been made available for human immunizations.

Toxoids. The toxins of several bacteria can be converted into non-toxic, but still antigenic, preparations called *toxoids*. Heat or formalin is used in the production of toxoids.

In most commercial preparations, 0.2 to 0.4 per cent formalin is added to bacterial toxins such as diphtheria and tetanus. The resulting mixture is incubated until the detoxification process is complete. Inert protein is then removed through purification. The resulting preparation is called *natural fluid* or *plain toxoid*.

Another type of toxoid can be prepared by the incorporation of certain aluminum compounds, e.g., alum, aluminum hydroxide, and aluminum phosphate. When alum is added to the toxoid, its antigenic component precipitates. This material is washed and suspended in sterile physiologic saline. In the case of diphtheria toxoid the preparation would be called *diphtheria toxoid, alum precipitated*. When aluminum hydroxide or phosphate is added to a toxoid preparation, the antigenic components adsorb onto the particles of these compounds. Resulting toxoid preparations (depending on which of the compounds were used) are called either *aluminum hydroxide* or *aluminum phosphate adsorbed toxoid*.

Both types of toxoids, alum-precipitated or aluminum hydroxide-adsorbed, produce a prolonged and relatively continuous antigenic stimulus. The aluminum compounds function as adjuvants slowly releasing the immunizing substances.

Currently available toxoids are shown in Table 26–2. A number of such preparations are combined for effective immunizations. An example of this practice is the DPT mixture, which consists of diphtheria and tetanus toxoids and killed *Hemophilus pertussis*. All ingredients of this preparation are either alum-precipitated or adsorbed onto the other aluminum compounds mentioned previously.

Table 26–2   Currently Employed Preparations for Active Immunizations (Vaccines)

Bacterial Diseases	Etiologic Agent	Means of Vaccine Preparation
Cholera	*Vibrio cholerae*	Heat-killed suspension of *V. (comma) cholerae*.
Diphtheria	*Corynebacterium diphtheriae*	Alum-precipitated toxoid preparation of *C. diphtheriae* toxin. This antigenic material is combined with tetanus toxoid and killed *H. pertussis* in the DPT vaccine.
Gonorrhea[a]	*Neisseria gonorrhoeae*	
Meningitis[a]	*Neisseria meningitidis*	
Plague	*Yersinia pestis*	Formalin-killed and alum-coated suspension of *Y. pestis*.
Shigellosis	*Shigella dysenteriae*	Two attenuated oral vaccines. One consists of a streptomycin-dependent mutant and the other contains a hybrid derived from a mating between an avirulent *Shigella* mutant and an *Escherichia coli*, K12 Hfr isolate (Chapter 16).
Tetanus	*Clostridium tetani*	Alum-precipitated toxoid preparation of *C. tetani* toxin. See diphtheria section above.
Tuberculosis	*Mycobacterium tuberculosis*	Bacillus of Calmette and Guérin (B.C.G.). Prepared from a strain of *Myco. tuberculosis var. bovis* attenuated by continuous subculture on glycerol-broth-bile-potato media.
Tularemia[a]	*Francisella tularensis*	
Typhoid and paratyphoid fevers	*Salmonella typhi*, *S. paratyphi*, *S. schottmuelleri*	Heat-killed, phenol-preserved, or acetone-dried preparations. Vaccines containing *S. typhi* alone, or in combination with *S. paratyphi* and *S. schottmuelleri* (TAB), are commonly employed.
Whooping cough	*Bordetella pertussis*	Alum-precipitated, or aluminum hydroxide- or aluminum phosphate-adsorbed, killed preparations of Phase I *H. pertussis*. See diphtheria section above.

[a] Vaccines are under development.

Rickettsial Diseases	Etiologic Agent	Means of Vaccine Preparation
Epidemic typhus	*Rickettsia prowazekii*	Formalin-killed suspension of *R. prowazekii* cultivated in chick embryo yolk sacs.
Rocky Mountain spotted fever	*Rickettsia rickettsii*	Formalin-killed suspension of *R. rickettsii* cultivated in chick embryo yolk sacs or obtained from infected ticks.

Viral Diseases	Means of Vaccine Preparation
Acute Respiratory Disease (ARD)	Attenuated adenovirus (ADV)-21, strain V-270, cultivated first in human embryonic kidney (HEK) cells and then in human diploid fibroblasts. This preparation is being used primarily on military bases.
German measles (rubella)	Three attenuated vaccines are in use, these are: (1) $HPV_{77}D_5$ obtained from tissue cultures of duck-embryo cells; (2) $HPV_{77}DK_{12}$ prepared from dog kidney cells; and (3) Cendehill obtained from rabbit kidney cells.
Influenza	Formalin-killed preparation of prevalent viral strains. The viruses are usually grown in embryonated chick eggs.
Measles (rubeola)	Two attenuated vaccines are in use. One preparation employs the Edmonston strain in combination with measles-immune gamma globulin. The other vaccine utilizes the Schwartz strain of measles virus. (See Chapter 31 for a more thorough discussion.) A new chicken embryo preparation is being evaluated.
Mumps	Formalin-killed preparation of virus obtained from chick embryo cultivation. An attenuated vaccine is currently in use. It is prepared by cultivation of the virus in embryonated chicken eggs and then in chick embryo cell cultures.
Poliomyelitis	Two vaccines are in use. The Salk vaccine is a formalin- or ultraviolet irradiation-inactivated preparation of the virus. The Sabin or oral vaccine is an attenuated preparation. Both of these vaccines contain types 1, 2, and 3 polio viruses.
Rabies (hydrophobia)	Two vaccines are available. The duck embryo vaccine (DEV) is a beta-propiolactone-inactivated preparation of fixed virus obtained from duck embryo cultivation. A nervous tissue vaccine (NTV) consists of fixed virus obtained from injected rabbit brain tissue and inactivated by either phenol at 37°C (Semple Vaccine) or ultraviolet irradiation. (See Chapter 38 for a more thorough discussion.) A new vaccine prepared from virus grown in human diploid cells and inactivated by tri(n)-butyl phosphate is under study.
Smallpox[b] (variola)	Attenuated cowpox virus obtained from calves.
Yellow fever	Attenuated strain of the virus (17D) cultivated in chick embryos.

[b] Hospital personnel should receive vaccines every three years. Refer to the section in this chapter that deals with the smallpox vaccination controversy.

Toxin-antitoxin complex. Although bacterial exotoxins are effective antigenic agents, they are extremely toxic, even in sublethal concentrations. Furthermore, several injections of sublethal concentrations must be administered in order to produce sufficient antibody levels. However, a highly effective immunizing agent was developed for diphtheria by the combination of toxin and antitoxin in a proportion which resulted in a slight excess of toxin. This diphtheria toxin-antitoxin complex is still used on a limited basis to provide protection against the disease.

Viral and Rickettsial Vaccines

Attenuated viral vaccines. Several viral vaccines are composed of microorganisms whose virulence has been greatly reduced, if not totally eliminated. Such organisms are referred to as being *attenuated* or weakened. The techniques used for attenuation are not limited to viruses alone, but are applicable to other microorganisms as well.

Several methods are known with which the virulence of microorganisms can be reduced. These include: (1) cultivation at temperatures above normal for the organism, (2) desiccation, (3) the use of unnatural hosts, e.g., tissue culture, or mice, for propagation of the microorganisms, and (4) continued and prolonged serial passages through laboratory animals. The first two of these techniques mentioned were discovered and effectively utilized by Louis Pasteur to combat the diseases of chicken cholera and rabies. An example of the procedures involved in attenuated viral vaccine preparation is that used for the smallpox vaccine.

Smallpox vaccine preparation. A well-known representative of viral vaccines employed today is the preparation used in smallpox vaccinations. Since its introduction by Jenner in 1796, the procedure has become one of the most universally practiced of all immunizations. The inoculum (vaccinia virus) used for smallpox vaccinations is generally produced from material of the infected skin of calves or sheep suspensions. Vaccines have also been prepared from chick embryos. However, the latter preparations have so far been employed only on a limited basis. The lyophilization (freeze-drying) of vaccines has resulted in better quality preparations, that retain their infectivity for prolonged periods of time in the absence of refrigeration. The following general description of the technical methods used in smallpox vaccine preparation is largely based on the excellent presentation of Rhodes and Van Rooyen, published in 1968.

In this context, the term *lymph* refers to the ground dermal material (pulp) from animals infected with vaccinia virus and consequently used in smallpox vaccinations. Before animals are inoculated with the *seed lymph*, i.e., the virus-containing material used to inoculate calves, sheep, or other animals used, they must be washed, shaved over the abdomen, thorax, and adjacent portions of the neck and thigh, scrubbed on all shaved areas with soapy water, and treated with an antiseptic (Figure 26-3A). As some time may elapse before these animals are utilized, the washing and antiseptic treatments are carried out again on the day of inoculation.

Next, the viral-containing "seed lymph" is introduced and rubbed into a series of long, parallel, superficial incisions made with the aid of a sterile scalpel. The pattern of incisions can be seen in Figure 26-3B.

After sufficient time has passed to allow for adequate viral multiplication,

FIG. 26–3. Various aspects of the procedure for vaccinia virus vaccine production. _A_. Inoculated calves at the King Institute of Preventive Medicine, Madras, India. Note the sterilized dressings covering their abdomens. _B_. The scraping of vesicles from the inoculated sites along the animal's abdomen. Note the pattern of incisions originally made to introduce the inoculum. _C_. Dispensing liquid vaccine into vials.

FIG. 26–3. *D*. Lyophilization procedure used for vaccine material in India. (Courtesy of World Health Organization, Geneva. Photos *A, B,* and *D* by P. N. Sharma, photo *C* by J. Mohr.)

perhaps 4 days, the inoculated animals are anesthetized, exsanguinated, and prepared for the harvesting of their viral-rich dermal pulp, which involves the washing, drying, and scraping of each line of vesicles with a surgical spoon (Figure 26–3*B*). After the dermal pulp is harvested, it is ground and treated to remove tissue fragments and to reduce the bacterial content.

If the vaccine is to be utilized in the liquid form (Figure 26–3*C*), glycerol is added to the preparation before it is ground. Such glycerolated pulp is generally stored at − 10°C, in order to reduce bacterial contamination substantially.

This is the classic method used for vaccine preparation. However, the lyophilized vaccines are being utilized more

and more. The retention of vaccine potency for a longer time period, and its effectiveness in areas without refrigeration, are among the major advantages of such preparations (Figure 26–3*D*).

Before any vaccine preparation can be issued, it must be tested both for potency and for freedom from pathogenic agents such as hemolytic staphylococci and streptococci, clostridia, and viruses other than vaccinia. In addition, vaccines must assayed for vaccinia virus, in laboratory animals or tissue cultures. Descriptions of the methods of vaccination and representative effects obtained with smallpox vaccines have been presented in earlier sections of this chapter.

Inactivated vaccines. In addition to attenuated organisms, viral vaccines also are available which consist of killed (inactivated) viruses. These include Salk polio vaccine, IPV (inactivated poliomyelitis vaccine), measles vaccine, and influenza vaccine (Table 26–2). Formalin is usually employed as the chemical killing agent.

Rickettsial vaccines are also formalin-killed preparations of the specific causative agent (Table 26–2). The vaccines currently being used are made by propagating the rickettsia in embryonated chick embryos, specifically in the yolk sac, harvesting the organisms, and then inactivating them with formalin. As Cox, in 1938, was the first person to cultivate rickettsia in this manner, vaccines so prepared are called *Cox vaccines*.

Currently Used Vaccines

One of the principal objectives of immunization is to produce a sufficiently solid degree of protection against infectious diseases. Vaccine-conferred immunity should provide as much or more resistance as would follow an actual infection. Preparations used for immunization should be safe, free from unpleasant side effects, and relatively simple to administer.

Several of the currently used vaccines, together with their methods of preparation, are listed in Table 26–2, while Table 26–3 provides a schedule for active immunization based in part on the recommendations in the Red Book of the American Academy of Pediatrics.

Combined vaccines. The appearance of increasing numbers of new vaccines makes it desirable to prepare combined forms of immunizing preparations, which will simplify their administration, reduce production costs, and minimize the number of required visits to health care facilities. Examples of combined preparations include DPT (diphtheria-pertussis-tetanus), MMR (measles-mumps-rubella viruses vaccine), and TAB (typhoid and paratyphoid A and B). Several studies have demonstrated excellent antibody responses with combined vaccine preparations. The combined vaccines provide simple, safe, and effective means with which to immunize against important infectious diseases.

Passive Immunization

As indicated previously, passive immunization is effective, immediate in action, and temporary in duration. The preparations used for the purpose of passive immunization are of two basic types, *antitoxins* and *antimicrobial sera*. Many of these preparations are produced in lower animals. They should only be used in clinical situations in which human sources of antitoxins and sera are not available, since these preparations present the possibility of hypersensitivity reactions (Chapter 25).

Antitoxins

Antitoxins are antibodies which are capable of neutralizing the toxin which stimulated their production. These protein substances may be referred to as comprising an *immune serum*. An antitoxin is specific in its action against its toxic counterpart, but it does not exert any effect on the microorganism which produced the toxin. Most commercial preparations used for the passive immunization of humans are produced in horses, although anti-sera from cows are available for use with individuals sensitive to horse products.

Preparation. The general preparation of antitoxins, such as those of diphtheria and tetanus, involves the administration of toxin solutions of suitable antigenicity to a horse or other appropriate animal until sufficient antitoxin titers are produced. At this time the animal is bled, and its serum or plasma is processed to concentrate the antitoxin and to eliminate a large proportion of native horse serum protein.

By removing as many of the horse protein components as possible, the likelihood of sensitizing individuals receiving antitoxin is greatly reduced, as is the precipitation of anaphylaxis or serum sickness in sensitized persons receiving antitoxin. It should be kept in mind that sensitization of an individual develops in response to the native horse serum protein and not to the antitoxins (antibodies) in the serum preparation.

Standardization. Before antitoxin preparations are released they are sterilized, usually by filtration, and then standardized. Following the sterilization step it is customary to introduce a chemical preservative to maintain the sterility of the preparation. Three procedures can be

Table 26–3   A Recommended Schedule for Active Immunization and
Tuberculin Testing

Recommended Age	Immunizing Agent
2– 3 months	Diphtheria toxoid ⎱ DPT Pertussis vaccine ⎰ (Combined Preparation) Tetanus toxoid Oral polio vaccine (OPV) (Type I or Trivalent Preparation)
3– 4 months	DPT OPV (Type III or Trivalent Preparation)
4– 5 months	DPT OPV (Type II or Trivalent Preparation)
9–12 months	Measles, mumps, and rubella vaccine. (Refer to the text for schedules used for the administration of this vaccine type.) These vaccines can be used in combined form or as individual preparations.[a] Tuberculin testing also is included at this point.[b]
15–18 months	DPT booster Trivalent OPV Smallpox vaccine[c]
3 years	DPT booster
6 years	DT (adult) booster Diphtheria and tetanus toxoids (DT) adult booster Smallpox vaccine[c] Trivalent OPV
12 years	DT (adult) booster Smallpox vaccine[c]
Thereafter: every 5–6 years	DT (adult) booster Smallpox vaccine[d]

[a] Children between the ages of 12 months and puberty may be vaccinated either with combined vaccines or with single vaccine preparations.

[b] Initial testing is recommended at one year of age. The frequency of testing thereafter depends on the risk of exposure and the prevalence of tuberculosis in the community.

[c] Routine immunization is not recommended by the American Academy of Pediatrics (AAP) or the U. S. Public Health Service (USPHS).

[d] Refer to text for recommendations for smallpox vaccination.

used for standardization of most antitoxins: animal (*in vivo*) protection procedures, tube flocculation tests, and skin challenge tests.

Animal protection tests basically are conducted by first injecting into test animals different quantities of a particular toxin mixed with one unit of the corresponding standard antitoxin. (The latter preparation is standardized and stored by a central controlling agency, such as the National Institute of Health, in Bethesda, Maryland, and dispensed to antitoxin manufacturers upon request.) In this procedure, the dose of toxin which can produce death in a laboratory animal of a certain weight in the presence of one standard unit of antitoxin after a specified length of time is determined. It is called "L_+." In the standardization of diphtheria and tetanus toxins, the L_+ dose is determined on the basis of the quantity of toxin needed to kill guinea pigs weighing 250 gm on the fourth day following the injection of the toxin-antitoxin combination. Once the L_+ dose of the toxin is obtained for the unit of standard antitoxin, it is used in the standardization of the newly processed antitoxin in determining the quantity of the new antitoxin preparation which will produce the same results as one unit of the standard antitoxin.

In the *flocculation test*, certain proportions of the respective toxin and antitoxin preparations are mixed in test tubes.

A flocculent precipitate generally forms in the tube which contains the proportions of toxin and antitoxin needed for neutralization.

The *skin challenge test* (or simply *skin test*) resembles the animal protection procedure discussed earlier except that the standard is the production of skin reactions by toxin-antitoxin combinations, rather than the causing of death in laboratory animals.

Commercial antitoxin preparations have been used principally in cases of diphtheria and tetanus. The designations for tetanus antitoxin preparations include ATS (antitetanic serum) and TAT (tetanus antitoxin). However, antitoxins also have been used in the treatment of other diseases, including botulism and gas gangrene.

When antitoxin is to be administered, a physician should be present. Frequent checks of the patient's blood pressure and pulse should be made during and after the treatment.

Immune serum globulin (gamma globulin). Human serum globulin (ISG), also referred to as gamma globulin, is one product derived from human blood, plasma, or serum. It contains most of the immunoglobulins (antibodies) found in whole blood. The concentrations of specific antibody vary among different preparations. Immune serum globulin contains primarily IgG (γG) immunoglobulins. Conspicuously absent are IgM-associated antibodies (important to the body's defense against bacterial pathogens) and secretory IgA (γA) immunoglobulins (important to the protective mechanism on mucus membranes). Nevertheless, ISG preparations have advantages which include: (1) the absence of serum hepatitis virus, (2) the presence of a large amount of antibodies in a small volume, and (3) stability during long-term storage. The value of human serum globulin has been shown unequivocally in cases of measles and certain congenital immune-deficiency disease states. ISG may be useful in cases of German measles during the first trimester of pregnancy, chickenpox exposed patients receiving immunosuppressive drugs, and posttransfusion hepatitis. The variability of successful results observed with immune serum globulin in these situations is probably due to the lack of sufficient specific antibody molecules in the preparations used.

Specific Immune Serum Globulin (SIG)

Specific immune serum globulins (SIG) contain a higher specific antibody concentration to the agent in question than found in immune serum globulin preparations. The more commonly used specific immune globulins include those employed for measles, mumps, whooping cough, tetanus, shingles, and the Rh_0 or D blood factor. These globulin preparations are made from sera obtained from individuals who have recently recovered from an active infection or disease state or from individuals who are hyperimmunized to a given material. Serum globulins are injected into persons either recently exposed to the particular infectious disease or currently experiencing the disease.

The Role of Allied Health Science Personnel

A basic understanding of immunologic principles is definitely needed and utilized by allied health science personnel, especially nurses. Immunization of susceptible persons against preventable diseases is one of the most important means available in the prevention and control of communicable disease epidemics. Nurses not only maintain and sterilize the needed instruments for such immunizing procedures, but frequently are given the added responsibility of administering vaccines and related preparations. In addition, nurses often have the responsibility of maintaining the immunization records of patients and informing parents as to the importance of certain immunizations to the health of their children and of the need to complete immunization schedules (Table 26–3).

In order for nurses, or other health science associated personnel, to be able to perform these duties efficiently and intelligently, they must be aware of the nature of the material to be administered, the correct method for administration, anticipated results, and contraindications or possible side-effects (Table 26–5) of the material to be used.

Complications Associated with Vaccinations

According to Michels undesirable and yet apparently inevitable side reactions have been reported to accompany immunization procedures ever since Jenner's variolation in 1796. Prior to the administration of any vaccine, patients should be questioned as to the history of previous reactions associated with vaccinations. This is especially important in cases of immunizations with egg-associated vaccines. Michels emphasizes that in cases of such adverse reactions, a full and careful documentation of the circumstances is important.

Some essential points which should be noted include the type of vaccine (its lot number and other pertinent features), the quantity of material administered, the route and site of injection, and a full description, if possible, of the reaction from the time of onset to its termination. Details of the patient's health, age, and family history also may be of significance and should be recorded. When an unfavorable reaction occurs after the administration of a specific immunization vaccine, the fact must be noted on the patient's record, and the individual must be made to fully understand the dangers

involved if he were to receive an additional exposure.

Representative reactions, their possible causes, and the types of complications which have been encountered with certain selected vaccines are given in Tables 26–4 and 26–5. Preventive measures and, in certain situations, treatments are also listed in these tables.

Other vaccines, such as those for cholera, typhoid fever, typhus, and yellow fever, are not regularly used in the United States, except by military personnel or persons intending to go into endemic regions, who may be required to receive certain of these vaccines. Unfavorable reactions from these preparations include acute febrile reactions (cholera, typhoid, and yellow fever), anaphylaxis (rare with the typhus vaccine), and encephalomyelitis (yellow fever). The latter reaction is highest in children less than one year old.

Immunization for International Travel

Several infectious diseases are considered to be "quarantinable" according to WHO International Sanitary Regulations. However, under these regulations individuals traveling to, through, or from certain specified regions must have been immunized only against cholera, smallpox, and yellow fever. Verification of smallpox vaccination is required by the majority of countries at the time of entry, and in certain situations it is needed for re-entry. Individuals traveling through regions considered as "yellow fever country" also are required to present verification of vaccination against the viral disease. Certain immunizations are recommended for American travelers. These are presented in Table 26–6. Vaccination against typhoid fever, it will be noticed, is not included. Generally, if the usual tourist facilities are used this immunization is not necessary.

Table 26–4   Representative Reactions, Their Possible Causes and Prevention

Reaction	Possible Cause	Prevention
Anaphylaxis	Immunologic interaction between antigen and skin sensitizing antibody. This consequently causes the release of reaction-mediating substances, including histamine and serotonin	1. Skin testing with diluted materials 2. Conspicuously labeling a patient's record for his allergic nature
Encephalomyelitis	1. Immunologic basis of antigen-antibody reaction 2. Possible predisposition to reaction because of neurologic disorders, mental retardation, etc.	Revaccination should be avoided to prevent recurrence of this reaction
Fetal injury	Effects of live vaccines	Avoidance of live vaccines in times of pregnancy
High fever	1. Possible intolerance of vaccine 2. Reduction of tolerance to heat stress	1. Not exceeding recommended dosages 2. Avoidance of administering multiple toxic vaccines on the same day 3. Use of fever-reducing medication, e.g., salicylates, after vaccinations
Induction of disease	1. Individual may be experiencing a sub-clinical infection with the disease agent against which vaccination is being given 2. Susceptibility of individuals with immunologic deficiency states, e.g., hypogammaglobulinemias, or patients under steroid or immunosuppressive therapy	1. Avoidance of inoculations which appear to be symptomatic for the disease against which vaccination is to be given 2. Avoidance of the administration of live vaccines to persons such as mentioned under item 2 of the cause for induction of disease
Serum-sickness-like reactions	Immunologic basis of antigen-antibody reaction	Epinephrine and antihistamines may be used in treatment
Severe local injury (abscess formation)	1. Bacterial contamination 2. Inadequate depth of vaccine administration	1. Proper cleansing of site for inoculation 2. Proper injection
Sepsis	1. Secondary abscess formation 2. Contaminated needles, syringes, or vaccines	1. Proper cleansing of site for inoculation 2. Use of disposable needle and syringes 3. Prevention of vaccine contamination during storage and subsequent use
Toxic reactions	Sensitivity of individual to vaccine	Reduction of immunizing dosages

Table 26–5 Common Reactions which Have Been Reported to Occur
with Certain Vaccines

Vaccine	Selected General Features of Side Reactions and Potential Dangers	Prevention or Treatment Used
B.C.G. (Bacillus of Calmette and Guérin)	1. Regional lymphadenitis, followed by suppuration and perforation with prolonged drainage in individuals under one month of age receiving greater than 0.025 cc dosages 2. Possible activation of quiescent tuberculosis can occur	Vaccine should not be administered to persons with positive tuberculin skin reactions
DPT and DT (Diphtheria, Tetanus Toxoids, and Pertussis Vaccine)	1. Toxic reactions 2. Encephalitis if it occurs is more commonly associated with the Pertussis component	1. Not exceeding recommended dosages, or reduction (tenfold) of diphtheria toxoid in DT preparation 2. Most adverse effects can be averted by immunizing healthy children, and administering the final DPT dose at 3 to 4 years of age 3. Skin testing beginning with the tetanus toxoid also can be helpful
Measles (attenuated)	Fever, malaise, and regional lymphadenopathy	1. Immunization should be performed with healthy children only 2. Children known to have histories of high fever reactions should be given adequate fluids and salicylates between the 5th and 8th day
Rabies (duck embryo preparations)	1. Local erythema, induration, and heat 2. Systemic reactions do not occur commonly	Skin testing for individuals with hen egg sensitivity. There may be some degree of cross-reactivity between the two egg sources
Rubella	1. Fever, rash, and mild local reactions 2. Pain, swelling, and stiffness in joints 3. Numbness and tingling sensations	Vaccine should not be given during pregnancy or if there is a possibility of pregnancy within 3 months of vaccination, or if there is any evidence of a fever, respiratory disease, or cancerous state
Smallpox	1. The major portion of problems occur with primary vaccination and include mild and local adenopathy and inflammation, fever, and tenderness around site of inoculation	1. Usually adequate rest and the use of salicylates will control the vaccination manifestations listed under item 1 of possible causes
	2. Toxemia, possibly caused by secondary bacterial infection or immunologic deficiency	2. Antibiotics should be used for the bacterial infections, and vaccine immune globulin (V.I.G.) for the immunologic deficiency. Methisazone is also of value here
	3. Myocarditis, nephritis, and osteomyelitis	3. The same types of procedure can be carried out for these states as mentioned in item 2 above
	4. Generalized vaccinia or eczema vaccination results most often from vaccination of an eczematoid individual	4a. Vaccination should not be conducted if open skin lesions exist 4b. Severe cases should receive treatment with V.I.G. and methisazone 4c. In addition, appropriate replacement of electrolytes, fluids, and protein may be warranted in severe cases

Table 26–6   Recommended Immunizations for American Travelers

Preparation	Areas Involved	Qualifying Remarks
Immune serum globulin	Africa, Asia, Central and South America	Used in the prophylaxis of infectious hepatitis
Plague vaccine	Cambodia, Laos, Viet Nam	Should be used in situations where sylvatic plague exists
Rabies (duck embryo vaccine) (*pre-exposure*)	Africa, Asia, South America	Recommended only for personnel resident in these areas and not for short-term visitors
Typhus fever vaccine	Endemic areas for the disease include Asia, Africa, Central and South America, Europe	The immunization should be used only for persons remaining in endemic regions for long periods of time

QUESTIONS FOR REVIEW

1. Define or explain the following terms:
   a. native immunity
   b. attenuated
   c. active immunity
   d. anamestic response
   e. passive immunity
   f. artificially acquired immunity
   g. toxoid
   h. gamma globulin

2. Discuss the general procedures used in the preparation of smallpox vaccine.

3. What general types of immunizing agents are currently available?

4. What is the difference between a toxin and a toxoid?

5. What is the nature of the immunizing material used with the following infectious diseases?
   a. typhoid fever
   b. whooping cough
   c. measles
   d. yellow fever
   e. tuberculosis
   f. influenza
   g. smallpox
   h. tetanus
   i. mumps
   j. polio
   k. rabies
   l. diphtheria

6. What are the characteristics of a functional vaccine?

7. Describe at least three routes of administration for vaccines, and give specific examples of preparations used.

8. What is a hypospray jet injector?

9. Does the administration of immune serum globulin have any value in combating the effects of disease agents? If so, with which diseases does this beneficial effect occur?

10. Can complications develop as a consequence of vaccinations? If so, describe several common examples.

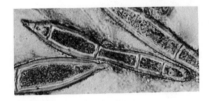
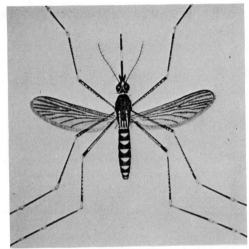

Microbial Diseases of Humans

DIVISION 7: Behavioral Objectives

After reading the chapters in this division, the individual should be able to:

1. Recognize the variety of ways in which pathogens can be transmitted.

2. Propose ways in which to prevent disease agents from spreading.

3. Describe the general clinical features of common infectious diseases and the microorganisms that cause them.

4. Relate basic laboratory procedures to the identification of disease agents.

5. Recognize the limitations of treatment and laboratory identification procedures as they pertain to microbial diseases.

6. Categorize specific microbial pathogens.

7. Discuss the relationship of microorganisms to the causation of cancers (see Chapter 40).

8. Appreciate the potential of microorganisms to cause disease under a variety of conditions.

9. Recognize the importance of proper handling of clinical specimens from the standpoint of laboratory identification of microorganisms and protection of personnel working with such specimens.

Principles of
Disease Transmission

Epidemiology is the study of the distribution and determinants of disease prevalence in man. It should be noted here that this area of investigation is not necessarily limited to the *communicable/infectious* type of disease only. In other words, the so-called noninfectious diseases, such as cancer, cardiovascular conditions, congenital defects, diabetes mellitus, emphysema, vitamin deficiencies (such as pellagra, rickets, and scurvy), and many more, have been and are continuing to be studied epidemiologically. The epidemiologist uses the inductive approach to solving problems; that is, he collects and analyzes data from many individuals, and draws conclusions about the epidemiology of the particular disease from this data.

Communicable diseases are known to be infectious. However, infectious diseases are not necessarily communicable. Examples include leprosy and certain forms of tuberculosis. Therefore, to prevent any misconceptions as to the scope of epidemiology, the combining expression *communicable/infectious* is used.

For centuries, communicable/infectious diseases have been noted to vary significantly in occurrence. The usual terms describing the prevalence of diseases are:

1. *Endemic*: This term refers to a constant presence of a disease, but one which involves a relatively small number of persons. Examples of such diseases, depending on the locality, could include coccidioidomycosis, leprosy, or tuberculosis.

2. *Epidemic*: Here, the emphasis is placed on an "unusual occurrence of a disease" involving large segments of a population for a limited period of time. Examples are influenza and poliomyelitis epidemics.

3. *Pandemic*: A pandemic is in reality a series of epidemics affecting several countries, or even the major portions of the world. The influenza pandemic of 1918 and 1919 exhibited such a worldwide distribution.

4. *Sporadic*: Diseases of this nature are not commonly encountered, appear at rather unusual or irregular periods, and affect only a relatively few persons.

Infections such as diphtheria and whooping cough (pertussis) occur sporadically. They and other communicable/infectious diseases may be sporadic or endemic in occurrence, but at other times, depending upon factors such as the immunity of the population and sanitation, they can assume epidemic proportions. This chapter will present the general principles underlying the epidemiology of infectious diseases, with respect to sources of disease agents, means of transmission, and problems posed by the hospital environment.

Morbidity and Mortality Rates

When an outbreak of a communicable disease occurs, or even a single case, numerous types of epidemiological data are gathered. Some of the principal findings frequently are expressed in terms of morbidity and mortality rates. *Morbidity* is generally defined as the number of individuals having the disease per unit of the population within a given time period. Usually 100,000 is taken as the unit of population for such calculations. The *mortality rate* refers to the number of deaths attributable to a particular disease per unit of the population (usually 1,000) within a given time period. Reports may be compiled weekly, monthly, yearly, or for even longer periods of time, depending on the purpose of the study.

Occasionally diseases occur which are more or less limited to particular segments of the population; consequently, morbidity and mortality rates may be calculated for that population segment. An *infant mortality rate* is an example.

Reporting Communicable/ Infectious Diseases

State administrative codes require the reporting of actual or even suspected cases of certain communicable/infectious diseases to local health authorities. The number and kinds of such reportable diseases may vary to some extent among states. The specific reportable infections in California are listed in Table 27–1, as an example of a fairly comprehensive list. Discussions of these communicable diseases can be found in later chapters.

Individuals who are charged with the responsibility of notifying local health authorities include physicians, coroners, directors of hospitals, clinics, and laboratories, and any persons knowing of a disease's existence.

Sources and Reservoirs of Infection

The sources of infectious disease agents are many and varied (Figure 27–1). Generally speaking, however, the most disabling and common infections of man are caused by microorganisms capable of using human tissues for purposes of reproduction and maintenance. In such cases man—specifically his tissues and secretions—collectively serves as a reservoir. The sources of infectious body fluids are referred to as *portals of exit*. They include: (1) the gastro-intestinal tract, (2) the genito-urinary system, (3) the oral region, (4) the respiratory tract, (5) blood and blood derivatives, (6) lesions of the skin and other areas, and (7) tissues of various types.

The individual who harbors infectious agents of disease but apparently suffers no ill effects is called a *healthy carrier*. The individual who is in an incubating state, undergoing the beginning disease but without apparent symptoms, is referred to as an *incubatory carrier*. Such persons may be infectious during the last stages of their incubation periods. Another category of carrier is the *convalescent*: in certain situations, patients recovering from an infection may serve as sources of pathogens.

Several other reservoirs of infectious agents are recognized. These include lower animals, e.g., dogs, cats, bats, etc.; arthroprods (bugs); soil; and inanimate contaminated objects, or *fomites*. Some of these sources also may serve as a means of disease transmission.

Zoonoses

Various warm-blooded animals are recognized as reservoirs of infectious disease agents for man (Table 27–2). Such sources include bats, birds, cattle, cats, dogs, horses, mice, monkeys, rabbits, rats, skunks, and various wild mammals. Diseases which primarily affect lower animals, but can also be transmitted to man by natural means, are referred to as *zoonoses*. Several animals also serve as sources of helminths. This group of diseases is discussed in Chapter 42.

Certain infectious agents can be transmitted through the bite of warm-blooded animals. Among the better-known diseases spread in this manner is rabies. The chief vectors of this viral infection include cats, coyotes, dogs, foxes, jackals, skunks, and a variety of bats. Since the turn of the century vampire bats have

Table 27–1   Reportable Communicable/Infectious Diseases

Disease	Nature of Causative Agent	Disease	Nature of Causative Agent
Acute infectious conjunctivitis of the newborn (includes gonorrheal ophthalmia)	Bacterial (B)	Scarlet fever	B
		Shigella infections	B
Anthrax	B	Streptococcal infections (including streptococcal sore throat)	B
Asiatic cholera	B	Syphilis	B
Botulism	B	Tetanus	B
Brucellosis	B	Trachoma	B[a]
Chancroid	B	Tuberculosis	B
Diarrhea of the newborn	B	Tularemia	B
Diphtheria	B	Typhoid fever (both actual cases and carriers)	B
Dysentery (bacillary)	B	Typhus fever	B
Food poisoning (excluding botulism)	B	Coccidioidomycosis	Fungal
Gonorrhea	B	Trichinosis	Helminth
Granuloma inguinale	B	Malaria	Protozoan
Leprosy	B	Dengue fever	Viral (V)
Leptospirosis	B	Encephalitis (acute form)	V
Meningitis (meningococcal or meningococcemia)	B	Infectious hepatitis	V
Paratyphoid fever A, B, and C	B	Measles (rubeola)	V
Pertussis (whooping cough)	B	Mumps	V
Plague	B	Poliomyelitis	V
Psittacosis	B[a]	Rabies (both human and lower animal)	V
Q fever	B[b]	Serum hepatitis	V
Relapsing fever	B	Viral exanthema in pregnant women	V
Rheumatic fever (acute)	B	Yellow fever	V
Rocky Mountain spotted fever	B[b]		
Salmonella infections (exclusive of typhoid fever)	B		

Source: Adapted from "Morbidity and Mortality Reportable Diseases," 14th Report, week ending April 11th, 1970, County of Los Angeles Health Department.

[a] These infections formerly were considered to be viral in nature.

[b] These infections are also referred to as rickettsial in nature. However, in the light of recent findings, the causative agents are considered to be a form of bacteria.

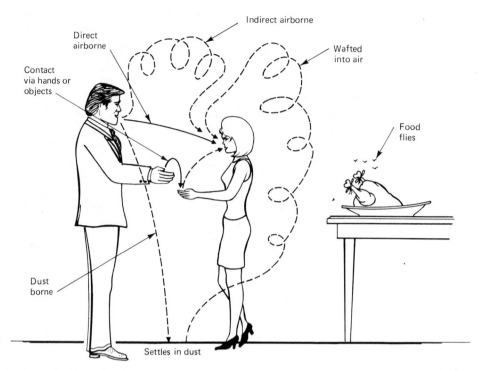

FIG. 27–1. A diagrammatic representation of some common sources of infection and portals of exit. Note that certain of these can also function as a means of disease transmission.

been incriminated as vectors of the disease in cattle in various regions of the world, including Central and South America. When in a rabid state, these bats can bite one another as well as cattle and man. The reports of bat-associated rabies in man has been steadily increasing. Figure 27–2 shows some representative bats of California.

Most species of bats are colonial in nature, congregating together in buildings, caves, mines, and trees. In general, bats are considered beneficial to man because they consume large quantities of insects and rodents. However, rabies has been reported to occur in over 20 species of bats, including fruit-eating, insectivorous, and vampire varieties. It is also known that rabies may be latent in these animals, and consequently such infected bats may serve as carriers, excreting the viral agents in their saliva and feces for several months.

Bat colonies may be removed through the use of repellents, batproofing, or simple destruction. Repellents which have been used include napthalene and para-dichlorobenzene. Several toxic chemicals, such as chlordane, dieldrin, and DDT, have been employed for the destruction of bat colonies.

Batproofing is apparently the only truly satisfactory method for the removal of bats. This procedure involves determining the bats' actual roosting site and then sealing the various means of access to it. The performance of the batproofing procedures should take into consideration the seasonal habits of the colony, the possibility of trapping bats before they have had an opportunity to leave, and insuring that all entries have been eliminated.

Table 27–2 Representative Zoonoses Produced by Microorganisms

Disease	Associated Animals	Mode of Transmission
Bacterial and Related Infections		
Anthrax	Domestic livestock	Direct contact with infected tissues and contaminated soil
Brucellosis (undulant fever)	Domestic livestock	Direct contact with infected tissues; ingestion of milk from diseased animals
Bubonic plague	Rodents	Fleas and ticks
Leptospirosis	Dogs, rodents, wild mammals	Direct contact with infected tissues and urine
Relapsing fever	Various rodents	Lice and ticks
Rocky Mountain spotted fever	Dogs, rodents	Ticks
Salmonellosis	Dogs, poultry, rats	Ingestion of infected meat; contamination of water
Tularemia	Wild rabbits	Direct contact with infected tissues; deer flies, ticks
Fungus Infections		
Severals forms of ringworm	Various domestic animals, e.g., cats, dogs	Direct contact
Protozoan Infections		
African sleeping sickness (trypanosomiasis)	Man, wild game animals	Tsetse flies
Chagas' disease	Man, wild animals	Kissing bugs
Kala-azar leishmaniasis	Cats, dogs, rodents	Sandflies
Toxoplasmosis	Birds, wild rodents, domestic animals, e.g., cats	Generally unknown; possibly contamination of food and water
Viral Infections		
Eastern equine encephalitis (EEE)	Birds; horses and related animals	Mosquitoes
Influenza	Man, swine, horses	Direct contact with droplets
Jungle yellow fever	Various species of monkeys	Mosquitoes
Rabies	Bats, cats, dogs, man, skunks, wolves, etc.	Bites, contamination of wounds with infectious saliva

Principal Modes of Transfer for Infectious Disease Agents

Infectious disease agents may be transmitted to susceptible individuals in a variety of ways, including: (1) direct contact with obviously infected persons or carriers; (2) indirect contact with inanimate objects, food, or water contaminated by infected individuals; (3) the inhalation of air-borne dust or droplet nuclei containing infectious agents; (4) through inoculation; and (5) by arthropods, which may serve either as mechanical or biological vectors. *Mechanical transmission* here refers to an insect physically transporting a pathogen from contaminated material such as food or water to other objects. Cockroaches and flies are good examples. In the case of *biological transmission*, a portion of the pathogen's life cycle is carried out in the vector. The relationship between the

Big Brown Bat
(Eptesicus fuscus)

Pallid bat
(Antrozous pallidus)

Little brown bat
(Myotis lucifugus)

Red bat
(Lasiurus borealis)

Hoary bat
(Lasiurus cinereus)

Freetail bat
(Tadarida brasiliensis)

FIG. 27–2. Some common California bats. (Courtesy of K. E. Murray, Bureau of Vector Control, California State Department of Public Health.

Drawn by Joe E. Brooks, Bureau of Vector Control.)

anopheline mosquitoes and the malarial parasite is representative of biological transmission. (See Chapter 41 for a discussion of malaria.)

The mechanical means of disease transmission includes the 5 Fs—food, fingers, flies, feces, and fomites. The biological means of transmission include the injection of blood and blood products, warm-blooded animal bites, arthropod bites, and the introduction of arthropod feces into bites or wounds. It is important to note that several diseases may be spread by a variety of ways.

Direct Contact

The direct contact with infectious lesions, such as open sores, boils (Color photograph 60), and draining abscesses (Color photograph 61), obviously opens the door to the potential danger of acquiring the disease agent involved. Contagious diseases, from the Latin word *contagio* meaning touch or contact, include anthrax, syphilis, and gonorrhea. Many of the disease states spread by direct contact also gain access to the body through the nose and throat.

Shaking hands or kissing can transmit pathogens. Examples of diseases spread in this manner include poliomyelitis, chickenpox, the common cold, bacillary dysentery, and streptococcal infections. Certainly washing hands after blowing the nose (Figure 27–3), defecation, urination, or working with infected persons would contribute greatly to preventing the spread of disease agents.

Indirect Contact

Various microorganisms can be transferred to susceptible persons by means of food and water and, quite often, by contaminated inanimate objects. The latter

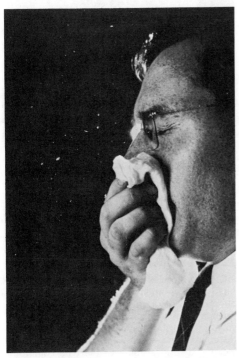

FIG. 27–3. Note how even with this stifled sneeze droplets still are produced. The photo also shows how easily the hands and arms can become contaminated with nasal secretions. (Courtesy of M. W. Jennison, Department of Bacteriology and Botany, Syracuse University, and the American Society of Microbiology. LS–10.)

are referred to as *fomites*. Moist foods that are not highly acid can be excellent culture media for pathogenic microorganisms, including the causative agents of amebic dysentery, bacillary dysentery (shigellosis), cholera, and typhoid fever. These diseases can also be spread through contaminated water supplies.

Raw or inadequately cooked meat from infected animals is a well-known source of disease agents. In addition to microorganisms, such products can contain worms (helminths) capable of causing trichinosis and tapeworm infections. Observing proper sanitary measures and adequate meat inspection can substantially reduce the possibility of acquiring these diseases. Many states have stringent requirements of sanitation for farms and ranches which supply meat for human consumption. Such measures are also important for bacterial disease control. Included in this last category are infections such as undulant fever (brucellosis) and bovine tuberculosis. Milk from infected cows also is an important source of disease agents.

The handling of food for human consumption by an undiscovered carrier always is a serious hazard. Such individuals may cough or sneeze onto foods. They may handle utensils or food during preparation procedures with hands unwashed after toilet use or nose-blowing. Occasionally food handlers or dishwashers may have a draining abscess or boils, which provide other sources of disease agents. Regular inspection of restaurant personnel and equipment, including dishwashing machines, is necessary for effective prevention of infections spread by food.

Eating utensils and drinking glasses can also be important factors in the transmission of diseases. Proper disinfection and thorough washing of such items is essential to good sanitation. Various types of commercial dishwashing equipment are available which clean and disinfect mechanically. There are standardized methods for bacteriological examination of dishes and related items. Specimens can be taken directly by means of a sterile cotton swab or, if possible, the utensil can be introduced directly into sterile media. The American Public Health Association publishes appropriate methods, media, and other details for this purpose.

The maintenance of adequate sanitation in restaurants can be difficult, costly, and quite time-consuming. It is therefore not surprising to find an increasing tendency for snack bars and food take-out stands to use disposable paper and plastic dishes and eating utensils. This greatly reduces the cost of operation, and—what is more important—sanitation levels become substantially higher. Bacterial counts of such plastic and paper products are negligible, and pathogens are seldom found.

Air- and Dust-Borne Infections

Particles bearing microorganisms are released into the general environment in two major ways. Some are produced during normal activities involving the respiratory tract, talking, coughing, and sneezing (Figures 27–3 and 27–4). Significantly larger numbers of organisms are liberated by sneezing than by the other two activities. People also produce microorganism-bearing particles as a result of normal body movements, from the skin, clothing, and even from dressings covering wounds.

The second major means by which particles are introduced into the general environment is by a redistribution of accumulated particles in room dust. This is due to drafts and to procedures such

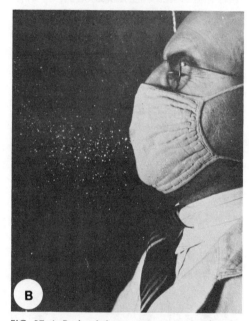

FIG. 27–4. Both of these pictures were taken by high-speed photographic techniques to show the atomization of droplets into the air as a consequence of a sneeze. _A_. A full-blown unstifled sneeze. Note the heavy cloud of material introduced into the air. _B_. The individual shown is wearing a surgical mask of the type commonly worn by hospital and related personnel. Despite the presence of the mask, several droplets resulting from an unstifled sneeze still are propelled into the air. (Courtesy of M. W. Jennison, Department of Bacteriology and Botany, Syracuse University, and the American Society of Microbiology. LS–5, LS–15.)

as sweeping and dusting. Dust-borne infections include the fungal diseases of coccidioidomycosis and histoplasmosis.

After droplets are released into the air, they fall to the ground at a rate depending upon their size. On the ground these droplets stick to, or become mixed with, a variety of animal, plant, and mineral debris, which is commonly referred to as "house dust." Evaporation, or drying, takes place next. The rate of evaporation depends on the size and composition of the droplets and the relative humidity of the atmosphere. The higher the humidity, the slower the rate of evaporation.

Depending on the types of microorganism present and the composition of droplets, bacteria and related organisms may be able to survive for long periods of time. This is especially true with droplets containing saliva, sputum, or other discharges. What remains of a droplet after evaporation is called the *"droplet nucleus."* Droplet nuclei do not settle quickly after being disturbed, but remain suspended in the air, thus possibly giving rise to droplet nucleus airborne infections. This is in contrast to dust particle borne microorganisms, which settle quickly. According to Riley and O'Grady, droplet nuclei settle at a rate of 0.04 feet per minute, while the dust particles settle at a rate of 1 to 5 feet per minute.

It is quite obvious that coughs or sneezes either stifled or not produce a microbial spray. In an effort to prevent hospital (*nosocomial*) infections, hospital personnel frequently wear masks to reduce the possibility of producing droplet nuclei. Unfortunately, preventing such sprays from occurring is impossible. Procedures and practices used to control disease transmission by such means include the application of bactericidal compounds to floors, and the use of special floor coverings to aid in trapping dust.

Fomites

Inanimate objects or substances which are capable of absorbing and transferring infectious microorganisms are referred to as *fomites*. A wide variety of materials can spread human diseases, including clothing, eating utensils, instruments, soiled bed linens, toys, and even fossils (Figure 27–5). Reports have appeared which indicate that Indian relics and fossils from endemic areas pose a definite public health hazard. Dust and dirt in contact with such objects may contain spores of infectious agents. The inhalation of such material would not be difficult during the removal of dirt and cleaning of collected items.

Plant pathogens also are transmitted by such fomites as gardening tools, gloves, and soil.

FIG. 27–5. A fossilized sea shell removed from a dry creek bed in Simi Valley, California, which was incriminated as a source of the fungus *Coccidioides immitis,* the causative agent of coccidioidomycosis. Apparently a case of this disease developed from the inhalation of fungal spores during the cleaning of the shell. (From Rothman, P. E., Graw, R. G., Jr., Harris, J. C., Jr., and Onslow, J. M.: *Amer. J. Dis. Child.,* **118**:792, 1969.)

Accidental Inoculation

Occasionally, individuals working with clinical specimens may directly introduce a pathogen into their bodies through a pre-existing cut or an accidental wound with a contaminated hypodermic needle, inoculating loop, etc. Great care must be exercised during the times animals are injected with infectious material, and during the processing of clinical specimens.

Infections also can develop from the direct introduction of pathogens during surgery.

Mention should be made here of the possible sources of potential or actual pathogens in laboratories associated with microbiology courses. Examples of such hazards include improperly handled or sterilized inoculating needles, culture tubes or flasks left unplugged in incubators, walking around laboratories with partially opened culture flasks, the inadequate disinfection of spilled microbial cultures, and eating and drinking in laboratories.

Arthropods and Disease

Through the centuries "bugs" have thwarted man's efforts to establish stable environments for himself. As he attempted to develop new cities or agricultural communities, devastating diseases associated with arthropods made their appearance. This was especially true during the sixth century B.C., when malaria and plague flourished in newly established cities. One of the few recourses left to man was to escape from these centers of disease and to return only long after the epidemic dangers had passed.

Although various arthropods were known to be ectoparasites on mammals, little information of any consequence was available to demonstrate the relationship between insects and disease agents. In

the latter part of the nineteenth century, an intensive systematic approach to the study of infectious diseases was undertaken. One of the most significant discoveries came to the attention of the scientific world in 1893, when T. Smith (Figure 27–6) and F. L. Kilbourne demonstrated the tick transmission of the protozoa *Babesia bigemina,* the causative agent of Texas cattle or red-water fever. This disease had been recognized in the United States since 1796, but its true etiology was masked until the investigations by Smith and Kilbourne.

The discovery of this arthropod-microbial association provided a basis with which other investigators were able to show the significance of other arthropods to disease epidemiology. Such was the

FIG. 27–6. Dr. Theobald Smith (1859–1934), one of the true pioneers in microbiology. In addition to demonstrating the arthropod-microbial cause of Texas cattle fever, he showed the immunizing effect of killed viral preparations, differentiated between bovine and human tubercle bacilli, and made significant contributions to the elaboration of the anaphylactic shock mechanism. (Courtesy of the Rockefeller Institute.)

case with Sir Ronald Ross (Figure 27–7) and his demonstration of the importance of *Anopheles* spp. mosquitoes to malaria.

In recent years knowledge of the arthropod-borne diseases has increased immeasurably. Consequently, several areas of intensive investigation have evolved which collectively form the specialization referred to as medical entomology. This field of study includes the recognition and description of arthropods, the distribution of arthropod-associated diseases, the effects of disease agents on the arthropod vector, the effects of the disease agent on the host, and the control of arthropods.

The Arthropoda

The phylum of Arthropoda constitutes the largest portion of known animals. According to Cheng, 740,000 species of this phylum were known in 1964. The number of subdivisions within this group of organisms varies according to the authority consulted.

Many arthropods are of medical and economic importance. This is true not only because of their capabilities to produce traumatic or necrotic injuries, or even sensitization, as in the case of centipedes, wasps, and spiders (Figure 27–8), but because several of these organisms

can serve either as intermediate hosts for parasites, or as vectors for pathogenic microorganisms. It is with the latter aspect that we shall be concerned. The arthropod species of medical importance, which are considered here, belong to the taxonomic classes of Arachnoidea (Arachnida) and Insecta (Table 27–3).

Although arthropods exhibit a wide range of characteristics, they share several major properties, including: (1) a rigid or semirigid chitinous exoskeleton, (2) a complete digestive tract, (3) an open circulatory system (with or without a dorsally situated heart) which forms a body cavity (hemocoel), and (4) excretory, nervous, and respiratory systems. Members of the class Insecta are noted for a segmented body possessing jointed appendages.

A classic example of an arthropod which transmits disease agents mechanically is the common house fly, *Musca domestica,* a member of the Diptera. The

FIG. 27–7. Sir Ronald Ross (1857–1932). (Courtesy of the National Library of Medicine, Bethesda, Maryland.)

FIG. 27–8. *Loxosceles reclusa* (the brown recluse spider). It produces a strong necrotizing toxin. Note the distinguishing figure of a violin (arrow). (Courtesy of the Bureau of Vector Control, California State Department of Public Health.)

Table 27–3   Classification of Selected
Medically Important Arthropods

Phylum Arthropoda
    Class Arachnoidea (Arachnida)
        Order Acarina
            Suborder Ixodides
                Family Argasidae
                Family Ixodidae
    Class Insecta
        Order Anopleura
        Order Diptera
        Order Hemiptera
        Order Siphonaptera (Aphaniptera)
        Order Orthoptera

etiologic agents of diseases, such as infectious hepatitis, polio, and salmonellosis, may be picked up by flies during
their contact with fecal matter containing
viable infectious microorganisms. These
pathogens may contaminate various body
parts of the fly, mouth parts (probocius),
legs, and alimentary canal. The depositing
of microorganisms on food intended for
human consumption occurs when the fly
comes to rest or to feed on such substances. Important in this type of transmission are factors affecting the survival
of pathogenic agents in the environment,

the availability of suitable arthropods,
and the rapidity of transfer.

Most arthropod-borne diseases are
transmitted biologically. Many animal
and plant pathogens require an arthropod
for purposes of development, multiplication, or both. Susceptible hosts become
infected through the bites of such patho-
gen-carrying arthropod vectors.

Arachnoidea or Arachnida

Ticks and mites.   These arthropods belong to the taxonomic class of Arachnoidea (Arachnida) and the order of
Acarina. They abound almost everywhere. Characteristics of this group include a fused head and thorax forming
a cephalothorax, the general absence of
body segmentation, separate sexes, the
absence of antennae and wings, and the
possession by adults of four pairs of legs.

Ticks are important medically because
they may: (1) serve as reservoirs of infection, (2) transmit infectious disease
agents (Table 27–4), and (3) be the

Table 27–4   Representative Tick-Borne Diseases of Man

Vector	Disease	Etiologic Agent	Geographic Distribution (Endemic Areas)
Americanum spp. *Dermacentor* spp. *Amblyoma* spp.	Q fever	*Coxiella burnetii*	Worldwide
Ixodes spp.	Queensland tick typhus	*Rickettsia australis*	Australia
Hyalomma spp. *Dermacentor* spp.	Tick-borne hemorrhagic fever		Asia Minor, Southeastern Europe, U.S.S.R.
Ornithodoros spp.	Tick-borne relapsing fever	*Borrelia recurrentis* and *Borrelia* spp.	Central and Northern America, Central Asia, Rocky Mountains and Pacific Coast in the United States
Amblyomma spp. *Haemaphysalis* spp. *Hyalomma* spp. *Rhipicephalus* spp.	Tick-borne typhus	*Rickettsia conori*	Africa, Mediterranean areas
Amblyomma spp. *Dermacentor virabilis Dermacentor* spp.	Rocky Mountain spotted fever	*Rickettsia rickettsii*	Portions of Canada and South America, Mexico, the United States
Amblyomma spp. *Americanum* spp. *Dermacentor* spp. *Haemaphysalis* sp. *Rhipicephalus* sp.	Tularemia	*Francisella tularensis*	Western United States

Source: Adapted from Cheng, T. C.: *The Biology of Animal Parasites*. W. B. Saunders Company, Philadelphia, 1964.

direct cause of disease, such as tick paralysis. Two main groups of ticks are recognized, the hard- and soft-shelled ticks (Figures 27–9 and 27–10). Hard-shelled ticks belong to the family of Ixodidae, and soft-shelled ticks are Argasidae. Figure 27–9 shows the scutum or dorsal shield which is a characteristic structure of hard-shelled ticks, such as *Dermacentor* spp. Approximately 800 different species are known.

The life cycle of both ticks and mites begins with an egg. Six-legged larvae hatch from the eggs, and subsequently develop into eight-legged nymphs. These forms later become adults. Certain infectious disease agents are known to pass into the eggs of infected ticks and the larvae of mites, thereby making their transmission to succeeding generations possible and the particular arthropods important reservoirs. This is known as *transovarial passage* or *transmission*.

Differentiating between ticks and mites can be confusing. Certain characteristics aid in distinguishing between the two types of arthropods, including: (1) the larger size of ticks, (2) the absence or almost complete absence of short hairs on the bodies of ticks (in contrast to the long hairs present on the membranous body of mites as shown in Figure 27–11), (3) the leathery appearance of the body of ticks, and (4) the exposed and teeth-bearing *hypostome*, used for attachment purposes.

Several species of mites infest man and can thereby transmit certain diseases,

FIG. 27–9. A dorsal view of a male and female hard-shelled dog tick (*Dermacentor variabilis*). (Courtesy of the Rocky Mountain Laboratory, U.S. Public Health Service, Hamilton, Montana.)

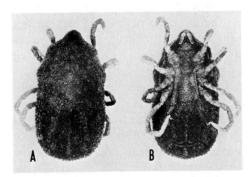

FIG. 27–10. Dorsal (*A*) and ventral (*B*) views of a female soft-shelled tick (*Ornithodoros concanensis*). (Courtesy of the Rocky Mountain Laboratory, U.S. Public Health Service, Hamilton, Montana.)

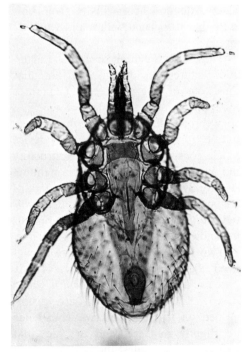

FIG. 27–11. A female mite, *Liponyssus bacoti*. (Courtesy of the Rocky Mountain Laboratory, U.S. Public Health Service, Hamilton, Montana.)

including rickettsialpox and scrub typhus. Furthermore, sarcoptic acariasis, a non-infectious disease, is caused by the skin-burrowing mite *Sarcoptes scabies*. The term *acariasis* is used to denote a mite infestation.

The Insecta

Lice.   These insects are parasitic on the surfaces of birds and of several mammalian species—cats, cattle, dogs, goats, horses, and man. Two orders of lice are known, Anoplura and Mallophaga. Generally speaking, the Anoplura have mouth parts which are adapted for sucking the blood and tissue fluids of mammals, while the Mallophaga species possess mouth parts adapted for chewing epitheloid structures associated with the skin of their hosts. However, certain species of the Mallophaga have been reported to feed on the blood and tissue fluids of their hosts. Attention here will be given only to the lice associated with man, *Anoplura* spp.

These insects exhibit several characteristic features, including: (1) antennae consisting of five segments; (2) three pairs of legs, the third pair of which is often broad, flattened, and the largest; and (3) an effective grasping device which consists of a hook-like structure and an opposing tibial process, or thumb (Figure 27–12). Two different genera of lice are associated with man, *Pediculus* and *Phthirus*. Members of the latter genus are known as the pubic or crab lice.

Two forms of *Pediculus* are recognized, *P. humanus var. corporis* (body louse) and *P. humanus var. capitis* (head louse). The two varieties are distinguished on the basis of size (head lice are slightly smaller), and the fact that body lice seldom infest the head region of the host. Head lice apparently roam over the entire body.

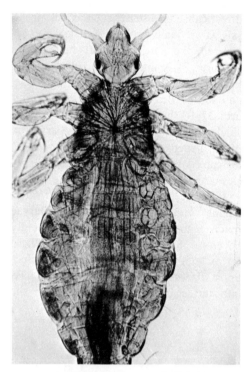

FIG. 27–12. The body louse, *Pediculus humanus var. corporis*. Note the characteristic features of this insect.

Several infectious diseases of man are transmitted by lice. Diseases such as cholera, impetigo, and trachoma are spread by mechanical means. The rickettsial diseases of epidemic typhus, and trench fever and the bacterial infection of relapsing fever are biologically transmitted.

The life cycle of lice includes the egg (nit), nymph, and adult stages. The sexes are separate. Blood meals can be taken by both the nymph and adult forms. Lice can be found clinging to hair or in clothing. One of the primary control measures used against human lice is effective personal cleanliness. This is especially important in crowded areas and during disasters such as earthquakes and floods. Control of these insects also can be accomplished through the judicious use of chemical agents, including chlordane, DDT, gammexane, and toxaphene.

The "true bugs." These insects belong to the taxonomic order of Hemiptera. Most of these insects are *phytophagous* (plant-eaters). However, several species apparently have abandoned such plant feeding, and have adopted *entomophagy* (insect-eating). Probably no other group of arthropods exert as pronounced an effect on the welfare of man as these "bugs" do. Several of them, such as the leaf hopper and plant lice, cause extreme destruction of plants. Other members of the order are vectors for viral plant disease agents and for protozoan pathogens of man and animals. Certain reduviid bugs, commonly referred to as "assassin bugs," attack higher forms of animals, including man. Chagas' disease (American Trypanosomiasis) is transmitted by species of the genera *Panstrongylus, Rhodnius,* and *Triatoma.*

These blooksucking bugs vary in size, usually are black or brown, and occasionally exhibit bright red or yellow markings (see Color photograph 110). An additional characteristic is a long, narrow head with a thin neck-like region immediately behind the eyes of the insect. Life cycles of the reduviid bug include the egg, nymph, and adult stages. The sexes are separate.

Fleas. These bloodsucking ectoparasites belong to the order of Siphonaptera. Well over 1,300 species of fleas have been described, undoubtedly leaving many more to be discovered.

These arthropods are wingless, possess laterally long, thin, compressed bodies, and range in size from 1.5 to 4.0 mm (males are generally smaller than females). The large first segments of the legs are collectively called *coxa.* They are important to the well-known jumping ability of fleas (Figure 27–13).

Another characteristic feature of these arthropods are the combs (*ctenida*), which are backward-pointing rows of

FIG. 27–13. *Pulex irritans,* the human flea. (Courtesy of the Bureau of Vector Control, California State Department of Public Health.)

spines. The cheek comb, referred to as the *genal* form, is located just above the mouth parts, while the *pronatal* comb is situated on the back of the first segment. (Figure 27–13). The cheek row of spines primarily serves to prevent the hairs or feathers of the host from interfering with the flea's mouth parts during its feeding. The pronatal ctenidium aids the flea's movements through the feathers or hairs of the host and protects its underlying parts. The presence or absence of these combs is important in classification. In certain species, the location of the ocular bristle (Figure 27–14) is also of taxonomic importance.

During the life cycle of the fleas, these arthropods pass through the egg, larva, pupa (cocoon), and adult stages. The pattern of development is an example of complete metamorphosis; the larvae transform into the highly complex adult female and male fleas during the pupal stage. This stage is characterized by a silky cocoon spun by the larva. When the development of this stage is completed, adult fleas emerge. The larvae feed mainly on any nutritive debris, including blood-containing feces of adult fleas. Adults feed on their particular hosts.

Fleas are of medical interest primarily in relation to the transmission of plague

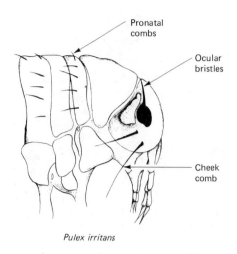

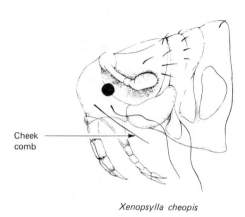

Fleas

FIG. 27–14. The characteristic combs of ocular bristles of the flea. The latter structures serve to distinguish between *Pulex irritans* (human flea) and *Xenopsylla cheopis* (rat flea).

and endemic typhus. *Xenopsylla cheopis* (rat flea) is considered the most important vector for both of these diseases. *Nosopsyllus fasciatus* as well as any other species of flea associated with rats may act as common vectors of endemic typhus.

Fleas can also serve as mechanical vectors for a number of helminths, such as the dog tapeworm (*Dipylidium caninum*) and the rat tapeworm (*Hymenolepis diminuta*).

Mention should be made of the cutaneous irritations that can be caused by infestation of fleas. The chigger or burrowing flea (*Tunga* spp.) burrows into the skin of mammals, including man, and produces intense itching which may lead to ulceration.

Mosquitoes. Several species of mosquito are known to transmit numerous helminthic, protozoan, and viral diseases of man and lower animals (Table 27–5). The insects are probably best known as the vectors for *Plasmodium* spp., the causative agents of malaria. They belong to the order of Diptera. Approximately 2,000 mosquito species have been described. Several species may be encountered in almost every country.

These "delicate flies of evil reputation" (so called by Brown and Belding in 1964) have long legs and slender bodies (Figure 27–15). Other distinguishing features of mosquitoes include: (1) the elongated mouth parts of adult females (proboscis) which are adapted, in most cases, for blood-sucking; (2) the bushier (plumose) antennae of males (Figure 27–16); and (3) the characteristic wing veins and scales (Figure 27–17).

In general, mosquitoes can be distinguished from other diptera on the basis of wing venation. Of particular value is the presence of two "bifurcated" wing veins near the apex of each wing.

The life cycle of these insects involves the general egg, larva, pupa, and adult stages (Figure 27–18). The larval form is called *instar*. Moisture is a major factor in larval development. Most mosquitoes utilize fresh water; however, species of

Table 27–5   Representative Human Viral Diseases Transmitted by Mosquitoes

Major Arthropod Vector	Disease	Geographical Distribution
Aëdes aegypti	Dengue fever (breakbone fever)	Caribbean area, Southeast Asia, Southwest Pacific
Aëdes sollicitans *Culex salinarius* *Mansonia perturbans*	Eastern equine encephalitis (EEE)	In the United States along the Atlantic coast to the Gulf coast, and occasionally in Kansas and Wisconsin; Mexico, South America
Culex tritaeniorhynchus	Japanese B encephalitis	Far East
Culex annulirostris *C. tarsalis*	Murray Valley encephalitis	North Australia, New Guinea
Culex quinquefasciatus *C. tarsalis*	St. Louis encephalitis	Western and Mid-western United States
Mansonia titillans	Venezuelan equine encephalitis (VEE)	South America, including Columbia, Ecuador, and Venezuela; Panama and Trinidad
Culex spp.	West Nile encephalitis	Egypt, India, Israel, Sudan
Aëdes spp. *Anopheles* spp. *Culex tarsalis* *Culiseta* spp.	Western equine encephalitis (WEE)	Western United States
Aëdes aegypti *Haemagogus mesodentatus* *Haemagogus* spp.	Yellow fever	South America; epidemic in Central and North America

SOURCE: Adapted from Cheng, T. C.: *The Biology of Animal Parasites.* W. B. Saunders Company, Philadelphia, 1964.

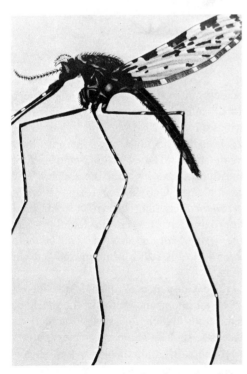

FIG. 27–15. One vector of malaria, *Anopheles gambiae.* (Courtesy of World Health Organization, Geneva.)

certain genera, e.g., *Aëdes, Culex,* and *Mansonia,* breed in brackish or salt water. Pupae are equipped with respiratory trumpets on the thorax and a pair of overlapping paddles on the last abdominal segment. The paddles help them to dive rapidly when exposed to unfavorable stimuli.

The principal genera involved in the transmission of disease agents of man and lower animals include species of *Aëdes, Anopheles, Culex, Haemagogus,* and *Mansonia.*

The control of mosquitoes requires knowledge of the habits of these insects, the topography and climate of the region involved, and the socio-economic status and living habits of the population in and around the breeding grounds of the insects. Generally speaking, the most effective measures include elimination of breeding sites and the destruction of larval and adult mosquitoes.

Cockroaches.   These insects belong to the order of Orthoptera. Adult forms

FIG. 27–16. A comparison of anopheline mosquito antennae. _A._ Male. _B._ Female. Note the jointed nature of these structures.

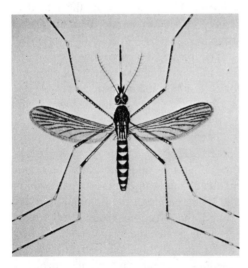

FIG. 27–17. _Culex tarsalis,_ female. The characteristic features of the mosquito include long legs, proboscis, and wing venation. (Courtesy of the Bureau of Vector Control, California State Department of Public Health.)

possess an oval body, three pairs of legs (well adapted for running), and four wings (Figure 27–19). The life cycle of cockroaches includes egg, nymph, and adult stages. The coloration and size of these insects varies with the species. For example, the German cockroach (_Blatella germanica_) is light brown in color, and approximately 1.3 cm in length, while the American cockroach (_Periplaneta americana_) is reddish-brown and 3.8 cm long.

The German cockroach is considered to be an important vector in the mechanical transmission of several infectious diseases, such as amebic dysentery, infectious hepatitis, salmonellosis, and shigellosis. Cockroaches are very widely distributed and survive under a wide variety of conditions.

FIG. 27–18. Development stages of *Culex tarsalis*. *Left,* instar stage. *Right,* pupa stage. Note the trumpet (*T*) and paddle (*P*) structures. (Courtesy of the Bureau of Vector Control, California State Department of Public Health.)

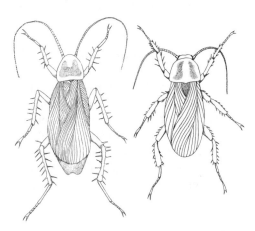

FIG. 27–19. Representation of two cockroaches. *Left, Periplaneta americana* (male American cockroach). *Right, Blatella germanica* (female German cockroach).

Pesticides (Friends or Foes)

The use of various pesticides for the control of insect pests, in particular the chlorinated hydrocarbons, e.g., DDT, has has been of great concern since Rachel Carson's publication "Silent Spring" appeared in 1962. The violent controversy that has developed still remains to be resolved. Arguments supporting the use of pesticides continually emphasize the dramatic effectiveness of DDT in reducing the numbers of various arthropods responsible for the transmission of insect-born microbial diseases of both animals and plants. Yet, on the other hand, those individuals demanding the restriction or total elimination of pesticide usage, have clearly established that the accumulation of pesticides by animals and plants has resulted in a most serious threat to the existence of life on earth. The chlorinated hydrocarbons pose a particular problem, since they, unlike other pesticides such as the organophosphates, are not biodegradable. Moreover, since 1964 numerous insect species have been found which were resistant to one form of a pesticide or another.

As this brief discussion indicates, the pesticide issue is a complex one, and since space limitations do not permit, a more thorough treatment of the subject is not possible. However, it would appear that the control of particular pests requires a carefully controlled and integrated approach incorporating the appropriate and combined use of a pest's natural enemies (predators), pesticides and even insect microbial pathogens such as those discussed in Chapter 5. The careful selection of these active participants for control, and their implementation should not add significantly to the current pesticide pollution problems. Moreover, it should serve as a more effective and well-balanced control device.

The Hospital Environment

Hospital Infections

The hospital environment can be considered a potential reservoir of infection, for it houses both patients with a variety of pathogenic microorganisms, and a large number of susceptible individuals. Today, *nosocomial*, or hospital-acquired, infections are posing serious and far-reaching problems. For example, since 1950 marked increases have been reported in bacteremia and deaths caused by staphylococci and Gram-negative organisms such as *E. coli, Enterobacter* spp., *Pseudomonas* spp., and *Proteus* spp.

Many factors have contributed to the problem of nosocomial infections, including: (1) overcrowded hospitals and staff shortages, (2) the closing of most communicable disease hospitals, (3) the indiscriminate, frequent, and prolonged use of broad-spectrum antibiotics, (4) longer and more complicated surgical procedures, (5) a false sense of security which has fostered neglect of aseptic techniques, and (6) the use of immuno-depressing agents such as steroids, anti-cancer, drugs, and irradiation. Such practices have provided fertile fields for the development of previously innocuous bacteria, which have emerged as major causes for over 60 per cent of hospital-acquired infections. It is estimated that approximately 5 per cent of all patients admitted to hospitals for reasons other than infectious states develop nosocomial infections. Such diseases may involve the majority of individuals, equipment, and procedures associated with patients.

Hospital personnel are considered to be important sources of infectious agents, as various parts of their bodies and clothes may serve to transport pathogens.

Reported sources of contamination for specific outbreaks of nosocomial infections have included intravenous infusion products, respiratory therapy equipment, stethoscopes, medicinals and lotions, catheters, and shaving brushes used in the preoperative shaving of patients. A recent study has implicated rolls of adhesive tape, which are exposed to a variety of patients, as potential sources of nosocomial infections. This finding is quite logical in view of the variety of uses of adhesive tape, the exposure of unused and used portions of tape to patient secretions, and the fact that contaminated rolls of tape can in turn contaminate the hands of personnel who handle them.

Certain areas of the hospital are considered as high-risk areas in the transmission of diseases. Among these areas is the central supply unit, where most of the equipment used in patient care is cleansed when soiled, and subsequently stored until needed again. Other high-risk areas are the nurseries. Because of the limited resistance of newborn infants to infection, the transmission of pathogenic organisms is of greater concern here. Because broken skin is a good portal of entry for pathogenic organisms, the operating room and the obstetrical delivery rooms also are considered high-risk areas in disease transmission.

Principles of Control

Many health care personnel (and perhaps the nurse more than any other) are responsible for patients 24 hours a day. In safeguarding the well-being of patients and preventing the transmission of infectious diseases, respective health care personnel employ basic measures: *medical asepsis* and *surgical asepsis*.

Medical Asepsis

Medical asepsis refers to those techniques used to reduce the direct or indirect transmission of pathogenic microorganisms. Medical asepsis is employed by the nurse to reduce the number of pathogenic microorganisms and hinder their transfer from one person or place to another. A variety of techniques are used in helping to achieve this condition. These include washing, dusting, disinfection, and isolation.

Surgical Asepsis

Surgical asepsis means those practices which make and keep objects and areas sterile, free from *all* microorganisms. Aseptic techniques are necessary in all surgical procedures or other procedures involving the body's deeper tissues. Injections are a good example; during such procedures a break is made into the body tissues, rendering them more susceptible to infection. Surgical asepsis is also used throughout the operating and delivery rooms and in nurseries to protect susceptible newborns. It is applied to the care of surgical wounds for several days following an operation, or until the injured tissues are healed sufficiently.

All materials used during these procedures are sterilized. Certain articles, such as linen or gauze, may be obtained from the stock supply of sterile packages. The surgeon and all other personnel involved in the procedure limit the introduction of microorganisms into the operative area by their utilization of sterile gowns, caps, masks, and rubber gloves, and by the adequate washing of their hands and associated areas.

The following principles of sterile technique or surgical asepsis may be applied in various ways depending on the procedure:

1. If in doubt about an article's sterility, consider it unsterile.
2. The rims or edges of any object or material that encloses sterile con-

tents (such as the wrapper on a sterile package) are considered unsterile.
3. Moisture may cause contamination because it provides a means of transporting bacteria to the sterile area. Therefore, sterile packages must be kept dry.

The nurse, in protecting patients from infection, must be able to understand and apply these principles of sterile technique, since a break in technique may become a threat to the patient's life. Even mild infections delay recovery and are expensive.

Control Measures

Hand Washing

Hands should always be washed before and after each patient contact, especially with those individuals considered to be potential sources of infectious agents. Using mechanical friction, all areas of the hands should be well lathered and scrubbed. Special attention should be given to the nails and nail beds. All rinsing should be performed under running water. The rinsing and washing steps should be repeated and followed by adequate drying. A cream or lotion may be applied to prevent chapping. In order to prevent pathogenic bacteria from becoming residents of the skin, soaps used for purposes of handwashing should contain a bacteriostatic agent such as hexachlorophene. The value of hexachlorophene has been questioned. However it is still being used to control staphlococcal infections.

Isolation

The purpose of isolation is to contain an infectious agent within a prescribed area to prevent the spread of infection. A patient is placed in isolation for one of two reasons—to prevent the spread of a communicable disease to other persons, or to protect an unusually susceptible patient. The physician initiates the order for admitting a patient to isolation and for discontinuing isolation. The nurse is responsible for maintaining the isolation of the patient. To accomplish this, she must understand the principles of medical asepsis and be aware of the microorganism involved and its specific characteristics. Isolation procedures for patients with communicable diseases need not be rigid routines. They should be determined by:

1. The mode or route by which the organism is transmitted from one person to another.
2. The location of the microorganism within the host and its portal of exit, e.g., feces, wound drainage, and respiration secretions.
3. The portal of entry of the organism into the body, e.g., the skin, the gastro-intestinal tract, the respiratory tract, etc.
4. The nature of the specific organism, e.g., its virulence and its vulnerability to destruction.

The nurse must interpret for the patient, as well as his immediate family members and visitors, the reasons for the isolation and the procedures to be followed. Isolations can be carried out on the basis of a particular syndrome or microorganism or the dictates of a specific hospital service, such as pediatrics or geriatrics.

Isolation on the basis of syndrome. This general category includes conditions such as diarrhea, purulent discharges, draining lesions, burns, and pediatric upper respiratory diseases. Meningitis cases should be isolated until laboratory findings are available to rule out *Neisseria meningitidis* infection. Meningococcal meningitis can be considered to be noncommunicable after 24 hours of antibiotic therapy. Individuals diagnosed as having aseptic meningitis should remain in isolation until the end of the febrile period in order to prevent cross infections with a variety of viruses, such as poliomyelitis, mumps, and enteroviruses. This procedure is also recommended for cases of viral hepatitis, pediatric conjunctivitis, active venereal disease, mumps, and pneumonia. With staphylococcal pneumonia, patients must always be isolated.

Isolation by service. Particular caution should be exercised with infant diarrhea and the yeast infection moniliasis in the nursery, and whooping cough and gonococcal vulvovaginitis in pediatric patients. Similar precautions should be observed with geriatric patients, as they often are hypogammaglobulinemic, with insufficient antibodies, and particularly susceptible to pneumonia due to any etiological agent.

Isolation by microorganism. The more significant communicable diseases which should be considered for isolation in this category are caused by microorganisms which include *Streptococcus aureus, Pseudomonas aeruginosa,* Group A beta hemolytic streptococci, *Mycobacterium tuberculosis, Treponema pallidum, Neisseria meningitidis,* and *Salmonella* and *Shigella* spp. Significant organisms encountered less often include *Bacillus anthracis, Vibrio cholerae, Corynebacterium diphtheriae, Yersinia pestis, Pseudomonas pseudomallei, Actinobacillus mallei, Leptospira* spp., and the agents of psittacosis and rabies.

Reverse isolation. This procedure is used for shielding highly susceptible patients from pathogens found in the hospital environment. Patients who for one reason or another have a lowered resistance to infection include premature infants, organ-transplant patients, severely burned and leukemia patients, and individuals receiving radiation therapy. The person in reverse isolation is placed in a single room which has been thoroughly cleaned and disinfected prior to his admission. Gowns are worn by those entering the room to prevent transmitting pathogens into the room from clothes. No one with a known infection is allowed to enter the room.

If a more strict reverse isolation procedure is needed, the patient may be placed into an isolator or plastic tent which provides a germ-free environment. The isolator has a sterile air supply, and only sterile equipment is passed into it through special portholes. Attached to the sides of the plastic tent are rubber gloves with long sleeves which make it possible for nursing and medical personnel to render adequate patient care, while at the same time protecting him from exposure to pathogens.

In environments outside of the hospital, much less attention is directed toward isolating individuals than was formerly practiced. It is generally felt that if a patient requires isolation, he should be sent to a hospital. Today quarantine is rarely practiced.

Institutional Policies for Control

Hospitals vary greatly in their specific policies for the care of communicable diseases. Each institution should put its policies in writing, and complete details of care should be available to all staff members. Some of the generally accepted policies are listed below.

1. Correct hand washing is one of the most important measures in preventing the spread of infection.
2. Isolation gowns should be worn by persons giving direct nursing care to the patient or by persons whose uniforms are likely to come in contact with contaminated material.
3. There is no consistent policy on the use of masks, but it must be remembered that a wet or ill-fitting mask provides little or no protection.
4. Disposable equipment and supplies should be used whenever possible. Non-disposable equipment should be disinfected and/or sterilized if considered feasible. All used equipment should be disinfected as soon as possible and with a minimum of handling. Such items should be removed from the patient's room for sterilization or if disposable for incineration.
5. All contaminated material, including equipment, trash, linen, and specimens should be removed from the patient's room by a double bagging technique. This method involves placing contaminated material in a paper or plastic bag and having someone outside the patient's room receive this first bag in another clean one. The latter then is properly labeled "isolation" and identified as to contents (Figure 27–20).
6. Terminal disinfection is done when the patient has recovered, been transferred, or has died. This procedure includes sterilizing or disinfecting all possibly contaminated material and equipment, such as mattresses, pillows, furniture, floors, and walls. Details are given in Chapters 17 and 18.

Diseases of Plants

The causative agents of plant infections and crop spoilage are for the most part of the same general types as those encountered with animal infections, and

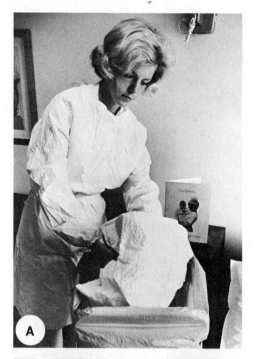

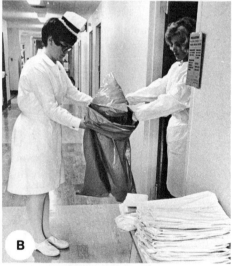

FIG. 27–20. The double bag technique. *A*. A nurse discards disposable paper bed linen and patient gown in a plastic hamper. The nurse also wears a disposable paper gown, which she deposits in the hamper before leaving the room. *B*. The bag is secured at the top and placed in an uncontaminated bag at the unit door for transmittal to the incinerator. (Courtesy of Andrew McGowan, St. Luke's Hospital Center, New York.)

include bacteria, fungi, viruses, and parasitic nematodes. Fortunately, however, none of these organisms have thus far been shown to be capable of producing infections in man or other animals. Plant disease agents can be transmitted in a wide variety of ways which can involve arthropods, contaminated soil and tools, grafting practices, mechanical inoculation (rubbing abrasives on the surfaces of leaves), seeds, and even certain species of fungi and nematodes. Numerous factors, such as host resistance, temperature, moisture, and the virulence of the disease agent are known to be important in the development of plant diseases. In many ways the disease process closely resembles that of animals.

QUESTIONS FOR REVIEW

1. Define or explain the following terms:
   a. epidemic
   b. sporadic infection
   c. pandemic
   d. communicable disease
   e. endemic
   f. epidemiology

2. What are Koch's Postulates?

3. Differentiate between morbidity and mortality rates.

4. What is a carrier? What types of diseases are associated with such individuals?

5. What are the Five Fs and why are they important?

6. What are fomites?

7. What types of fomites could one encounter in the following situations?
   a. physician's office
   b. dormitory
   c. dentist's office

d. restaurant
e. hospital room
f. clinical laboratory

8. List at least six infectious diseases which could be transmitted by fomites.

9. Periodically, newspapers report the occurrence of both natural and man-made disasters. Discuss the types of conditions favorable for the spread of diseases which could prevail in the situations listed, and the infectious diseases which could be present.
a. earthquake
b. war
c. flood
d. famine
e. fire
f. blizzard

10. Differentiate between biological and mechanical means of disease transmission.

11. What contributions did the following individuals make toward the understanding of disease transmission and processes?
a. Sir Ronald Ross
b. Theobald Smith
c. Robert Koch

12. What dangers do bats pose for the well-being of man and the various domestic animals in his environment?

13. What arthropod vectors are associated with the following diseases?
a. malaria
b. Rocky Mountain spotted fever
c. Western equine encephalitis
d. plague

e. typhoid fever
f. African sleeping sickness
g. typhus fever
h. yellow fever
i. dog tapeworm
j. amebic dysentery

14. What methods are commonly available for the control of arthropods?

15. Discuss medical asepsis.

16. What practices are involved in surgical asepsis?

17. What is reverse isolation?

18. Associate specific infectious diseases with the following potential means of disease transmission (mark your answers down on paper and keep for future reference).
a. flies
b. ticks
c. water (contaminated)
d. mosquitoes
e. hypodermic syringe
f. cockroaches
g. mouthpiece (used)
h. nasal secretions
i. milk
j. kissing
k. fleas
l. sexual relations
m. dogs
n. soil
o. mites
p. lice

19. *After you have read the remaining chapters in this section, come back to question 18 and your answers. Have your views changed?*

Selected Techniques in the Identification of Disease Agents

The accurate identification of pathogenic organisms is dependent upon a close working relationship between various members of the allied health team. Upon recognizing the presence of the clinical symptoms of a particular infectious disease, the physician will request that specific specimens be taken. This procedure may be performed by a registered nurse, medical technologist, or other health personnel. Then the specimen is sent to the laboratory for processing and examination by qualified personnel. With the proper handling, the organisms in the specimen can be identified. Careful attention to details and good communication between members of the team are desirable for the most rapid and intelligent identification of disease agents. Laboratory findings are transmitted as quickly as possible to the attending physician.

Protozoa and Helminths

The numbers and kinds of procedures required for the identification of a disease agent varies significantly with the type of organism involved. For example, the examination of feces for helminth ova and other forms of parasites usually involves preparation of a wet mount of fresh or preserved material. A permanent, stained preparation may be made in some cases to assist in identification. For example, the identification of malarial parasites involves the examination of Wright and/ or Giemasa stained blood smears. With a certain degree of luck and extensive searching, a single smear of this type will be sufficient to locate various stages in the parasite's life cycle. (Color photographs 107 through 120). Thus repeated blood samples and examinations are not necessary.

Fungi

Fungi require inoculation on a selective medium and incubation at room (25°C) and body (37°C) temperatures. Once growth appears, these organisms can usually be differentiated on the basis of microscopic examination. Finding such structures as hyphae, spores, yeasts, arrangements of spores, etc., can provide a suitable identification. Yeasts may require one or several additional steps. For example, *Cryptococcus neoformans* has a broad capsule evident in organisms from clinical specimens (Figure 10–2) and can be differentiated from other yeast cells by detecting the presence of the enzyme urease. This is the only genus of pathogenic yeasts that has the enzyme. Other yeasts, *Candida* spp., are generally differentiated from similar organisms by their forming pseudo-mycelia; cells remain together forming a chain of yeasts in corn meal Tween 80 agar. Characterizations of the species in this genus are done by examination of the pseudo-mycelia. Confirmation is accomplished by means of sugar fermentation and oxidation tests.

Bacteria

The isolation and identification of pathogenic bacteria may require few or many different tests and media. For this reason, and also because many laboratories only occasionally encounter parasites and fungi, the differential identification of bacteria is stressed in this chapter. Additional details concerning individual organisms described here will be provided by later chapters. This chapter will serve only to introduce some of the common problems involved in the collection and handling of specimens. Attention is also given to the isolation and identification of possibly significant microorganisms. In short, this chapter will serve to orient the reader to the overall view of the problems associated with diagnostic microbiology.

Specimen Collection and Handling

Laboratory personnel involved with the identification of disease agents can only report those organisms that are isolated from clinical specimens (Tables 28–1 and 28–2). Initially the physician must decide which type of specimen or specimens will enable him to confirm his clinical diagnosis. Such specimens must be taken from a patient as ordered and sent to the laboratory, with appropriate precautions to keep the specimen in good condition.

It is a good practice for physicians to indicate their particular reasons for the specimen on the order slip. Information of this sort may assist laboratory personnel in the proper selection of media and/or conditions which would make recovery of a suspected pathogen more likely. This would be particularly true in the case of certain fastidious, unusual, or slow-growing organisms.

In a hospital situation, except for blood cultures, most specimens are collected by physicians or nurses. Blood samples are generally obtained by medical technologists. Many different types of specimens are used in laboratory diagnosis. Representative ones, together with the bacterial and mycotic diseases with which they may be associated, are listed in Tables 28–1 and 28–2. Additional information concerning specimens for other pathogenic types will be found in later chapters.

Certain types of specimens are taken with swabs, and if these dry out after collection or during transit to the laboratory, they may prove to be unsatisfactory. The recent introduction of Dacron swabs has helped this situation immensely, since many organisms will survive well on dry Dacron. One method for transporting a throat swab specimen from the office to a laboratory is shown in Figure 28–1. It is still advisable to transport a swab specimen in a tube containing a small amount of holding medium: any of several liquid or semi-solid media which

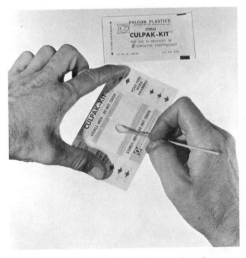

FIG. 28–1. An aid in the recovery of pathogenic streptococci from a throat swab when the specimen must be transported some distance to a laboratory. The organisms survive well for a day or more. (Courtesy of Falcon Plastics, Division of BioQuest, Los Angeles.)

Table 28–1   Representative Types of Specimens Used for the Laboratory Diagnosis of Selected Bacterial Infections

	Autopsy Material	Biopsy Material	Blood	Spinal Fluid	Sputum	Stool	Vesicular Fluid or Skin Scraping	Throat Swab	Throat Washing	Urethral Discharge	Urine
Actinomycosis (lumpy jaw)		+			+						
Boils		+					+				
Diphtheria								+	+		
Enteritis (salmonellosis)		+	+			+					+
Gas gangrene	+	+									
Gonorrhea										+	
Meningitis	+		+	+							
Shigellosis						+					
Syphilis		+		+							
Tuberculosis	+	+	+	+	+				+		+
Urinary tract infection		+								+	+

Table 28–2   Representative Types of Specimens Used for the Laboratory Diagnosis of Selected Mycotic (Fungal) and Related Infections

	Autopsy Material	Biopsy Material	Blood	Hair	Mucous Membranes or Skin Scrapings	Nail Material	Sputum	Vaginal Smear
Athletes's foot (Tinea pedis)					+	+		
Coccidioidomycosis	+	+	+				+	
Histoplasmosis	+	+	+				+	
Moniliasis (oral thrush)					+		+	
Nocardiosis	+	+					+	
North American blastomycosis	+	+					+	
Ringworm of the scalp (Tinea capitis)				+	+			
Vaginal thrush								+

FIG. 28–3. A sterile container with a tight-fitting lid to prevent spills when used with urine specimens. This type of container is very satisfactory for sputum specimens as well. (Courtesy of Falcon Plastics, Division of BioQuest, Los Angeles.)

FIG. 28–2. Sputum collection kit. A tight-fitting lid covers a funnel into which sputum is coughed. The funnel directs the specimen into a graduated, threaded plastic centrifuge tube. The screw cap is shown near the bottom of the tube. Processing of the sputum for culture requires only that the bottom cap be removed, followed by the removal of the centrifuge tube and the screw cap. (Courtesy of Falcon Plastics, Division of BioQuest, Los Angeles.)

prevent dessication of the pathogenic organisms without allowing overgrowth of normal flora or contaminants.

If the material cannot be cultured immediately, most specimens will be adequate for culturing if they are refrigerated for several hours prior to planting. However, bacteria such as *Neisseria meningitidis* are sensitive to the cold, so a cerebrospinal fluid specimen suspected of containing this organism must be cultured immediately. Wound specimens should also be processed immediately, since anaerobes may be present and they die rapidly upon exposure to oxygen. Refrigeration is generally adequate for urine,

feces, and sputum. Sputum collection is best done in the collection kit shown in Figure 28–2.

Urine is the only specimen for which a bacterial count is performed as a clinical test. (See Chapter 37 for discussion of this type of specimen.) It must be collected in a sterile container (Figure 28–3).

Samples of several types of clinical specimens (throat swabs, feces, blood) can be rapidly frozen and kept in this state for later viral examinations, or they may be shipped in dry ice to a reference laboratory for further study. Serum for such viral or other serological testing must be separated from the whole blood and sent in a sterile tube. Whole blood, if frozen, will prove unsatisfactory for serological tests. If clotted blood is to be sent, it should be refrigerated or transported in ice.

This brief discussion has barely touched the overall problem of proper collection and handling procedures. Many microorganisms have unique requirements which makes it necessary for laboratory personnel to be familiar with the various usual and unusual organisms in order to find them in clinical specimens. For instance, some anaerobic bacteria will not survive even the briefest exposure to oxygen. Moreover, some parasitic forms degenerate rapidly. Thus stool specimens must be placed into preservative solutions to guarantee recognition of the organism at the laboratory.

The Transport of Microbial-Containing Specimens

The rapid isolation and subsequent identification of microbial pathogens are important in determining the specific chemotherapeutic approach to curing or arresting a disease process. The majority of microbial pathogens are fragile and short-lived. Because these life forms deteriorate in transit, or when subjected to unfavorable environmental conditions of humidity and/or temperature, a lack of adequate nutrients, or the presence of toxic substances, clinical specimens should be shipped by the most rapid means available to a laboratory.

Consideration also must be given to the risk posed by specimens containing pathogens to human life. This factor emphasizes the need for proper packaging of such specimens (Figure 28-4), whether transported by passenger commercial aircraft or by other means. The details of the regulations relating to packaging and other requirements applicable to the transportation of clinical and related specimens are specified in the following Code of Federal Regulations (CFR):

Title 42—Public Health

Chapter 1, Subchapter F—Quarantine, Inspection, Licensing

Part 72—Interstate Quarantine

Subpart C—Shipment of Certain Things

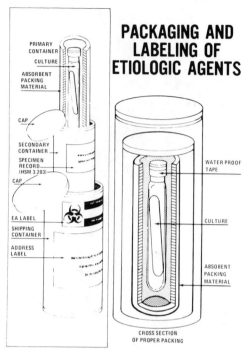

FIG. 28-4. Cross section of the approved container arrangement for the shipping of Etiologic Agents/Biomedical Material. (Courtesy of Biohazards Control Office, Center for Disease Control, Atlanta, Ga.)

In this CFR three categories of etiologic agents are defined: (1) a viable microorganism or its toxin which causes or may cause human disease, (2) a diagnostic specimen including human or lower animal material such as blood, fecal matter, tissue, or tissue fluids being transported for diagnostic purposes, and (3) a biological product prepared, manufactured, and licensed or authorized in accordance with other portions of the Code of Federal Regulations. In addition to defining the nature of an etiologic agent, Title 42 CFR specifies (1) the types of containers to be used for the shipment of different volumes of clinical specimens, (2) the use of shock absorbent material with volumes of 50 milliliters or greater, (3) the precautions to be taken with dry ice, (4) the

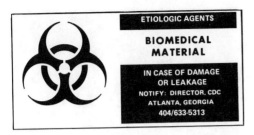

FIG. 28–5. The shipping label for Etiologic Agents/Biomedical Material. The symbol for etiologic agents shown at left is red and centered in a white square. (Courtesy of Biohazards Control Office, Center for Disease Control, Atlanta, Ga.)

features of the label for etiologic agents (Figure 28–5), and (5) the procedures to be followed with damaged packages, cases of failure of delivery of specimens, and the use of registered mail or an equivalent system. A provision also is included for the approval of variations to the shipping requirements.

Quite obviously adherence to these regulations is important not only to the safeguarding of passengers on commercial aircraft but also to the safety of all personnel handling specimen-containing packages. It should be noted that failure of the shipper to adhere to Title 42 CFR will result in penalties.

Laboratory Philosophy

A small clinical laboratory, which processes only a few specimens per day, generally can be academic in its approach to identifying microorganisms. By this is meant that each specimen can be examined soon after its arrival, and depending on the type of organism observed in wet mount or stained smear, an appropriate isolation medium can be selected and inoculated accordingly. In examining the growth which appears, an experienced microbiologist can note several additional important clues as to the identification of the suspected disease agent. Included in

this group of properties would be odor, colonial appearance, and staining reactions.

As the volume of specimens increases, the amount of time that can be spent on each decreases and general procedures must be adopted. Often, specimen smears cannot be stained immediately and observed soon enough to allow the selection of appropriate isolation media. In such situations, media must be chosen to isolate the significant pathogens usually associated with a particular type of specimen.

A wide variety of selective and differential media are available to assist the microbiologist. However, these should not be used as a substitute for careful observation. The fact that a certain organism will not only grow but produce a characteristic colony on some medium is only presumptive evidence for its identification. Biochemical testing and in some cases serotyping may be necessary for adequate identification.

Multiple-test and rapid-method systems. The identification of bacterial species is based on schemes or keys that take into consideration a variety of characteristics, such as differential-staining reactions, colonial properties and biochemical tests that determine the ability of a particular organism to utilize or to attack certain substances (substrates), and production of chemical products that can be analyzed. Traditionally, the use of a variety of well-chosen biochemical tests has offered the best means of specific or near-specific identification of unknown bacterial cultures. Assistance in this type of activity is provided by numerous reference works and identification schemes that contain the results of key reactions obtained with known bacterial species.

In many cases the biochemical tests used in the identification of unknown cultures are performed in separate Petri plates and/or test tubes (Color photographs 37 through 42). These rather standardized procedures not only are costly but also are time consuming. It is no small wonder, then, that investigators have long been interested in reducing the economic expense and drudgery associated with microbiological methods. The efforts of many individuals have resulted in the development of at least three general categories of improved biochemical testing procedures and materials. These are: (1) several test substrates combined in one or two tubes, which are inoculated and incubated in the conventional manner (Color photograph 51), (2) separate biochemical tests contained in miniaturized, multi-compartment devices, which are inoculated by unconventional methods, but incubated according to standard practices (Color photographs 52 and 53), and (3) biochemical substrates impregnated into paper strips, which are inoculated by unconventional methods and which produce reactions in significantly less time than in conventional tests (Figure 28–6).

The first category includes several widely accepted media such as Triple Sugar Iron Agar (Color photograph 51). This medium is used for the differentiation of Gram-negative enteric organisms by their ability to ferment dextrose (glucose), lactose, or sucrose and to reduce sulfites to sulfides. It is dispensed in the form of an agar slant.

The second category includes several commercially available miniaturized multiple-test systems and devices designed to make identification of unknown bacterias easier (Figure 28–6). Complete instructions together with accurate identification keys based on established biochemical reactions are provided by the respective manufacturers. Several systems, including

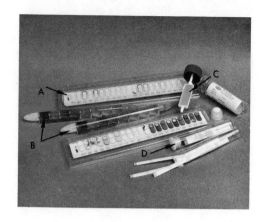

FIG. 28–6. Representative examples of multiple- and rapid-test systems used in the identification of unknown bacterial cultures. Explanation of labels: _A_. API Enteric 20 (Analytab Products Inc.); _B_. Enterotube (Roche Diagnostics); _C_. Urine dipslide (Oxoid, Ltd.); and _D_. Pathotec strips. (Photo by C. Righter.)

API 20 Enteric (Analytab Products, Inc.) and the Enterotube (Roche Diagnostics), consist of manufacturer-selected combinations of substrates that are ready for use, require minimal storage space, and are stable at either room or refrigerator temperatures for significant time periods. The API system mentioned employs a plastic strip that holds 20 miniaturized compartments, or capsules, each containing a dehydrated substrate for a different test. Specifically, 22 standard biochemical tests can be performed using this system. The dehydrated substrates are inoculated with a bacterial suspension and subsequently incubated according to a procedure described by the manufacturer.

The Enterotube incorporates conventional media into a single, ready-to-use, multi-compartment tube with an enclosed inoculating needle. The rather unique inoculating arrangement permits simultaneous inoculation of all compartments. The design of the Enterotube allows 11 standard biochemical tests to be performed.

Recently, a multiple-test system has become available which, when compared to other conventional systems, provides a greater degree of flexibility in selecting tests to be used for bacterial identification. The new system, Minitek (Bio Quest), incorporates paper disks impregnated with individual substrates. These disks are placed into individual wells in a plastic plate and inoculated with a broth suspension of the unknown organisms. Subsequent identification is based on the color reactions that occur in the disks following a suitable incubation period. More than 30 different substrate disks are presently available, which gives the user a wide range of choices from which to select those tests that are appropriate for his or her identification scheme.

The third category includes rapid methods for cultural identification. One example of this approach is represented by Pathotec strips. This commercial system consists of paper strips impregnated with a test substrate. By exposing the test area to a heavy bacterial suspension during incubation, a color reaction will appear within a short period of time.

The various systems and techniques described are representative of approaches to providing convenient means for performing the traditional biochemical tests used in the identification of unknown bacterial cultures. Each has certain advantages and disadvantages that should be duly considered before a decision is made to adopt a particular system.

Blood Cultures

The presence of bacteria in blood, i.e., bacteremia, may be of significant importance clinically. Various microorganisms gain access to the circulatory system as a consequence of their spreading from a diseased area by direct extension. The bloodstream if invaded aids the dissemination of pathogens, which may lead to involvement of any or eventually all organ systems. The speed with which a positive blood culture is recognized and the attending physician notified is of critical importance to proper patient treatment. When a patient exhibits an elevation of temperature, unexplainable on a clinical basis, blood cultures are usually taken. Although techniques vary, one common practice involves the taking of three blood specimens at approximately 2-hour intervals, and using them to inoculate appropriate culture media. Careful preparation of the skin before obtaining the blood specimens is mandatory. Although many antiseptic preparations are available, the use of tincture of iodine is still probably the best choice for adequate skin disinfection. After application, the tincture of iodine is allowed to dry and subsequently wiped off with isopropyl alcohol. Proper technique at this point will minimize the possibility of contamination of the blood specimen by skin bacteria.

Media. A variety of media are available for blood culture; these include Trypticase Soy and Tryptic Soy broths, Thiol, and Liquoid. Some microbiologists feel that addition of anticoagulants to the media will enhance the isolation of organisms. Certain compounds may also be added to neutralize some antibiotics that a patient may have received prior to collection of the blood specimen. In general, the growth-inhibiting effects of natural sera, various antimicrobial compounds, and antibiotics can be reduced or even eliminated by dilution of the blood specimen. This can be accomplished by adding the blood to the broth medium in a ratio of 1 to 10.

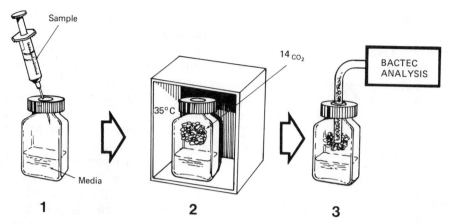

FIG. 28–7. The BACTEC Principle. *1*. A specimen is inoculated into a culture medium containing ^{14}C substrate. *2*. During bacterial metabolism $^{14}CO_2$ is produced from the organisms' utilization of the ^{14}C-containing substrate. *3*. The BACTEC instrument (Figure 28–8) is used to measure the released $^{14}CO_2$.

Examination. In the case of bacterial infections, it is imperative that blood cultures be examined daily for the presence of growth or any indication of a microorganism's presence. If growth is detected, subcultures should be made using fresh media and incubated under aerobic and/or anaerobic conditions. In addition, microscopic examination of the positive culture should be made. At this point the attending physician is notified so that he can evaluate the patient's treatment in light of this new information. Any and all additional information, including tentative identification of the isolated organism, antibiotic sensitivity, etc., also should be directed toward the physician as quickly as possible.

Although tedious, the examination procedure outlined above is critical to the analysis of blood cultures. Alternate methods have been proposed. Some of these have involved the successful use of membrane filtration with a more exotic procedure using liquid culture media with the incorporation of radioactive carbon (^{14}C) into some culture medium components. During bacterial metabolic activity the

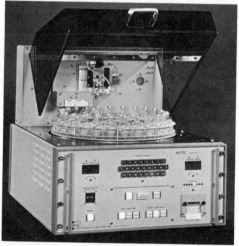

FIG. 28–8. The BACTEC 225 automated system. (Courtesy of Johnston Laboratories, Cockeysville, Maryland.)

radioactive carbon is released as $^{14}CO_2$. A special sensing device can detect the gas in this form. Figure 28–7 illustrates the principle of a radiometric BACTEC instrument (Figure 28–8), which is available commercially. This device is a fully automated model and can be used to analyze multiple cultures in a controlled environment.

General Identification Procedures

Familiarity with the pathogens most likely to cause particular clinical symptoms and those organisms most likely to be present in a certain specimen is important to good clinical microbiology. Other chapters of this book cover the various microorganisms encountered in the disease states and associated specimens. One purpose in this chapter is to indicate generally acceptable techniques for various specimens.

Each specimen must be handled aseptically. After its use for the inoculation of appropriate media, one or more smears should be made of it for microscopic examination. Smears or wet mounts are usually omitted with fecal specimens, except in the case of a request for worms' ova and parasite examination. However, some clinical microbiologists recommend the routine examination of a Gram stain of feces or rectal swabs. The reasoning behind this practice is to acquaint the medical technologist with the typical assortment of Gram-negative and Gram-positive organisms so that he will recognize an atypical assortment that might be diagnostic. For example, this would be important in cases of staphylococcal enterocolitis or *Clostridium perfringens* food poisoning.

In addition to a routine Gram stain of sputum, the preparation of a second smear for the acid-fast staining procedure may result in the detection of an undiagnosed case of tuberculosis. In any event, the clinical microbiologist and medical technologist should be familiar with the morphological characteristics of many pathogens.

Guidelines for the Identification of Selected Microorganisms

Gram-Positive Aerobic Bacteria

Certain characteristics, including colonial and cellular morphology, type of hemolysis, and various biochemical tests, are quite useful in making a limited clinical identification of Gram-positive aerobic bacteria. Included in this group are *Staphylococcus aureus, S. epidermidis, Streptococcus* spp., *Streptococcus pneumoniae, Corynebacterium diphtheriae*, diphtheroids, and *Bacillus* spp.

Pathogenic cocci

Staphylococci. Staphylococcus aureus often is distinguished from *S. epidermidis* on the basis of coagulase production alone (Color photograph 64). However, other characteristics, such as pigmentation and mannitol fermentation (Color photograph 62), are also important for confirmation.

The following procedure illustrates how these properties are used for identification purposes. Specimens suspected of harboring *S. aureus* may be planted on Mannitol Salt Agar and on blood agar. The former preparation consists of several ingredients, the most important of which are mannitol, 7.5 per cent sodium chloride, and the pH indicator phenol red. Blood agar generally contains as basic ingredients protein, salt carbohydrate, and sheep blood.

Both species of staphylococci grow on these media. In the case of *S. aureus*, however, the organism produces acid from mannitol, which is recognized by the medium turning yellow around the bacterial colonies (Color photograph 62). On blood agar plates (BAP), these organisms may cause a breakdown of hemoglobin, recognized by the appearance of clear zones around the colonies (Color photograph 45B). This reaction is known as beta hemolysis. Organisms exhibiting these effects are tested further for the production of the enzyme coagulase, a substance characteristically produced by pathogenic staphylococci. While pigment production is much less stable as a characteristic, mannitol fermentation agrees fairly well with coagulase production. It must be noted that rare cultures of *S. aureus* may not produce coagulase on initial isolation from a clinical specimen. However, on subculture typical results appear.

While *S. epidermidis* is not considered a significant pathogen, it has been implicated in a number of disease states, including abscesses and bacterial endocarditis. Thus *S. epidermidis* should be treated with respect.

Streptococci. During the primary isolation of pathogenic bacteria on BAP, the luxurient growth of staphylococci can often be easily distinguished from the pin-point type of colony of streptococci. However, sometimes all colonies may be small and the Gram stain reactions may be difficult to interpret. This may be due to: (1) inexperience on the part of the laboratory personnel, (2) the selection of a specimen for a smear from mixed colonies, or (3) lack of adequate time for careful observation.

In this type of situation, the test for the enzyme catalase is justified. Staphylococci produce catalase, and streptococci do not. This enzyme rapidly degrades hydrogen peroxide (H_2O_2) into oxygen and water. The reaction can be easily observed. When some staphylococci are removed from a culture and emulsified in 3 per cent H_2O_2 the resulting activity is sufficiently vigorous to cause bubbling. A drop of H_2O_2 on a colony will cause the same oxygen gas release.

The hemolytic reaction shown in Color photograph 45*B* is very useful for the categorization of the various streptococci in clinical specimens. The majority of human pathogens are group A beta hemolytic organisms, which are also sensitive to a low concentration of the anti- biotic bacitracin. This fact is used to differentiate group A members from other beta streptococci which are resistant to this level of the antibiotic. In practice, the beta streptococci are restreaked into a clear area of the BAP, or a fresh plate and a disk containing 0.04 units of bacitracin is placed onto the streaked area. Formation of a zone of inhibition is interpreted as identification of the group A beta hemolytic streptococcus.

Other streptococci of clinical significance include group B and D beta, and several gamma and alpha hemolytic strains. The enterococci or group D beta hemolytic strains should be differentiated from other non-group A organisms, since their susceptibility to chemotherapeutic agents differs greatly. They are generally resistant to sulfa drugs and tetracyclines, while being sensitive to the penicillins and streptomycin. The other groups are generally sensitive to sulfonamides and tetracyclines as well.

Pneumococci. One other Gram-positive coccus of common clinical significance is *Streptococcus pneumoniae*. The colonies of this organism closely resemble those of the α-hemolytic viridans streptococci. Microscopically, *S. pneumoniae* appear as lancet-shaped diplococci.

One procedure for *S. pneumoniae* isolation and identification involves the application of a disk containing optochin (ethylhydrocupreine hydrochloride) to a portion of a streaked area on a primary isolation plate, i.e., BAP or blood azide. Optochin is a chemotherapeutic drug which was used for treatment of pneumococcal infection prior to the advent of sulfonamides. While the colonies are somewhat similar to alpha streptococci, they will not grow in the immediate area about the optochin disk.

If any question should arise regarding the colonies on the plate, a bile solubility test may be performed. Pneumococci are noted for their susceptibility to lysis by bile. The test may be performed by placing a drop of a 10 per cent desoxycholate solution or a small crystal of the compound next to the colonies in question. Within 5 or 10 minutes, pneumococci lyse and the colonies will disappear. Streptococci are unaffected in this procedure.

Gram-positive bacilli (rods). Probably from a clinical standpoint the most significant aerobic, non-spore-forming bacterium in this category is *Corynebacterium diphtheriae,* the causative agent of diphtheria. This organism generally resides in the upper respiratory tract of healthy carriers or infected persons. Rarely, if at all, is it found anywhere else. Blood or chocolate agar supplemented with tellurite or Loeffler serum medium is used for the isolation of this organism. Tellurite salts inhibit most contaminants from growing. Moreover, with this substance in the medium, differentiation is made possible among the three generally accepted varieties of *C. diphtheriae.*

Several distinguishing morphological features of this pathogen are helpful in diagnosis. These include the Y, L, and V arrangements exhibited by cells and the demonstration of metachromatic granules by Loeffler methylene blue staining. When diphtheria is suspected on the basis of clinical signs, the attending physician must be notified immediately of any confirmatory laboratory findings. Furthermore, the local public health department is also notified, and a subculture of the suspected culture is generally sent to them to determine if the isolate produces diphtheria toxin.

Three other species of *Corynebacterium* that may be found in clinical specimens are *C. pseudodiphtheriticum, C. acnes,* and *C. xerosis.* Commonly these organisms are called *diphtheroids.* They are also present in water and surface contamination studies which may be conducted in hospitals, restaurants, and clinics, and may be implicated occasionally in disease states. The usual identification of this group consists of the observation of Gram-positive club-shaped rods growing on routine isolation media. They are reported as diphtheroids.

Other common contaminants in surface specimens and occasionally in clinical specimens are the spore-forming rods of *Bacillus* spp. These organisms can be distinguished from diphtheroids by their colonial and cellular morphology. Moreover, after 24 to 48 hours of incubation the cultures will usually contain spores. Unless there is reason to suspect the presence of *B. anthracis* in a clinical specimen, the isolated organisms are considered to be soil or dust contaminants and they are reported as *Bacillus* spp.

Gram-Negative Aerobic Enteric Bacteria

These organisms are extremely common in clinical specimens and probably make up the major portion of the laboratory workload. Unfortunately, Gram stains of organisms from primary isolation media such as blood agar do not serve to differentiate among these organisms, since they look very much alike. Biochemical testing procedures are utilized to achieve differentiation and identification.

The procedure for identifying members of this group of bacteria depends largely upon circumstances. If the source of the organism is stool, then concern is primarily with the major enteric pathogens, *Salmonella* and *Shigella* spp., for children and adults, and enteropathogenic *Escherichia coli* for children under three.

Whenever one or more of the enteric Gram-negative bacteria are encountered in specimens other than stool, they may be significant and should be identified.

This is particularly true with urine, blood, sputum or bronchial aspirates, spinal fluid, and wounds. Sometimes they are in small numbers relative to organisms such as *S. aureus,* streptococci, and pneumococci, and may not seem important. Nevertheless they should be identified and reported to the physician. In this manner the physician can determine the best treatment in the light of possible opportunistic bacteria which continue the infection after a chemotherapeutic agent has brought the primary pathogen under control. This is particularly true with such difficult-to-treat organisms as certain strains of *Proteus* spp., *Serratia marcescens,* and *Pseudomonas aeruginosa.*

Non-Fermentative Aerobic Gram-Negative Bacteria

Often when a Gram-negative rod is found and inoculated onto routine media, colonies appear which do not ferment the sugars in differential media, such as Eosin Methylene Blue, MacConkey, or Hektoen-Enteric Agars. The sugars in these media are lactose and sucrose. The organisms are therefore suspected of being *Salmonella, Shigella, Proteus,* or *Providencia* spp., for example.

Since by definition all of the enteric Gram-negative bacteria ferment the glucose present in the Triple Sugar Iron Agar slant medium, the lack of any acid production indicates that organisms from some other group are involved. Nonfermenters commonly encountered include *Pseudomonas aeruginosa* and *Alkaligenes faecalis.* The former organism is of much greater significance as a pathogen. The properties of several of these organisms are given in later chapters of this division.

Gram-Negative Aerobic Diplococci

This grouping is comprised of the genus *Neisseria.* In the clinical laboratory, various nonpathogenic species are found in sputum, throat swabs, and cervical and vaginal swabs. Since these same specimens may be submitted in situations of suspected cases of meningococcal meningitis or of gonorrhea, which are caused by the two prime pathogens of *Neisseria,* it is important to differentiate these organisms from nonpathogens. The pathogenic *Neisseria, N. gonorrhoeae* and *N. meningitidis,* usually require blood or chocolate agar and 3-10 per cent CO_2 for isolation. In contrast, nonpathogenic species of *Neisseria* generally will grow on ordinary nutrient agar in the absence of CO_2.

In cases of suspected gonorrhea, the specimen should be planted onto Thayer-Martin chocolate agar which contains a mixture of antibiotics formulated to prevent the growth of practically all organisms but *N. gonorrhoeae* or *N. meningitidis.* While other organisms may grow on this medium, they can be differentiated on the basis of cellular morphology and the oxidase test (Color photograph 94). The neisseriae are oxidase-positive. So are *Pseudomonas* spp. and certain others, but the growth of oxidase-positive, Gram-negative diplococci on Thayer-Martin medium is presumptive evidence for one of the pathogenic neisseria.

Although the specimen or source of the organism is certainly indicative for species identification, most laboratories still prefer, and correctly so, to perform sugar fermentation tests. As a memory aid *N. (g)onorrhoeae* ferments (g)lucose only, while *N. (m)enin(g)itidis* ferments (m)altose and (g)lucose (Color photographs 96 *A, B*).

Fastidious Aerobic Gram-Negative Bacilli (Rods)

This fairly broad grouping of bacteria includes species of *Hemophilus, Bordetella, Brucella, Pasteurella,* and *Francisella.* Except for *H. influenzae,* these organisms are not routinely encountered in the clinical laboratory and therefore the reader should refer to the individual descriptions in other chapters.

Anaerobic Bacteria

The routine clinical laboratory, as a rule, cultures wound and blood specimens for anaerobic bacteria. These organisms are also cultured from other types of specimens (e.g., urine) and biopsies, if their presence is suspected from clinical findings.

Representative cultivation procedures for anaerobic bacteria have been outlined in Chapter 12. Generally, specimens are inoculated into thioglycollate broth and on a BAP. The latter medium can be incubated in a special anaerobic incubator, Brewer jar, or in a Gas Pak system. The introduction of the Gas Pak system has enabled more laboratories to carry out isolation procedures for anaerobic pathogens, e.g., *Clostridium, Peptostreptococcus,* and *Bacteroides* spp. A multi-test system for anaerobe identification has recently been developed.

Clostridia. *Clostridium* spp. are characterized as Gram-positive, anaerobic, spore-forming rods, and differentiated from one another on the basis of hemolytic patterns and sugar fermentations. Formation of spores by clostridia usually requires a slightly alkaline, high-protein medium, e.g., Trypticase Agar-Base.

Peptostreptococci. *Peptostreptococcus* spp. (anaerobic streptococci) may appear in association with various wounds, sinus and ear infections, and abscesses. Their identification is usually based upon the observation of Gram-positive chained cocci growing anaerobically but not aerobically.

Bacteroides. The group of anaerobic, Gram-negative bacteria known as bacteroides include organisms which are non-spore-forming, rod-like, have rounded or pointed ends, may be filamentous, and may have spherical bodies. Most of these organisms are very difficult to isolate because of their extreme sensitivity to free oxygen. Genera included in this group are *Bacteroides, Sphaerophorus, Fusobacterium* and *Streptobacillus.* Species of *Bacteroides* and *Sphaerophorus* are probably encountered most often as pathogens. They are generally differentiated by colonial and cellular morphology and selected biochemical tests.

Acid-Fast Bacteria

The two bacterial genera which are routinely acid-fast (Color photograph 17) are *Mycobacterium* and *Nocardia*. (On rare occasions isolates of the genus *Corynebacterium* may be acid-fast and thus may create some confusion.)

Mycobacteria. Various types of specimens can be used for the isolation of mycobacteria; these include bronchial lavage, gastric lavage, spinal fluid, sputum, tracheal aspiration, and lung tissues. With the exception of tissues and spinal fluid, most specimens are digested and decontaminated routinely. One of the procedures used involves breaking up of mucus in the specimen, not only to separate mycobacteria from this material, but to kill contaminating organisms. The latter aspect is accomplished by raising the pH of the preparation. Mycobacteria generally survive these treatments and thus can be isolated.

After a specimen has been suitably prepared it is generally used to inoculate two different media. Current recommendations suggest the use of an egg-base medium, such as Lowenstein-Jensen or Petragnani, and a clear agar medium, such as Middlebrook 7H-10. For more rapid results it is advisable to incubate the culture under an increased CO_2 tension of 5 to 10 per cent. (The Middlebrook medium must be incubated with CO_2.)

Characteristically, *M. tuberculosis* has a nonpigmented, tan-to-buff, heaped colony appearing in about 2 to 3 weeks. Whenever any growth appears on the media, acid-fast stains should be performed to determine if a mycrobacterium or some contaminant is present. Further details of the identification of *M. tuberculosis* are discussed in Chapter 33.

Nocardia. Specimens suspected of containing nocardiae are usually planted onto BAP and Sabouraud's dextrose agar slants and incubated at room temperature and at 35°C. Since these organisms may survive the decontamination and digestion procedures described earlier, they can be found on routine mycobacteria media. Their differentiation from mycobacteria and other bacteria includes observation of branching of acid-fast mycelia, colonial morphology, and biochemical tests.

It must be noted that the usual acid-fast staining procedures may not show these organisms to be acid fast. The nocardia are only slightly more resistant to decolorization than non-acid-fast organisms, and therefore greater care must be exercised. Growth of organisms in litmus milk will enhance acid-fastness.

Various species of *Nocardia* appear on BAP in several days as small colonies resembling *M. tuberculosis.* Within 5 to 10 days the colonies will become waxy, folded, and pigmented yellow to orange. Speciation is based upon colonial morphology and selected biochemical tests.

Quality Control Considerations

Satisfactory interpretation of any test result depends upon the degree of confidence in the quality of materials used and the personnel involved with testing. All media reagents and staining solutions should be evaluated in the context of their use under suitable control conditions.

For example, you cannot rely upon the interpretation of a Gram stain unless you have performed the procedure with selected known Gram-positive and Gram-negative organisms. Prepared smears of a *Bacillus* species and a *Neisseria* species are good controls since they represent organisms that are particularly sensitive to deviations in technique.

According to federal regulations, all laboratories engaged in interstate commerce must perform quality control as outlined in Table 28–3.

In addition to routine testing of new batches of media and other related materials, it is important that microbial unknowns be submitted periodically to appropriate laboratory personnel for identification to test their technical ability. This practice can be accomplished by subscribing to survey programs of the College of American Pathologists and the American Society for Clinical Pathologists, or by cooperative efforts between local and regional laboratories of universities and public health departments.

In contrast to the above external controls, it is often desirable to have periodic internal controls. In this case routine specimens are submitted to the clinical laboratory by the chief microbiologist in cooperation with hospital staff physicians. In appearance this type of specimen would be no different than many others; however, it is used to familiarize the technologists with unusual organisms or pathogens which are not encountered routinely. Bacteria in this category might include *Pasteurella multocida, Brucella* spp., or *Bordetella pertussis.*

An important aspect of quality control involves preventive maintenance of equipment and the routine monitoring of equipment performance. Centrifuges must be checked periodically to see if operating speeds are accurate. All incubators, refrigerators, freezers, water baths, and

Table 28–3 Quality Control Items Required for Laboratories Engaged
in Interstate Commerce

Item	Particular Requirements
Laboratory Manual	1. Must be current 2. Procedures dated when they go into effect 3. Listing of complete references 4. Listing of criteria for quality control
Records	1. Must show any and all changes in procedure 2. Evidence of monitoring of materials and methods 3. Indications of remedial action when necessary
Stains	1. Must incorporate procedures for control
Media	1. Must incorporate procedures for testing prior to or concurrent with use
Serology	1. Positive controls tested 2. Negative controls tested 3. Selected weak or variable controls tested

thermal blocks should have minimum-maximum recording thermometers or frequent readings should be made by means of ordinary thermometers to monitor the performance of the equipment. Significant deviations from the norm usually indicate a pending failure of the control mechanism. With a minimum of effort in recording temperatures, thermostat failures can be prevented. Thus the "cooking" of cultures or the thawing of expensive frozen serological reagents can be averted.

QUESTIONS FOR REVIEW

1. What importance do you attach to:
   a. specimens being obtained correctly?
   b. specimens being delivered to the laboratory promptly?
   c. specimens being inoculated properly?
   d. smears and wet mounts being examined routinely?
   e. pathogenic organisms being identified correctly?
   f. information concerning a specimen being communicated promptly?

2. Considering the infectious diseases listed in Table 28–1, indicate a causative agent for each and selected differential characteristics necessary for its identification. It will be necessary to refer to other chapters of this division for some of the required information.

29

Bacterial Diseases Associated with the Skin

The skin, together with certain derivatives of the skin, such as hair, nails, and various glands, makes up the *integument* of the human body. The structural arrangement of the skin consists of two main parts, the *epidermis* (outer layer), and underneath this layer, the *dermis* or *corium*. A *subcutaneous tissue* layer composed of loose connective tissue is located below the corium and serves to attach the skin to various underlying structures. The thickness of the skin and of the individual layers varies in different parts of the body (Figure 29–1).

The dermis region consists of dense, irregularly arranged connective tissue. Various types of cells, including fibroblasts, histiocytes (phagocytes), mast cells, blood, and lymphatic vessels and nerves are also found in this layer. Additional components, including hair follicles, sweat glands, superficial sebaceous glands, and a variable amount of muscle, also reside within the dermis.

The subcutaneous layer contains a large number of components, including adipose (fat) tissue, blood vessels, certain special nerve endings, nerve trunks,

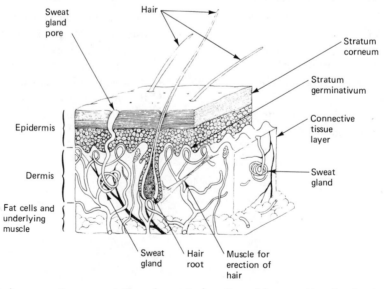

FIG. 29–1. A diagrammatic representation of a vertical section of human skin, showing its structural arrangement.

hair follicles, sebaceous glands, and sweat glands.

In addition to its functions of excretion, receptor of external stimuli, secretion, and temperature regulation, intact skin serves as a natural protective barrier to the majority of infectious disease agents, as discussed in Chapter 20. However, hair follicles and the openings of secreting glands constitute potential invasion avenues or portals of entry for pathogens. Certain physiologic factors are also important in providing barriers to skin-invading microorganisms. These include the acidity of the skin, the presence of an indigenous flora, and a temperature suboptimal for microbial growth, which may prevent the growth of certain disease agents. Another extremely important factor, which applies not only to skin invasion but to injuries of other anatomical regions, is the inflammatory reaction. The outcome of an infection is largely determined by this local response which incorporates the elements of blood and the surrounding tissues.

During the course of normal living, breaks of various types occur in the skin, thus providing means for infectious agents to gain entrance into the body. The nature and extent of injuries usually affect host-parasite relationships to varying degrees. So-called minor infections can constitute a serious problem if they are spread and involve contiguous tissues, cause hemorrhage, produce an ischemic area (local anemia due to stoppage of circulation) or result in edema (swelling). Table 29–1 provides brief descriptions of terms used in the symptomatology of infectious disease of the skin.

This chapter will be limited to certain bacterial infections associated with the skin (Table 29–2). Diseases caused by fungi and viruses are discussed in Chapters 30 and 31, respectively.

Specific Bacterial Diseases

Anthrax

If the descriptions contained in the writings of the ancients are relatively accurate, this bacterial disease has long caused the death of vast numbers of humans and domestic animals. Unfortunately, although the literature of the ancient Arabic, Greek, Hebrew, Hindu, Indian, and Roman civilizations contains various descriptions of diseases which affected tens of thousands of animals, a true distinction among these infections was not made. Accounts of the destructive effects of an anthrax-like disease have appeared describing severe losses in Europe during the seventeenth, eighteenth, and nineteenth centuries. In 1780, Chabert presented one of the first accurate descriptions of anthrax as it occurs in animals. Anthrax is primarily an infection of domestic animals such as cattle, goats, and sheep. It has also been reported in other warm-blooded animals, including camels, cats, chickens, elephants, horses, rodents, and wild deer. The descriptions of the "malignant pustule" by Maret in 1752 and Fournier in 1769 were among the first describing the features of anthrax in man, but it was not recognized as related to the disease of animals.

Many reports during the 1880s were concerned with the infectious nature of this disease. Barthelémy in 1823 clearly showed that he could transmit the infection by inoculating healthy animals with blood taken from diseased ones. Rayer confirmed this point, and, in addition, demonstrated the presence of small, nonmotile filaments in the blood of sheep which had died of anthrax. Davaine in 1863, utilizing the findings of several investigators, emphasized the fact that

Table 29–1   Brief Descriptions of Selected Elementary Skin Lesions

Type of Lesion	Description
Bullae (blebs, blisters)	Thin-walled, rounded or irregularly shaped blisters containing serous or seropurulent fluid
Carbuncle	An ulcerated lesion of the skin and subcutaneous tissue. Usually a hardened border and draining of pus are evident
Crusts (crustae or scabs)	Dried accumulations of blood, pus, or serum combined with cellular and bacterial debris. Detachment of thin crusts may leave dry or moist red bases. These generally heal, resulting in a smooth skin surface. Scar formations usually are associated with thick crusts covering ulcers
Furuncle	Localized inflammed regions which develop soft centers and eventually discharge pus
Macules (maculae, spots)	Usually round, circumscribed alterations in the color of the skin. The lesion is neither elevated nor depressed. The outline of a macule may either be quite distinct or may blend into the surrounding region
Maculopapules	Slightly raised macules
Papules (papulae or pimples)	Circumscribed, solid, elevated lesions without visible fluid contents. The color, consistency, and size of papules vary
Pustules (pustulae)	Small elevated skin lesions containing pus. They may develop from papules or vesicles. These lesions also vary in color, size and contents (pus, blood or both). Pustules may consist of a single cavity (unilocular) or several compartments (multilocular) with fluid
Scars (cicatrices)	Newly formed connective tissues which replaces tissue lost through injury or disease. These secondary lesions tend to be pink at first, then they assume a glistening appearance. Scars are normal components of the healing process
Ulcers	Rounded or irregularly shaped depressions or excavations. These lesions vary in size
Vesicles (small blisters or vesiculae)	Circumscribed elevations which may occur irregularly or in groups or rows. They may contain blood, seropurulent matter, or serum. The color of the lesion depends upon its contents. Vesicles may arise from a macule or papule and develop into pustules. These lesions may be uniocular or multiocular

anthrax could not be transmitted unless a living organism, which he designated as *Bactéridie,* were present in the material to be used as the inoculum.

In 1864, Davaine and Raimbert demonstrated the presence of similar organisms in the malignant pustules of a human patient. This was the first evidence suggesting the possibility that the causative agents of anthrax and malignant pustule were identical.

The clear-cut proof of the specific etiologic role of *Bacillus anthracis* in the infection was provided by Robert H. Koch. In his crucial experimentation, he isolated the microorganisms, grew it in pure cultures, produced the disease in animals with these cultures, and finally was able to recover the causative agent from the dead animals. Koch's investigations brought him great fame, as his results not only were the first to demonstrate the bacterial nature of an infectious process, but, as indicated previously, established the procedure, known as Koch's Postulates, which subsequently were employed to uncover other causative agents.

Mode of transmission. Anthrax is found worldwide. However, it appears to be most prevalent in Africa, Asia, and Central and Southern Europe. Most human cases of the disease are acquired through the handling of infected animals and their products, such as meat, hides, hair, wool, bristles, bones, and manure. Oral forms of anthrax have developed from the use of unsterilized toothbrushes made from bristles contaminated by *B. anthracis* spores. Infection results from direct contact (Color photograph 81), inhalation, or even possibly the ingestion of the etiologic agent. Insect bites have also

Table 29–2 Representative Bacterial Diseases of the Skin and Related Tissues

Disease and/or Manifestation	Etiologic Agent	Gram Reaction	Morphology	Possible Treatment
Actinomycosis	*Actinomyces bovis, A. israelii*	+	Rods	Cephalothin, chloramphenicol, penicillin, tetracyclines
Anthrax	*Bacillus anthracis*	+	Rod	Chloramphenicol, erythromycin, penicillin, tetracyclines
Boils, carbuncles, furuncles	*Staphylococcus aureus*	+	Coccus	Appropriate antibiotics; for penicillin-resistant organisms, semi-synthetic penicillins not affected by penicillinase
Cellulitis	*Staphylococcus aureus, Streptococcus pyogenes*	+	Cocci	Cephalothin, methicillin, vancomycin
Erysipeloid	*Erysipelothrix rhusopathiae*	+	Rod	Tetracycline
Gas gangrene[a]	*Clostridium perfringens,* other clostridia	+	Rods	Surgical removal of devitalized tissue (surgical debridement), polyvalent antitoxin, appropriate antitoxin
Glanders[b]	*Actinobacillus mallei*	—	Rod	Streptomycin, tetracyclines
Impetigo	*Stapylococcus aureus, Streptococcus pyogenes*	+	Cocci	Cephalothin, erythromycin, lincomycin, penicillin, vancomycin
Leprosy	*Mycobacterium leprae*	Not done. Acid-fast	Rod	Sulfones, including 4,4'—diaminodiphenylsulfone (DDS)
Leptospirosis	*Leptospira icterohemorrhagiae, L. canicola, L. pomona*	Not done	Spirochetes	Early administration of tetracyclines
Nocardiosis	*Nocardia asteroides[c],* other nocardiae	+	Rods	Sulfonamides, cycloserine
Pemphigus neonatorum (impetigo of the newborn)	*Staphylococcus aureus*	+	Coccus	Penicillin
Pinta	*Treponema carateum*	Not done	Spirochete	Antibiotics, including erythromycin, penicillin, tetracycline
Pseudomonas infections, including green nail and pyoderma	*Pseudomonas aeruginosa*	—	Rod	Sulfonamides, carbenicillin, gentamicin
Rat-bite fever	*Spirillum minor*	Not done	Spirillum	Penicillins, streptomycin, tetracyclines
	Streptobacillus moniliformis	—	Rod	
Scarlet fever and other diseases caused by Group A Beta hemolytic streptococci	*Streptococcus pyogenes*	+	Coccus	Penicillin, or erythromycin, symptomatic
Tetanus	*Clostridium tetani*	+	Rod	Tetanus antitoxin, appropriate antibiotics, surgical debridement
Verruga peruviana (a form of bartonellosis)	*Bartonella bacilliformis*	—	Coccobacillus	Chloramphenicol, penicillin G, streptomycin, tetracycline
Wound botulism	*Clostridium botulinum*	+	Rod	Specific botulism antitoxin, surgical debridement, drainage and irrigation of the wound site, appropriate antibiotics
Yaws (frambesia)	*Treponema pertenue*	Not done	Spirochete	Erythromycin, penicillin, tetracyclines

[a] *Staphylococcus aureus* and *Streptococcus pyogenes* functioning together can produce a form of this disease referred to as *synergistic gas gangrene.*
[b] A disease of horses communicable to man.
[c] This organism is weakly acid-fast.

been implicated as a means of transmission.

Clinical features.   When *B. anthracis* is introduced into the skin, a malignant pustule (Figure 29–2) develops, which may remain localized in the form of a furuncle-like lesion, or it may disseminate and cause death within a week's time. In the latter case, an elevated, reddened, and swollen area develops at the site of infection which leads to septicemia (bacteria in the bloodstream) and death of tissues. Oral lesions show considerable reddening and swelling of the soft tissues around the initial point of entry. The disease in this case may spread quite rapidly, becoming a full-blown septicemia with a poor prognosis.

In cases of pulmonary infection (Woolsorter's disease), a malignant pustule develops in the lung. The primary effect is an acute pneumonia, which in the majority of cases results in death.

Ingestion of *B. anthracis*, usually in the form of spores, may also have fatal consequences. An acute inflammation of the intestinal tract can develop.

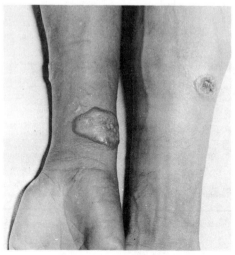

FIG. 29–2. Malignant pustule. (Courtesy of the Armed Forces Institute of Pathology, Washington, D.C., Neg. No. D–45409–10.)

Laboratory diagnosis.   *B. anthracis* is a Gram-positive, large (4 to 8 μm in length, and 1 to 15 μm in width), non-motile, spore-forming rod. In smears prepared from infected tissue, the organism appears as short rods, generally encapsulated (the capsule is composed of a γ-polypeptide of D-glutamic acid). Spores of *B. anthracis* are not found in such specimens.

Diagnosis generally includes the demonstration of *B. anthracis* in tissue biopsy material and the finding of the characteristic medusa head or "curled hair-lock" appearance of colonies on cultivation. Common media of the enriched variety, e.g., blood agar or egg-yolk agar, can be used. The organism grows best under aerobic conditions, which are necessary for sporulation. Oval spores are numerous after 48 hours of incubation. Testing for susceptibility to gamma phage can provide evidence that an isolate is a strain of *B. anthracis*.

Animal inoculations involving guinea pigs or mice also are used to determine the pathogenicity of pure cultures of the isolates.

Serologic diagnosis depends on the results of the Ascoli test. This method determines if soluble anthrax antigens are present in the tissues of diseased animals, or those suspected of having the infection. Specimens are first subjected to an extraction step performed at 100°C in saline. This material is then layered on the surface of a highly active anthrax anti-serum. If antigen is present in the specimen, a precipitate forms at the interface of the two reactants (see Color photograph 55). Naturally, suitable controls also are carried out. The Ascoli (*thermoprecipition*) test is especially helpful in situations where *B. anthracis* cannot be isolated.

Control measures.   In 1881, at Pouilly-le-Fort, Pasteur conducted a field trial to demonstrate the immunogenic properties of a vaccine against anthrax. The preparation contained organisms which were attenuated by cultivation at higher than optimal temperatures, 42° to 43°C. His experiment was a complete success, and so today similar vaccines are routinely used. Unfortunately, these preparations do not produce long-lasting immunity—protection ranges from 9 to 12 months, so vaccination affords only partial control.

Other anthrax control methods include the disposal of infected carcasses, either by cremation or deep burial, and the disinfection of infected animal products by boiling and the use of formaldehyde.

Gas Gangrene

Several species of the genus *Clostridium* are recognized as the etiologic agents of this disease, including *C. novyi*, *C. perfringens*, and *C. septicum*. In general, most organisms causing this disease state are not highly invasive. However, they are capable of elaborating highly injurious toxins during their growth in damaged tissues. Such toxic substances may be of a hemolytic, necrotizing, or lethal nature. The growth of clostridia in tissues often results in the accumulation of gas, predominantly hydrogen, and of toxic degradation products of tissues. The latter can bring about extensive connective and muscle tissue destruction, as well as serious systemic involvement.

Mode of transmission. The infection process is similar to that of tetanus. Specifically, the contamination of open wounds (incisions, lacerations, etc.) by clostridial spores initiates the infection. The process continues when the spores of the etiologic agent germinate in tissues with a sufficiently low oxidation-reduction potential. Such germinated cells undergo multiplication, grow, and elaborate toxins

which bring about clinical effects. Infections have been associated with wounds or injuries resulting from attempted abortions (Figure 29–3), automobile accidents, frostbite, and military combat.

Clinical features. A milder form of gas gangrene, *anaerobic cellulitis*, may resemble localized infections caused by staphylococci. Anaerobic cellulitis does not involve the muscles, while gas gangrene usually affects muscle tissue. Individuals with gas gangrene commonly experience symptoms including fever, fast heartbeat (*tachycardia*), and severe pain. Infected wounds frequently have a foul-smelling serous discharge. The presence of gas accumulating in the subcutaneous tissues can be detected during physical examination, usually by noting crepitation (creaking joints). The involved tissues are like inflated balloons. Death can result.

Laboratory diagnosis. The finding of Gram-positive spore-forming rods in stained preparations made from clinical specimens usually is accepted as a tentative identification. It should be noted that other bacterial species can cause this infection, notably *Klebsiella* and

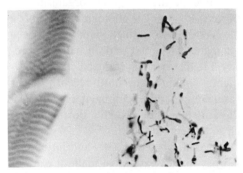

FIG. 29–3. A smear of a specimen from a woman following an attempted abortion. This woman developed gas gangrene and died. The photo shows clostridia and a muscle fiber below. (Courtesy of the Armed Forces Institute of Pathology, Washington, D.C., Neg. No. AFIP 56–8091.)

Escherichia. The laboratory diagnosis of gas gangrene is complicated, because most of the infections are of a mixed type. The presence of gas in the host's tissues does not necessarily incriminate *Clostridia* since other organisms can produce this effect (Table 29–2). Therefore, clinical specimens should always be cultured for purposes of a laboratory confirmation of the tentative diagnosis.

Media and cultivation conditions should be used which will favor the growth of aerobic and anaerobic bacteria. If, for example, Gram-positive spore-forming rods appear in thioglycollate medium in the proper region (Color photograph 28), and on blood agar, or other suitable media incubated anaerobically, the presence of clostridia should be suspected. Additional tests, such as differential biochemical fermentations, toxin neutralization, and the demonstration of capsules, are used to determine the species of the causative agent.

Leprosy (Hansen's Disease)

Leprosy is a chronic infectious disease of humans caused by the acid-fast rod *Mycobacterium leprae*. This microorganism was first observed in the skin lesions of leprosy patients in 1873 by Armauer Hansen. Despite the fact that *M. leprae* was one of the first microorganisms reported to be the etiologic agent of a human disease, it has to date not been "convincingly" cultured *in vitro*. Moreover, it has been introduced into experimental animals but until recently never resulted in the development of a typical disease state. Thus Koch's Postulates are close to being fulfilled.

Several of the early descriptions of leprosy-like disease have made it exceedingly difficult to determine the period when the infection made its appearance. Contrary to common opinion, the descriptions of skin eruptions appearing in the Old Testament (Leviticus) are not what we now term leprosy. Lendrum, in 1950, drew attention to the fact that the word "lepra" was applied by early physicians in a rather vague way to any scaly skin eruptions. The purpose of this practice was simply to prevent confusion of such disease states with any of the better-recognized infections. Despite the early recorded vague descriptions, it appears that leprosy was present in various parts of Africa and the Far East before the Christian era. Leprosy subsequently spread through the European continent as a consequence of military actions and an increase in migration.

It appears quite likely that leprosy was introduced into the American continent by European immigrants and infected slaves from Africa. Today, this disease predominantly occurs in warm and tropical areas.

Predisposing factors.   No conclusive statement can be made about racial susceptibility. Leprosy usually is acquired during childhood, although exposure and resultant infections are known to occur in adults. In general, the more prolonged and intimate contact is with infectious persons, the more likely the infection will be transmitted.

The sex of individuals apparently is a factor with lepromatous leprosy. This form of the disease occurs more frequently in males than in females, for unknown reasons.

Sources of infection and the mode of transmission.   Sources of infection are human cases. It is important to note that there is no relationship between human and rat leprosy. Rat leprosy is caused by another microorganism, *M. lepraemurium*.

Leprosy is probably transmitted by prolonged direct contact with infected (lepromatous) patients, or by inhaling organisms from sputum, nasal, or other types of discharges. Indirect contact with contaminated objects, and various insects also has been implicated. The portal of entry is open to question; the skin and the mucous membranes of the nose and throat have been considered.

Clinical features.   The association of *M. leprae,* or Hansen's bacillus, with leprosy has largely been based upon the consistent demonstration of the microorganism in smears or tissue biopsy specimens from infected persons. As Hansen's bacillus exhibits a particular predilection for the skin and nerve tissues, clinical manifestations are observed chiefly affecting the skin, mucous membranes of the upper respiratory tract, and certain peripheral nerves.

According to the Medical Bulletin issued by the U.S. Department of Medicine and Surgery, four different types of this disease are recognized. Two of these phases, namely, the lepromatous (Figure 29–4*A*) and tuberculoid (Figure 29–4*B*), are considered major manifestations. The remaining two recognized forms are the borderline (dimorphous) and the indeterminate (uncharacteristic) phases. The classification of leprosy is shown in Figure 29–5.

The *lepromatous* or *progressive form of leprosy* is characterized by skin lesions which develop from small histiocyte (macrophage) infiltrations around blood vessels, nerves, etc. The first commonly encountered cutaneous lesions are either lepromatous macules or plaques. The former exhibits an indefinite border (and may be hypopigmented or hyperpigmented), while the latter is elevated and flat. The plaque does not have a

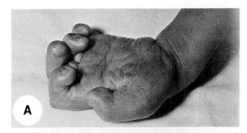

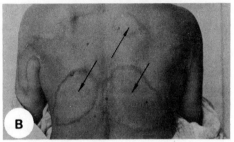

FIG. 29–4*A*. The "claw" hand found associated with lepromatous leprosy. (Courtesy of the Armed Forces Institute of Pathology, Washington, D.C., Neg. No. AFIP 56–14075–2.) *B*. A feature of tuberculoid leprosy. The skin within the nodules (arrows) is completely anesthetic. (Courtesy of The Pathology Research Laboratory, Leonard Wood Memorial, Armed Forces Institute of Pathology, Washington, D.C.)

sharp margin. Both lesions contain *M. leprae* and show histopathologic changes. Infiltrations of the skin without such changes are common in this phase of leprosy. Involvement of the entire body with the exceptions of areas such as the scalp, axillae, etc., can be observed. The condition known as *facies leontina* (lionface) develops as a result of infiltration of the facial skin (Figure 29–6).

Histiocytes apparently do not prevent, but rather encourage, the multiplication of *M. leprae.* Aging macrophages, commonly called "lepra cells," containing numerous microorganisms and exhibiting a fatty vacuolization of their cytoplasm (foamy appearance), eventually infiltrate blood vessels, epithelial cells of hair follicles, and small nerves. In advanced cases, the nasal mucous membranes are usually affected. Moreover, ulcerations

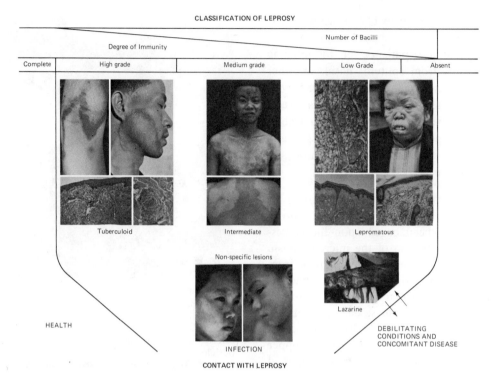

FIG. 29–5. The classification of leprosy. This composite photo shows the various forms of leprosy after contact with *Mycobacterium leprae*. An indication of the degree of immunity and the number of bacilli in these different types of leprosy is shown. (From Skinsnes, O. K.: *Ann. N.Y. Acad. Sci.,* **154**:19, 1968. © The New York Academy of Sciences, 1968; Reprinted by permission.)

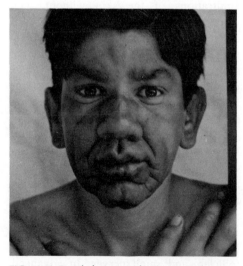

FIG. 29–6. Facial changes in lepromatous leprosy. (Courtesy of the Pathology Research Laboratory, Leonard Wood Memorial, Armed Forces Institute of Pathology, Washington, D.C.)

of the skin, keratitis, and loss of the eyebrows may all occur. The latter condition is characteristic of the lepromatous form of the disease. The lepromin skin test is negative.

In *tuberculoid leprosy* bacilli, if present, are few in number. Cellular evidence of resistance on the part of the host is apparent. The most characteristic early sign is the distinct, well-defined, erythematous or hypopigmented patch (leprid), which demonstrates a definite impairment of sensation. Anesthesia is a well-known cardinal sign of the disease. Nerve destruction in lesions occurs early and serves as an indication of the leprosy. The tuberculoid patches appear to be confined to the posterior and lateral surfaces of the hands, legs back, and face. The skin test is positive in the majority of cases with this phase of leprosy.

Intermediate leprosy is characterized by the appearance of the macular lesions. These macules may develop into lepromatous, tuberculoid, or borderline forms, or they may simply regress. Histiopathologic features may include the demonstration of lepra cell infiltrations and the limited involvement of nerves with *M. leprae*. The lepromin test may be either negative or positive.

Borderline leprosy is not well understood. In general, individual cases may exhibit histologic features of both lepromatous and tuberculoid lesions. Skin lesions usually are bacteriologically positive. The skin test generally is negative, although weakly positive reactions have been observed. Patients exhibiting the latter type of reaction should be considered infectious.

Laboratory diagnosis. Bacteriologic diagnosis is generally based on the demonstration of acid-fast bacilli in either smears of skin scrapings, etc., or biopsy preparations from patients with clinical signs of leprosy. A true diagnosis includes bacteriological evidence as well as the presence of peripheral nerve damage, or definite impairment of sensation in skin lesions.

The *intradermal lepromin test*, which utilizes a heated preparation of lepromatous material, is employed in following the prognosis of the disease. Lepromin was first prepared by Mitsuda in 1914. Its injection in patients results in the development of an inflammatory reaction, similar to the tuberculin reaction, within 24 to 48 hours (Figure 29–7). The test is generally negative in the lepromatous and borderline phases, positive in the tuberculoid state, and either positive or negative in the intermediate phase. A weak positive reaction may be observed

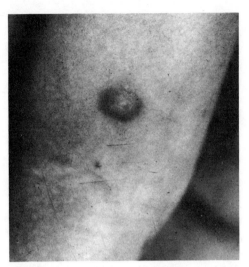

FIG. 29–7. A positive lepromin test. (Courtesy of The Pathology Research Laboratory, Leonard Wood Memorial, Armed Forces Institute of Pathology, Washington, D.C.)

occasionally in the borderline forms of leprosy.

Prevention. Naturally the reporting of leprosy cases and the hospitalization of the patients is desirable. Hospitalization is especially important for all individuals with the lepromatous form of the disease. One important aspect of hospitalization that is frequently overlooked is that it offers an opportunity to inform and educate patients, especially with respect to their treatment.

Contaminated articles should be adequately disinfected in all situations involving suspected as well as known cases of leprosy.

Pseudomonas Infections

Pseudomonas aeruginosa has been largely ignored in dermatologic literature as a causative agent of several specific skin diseases. This Gram-negative rod has been reported to produce a variety of skin manifestations (Color photograph 103) in situations associated with epidermal destruction, such as burns. *Pseudom-*

onas septicemia may develop from such cases, as well as from changes in the normal human flora or immune mechanisms of the individual, brought on by the use of antibiotics or drugs capable of suppressing antibody production. In healthy persons the pathogenic effects of this organism are limited. Examples of these dermatologic infections include "green nail" syndrome (Color photograph 104) and toe web infection (Color photograph 106).

Clinical features. Hall and his colleagues describe the *"green nail" syndrome* as a greenish discoloration of the nail plate which cannot be altered by topical cleansing. This clinical entity usually occurs in patients with histories of long submersion of hands in water, such as dish washers and housewives. The condition is caused by the diffusion of green pigment (pyoverdin) of *P. aeruginosa* into the nail.

Toe web infections are characterized by the formation of thick, white, scaling lesions (toe web scaling) (Color photograph 106). This condition is influenced greatly by high humidity and temperature.

The specific condition known as *"classical" ecthyma gangrenosum* is characteristically associated with *Pseudomonas* septicemia. This disease condition can occur in debilatated, leukemic, moribund, or severely burned patients. Individuals receiving antibiotic therapy also may be affected. Lesions are usually tense vesicles (blisters) surrounded by pink-to-violet-colored halos, which later rupture spontaneously and ulcerate.

Pseudomonas aeruginosa is also capable of producing a superficial skin infection known as *Pseudomonas pyoderma*. Characteristically, individuals with the condition exhibit eroded and macerated epidermis, bluish-green pus, and a grape juice aroma. The infection develops more commonly as a complication of eczematous eruptions, infected bed sores, burns, or grafted tissues, or tinea pedis (ringworm of the foot).

Rat-Bite Fever (Soduku)

This disease can be caused by two different bacterial species, *Spirillum (minus) minor* and *Streptobacillus moniliformis*. As the infection occurs in two forms, the causative agents will be discussed separately.

Spirillum minus

Mode of transmission. This organism is naturally found in various wild rodents, including rats. As the name of the disease implies, *S. minor* is acquired through a rat bite.

Clinical features. Individuals with the infection generally experience local inflammatory involvement, enlargement of regional lymph glands (lymphadenitis), skin rash, and a relapsing fever.

Laboratory diagnosis. *S. minor* is a rigid spiral which measures approximately 2 to 5 μm in length. It possesses one to seven polar flagella at each end and is quite motile. The organism, as of 1971, has not been cultured on artificial forms of media. In general, inoculation of laboratory animals—guinea pigs, mice, and white rats—is used for cultivation.

The laboratory diagnosis of *S. minor* may incorporate both direct microscopic examination of clinical specimens and animal inoculations. Specimens of choice include blood and biopsy material from local lesions or lymph nodes. The Wright stain, or other procedures using ordinary aniline dyes, may be employed in the examination of material from infected individuals.

Streptobacillus moniliformis. This is a normal inhabitant of the upper respiratory tract of both wild and laboratory rats. In addition to being one of the two etiologic agents of rat-bite fever in humans, this bacterial species is also responsible for a spontaneous disease characterized by an arthritic condition in mice, which results in the swelling of the feet.

S. moniliformis is an aerobic, Gram-negative, pleomorphic bacterium. As its name implies, the organism tends to form chains of rods. This property is particularly noticeable in older cultures and with those organisms grown on solid media. In certain instances spherical or sac-like swellings may project laterally from these chains of bacilli. *S. moniliformis* is non-capsulate, non-motile, and non-spore-forming.

Mode of transmission and clinical features. In man, *S. moniliformis* associated rat-bite fever is quite similar clinically to the form of the disease produced by *Spirillum minor*. However, arthritis is more commonly produced and endocarditis (inflammation of the inner portions of the heart) may be an added complication. This infection may be acquired by several means, including rat bite, contamination of skin abrasions, and the ingestion of contaminated food. In 1929 a milk-borne epidemic of streptobacillus disease was reported in Haverhill, Massachusetts. Infected persons exhibited a fever, rash, and arthritis. In cases of this disease in which a rat bite cannot be incriminated, there is a tendency on the part of investigators to designate the infection as Haverhill fever.

Laboratory diagnosis. The laboratory diagnosis involves culturing the organism from clinical specimens (e.g., blood or aspirated joint fluids) blood, or serum is

necessary for good cultivation. The colonies are small and usually develop within the medium (L-type colonies). These growths represent the L forms of the disease agent and are composed of cells possessing defective mechanisms for the formation of cell walls.

Staphylococcal Infections

Staphylococcus aureus is a Gram-positive, spherical bacterium which usually appears in grape-like clusters (see Color photograph 63). In humans, staphylococci can produce a variety of infections which can involve any and all tissues of the body. The disease states are characterized by pus formation (suppuration) and include carbuncles (Color photograph 60), deep tissue abscesses, empyema, endocarditis, furuncles, boils, impetigo contagiosa (Color photograph 69), meningitis, osteomyelitis (Color photograph 61), pneumonia, and wound infections. Additional diseases caused by these agents are discussed in later chapters.

In recent years, staphylococcal infections have gained additional significance because of the appearance of so-called drug-resistant mutants. It should be noted that these bacteria are not the only agents of disease which have been found to be resistant to antibiotics.

Transmission and predisposing factors. The exact mode of transmission involved in staphylococcal diseases is not obvious in all cases. Droplet nuclei, airborne organisms in the form of aerosols, carriers, and direct contact with patients having open infected wounds have all been implicated as sources of disease agents. Hospital environments and hospital personnel have been noted in particular to serve as sources of staphylococci in epidemic situations. Intimate contact with attendants, nurses, and physicians harboring these organisms in their nasopharyngeal regions poses serious problems in control. Carriers who happen to be food handlers constitute a difficult control situation.

In general, infections caused by *S. aureus* occur in persons whose local, as well as general, defense mechanisms are significantly lowered. Individuals with chronic debilitating diseases, including cancer, diabetes mellitus, and cirrhosis of the liver, are quite prone to staphylococcal infections. Furthermore, infections can result from exposure to skin irritants, or as a complication of burns and of wounds produced either accidentally or from surgical operations. Humans are constantly exposed to staphylococci, and it appears that frequent recurrent skin-limited infections occur during the years of puberty. Examples of such diseases include inflammations of hair follicles (folliculitis) and acne vulgaris. The latter state is a chronic condition which is characterized by inflammations of the sebaceous glands located on the back, chest, and face of an individual.

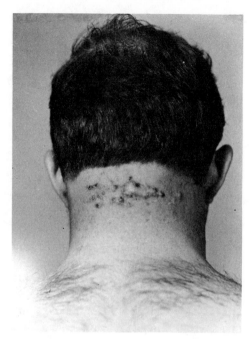

FIG. 29–8. An example of chronic furunculosis. This patient also has inflammations of hair follicles and the accumulation of tumorous growths called *keloids*. All of these conditions are due to staphylococcal infections. (Courtesy of the Armed Forces Institute of Pathology, Washington, D.C., Neg. No. AFIP 53–12335.)

Furuncles and Carbuncles

Poor hygenic habits and nutrition, as well as the irritation produced by the rubbing effects of clothing and uncleanliness, can contribute to the formation of both furuncles and carbuncles.

Clinical features. Furunculosis (Figure 29–8) is a relatively mild infection characterized by the initial appearance of *furuncles,* localized swollen areas which develop soft centers and eventually discharge pus. As these lesions heal, small, fleshy masses of tissue accumulate. There are no generalized symptoms, such as fever or pain.

Carbuncles are a more severe form of staphylococcal infection (Color photograph 60). Persons with these lesions exhibit fever and general discomfort (malaise). In cases of extremely severe

carbuncles, which are ulcerations of the deeper skin layers, *S. aureus* enters the blood stream, thus causing a septicemia. Such infected individuals experience a high fever and toxemia. The central nervous system may be involved. If infections of this type are not treated soon, the septicemic state can and does involve other tissues and organs of the body. Abscesses form in and spread from the appendix, bone, brain, heart, kidneys, liver, lungs, and other body structures. Mortality rates are quite high in untreated cases.

Impetigo Contagiosa

This communicable infection of the superficial skin layers is commonly encountered in areas where hygienic conditions are poor. Occasionally the disease is epi-

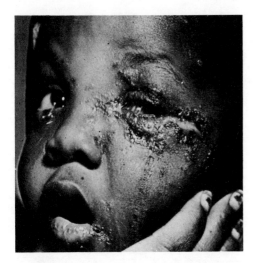

FIG. 29–9. *Staphylococcus*-caused impetigo. Children under 10 years of age are prime victims of the disease. The child shown has an obvious involvement of the face and lips. (Courtesy of the Armed Forces Institute of Pathology, Washington, D.C., Neg. No. AFIP 13966–6.)

demic, but in most situations it is sporadic and children under 10 appear to be the most common victims (Figure 29–9 and Color photograph 69). Orphanages and nurseries of various types can offer favorable environments for the spread of impetigo.

Transmission and clinical features. Impetigo contagiosa is spread by direct contact with infected persons or indirectly by contact with contaminated objects, such as bed sheets, handkerchiefs, pencils, or towels. The crusts from lesions also serve as a source of *S. aureus*. Staphylococci generally are introduced into the body through some form of abrasion or other lesion. The premature removal of scabs or crusts of viral skin infections, e.g., chickenpox or smallpox, may provide additional portals of entry.

Laboratory diagnosis. The findings of Gram-positive cocci arranged in clusters in stained smears prepared from clinical specimens, such as blood or pus, is not sufficient to identify *S. aureus*. Several

other bacterial species produce a similar morphological picture. Thus, additional tests are necessary to differentiate *S. aureus* from other Gram-positive cocci, and to firmly establish it as the causative agent.

In general, most pathogenic staphylococci golden-colored colonies: typically are beta hemolytic (Color photograph 45*B*), grow in the presence of 7.5 percent salt, and ferment mannitol. Both ingredients are contained in the medium mannitol-salt agar (see Color photograph 62).

The characteristic of *S. aureus* which correlates best with the property of pathogenicity is its elaboration of the enzyme *coagulase*. The test for this staphylococcal product is performed by inoculating a small volume of human or rabbit citrated plasma and incubating the preparation for a period of time ranging from 3 to 18 hours. An uninoculated tube of plasma is included as a control. The presence of a plasma clot only in the tube containing the *S. aureus* is considered a positive test for pathogenicity. Organisms of this type are referred to as *coagulase-positive staphylococci* (see Color photograph 62 through 66 for a typical diagnostic procedure).

Prevention. Great care must be excised in the treatment of patients with staphylococcal infections. The proper handling and disposal of contaminated objects must be observed in hospital, as well as home environments. Patients with infections of this type should be made aware of the potential danger they can pose to others if adequate hygienic habits are not observed.

Streptococcal Infections

The streptococci include several organisms which, given the right set of circumstances, are capable of infecting virtually all areas of the body. Primary infections can involve components of the respiratory, circulatory, and central nervous systems, as well as the skin (Color photographs 67 and 68), genital, and urinary tracts. Streptococci are also known for their frequent secondary invasion of body tissues. Various strains of these organisms can all cause the same disease state, and, conversely, a single given streptococcal species can produce several kinds of infections.

The virulence of streptococci (as in the case of numerous other "parasitic" microorganisms) appears to be dependent upon its cellular products, surface components, and related substances. These factors are important in the organism's establishing itself in the host. Included in this group are: (1) the type-specific M protein which renders streptococci less susceptible to phagocytosis; (2) the hyaluronic acid component of capsules which acts in a similar manner to the M-substance; and (3) streptodornase, which functions in breaking down tissue barriers.

In 1895, Mamorek first observed that streptococci were capable of causing the *in vivo* as well as *in vitro* lysis of red blood cells. In 1903 Schottmuller suggested that this hemolytic activity be utilized for classiflcation purposes. This suggestion wasn't fully explored until J. H. Brown undertook an intensive study in 1919. Based on his findings and those of others, streptococci were categorized into one of three groups on the basis of their hemolytic activity on blood agar plates. These categories were: (1) *alpha* (*α*) *hemolysis*, a greenish zone surrounding the bacterial colony (Color photograph 45*A*); (2) *beta* (*β*) *hemolysis*, a clear zone surrounding the colony (Color photograph 45*B*; and (3) *gamma* (*γ*) *hemolysis*, no obvious change developed on the medium (Color photograph 45*C*).

In the early 1930s, the hemolytic streptococci were further subdivided into groups, based on immunological differences. These groups were designated by the capital letters A through O. The group A beta hemolytic streptococci contain the greatest number of human pathogens.

Mode of transmission. Humans are the "ultimate" sources of pathogenic streptococci. Factors involved in the transmission of these organisms to susceptible persons include climate, crowding, improper sanitation, and the creation of aerosols.

Erysipelas

This disease occurs worldwide, but with greater frequency in the temperate zone. Erysipelas (Figure 29–10) is an acute

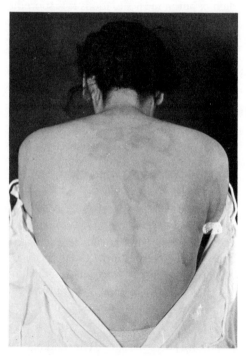

FIG. 29–10. Erysipelas caused by group A streptococci. (Courtesy of the Armed Forces Institute of Pathology, Washington, D.C., Neg. No. AF 18 58–6180.)

infection arising as a complication of surgery or of accidental wounds. Usually victims of the disease show a history of minor traumatic experiences. Group A streptococci are the ones most often found causing this disease.

Clinical features. Usually the incubation period is short. The onset of symptoms is quite abrupt. Patients experience fever, stinging, or itching at the involved area, headache, and vomiting. A small lesion soon appears, which develops into a widespread thickened reddened area. The face, extremities, and the body proper (Figure 29–10) are most frequently involved. The latter usually is affected separately.

Scarlet Fever

Various strains of group A beta hemolytic streptococci are known to cause scarlet fever. Many of these organisms also produce other types of infections, including septic sore throat, erysipelas, tonsillitis, puerperal fever, and wound abscesses. Typically, scarlet fever is an acute inflammation of the upper respiratory tract that may be accompanied by a generalized rash. In recent years this infection appears to be milder in its effects, and both morbidity and mortality rates have declined. The term *scarlatina* has been used by many individuals to designate milder forms of scarlet fever. The various effects of the infection are directly related to a toxin produced by streptococci, which usually spreads from the infected site to other parts of the body.

Although scarlet fever apparently was known to Hippocrates, considerable confusion developed among medical practitioners in attempting to distinguish it from other disease states, such as measles and diphtheria. The first accurate description of scarlet fever was made by Lydenham in 1675.

Mode of transmission. Scarlet fever infection is spread by means of: (1) droplet nuclei, (2) aerosols, (3) contaminated food, e.g., milk and water, and (4) direct contact with carriers, individuals in the acute stage of the disease. Fomites have been implicated, but it is believed such contaminated objects are not commonly involved.

Predisposing and related factors. This infection is worldwide. However, the development of a rash occurs more frequently in the temperate zones. Scarlet fever occurs most commonly during the fall, winter, and early spring months.

Studies indicate that this disease appears more frequently in Caucasians than in members of the Negro race. Scarlet fever infection may occur in persons of any age. In general, however, it is more commonly found in children under 10 years of age.

Clinical features. In general, the incubation period for scarlet fever varies between 1 and 10 days. The onset of the disease is rather severe, demonstrated by a sudden rise in temperature, which ranges between 101° and 104°F. Infected individuals usually experience the four characteristic symptoms of fever, headache, sore throat, and vomiting. A raised reddened rash (Color photograph 82) develops 2 days after onset. It generally first appears on the back and upper chest, and later spreads to other regions of the body. The rash does not routinely affect the face of Caucasians, but does in half the Negro patients. Peeling, or desquamation, occurs in many scarlet fever cases. This condition may begin about the fifth day of the disease, or only after several weeks. In many instances this peeling starts at the regions of the body where the rash first developed, and then spreads to the other areas of involvement.

A generalized inflammation also occurs, involving skin, mucous membranes, and tongue. About the time the rash appears, the tongue becomes heavily coated and gray. Its papillae (surface projections) become swollen and stand out. This condition is known as "strawberry tongue." The tongue may also undergo peeling. Usually this results in a denuded upper surface ("raspberry tongue"), which is moist, blood red, glistening, and sore. The normal surface is restored in about 2 weeks. At least five different categories of this disease have been recognized based on the degree of severity of effects.

Clinical diagnosis.   Average cases of this streptococcal disease, which are accompanied by a rash, generally offer little trouble in diagnosis. Other clinical findings are used for this purpose, including the cardinal features of fever, headache, sore throat, and vomiting; peeling of the patient's tongue; and general desquamation. Evidence of direct contact with a known case of scarlet fever also is quite helpful.

Because of its lower incidence, scarlet fever may pose problems of diagnosis in differentiating it from the other disease states which are accompanied by rashes. This group includes German measles, smallpox, and conditions produced by a number of coal-tar-derived drugs. One particularly good aid in diagnosis of scarlet fever is the Schultz-Charlton or "blanching" test. This procedure involves the intracutaneous injection of either 0.1 ml of the scarlet fever antitoxin, or 0.2 to 0.5 ml of convalescent serum, into a heavily involved area with pronounced rash. A clearing or blanching

will occur around the site of injection within 4 to 8 hours if the rash is associated with scarlet fever infection.

Mention should be made here of another procedure, the Dick test, which is used to determine the susceptibility of individuals to the erythrogenic toxin. This procedure shows the presence or absence of "antitoxic immunity" only. The Dick test involves the intracutaneous injection of 0.1 ml of a diluted erythrogenic toxin preparation. The development of redness around the injection site within 24 hours is a positive test. This procedure also can serve as a confirmation of a scarlet fever diagnosis. If the test is performed during the early stages of the disease, and then repeated within 7 to 10 days time, the Dick reaction should turn negative. This type of finding would indeed be suggestive, if not direct evidence for the presence of the streptococcal infection.

Impetigo Contagiosa

Although this infection is caused more commonly by staphylococci (Figure 29–9), the streptococci also have been associated with the condition. The streptococci are considered to act more in the nature of secondary invaders. Group A organisms appear to be the ones more generally involved.

Streptococcal impetigo is a universal disease which usually occurs in areas where sanitation and personnal hygiene are poor. The disease largely affects young children, although when the above-mentioned conditions exist during the time of natural disasters and war, adults also can develop the infection.

The infectious agents can be transmitted by means of fomites (e.g., napkins, bed clothes, pencils) or by direct inoculation with infectious discharges from persons having the disease.

Clinical features. The development and features of impetigo contagiosa caused by streptococci are quite similar to those produced by staphylococci. However, certain differences do exist between the two states. The streptococcal form is the more severe.

Ludwig's Angina

Certain serious complications can develop as a consequence of infected teeth. One of these states involves beta hemolytic streptococci and is known as Ludwig's angina (Figure 29–11). Microorganisms from such sites of infection pour into the surrounding tissues of the oral cavity. Ludwig's angina is a particularly dangerous infection of the throat and neck, since the swelling which develops during the course of the disease can occasionally block the air passages.

Puerperal Sepsis

Puerperal sepsis is an infection which develops from the invasion of open wounds in the genital tracts of women who have just given birth. Several bacterial pathogens are recognized as causes of puerperal sepsis; these include streptococci from groups A, B, C, D, and G. Anaerobic streptococci are the second most commonly found etiologic agents.

Infections are acquired through direct contact with persons harboring pathogens in their upper respiratory passages. Even the patients may be included in this category. Droplet nuclei and fomites also may serve as sources of infectious agents. Group A streptococci are the most common causes of puerperal sepsis. With organisms of low virulence, the disease remains limited to the uterus. However, with more virulent streptococci, other disease states, such as cellulitis (inflammation of deeper tissues) and septicemia may develop.

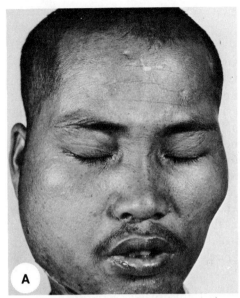

FIG. 29–11. Ludwig's angina. <u>A</u>. This photograph shows the typical swelling which can occur. The infection probably developed from an infected tooth on the left side of the individual's face.

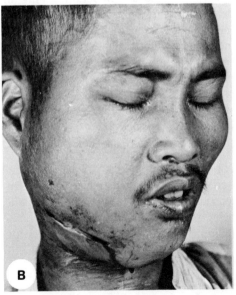

<u>B</u>. The result of treatment, which included an incision to produce drainage. (Courtesy of the Armed Forces Institute of Pathology, Washington, D.C., Neg. No. AFIP 44713–1 and 44713–2.)

Consequences of Group A Streptococcal Infections

Several consequences, or *sequelae,* can develop from streptococcal infections, especially throat involvement. In general, acute hemorrhagic glomerulonephritis and rheumatic fever are the most common. The disease known as *erythema nodosum* also may occur. However, it is not a frequent consequence. This infection is characterized by the formation of tender, subcutaneous nodules, primarily on the arms and legs. Fever and general malaise accompany the formation of these typical lesions.

Acute Hemorrhagic Nephritis (Glomerulonephritis)

This complication often develops following mild or moderate streptococcal infections. The intensity of the disease varies from a slight involvement of the kidney to a severe infection ending in death. Most victims recover with varying degrees of kidney damage. The mechanism which operates during the course of this complication is not fully understood. However, the suggestion has been made that the disease represents a situation of *autoimmunization,* in which individuals produce antibodies against substances derived from their own tissues.

Laboratory diagnosis. Several procedures are utilized in identifying streptococci in the laboratory. These include hemolytic reactions on blood agar medium, Gram-stain, bacitracin sensitivity, and a variety of serological tests.

Rheumatic Fever

There is a relationship between the occurrance of this disease and the incidence of other streptococcal-caused states, including erysipelas and puerperal and scarlet fevers. It has been reported that approximately 3 per cent of Canadian and United States military personnel having some form of streptococcal infection develop rheumatic fever. Immunological studies have shown that group A streptococcal diseases occur just prior to most cases of acute rheumatic fever. The causal role of streptococci in this disease appears to be quite evident; however, the mechanism of action still remains unknown.

The severity of acute rheumatic fever lies in the possible development of a chronic disease of the heart valves. The infection mainly affects children in the age group from 3 to 15 years, but attacks may occur during adult life. In general, once an acute case of rheumatic fever is initiated, the clinical course of the disease state is unpredictable. Every attempt must be made to control it. This is usually done with the aid of antibiotic therapy. Another streptococcal infection in addition to rheumatic fever can be disastrous. It is important to mention here also that individuals who have had this disease are subject to recurrences upon additional attacks caused by streptococci. Upper respiratory tract infections, e.g., nasopharyngitis and tonsillitis, have been reported to be responsible for recurrences.

Clinical features. In general, three stages or phases of rheumatic fever are recognized. Individuals in the first stage exhibit an upper respiratory infection, such as tonsillitis, sore throat, or a nasopharyngitis. In the second phase, symptoms subside and generally disappear. The third or "rheumatic" stage is characterized by painful joints (polyarthritis), sore throat, and a generalized malaise.

Tetanus

This disease was described by Hippocrates some 24 centuries ago. Tetanus is caused by a neurotoxin known as tetanospasmin, which is among the most poisonous substances known to man, second only to botulinus type A toxin. Tetanospasmin is produced by the ubiquitous anaerobic bacterium *Clostridium tetani*—an organism present in dust, soil, and the feces of both domesticated and wild animals.

Mode of transmission. The disease is associated with wounds of all types. However, any break in the skin, whether a superficial scratch or a puncture, is subject to contamination by the spores of *C. tetani* (Color photograph 23). Once these structures gain access to the injured area, if there is enough dead or dying tissue to provide reduced oxygen tension —"environmental oxidation-reduction potential"—the spores may germinate into the growing cells which produce the tetanus-causing toxin.

Clostridium tetani is considered, for the most part, to be a relatively noninvasive organism. Foreign objects, including glass, slivers of metal or wood, and other pathogens, can enhance the "wound environment." A newborn infant may develop *tetanus neonatorum* from infection of its severed umbilical cord. Tetanus can affect people of all ages, and can develop from abortions, circumcisions, ear-piercing, injections of drugs, and negligent surgical procedures.

Tetanus develops in three stages: (1) the initial "wound-bacterial" stage, (2) a "silent tetanotoxemic" stage, and (3) the "critical neurological stage." The first stage requires a suitable wound environment and the spores of the causative agent. The second phase is initiated by the liberation of the neurotoxin, which is carried by blood and other body fluids or along the intracellular spaces of adjacent nerve trunks to the central nervous system. Fixation of the toxin by "tetanophilic" cells ushers in the final and most severe stage of the tetanus, the critical neurologic stage or clinical tetanus.

Clinical features. The incubation period of tetanus varies. The appearance of manifestations is determined not only by the extent and location of the injury, but also by the numbers of *C. tetani* present. Symptoms of clinical tetanus develop from the interactions between the tetanus neurotoxin and certain neuromotor cells of the central nervous system (brain stem and spinal cord). These manifestations are characteristically sudden and violent involunatry contractions of voluntary muscles, frequently referred to as "tetanospasms." Tonic spasm (persistent rigidity) predominates. Generally, the muscles in the area of the infection are first to be involved. This is followed by involvement of the muscles of the jaws and face. These states are called, respectively, trismus and risus sardonicus, or sardonic smile. The muscles of the neck and trunk (the clinical condition is known as *opisthotonos*) as well as the extremities are subsequently attacked by the tetanus toxin.

In patients with severe tetanus, convulsive seizures may be brought on by a simple adjustment of the bed, or sudden noises. Death generally occurs because of the impairment of the respiratory mechanism. Chills, fever, leukocytosis, and malaise commonly are not found in the early clinical tetanus. However, they may occur later if the disease increases in severity or complications develop.

Diagnosis. Clinical findings primarily

serve as the basis of diagnosis. In general, laboratory procedures are of limited value. The clinical diagnosis of tetanus and the beginning of therapeutic measures should not await the results of bacteriological tests. Moreover, neither the isolation of the gram-positive *C. tetani* from clinical specimens (e.g., pus and tissues) nor the absence of this organism necessarily establishes a clinical diagnosis of tetanus. The presence of *C. tetani* may be recognized in smears by the typical "drumstick" or "tennis racket" appearance of its spores (Color photograph 23).

Laboratory diagnosis generally includes the use of the Gram- and spore-staining procedures, and the demonstration of toxin production with the aid of a mouse protection test.

Prophylactic immunization is the only effective means available to control the disease. An initial course of three injections of tetanus toxoid is generally used, and a single booster injection is commonly administered after one year. Immunization schedules and the applications of toxoid and antitoxin preparations are presented in Chapter 26.

Wound Botulism

Fifteen cases of wound botulism have been reported in the United States since 1943. Ten of these cases have been reported since 1970, with five cases reported in 1974 alone. Although wound botulism is still a relatively rare disease, the marked increase in reported cases should serve as a signal of its potential significance. The causative agent of wound botulism as well as of the more familiar food poisoning is *Clostridium botulinum* (see Chapter 38). This organism is described as a Gram-positive, anaerobic spore-forming rod. The spores of this bacterium are commonly found in the soil. Although *C.*

botulinum is virtually non-invasive, it produces a potent exotoxin.

Mode of transmission. Although the number of reported cases of wound botulism is not large, it appears that most victims acquire the disease in a manner similar to that of acquiring tetanus.

Clinical features. Symptoms of wound botulism are similar to those of food botulism; however, there are some marked differences. A fever may be present in wound botulism, whereas it is rare in food poisoning. As a rule, gastrointestinal symptoms are not present in the wound form of botulism. If the wound is severe and is located on an extremity, unilateral sensory changes may develop in association with the trauma or infection; in food botulism, on the other hand, no sensory abnormalities are seen. Wound botulism often has an incubation period of 4 to 14 days as compared to incubation period of the food-borne form, which ranges from several hours to 7 days. This situation is presumably due to the length of time required for the organism to multiply and to produce the toxin at the wound site. Double vision, difficulty in talking and swallowing, and neck weakness may also occur.

Diagnosis. The diagnosis of wound botulism currently is based on clinical findings. In general, as is the case in tetanus, laboratory tests are of limited value. The laboratory procedures used are similar to those described for tetanus.

Treatment. Treatment for any form of botulism is very specific, namely, intravenous and intramuscular injections of botulism antitoxin. Treatment for wound botulism also includes thorough surgical debridement, drainage, and irrigation of the wound site after the administration of antitoxin. Antibiotics such as penicillin also may be administered.

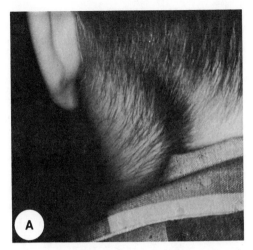

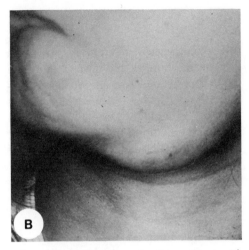

FIG. 29-12_A_. The extreme swelling of lymph nodes in a case of cat-scratch disease. _B_. Swollen submandibular lymph nodes in a patient with cat-scratch fever.

Cat-scratch Disease

This state was first reported as "maladie des griffes de chat," a new disease entity, by Debre *et al.* in 1950. The nature of the causative agent has been in dispute; both a virus and a bacterium have been implicated. The agent of cat-scratch disease is transmissible to monkeys and to man and shows a serologic relation to the Chlamydia, the etiologic agents of inclusion conjunctivitis, lymphogranuloma venereum, psittacosis, and trachoma. Some patients have contracted the disease from contact with a sick bird rather than a cat.

Clinical features. The scratch of a cat resulting in an open wound is followed in a few days by swelling of the lymph nodes which drain the injured area. Many cases are mild and uncomplicated. However, the victim often experiences a lack of energy coupled with a low-grade fever, chills, and nausea which lasts for weeks or months. The swollen lymph nodes (Figure 29–12) are painful and may be markedly enlarged, with the overlying skin also showing inflammatory changes.

The main clinical problem associated with this disease is in the differential diagnosis of lymph node enlargements, since cat-scratch disease, which has an excellent prognosis, may mimic the more serious granulomatous diseases.

Diagnosis. In general, the following criteria might be used in diagnosing cat-scratch fever: (1) swollen lymph nodes, (2) positive skin test reactions with an antigen specific for the disease, (3) the presence of an identifiable inoculation site, (4) a history of contact with a cat, and (5) an absence of other diseases.

Treatment. In most cases of cat-scratch disease, only symptomatic treatment is indicated. Most patients can continue with their daily routine, restricting only vigorous exercise. Excision of a lymph node may be indicated because of a persistently draining sinus, or in those rare cases when a malignancy or some other serious disease makes diagnosis of an equivocal case urgent.

QUESTIONS FOR REVIEW

1. What types of microorganisms make up the flora of the normal skin (see chapter 20)? Are any of these organisms capable of invading normal skin? Explain. Does the microbial flora of the skin serve any useful function? Explain.

2. Define or explain the following terms:
   a. cellulitis
   b. impetigo
   c. débridement
   d. inflammation
   e. vesicle
   f. neurotoxin
   g. exudate
   h. pustule
   i. abscess

3. Select five bacterial species which are associated with diseases of the skin. Construct a table and compare these agents with respect to the following properties:
   a. morphology
   b. Gram reaction
   c. method of diagnosis
   d. determination of pathogenicity (if applicable)
   e. preventive and/or control measures

4. Does there appear to be any form of immunity toward bacterial agents capable of causing skin infections? If so, which ones? Are vaccines available against these organisms?

5. What is the association between pathogenicity and coagulase production?

6. Discuss the nature of rat-bite fever with reference to the following categories:
   a. causative agents
   b. diagnosis
   c. means of transmission

7. What types of microorganisms are associated with wounds? Are any of these agents aerobic? With what types of wounds, e.g., abrasions, lacerations etc., is tetanus associated?

8. Compare the properties of an endotoxin with that of an exotoxin (see Chapter 21).

9. What is gas gangrene? How does it differ from an ordinary case of gangrene? How is gas gangrene treated?

10. a. Discuss the prevalence and importance of leprosy.
    b. How is this disease transmitted?
    c. Describe the clinical stages of leprosy.
    d. How is the disease diagnosed?
    e. Are control methods necessary for this disease? Explain.

11. What is cat-scratch disease?

12. How does wound botulism differ from botulism associated with food?

Mycotic Infections of the Skin, Nails, Hair, and Mucous Membranes

Human skin, nails, and hair are particularly vulnerable to attack by certain pathogenic fungi. Of the 50,000 to 200,000 known species of fungi, about 50 are recognized as human pathogens. Most of these are of the class Deuteromycetes (Fungi Imperfecti). Several of these agents are capable of affecting the skin and related tissues. The basis of the predilection of fungi that infect the skin and its appendages is the presence of the protein keratin. These fungi are also called *dermatophytes.*

It is customary and quite useful to group the fungal diseases, or *mycoses,* according to the tissues and organs affected and the clinical pattern or patterns produced by the causative agent. Our consideration of these diseases follows the terminology observed in the *Ciba Foundation Symposium, Systemic Mycoses* (1968).

Before discussing certain common mycotic infections, a brief consideration will be given to the classification of the mycoses, diagnostic features of causative agents, and certain other related properties.

Classification of Mycotic Infections

Superficial Mycoses

Fungi which predominantly attack the epidermis, hair, nails, and mucosal surfaces are referred to as the *superficial fungi.* The disease caused by such agents would include the various forms of ringworm or tinea (from the Latin meaning "growing moth"), other epidermophytoses, and *Candida* infections of mucosal surfaces, such as thrush and vulvovaginitis. These infections are frequently referred to as the *superficial mycoses* or *surface mycoses.*

Superficial mycoses are further classified on the basis of the location of the lesions produced by the causative fungus (Table 30–1). For example, ringworm of the scalp is referred to as *tinea capitis,* whereas involvement of the feet by a dermatophyte is called *tinea pedis,* more commonly known as "athlete's foot."

Deep-Seated or Systemic Mycoses

Infections in which the causative agents invade the subepithelial tissues (dermis and deeper regions) are known as *deep-seated, deep* or *systemic mycoses.* Some mycotic diseases which attack the dermis and subcutaneous tissues, such as chromomycosis and sporotrichosis, are occasionally grouped with the superficial diseases.

Opportunistic Fungi

Another designation which is frequently used for some fungi is *opportunistic infection.* Several fungi are not normally pathogenic to healthy persons. However, under certain condtions, which are generally unrelated, they can produce severe

Table 30–1   Representative Superficial Mycoses

Disease	Causative Agent	Source of Infection	Geographical Distribution	Possible Treatment
Tinea barbae (ringworm of the beard)	*Microsporum canis* (rare); *Trichophyton mentagrophytes; T. rubrum, T. sabouraudi, T. verrucosum, T. violaceum*	Infected animals and children	Worldwide	Griseofulvin Application of warm saline compresses Antibiotics to prevent secondary bacterial infections
Tinea capitis (ringworm of the scalp)	*M. audouini, M. canis, M. gypseum, T. mentagrophytes, T. sabouraudi, T. schoenleini, T. sulfureum, T. tonsurans, T. violaceum*	Infected animals, people, and fomites	Worldwide	Griseofulvin Antibiotics to prevent secondary bacterial infections
Tinea corporis (ringworm of the body)	*M. audouini, M. canis, M. gypseum, T. concentricum, T. mentagrophytes, T. sabouraudi, T. schoenleini, T. sulfureum, T. tonsurans, T. violaceum*	Infected animals and articles of clothing	Worldwide	Griseofulvin For small lesions, fungicides such as Tinactin, Verdefam, or Whitfield's ointment
Tinea cruris (ringworm of the groin)	*Candida albicans, Epidermophyton floccosum, T. mentagrophytes, T. rubrum*	Infected articles of clothing, or athletic supports	Worldwide	Whitfield's ointment One percent gentian violet
Tinea manuum and Tinea pedis (ringworm of the hand and feet)	*C. albicans, E. floccosum, M. canis, T. mentagrophytes, T. rubrum, T. schoenleinii*	Direct contact with fungi in moist environments including showers, swimming, and wading pools	Worldwide	Aqueous potassium permanganate soaks Griseofulvin Antifungal ointments and powders
Tinea nigra (ringworm of the palms)	*Cladosporium werneckii*		Worldwide	Most antifungal preparations
Tinea unguium (ringworm of the nails)	*C. albicans, E. floccosum, T. mentagrophytes, T. rubrum, T. schoenleinii, T. violaceum*	Infected individuals or regions of the body	Worldwide	Griseofulvin
Tinea versicolor (branny scaling of the skin involving the body surface)	*Malassezia furfur*		Worldwide	Ten percent sodium hyposulfite, or one percent tincture of iodine
Black piedra	*Piedraia hortai*	Infected hair (beard, mustache, scalp)	Tropical countries	Shaving infected area, or adequate cleaning of hair followed by application of a mild fungicide
White piedra	*Trichosporon beigelii*	Infected hair (beard, mustache, scalp)	Temperate and tropical regions	

infections. Included among these opportunistic agents are species of *Aspergillus, Candida, Cryptococcus, Geotrichum, Mucor,* and *Rhizopus.* Factors which have been found to predispose individuals to opportunistic infections include chronic anemia, leukemia, metabolic disorders (such as *diabetes mellitus*), and intensive treatment with broad-spectrum antibiotics and drugs which suppress anitbody formation, e.g., corticosteroids.

Diseases caused by certain filamentous bacteria, e.g., *Actinomyces, Nocardia,* and *Streptomyces,* are conventionally considered fungus infections because of their clinical similarity to the mycoses. Some of these infections will be mentioned in this chapter, while others are discussed in other portions of the textbook.

Diagnostic and Related Features of the Dermatophytes

Unlike some systemic fungi, dermatophytes are not dimorphic; they do not have yeast and hyphal stages. Most dermatophytes appear similar in skin lesions. Culturally, however, their properties are quite different (Color photographs 73 and 78). As indicated in Chapter 12 one of the most widely used media for the cultivation of fungi is Sabouraud's dextrose agar, which contains neopeptone and dextrose as the sole source of nutrients. This medium is acid (approximately pH 5.6) and is especially suited for the majority of fungi because they are able to survive in this type of environment which prevents certain bacteria from growing. Media can be made more selective by adding antibiotics which will discourage the growth of bacteria and saprophytic fungi. Other types of common laboratory media also are used for fungal cultivation.

The identification of several fungi is based on the presence and characteristics of hyphae and spores in cultures (Figure 30–1). Hyphae may undergo development and acquire new features, such as coiling or twisting. The types, form, and arrangement of asexual spores which appear at the ends and sides or within hyphae are of extreme importance. Examples of non-specialized asexual spores are *arthrospores* and *chlamydospores* (Figure 30–1). Fragmentation of hyphae results in the formation of arthrospores, while the thick-walled and heat-resistant chlamydospores are probably formed like bacterial spores, by endosporulation, and are examples of *specialized asexual spores*. Both large asexual spores, called *macroconidia* (Color photographs 79 and 80), and small forms called *microconidia* are quite helpful in the laboratory identification of the various dermatophytes.

Detection of fungi in specimens involves techniques for their isolation and cultivation and also may include a direct microscopic examination of tissues. One of the procedures generally employed involves the digesting of particular specimens in 10 per cent potassium or sodium hydroxide with the aid of heat. This is performed on a slide and is carried out to enable the investigator to see the fungus if it is present. The various organic substances, e.g., fats, some polysarcharides, and proteins, of the tissue become hydrolyzed, thus making the specimen optically clear. In certain cases of especially alkali-resistant organisms, the procedure utilizes a 20 per cent solution of the chemicals. The examination of infected hairs (described below) utilizes techniques of this nature.

Staining procedures are also used in diagnosis, including the Gram stain and the periodic acid-Schiff (PAS) stain. These techniques are not specific for fungi.

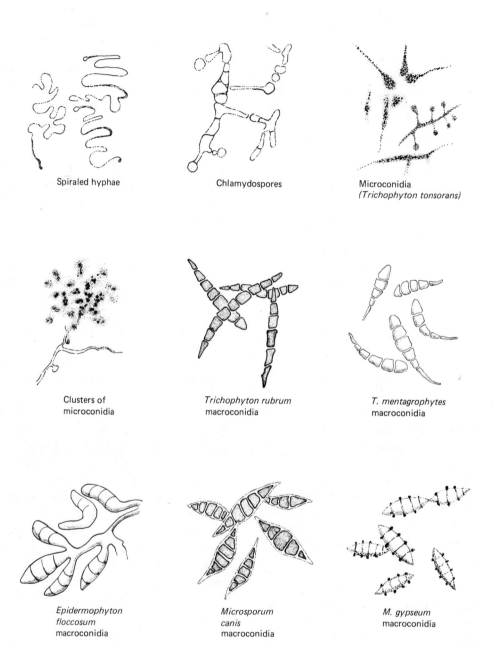

Spiraled hyphae   Chlamydospores   Microconidia
                                                 (Trichophyton tonsorans)

Clusters of   *Trichophyton rubrum*   *T. mentagrophytes*
microconidia   macroconidia   macroconidia

Epidermophyton   *Microsporum*   *M. gypseum*
floccosum   *canis*   macroconidia
macroconidia   macroconidia

FIG. 30–1. Representative microscopic features of the true dermatophytes.

Representative Dermatophycoses

Tinea Barbae

This fungal infection is a chronic condition involving the bearded regions of the face and neck (Figure 30–2). Only men are affected. Causative agents for tinea barbae mainly are *Trichophyton mentagrophytes* and *T. verrucosum*. Other fungi rarely produce the infection.

Clinical features. Generally, individuals with tinea barbae exhibit an inflammation on one side of the face. The infection commonly is sharply localized and may become ulcerated

Diagnosis. Laboratory diagnosis primarily requires the demonstration of the causative agent not only microscopically in clinical specimens, e.g., infected hairs, but in culture as well.

Fungi that attack hair or hair follicles can produce *ectothrix* or *endothrix* infections. The ectothrix condition is characterized by the growth (in the form of arthrospores) of the fungal agent within and on the external portions of the hair shaft. In the latter type of infection, the organism grows only within the hair shaft. Diagnosis of these conditions usually is made by examining infected hairs, which have been exposed to potassium or sodium hydroxide.

Tinea Capitis

This highly infectious mycotic condition is produced by species of *Microsporum* and *Trichophyton*. The disease involves the scalp and the follicle and shaft of the hair. Tinea capitis may be acquired by direct contact with infected animals, humans, or fomites. The disease is commonly found in individuals living in overcrowded areas who practice poor hygienic habits. Children are most commonly affected (Color photograph 75).

Clinical features. Clinically, four forms of the disease are recognized: block-dot ringworm, favus (Figure 30–3), gray patch, and inflammatory ringworm (including kerion formation, which is a boggy, elevated inflamed, pus-containing mass).

Black-dot ringworm is a chronic condition in which infected hairs break off at the scalp's surface, producing a dotted appearance. Crusting, scaling, varying de-

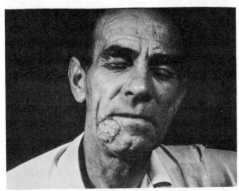

FIG. 30–2. Tinea barbae. Note the localized, boggy appearance of this infection. (Courtesy of the Armed Forces Institute of Pathology, Washington, D.C., Neg. No. 56–4858.)

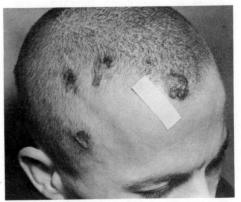

FIG. 30–3. Favus, a severe form of tinea capitis. (Courtesy of the Armed Forces Institute of Pathology, Washington, D.C., Neg. No. B–535–1.)

grees of inflammation, and a kerion may occur. *T. tonsurans* and *T. violaceum* are the common etiologic agents.

Favus also is a chronic state, characterized by the development of red, scaly patches, which form yellow crusts referred to as *scutula*. Penetration of these crusts by hairs also occurs. The crusts slowly spread over the scalp. Hair loss commonly follows. *T. schoenleinii* causes the infection.

In the *gray patch* form of tinea capitis, the involved skin surface is mildly inflamed and scaly. The infected hairs in the area become discolored and brittle, and patchy losses of hair (*alopecia*) occur. Two species of *Microsporum*, *M. audouini* and *M. canis*, are the etiologic agents of gray patch.

Individuals with the *inflammatory* form of ringworm exhibit varying degrees of inflammation, together with scaling and crusting. Kerion formation occurs in severe cases of the infection. Infected hairs loosen and fall out. *M. canis*, *M. gypseum*, *T. mentagrophytes*, and *T. verrucosum* are commonly associated with this form of tinea capitis.

Diagnosis. Diagnosis of tinea capitis can be made in one of three ways: (1) the use of Wood's light (the fluorescence test), (2) microscopic examination of infected nails, and (3) culture.

With *M. audouini*, *M. canis*, or *T. schoenleinii*, diagnosis can be made with the aid of the fluorescence test. Hairs infected with the first two organisms, when exposed to Wood's light, produce a bright green fluorescence, while the last-mentioned fungus causes hair to fluoresce grayish-green.

The partial digestion of infected hair specimens by a 10 per cent solution of either potassium or sodium hydroxide is used to reveal the arrangement of fungal spores. In *Microsporum* spp. infections,

spores are situated around the hair shaft in the form of a sheath. *T. tonsurans* and *T. violaceum* usually have their characteristic spores arranged in chains in hair (endothrix infection). With other *Trichophyton* spp., such as *T. mentagrophytes* and *T. verrucosum*, spores are located outside of the hair (ectothrix infection). The causative agent of favus, *T. schoeinlenii*, produces an endothrix infection with bubble formation in the hair shaft.

On cultivation many of these fungi produce characteristic mycelia which exhibit distinctive coloration (Color photographs 73, 74, and 78). The macroscopic and microscopic appearance of cultures after 5 to 10 days are used to complete the diagnosis.

Prevention. Preventative measures are important with tinea capitis. Parents should be made aware of its contagious nature. Shampooing after haircuts may be of value in the prevention of this disease.

Tinea Corporis

The non-hairy (glabrous) skin of an individual's body is affected in this chronic mycotic disease. The infection can be found in both sexes, with a greater frequency in moist and hot regions. The disease agent in children often is *M. canis*, whereas in adults several *Trichophyton* species produce the infection (Color photograph 70).

Clinical features. The lesions of tinea corporis are asymmetrically distributed and appear in various shapes and sizes. In general, these lesions begin as small, round, red, scaly, raised areas (erythematous and maculopapular) which tend to clear up in the center while spreading from their edges. Concentric rings (circinate lesions) may develop during the infection. The borders of several lesions often are found to contain vesicles. Itching is a common symptom.

In certain patients, the causative agent may invade the deeper portions of skin, thus producing *tinea profunda,* a tumor-like growth or granuloma forms, which is comparable to the kerion associated with *tinea capitis.* A mycotic disease known as *tinea imbricata,* caused by *T. concentricum,* also involves the skin. The infection is characterized by the formation of concentric ring lesions which produce a wavelike, scaly appearance of the infected area. Most of the skin surface can be involved. The disease is found in Africa, the Far East, and South America.

Diagnosis.   Tinea corporis must be differentiated from various fungus diseases as well as other conditions which can affect the smooth skin; these include eczema erythrasma, psoriasis, and certain forms of syphilis. Diagnosis generally must be confirmed by the demonstration of the causative agent in skin scrapings and the macro- and microscopic characteristics of cultured organisms.

Tinea Cruris

This chronic, superficial infection generally is confined to the inner surfaces of the inguinal region. Perianal and axillar involvement can also occur. The disease is caused primarily by *Epidermophyton floccosum* (Color photograph 80), although *Candida albicans* and *Trichophyton* species have been reported to produce it (Color photograph 72).

Clinical features.   Lesions of tinea cruris occur on the upper surfaces of the inner thigh. They are generally brownish in color, with abrupt margins. The borders of the lesions may be inflamed. The eruptions exhibit a bilateral symmetry. Other areas, including the axillae and genitalia, may also become involved. It is not uncommon for the involved areas

to extend backward to the buttocks and upward to the abdomen.

Diagnosis.   Diagnosis is based on the demonstration of hyphae in skin scrapings and the characteristic macro- and microscopic features. The macroconidia of *E. floccosum* are club-shaped and appear as "bunches of bananas" (Color photograph 80).

Tinea Manuum and Tinea Pedis

These mycotic manifestations are chronic and usually develop as a result of the causative fungi spreading from the toe webs, after being acquired through contact with contaminated showers, swimming and wading pools, and wet, tropical terrain. Species of *Microsporum* and *Trichophyton,* as well as *Candida albicans* and *E. floccosum,* are the causative agents (Color photograph 76).

Clinical features.   The degree of involvement and the severity of the disease depend both on the causative agent and the defenses of the host. In the inflammatory form of tinea pedis, the infection begins on the sides of toes or toe webs. Considerable redness, blisters, and soreness usually are present. These effects are followed by the formation of grooves or fissures in the affected areas. Lesions are cracked, moist, and swollen. Infected persons experience burning, itching, pain, and a general discomfort. In certain cases tinea pedis becomes so severe as to be incapacitating. Secondary bacterial infections can also result. *E. floccosum* and *T. mentagrophytes* are common causes of this form of disease (Color photograph 71).

With the absorption of fungal products by infected persons, various types of nonfungal eruptions can occur on the extremities and trunk. These are indicative of the so-called "id" or trichophytid reaction, an allergic reaction to the products of the causative fungus, *Trichophyton* spp. Such skin reactions are reddened areas which appear on areas distant from infected regions. These eruptions are sterile (i.e., no fungi are present).

Chronic manifestations of tinea pedis are generally seen on the soles (Figure 30–4). Usually redness, scaling, and thickening of the infected area are the most noticeable features of the disease. Involvement of the hands occurs with the spreading of the infection. This form of tinea pedis is generally caused by *T. rubrum*.

Diagnosis. Tentative identification is obtained by examination of skin and nail from infected persons. The final identification of the etiologic agent, however, is made on the basis of mycelial characteristics and microscopic morphology of cultures (Color photographs 78 and 79).

Prevention. Preventive measures are extremely important in the control of tinea

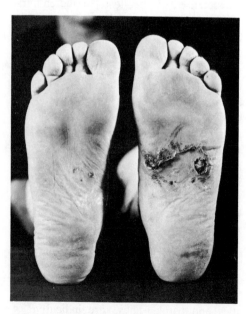

FIG. 30–4. Tinea pedis. (Courtesy of the Armed Forces Institute of Pathology, Washington, D.C., Neg. No. 53–14665–1.)

pedis. These include keeping potential areas of infection clean and dry.

Tinea Nigra

Cladosporium werneckii is considered the causative agent of this tropical mycosis. The disease, although not commonly encountered in the United States, has been reported to have a widespread geographical distribution. Cases occur in Asia and Central and South America.

Clinical features. Individuals with this disease exhibit macules (spots) of varying size, ranging in color from gray to black, on the palms of their hands. These lesions have been likened to silver nitrate stains. Inflammation is not present.

Diagnosis. Diagnosis of tinea nigra can be relatively simple, because of its characteristic clinical appearance. Laboratory confirmation is made by the demonstration of the branched hyphae of *C. werneckii* in epidermal scrapings and the cultivation of the etiologic fungus. The organism produces shiny, yeast-like, greenish-black colonies.

Tinea Unguium (Onychomycosis)

Infection of the toe and finger nails is a chronic mycotic disease. Usually the infection is secondary to tinea pedis or tinea manuum. Causative agents of this disease include *Candida albicans, Epidermophyton floccosum,* and *Trichophyton* species.

Clinical features. Nails which are infected with any pathogenic fungus except *C. albicans* generally are brittle, dry, lusterless, opague, pitted, and yellow in color. Only one or a few fingernails are infected. Moreover, infection usually is limited to one hand. With infected toenails, the disease commonly involves both feet. (Nail involvement by *Candida* species is discussed later.)

Diagnosis. As in the case of other fungus infections, diagnosis is based on the demonstration of the causative agent in clinical specimens (e.g., scales, scrapings from nail bed or plate) and the characteristics of the cultured organism.

Tinea Versicolor

Malassezia furfur is the causative agent of this chronic fungus infection. Generally, the condition is an asymptomatic one, although infected individuals may experience mild itching. The disease is most commonly associated with young adults.

Clinical features. *M. furfur* affects the most superficial portion of the skin only, usually on the trunk. Lesions are small, macular, scaly patches which vary in color from that of the normal skin to dark brown. A slight degree of inflammation and itching may be present. When lesions are examined under Wood's light (3650Å), they have a yellowish-brown appearance.

Diagnosis. The clinical features, together with the results of a Wood's light examination procedure, are quite distinctive. However, laboratory confirmation by means of microscopic examination of skin scrapings is used to differentiate tinea versicolor from other superficial fungus infections. *M. furfur* appears as short hyphae with clusters of round spores in such specimens. The cultivation of the causative agent on artificial media has not been successful.

Piedra

In this disease fungal growths securely attach to the hair's surface, forming black, brown, or white firm nodules. Two forms of the infection are recognized, black and white piedra. Black piedra is caused by the *Piedraia hortai* and white piedra by *Trichosporon beigelii*. All ages and both sexes appear to be vulnerable to the infection.

Clinical features. Inflammatory reactions do not occur, since the skin is not involved. Hairs of the beard, mustache, and scalp can be infected. The nodules produced as a consequence of the disease may impart a gritty or coarse feeling to the hair. Such nodules are more firmly attached in the case of *P. hortai* (black piedra) infection (Color photograph 77) than with those of *T. beigelii* (white piedra).

Diagnosis. Laboratory diagnosis is made on the basis of demonstrating the hyphae and arthrospores of the respective causative agents in microscopic examinations, and the cultivation of these fungi.

In black piedra usually dark, branching hyphae and spores (ascospores) of *P. hortai* surround the hair (Color photograph 77). With white piedra infections, the hyphae encircle the hair shaft and extend along its length.

Other Diseases of the Skin and Mucous Membranes Caused by Fungi and Filamentous Bacteria

Several superficial fungi are capable of attacking tissues in addition to the skin. Certain properties of selected representatives of the group, agents of chronic mycotic diseases, and fungi-like (filamentous) bacteria that cause skin infections are listed in Table 30–2. Discussions of their respective clinical features and diagnosis are presented by groups in the following section.

Table 30–2   Other Fungal and Fungus-like Bacterial Diseases of the Skin

Disease	Causative Agent (Superficial fungus—S) (Deep-seated agent—D) (Filamentous bacterium—F)	Source of Infection	Geographical Distribution	Possible Treatment
Actinomycosis	*Actinomyces bovis* *A. israelii* (F)	Soil, oral cavity	Worldwide	Choramphenicol Penicillin Tetracyclines Streptomycin Surgical drainage Irrigation of infected areas
Candidiasis (Moniliasis)	*Candida albicans* and *Candida* spp. (S)	Skin, gastrointestinal tract, oral cavity	Worldwide	Amphotericin B Gentian violet (5 per cent) rarely used
Chromoblastomycosis	*Hormodendrum (Fonseccaea) compactum* *H. pedrosoi, Philophora verrucosa* (D)	Soil, wood	Worldwide	Amphotericin B Surgical excision of lesions
Cryptococcosis	*Cryptococcus neoformans* (D)	Soil, pigeon droppings	Worldwide	Amphotericin B
Mycetoma	*Nocardia* spp. *Streptomyces* spp. (F)	Soil	Tropical and subtropical areas	Surgical drainage of lesions Amputation (severe cases) Antibiotics, including aureomycin, chloromycetin
Sporotrichosis	*Sporotrichum schenckii* (D)	Soil, decaying vegetation, moss (Sphagnum), thorns of shrubs	Worldwide	Potassium iodide Amphotericin B

Candidiasis

This disease dates back to the early beginnings of microbiology. Its effects range from simple, localized infections to fulminating fatal septicemias. *Candida albicans* is considered the usual causative agent of bronchopulmonary candidiasis, dermal candidiasis, oral thrush and vaginitis, and paronychia, i.e., inflammation of the nail bed. Other *Candida* species also have been associated with certain infections: *C. parapsilosis, C. guilliermondii,* and *C. tropicalis* with endocarditis, and *C. stellatoidea* with vaginal manifestations. It should be noted that the mere presence of the fungus is not enough to cause disease, since it has often been isolated from the skin, oral cavity, and intestinal tract of healthy individuals.

The organisms are present in many areas of the body and can manifest themselves as etiologic agents of a fungal infection when host resistance is lowered, when there is some form of nutritional deficiency, or as a complication of bacterial or viral diseases. Candidiasis is commonly seen at both extremes of life, in the very young and the very old, as well as in debilitated persons. Predisposing factors include diabetes mellitus, pregnancy, obesity, and avitaminosis. The infection has shown an increase in recent years as a complication of therapy with antibiotics, corticosteroids, and cytotoxic drugs used in cancer therapy. *Candida* species have been, in many instances, grouped with the so-called opportunistic fungi.

Clinical features. The common sites of infection are in the mucous membranes of the mouth, the vagina, vulva, and the uterine cervix. The effects of *C. albicans* and related species are numerous and varied. Local areas of the skin may be involved, or the disease may be of a systemic nature. The following descriptions represent selected examples of clinical manifestations caused of *Candida* species.

Intertriginous Candidiasis

Infections of this type generally occur in regions of the skin which are wet and macerated. People whose hands are constantly immersed in water—dishwashers, fruit canners, and housewives—are particularly prone to intertriginous candidiasis. Other areas can also be involved. Infected persons generally complain of pain rather than of itching sensations. Vesicles (small blisters) and pustules (elevated portions of the cuticle containing pus) may be present.

Paronychia

Candida spp. can invade the subcutaneous tissues at the base of nails (eponychial tissue), usually creating typical inflammation of the region. Pus is found in small quantities. The nails may become secondarily invaded resulting in the condition known as onychia or onychomycosis (Figure 30–5). Infected nails exhibit irregular surfaces, with a brownish coloration. Striations and destruction of the tissue also may be evident.

Generalized Cutaneous Candidiasis

Individuals with diabetes or with certain congenital defects may develop this condition. In general, the axillae, groin, oral, and closely related regions are more severely affected.

Laboratory diagnosis. The diagnostic procedures for *Candida* infections are given in Chapter 32.

Prevention. Preventive measures generally are directed toward keeping susceptible skin areas as dry as possible. Rubber gloves and the avoidance of excessive exposure to detergents and re-

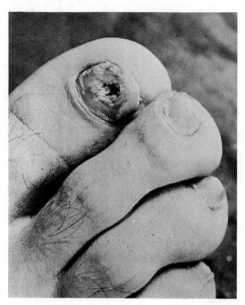

FIG. 30–5. *Candida*-caused onychomycosis. Note the brittle appearance of the infected toenail. (Courtesy of the Armed Forces Institute of Pathology, Washington, D.C., Neg. No. 58–13966–4.)

lated substances may be of value in controlling the disease.

Selected Deep-Seated Mycoses Involving the Skin

Chromomycosis (Chromoblastomycosis Dermatitis Verrucosa)

Three fungal agents have been listed as causative agents of this chronic mycotic disease state. These are *Hormodendrum (Fonsecaea) compactum, H. pedrosoi,* and *Phialophora verrucosa*. Infections are found with wounds associated with wood. The majority of chromoblastomycosis patients have been males.

Clinical features. The lesions of chromoblastomycosis may involve several sites on the skin, but generally the foot or leg is affected. Initial effects of the disease may begin with a brown, purple, or red

warty nodule, or as an ulcer. Within several months to years, such lesions may run together. So-called cauliflower-like growths also may develop. Secondary bacterial infection of ulcers can occur.

Diagnosis. The causative agents of this disease are oval to spherical dark brown cells. Their identification is generally possible on the basis of mycelial characteristics and on the corresponding microscopic examinations of these fungi.

Cryptococcosis

This chronic fungal disease may involve the lungs, skin, subcutaneous tissues, joints, meninges, and oral mucous membranes. The chief lesions are usually found in the central nervous system. The disease is caused by *Cryptococcus neoformans*. Other names for the infection include torulosis, European blastomycosis, and Busse-Buschke's disease. Causative organisms have been found in large numbers in pigeon droppings, even though the birds are not systemically infected. Wilson in 1957 observed that men may carry the organism while maintaining good health, and later become infected from these organisms or from an outside source, such as soil. It appears likely that several host factors determine whether infection takes place. The respiratory tract is considered to be the portal of entry.

Clinical features. Primary lesions usually occur in the lung, or on the skin (Figure 4–15*A*). Occasional cases of oral infections have been reported. Most oral disease develops in markedly debilitated persons, commonly patients suffering from leukemia.

Diagnosis. Laboratory diagnosis generally involves the demonstration of *C. neoformans* in various types of specimens, including pus, skin, spinal fluid (Figure

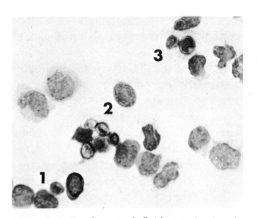

FIG. 30-6. Cerebrospinal fluid examination in meningoencephalitis. Cells from a patient with *Cryptococcus neoformans* meningitis stained by Wright's procedure. Explanation of numbers: (1) *Cryptococcus* to the right of label; (2) five crytococci below the label surrounding the right side of small lymphocyte; (3) another extracellular *Cryptococcus* with a bud to the right of the label. (From Tourtellotte, W. W.: *Modern Treatment,* **415**:879–897, 1967.)

30–6), and tissue sections. India ink and Wright's stain are particularly useful for this purpose. *C. neoformans* is a thin-walled, spherical fungus, with a polysaccharide capsule which varies in thickness and often equals the diameter of the cell. Unlike other fungi that produce disseminated disease, this organism is not dimorphic. Cultivation of the pathogen is necessary for confirmation of the diagnosis (Color photograph 36). *C. neoformans* produces yeast colonies on a number of different media, either at 37°C or at room temperature. Animal inoculations are used to demonstrate pathogenicity.

Sporotrichosis

This subcutaneous mycosis, caused by *Sporotrichum schenckii,* is characterized by the development of granulomatous nodules or ulcers in mucous membranes, skin (Figure 30–7), and superficial lymphatics associated with the primary site of inoculation. On rare occasions it may be disseminated to the lungs, meninges,

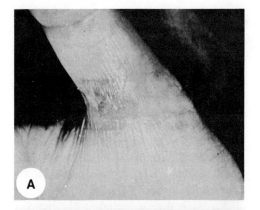

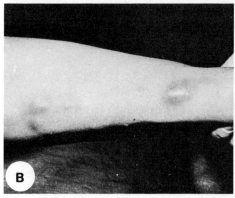

FIG. 30-7*A.* A skin ulcer resulting from *S. schenckii* infection at the base of the right thumb. *B.* Nodular lymphangitis (inflammation of lymph vessels). (Courtesy of Drs. J. B. Hanrahan and E. R. Erickson, Western Pennsylvania Hospital, Pittsburgh.)

or viscera. Sporotrichosis commonly affects farmers and florists. The disease is not confined to man, as it has been noted in horses, mules, dogs, and cats, and has been transmitted by animal contact. Infection often results from accidental implantation into the skin or mucous membranes. It is commonly referred to as an inoculation disease.

Diagnosis. *Sporotrichum schenckii* is dimorphic. The parasitic stage occurs in tissues, with the extremely small organism (1 to 2 μm) being very difficult to demonstrate. The organisms are seen as small, cigar-shaped, budding yeasts. Unfortunately, specimens may contain few fungi. The periodic acid-Schiff (PAS) staining and fluorescein-labeled antibody techniques have been used in diagnosis.

Laboratory diagnosis may be made by isolating and culturing the fungus from lesions. Microscopic examination of cultures reveals septated thin hyphae with lateral and terminal projections of pear-shaped microconidia. These conidia are attached individually by means of a common conidiophore.

Serological tests including the indirect fluorescent antibody technique and a slide latex agglutination procedure can be used for diagnostic purposes.

Fungi-Like (Filamentous) Bacterial Skin Diseases

Actinomycosis (Actinomycosis Cervicofacialis, Lumpy Jaw)

The disease is produced by two species of *Actinomyces, A bovis* and *A. israelli.* The members of this genus were long regarded as fungi, largely because of the resemblance of their colonial formations to mycelia and the indistinguishability of certain clinical manifestations from those produced by some fungi.

Today, however, actinomycetes are considered to be more related to bacteria, primarily on the basis of certain biological properties of the genus. These characteristics include (1) the inhibition of growth by antibiotics known to be effective against bacteria e.g., penicillin and the tetracyclines, (2) the ineffectiveness of antimycotics on growth, (3) the presence of a poorly defined nucleus, (4) the presence in cell walls of compounds typical of bacterial cells, namely diaminopiemelic and muramic acids, (5) the absence of compounds typically associated with fungal cell walls (e.g., chitin and glucans), and (6) the susceptibility of certain antinomy-

cetes to phages (actinophages). This susceptibility has not been observed in the majority of fungi.

Many of the *Actinomycetes* normally exist in the environment and seemingly cause no damage to man. Others, such as *A. israelii* and *A. bovis,* can produce serious infections in man. Both pathogens are microaerophilic, Gram-positive, filamentous microorganisms requiring rich media for growth. They can cause a number of disease conditions in man, including cerviocofacial, thoracic, abdominal, and other forms of actinomycosis. Infections of the face, neck, and oral cavity (Figure 30–8) are the most commonly seen, probably accounting for nearly 60 per cent of the cases. Organisms have difficulty in penetrating intact epithelium. Consequently, most infections are associated with trauma or accidental damage, or with dental defects such as open cavities with exposed pulps or extraction sockets.

Clinical features.   Two principal types of lesion have been described. One is chronic, slow growing, and very firm. The second is a more acute, rapidly progressive type in which the discharge of pus predominates. The latter lesion closely resembles most other abscesses. There

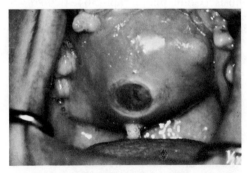

FIG. 30–8. Actinomycosis of the palate showing the rather extreme nodular swelling which has ulcerated at the surface. (Courtesy of Dr. N. H. Rickles, Pathology Department, University of Oregon Medical School.)

may be all grades of chronicity between the two extremes.

Early, there is moderate pain accompanied by non-characteristic inflammatory swelling which does not subside following routine therapy. It then develops into a chronic hard, nodular, indurated area with subsequent formation of multiple deep, winding ulcers (fistulas) which discharge pus containing the so-called yellowish "sulfur granules" (Figure 30–9). Such granules are in reality clumps of bacteria

When untreated, the chronic condition proceeds slowly and irregularly, with areas of healing and new areas of infection, all of which result in a maze of infiltrations, abscesses, and fistulas. The infiltration proceeds without regard for existing normal tissue borders. When blood vessels are invaded blood-borne infections carried to distant parts of the body may occur (*hematogenous metastasis*). The lymph nodes usually are not involved in this disease.

Laboratory diagnosis. The diagnosis of actinomycosis is confirmed by the demonstration of bacterial clumps in the form of "sulfur granules" and of Gram-positive, granulated, branching threads, upon microscopic examination of the pus, even if the result of bacteriologic culture is negative. Growth of these organisms on artificial media is difficult, especially when patients suffering from actinomycosis have been previously treated with antibiotics. Anaerobic cultivation is commonly employed.

Mycetoma

This clinical syndrome is characterized by localized granular, pus-forming lesions. It is produced by either of two major groups of microorganisms, the bacteria-like aerobic actinomycetes and a variety of fungi. Examples of the former group include *Nocardia asteroides, N. brasiliensis, Streptomyces madurae, S. pellatieri,* and *S. somaliensis.* The fungal pathogens include *Cephalosporium falciforme, C. recifer, Leptosphaeria senegalensis, Madurella grisea,* and *M. mycetomi.* Mycotic mycetomas and at least eight other fungal diseases are frequently called *maduromycosis.*

In general mycetomas develop as a consequence of introducing the causative agent through some form of injury. Most infections affect the foot, although other body parts may become involved. *Mycetoma pedis* is the designation for this manifestation. When the hand is involved the disease is called *mycetoma manus.*

Clinical features. In a typical case of mycetoma, the affected part of the body swells, and discharging sinuses exude pus containing clumps (mycelia) of the causative agent. The accumulations usually take the form of grains, which vary in color, shape, size, and texture, depending on the pathogen. Generally one site is affected; however, multiple lesions may develop. An important characteristic of the disease is bone penetration.

The degree of involvement is determined by the causative microorganism.

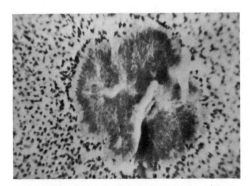

FIG. 30–9. A clump of *Actinomyces israelii* surrounded by a "sea" of polymorphonuclear leukocytes. This is a typical "sulfur granule." (Courtesy of Dr. N. H. Rickles, Pathology Department, University of Oregon Dental School.)

In a large number of cases, although not in all, a striking massive enlargement and distortion of the involved tissue occurs with multiple deep abscesses. Victims of the disease may experience little or no pain, or may have severe pains. This disease has been known to exist for several years before patients sought treatment.

Diagnosis. Clinical diagnosis is readily made in advanced cases, as a typical disease picture is present. However, this is not so in the early stages of mycetoma. The confirmation of the clinical diagnosis, as well as the identification of the causative agent, is based upon biopsy examinations and the results of culturing material from specimens.

QUESTIONS FOR REVIEW

1. Differentiate between superficial and deep-seated mycoses.

2. What is a dermatophyte? Give six examples.

3. How can one distinguish between endothrix and ectothrix infections?

4. Explain dimorphism.

5. Define or explain the following terms:
   a. hyphae
   b. chlamydospore
   c. conidia
   d. arthrospore
   e. macroconidia
   f. microconidia

6. Which of the structures listed in question 5 are of diagnostic importance? List at least three organisms that can be identified on this basis.

7. How can the following diseases be contracted?
   a. tinea capitis
   b. tinea cruris
   c. tinea pedis
   d. tinea corporis
   e. tinea versicolor
   f. tinea unguium
   g. mycetoma
   h. white piedra
   i. black piedra
   j. sporotrichosis
   k. mycetoma pedis
   l. tinea nigra

8. What methods are conventionally used in the diagnosis of dermatophytosis?

9. Discuss the manifestations of *Candida albicans* as to their various forms and possible means for their prevention.

10. What is actinomycosis?

11. If you were traveling in a tropical or subtropical area of the world, what mycotic infections might you find? How could these diseases be prevented?

Viral Infections of the Skin

Several viral infections are either limited to the skin proper or involve it in the pathogenesis of the disease process (Table 31–1). Some of the better-known of these viral diseases, including chickenpox, cold sore, measles, smallpox, and warts, will be presented.

General Symtomatology

The clinical features associated with a large number of skin diseases vary widely. Yet, according to the nature of the pathologic process, certain diseases may possess identical features, which creates a problem in diagnosis.

Familiarity with the terminology of skin diseases presented in Chapter 29 is helpful, not only in diagnosis, but also in following the development of a disease process.

Treatment

Promising results have been obtained by several investigators in treating various viral skin infections (Table 31–1). Unfortunately, all forms of such diseases do not respond equally well. In many instances treatment of viral skin diseases consists only of preventing secondary bacterial infections with antibiotics, and

Table 31–1   Representative Viral Diseases of Humans that Affect the Skin

Common Designation of the Disease	Viral Group	Accepted or Proposed Genus Designation	Possible Treatment
Herpes simplex, cold sore, fever blister	Herpesvirus	*Herpesvirus*	5-iodo-2' deoxyuridine (IUDR) (promising medication); other DNA synthesis inhibitors and certain dyes, such as neutral red and proflavine
Herpes zoster, shingles			
Varicella, chickenpox			5-iodo-2' deoxyuridine (IUDR); zoster immunoglobulin[a]
			5-iodo-2' deoxyuridine (IUDR). X-ray for early stages of shingles. Symptomatic treatment
Warts, verruca vulgaris	Papillomavirus	*Papillomavirus*	Surgical or chemical removal of warts. Certain vaccines under development
Classic measles (rubeola or morbilli)	Paramyxovirus	*Paramyxovirus*	Antibiotics to prevent secondary bacterial infections. Symptomatic treatment
German measles, rubella		This agent resembles the paramyxoviruses	Immune globulin preparations
Contagious pustular dermatitis (or virus infection)	Poxvirus	*Dermovirus*	Self-healing
Molluscum contagiosum		*Molluscovirus*	Excision of lesions
Smallpox		*Poxvirus*	Hyperimmune serum. Antibiotics to prevent secondary bacterial infections.
Vaccinia			Self-healing

[a] Recently made available.

relieving the victim's discomfort (symptomatic treatment).

The Herpesvirus Group

The viruses belonging to this group (Table 31–2) are characterized on the basis of several properties, including: (1) the possession of double-stranded DNA, (2) the presence of a nucleocapsid with cubical symmetry, (3) inactivation by chloroform and ether, (4) viral multiplication in the nucleus of infected cells, (5) the production of clinical manifestations such as vesicular eruptions of the skin and mucous membranes, and occasional neurotropic involvement, and (6) the formation of intranuclear eosinophilic inclusions. These inclusions are referred to as Lipschütz or type A inclusions. During the early stages of viral development, such inclusions are basophilic when they contain viruses. The eosinophilic state results after the viruses have been released. Thus, the Lipschütz inclusion body is an empty shell, a "token" of viral infection.

The Provisional Committee for Nomenclature of Viruses officially placed the genera of *Herpesvirus* and *Cytomegalovirus* (see Chapter 36) as members of the family *Herpesviridae. Herpesvirus*

hominis, commonly referred to as herpes simplex or "cold sore virus," is designated as the type species. A representative number of herpesviruses are listed in Table 31–2. As investigations of viruses continue, more of them will be added to the group of herpesviruses.

Herpes Simplex

Clinically, the manifestations of herpes simplex virus can be placed into four groups. These categories include: (1) localized lesions of the skin or mucous membranes, (2) central nervous system involvement, (3) eczema herpeticum, and (4) a disseminated form of herpes.

Clinical symptoms.   The localized skin or mucous membrane lesions of herpes can develop as vesicular eruptions on the lips (Figure 31–1*A*), face, or ears (Figure 31–1*B*). Generally these vesicles are painful, but there is no fever. A similar pattern of eruptions, referred to as *herpes febrilis,* can occur during febrile periods.

Lesions can also occur on the external genitalia (*herpes genitalis*) and on fingers (*herpetic whitlow*). The latter is commonly contracted by nurses and physicians. Genital herpes infection is discussed in Chapter 37. Herpetic keratitis, the involvement of the cornea, is discussed in

Table 31–2   Representative Herpesviruses

Common Designation of Agent	Genus and Species (if applicable)	Natural Hosts Involved
Fever blister of herpes simplex virus	*Herpesvirus hominis*	Humans
B virus of monkeys	*Herpesvirus simiae*	Monkeys, humans
Virus III of rabbits	*Herpesvirus cuniculi*	Rabbits
Pseudorabies	*Herpesvirus suis*	Cats, cattle, dogs, foxes, mink, and pigs
Varicella (chicken pox), Herpes zoster agent	*Herpesvirus varicellae*	Humans
Infectious bovine rhinotrachetis		Cattle
Equine rhinopneumonitis		Horses
Canine herpesvirus		Dogs
Feline viral rhinotracheitis		Cats
Infectious mononucleosis, Epstein-Barr virus		Humans
Cytomegalic inclusion disease virus	*Cytomegalovirus*	Humans

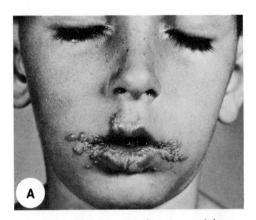

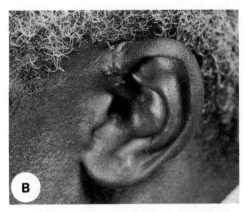

FIG. 31–1. Common manifestations of herpes simplex. _A_. Involvement of the lips. (Courtesy of the Armed Forces Institute of Pathology, Washington, D.C., Neg. No. 55–11961–1.) _B_. Vesicular eruptions on the external ear. This is a case of recurrent infection. Note the clustered appearance of the vesicles. (Courtesy of Dr. Y. L. Lynfield, Veterans Administration Hospital, Brooklyn. Photo by F. G. Hertling.)

Chapter 38. Some of the other categories of herpes virus infection are discussed elsewhere in the text.

The most common form of herpes simplex virus infection is _herpetic gingiostomatitis_. This manifestation represents the individual's first encounter with the viral agent (primary infection). This disease phase occurs chiefly in children between the ages of 1 and 5. Similar primary involvement in adults may be quite severe. After recovery, the virus assumes a latent form. However, infections can recur quite readily as a consequence of precipitating causes, such as emotional disturbances, infections, lymphoma (Figure 31–2), menses, and sunburn. Although persons with recurrent herpes have circulating antibodies, they do not prevent the manifestation from occurring.

Transmission of the virus can be accomplished by direct contact, including kissing, hand touching, and sexual relations, and by fomites.

Diagnosis. Laboratory diagnosis usually involves the examination of any of a wide variety of clinical specimens, e.g.,

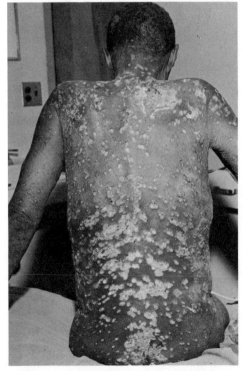

FIG. 31–2. Patient with generalized herpes simplex infection. This individual's immune state was altered by lymphoma. Identification of the viral agent was made by tissue culture studies of vesicle fluid. (Courtesy of Dr. Y. L. Lynfield, Veterans Administration Hospital, Brooklyn. Photo by F. G. Hertling.)

biopsy material of the liver (Figure 31–3), corneal and skin scrapings, spinal fluids, and vesicular fluid. The etiologic agent characteristically forms intranuclear inclusions in certain giant cells.

Viral isolation procedures also are used. These include inoculations of common laboratory animals, chick embryos, and tissue culture systems such as human embryonic lung fibroblasts. Such cells are available from commercial firms. Serological tests for the detection of antibodies are widely employed. The fluorescent antibody complement-fixation and virus neutralization tests are generally used for this purpose. Herpes simplex manifestations must be differentiated from those of other viruses and other causative agents.

Varicella (Chickenpox)-Herpes Zoster (Shingles) Virus

Intensive studies have been carried out concerning the antigenic and biologic characteristics of the etiologic agents of varicella (chickenpox) and herpes zoster (shingles). A variety of immunologic tests—agglutination, complement-fixation, and viral neutralization—have demonstrated the viruses to be immunologically identical. Furthermore, the morphological examination of the virions and inclusion bodies associated with these agents found them to be physically indistinguishable. Both viruses also produce similar cytopathic effects in tissue cultures, and fail to cause infections of certain experimental laboratory animals. The identity of these agents has been further established by the production of typical cases of chickenpox in children following inoculation of shingles vesicle fluid. On the basis of these and related investigations, the majority of investigators believe that varicella and herpes zoster represent different clinical manifestations of infection with the same agent, the V-Z virus.

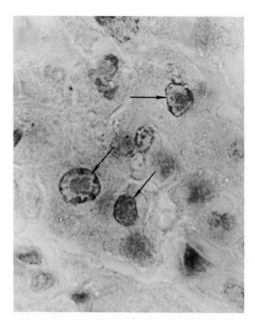

FIG. 31–3. A liver biopsy from a 10-day-old child showing typical inclusions of herpes simplex virus (arrows). (Courtesy of the Armed Forces Institute of Pathology, Washington, D.C., Neg. No. 56–2952.)

Varicella

Chickenpox is one of the most common diseases in residential schools. This viral disease is primarily a childhood infection. However, approximately 20 percent of cases are adults. Varicella is the primary disease state produced in an individual without immunity. Infections are transmitted via droplets (e.g., respiratory secretions) and contact, either direct or indirect, with infectious skin surfaces. It should be noted that an individual with shingles (herpes zoster infection) may be a source of infectious material for an outbreak of chickenpox.

Clinical features. Generally speaking, the incubation period for chickenpox ranges from 11 to 20 days. The disease begins suddenly and the rash (Figure 31–4) is the first manifestation. A patient usually is infectious from approximately 1 day before the rash appears to about 7 days later.

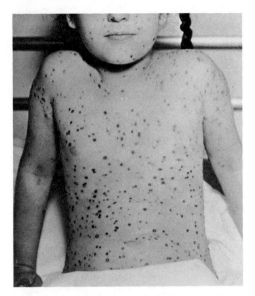

FIG. 31-4. A typical case of chickenpox. (Courtesy of the Armed Forces Institute of Pathology, Washington, D.C., Neg. No. AMH-10529E.)

The lesions pass from the macular stage to the papular one, which is then followed by the formation of vesicles. These manifestations generally develop in successive crops, so that all of the aforementioned stages can be seen at one time. The rash is mainly distributed over the trunk and face, leaving the feet, scalp, and hands with fewer manifestations. However, this is not always the case. The skin lesions of chickenpox closely resemble those associated with shingles.

Complications with varicella are generally uncommon. However, they occasionally occur. Examples of such complications include abscess formation, corneal ulceration, encephalitis, otitis media (middle ear infection), and pneumonia. Severe secondary bacterial infections are treated with antibiotics.

Laboratory diagnosis. A laboratory confirmation of chickenpox is generally not needed. However, a distinction from smallpox may be necessary. Smear prep-

arations for the detection of typical varicella giant cells, serological tests, and tissue culture techniques are of value. Material for such preparations is obtained by scraping the bases of vesicular lesions. Fluorescent antibody tests and electron microscopy can be used to provide rapid confirmation.

Immunity. Generally recovery from an attack of chickenpox provides a relatively long-lasting active immune state. Recurrent infections are extremely rare.

Control. Control measures for this disease include isolation of infected persons and the administration of immunoglobulin to contacts. Both of these means, however, are limited in effectiveness. No effective vaccine exists at the current time.

Herpes Zoster (Shingles)

This viral infection is uncommon in children; most cases occur in adults. At least 70 per cent of adults have had previous exposure to the varicella-zoster virus, as indicated by the presence of circulating antibodies. Shingles represents a reinvasion, or recurrence of varicella-zoster virus in persons partially immune to varicella.

The natural means of transmission for shingles is not known. The possibility exists that the virus gains extrance to the body by way of the pharynx. From here it enters the bloodstream and then localizes in ganglionic nerve cells. In this location the virus remains latent for varying periods. Activation of the viral agent may be precipitated by several factors, including cancer, trauma, and certain drugs, e.g., antimony and arsenic.

The characteristic eruptions of herpes zoster are vesicular in appearance, and remain localized, usually involving one side of the body only. Sites commonly affected include the head and neck (Figure 31-5) and the trunk, especially the

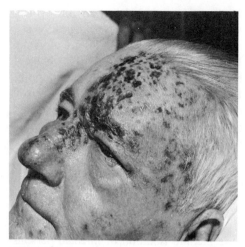

FIG. 31–5. Herpes zoster in an adult patient, specifically, involvement of the ophthalmic nerve. (Courtesy of the Armed Forces Institute of Pathology, Washington, D.C., Neg. No. 58–15409–4.)

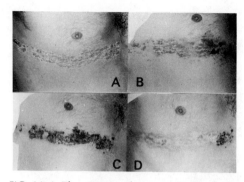

FIG. 31–6. The pattern of treatment of vesicular herpes zoster. _A._ Before treatment with ICDR (5-iodo-2-deoxyuridine). _B._ Drying and excoriation of blisters (bullae) 4 days later. _C_ and _D._ Healing and scar formation. (From Calabresi, P.: Ann. N.Y. Acad. Sci., **130**:192–208, 1965. © The New York Academy of Sciences; 1965; Reprinted by permission.)

chest. The manifestations of the infection may remain for several weeks. Figure 31–6 shows the various stages of healing of vesicular herpes zoster.

Diagnosis. Generally, a laboratory diagnosis is not necessary in the case of shingles, as its clinical symptoms are quite characteristic. However, as in the case of varicella, a differentiation must sometimes be made in order to exclude infections caused by herpes simplex and smallpox viruses. Diagnostic procedures used include inoculations of chick embryos and animals with vesicular fluid. These tests are all negative with herpes zoster, which does not produce lesions.

Papilloma Virus Infection

Human (Papilloma) Warts

Verruca vulgaris, otherwise known as the common wart or condyloma (Figure 31–7), is caused by human papilloma virus, which is a DNA virus. The Provi-

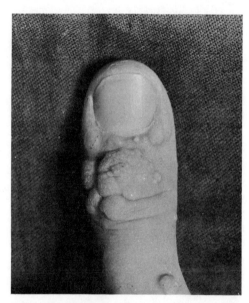

FIG. 31–7. The common wart, verruca vulgaris. This infection commonly manifests itself on the backs of hands, generally in the area of the nail folds. (Courtesy of the Armed Forces Institute of Pathology, Washington, D.C., Neg. No. AMH 10737–2.)

sional Committee for the Nomenclature of Viruses categorized these agents into the family of *Papillomaviridae*. This group, formerly and better known as the papovaviruses, is composed of viruses which cause warts in man and several other animal species (dogs, goats, mice, pigs, and rabbits) and those which produce tumors in laboratory animals.

Human wart virus particles exhibit cubical symmetry with a size range of 40 to 58 nm. The transfer of warts appears to be through scratching. In addition, indirect spreading of viruses has been reported through scratching. In addition, indirect spreading of viruses has been reported to occur by contact with contaminated bathroom and swimming pool floors, communal washroom facilities, and gymnastic equipment. Barbers, chiropodists, and masseurs also have been implicated in spreading the disease. Genital warts, or condylomata acuminata, are transmitted through venereal contact.

Clinical features.   The incubation period for human papilloma may be several weeks. Warts can develop on the backs of hands, palms, soles, or on various parts of the genitourinary system (e.g., glans penis, labia, or prepuce). Several types of warts may become malignant if they are not removed. Human papillomas are of considerable interest today because the causative agent of this disease is grouped together with certain oncogenic (cancer-producing) viruses, polyoma and simian virus 40 (SV40).

The Paramyxoviruses

The viruses belonging to this group are characterized on the basis of several properties, including: (1) the possession of one large molecule of single-stranded RNA, (2) the existence of an envelope with a lipid composition similar to that of the host's cell membrane, (3) replication that takes place in the cytoplasm, and (4) possession of hemagglutinating activity, which most strains in the group have. The

paramyxoviruses include the agents of classic measles (morbilli), German measles (rubella), mumps, Newcastle disease, and several human and lower animal respiratory infections.

Measles (Morbilli)

This is a highly contagious disease usually contracted by exposure to respiratory secretions. The term *rubeola* is occasionally used for this disease. Unfortunately, the very similar designation of *rubella* has been applied to German measles, thus creating confusion. In general, the virus manifests itself in areas where large numbers of susceptible young children reside. Most outbreaks primarily affect children, as older persons generally have acquired a definite degree of immunity from previous exposures to the causative agent. However, when susceptible adults are infected, symptoms are generally more severe.

The frequency of epidemics differs in various parts of the world. In so-called highly developed regions, for example, Britain and North America, measles outbreaks occur every 2 years or so. However, in the less developed areas, such as Nigeria and other portions of Africa, yearly epidemics are observed. Furthermore, if measles is introduced into "virgin territory," isolated communities in which exposure to the viral agent has been rare or nonexistent, severe infections can result. Several instances of such epidemics have been reported. Notable in this regard are the epidemics in the Faroe Islands, Fiji, and parts of South America.

Clinical features.   The incubation period for measles varies from 7 to 21 days. The rash (*exanthem*) generally appears 14 days after the initial exposure. Near the end of the incubation, general symptoms (or complaints) appear; these include coryza, cough, fever, general malaise, muscle pains, photophobia, and redness of the eyelids. Koplik's spots, the pathognomonic (characteristic) feature of measles, occur on the buccal mucosa opposite the molar teeth of the majority of infected persons. These are bright red spots, 1 to 3 mm in diameter, with centrally located bluish-white dots. The rash (Color photographs 83 and 84), which is papular in nature, first appears on the face or behind the ears. The trunk and limbs are involved next. Fading of the rash generally occurs in 4 or 5 days, followed by a powdery ("branny") desquamation.

Complications may follow a measles virus infection, the most common of which include bacterial secondary infections such as bronchitis, bronchopneumonia, and otitis media. In general, it is advisable to administer antibiotics prophylactically to infected children under 3 years of age and to other persons with debilitating diseases, e.g., bronchitis and tuberculosis.

The virus of measles can also produce serious complications such as encephalitis and pneumonia. Fortunately, such cases are not frequent. At the present time no definite evidence exists to implicate measles virus in the mother as the cause of congenital effects in the fetus. Pooled human immune globulin preparations can be employed to modify the course of the disease. While the general effects of the illness may be lessened with this procedure, the incidence of encephalomyelitis is not. Timing and dosages are quite important. Recovery from measles generally provides a long-lasting state of naturally acquired active immunity. Second bouts with the virus are uncommon.

Diagnosis. Generally speaking, the clinical features of measles are sufficient for diagnosis. If a laboratory confirmation is necessary, evidence of the virus infection can be provided by the use of several procedures, including smear preparations of nasal mucosal cells, viral isolations in cell cultures, and serological tests, such as complement-fixation and hemagglutination-inhibition. Blood, nasal, and pharyngeal secretions and urine specimens can be used for the cell cultures.

Prevention. Several types of vaccines have been prepared for the express purpose of eradicating measles. The success of these preparations was made possible through the pioneering experiments of Enders and Peebles. In 1954, these investigators propagated measles virus in cell cultures, thus providing a satisfactory procedure for the development of vaccines. As a result of successive passages through cell cultures and chick embryos, Enders and his colleagues were able to attenuate a strain of measles virus called the Edmonston strain. Vaccine preparations derived from Ender's Edmonston strain have gained wide usage. Several studies have demonstrated that vaccination with a single dose of this preparation provided protection to virtually 100 per cent of the children receiving the inoculation. Moreover, the resulting active immunity appears to be long-lived.

Attenuated vaccine occasionally produces mild side effects which resemble measles-like symptoms; these include coryza, cough, fever, and modified rash. Fever is generally experienced by 80 per cent of the inoculated persons. In 20 to 40 per cent, the temperature may exceed 103°F. Encephalitis associated with measles vaccination has been rare.

Contraindications for the use of the attenuated vaccine include pregnancy, several types of malignancies, and "severe" febrile illness. In addition, vaccination should not be carried out with infants under 1 year of age, or with children who have been given whole blood or blood derivative (e.g., immune globulin and plasma) during the preceding 6 weeks.

Further attenuation of the Edmonston strain has resulted in preparations, e.g., Schwarz and Beckenham (United Kingdom Vaccine), which produce less side reaction. Formalin-inactivated vaccines have been developed also. However, these preparations have not been as effective as attenuated vaccines.

Several programs for the eradication of measles have been carried out. The immunization schedules used have incorporated different vaccine preparations (Table 31–3). One major approach to measles eradication involves the immunization of all children at 1 year of age, administration of a vaccine to any other children upon their entry into school, vaccination of all other susceptible children not previously immunized, and ad-ministration of measles immune globulin to all "exposed susceptible persons."

Rubella or German Measles

This disease occurs in either epidemic or sporadic form worldwide. Generally speaking, German measles is considered to be a typically mild disease with very few and rare complications. However, the disease takes on an entirely different perspective in light of the anomalies the viral agent can induce in fetuses during the early stages of pregnancy. This capacity of the virus to produce congenital defects was first reported in 1941 by the Australian ophthalmologist Gregg. These various clinical manifestations are frequently referred to collectively as the "rubella syndrome," and include cataract formation, congenital heart disease, permanent deafness, mental retardation, spontaneous abortion, and stillbirth. The consequences of rubella not only are

Table 31–3   Immunization Schedules used for Measles

Preparation Used	Age of Individuals Receiving Vaccines	Dosage and Other Pertinent Points of Administration[a]
Edmonston strain (attenuated vaccine)	Generally one year of age and older	One
Edmonston strain plus measles immune globulin	Generally one year of age and older	One of the viral vaccines and the simultaneous administration of the immune globulin preparation (0.1 cc per each pound of body weight) at a site distant from the one used for the vaccine[b]
Schwarz strain (attenuated vaccine)	Generally one year of age and older	One
Inactivated vaccine	Any age	Three at monthly intervals, and a booster shot at one year
Inactivated vaccine plus attenuated vaccine	Generally one year of age and older	One dose followed by one dose of an attenuated vaccine 1 to 3 months later
Inactivated	Under one year of age	Three doses of the inactivated preparations at monthly intervals, followed by the attenuated vaccine at one year of age or older
Measles, Mumps, and Rubella (M-M-R) attenuated vaccine	One year of age	One[c]

SOURCE: *Morbidity and Mortality Weekly Report,* April 23, 1966, Los Angeles County Health Department.

[a] The directions of the vaccine's manufacturer always should be consulted before use, especially in relation to dosages and other pertinent details.

[b] This procedure varies.

[c] A trivalent vaccine. Each component can be given separately also (see Chapter 26).

varied, but unpredictable. It appears that virtually any organ of a developing fetus may fall victim to the effects of the virus.

Many case histories have been compiled to determine the time relationship between maternal infection and the appearance of specific congenital anomalies. Most appear when maternal infections occur during the first trimester. Cataracts and cardiac defects develop predominantly after maternal infection during the first 2 months of pregnancy, while the loss of hearing and "psychomotor retardation" occur at any time during the first 3 months of the gestation period. Rubella has been placed into the TORCH group of disease agents because of the similarities in effects and in approaches to identification (refer to Chapter 37).

The mechanism or mechanisms contributing to the embryopathic effects of the rubella virus are not known. However, in view of studies of autopsied rubella infant victims showing underdeveloped organs, and tissue culture investigations which have demonstrated pronounced chromosome breakage in lymphocytes from 1-year-olds demonstrating the "rubella syndrome," several investigators suggest that the virus may induce an inhibition of cell multiplication in the fetus.

Transmission of rubella usually occurs through direct contact with persons harboring inapparent infections. The nasal secretions of infected individuals are highly contagious. Children 5 to 14 years old are the major sources of the virus. In addition, normal-appearing infants born to women who have had clinical rubella during the first 3 months of pregnancy excrete virus at birth. Such newborns come into close contact with various health care personnel, expectant mothers, and other children.

Clinical features.   The incubation period of German measles from the time of viral exposure to the onset of the eruption is 2 to 3 weeks. The face usually is first affected by the macular rash, which is followed by involvement of the trunk. A slight fever and general discomfort may be present. Lymphadenopathy, especially of the post-cervical lymph nodes, is a prominent clinical feature of the disease. Koplik spots are absent. Rubella apparently exerts more severe effects in adults than in children.

Diagnosis.   The effects of rubella virus may be confused with those of several other infectious agents, including, coxsackie and ECHO viruses, infectious mononucleosis, and red measles. In the majority of cases, however, the clinical picture is sufficient for diagnosis. If a laboratory confirmation is required, tissue culture, animal inoculations, and serological testing procedures (e.g., complement-fixation and neutralization) are generally utilized. The hemagglutination-inhibition test is the current test of choice. Chapter 23 presents the details of this procedure and its significance to rubella.

Control.   Recovery from German measles generally imparts a long-lasting active immunity to the viral agent. Although vaccines against this disease are available, considerable disagreement exists as to their value for young children. If girls in their teens have not had German measles, vaccination is generally recommended, since it is highly desirable for young girls to be exposed to the viral agent before reaching childbearing age.

Pooled preparations of immune globulin are administered to pregnant women as soon as possible after exposure, if these women are in their first trimester. The effectiveness of this procedure still is questionable, especially in relation to the prevention of congenital defects. Some physicians recommend a therapeutic abortion to their patients in the event of a rubella infection during the first trimester of pregnancy.

The Poxviruses

More than two dozen disease agents of humans and lower animals belong to the poxvirus group (Table 31–4). In relation to human infections, the viruses of major significance include variola and alastrim (the etiologic agents of smallpox), and vaccinia (the virus employed in smallpox vaccinations). Molluscum contagiosum is a skin disease of minor importance.

Some of the following characteristics apply to most members of the poxvirus group: (1) the multiplication and production of inflammatory lesions (pocks) after inoculation onto the chorioallantoic membranes of chick embryos, (2) possession of double-stranded DNA, (3) viral replication within the cytoplasmic regions of cells, (4) the agglutination of fowl or mouse red blood cells, (5) brick-shaped to ovoid viral particles, and (6) resistance while in dried form to a wide variety of adverse environmental conditions (infectivity can be retained for long periods of

time). These viral agents usually are inactivated by chloroform and common disinfectants, e.g., alcohol and phenol, within an hour at room temperature, 25°C. The poxviruses can be placed into several subgroups on the basis of their viral particle morphology, their antigenic properties, and their natural hosts. Only two viruses, smallpox and vaccinia, will be considered in detail.

Smallpox

This viral infection is known to occur in two forms, variola major (Asiatic smallpox), which is more severe, and variola minor (alastrim or amaas). The etiologic agents are designated as *Poxvirus variolae* in situations when differentiation is unnecessary. However, when differentiation is called for, the causative agents of the abovementioned disease states can be referred to as variola major virus and alastrim virus.

Generally speaking, these viruses are antigenically indistinguishable. However, differentiation can be accomplished through several means, including the clinical and epidemiologic characteristics of their respective disease manifestations.

Geographical distribution. At the present time, smallpox is primarily limited to Africa, Southeast Asia, and South

Table 31–4   Representative Members of Genera Comprising the Poxviridae

Common Designation for Disease	Genus Designation	Host Affected
Rabbitpox	*Poxvirus*	Rabbits
Variola (smallpox)		Humans
Vaccinia		Calves, humans, sheep
Contagious pustular dermatitis	*Dermovirus*	Humans, sheep
Camelpox	*Pustulovirus*	Camels, humans
Horsepox		Horses, humans
Lumpy skin disease		Cattle
Fowlpox	*Avipoxvirus*	Chickens
Rabbit myxoma	*Fibromavirus*	Rabbits
Molluscum contagiosum	*Molluscovirus*	Humans

America, although sporadic outbreaks have occurred in various parts of Europe and North America. The disease still constitutes a potential public health problem because of increased travel to endemic regions by recently vaccinated or unvaccinated persons who may acquire the viral agent and upon their return disseminate the disease into a non-endemic country. Increased world trade is another important factor in the introduction of the disease into countries where smallpox is not endemic. Several outbreaks have been initiated by contaminated products. Other diseases, such as anthrax, and foot and mouth disease, also have been spread in this manner.

Transmission.   The etiologic agents of smallpox usually enter the body via the upper respiratory tract. The transmission of the disease can be accomplished through person-to-person contact or exposure to infected dust, contaminated articles, or secretions such as mucus, fluid from vesicles, or dried crusts containing virus. Insects of various types also have been implicated. Generally speaking, victims of smallpox are infectious at the end of the incubation period. Thus persons without any overt signs of disease can easily spread the virus to susceptible individuals.

Clinical features.   The incubation period of variola major ranges from 6 to 22 days, with the average period approximately 12 days. The sudden onset of the disease is accompanied by fever, headache, back pain, aching limbs, and general prostration. A pathognomonic diagnostic feature associated with this disease is a petechial "bathing drawers" rash occurring in the inguinal areas. The first lesions of the skin generally appear on the third to fifth day, at which time the temperature of the individual falls tem-

FIG. 31-8. Confluent smallpox. "Confluent" refers to situations in which lesions are extremely close together. This state is in contrast to "discrete" smallpox, in which lesions are farther apart. Certain patients may not exhibit any form of rash, but instead experience numerous hemorrhages in various regions of the body. Other victims may have both types of manifestations. (Photo Government Ivoirien, courtesy of the World Health Organization.)

porarily. These skin eruptions are macular, developing into papules and vesicles. Umbilication occurs later, followed by pustule and scab formation, effects begining about the twelfth day of the infection. The rash characteristically is most pronounced on the face, forearms, palms, soles, wrists, and in the mouth and throat regions of the infected individual (Figure 31-8).

Complications can develop, especially with bacterial secondary infections. Example of such complications include abscess formation, carbuncles, and osteomyelitis.

Variola minor or alastrim is much less severe in its effects than variola major. Convalescence is rapid and the mortality rate is under 0.5 per cent.

Laboratory diagnosis. Laboratory diagnosis of smallpox and/or serological surveys are directed toward the isolation or identification of the virus, the detection of viral antigens, or the demonstration of rising antibody titers in a patient's sera. The techniques used for these purposes are of great importance, especially in the early stages of an epidemic, and in cases of abortive or doubtful infections. Thus, diagnostic tests should produce accurate, easily interpreted results.

Smallpox can be diagnosed in the laboratory by the "four-test-combination" approach, which involves the combined use of electron microscopy, agar-gel precipitation, chorioallantoic membrane (CAM) inoculation (Figure 31–9), and tissue culture. The occasional shortcomings of one method are compensated for by the advantages of another. Naturally, adequate amounts of patient material should be on hand. Specimens should be obtained from maculopapular or vesicular types of lesions. Crust material is of little use.

The isolation of the infective viruses usually involves the inoculation of animals with clinical specimens, e.g., blood and scrapings from skin lesions. The technique of choice appears to be the inoculation of chick embryos, specifically their chorioallantoic membranes. Small gray-white pocks appear, usually within 2 to 3 days. These lesions are typical for both variola major and minor viruses. These pocks can be distinguished from the larger ones produced by vaccinia virus (Figure 31–9) as follows. Vaccinia virus produces large, opaque white pocks, usually with depressed centers. These lesions appear within 48 hours, whereas those caused by variola virus are barely evident at that time. It should be stressed that inoculation of chick embryos is of prime importance in distinguishing be-

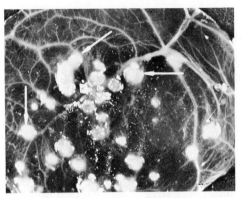

FIG. 31–9. Vaccinia virus-caused pocks (arrows) on the chorioallantoic membrane of a chick embryo. (Courtesy of the Armed Forces Institute of Pathology, Washington, D.C., Neg. No. AMS-1061–19.)

tween these two viruses. Immunological techniques including complement-fixation, immunofluorescence, and precipitation tests can be utilized to demonstrate the presence of viral antigens from inoculated chick embryos.

Immunity. Recovery from either variola major or alastrim virus infections usually produces a long-lasting natural active state of immunity to both of these agents. This resistance is believed to be dependent upon the antibody response of the individual to the antigen which is shared by several members of the poxviruses. It is because of the cross reactivity associated with this antigen that vaccinia virus can be utilized to produce an artificially acquired, active state of resistance against smallpox.

Prevention. Control measures in the case of smallpox include isolation and vaccination of recently exposed persons, proper sterilization of all articles contaminated by infected individuals, surveillance of contacts, and prophylactic vaccination. (Consult Chapter 26 for a discussion of vaccines and their administration.) Smallpox vaccination for European travel for visiting Americans is no longer required. Other changes in vaccination requirements are under consideration.

Vaccinia

The virulent and contagious nature of smallpox virus has limited investigations concerned with the pathogen. However, the closely related vaccinia virus was found not to pose such handling difficulties. For practical purposes, this viral agent is considered as the prototype of the poxvirus group. Vaccinia virus has gained importance primarily because of its use as the tool with which to determine the characteristics of poxviruses—their antigenic constitution, chemical composition, morphology, physical measurements, and replication cycle, and as the immunizing agent against smallpox.

Vaccinia virus does not occur in nature. The agent is maintained in the form of several laboratory strains. These viral preparations have a wide range of hosts and varying degrees of virulence, but a low level of virulence for humans. Two general categories of vaccinia strains have been established on the basis of viral tissue affinities in animals. These are the dermal and neural strains. The former is used for the production of smallpox vaccine.

QUESTIONS FOR REVIEW

1. Differentiate between the following terms:
   a. macule and pustule
   b. vesicle and scar
   c. maculopapule and crust
   d. ulcer and papule
   e. papule and pustule

2. Describe the various manifestations of *Herpesvirus hominis*. Are there any precipitating causes?

3. List at least two distinguishing characteristics of recurrent herpes as compared to primary herpes.

4. Compare the modes of transmission of the viral skin diseases discussed in this chapter. What control measures could be employed to limit infection?

5. What is the relationship between varicella and shingles?

6. What types of complications are associated with viral skin disease?

7. Differentiate between German measles and morbilli.

8. With which of the viral skin diseases discussed in this chapter is a laboratory diagnosis essential?

9. Can all viral pathogens cause congenital defects? Explain.

10. Which of the infections discussed in this chapter have you experienced?

11. Against which viral diseases of the skin are vaccines currently available?

12. Define or explain the following terms:
    a. vaccinia
    b. Lipschütz body
    c. variola major
    d. rubella syndrome
    e. alastrim
    f. herpetic whitlow
    g. morbilli
    h. verruca vulgaris
    i. poxvirus
    j. herpetic keratitis
    k. Koplik's spots

Infections and Disease States Affecting the Oral Regions

Structure of the Mouth

The oral cavity or mouth is situated at the beginning of the gastro-intestinal tract. This space is bounded laterally by the lips and cheeks, above by the hard and soft palates, and below by the floor of the mouth and the tongue. The lips are covered on the outside by skin and on the inside by mucous membrane. Small glands are present beneath the mucosa, and numerous muscle bundles are contained within the lips to allow their many movements. The red or vermillion of the lips is a transitional area between the outer skin and the inner "wet" mucous membrane (Figure 32–1).

The cheeks are lined by non-keratinizing mucous membrane which overlies the connective tissue, muscle, and the buccal (mouth) fat pad. The surface usually shows a slightly elevated, often lighter linear mark known as the bite line, which corresponds to the occlusal line at which the upper and lower teeth meet.

The palate or roof of the mouth is divided into an anterior hard and posterior soft palate. The former region is covered by a thick layer of firm but soft tissue which covers the palate bones. The soft palate connects with the pillars of the fauces (the passageway leading from the mouth to the throat). It is continuous with the tissues encircling the opening to the pharynx, and ends behind as a free

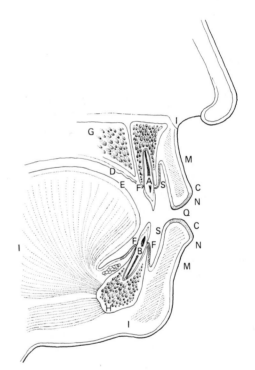

FIG. 32–1. Diagrammatic representation of a cross-section through the maxilla and mandible showing (a) a maxillary incisor, (b) a mandibular incisor, (c) the lips, (d) the palate with rugae, (e) the tongue, (f) the gingiva, (g) maxillary bone, (h) mandibular bone, (i) muscles, (m) skin, (n) junction of vermilion and skin, (q) vermilion of lip, and (s) the oral mucosa. (Courtesy of Dr. William B. Wescott. Modified from Sicher, H.: *Oral Anatomy*, C. V. Mosby Co., St. Louis, 1960.)

projection called the *uvula*. This structure is a small, fleshy mass hanging above the tongue and at the entrance to the oropharynx.

The floor of the mouth lies in a horse-shoe around the tongue, and is continuous laterally with the *gingiva* (the gum) (Figure 32–1) and centrally with the tongue. Near the anterior end are the openings of the submandibular and sublingual *salivary glands.* The tongue is a muscular organ which is attached at its posterior base and along the floor of the mouth. It is covered by a mucous membrane and four types of *lingual papillae* (projections) on its surface.

The human is supplied with two sets of teeth, the deciduous and the permanent. The former are the baby teeth or milk teeth. The deciduous teeth number 20, while the permanent group generally contains 32. Teeth are categorized into four groups, *incisors, canines, premolars* or *bicuspids,* and *molars.* Incisors are used for cutting food, canines for tearing food, and the latter two are grinders. Each tooth has three parts (Figure 32 –2); these are the *crown,* the portion above the gum; *root,* the structure embedded in the jaw; and *neck,* which is the constricted region between the crown and the root.

A tooth's crown is coated with *enamel*

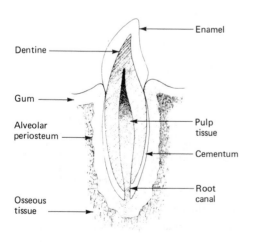

Dentine

Gum

Alveolar periosteum

Osseous tissue

Enamel

Pulp tissue

Cementum

Root canal

FIG. 32–2. The basic structure of a human tooth.

(the hardest substance found in the body) while the rest is covered by a layer of modified bone called the *cementum.* Under the enamel coating is an ivory-like tissue called *dentine.* It comprises the bulk of a tooth and is quite hard and striated. Within the dentine is a cavity, containing blood vessels, connective tissue, and nerve endings, called the *pulp chamber.* The contents of this chamber are frequently referred to as the *dental pulp.*

Teeth tend to be covered with a gummy accumulation of salivary mucin and bacteria, called the *dental plaque,* that may be visible to the naked eye.

The Oral Flora in Health

The mouth, being warm and moist and having a regular supply of fresh food introduced, makes an ideal growth chamber for microorganisms. The study of *oral ecology* (ecology is the relationship of an organism to its natural habitat and to other living creatures in that habitat) is both interesting and complex. If a sample of plaque-like material is taken from a tooth's surface and examined microscopically, a wide variety of bacteria are often seen (Figure 32–3). Many studies have been conducted in an attempt to decide which organisms, and in what concentration, predominate in the oral cavity. Perhaps the first of these was reported in 1690 by Leeuwenhoek. Using a microscope which he developed, he described several of the basic bacterial types of the mouth.

Generally, the organisms of the human mouth can be divided into three groups with regard to their tolerance of, or requirement for, oxygen—the strict anaerobes, strict aerobes, and the "facultatives." This last group encompasses all of the various gradations between the two extremes—all those which are able to

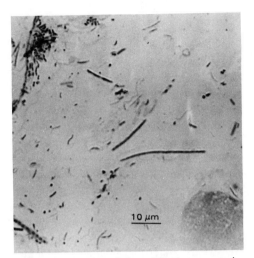

FIG. 32–3. Mixed oral flora. The long, granular organisms are *Leptotrichia*. A few rods, diplococci, and threadlike forms are also seen. (Courtesy of Dr. Richard Parker.)

tolerate some concentration of oxygen, from very high to very low.

The oral flora is relatively stable as to the types of organisms present. Although others may be introduced, perhaps with food, they are usually transients and seldom take up permanent residence.

Most of the basic groups of bacteria usually encountered in the oral flora are described in this section.

Bacteria in the Mouth

Streptococci

The organisms which, in sheer numbers, make up the largest bacterial group in the oral cavity are the Gram-positive streptococci. Streptococci can be isolated in great quantity from the tongue and saliva and in lesser numbers from tooth surfaces, plaque, and gingival areas. Characteristically, when grown in a carbohydrate-rich environment, they produce large amounts of organic acids. For this reason the pH of the mouth may drop considerably after the ingestion of food with a high sugar content.

The alpha hemolytic streptococci, or viridans group, are found in great numbers in the normal mouth and are a constant source of danger to persons who have suffered previous heart valve damage. During tooth extraction or other dental procedures (and sometimes during the food chewing process) viridans streptococci may enter the patient's bloodstream and lodge in the scarred heart valve tissue. In this rather inaccessible position they may grow and thrive, causing tissue damage and constantly threatening the individual with bacteremia (bacteria in the bloodstream). The beta streptococci are found in relatively small numbers and usually in the throat. Such streptococci are responsible for diseases including scarlet fever and "strep throat." The last group, the gamma-strep, seems to be least harmful to man. It should be noted, however, that the consequences of any streptococcal infection, even a mild one, may include the enlargement of lymph nodes and permanent kidney damage.

Lactobacilli

Related to the streptococci but morphologically quite distinct are the lactobacilli (Figure 32–4). These are Gram-positive, facultative, rod-shaped organisms which produce large quantities of organic acid from carbohydrate substrates. It is this latter fact upon which the Snyder test (Color photograph 44) is based.

The Snyder test. At a time when caries (teeth cavities) were thought to be caused by the presence of organic acids in the mouth the Snyder test was intended to be a caries index of an individual. The test calls for the inoculation of patient saliva into a low pH medium (4.7-5.0) containing a metabolizable carbohydrate (dextrose) and a dye, bromcresol green. This indicator changes color as the pH

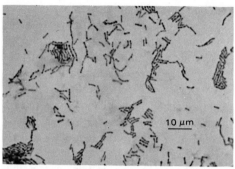

FIG. 32–4. A pure culture of lactobacilli. Note the polar staining in these organisms. (Courtesy of Dr. Richard Parker.)

of the medium varies. As organisms grow, the sugar is utilized, acid is produced, and the indicator dye is changed from blue-green to yellow (below pH 4.0). Theoretically, the lower the pH, the more organisms (usually lactobacilli) are present which could contribute to mouth acid and thence to caries. However, as scientists have moved away from the simple, one-cause answer to caries, the Synder test has lost some of its intended importance.

Neisseriaceae

Another major factor in the oral flora are the Gram-negative diplococci of the family Neisseriaceae. The organisms of its aerobic genus, *Neisseria,* are relatively nonpathogenic, except for two species which cause meningitis and gonorrhea. Members of the anaerobic genus *Veillonella* (Figure 6–29) are similar in appearance to *Neisseria* except that the cells are much smaller. These species are thought to be entirely nonpathogenic; however, they have been implicated in urogenital and central nervous system diseases. With appropriate techniques, both genera can be isolated from the saliva and oral surfaces. Recent studies have implicated a related organism in caries production, namely, *Branhamella catarrhalis.*

Actinomycetaceae

Filamentous forms make up a large portion of the tooth plaque material. This group includes the *Nocardia, Actinomyces,* and *Bacterionema.* All are Gram-positive and are characterized by the development of filaments which exhibit true branching. However, all are extremely pleomorphic and have been found, using fluorescent antibody techniques, to exist in the mouth as either coccus-like or short rod forms. The *Nocardia* and *Bacterionema* are aerobic to microaerophilic, while the *Actinomyces* are strictly anaerobic to microaerophilic. Several species have been implicated in disease processes within the body. These organisms can usually be isolated (often with difficulty) from plaques and other areas in the mouth which are not subject to adequate cleansing, such as the gingival sulcus (gum grooves) and between the teeth.

Leptotrichia

The *Leptotrichia* (Figure 32–3) are almost a family unto themselves. They are often included with the Actinomycetaceae even though they do not branch. Being highly anaerobic, they are quite fond of oral recesses and crevices, and can be recognized in smears as very thick, long, non-branching rods with rounded ends. However, they are somewhat pleomorphic and often exhibit bulb-like swellings at one end. In stained preparations they appear granular, and always have a buckshot appearance. Based on their cultural and biochemical characteristics, an attempt has been made to classify them with the family Lactobacillaceae.

Bacteroidaceae

The family Bacteroidaceae is represented by two main genera in the mouth, *Bacteroides* and *Fusobacterium.* Both are

Gram-negative and strictly anaerobic. The *Bacteroides* are short, poorly-staining rods which are found only in small percentages in healthy mouths. However, this percentage increases markedly when the normal oral environment is disturbed, as in *necrotizing ulcerative gingivitis* (N.U.G.). It cannot be said for certain whether this increase is due to the disease process, or whether the disease process is due to the increased number of organisms. It has been postulated that, since those organisms are Gram-negative, they may produce endotoxins and/or enzymes capable of causing severe inflammation in the tissues surrounding the teeth. This fact remains to be definitely proven.

What has been said regarding *Bacteroides* and N.U.G. can also be said for the fusobacteria. In fact, these microorganisms were one of the first to be noted as possible etiologic agents in Vincent's disease (trench mouth). On direct smear, fusobacteria are long, thin, Gram-negative rods with pointed ends. In culture, many of the species have a distinctive foul odor. They can easily be demonstrated in diseased mouths, or mouths with poor oral hygiene. Often these organisms may appear as long, twisting, Gram-negative filaments. It must be emphasized that all the members of this group are normal inhabitants of healthy mouths and any association with disease processes may be only coincidental, or a matter of environmental opportunity.

Diphtheroids (Corynebacteriaceae)

The diphtheroids (diphtheria-like) constitute a sizeable addition to the oral flora. In stained smears they can be seen as Gram-positive, club-shaped bacilli, which tend to orient themselves to one another in a manner suggestive of Chinese characters. The diphtheroids belong to the family Corynebacteriaceae, and are usually aerobic to microaerophilic. In certain stained preparations these cells often appear banded or beaded with metachromatic granules, a fact which can be used in their identification. *Corynebacterium diphtheriae* is the most important pathogen of this group. However, many avirulent corynebacteria are found as regular normal inhabitants of the mouth.

Treponemataceae

The family Treponemataceae contributes two genera, the *Borrelia* and the *Treponema,* to the oral environment. Both of these contain strict anaerobes that are highly motile. Treponemes are distinguished from the *Borrelia* by their more tightly coiled appearance and by the fact that they cannot be stained except with special procedures. For this reason, and because they are not visible in a wet mount under a light microscope, examination for their presence is usually done using dark field microscopy. Of the *Treponema,* perhaps the most notorious species is *T. pallidum,* the cause of syphilis in man. However, there are other species found in the mouth which are evidently nonpathogenic.

Borrelia (Figure 32–5), by contrast, can be stained with ordinary aniline dyes. Along with fusobacteria, *Borrelia* were named as possible etiologic factors in periodontal disease, since numbers of them can be found in afflicted individuals. However, no direct relationship between the *Borrelia* and N.U.G. has been proved. Both of these organisms are part of the normal oral flora, although they may not always be demonstrable in all individuals.

Mycoplasma (PPLOs)

Mycoplasma, or PPLOs (PleuroPneumonia-Like Organisms), also have been isolated from many areas of the human

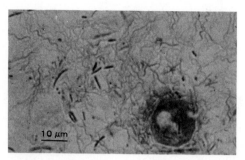

FIG. 32–5. Necrotizing ulcerative gingivitis. This smear was taken from a patient suffering from Vincent's infection. Note the large numbers of *Borrelia* and a variety of other cells. The large dark cell is a phagocytic inflammatory cell. (Courtesy of Dr. N. H. Rickles, Pathology Department, University of Oregon Dental School.)

mouth. Though some oral disease has been attributed to them, their pathogenicity has been questioned. More research is needed in this area.

Microorganisms Other than Bacteria

Although bacteria are the most obvious inhabitants of the oral cavity, many other microorganisms are often seen. These include several species of fungi, viruses, and protozoa.

Of the fungi, probably those most commonly found are of the genus *Candida*. It has been estimated that in approximately 40 per cent of the "normal" population these organisms can be cultivated from saliva. In a healthy mouth, they make up only a small percentage of the total oral flora. However, in children, the aged, and the debilitated, these organisms are of major importance. Frequently, *Candida* infections of the oral tissues follow heavy patient dosage with antibiotics. This is undoubtedly due to the change in the bacterial population and the resulting imbalance in oral ecology. (See the section on oral fungal diseases.)

Viruses, both human and bacterial, have been recovered from the oral cavity. The causative organisms of herpes sim-

plex and of measles can be found in oral lesions during obvious disease. Little is known regarding the place of viruses in the normal ecology of the human mouth. Undoubtedly, many types could be isolated if research efforts were directed to this area.

Concluding Points Concerning Oral Flora (Microbiota)

The oral cavity of the fetus is essentially germ-free until it passes through the birth canal. At this time microorganisms are derived from many sources and include lactobacilli, micrococci, alpha and gamma anaerobic streptococci, coliforms, corynebacteria, yeasts, viruses, and protozoa from the vaginal and urogenital tract. Staphylococci and pneumococci may be added from the air. As soon as feeding begins many more organisms are added along with those gained from contact with people and new environments. The oral flora persists for the life of the individual and is subject to change with the aging process. The organisms present at any one time exist in balance with one another, and any change in this balance may result in disease. Attempts to study the oral microbiota in the laboratory have proved most difficult, since duplication of the environment is almost impossible. Mixed culture studies have yielded some information, but to date no one has developed a system capable of duplicating the multivaried environments required by oral microorganisms.

Non-Specific Infections of the Oral Regions

Infections of the face, oral cavity, and neck may be extremely serious, depending upon their location and the microorganisms involved. Specific infections caused by bacteria, fungi, or viruses may occur here, as well as in other sites in the body. More commonly, mixed bacterial infections are seen either in association with deep cavities in teeth, or as a result of tissue injury. Keeping these thoughts in mind, consideration will be given to selected oral disease conditions.

Dry Socket

This term simply means that the blood clot which formed following the removal of a tooth has been dislodged and lost from the extraction site, thus exposing the bone and allowing some degree of infection to develop. Any of the following factors have been implicated as causes of dry socket: (1) contamination of the area during extraction; (2) excessive injury, such as crushing the surrounding tissues; (3) extended surgical procedures followed by inadequate clotting of blood; (4) rinsing the mouth with hot fluids; (5) vigorous rinsing and dislodging of the clot; (6) lowered resistance of the tissues due to local or systemic disease of the patient; (7) mechanical loosening of the clot by chewing rough food and forcing it into the socket; and (8) implanting of bacteria or foreign material, resulting in an infection.

The bony walls of the socket often become necrotic, and infiltrated with bacteria of many types. A foul odor also develops. The soft tissues in the region commonly are swollen, inflamed, and have a slough (a mass of dead tissue) along the margin nearest the socket. Severe pain is experienced.

Treatment. Treatment usually involves flushing the debris and bacteria from the socket and removing the dead tissue slough. A dressing is placed over the area which will cover the bony walls and prevent further bacterial growth. Healing of the lesion is slow and must progress from the deepest part of the socket to the

surface. Otherwise, deep pockets of infection may remain, allowing bacteria to spread through the relatively loose meshwork of the alveolar bone and produce an osteomyelitis.

Osteomyelitis

Inflammation of the bone (*osteo*) marrow (*myelo*) may occur from the introduction of many different types of bacteria either as pure or mixed cultures. The resulting infection leads to inflammation, cellular degeneration, and necrosis of the tissues involved, often including the bone (osteitis) and the *periosteum* or surrounding membrane (periostitis).

Several different factors may cause osteomyelitis. These include: (1) infected or gangrenous pulps; (2) traumatically implanted foreign material accompanied by contaminating microorganisms; (3) severe infections of the maxillary sinus (Figure 32–6); (4) residual infections following the extraction of teeth; (5) severe periodontal disease, with extension of the infection to bone; (6) many forms of traumatic injury; and (7) specific infections such as tuberculosis, syphilis, or actinomycosis.

The disease may be acute or chronic, depending upon many factors, such as

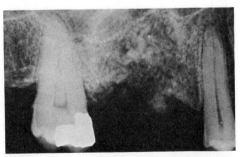

FIG. 32–6. Chronic osteomyelitis involving the maxilla. A draining sinus was present on the gingiva between the molar and bicuspid. This radiograph demonstrates the moth-eaten appearance of the bone. (Courtesy of Dr. N. H. Rickles Pathology Department, University of Oregon Dental School.)

the type and number of organisms involved, their virulence, and the age and resistance of the host. Manifestations of the infection usually include severe pain, elevated temperature, and swollen lymph nodes (lymphadenopathy) associated with the area. In addition, the teeth in the area may be loose, resulting in pain and difficulty in eating. Thus the patient's nutritional status also can be affected.

Tuberculous osteomyelitis.   Although rare, this disease may be seen in patients with advanced tuberculosis. Tubercle bacilli may enter the bone following trauma or tooth extraction, or via the blood stream (hematogenous spread). Generally, the mandible is involved with the development of swelling, suppuration (pus formation), and sequestration (deposition of devitalized bone). This condition is described in another portion of this chapter.

Syphilitic osteomyelitis.   This disease can occur in both the congenitally acquired and tertiary forms of syphilis (see Chapter 37). Quite frequently the palate is involved and may be perforated. The mandible may be extensively affected by syphilitic osteomyelitis, causing pain, swelling, suppuration, and necrosis. This syphilitic form can be differentiated from those produced more commonly by other bacteria. It has a more progressive course, and generally does not improve following the usual treatment with anti-syphilitic drugs.

In severe cases of osteomyelitis of the mandible, fracture of the bone may result.

For many years, surgical intervention coupled with the administration of antibiotics was the major form of treatment. However, in recent years reports have appeared indicating that antibiotic therapy alone is sufficient.

The complication of osteomyelitis following mandibular fractures has become a relatively rare occurrence, due to antibiotics. However, cases are occasionally reported which illustrate the ever-present problem of infections caused by resistant strains of bacteria, notably the staphylococci.

Pericoronitis and Cellulitis

Infections may begin in a flap of tissue overlying an erupting tooth and around an impacted or partially erupted third molar. This periocoronitis, or inflammation (-*itis*) around (*peri-*) the crown (*coronal*), of the tooth may spread into the surrounding tissues, resulting in a cellulitis, or diffuse inflammation of the soft tissues. The bacteria involved here produce large amounts of hyaluronidase and fibrinolysins, enzymes capable of breaking down tissue cohesiveness, thus allowing the spread of the infection. Many such spreading infections are caused by streptococci. Cellulitis may follow any procedure which permits microorganisms to enter deeper tissues. Examples include infections following extractions, and the introduction of organisms into these regions by contaminated instruments.

As an infection spreads, the entire face on the side involved swells and the firm tissues may become discolored. Generally, the advanced, diffuse infections tend to form a localized pocket which often will erupt or "point" to the nearest surface and begin draining. Early treatment will usually prevent this, although in severe cases the surgeon must incise and drain the area, as well as treat the original cause of the cellulitis.

Periodontal Disease

The diseases of the tissues surrounding and supporting the teeth, gingivitis and periodontitis in their many forms, can be grouped under the general heading of periodontal disease. However, certain educators and investigators would like to reserve this term for one particular type of oral disorder, one which is perhaps more serious and involves the supportive structures and tissues around the tooth. As in all specialty areas there are a great number of divisions and subdivisions for each disease. However, for our purposes in might be well to view all of these diseases as examples of one phenomenon, a continuum from normal to simple gingivitis to acute periodontitis. Quite often the diagnosis is based upon the severity of the disease (Figure 32–7).

Clinical features. Periodontal disease is a worldwide affliction of humans which clinically appears as an inflammation of the soft tissues around the teeth. The disease may affect all of the tissues around the teeth, or it may involve only one area, or a few isolated areas. In the advanced stages, destruction of cementum and periodontal membrane accompanied by loss of alveolar bone occurs (Figure 32–8). The net result is the formation of a pocket between the root and the overlying soft tissue, usually with marked inflammatory changes and exudation of pus. Unfortunately for the patient, there are few clinical symptoms, and the disease progresses relentlessly until the teeth are lost. In people over 35 years of age, this disease—not dental decay—is the major source of tooth loss.

Etiology. It is quite possible that no one case or factor is responsible for the infection, but rather many factors acting in concert. Several of the currently held views concerning this question are as follows.

One hypothesis, favors the view that periodontal disease is not caused by a particular bacterial species, but rather, results from certain enzymatic and related activities of organisms in intimate contact with tissues surrounding teeth. It is well known that food, debris, and bacteria

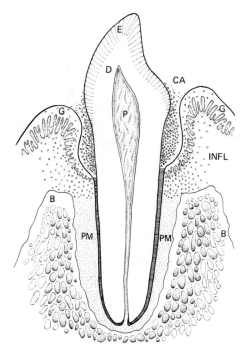

FIG. 32–7. Diagrammatic representation of periodontal disease. The specific tooth components and the manifestations associated with them are (E) tooth enamel, (D) dentin, (P) pulp, (PM) periodontal membrane, (C) cementum, (G) gingival tissue, showing inflammation, swelling, and loss of stippling, and (CA) plaque and calculus extending down the root, creating a market inflammatory reaction with resultant loss of bone (B). A purulent exudate could be expressed from the pocket. (Courtesy of Dr. N. H. Rickles, Pathology Department, University of Oregon Dental School.)

collect in the area of the gingival sulcus (groove). Here, microbial growth and reproduction may go on unhampered by ordinary cleansing procedures. During such processes several bacteria produce extracellular enzymes capable of attacking proteins and carbohydrates. In addition, Gram-negative organisms in this area may be a source of endotoxins. The total effects of all of these compounds upon human tissues is not known.

In recent years the roles of dental plaque and calculus (Figure 32–9) in the overall process have been studied.

FIG. 32–8. Almost total destruction of the bone surrounding this lower molar has occurred as a manifestation of periodontal disease. Clinically the patient has a periodontal abscess with swelling and acute inflammation. (Courtesy of Dr. N. H. Rickles, Pathology Department, University of Oregon Dental School.)

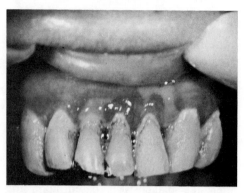

FIG. 32–9. Gingivitis. Note the severe involvement of the gingiva around the anterior teeth. The teeth also have heavy plaque and calculus present. (Courtesy of Dr. N. H. Rickles, Pathology Department, University of Oregon Dental School.)

Clinical observations support the fact that there is a definite relation between these entities and periodontal disease. The crowns of extracted teeth, when examined histologically, show an almost constant presence of an acquired cuticle. The cuticle is acellular, essentially bacteria-free, 0.3 to 0.8 μm thick, and consists of modified salivary muco- or glycoproteins together with some lipid material.

Plaque formation is of great importance, especially since it may well be the initiator of dental decay as well as periodontal disease. Certain studies have demonstrated plaque development on the cuticle and the accumulation and growth of microorganisms beginning as early as the second day. Another study demonstrated that bacteria may attach directly to the enamel without having the cuticle present. In either event, bacteria aggregate in large numbers in such regions. The early bacterial forms seen are coccoid, with increasing numbers of filamentous forms appearing as the age of the plaque increases (Figure 32–10). In mature calculus the filamentous forms account for approximately 40 percent of the bacteria grown from this material.

FIG. 32–10. A scanning electron micrograph of human dental plaque material taken from the gum line (cementum-enamel junction). The corncob structures seen are composed of streptococci adhering to a central filamentous organism. (Courtesy of Dr. Z. Skobe, Forsyth Dental Center.)

A number of studies in experimentally produced gingivitis in man showed that the early plaque bacteria essentially represented a proliferation of the resident Gram-positive cocci and rods, with streptococci, neisseria, and nocardiae soon followed by a proliferation of fusobacteria and filamentous bacteria. In the final phase, spirilla and spirochetes appeared to complete the complex flora. It has

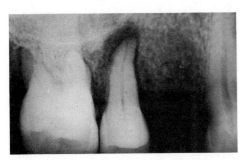

FIG. 32–11. The very dark area at the apex and along the root surface of the tooth represents total destruction of the normal tissue. The area is an abscess which drains to the surface along the side of the tooth. Calculus is evident between the bicuspid and molar. Note that the teeth are free from evidence of decay. (Courtesy of Dr. N. H. Rickles, Pathology Department, University of Oregon Dental School.)

been suggested that the early growth of aerobes and the build-up of plaque may be necessary to provide a suitable environment for the growth of anaerobes. The latter organisms seem to predominate in older plaque. The result is that large numbers of bacteria are in apposition with the gingival tissues, and the rough, ragged calculus further increases the irritation to the periodontium (supporting tissue surrounding teeth).

Calculus is an almost constant companion of periodontal disease and is considered by many to be the major etiologic factor in its development (Figure 32–11). Clinically, calculus is a hard, calcified substance which adheres firmly to the teeth, or to appliances worn in the mouth. The external environment coupled with systemtic factors of the host apparently determine whether the plaque will calcify or become associated with dental decay. Calcification of plaque begins in numerous foci which enlarge and coalesce to form large areas of calculus. The calcifying plaques have a relatively high calcium and phosphorus content even in the very early stages. The external surface is usually very rough and irregular and in radiographs often appears as small, wedge-shaped spurs in the interproximal area.

The possibility that certain types of periodontal lesions in humans are virus-induced has been suggested. Another possible etiologic mechanism involved in the production of periodontal disease is that of allergic inflammation produced by bacterial antigens in gingival tissues. Antibody-containing plasma cells accumulate in tissues with experimentally induced allergy. These cells tend to accumulate in human gingival tissue. This finding may well be related to the introduction of several antigens from the multitudes of bacteria within the gingival crevice.

Several other conditions or states have been considered as having some role in the etiology of periodontal disease. Implicated in the disease process are factors of a local type such as faulty toothbrushing, food impaction, habits which traumatize tissue (e.g., improper use of dental floss or toothpicks and mouthbreathing), malformed teeth, malocclusion (poor closure of the jaws), and factors of a systemic or general nature, including allergies, drug intake, endocrine function, the genetic make-up of the individual, nutrition, and psychic disturbances. This brief discussion demonstrates the complicated nature of the process and paves the way for a consideration of some of the clinical findings resulting from the complex interplay of the clinical findings resulting from the complex interplay of etiologic factors.

Gingivitis

This condition is defined as an inflammation of the gingiva (that portion of the oral mucous membrane which surrounds a tooth). Such involvement of the marginal gingiva is the most common disease affecting the soft tissues of the oral cavity. If the inflammatory process is not interrupted, it is progressive and eventually results in severe periodontal disease.

Improper or inadequate oral hygiene is probably responsible for most gingivitis, since remnants of food attract and lodge bacteria and provide good culture media for them. Gingivitis also may begin as a result of food impaction between malposed teeth, or around teeth badly broken down by caries.

Clinical features. Tissue changes result from the body's primary defense in response to irritation, and to exudative inflammation. The gingiva are swollen by edema, reddened from engorgement of blood vessels, and bleed easily due to loss of *tissue tonus,* i.e., slight, continuous contraction of muscles. The tissue is shiny or glossy and the normal stippling is lost. A purulent exudate can usually be expressed from the sulcus.

Necrotizing Ulcerative Gingivitis (N.U.G.)

This disease is also commonly called Vincent's infection or trench mouth, a name it earned during World War I due to its common occurrence among soldiers. The outbreaks of N.U.G. among soldiers, and in other crowded groups under emotional or physical stress, convinced many clinicians that it was an infectious and communicable disease. Recently a number of studies have concluded that N.U.G. is not a communicable disease and it is no longer required to be reported by physicians and dentists.

The infection is essentially found among adolescents and young adults. Fatigue and anxiety evidently play a most important role in the predisposition of the oral cavity to this necrotizing lesion. Other systemic forms of stress such as severe deficiency diseases and debilitating illnesses also appear to lower the resistance of the oral tissues to this disease.

All of these factors may be intimately related to the changes which occur in the adrenal cortex during periods of stress.

Increases in the corticosteroid output are followed by a sharp and prolonged decrease in the number of circulating lymphocytes and in a marked depression of the circulatory antibody titer. It would seem that stress in any form may result in a sharp decrease in the ability of the tissues to overcome and neutralize the effects of the powerful and destructive antigens in the tissues around the teeth. In addition, local irritations such as deep gingival pockets, calculus, or overhanging fillings are also important in establishing a favorable environment for the disease.

Many types of organisms have been indicated as causative agents of N.U.G., but the exact cause is still undetermined. As *Fusobacterium fusiforme* and the spirochete *Borrelia vincentii* increase in numbers during the manifestation, they have been incriminated as factors in the etiology of the disease. However, these organisms are present in the healthy mouth and may be only secondary invaders in the diseased tissues.

The infection can be a mixed one, characterized by a necrotizing process which may involve the gingivae as Vincent's infection, the oral mucosa as Vincent's stomatitis, or extend to the pharynx as Vincent's angina.

Clinical features. In the acute phase of N.U.G. general pain, malaise, and fever of 100 to 101°F are evident. The interdental papillae (projections) are markedly involved early (Figure 32–12) and show sloughing, ulceration, and bleeding, with subsequent exposure of the connective tissues and pain. Necrotic material remains between the teeth and these patients complain of a fetid odor and foul or metallic taste. The bleeding further entraps material as clotting takes place

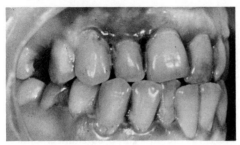

FIG. 32–12. Trench mouth or N.U.G. The clinical appearance of Vincent's infection with "punched-out" necrotic papillae (projections) accompanied by swollen and inflammed gingiva. (Courtesy of Dr. Francis Howell, Pathology Department, University of Oregon Dental School.)

and a pseudomembrane forms. This newly formed structure contains extravasated blood, dead epithelial cells, neutrophilic leukocytes, salivary materials, food debris, and microorganisms. The clotted blood serves as an excellent culture medium for the growth of bacteria with their associated toxins.

These areas continue a cycle of sloughing, hemorrhage, formation of the pseudomembrane with microorganisms, deterioration, necrosis, and sloughing, as a self-propagating form of the disease. The interdental papillae give the appearance of being punched out as a result of the above processes. In long-standing severe cases the papillae do not reform but remain as depressed, trough-like areas. Furthermore, in severe cases where the lesions progress, even the bone is affected and the bordering bone in interproximal areas is rapidly destroyed by the virulent toxins released into the necrotic debris. The craters that remain in the bone and gingiva after healing permit trapping and impaction of food between the teeth. This in turn may lead to calculus formation, periodontal disease, and eventually to the return of N.U.G.

Treatment. The treatment for N.U.G. is essentially the same as for other types of gingivitis, with removal of any irritating material and cleansing being the most important aspects. Careful scaling, scraping, and polishing of the teeth with the removal of all irritating factors is essential. Antibiotics should be used cautiously, since they suppress the process temporarily but do not eliminate it. Obviously, adequate nutrition and rest should also be prescribed. The important point here is that the disease will recur in either the acute or chronic form if all local irritating factors are not considered in the control of the acute manifestations of N.U.G.

Periodontitis

Inflammation of the periodontium is the direct result of untreated gingivitis. A common synonym for the condition is *pyorrhea*.

Clinical features. Clinically the gingiva is inflamed, enlarged, smooth, glistening red or cyanotic (bluish-red), and bleeds easily. Additional effects include increased depth of the sulcus and a loss of bone around the teeth, with the result that they may loosen in advanced cases. Radiographs show loss of the bordering portion of interproximal bone, and these areas are blunted. Spurs of calculus are often seen in the interproximal spaces. As destruction of the bone progresses, bone loss in bifurcation (two-branches) and trifurcation (three-branches) between the roots of the teeth near the crown may be seen (Figure 32–13). In very severe cases all of the supporting tissues around the tooth may be lost and the tooth may spontaneously dislodge. These very deep pockets contain large numbers of microorganisms and initiate periodontal abscess formation, with considerable swelling and pain.

Unfortunately, in many cases the disease is chronic with few symptoms. The patient really is unaware that anything

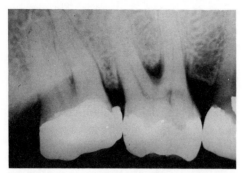

FIG. 32–13. Radiograph showing periodontal disease. The bifurcation of the roots of the first and second molar show bone destruction. There is an overhanging restoration on the second molar which may result in interproximal inflammation and bone loss. (Courtesy of Dr. N. H. Rickles, Pathology Department, University of Oregon Dental School.)

so serious is wrong. Many cases are not discovered until it is too late to save the patient's teeth and they must all be extracted. It is somewhat ironic that people blessed with teeth free from cavities quite often have severe periodontal disease since they may seldom or never see a dentist or hygienist to have the calculus and debris removed from their teeth.

Treatment. The treatment of periodontal disease will vary widely, depending upon the degree of involvement of the patient's tissues at the time of examination. In treating periodontal disease, certain principles are kept in mind, such as correcting dietary and improper oral hygiene habits, eliminating all irritating and trauma-inducing factors which are damaging to the periodontal tissues, and restoring the proper form and function to the teeth.

Dental Caries

Tooth decay is a worldwide problem, although not all areas and peoples are affected equally. Factors which influence the incidence of caries include climate, composition and quantity of saliva, hormonal balance, nutritional balance, oral

hygiene, the fluoride level in the drinking water, and diet, and race, to name a few. The following discussion will be limited essentially to the role of bacteria in dental caries formation.

Dental caries is a disease of the calcified tissues of the teeth and is characterized by a decalcification (loss of calcium salts) of the inorganic substance, either followed or accompanied by a disintegration of the organic portion. The etiology is complex, and considerable controversy has existed regarding the exact mechanism of caries development. The development of dental decay in teeth is the result of an interaction between the host tissues and extremely specific cariogenic (caries-producing) microorganisms utilizing a suitable substrate provided by the individual's diet.

The streptococci produce extracellular polysaccharides from sucrose which enable them to adhere to one another and thus form colonies on the tooth's surface. Their extracellular product forms the plaque matrix of dextrans and some levans. All bacteria known to cause decay on smooth surfaces of teeth are plaque-formers and also are known to secrete the complex polysaccharides which are derived chiefly from sucrose (table sugar). The plaque-forming ability of oral bacteria can be assessed by testing their ability to produce adhesive microbial deposits on wires immersed in a growth medium containing 5 percent sucrose (Figure 32–14). The streptococci are not the only bacteria known to synthesize polysaccharides, but they are the only ones that form plaque. Only those large molecules of dextran and levan with molecular weights too high to be soluble have the gumminess that makes plaque adhere to smooth surfaces. Several bacteria synthesize only smaller, lighter varieties of dextran.

Three polysaccharide-producing streptococci are found in large numbers in hu-

FIG. 32–14. *In vitro* plaque formation in a growth medium that contains 5 percent sucrose. The tube on the left shows the wire and the early growth and adherence of plaque-forming organisms. The tube on the right shows the growth after several days. Note the increased accumulation of organisms. (Courtesy of M. L. Freedman and J. M. Tanzer.)

mans: *Streptococcus mutans, Streptococcus sanguis,* and *Streptococcus salivarius* (Color photograph 46). Both water-soluble and insoluble polysaccharides may be produced by them. Various experiments have demonstrated that these streptococci and certain others, whether of human or rat origin, can produce tooth decay in germ-free rats. Attempts to produce caries in germ-free rats with *Streptococcus lactis, S. fecalis var. zymogenes, Lactobacillus acidophilus,* and *L. fermenti* have not been successful. The bacteria work inward on the tooth from the enamel to the dentin (Figure 32–15).

Once the bacteria reach the pulp of the tooth (Figure 32–15*C*) a soft tissue infection occurs and if untreated soon involves the entire root canal and apical area (Figure 32–15*D*). As long as the pulp chamber is exposed to the environment so that drainage may occur, or if the host resistance is high, or the virulence of the organism is low, then a dental granuloma may occur at the apex of the involved root. The granuloma is essentially chronically inflamed tissue, which may or may not contain bacteria.

Sometimes the bacteria remain within the root canal. Their toxic products, along with tissue breakdown substances, create a source of chronic irritation to the tissue. If the infection becomes acute and cannot drain through the tooth we may clinically see a *gum-boil* or *parulis* (Figure 32–16), a sinus tract with an opening onto the skin, or an enlarged fluctuant mass of pus. These patients often are quite ill, with elevated temperature, loss of appetite, considerable pain, and general malaise. These infections may lead to osteomyelitis, cellulitis, bacteremia, or other conditions previously discussed.

On occasion the acute infection may gradually revert to a chronic infection and then the patient experiences few symptoms. Chronic irritation may stimulate the epithelium, left in the tissues as remnants during development, resulting in a *radicular cyst* (Figure 32–17) which will slowly enlarge at the expense of the surrounding tissues. These cystic lesions may become secondarily infected resulting in an acute infection.

Treatment and prevention. Dental decay and the defects produced by caries can be treated and the tooth restored to proper form and function in most cases. In recent years more and more effort has been expended on preventive measures which could eliminate this costly and

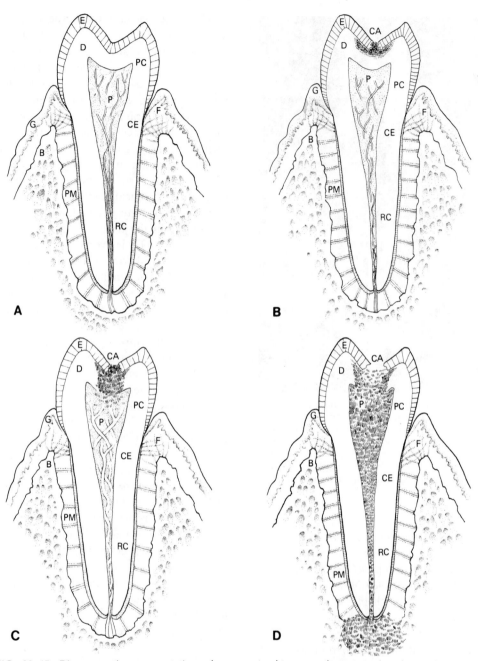

FIG. 32–15. Diagrammatic representation of a section through a pre-molar tooth, showing the progress of decay on the occlusal (chewing) surface. _A_. A normal tooth and its surrounding tissues. _B_. A carious lesion on the occlusal surface. _C_. The decay has passed through the dentin into the pulp, which has become inflammed, with many engorged vessels. _D_. The decay has spread to involve the tissues around the end of the root. At this stage there is a dental granuloma with some destruction of bone. Symbols: (E) enamel barrier, (D) dentin, (G) gingiva, (C) cementum, (P) pulp tissue, (PC) pulp chamber and canal, (RC) root canal, (B) alveolar bone, (PM) periodontal membrane; (F) fibers, (CE) cemento-enamel junction, (CA) carious lesion. (Courtesy of Dr. William B. Wescott, Pathology Department, University of Oregon Dental School.)

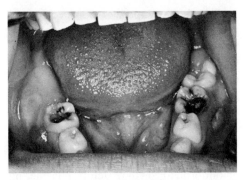

FIG. 32–16. Bilateral "gum-boils" in a child with extensive caries of the primary second molars. The dark areas of the teeth represent advanced caries which have infected the pulp. Note the pus-containing swelling on the gingiva adjacent to these teeth. (Courtesy of Dr. N. H. Rickles, Pathology Department, University of Oregon Dental School.)

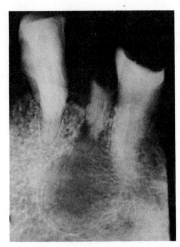

FIG. 32–17. A radicular cyst within a bone associated with the badly broken-down, decayed, and infected lateral tooth. (Courtesy of Dr. N. H. Rickles, Pathology Department, University of Oregon Dental School.)

often painful disease of humans. At present plaque is most effectively eliminated by mechanical means such as brushing and flossing. However, effective plaque control by these means is time-consuming and is generally achieved only by patients who are above average in dental knowledge, motivation, and manual dexterity. An anti-plaque chemotherapeutic agent contained in an easy-to-use, palatable vehicle would make effective oral hygiene easily attainable. Such a drug could drastically reduce the prevalence of periodontal disease while increasing the reduction of dental caries already generated by fluorides.

Chlorhexidine gluconate, which can prevent plaque formation, shows promise as a potential plaque-control drug. The anti-bacterial action of Chlorhexidine gluconate has received considerable attention in the past few years. The chemical has not been widely available to investigators in the United States. Most of the reported research has been carried out in Europe. Chlorhexidine's mode of action for plaque control is total suppression of the oral flora to prevent bacterial coloni-

zation on the tooth surface. Before it can be considered for long-term plaque control, however, the chemical must be thoroughly investigated for possible undesirable, if not harmful, side effects, including possible effects resulting from the total suppression of oral microflora.

At present there is no chemotherapeutic agent that can be safely administered for long-term control of bacterial plaque. Antibiotic compounds can be considered only for short-term plaque control due to their systemic side effects and limited spectrum of activity. All other compounds are limited in their usefulness due to: (1) local or systemic side effects that are unpleasant or toxic, (2) lack of clinically significant effectiveness, and/or (3) inadequate experimental evidence.

Mechanical cleansing of the teeth is a most important factor. If all adherent material is removed by proper toothbrushing and careful use of dental floss, decay will not occur. However, there are areas which are difficult to clean, and periodic prophylaxis by the dentist or hygenist is needed.

Numerous chemicals have been used in attempts to eliminate or reduce the numbers of bacteria, change the flora to harmless non-acid formers, inhibit enzyme activity, and alter the tooth surface. One of the most popular but controversial compounds is sodium fluoride. This material has been shown to have significant effects on caries incidence without causing ill effects in the person when taken in proper amounts. Many other compounds, including sodium phytate, dibasic sodium phosphate, and sodium metabisulfite, as well as numerous antibiotics, are also being tested.

Focal Infections

A localized area of infection within the oral tissues or elsewhere is called a *focus of infection*. When organisms or their toxic products spread from this focus to distant tissues, either to form another site of infection or to produce a hypersensitive reaction, the process is known as a *focal infection*.

The concept of focal infection has had a long and stormy history. Shortly after the concept was introduced, medical and dental practitioners enthusiastically condemned infected teeth and oral tissues as the cause of many unexplained conditions within the body. The criteria used to justify the extraction of teeth and related procedures were based upon subjective clinical experiences. Consequently, countless thousands of teeth were sacrificed to the cause. Then the pendulum swung too far to the other side, and the oral regions were almost ignored as a source of focal infection. At present, certain conditions are known to be related to oral foci of infection. The importance of good oral hygiene, along with elimination of infection, is considered an important part of restoring and maintaining good health.

Selected examples of nonspecific oral foci of infection include those existing in the periodontium or supporting structures of the teeth, such as gingivitis, periodontal disease, and necrotizing ulcerative gingivitis or Vincent's infection (trench mouth), and dental caries (Figure 32–18) and the resultant changes in the tissues from infected teeth, including abscesses and apical granulomas (a form of tumorous growth). Before considering these foci of infection mention should be given to certain specific effects attributed to them.

Rheumatic Heart Disease and Sub-Acute Bacterial Endocarditis (SBE)

Relationships have been known to exist between many diseases, including those of the eye, skin, gastro-intestinal tract, bones and joints, and heart. One of the most important disease conditions related to oral foci of infection is subacute bacterial endocarditis. The management of patients with a history of rheumatic heart disease has become increasingly important in the practice of dentistry. Heart valves which have been scarred by rheumatic fever are readily implanted with

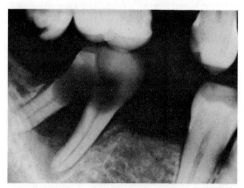

FIG. 32–18. The lower molar tooth shows a crown almost completely destroyed by caries. There is a large area of bone destruction between the roots of the molar, indicating severe periodontal disease in this area. (Courtesy of Dr. N. H. Rickles, Pathology Department, University of Oregon Dental School.)

bacteria, which can lodge in the irregular recesses and roughened portions of the valve cusps. Less commonly, endocarditis may develop in valves altered by congenital malformations, infections other than rheumatic fever, and roughened irregular areas resulting from arteriosclerosis. Contrary to the popular belief that rheumatic heart disease is practically restricted to the young of the lower income groups in cold, wet countries, it is a disease of universal distribution, found in all climates, races, and social strata and at all ages.

Subacute endocarditis may be a very serious complication of any dental procedure which allows bacteria to enter the bloodstream of a patient with heart valve damage. Bacteremia commonly results from extractions, endodontics, gingival surgical procedures, or from deep scaling (removing infected material from the tooth's surface) and currettage (removal of material by means of scraping). Any manipulation of infected or inflammatory vascular tissues within gingiva, or even chewing, can open small capillaries or force microorganisms into the bloodstream. The greater the trauma of manipulation, the greater the incidence of bacteremia.

Reports of many cases have been published which forcefully demonstrate the real danger of so-called simple manipulative procedures, not involving surgery, and their potential in causing subacute bacterial endocarditis. The patients involved often had heart murmurs which were not made known to the dentist. Consequently, they did not receive prophylactic antibiotics prior to the treatment. Endocarditis has developed following root canal therapy, periodontal treatment, and deep scaling and prophylaxis, as a result of the bacteremia created by these procedures. Fortunately,

these showers of bacteria are disposed of by the defense mechanisms of the body except when the valves are irregular and misshapen as a result of prior disease.

Extensive periodontal treatment and multiple extractions should be avoided in rheumatic heart disease patients. It is critical that any individual with this condition or other predisposing disease be made aware of the problem and every effort made to prevent the need for extensive oral manipulative procedures. If extractions are necessary, only one tooth should be extracted at a time, the exposed crown and root surface should be as clean as possible, and the patient should receive prophylactic penicillin treatment. Sterilization of the dried gingival sulcus (groove) with 2 per cent iodine may also be of value.

For many years only 20 to 30 per cent of all cases of bacterial endocarditis were caused by beta hemolytic streptococci, the *Streptococcus viridans* microaerophilics, and enterococci. These organisms now account for approximately 45 per cent of all cases. In recent years there has been an increase in the frequency of this disease state caused by penicillin-resistant staphylococci, Gramnegative organisms, and certain fungi.

Clinical features. Bacterial or vegetative endocarditis is a severe infection. It is characterized by a prolonged septic febrile course, a changing cardiac murmur, and the growth of bulky, bacterial "vegetations" on the heart valves. These accumulations consist of irregular, amorphous, tangled masses of fibrin strands, platelets, and blood cell debris along with the bacterial masses.

Vegetations vary in size and hang from the free margin of the valve cusps as friable, irregular masses (Figure 32–19), which may cause perforation of the

FIG. 32–19. Vegetative bacterial endocarditis of the aortic valve, with massive friable masses involving the valve leaflets. (Courtesy of Dr. N. H. Rickles, Pathology Department, University of Oregon Dental School.)

valve cusps or erosion of adjacent tissues. Furthermore, vegetations may undergo a progressive fibrosis and organization as scar tissue, which may exentually calcify. Patients also may develop uncontrolled infections by resistant organisms, which usually terminate in death. The mitral valve (the valve interconnects the left atrium and ventricle of the heart) and the aortic valve are most commonly affected. In congenitally deformed hearts, the endocarditis develops at the site of the defect. The changing characteristic of the heart murmur is related to the buildup and fragmentation of the valvular vegetations.

The successful management of bacterial endocarditis depends upon prompt initiation of an effective antimicrobial regimen. Naturally, early recognition is the first step in treatment. Penicillin generally is the drug of choice.

Selected Bacterial Infections

Various bacterial pathogens can and do involve the oral cavity (Table 32–1) at some time during their development cycles. Only a representative number of such agents is presented here. Other pathogens are discussed in other chapters of this division.

Gonococcal Infections

On rare occasions the oral cavity may be infected by *Neisseria gonorrhoeae* from the hands of a person with gonorrhea, or by other contact with the infection. The oral lesions resemble an acute necrotizing gingivitis with whitish gray or yellow patches which may cover large areas of the mucosa. These adherent membranes will slough off in time, leaving a raw bleeding surface. The lesions are painful and are accompanied by inflammation and swelling.

Tuberculosis

Although the common site for primary disease in man is the lungs, any tissue or organ may be involved either primarily or as a lesion secondary to the chronic lung disease.

Oral lesions may involve any of the tissues of the mouth. However, infections are more common in the nasopharynx, pharynx, and tongue (Figure 32–20). Only a few reports have appeared concerning gingival or mucous membrane involvement. The dentist or dental hygienist may be the first to note the oral lesion which in turn may lead to discovery of another case of pulmonary tuberculosis. These oral lesions do not have a characteristic diagnostic appearance, so they often require biopsy with special stains for the organisms. The diagnostic characteristics of *Mycobacterium tuberculosis,* e.g., morphology, staining properties, and cultural features, are presented in Chapter 33.

Clinical features.   Oral lesions present a roughened, ulcerous, ragged appearance

Table 32–1   Bacterial Infections Involving the Oral Cavity

Disease Entity	Etiologic Agent	Gram Reaction	Symptoms and Clinical Appearance	Treatment
Actinomycosis	*Actinomyces israelii* *A. bovis*	+	Cervicofacial swelling, usually involving the mandible, with induration and draining sinuses	Penicillin Sulfonamides Incision and drainage
Anthrax	*Bacillus anthracis*	+	Rare primary oral infections results in marked swelling of soft tissue, bone may be affected by rapidly destructive osteomyelitis	Penicillin Erythromycin Tetracycline
Gonococcal Infections	*Neisseria gonorrhoeae*	−	Whitish-yellow to gray adherent membranes which slough and leave an inflamed surface, appear on gingiva, tongue, and soft palate	Penicillin Tetracycline Streptomycin Sulfonomides
Leprosy	*Mycobacterium leprae*	a	Nodular tumor-like leproma or masses of granulomatous tissue may involve the oral mucosa, tongue, lips, or palate	Diaminodiphenylsulfone Sulphetrone Sulfoxone sodium Glucosulfone sodium Diphenylthiourea
Syphilis	*Treponema pallidum*	a	Primary oral chancres, secondary mucous patches, tertiary gummas, chronic proliferative inflammatory destructive lesions	Benzathine penicillin G Procaine penicillin G with 2% aluminum monostearate Tetracycline Erythromycin in penicillin—sensitive patients
Tuberculosis	*Mycobacterium tuberculosis*	a	Ulcerated punched-out lesions on mucosa or involving the tongue. Primary oral tuberculosis lesions are rare. Fatigue, malaise, night sweats, productive cough when respiratory system involved	Streptomycin Isoniazid Tetracycline Para-aminosalicylic acid
Tularemia	*Francisella tularensis*	−	Sudden onset of fever, chills, nausea, vomiting, and prostration. Papule to ulcerated pustule at site of inoculation	Streptomycin Tetracyclines
Yaws	*Treponema pertenue*	a	Oral lesions "daughter yaws" secondary to skin lesions. Affect mucous membranes and mucocutaneous junctions	Penicillin

a Gram stain reactions are not significant.

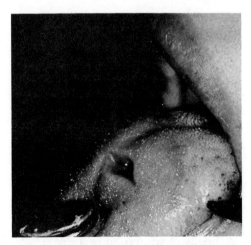

FIG. 32–20. A tuberculosis ulcer of the tongue in a young girl suffering from systemic disease. (Courtesy of Dr. Frank Everett, Pathology Department, University of Oregon Dental School.)

and resemble several other lesions. They often become secondarily infected and painful. Microscopically, they show tubercle formation with central caseation necrosis (cheese-like masses) surrounded by epithelioid cells, Langhans' giant cells, and lymphocytes (Figure 32–21). The surrounding tissue may show increased fluid (edema) and some inflammatory cell infiltrates around blood vessels (perivascular cuffing).

Most authors agree that primary tuberculosis of the mouth is extremely rare and that most lesions are secondary to long-standing pulmonary tuberculosis. The saliva exerts a bacteriostatic effect on tubercle bacilli which apparently is partly responsible for the paucity of oral lesions.

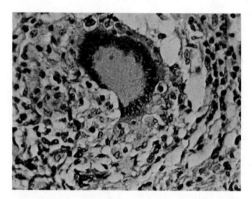

FIG. 32–21. The microscopic appearance of tuberculosis oral lesions. Tubercle formation with central caseation necrosis surrounded by epithelioid. Langhans' giant cells and lymphocytes are shown. (Courtesy of Dr. N. H. Rickles, Pathology Department, University of Oregon Dental School.)

Oral lesions of tuberculosis are classified according to the tissues involved. Four general groupings are recognized as follows: those involving (1) the tooth apex and socket, (2) the oral mucous membrane, (3) the maxilla and mandible, and (4) associated lymph nodes.

Tuberculous involvements of the apical area and tooth socket are much more common than generally believed. Dental granulomas are positive from *M. tuberculosis* in about 10 per cent of tubercular patients with these lesions. The secondary infection of extraction sites by organisms contained in positive sputum seems a reasonable sequelae to the extraction. Fortunately, not all extraction sites become infected, and those that do heal well after surgical removal of the infected "tuberculous granulation" tissue. Lesions of the soft and hard palates and the tongue are less common and seem to occur in patients with far-advanced pulmonary lesions. Lesions of the tongue are often associated with local trauma or irritation from rough, jagged teeth or broken dentures.

When the bones of the maxilla or mandible are infected, the result is a *tuberculous osteomyelitis,* which probably is the result of an extension from infected soft tissue. This form of osteomyelitis closely resembles that caused by many other organisms. Proper diagnosis is not easy, since careful study is necessary to demonstrate the acid-fast organisms. Tuberculous osteomyelitis tends to spread rapidly through the bone, leaving fragments of devitalized bone known as *sequestra,* all accompanied by severe pain. The involved area usually breaks out to the surface, appearing clinically as a draining sinus.

Scrofula, or tuberculosis of the cervical lymph nodes, may occur as a result of primary tuberculosis of the tonsils or adenoids. Clinically the patient will eventually have a sinus draining through the overlying skin. When the tubercle bacilli are filtered out by the lymph node, an acute inflammatory reaction results with swelling, heat, and tenderness of the area. Soon caseation necrosis develops and much, if not all, of the lymph node is destroyed.

Treatment.   Successful treatment lies in the administration of anti-tuberculous drugs in combinations which are known to be effective in preventing the emergence of resistant organisms.

Mycotic Infections

Fungus pathogens, as well as bacterial and viral agents of disease, involve the oral cavity either in a superficial manner or as a consequence of systemic disease. A select few mycotic infections are discussed to illustrate this point, while others are briefly characterized in Table 32–2.

Candidiasis (Moniliasis)

In 1965 Cohen reported that vitamin deficiencies, iron deficiency anemia, preg-

Table 32–2   Mycotic (Fungus) Infections Involving the Oral Cavity

Disease Entity	Etiologic Agent	Symptoms and Clinical Appearance	Treatment
Candidiasis (moniliasis, thrush)	*Candida albicans*	Superficial lesions of skin or mucous membranes in skin folds or creases, often involves commissures of lips. Oral lesions soft, grayish-white, and strip off, leaving raw, bleeding surfaces. May accompany denture sore mouth	Nystatin Amphotericin B Gentian or crystal violet Potassium iodide
Coccidioido-mycosis	*Coccidioides immitis*	Approximately 60% show no symptoms; 40% have symptoms of influenza. Pulmonary lesions, skin, and oral mucosal granulomatous lesions	Symptomatic treatment Bed rest Amphotericin B
Cryptococcosis (torulosis)	*Cryptococcus neoformans*	Fever, cough, and pleural pain following inhalation of dusts containing the organism. Oral lesions usually seen in systemically debilitated as ulcerations	Amphotericin B Sulfadiazine Sulfapyridine
Geotrichosis	*Geotrichum candidum* (other *Geotrichum* species)	White patches on oral mucosa. May develop pulmonary and intestinal lesions	Nystatin Amphotericin B
Histoplasmosis	*Histoplasma capsulatum*	Lesions of the skin and involvement of reticuloendothelial system. Nodules may occur in the mouth or throat and involve the respiratory tract	Amphotericin B
Mucormycosis	*Absidia* *Rhizopus* *Mucor*	Purulent nasal discharge. Inflammatory, gangrenous mucosa. Progressive systemic involvement with fatal outcome if untreated. Rarely involves the oral region	Amphotericin B Correction of diabetes mellitus or underlying disease
North American blastomycosis	*Blastomyces dermatitidis*	Indurated (hard) or fluctuant (wavy) granulomatous swellings often with ulceration, drainage	Amphotericin B
South American blastomycosis	*Blastomyces brasiliensis* (*Paracoccidioides brasiliensis*)	Fever, rales, and cough. Chronic granulomatous lesions on the skin or mucous membranes and in various organs. Oral lesions common	Amphotericin B
Sporotrichosis	*Sporotrichum schenckii*	Primary nodule often with ulceration. Infection spreads along lymph channels and involves lymph nodes. May have oral nodules with ulceration	Potassium iodide Sulfonamides Amphotericin B

nancy, and diabetes may predispose an individual to the development of monilial stomatitis. Woods suggested in 1951 that the growth of *Candida* spp. appears to be restricted by the co-existing bacterial flora, but this flora is suppressed by antibiotics, the *Candida,* which are not affected, grow without restraint. As a result, patients may develop monilial infections of the oral cavity (Figure 32–22) or a more severe, generalized monilial infection of the blood involving the heart valves, respiratory system, gut, and brain.

Clinical features.   The oral lesions involve the tongue, palate, cheeks, and lips, and may further extend to the tonsils, pharynx, and larynx. Ioannovich reported

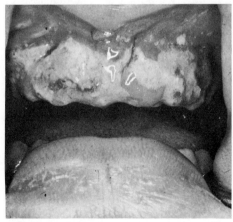

FIG. 32–22. Candidiasis. Anterior view of the gingiva, showing the extent of the grayish-white membranous growth. (Courtesy of Dr. N. H. Rickles, Pathology Department, University of Oregon Dental School.)

in 1961 *Candida* spp. may enter tissues
at the time of tooth extraction. Localized
infection with dull pain, low-grade fever,
foul odor, and a persistent drainage of
purulent material from the nostril result.

Perleché is a candidal infection which
involves the corners of the mouth, and
the superficial tissues, and appears clinically as a grayish-white membrane with
red borders. Often deep cracks appear
and the tissues are tender.

Thrush is a candidal infection of the
mouths of infants which may be contracted from an infected birth canal or
from contaminated equipment in the
nursery.

Oral lesions appear as soft, white,
slightly elevated plaques which resemble
milk curds. They adhere to the underlying
mucosa and when removed leave raw,
bleeding surfaces. The plaque contains
epithelial cells, polymorphonuclear leukocytes, and the fungus. The tissues show
a superficial penetration by the organisms,
which appear microscopically as budding
yeast-like cells in the form of a pseudohyphae (Figure 32–23).

Laboratory diagnosis. The diagnosis of
candidiasis may include a direct examination of freshly obtained clinical specimens (e.g., pus, tissue scrappings, sputum) and specimen cultivation. Animal
inoculations and serological tests are
generally of little practical value.

In smear preparations of clinical specimens *Candida* spp. appear as small, oval,
budding yeasts measuring approximately
3 to 6 μm in diameter (Figure 32–23).
Gram-staining, the use of simple stains, or
mounting specimens in lactophenol cotton
blue is sufficient for direct examination
purposes. Demonstration of abundant
yeast cells and hyphae can be taken as
presumptive evidence of this disease.

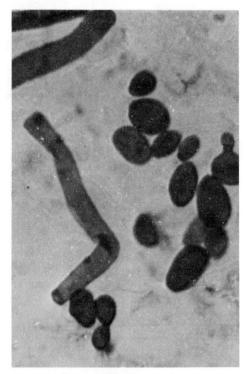

FIG. 32–23. *Candida albicans* in a direct smear
from sputum. (From Kozinn, P. J., and Taschdjian,
C. L.: *JAMA*, **198/2**:170–172, 1966.)

Sabouraud's modified agar with chloramphenicol is generally used for isolation
(Color photograph 36). On this type of
medium *Candida* spp. appear as moist,
creamy colonies which produce a yeasty
odor. The most characteristic diagnostic
feature of *Candida albicans*, however, is
its formation of spherical macroconidia
(chlamydospores) on corn meal or rice-
Tween 80 agar (Figure 32–24). Spherical
clusters of blastospores or yeasts are also
characteristically produced.

Nystatin (Mycostatin) and ampho-
tericin B (Fungizone) are effective, specific antifungal drugs for candidiasis.
Aqueous suspensions are helpful for oral
lesions if used several times daily by
holding the solution in the mouth as long
as possible and then swallowing it.

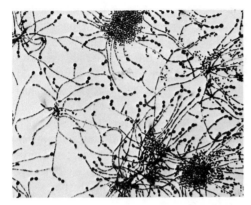

FIG. 32–24. *Candida albicans* grown on rice-Tween 80 agar. Pseudohyphae, blastospores, and chlamydospores may be seen. The pseudomycelium is composed of elongate budding cells that have failed to detach. A few budding cells or clusters of blastospores may be borne at the pseudohyphal constrictions. (Courtesy of Dr. Richard Parker.)

Mucormycosis

This mycotic infection of man is extremely rare in the oral cavity. The organisms responsible for the infection belong to the class Phycomcetes, order Mucorales, and are of three genera, *Absidia, Rhizopus,* and *Mucor.* They are generally considered nuisance fungi and are found in soil and decaying vegetable matter. Common designations for the fungi are "bread molds" or "sugar molds." The organisms exhibit a low degree of pathogenicity. Generally, mucormycosis occurs in patients who are debilitated by other diseases such as diabetes or leukemia.

Diagnosis. The organisms cultured on Sabouraud's glucose medium show rapid growth, with the formation of a large aerial mycelium. When these are examined microscopically, sporangia (large globular structures) can be seen. Tissue sections stained by the periodic acid-Schiff (PAS) technique show the very thick, non-segmented mycelia.

South American Blastomycosis

This chronic granulomatous fungal infection is presumed to be limited to South America. It occurs with some frequency in coffee plantation workers, possibly due to their habit of cleaning their teeth with small fragments of wood and of chewing on stems and leaves of various plants, which might carry the causative agent, *Paracoccidioides brasiliensis,* which is also known as *Blastomyces brasiliensis.* In addition, perianal lesions also have been reported, probably because of "comparable toilet habits" (the use of contaminated leaves). Man-to-man transfer does not occur. Discussion of North American blastomycosis is given in Chapter 34.

Clinical features. The primary lesion is commonly on the oral mucosa and may involve the tongue, gingiva, palate, cheeks, lips (Figure 32–25), or nose. A small papule forms and soon ulcerates, leaving a granulomatous mass which extends into the underlying tissue and soon produces closely accompanying satellite lesions. The lesions are painful and make eating difficult, which leaves the patient debilitated. The lymph nodes draining the area soon become involved, rupture, and leave draining sinuses. Skin, viscera, and other areas may become involved secondarily, or they may be primary sites of infection.

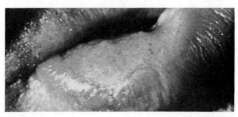

FIG. 32–25. Blastomycosis of the lower lip with central ulceration and a raised, swollen border. (Courtesy of Dr. N. H. Rickles, Pathology Department, University of Oregon Dental School.)

Laboratory diagnosis. This is generally based on the properties of cultures and the microscopic appearance of the organisms, as well as the detection of *P. brasiliensis* in tissue sections. Suspected material can also be injected intraperitoneally into mice or intratesticularly into guinea pigs. Lesions develop in tissues of the mouse in approximately 6 weeks and in 2 weeks in guinea pigs.

P. brasiliensis is a dimorphic fungus, which appears in tissues and exudates as multiple-budding yeast cells approximately 2 to 60 μm in diameter. These multiple buds are arranged around the mother cell in a distinguishing manner which is frequently referred to as a "pilot wheel." The parasitic or yeast

phase occurs both *in vivo* and *in vitro* when the organism is grown on glucose blood infusion agar at 37°C. The mycelial phase develops on Sabouraud's glucose agar at room temperature as a white and later brown wrinkled mycelium that has branching hyphae and oval forms. Cultures should be kept for at least 4 weeks, since growth is slow and may not appear before the third week. The septated mycelium supports aerial hyphae to which the chlamydospores and blastospores are attached.

Viral Infections

A representative group of viral infections of the oral cavity are listed in Table 32–3 and discussed here.

Table 32–3   Viral Infections Involving the Oral Cavity

Disease Entity	Etiologic Agent	Symptoms and Clinical Appearance	Treatment
Chickenpox (varicella)	Varicella-Herpes Zoster virus	Vesicles with a surrounding erythematous zone appear on the mucosa and soon ulcerate	Symptomatic
Hand, foot, and mouth disease	Coxsackie virus Group A, Types 16, 5, and 10	Vesicles and ulcerations involving buccal mucosa, tongue, gingiva, and lips. Ulcers are painful and interfere with eating. Lesions also present on hands and feet	Symptomatic
Herpangina (aphthous pharyngitis)	Coxsackie virus Group A, Types 2, 4, 5, 6, 8, and 10	Sudden onset of high fever, headache, and sore throat, accompanied by papules, vesicles, and later ulcers on the pillars of the fauces, the uvula, and soft palate	Symptomatic
Herpes simplex (fever blister)	*Herpesvirus hominis*	Primary lesions usually in oropharyngeal mucosa as multiple, very small vesicles, which rupture and ulcerate. A bright red zone is present around the periphery. Fever, malaise, anorexia, and lymphadenopathy are present. Recurrent lesions of mucosa and lips common	Supportive *Lactobacillus acidophilus* preparations, certain drugs that inhibit DNA synthesis (currently under study)
Herpes zoster (shingles)	Varicella-Herpes Zoster virus	Vesicles form along the distribution of a sensory nerve and soon ulcerate	Symptomatic
Hoof and mouth disease	Foot and mouth disease virus	Vesicles and ulcerations involving lips, tongue, palate, and mucosa. Heal within two weeks	Symptomatic
Measles (rubeola)	Paramyxovirus	Koplik's spots appear on buccal mucosa as bluish-white spots with a reddish surrounding zone, followed in a few days by a diffuse rash, fever, and catarrhal inflammation	Symptomatic
Molluscum contagiosum	Molluscovirus	Usually on skin of face; may rarely involve the intraoral tissues with slightly elevated lesions showing a superficial purulent discharge	Curretage Electrodessication
Mumps	Mumps virus	Painful swollen salivary glands, usually the parotid	Symptomatic Convalescent serum
Smallpox (variola)	Poxvirus variolae	Ulcerations of the oral mucosa. The tongue may be involved. Severe symptoms with fever, headache, nausea	Hyperimmune vaccinia Gamma globulin Thiosemicarbazone

Foot and Mouth Disease (Epidemic, Epizootic, or Aphtho-bullous Stomatitis, Aphthous Fever, FMD)

This infection is mentioned here only because of the severe inflammation of oral mucosa which can occur in humans.

Clinical features. Patients who are infected experience general ill-feeling with fever, nausea, and vomiting accompanied by painful red ulcerative lesions involving most oral tissues, and possibly some vesicular lesions of the skin. The ulcerated lesions usually heal within 2 weeks without scarring, unless they become secondarily infected, which may delay the healing.

Laboratory diagnosis. The isolation of the causative agent by means of tissue culture, and serologic testing, e.g., complement fixation and neutralization tests, are important to the identification of FMD virus.

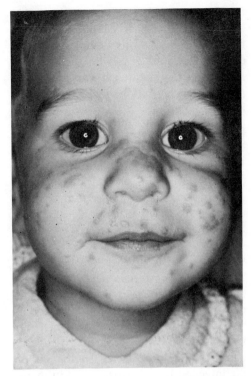

FIG. 32–26. Facial skin lesions of hand, foot, and mouth disease with a perioral distribution. (Courtesy of Dr. Gerald H. Prescott.)

Hand, Foot, and Mouth Disease

This condition primarily affects young children (Figure 32–26). It is characterized by vesicular lesions of the mouth (Figure 32–27), hands, and feet. Many epidemics have been reported since the first description of 60 cases in Toronto in 1958, including reports of epidemics in England, California, Oregon, Arizona, and numerous Eastern states.

The etiologic agents, Coxsackie viruses, are enteroviruses and share many properties in common with other members of this group (see Chapter 36), including the prevalence of infections during the summer months in temperate climates, and the symptomless carriers among family contacts. The Coxsackie A viruses type A16, A5, and A10 have been isolated from the vesicle fluid, mouth, and stools of patients with the disease. The A16 virus is seldom isolated

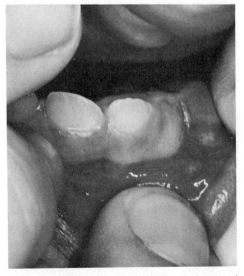

FIG. 32–27. Intraoral lesions of hand, foot, and mouth disease in the area of the unerrupted cuspid. (Courtesy of Dr. Gerald H. Prescott.)

from normal children as are the types A5 and A10, which can be recovered from their stools. This finding may help explain why infections with the A5 and A10 types do not reach epidemic proportions, since some immunity may have been acquired.

Diagnosis.   The diagnosis generally is made on the basis of the clinical picture. Virologic confirmation is not always necessary. However, tissue culture and animal inoculations can be used to determine the presence of virus in vesicle fluid and feces.

Herpangina (Aphthous Pharyngitis)

This infection is specific and highly contagious. The disease is transmitted from one person to another through direct contact. It was first described in 1920 by Zahorsky, who later proposed the name herpangina. Sporadic outbreaks of the infection have been reported in many parts of the United States, usually during the summer months. It begins during the warm weather and disappears with the first plant killing frost. Children up to 15 years of age are commonly affected.

Diagnosis.   Laboratory confirmation of herpangina includes animal and tissue culture inoculations and serological testing.

Herpes Simplex

This common viral disease affects the oral tissues (Figure 32–28), often remains localized, and produces considerable pain and discomfort for the patient. The lesion has been called by many names, including canker sore, fever blister, cold sore, aphthous ulcer, and herpes labialis. *Herpesvirus hominis* is often classified as a dermatropic virus since it resides within cells of ectodermal origin, chiefly the dermis. Many factors may stimulate the virus to produce clinical lesions; among these are excessive exposure

FIG. 32–28. Herpes simplex virus involving the inner surface of the lip. This is an older lesion with secondary infection and a thin necrotic slough over the surface. (Courtesy of Dr. N. H. Rickles, Pathology Department, University of Oregon Dental School.)

to sun, fever, allergy, mechanical trauma, gastrointestinal upsets, and certain psychogenic factors. The etiology of the lesions was conclusively demonstrated in 1939 when herpes simplex virus was isolated from 27 of 28 patients. Neutralizing antibodies were found in the blood of patients from whom oral herpes virus was isolated and in the blood of most normal adults who also frequently experienced herpetic lesions even when antibodies were present. Herpesvirus is recovered approximately three times as often from patients with illness as from healthy patients; however, there is often no clear etiologic association between the presence of the virus and the patient's illness.

Herpes simplex neonatorum is seen in infants who become ill on the fourth or fifth day after birth and die in shock a few days later. The clinical symptoms of the disease are fever, cough, lethargy, jaundice, and an increase in the sizes of the liver and spleen. Pathologically, the disease is characterized by sharply outlined areas of focal necrosis in many tissues, principally the liver and adrenal glands, but also in other organs, including the spleen, lungs, brain, kidneys, and bone marrow.

Generalized herpetic infection of the newborn might be acquired transplacentally before birth or postnatally by contact with herpes-infected persons in the environment.

Mumps (Epidemic Parotitis)

This worldwide acute, communicable disease is caused by a paramyxovirus. Man is the only natural host for the causative agent. The virus apparently is spread as a droplet infection or by direct contact with saliva and respiratory secretions.

Mumps most frequently affect children between 8 and 15 years of age, with an overall incidence of at least 60 per cent of the population. Adults may develop mumps and often suffer severe complications. The oral tissues involved are the salivary glands, most commonly the parotid glands. Unilateral swelling of one salivary gland will produce the same degree of immunity as found in multiple gland involvement.

A temporary passive immunity toward the virus may be obtained by giving injections of gamma globulin from serum known to contain mumps antibody in high titer. Active immunization by vaccination with inactivated virus preparations or with live virus attenuated by chick embryo passage has shown some reduction in the incidence of mumps. The immunity resulting from having the disease is of long duration and may develop following subclinical infections. Subsequent attacks have rarely been reported.

Diagnosis. The mumps virus may readily be isolated from the saliva of patients with parotitis. It grows slowly in the yolk sac or amniotic sac of chick embryos. The virus has a number of immunologic properties, including hemagglutination, fixation of complement, and hemolysis, and brings forth a delayed type of skin reaction. Cases of sub-clinical mumps do exist and are diagnosed by a rise in complement-fixing antibody titer after 2 to 3 weeks.

QUESTIONS FOR REVIEW

1. Consider the various components of the oral cavity. List at least five of these and a particular infection or disease state associated with each of them.

2. What types of bacteria make up the largest microbial group of the oral cavity? Which one can cause diseases?

3. What is N.U.G.?

4. Discuss the following clinical states as to general features, cause or causes, and treatment, if any.
   a. dry socket
   b. Vincent's infection
   c. osteomyelitis
   d. periodontitis
   e. pericoronitis
   f. dental caries
   g. periodontal disease
   h. sub-acute bacterial endocarditis

5. What is the role of calculus in periodontal disease?

6. Construct a table comparing the diseases listed below as to: (1) causative agent, (2) means of transmission, (3) laboratory diagnostic features and possible means for prevention.
   a. actinomycosis
   b. foot and mouth disease
   c. gonorrhea
   d. herpangina
   e. syphilis
   f. hand, foot, and mouth disease
   g. tuberculosis
   h. fever blister
   i. candidiasis
   j. mumps
   k. South American blastomycosis

7. What etiologic mechanisms have been offered to explain periodontal disease?

8. What is pyorrhea?

9. What is a focal infection? How important is it to the general health of the body?

10. What precautions should be observed in the case of a dental patient with a history of rheumatic fever?

Selected Bacterial Diseases of the Respiratory Tract

The human respiratory system (Figures 33–1 and 33–2) includes the nose, pharynx (throat), larynx (voice box), trachea (wind pipe), bronchi, and lungs. As certain of these structures will be referred to in relation to respiratory diseases, it is appropriate to include brief descriptions of them at this point.

The Pharynx

The throat is a tubelike structure which, in addition to other functions, serves as a passageway for both food and air. The pharynx is characterized by its association with certain lymphoid tissues called *tonsils,* including the pharyngeal tonsils or adenoids and the lingual tonsils. A total of seven openings lead to or from the throat. There is one with the mouth, two with the nose, two with eustachian tubes, one with the larynx, and one with the esophagus.

The Trachea

The trachea, commonly called the windpipe, is a thin tube averaging about one

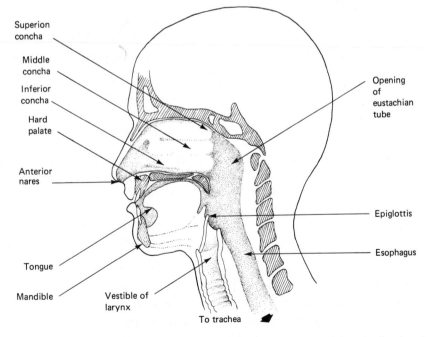

FIG. 33–1. A diagram showing portions of the respiratory system contained within the head and neck region.

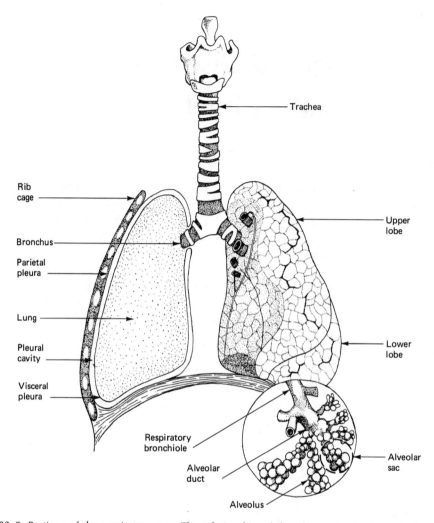

FIG. 33–2. Portions of the respiratory tree. The relationship of the pleurae to the lungs is also shown.

inch in diameter. It descends from the larynx and terminates in the thoracic or chest cavity where it divides into the two primary *bronchi*. The trachea is lined by ciliated epithelial cells.

The Thoracic Cavity

The chest or thoracic cavity is the space bounded by the walls of the thorax. The anterior, lateral, and posterior limits or boundaries of the cavity are formed by the ribs and associated cartilages, the

sternum (breastbone), and the thoracic vertebrae. The connective tissue and muscles between these bones and cartilages also are included. The diaphragm separates the thoracic cavity from the abdominal cavity.

The Pleurae

Two membranes in the form of a closed sac envelop the lungs (Figure 33–2). The inner membrane, the *visceral pleura,* covers the outer lung surface. The outer membrane layer, the *parietal pleura,* lines the inner surface of the thoracic wall. The potential cavity between these two membranes is called the *pleural cavity.* A serous (serum-like) fluid is found in this region which enables the two pleurae to glide over one another during respiratory movements.

The Lungs and the Primary Bronchi

These conical organs of respiration are soft and spongy. Each lung is divided into *lobes.* The right lung is composed of three lobes and the left of two. Most of the chest is taken up by the lungs.

A depression on the medial (middle) surface of each lung is the region through which the primary bronchus, blood vessels, lymphatic, and nerves penetrate the structure. The bronchial tree (Figure 33–2) is formed from both bronchi dividing and subdividing into smaller bronchi, leading into several sizes of tubelike structures called *bronchioles.* The smallest of these, approximately 0.5 mm, are known as *terminal* bronchioles. These divide and give rise to *respiratory* bronchioles, which in turn branch into several alveolar ducts. Alveolar sacs develop from the ducts. The walls of these sacs form *alveoli,* the pulmonary unit in which gaseous exchange (external respiration) occurs.

Introduction to Microbial Infections of the Respiratory Tract

Several microorganisms can cause respiratory tract infections. Many of the resulting diseases are quite common and are among the most damaging of any which affect man. A selected number of such respiratory infections will be presented in the remaining portions of this chapter.

Various microbial pathogens—bacteria, fungi, and viruses—are provided with a suitable avenue for entry, as well as a site for multiplication, by the respiratory tract. The mechanisms utilized by such disease agents vary, which taxes the defenses of potential hosts. Even though these microorganisms utilize the respiratory tract as a "port of entry" and at times as a "portal of exit," the resulting infectious process may easily extend to other regions of the body.

Another important aspect of respiratory infections is that the various secretions associated with this system can be infectious. Relatively few microorganisms are introduced into the environment during normal breathing, even by an infected individual. However, an infected person or carrier who does not cover his nose or mouth while sneezing or coughing can easily contaminate his environment with disease agents. Naturally, the communicability of infectious diseases is influenced by several factors, including: (1) the survival of respiratory pathogens on fomites or in the air, (2) the number of microorganisms inhaled, (3) the duration of contact, and (4) the anatomical site involved in the localization of the infectious agents.

Control Measures

Numerous advances within the past 50 years have greatly increased and improved measures used in the control and prevention of infectious diseases involving the lungs. The future appears to hold additional promise, especially in relation to the effective control of respiratory diseases, such as the common cold. Although a representative number of general control methods have been discussed in earlier chapters, some of them will be reviewed here in order to emphasize their importance.

Many of the measures used in the control of respiratory tract infections are quite similar, if not identical, to those employed for other types of diseases. In general, the procedure or procedures followed are determined to a great extent by the characteristic features of the pathogen or the particular disease process it causes. Measures involved in the control of respiratory tract infections may include: (1) isolation of infected persons, (2) concurrent disinfection or sterilization of equipment used by patients, such as mouthpieces, thermometers, rubber tubing, and any and all contaminated articles such as eating utensils and dishes, (3) the use of and proper disposal of gowns following contact with infectious individuals, (4) the disinfection of rooms or associated facilities used by infected persons; and (5) the washing and disinfecting of hands of appropriate personnel before and after contact with patients or with any and all articles handled by such individuals, blankets, dishes, laundry, pillows, etc.

Bacterial Diseases of the Respiratory Tract

Several bacterial infections of the respiratory tract (Table 33–1) are of great importance because of the ease with which they are transmitted and contracted, and the difficulties encountered with measures used in eradication of the respective disease agents. The characteristics of a number of these pathogens are presented in this section. (Treatment usually includes the administration of antibiotics that are effective against these agents.)

Diphtheria

Historical Background
This acutely infectious communicable disease has been known and often described since ancient times, but its specific nature was not recognized until approximately 1826. Pierre Bretonneau made the important contribution of accurately describing diphtheria and differentiating it from other respiratory tract diseases. He also coined a name for the infection, "dipheritie," derived from the Greek word *diphthora,* meaning skin or membrane. The designation has since been altered to *diphtheria.*

Although Bretonneau was firmly convinced that the infection he described was a highly communicable one, and furthermore was caused by a specific agent, it was not until 1883 and 1884 that proof of his concept was provided. The bacterial etiology of diphtheria from stained smears was demonstrated by Klebs in 1883. The actual cultivation of the causative agent was achieved one year later by Loeffler, who also demonstrated its causal relationship to the disease.

Intrigued by certain histological findings with diseased laboratory animals, Loeffler pursued the investigation of diphtheria's pathogenesis. He concluded from his studies that the bacteria which were injected into the guinea pigs remained localized, and during the course of their growth and metabolic activities produced a powerful toxin. The disease state developed as a consequence of the poisonous material being transported via the bloodstream to other parts of the animal's body. The proof of Loeffler's hypothesis was provided in 1888 by Roux and Yersin, who clearly showed the presence of a soluble exotoxin in *Corynebacterium diphtheriae* cultures. By separating organisms from their liquid environment, Roux and Yersin were able to demonstrate the presence of the *C. diphtheriae* toxin in the liquid phase of the medium.

Further insight into the ability of this pathogen to produce toxin was brought to the attention of the scientific world by

Table 33–1 Representative Bacterial-Caused Respiratory Tract Infections

Disease	Pathogen	Gram Reaction	Morphology	Possible Treatment
Diphtheria	Corynebacterium diphtheriae (Klebs-Loeffler bacillus)	+	Rods appearing in aggregates resembling X's, Y's, and Chinese letters	1. Diphtheria antitoxin therapy combined with antibiotic therapy 2. Antibiotics include erythromycin, penicillin, and tetracyclines
Leprosy	Mycobacterium leprae (Hansen's bacillus)	[a]	Rod	Antibiotics include chloromycin, kanamycin, novobocin, tetracyclines
Melioidosis	Pseudomonas pseudomallei	−	Rod	Antibiotics (limited effectiveness)
Nasopharyngitis[b]	Neisseria meningitidis	−	Diplococcus	Antibiotics
Ornithosis	Chlamydia ornithosis	−	Rod	Chloramphenicol and oxytetracycline
Parapertussis	Bordetella parapertussis	−	Rod	Tetracyclines
Pneumonia	Streptococcus (Diplococcus) pneumoniae	+	Diplococcus	Penicillin and broad-spectrum antibiotics
	Hemophilus influenzae (Pfeiffer's bacillus)	−	Rod	Ampicillin, chloramphenicol, streptomycin, and tetracyclines
	Klebsiella pneumoniae (Friedlander's bacillus)	−	Rod	Chloramphenicol, streptomycin, and tetracyclines
	Serratia marcescens, S. rubidaea	−	Rod	Chloramphenicol, genatamicin, kanamycin
	Staphylococcus aureus	+	Staphylococcus	Penicillin, tetracycline
	Streptococcus pyogenes	+	Streptococcus	Penicillin, tetracycline
Pneumonic Plague	Yersinia (Pasteurella) pestis	−	Rod	Chloramphenicol, oxytetracycline, streptomycin, and combinations
Primary atypical pneumonia	Mycoplasma pneumoniae (Eaton's agent)	[c]	Pleomorphic	Antibiotics, tetracyclines
Psittacosis	Chlamydia psittaci	−	Rod	Chloramphenicol and oxytetracycline
Streptococcal lymphoiditis[d]	Streptococcus pyogenes	+	Streptococcus	Antibiotics, penicillin, and tetracyclines
Tuberculosis	Mycobacterium tuberculosis	[a]	Rod	Isoniazid (INH), P (para) aminosalicylate (PAS), Streptomycin, rifampin, and the combination of two or more drugs for drug-resistant tubercle bacilli
Whooping cough (pertussis)	Bordetella pertussis (Bordet-Gengou) bacillus	−	Rod	1. Antibiotics including chloramphenicol, oxytetra-cycline, and penicillin 2. Symptomatic

[a] The Gram-stain reaction is not used diagnostically. The acid-fast staining procedure is used instead.
[b] Note that this is the most common manifestation of the bacterial pathogen.
[c] Gram reactions are of little value with this pathogen.
[d] Grouped here because they are characterized by involvement of the lymphoid tissue of the upper respiratory passages.

V. J. Freeman in 1951, some 63 years later. From his investigations Freeman discovered that toxin production was dependent upon the presence of a lysogenic state in *C. diphtheriae* strains (see Chapter 16). In other words, only those strains of this bacterial species which were supporting a specific bacteriophage on their own could elaborate the toxin responsible for causing diphtheria. Moreover, *C. diphtheriae* strains either lacking such viruses or losing them could not produce toxin.

The discovery of the diphtheria toxin had great immunological significance, primarily from the standpoint of potential immunization against the disease. Von Behring and his associates in 1890 were able to immunize laboratory animals with a heat-attenuated toxin preparation and also obtain antitoxin with which to treat human victims of the disease. Unfortunately, the heat-attenuated form of diphtheria toxin proved to be too toxic for human immunization purposes. Not until 1923 was an effective and safe immunizing preparation developed. Then Ramon developed a modified toxin by treating the toxin with formalin. The resulting toxoid retained its antigenicity, but was found to be incapable of disease production (see Chapter 26).

Means of transmission. Most instances of diphtheria result from direct contact with droplets. *C. diphtheriae* is a hardy organism, as evidenced by its ability to withstand cold, heat, and drying.

Diphtheria has a worldwide distribution, and appears to be more common in the colder months of the year. Individuals who are attacked by the disease generally are older than 6 months of age, but not past middle age. Among the major sources of *C. diphtheriae* are the carriers. Such individuals are believed to account for approximately one-fourth of the known cases of the disease. Of course, exposure to a recognizably infected person is far more likely to result in a case of diphtheria. Infected persons may be a source of disease agents for as long as 1 to 2 weeks.

Predisposing factors associated with the disease include chilling, improper nutrition, overcrowding, and operations involving the nose and throat. In the last case, diphtheria may result from the exposure of a normal individual to the pathogen, or from *C. diphtheriae* already being present, as in the case of a carrier.

Clinical features. The incubation period for diphtheria is generally between 1 and 10 days. The disease begins rather suddenly. Typical symptoms include fever (approximately 102°F), a sore throat, and general malaise. The well-known *diphtheritic pseudomembrane* forms on one tonsil, and soon involves the remaining side. This pseudomembrane usually remains limited to the area if the disease is detected and treated early. However, if diphtheria is not treated the membranous material extends well into the nasopharyngeal area. Infections also may commence from the nose and extend downward.

The more commonly encountered clinical forms of diphtheria are designated according to the regions affected. They include *tonsillar, pharyngeal, nasopharyngeal,* and *laryngeal* diphtheria. Less common forms of the disease are the *nasal,* the *hemorrhagic,* the *cutaneous,* and the *ocular.*

Complications. In general, severe complications of diphtheria are associated with the laryngeal and nasopharyngeal forms of the disease. With myocarditis, an inflammatory state of heart muscle is the earliest of the severe complications.

Additional complications reported to occur with nasopharyngeal diphtheria include palatal, pharyngeal, and respiratory paralysis and pneumonia. The respiratory form of a paralysis involves the intercostal muscles and is a greatly feared condition. Respirators have been used beneficially in the treatment of some patients with this complication.

Complications of laryngeal diphtheria include pneumonia and suffocation.

Individuals with the milder types of diphtheria (nasal, pharyngeal, and tonsillar) may also develop complications; these include middle ear infection (otitis media) and peritonsillar abscess.

Laboratory diagnosis. Clinically, diphtheria may be confused with other disease states. Principal among them are acute tonsillitis, catarrhal laryngitis, infectious mononucleosis, scarlet fever, streptococcal sore throat, and Vincent's agina.

In a typical laboratory diagnosis of diphtheria, clinical specimens, e.g., exudate from the lesion and throat, are used to inoculate three types of media: a blood agar plate, Loeffler's slant, and a medium containing potassium tellurite (Color photograph 49). After an incubation period of 24 to 48 hours at 37°C, careful microscopic examination should be made of representative types of colonies appearing on each of the media used. *Corynebacterium diphtheriae* characteristically is a Gram-positive rod. When stained by Loeffler's methylene blue, it exhibits pronounced metachromatic granules (Figure 8–21). *C. diphtheriae,* as well as other members of the genus, are noted for their aggregations in the form of Chinese letters, X's, and Y's. It also is important to note whether growth appeared on all of the media mentioned previously. If colonies are not found on the medium containing potassium tellurite, generally *C. diphtheriae* can be tentatively ruled out as the causative agent of the disease state in question.

Occasionally, other species of Corynebacterium are isolated clinically from the ear, eye, or nasopharyngeal region. Such organisms include *C. hofmannii* and *C. xerosis.* Differentiation from *C. diphtheriae* can be accomplished by means of fermentation reactions (Table 33–2).

In the event that *C. diphtheriae* is isolated, it should be subcultured and tested for toxin production. This property can be determined either by the *in vitro* gel diffusion procedure (see Chapter 23) or by the guinea pig or rabbit virulence test. Tissue culture techniques for the demonstration of toxin production are under study.

Immunity and prevention. A relatively long-lasting acquired immunity results from one attack of diphtheria. Infants born to mothers immunized against *C. diphtheriae* infection usually have temporary protection. Unfortunately, such immunity only ranges from a few weeks to approximately 3 months. Consequently,

Table 33–2   Differentiation of *C. diphtheriae* from Other Corynebacterium by Means of Fermentation Reactions

Species	Carbohydrate[a]		
	Glucose	Maltose	Sucrose
C. diphtheriae	A	A	V
C. hofmannii	N.C.	N.C.	N.C.
C. xerosis	A	N.C.	A

[a] A=acid; N.C.=no change or negative; V=variable.

widespread immunization of such infants is practiced. In the United States, the DPT vaccine (diphtheria, pertussis, and tetanus) is used to induce immunity (see Chapter 26). This preparation contains diphtheria and tetanus toxoid and killed *Bordetella pertussis*. Later booster injections and exposure to infected persons contribute to maintaining adequate antitoxin levels in the person. It is important to note that the antibody response of individuals varies widely. Therefore, it may be necessary to administer several booster shots during childhood and later in life to bring a person's degree of immunity up to a functional level.

Schick test. A skin test for the determination of susceptibility and the need for active immunization was developed by Bela Schick in 1913. The Schick test is used in the testing of large groups of people. It is reliable in most, but not all, situations. The procedure used involves the intradermal injection into the arm's flexor surface of 0.1 ml of a standardized preparation of diphtheria toxin. Susceptibility to the disease is evident from the appearance of a reddened, swollen, tender area around the site of injection. Changes of this type do not occur within persons resistant to infection.

Hypersensitivity to the toxin preparation has been reported. This reaction may be the consequence of the development of sensitivity to other antigenic components of the skin test material. In order to distinguish such responses from a true indication of susceptibility, toxoid is injected into the opposite arm. The types of responses are shown in Table 33–3.

Moloney test. Measures are taken to prevent hypersensitivity from developing, in case reimmunization is necessary. A procedure known as the Moloney test is used. This involves testing persons for sensitivity by intradermally injecting 0.1 ml of a 1:10 dilution of diphtheria toxoid. If the patient exhibits a localized reddening around the site of injection, diluted preparations are injected cautiously. If no indication of sensitivity appears, the normal inoculation procedure is followed. It has been noted quite often that the quantity of toxin given in the Schick test may be sufficient for immunization purposes. Consequently, additional injections are unnecessary.

Diphtheria can spread through a community as a consequence not only of the contact susceptible persons have with actively infected individuals, but also with carriers of *C. diphtheriae*. Top in 1964 stated that this disease is less likely to be contracted from a carrier than from a "recognized case." As is the situation with other infections, patients recovering

Table 33–3　Reactions Observed in Hypersensitive Individuals

State of Immunity	Reaction Toward		Duration of Reaction
	Toxin	Toxoid	
Immune and non-sensitive	—	—	No reaction observed
Non-immune and non-sensitive	+	—	Persist for at least 6–7 days[a]
Immune and sensitive	+	+	Approximately 2 days[b]
Non-immune but sensitive	+	+	Reaction to toxin reaches peak at approximately 5 days. Response to toxoid subsides by this time[c]

[a] True positive reaction.
[b] Pseudoreaction.
[c] Combined reactions.

from diphtheria harbor and can disseminate the etiologic agent for several weeks. Nasal secretions are highly infectious and may contaminate objects and food. Carriers are detected as a consequence of isolating *C. diphtheriae* from persons without apparent illness.

Several measures adopted by health agencies to protect the susceptibles include large-scale immunization programs (see Chapter 26). Quarantine and the daily use of appropriate antibiotics with carriers can be especially helpful in reducing their numbers in a community. Quarantining of carriers should continue until bacterial cultures are negative.

Melioidosis

This bacterial disease is caused by the Gram-negative rod *Pseudomonas pseudomallei*. It is described as a fulminating and, if untreated, lethal infectious disease.

Means of transmission. The etiologic agent is either transmitted by contaminated food or acquired through an accidental inoculation with rat excreta.

Clinical features. Individuals with melioidosis predominately exhibit pulmonary symptoms, although septicemia has been observed. Clinically, patients have chills, fever, malaise, and a cough. Pneumonitis is suggested by physical findings. In untreated cases, death results from respiratory failure. With the septicemic form of the disease, abscess formation in all organs, high fever, and circulatory collapse are found. Such manifestations are indistinguishable from the septicemic form of plague and other causes producing "overwhelming septicemia."

Laboratory diagnosis. Diagnosis is dependent upon the recovery and subsequent identification of *P. pseudomallei*. Specimens of choice include sputum and in cases of septicemia, blood. Media used for isolation of the etiologic agent are blood agar or nutrient agar supplemented with 3 per cent glycerin, crystal violet, and penicillin. Differential diagnosis from *Pseudomonas aeruginosa* can be usually accomplished by comparing the odor of cultures, colonial morphologic features, and biochemical reaction patterns with certain tests (Table 33–4). The odor of *P. aeruginosa* is noticeably sweet, while that of *P. pseudomallei* has an earthy quality.

Chlamydial Respiratory Infections

Until fairly recently, the causative agents of psittacosis, lymphogranuloma venereum (LGV), and trachoma were considered by some investigators as biological forms intermediate between true viruses and rickettsia. Quite often they were called the *basophilic* group of viruses. However, at the time of writing, these agents have been placed into the bacterial

Table 33–4   General Differential Diagnosis of *Pseudomonas pseudomallei*

Microorganism	Colony Characteristics	Gelatin Liquefaction	Litmus Milk[a]	Fermentation Reactions[a]				
				Glu	Lac	Malt	Man	Suc
P. aeruginosa	Irregular, large, spreading, gray or greenish centers	Rapid	Alk, P and R	N.C.	N.C.	N.C.	N.C.	N.C.
P. pseudomallei	Circular, cream colored, opaque, and wrinkled	Moderate	Slow A, P variable	A	A	A	A	A

[a] Explanations of symbols used for reactions: Glu=glucose; Lac=lactose; Malt=maltose; Man=mannitol; Suc=sucrose; A=acid; Alk=alkaline; N.C.=no change; P=peptonization; R=reduction.

genus of *Chlamydia*. The formerly-called basophilic viruses are now considered to be *intracytoplasmic bacteria,* and not an intermediate form.

The *Chlamydia* are described as spherical, Gram-negative, non-motile, intracellular parasites. Other properties of the genus include: (1) a unique developmental cycle, (2) the presence of both DNA and RNA, (3) a size range from approximately 200 to 1000 nm, (4) the possession of certain portions of enzyme systems which are functional in producing energy, and (5) susceptibility to tetracyclines and certain other antibiotics.

Two respiratory diseases caused by members of the *Chlamydia,* psittacosis and ornithosis, will be discussed here. *C. psittaci* and *C. ornithosis,* respectively, are the etiologic agents of these infections.

Psittacosis

Psittacosis, or parrot fever, is the term generally given to respiratory infections contracted from psittacine birds (e.g., canaries, cockatoos, lovebirds, parakeets, parrots, and thrushes). Disease states contracted from non-psittacine birds, such as chickens, pigeons, sea birds, and turkeys, are referred to as *ornithosis*. In general, psittacosis is considered to be of a *zoonotic* nature, spread by lower animals through natural means to humans. However, some cases of the disease in man have resulted from direct contact with infected persons.

Means of transmission. In psittacine birds, this infection is usually spread by direct contact, droplets, and droppings. Latent disease states are quite common with these animals, and under conditions of stress—chilling, dampness, or overcrowding—the latent infection is known to develop into overt psittacosis. Infected birds generally have symptoms which include diarrhea, emaciation, and a mucopurulent discharge from the mouth. Many cases of human disease develop in pet owners, animal handlers, and pet store attendants.

Laboratory diagnosis of psittacosis in birds. This usually includes microscopic examination of smears prepared from tissue lesions, and the inoculation of chick embryos and mice. The microscopic procedure is used to demonstrate the characteristic inclusion and elementary bodies of the *Chlamydia psittaci,* while the *in vivo* technique is employed in isolating the causative organism. Great care must be exercised in handling specimens suspected of containing the psittacosis agents.

Clinical features in humans. The incubation period in human cases generally varies from 6 to 15 days. The individual experiences a sudden onset of symptoms, which include those of bronchitis and bronchopneumonia. Prostration, fever, and delirium are not uncommon in untreated patients. Subclinical infections also are known to occur.

Diagnosis. In human infections, diagnosis is generally made by isolating the causative agent or demonstrating a rise in the complement-fixation titer. In the former procedure, clinical specimens, such as blood, lung tissue, or sputum, are inoculated into mice and/or chicken embryos. Finding typical inclusions in these animals confirms the diagnosis.

Control. Control measures against psittacosis generally include the imposition of quarantine, usually 6 months, on shipments of psittacine birds, the use of spot laboratory examination on shipments of these animals, and the incorporation of antibiotics into the feed for psittacines. Chlortetracycline has proved to be extremely efficient in reducing the incidence of the disease in birds.

Ornithosis

This disease is caused by *C. ornithosis* and is an infection of nonpsittacine birds. Human infections occur generally with individuals handling infected birds, such as chickens, ducks, and turkeys. Ornithosis has become an important public health problem in recent years.

Clinical features. Individuals with the disease may experience symptoms of bronchitis, bronchopneumonia, or influenza. Generally, a high fever and a severe cough are present. Subclinical infections also occur. It should be noted that neurologic complications may develop. These include encephalitis, facial paralysis, and polyneuritis (inflammation of many nerves).

Diagnosis. The laboratory diagnosis for ornithosis is similar to that for psittacosis.

Bacterial Pneumonias

This group of diseases will be presented according to causative agents.

Pneumococcal Pneumonia

Streptococcus (*Diplococcus*) *pneumoniae* causes by far the majority of pneumonia cases in which a whole lobe or more than one lobe is involved, referred to as *lobar pneumonia*. Over 75 different serological types of *S. pneumoniae* have been reported. Differentiation among the various types is based on the existence of immunologically distinct polysaccharides which form the capsules of these organisms (Color photograph 21). The designations of these different types is by number, type 3, 7, etc.

Other microorganisms which also have been known to produce the disease, but far less frequently, include *Klebsiella pneumoniae, Mycobacterium tuberculosis, Yersinia pestis* (the causative agent of pneumonic plague), *Francisella tularensis* (the causative agent of tularemia or rabbit fever), and *Serratia marcescens*. It is im-

portant to note that *S. pneumoniae* is also capable of causing diseases other than pneumonia; these include infection of the middle ear (otitis media), pneumococcal meningitis, and inflammation of the sinuses (sinusitis).

Transmission and predisposing factors. Pneumonia produced by *S. pneumoniae* occurs during the winter months in temperate zones, among the members of the population ranging in age from 15 to 45. Although this disease is not considered to be highly communicable, its incidence has been noted to be greater where close contact among persons exists, as in households, barracks, dormitories, hospital wards, prisons, and similar group living quarters. Mortality rates have been substantially reduced, especially in the young, by the early and adequate administration of antibiotics.

Pneumococci usually are spread by droplet nuclei from nasal or pharyngeal secretions. Individuals exposed to such infectious material may contact the disease or become carriers. It is interesting to note that approximately 40 to 70 percent of normal adults have *S. pneumoniae* as normal inhabitants of their throats.

Several factors have been reported as predisposing individuals to pneumonoccal pneumonia. Among these so-called secondary causes are viral infections of the upper respiratory tract, and local or generalized pulmonary edema (fluid in the lungs). Pulmonary edema can be brought about by irritating anesthetics, cardiac failure, and influenza. More general predisposing causes which have been implicated include increasing age, debilitating disease states, (e.g. diabetes, malignancies), fatigue, and chilling. With many, if not all, of the factors mentioned the underlying feature is an impairment of the lung's defense mechanism, its phagocytic activity by tissue macrophages.

Clinical features. The incubation period of pneumococcal pneumonia is short, 1 to 3 days, and the onset of the disease is quite abrupt. Patients definitely show illness from the onset. Individuals experiencing the infection generally exhibit the symptoms of a mild cold and a severe shaking chill, a fever ranging from 102° to 106°F, an elevated pulse, a thick, scanty, rust-colored sputum, marked chest pain, and a dry cough. Occasionally, nausea and vomiting may occur. In extremely severe cases, convulsions, cyanosis (a bluish coloration of the skin), and delirium can be encountered. Because of the high fever, herpes simplex infection may develop.

Physical examination of infected persons clearly demonstrates the signs of lung consolidation; these include crackling sounds and dullness to percussion.

Complications. Unfortunately, complications arise with at least 15 to 20 per cent of the pathogen's victims. Commonly encountered complications include recurrence of the disease, inflammation of the pleura, otitis media, and sinusitis. Apparently, *S. pneumoniae* rarely produces residual injury to the lung. Recurrence of this form of pneumonia is generally produced by a different serological type of organism. Pleural inflammation (*pleurisy*) may be associated with a small collection of fluid or effusion; hence this state is referred to as "pleurisy with effusion." If the accumulated fluid becomes purulent (pus-containing) the condition is called *empyema*. This is a rare complication, especially since the advent of antibiotic therapy. Other rare complications include lung abscess, meningitis, and involvement of the heart.

Diagnosis. Quite often, pneumococcal pneumonia can be diagnosed clinically, utilizing the patient's history and clinical manifestations—chills, respiration, and the appearance of his sputum. X-ray examinations also are extremely helpful. Confirmation is made on the basis of laboratory findings, which include the examination of the patient's sputum and the isolation of the pathogen from such material, as well as from blood.

Sputum specimens are Gram-stained and used as inocula for blood and chocolate agar media. Blood samples, which should be taken prior to any antibiotic treatment, can be cultured in a similar manner. The Gram procedure is an extremely important one, as it enables one to distinguish to a certain degree between *S. pneumoniae* and other bacterial causative agents of pneumonia, such as *Klebsiella pneumoniae* and α-hemolytic streptococci. The acid-fast staining procedure may also be utilized, especially when tuberculosis is suspected.

S. pneumoniae on blood agar produces α-hemolysis, and can be confused with α-hemolytic streptococci of the viridans group. In general, the distinction between these bacterial species is made using the bile-solubility and the optochin (ethylhydro-cupreine) tests. The former test is done by adding sodium deoxycholate to a saline suspension of the isolated organism. Pneumococci are solubilized by this compound. Similarly, if a paper disc impregnated with optochin is placed onto the surface of a blood agar plate containing *S. pneumoniae,* the growth of these organisms will be inhibited.

Additional diagnostic procedures which are used, although the frequency of usage depends upon the particular laboratory, are the Quellung, mouse inoculation, and the fermentation of inulin tests.

Immunity and prevention. Individuals who have recovered from pneumococcal pneumonia quite often carry the causative agents in their upper respiratory tracts for long periods, despite the fact that they also have circulating antibody in their bloodstreams. These antibodies remain for several months. In most cases, if an individual suffers a second attack of pneumonia, it is in all probability due to a serological type of *S. pneumoniae* other than the one which caused the first infection.

Preventive measures against pneumonoccal diseases generally include the adequate treatment and isolation of infected persons. Indiscriminate usage of antibiotics is to be avoided. The possibility of inducing drug reactions, and of enhancing the survival of drug resistant organisms, is always a potential danger.

Staphyloccal Pneumonia

Several factors and practices have been implicated as initiators of this disease state. These include a general lowering of defense mechanisms as a consequence of irradiation therapy or the administration of steroid compounds, uncontrolled diabetes mellitus, certain respiratory infections (e.g., influenza, measles), and diseases associated with the reticuloendothelial system (e.g., viral hepatitis). Certain medical practices have been suggested as possibly playing an important role in the establishment of staphylococci in the lungs. Organisms may be introduced through the use of intranasal tubes. In this case, staphylococci residing in the nasopharyngeal area may be simply carried along by the tubing. Excessive administration of intravenous fluids causes wet, "soggy" lungs, a condition which apparently provides a suitable environment for infectious agents.

Clinical features. In infants, staphylococcal pneumonia is an extremely serious infection. These patients generally exhibit a fever of 102° to 103°F, cyanosis, frequent cough, rapid breathing, and the presence of a pus-laden discharge from the eyes, nose, or both regions. The patients obviously are acutely ill.

In young adults, staphylococcal pneumonia usually develops as a complication of viral influenza, and the symptoms usually observed are similar to those described for infants, though of lesser severity. The infection tends to mimic pneumococcal pneumonia; however, a more extensive lung involvement develops (Figure 33–3).

In recent years, the incidence of *S. aureus*-caused pneumonia has increased in elderly, debilitated persons. Generally the symptoms observed are similar to those described for young adults. Some individuals also may exhibit mental confusion.

From the pathological viewpoint, consolidation and abscess formation (Figure 33–4) can occur on one or both sides of the lungs. The size of abscesses correlates with the length of the illness. Tissue destruction accompanied by hemorrhage,

FIG. 33–3. The appearance of the human lung in staphylococcal pneumonia. (Courtesy of the Armed Forces Institute of Pathology, Washington, D.C., Neg. No. AFIP 55–6150.)

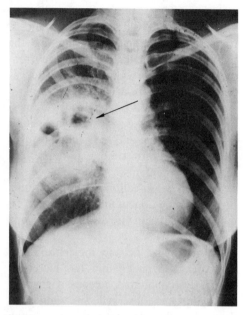

FIG. 33–4. Lung abscess formation caused by *Staphylococcus aureus*. X-ray shows lung area (arrow) with abscess before treatment. (Courtesy of Dr. Marcel Bilodeau, Hospital Laval, Quebec, Canada.)

as well as the presence of a thick, yellowish pus are commonly observed at autopsy of patients with staphylococcal involvement.

Diagnosis. Clinically, x-ray examination is extremely helpful. The finding of Gram-positive staphylococci in sputum specimens also is of value in establishing the diagnosis of staphylococcal pneumonia. Additional details of procedures used in laboratory diagnosis are given in Chapter 28.

Prevention. Precautionary measures should be practiced by nurses and physicians involved with patients. The following procedures should be included: (1) thorough hand washing; (2) avoiding the introduction of organisms via intranasal or intratracheal devices; (3) establishing a carrier-control program, especially in nurseries; and (4) an increased

surveillance of patients recovering from viral infections and of individuals with some form of debilitating disease such as diabetes or cancer.

Streptococcal Pneumonia

As mentioned earlier, streptococci can be divided into three broad categories on the basis of their hemolytic reactions on blood agar media: alpha (α), beta (β), and gamma (γ). The most commonly encountered human pathogen of these streptococcal categories is the β-hemolytic *Streptococcus pyogenes*. Its members are further subdivided into different immunological groups which are designated by the letters A through O. The basis for this classification is a difference in type-specific protein antigens. Human pathogens are found in large numbers in Group A. More than 50 different types belonging to this category have been reported since 1935.

Streptococcal pneumonia is an example of a suppurative (pus-producing) disease. Other suppurative infections produced by this type of organism include acute streptococcal pharyngitis, mastoiditis, meningitis, otitis media, peritonsillar abscesses, and various skin diseases. Acute glomerulonephritis and rheumatic fever are representative of the nonsuppurative category of streptococcal infections.

As with other bacterial pathogens, such as *Streptococcus pneumoniae* and *Klebsiella pneumoniae*, the invasive nature of streptococci depends to a very large extent on their antiphagocytic characteristics. The principal factors involved are their two surface components, the M protein and the hyaluronic acid capsule. The M protein is a cell wall component. It is the antigenic substance which makes the differentiation of Group A streptococci possible. The capsules of Group A organisms are composed of hyaluronic acid. This major component is not immunogenic. The reason for its invasive property apparently is related to the compound's similarity to the ground substance of connective tissues.

Clinical features. Streptococcal pneumonia may be a primary manifestation. It may also be a complication of other respiratory disease states, such as asthma, influenza, or measles, or it may follow shortly after other streptococcal infections, such as erysipelas or tonsillitis.

Streptococcal pneumonia generally has been reported to occur in individuals older than 10 years of age. Its incidence has been substantially reduced in recent years due to the advent of antibiotic therapy.

Persons with Group A, β-hemolytic streptococcus-caused pneumonia generally experience chills, cough, dyspnea (difficulty in breathing), fever, and malaise. Consolidation of the lungs is a rare finding. Complications that have been reported include endocarditis, meningitis, and pericarditis.

Laboratory diagnosis. The identification of β-hemolytic *Streptococcus pyogenes* generally involves inoculating blood agar plates with clinical specimens. The Gram stain procedure should demonstrate the presence of Gram-positive cocci appearing in pairs and short chains (Color photograph 15). Another procedure which has been found to be useful in providing a tentative identification of Group A streptococci incorporates filter paper discs impregnated with the antibiotic bacitracin on to the medium. As the β-hemolytic organisms of this category are particularly sensitive to this antibiotic, growth around the treated disc should be scanty.

Bacterial Pneumonias of Low Incidence

This disease of children under 10 also can be caused by two Gram-negative organisms, the cocco-bacillus *Hemophilus influenzae* and the short rod *Klebsiella pneumoniae*.

Hemophilus influenzae. In addition to its respiratory manifestations, *H. influenzae* is known to cause meningitis, otitis media, and other related conditions. The organism is transmitted by means of droplet nuclei, and gains entrance into the body via the respiratory tract. Only about 0.3 per cent of pneumonia cases are the result of *H. influenzae* infections. The organism's clinical features are indistinguishable from those of *Streptococcus pneumoniae*.

H. Influenzae infections have additional properties which are similar to *S. pneumoniae*. These include the presence of a fairly large percentage of carriers and the association of the organism's virulence with its capsule. At the present time, on the basis of the antigenic properties of *H. influenzae* capsular antibodies, 6 types are known, designated a through f. Severe infections are apparently caused by Type b.

Laboratory diagnosis. *H. influenzae* is a rather particular organism in that it will not grow on nutrient agar. It is usually grown on blood and chocolate agars, because it requires the growth factors designated as X and V. The X factor is heat-stable while the V factor is heat-labile. Blood agar contains both of these substances, but because the preparation of chocolate agar involves the heating of blood, it contains only the X factor.

The isolation of *H. influenzae* usually incorporates 5 to 10 per cent CO_2 (capneic incubation) which can be provided by a candle jar. Depending upon the disease state, specimens may be taken from the nasopharyngeal region, from blood, or from spinal fluid. This Gram-negative organism does not produce hemolysis. In addition, the Quellung test can be used with specific anti-serum to establish the identity of *H. influenzae.*

Active immunization against *H. influenzae* is not done. One reason for this is that by the time most children reach 10 years of age they possess a naturally acquired active state of immunity.

Klebsiella pneumoniae. This bacterial species, also known as Friedländer's bacillus, can be commonly found in the nasopharyngeal regions and intestinal tracts of healthy persons. However, the organism is also known as a secondary invader in various types of chronic pulmonary diseases. *K. pneumoniae* causes approximately 1 to 3 per cent of the bacterial pneumonias. The organism is similar in many ways to *Streptococcus pneumoniae,* especially, in relation to invasive properties, clinical features, and the existence of several serological types. The "type" designation refers to capsular antigens, of which there are 14. There are, however, significant differences from *Streptococcus.* Among them is the fact that *K. pneumoniae* is resistant to penicillin therapy.

Friedländer's pneumonia is both endemic and sporadic in nature. The highest number of cases appear during the summer months. Older male members of the population show a higher incidence of infection than females and younger males.

In addition to *K. pneumoniae,* additional species of the genus have been associated with respiratory tract infections. Principally, these include *K. ozenae* and *K. rhinoscleromatis.* The latter organism is believed to cause a destructive tumorous condition involving the nose and pharynx, while *K. ozenae* has been found in cases of nasal muscosa destruction.

Clinical features. Pneumonia caused by Friedländers bacillus most commonly involves type 1. Infected persons generally experience the sudden development of fever ranging from 101° to over 102°F., chest pains, and the formation of a thick, reddish-brown sputum. Lung abscesses and the development of necrotic areas also may occur. Usually these are produced by large numbers of unphagocytized, encapsulated *K. pneumoniae.* This encapsulation also interferes with the effectiveness of antibiotic therapy.

Complications can develop with this disease state; empyema is an example. Chronic alcoholics and the elderly apparently are more commonly subject to such complications.

Laboratory diagnosis. Since *Klebsiella pneumoniae* is insensitive to penicillin, it is essential to identify the antibiotic sensitivities of this small Gram-negative rod as quickly as possible. Sputum is the specimen of choice in pneumonia cases. The laboratory identification of *K. pneumoniae* involves tests similar to the ones used for *Enterobacter* (*Aerobacter*) *aerogenes* (Table 33–5).

Mycoplasma Infections

Mycoplasma have only recently been considered to be of medical importance. These microorganisms have been known for several years to be the causative agents of many diseases of lower animals. However, only recently have investigations demonstrated that one such species is pathogenic for man. This is *Mycoplasma pneumoniae,* the etiologic agent of primary atypical pneumonia.

In 1898, Nocard, Roux, Borrel, Salimbeni, and Dujardin-Beaumetz described a highly contagious pulmonary disease of cattle which was rampant in Europe at

Table 33–5   Characteristic Metabolic Reactions of *Klebsiella pneumoniae* and
Enterobacter (Aerobacter) aerogenes

Microorganism	Tests[a]						Carbohydrates[a]			
	Mot.	U.	Indole	M.R.	V.P.	Cit.	Glu.	Lact.	Man.	Suc.
Enterobacter aerogenes	+	−	−	−	+	+	AG	AG	AG	AG
Klebsiella pneumoniae	−	−	−	−	+	+	AG	AG	AG	AG

[a] Explanations of symbols: Mot=Motility; U=Urease; MR=Methyl red; VP=Voges-Proskauer; Cit=Citrate; Glu=Glucose; Lact=Lactose; Man=Mannose; Suc=Sucrose; +=positive; −=negative; AG=acid and gas produced.

that time. Large losses of animals were caused by the disease, which became known as *pleuropneumonia* because large quantities of serous fluid characteristically accumulated in the lungs and pleural cavities of diseased animals. The agent was called a virus because it could not be seen microscopically in early investigations.

Attempts to culture the so-called virus of pleuropneumonia on bacterial media available at the time failed. However, the later use of an *in vivo* technique devised by Metchnikoff, Roux, and Salimbeni produced favorable results. Stimulated by these investigations, others developed additional media for the cultivation of the pleuropneumonia agent.

Clinical features.   The degree of illness varies considerably. Some persons appear to be quite unaffected. Children generally experience a sudden onset of the disease, often accompanied by a cough, malaise, and shivering. Similar symptoms are found to develop in adults, who usually have additional complaints of headaches and sore throats. Adults also produce a thick, or mucopurulent, sputum. Many of these symptoms persist for 7 to 10 days. Coughing is generally the most prominent feature during this period.

The prognosis of *M. pneumoniae* infection is generally good. Fatalities seldom occur. However, complications resulting from primary atypical pneumonia have been reported; these include encephalitis and polyneuritis (inflammation of many nerves).

Laboratory diagnosis.   Diagnosis of *Mycoplasma pneumoniae* infection generally incorporates isolation and serological procedures. Clinical specimens, including sputum and material from pharyngeal swabbing, are used for the inoculation of suitable liquid or solid media for the cultivation of pathogenic mycoplasma. The media are usually supplemented with yeast extract, penicillin, and serum or cholesterol. Lipid substances are extremely important to the nutrition and metabolism of these pathogenic microorganisms. Saprophytic strains apparently do not have this requirement. It is also customary to add thallium acetate, which inhibits possible contaminants and saprophytic mycoplasma.

Growth in liquid media may appear within a week or may take several weeks. Colonies of the organism in liquid preparation are usually free-floating. They are round, ranging in diameter from 10 to 200 μm. On solid media, colonies of human pathogenic strains look like fried eggs (Figure 33–5 and Color photograph 4*B*). This effect is caused by the organism's penetration of the agar.

Special staining methods are used to demonstrate and identify the presence of

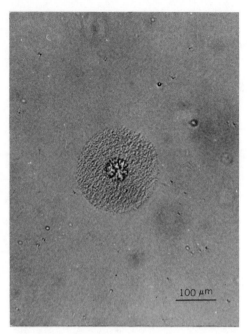

FIG. 33–5. A colony of the human T-strain *mycoplasma* Johnson. (From Manchee, R. J., and Taylor-Robinson, D.: *J. Bacteriol.*, **100**:78–85, 1969.)

the organisms in agar media, including the direct fluorescence antibody technique. The combination of methylene blue and azure II also is used to show colonies.

The presence in patients' sera of *cold agglutinins* (antibodies which can agglutinate human type O erythrocytes at 4°C) and the cells of an α–(alpha) hemolytic streptococcus of the MG variety, is diagnostically significant. Both types of antibody generally develop in persons with atypical primary pneumonia caused by *M. pneumoniae*. The complement-fixation test is used to demonstrate a rise in antibody titer during the course of the disease. It should be noted here that cold agglutinins may also be encountered with other disease states, e.g., acquired hemolytic anemia (see Chapter 24).

Streptococcal (Epidemic, Septic) Sore Throat

This condition is generally defined as an acute, severe inflammation of both the tonsils (tonsillitis) and the throat (pharyngitis). "Strep throat" can be caused by several strains of Lancefield's group A, beta hemolytic streptococci.

Means of transmission. The disease usually occurs in epidemic form and is associated with contaminated milk products and water—it is a milk- or waterborne disease. The nasopharynxes of individuals suffering from the disease during the acute or convalescent stages serve as the sources of infectious agents. There are also carriers. Milk products may become contaminated as a consequence of human handling, or as a consequence of obtaining milk from infected cows. In situations of epidemics involving the consumption of milk, the source of the food product usually can be traced to the same dairy. Furthermore, "strep throat" occurs more commonly in regions where pasteurization of milk is not practiced. Epidemics may last from 2 to 6 weeks. The incidence of this disease is greater during the winter and spring months.

Clinical features. The incubation period for septic sore throat varies between 1 and 3 days. All ages can be affected. Symptoms of the disease develop within 24 to 36 hours following the ingestion of contaminated food or water. Such stricken individuals may experience chills, fever ranging from 102° to 105°F, headache, nausea or vomiting, and a rapid pulse. Additional features of the infection include congestion of the mucous membranes of the soft palate as well as of the pharynx, reddened and swollen throat, swollen uvula, and the presence of a gray or yellow-white material covering the pharynx and throat. Swallowing is quite painful for the affected individual.

Complications that may be associated with streptococcal sore throats include arthritis, endocarditis, lymphadenitis (lymph node inflammation) of various types, otitis media (middle ear infection), nephritis (inflammation of the kidney), and septicemia.

Diagnosis. Clinically the disease must be differentiated from several other infectious diseases, including diphtheria, infectious mononucleosis, and Vincent's angina. The laboratory procedures used in the identification of streptococcal infections are discussed in other chapters.

Prevention. Control measures for this disease include pasteurization of milk, isolation of infected persons, and proper disinfection or disposal of objects contaminated by the discharges of infected persons. Such persons should not be allowed to come into contact with products for consumption during either the acute or convalescence stages of the disease.

Whooping Cough (Pertussis)

This disease was first described in 1578 by Baillou. Subsequently, several epidemics of pertussis occurred during the seventeenth century in England. Today, the disease exhibits a worldwide distribution and appears to be more prevalent in colder regions. Children under 5 years of age, especially newborns, are the primary victims, with females being affected more frequently than males. However, aged and debilitated individuals also are quite susceptible.

Means of transmission. Whooping cough is characterized by spasmodic coughing attacks and an inspiratory whoop. With this prominent feature of the disease in evidence, transmission no doubt is by droplet infection. However, fomites should not be ruled out.

The etiologic agent, *Bordetella pertussis* (formerly known as *Hemophilus pertussis*), was isolated by Bordet and Gengou in 1906. It is a small, non-motile, Gram-negative rod. Capsules are formed by virulent organisms. *B. pertussis* differs from *H. influenzae* in several respects, including: (1) the absence of the requirements for either the X or V factors for purposes of growth following primary isolation; (2) the production of a single, capsular antigen; and (3) the presence of limited invasive capabilities.

Clinical features. The incubation period of pertussis ranges from 5 to 21 days after exposure. Most authorities divide the disease into three stages—the *catarrhal,* the *paroxysmal,* and the *convalescent.*

The catarrhal stage lasts approximately 7 to 14 days. Infected individuals experience bronchitis and an accompanying dry, persistent cough. A slight fever, characteristic catarrhal symptoms (coryza, sneezing, and lacrimation or tearing), and poor appetite also are present. Children lack energy, and may vomit after a paroxysm (an intensification of the characteristic symptoms).

The paroxysmal stage occurs after about a week of the disease. With severe cases this phase may continue for up to 4 weeks. Recurrence of intense symptoms usually is experienced by patients 10 to 15 times per day. In severe cases the number of such attacks may exceed 30. During the coughing bout, the patient's face becomes deep red, and may even become cyanotic, or purplish red color. The characteristic "whoop" is caused by rapidly inhaling air, which passes quickly over the vocal cords. Usually at the end of a paroxysm of coughs a thick, stringy mucus mass is evident in the nose and mouth. Vomiting may also occur. Bouts of this type are extremely tiring, and children may fall asleep from exhaustion between attacks.

The convalescent stage develops approximately within 4 weeks after the onset of the infection. Attacks of coughing generally subside in severity as well as in frequency. However, the paroxysmal type of cough described in the previous stage can return. (It also should be noted that children may "fake" symptoms to gain certain benefits from their parents.)

Complications that may occur with whooping cough include atelectasis (collapsed lung), bronchopneumonia, interstitial emphysema, convulsions, and hemorrhages in various regions of the body (e.g., brain, conjunctivae, eyes, and skin).

Laboratory diagnosis. Bacteriologically, laboratory diagnosis has been commonly based on isolations made from the so-called "cough plates." Here, plates of the Bordet-Gengou agar (BGA) medium are held open in front of patients who are asked to cough. BGA contains glycerol, peptone extract and 20 to 25 per cent sheep's blood. This type of procedure has been largely replaced with the *nasopharyngeal swab* method for obtaining specimens. A cotton swab, usually on the end of a flexible wire approximately 8 inches long, is passed through a nostril to the posterior pharyngeal region (see Figure 33–1). The specimen-containing swab is removed from the patient and quickly touched to a drop of penicillin solution on a BGA plate. The penicillin serves to prevent the growth of sensitive contaminants. The specimen-containing-drop then is streaked onto the medium and the plate is incubated at 37°C for 48 to 72 hours. Identification of *B. pertussis* is made

on the basis of an agglutination test, using the isolated organisms and the specific anti-serum. Rapid bacteriological identification of this pathogen also can be obtained with the direct staining of nasopharyngeal specimen smears by fluorescein-labeled antibody. Serological tests are of little diagnostic significance early in the disease.

Prevention.   Active immunization is the most widely used practice for the control of pertussis. Generally children approximately 3 months old are given the DPT (diphtheria, pertussis, and tetanus) vaccine preparation. The pertussis portion is a merthiolate-killed virulent form (S) of the causative agent. The primary vaccination procedure is carried out with 3 injections, administered at 4 to 6 weeks intervals. Booster shots are advised at the ages of 1, 3, and 5 years.

This immunization procedure does not provide protection against the milder infection caused by *B. parapertussis.*

In situations of susceptible contacts, i.e., young children, isolation and the administration of human hyperimmune serum are carried out. Exposed individuals who have been vaccinated one year or more previously should be given a booster.

Parapertussis

Parapertussis is clinically indistinguishable from pertussis. Identification of the causative agent, *B. parapertussis,* is accomplished with specific agglutinating antisera. It should be noted that the treatment for this disease is similar to that followed with whooping cough.

Tuberculosis and Other Mycobacterial Diseases

Tuberculosis has been a worldwide plague of mankind for centuries, especially in areas of malnutrition and poor sanitary conditions. The clinical manifestations as well as the communicable nature of this infectious disease have been known since at least 1000 B.C. Both Aristotle and Hippocrates described it. During the so-called Hippocratic age, the disease was referred to by the term *phthisis,* translated into English as *consumption.* The designation of the infection as tuberculosis probably arose in part from the post-mortem observations of Sylvius, who noted nodular lesions in victims of the disease. He applied the term *tubercle* to such typical manifestations.

The fact that tuberculosis was not necessarily limited to the respiratory system but could also involve other regions of the body was not apparent until the early part of the nineteenth century. This discovery was first reported by Laennec, who invented the stethoscope—an instrument which has aided in the early detection of tuberculosis as well as of many other diseases.

Although the infectious nature of tuberculosis was formally established by Villemin in 1868, not until 1882 was the true cause of the disease demonstrated. Robert Koch, fulfilling the dictates of his famous postulates (see Chapter 2), clearly proved *Mycobacterium tuberculosis* to be the etiological agent of this infection.

Since Koch's discovery, a number of other species of the genus *Mycobacterium* have been reported to cause similar disease states in man and other animals. The suggestion has been made to refer to all such diseases, tuberculosis included, as a form of *mycobacteriosis,* but a final decision has not been made to adopt the term. Tuberculosis is still the preferred term for *M. tuberculosis, M. bovis,* and rarely *M. avium* infections. In their 1969 publication entitled *Diagnostic Standards and Classification of Tuberculosis,* the National Tuberculosis and Respiratory Disease Association recommends that other mycobacteria-caused diseases be reported in a manner which specifies the etiological agent (e.g., lung infection caused by *M. kansasii*).

The prevalence of tuberculosis in many western countries has been substantially reduced. Unfortunately, however, in regions of the world such as the Orient and the tropics, tuberculosis still reigns. Furthermore, unknown thousands of persons with the disease have escaped detection or have not been adequately treated after diagnosis. In short, tuberculosis still is very much with us today. Persons with active infections pose a serious threat to the well-being of others.

Transmission and predisposing factors. Today, infection with *M. tuberculosis* occurs primarily through the inhalation of droplet nuclei. Sputum, "coughing sprays," and droplets released through sneezing from infected persons serve as common sources of the disease agent. So does contaminated dust.

Other ways by which mycobacteria may gain entrance into the susceptible individual include ingestion and direct inoculation. Tubercle organisms may be swallowed by children as a consequence of placing contaminated objects into the mouth or consuming food containing these bacteria. The danger of acquiring tuberculosis from infected dairy products has been largely eliminated in many countries by the pasteurization of milk products and the tuberculin testing of dairy cattle. (Rarely, butchers may become infected through handling diseased meats or pathologists in examining infected tissues.) Congenital TB appears to be rare, as the placenta is usually an effective barrier to *M. tuberculosis.*

Predisposing or *secondary* causes of tuberculosis include advanced age, chronic alcoholism, poor diet, low economic status, certain metabolic diseases, some occupations, race, and prolonged stress. Tuberculosis itself is not inherited. The question of whether air pollution and/or cigarette smoking predispose one to tuberculosis has not been settled.

Active pulmonary tuberculosis among infants and children has been substantially reduced in the United States. In general, however, the disease is severe in infants whose susceptibility to tuberculosis increases with age after adolescence. For some unknown reason, the typical victims of the disease in the U.S. are white males 40 years of age or older. However, the ratio of death to active cases of tuberculosis is substantially higher in the non-white members of the population. This is true for both sexes of the American Indian, Eskimo, and Negro.

Tuberculosis is a disease associated with poverty. Overcrowding, poorly ventilated rooms, and malnutrition favor the establishment of *M. tuberculosis* infection. Quite possibly, factors such as these may account for the greater mortality among non-whites.

Among the metabolic diseases, diabetes mellitus appears to be the most frequently encountered one which predisposes persons to pulmonary tuberculosis.

Other factors that have been noted to be of significance include prolonged periods of fatigue or overexertion, dissipation, and chronic alcoholism. The latter stage is related most definitely to poor nutrition. Whether or not other respiratory diseases influence susceptibility to tuberculosis has not been firmly established. Frequent colds have been implicated, however.

Selected aspects of mycobacterial classification. The etiologic agent of human tuberculosis is the tubercle bacillus, or *Mycobacterium tuberculosis*. Occasionally *M. bovis* and rarely *M. avium* have been found to be the causative agents. The genus *Mycobacterium* contains pathogens as well as some saprophytic members. These organisms are characterized as being acid-fast, aerobic, non-motile, non-sporulating rods. Table 33–6 lists many of the recognized saprophytic and pathogenic species, together with their distribution and other properties.

Several mycobacteria isolated from human specimens have differed in certain properties from those noted in Table 33–6. On the basis of their respective growth rate and ability to produce pigment, four groups of these so-called atypical or anonymous organisms have been provisionally created. The classification scheme is based on one proposed by E. H. Runyon. Accordingly, the groups are designated as Runyon Groups I through IV. The selected properties of the respective groups are given in Table 33–7.

The properties of several mycobacteria strains have been recorded for many years. From these records, it appears that the characteristics remained relatively constant. Subsequently, several strains have been utilized as standards in studies, and as material for human prophylactic immunization. The *bacille Calmette and Guérin,* or BCG, is used for the latter purpose. This organism, a bovine tubercle bacillus, was originally isolated by Nocard in 1902.

Selected aspects of the pathogenesis and the pathology of tuberculosis. The pathogenesis and pathology of tuberculosis are relatively complex subjects. Due to space limitations, only a brief treatment of these subject areas can be presented. The discussion will deal with the characteristic responses of the body to tubercle bacilli. Additional information can be obtained from the reference sources given at the end of the text.

Table 33–6   Selected Pathogenic and Saprophytic Mycobacteria

Organism	Other Designations	Pathogen (P) or Saprophyte (S)	Distribution and/or Related Properties
M. avium	*M. tuberculosis var. avium*	P	Causes tuberculosis in birds and pigs
M. bovis	*M. tuberculosis var. bovis;* mammalian tubercle bacillus	P	Causes tuberculosis
M. leprae	Hansen's bacillus	P	Causes leprosy
M. lepraemurium	Stelansky's bacillus	P	Causes rat leprosy
M. marinum	*M. balnei*	P	Can cause infections of salt-water fish. Produces swimming pool granuloma in humans
M. microti	Vole bacillus or murine tubercle bacillus	P	Produces tuberculosis in voles, and localized infections in calves, guinea pigs, and rabbits
M. paratuberculosis	———	P	Causes a chronic diarrhea in cattle, known as Johne's disease
M. phlei	Timothy hay bacillus	S	Widely distributed in dust, soil, and on plants
M. platypoecilus	———	P	Causes infections of tropical and related fish
M. smegmatis	———	S	Widely distributed in nature
M. thamnopheos	———	P	Causes infection in garter snakes
M. tuberculosis	*M. tuberculosis var. hominis,* mammalian tubercle bacilli	P	Causes tuberculosis in humans
M. ulcerans	———	P	Causes skin ulcers in humans

Table 33–7   A Provisional Classification of the Atypical or Anonymous Mycobacteria

Runyon Group Designation	General Name	Example	Pigment Produced	Growth	
				25°C	37°C
I	Photochromogens	*M. kansasii*	Yellow[a]	Slow	Slow
II	Scotochromogens	*M. scrofulaeum*	Yellow-orange	Absent	Slow
III	Nonchromogens	Battey bacilli	Absent	Absent	Slow
IV	Rapid-growers	*M. xenopi*	Absent	Absent	Rapid[b]

[a] Light-dependent.
[b] Bacterial colonies appear within 5 to 7 days after inoculation.

The response of the individual to tubercle bacilli primarily is dependent upon his resistance, as well as the organism's virulence. The size of the initial inoculum and the location of the infection also are important factors. In man, a wide range of responses can occur. The tissue changes which develop, in simple terms, are mainly those associated with inflammation and repair.

Basically, an inflammatory process is produced from the presence of *M. tuberculosis*. This so-called "tuberculosis inflammation" chiefly incorporates wandering tissue phagocytes known as *macrophages*. These cells are also known as "histiocytes" and "phagocytic pneumocytes." Most other inflammatory processes utilize polymorphonuclear leukocytes (PMNLs).

The initial and characteristic lesion of tuberculosis, called the *tubercle,* appears as a nodule in the lung parenchyma (tissue). Infection sites may be found in any portion of the lung. However, the pleura appear to be commonly involved. Single localized lesions (single foci) result in most cases, although multiple foci are known.

Pulmonary lesions develop in the most aerated regions of the lungs. The presence of a high O_2 tension, which *M. tuberculosis* requires, may account for the development of lesions in the top parts (apices) of the upper lobes of human lungs. In cattle, the dorsal region of the lower lung lobes is involved.

From the histo-pathological standpoint, two types of reactions are recognized—*exudative* and *productive lesions.* Exudative lesions are found in cases of initial infection, or in persons with a low level of resistance. Organisms multiply rapidly in such individuals, as there is little host resistance. Exudative lesions are characterized by the presence of acute or subacute inflammation accompanied by the outpouring of fluid from the surrounding tissue, and the accumulation of polymorphonuclear leukocytes around the causative agents of the disease.

The productive lesion develops in persons with tuberculo-protein sensitivity. In general, elongated epithelioid cell tubercles are formed by macrophages that come into contact with *M. tuberculosis* or its products. These cells are arranged concentrically. In the center of the lesion some of these cells may fuse to one another, forming giant cells. In addition, numerous cell nuclei are arranged around the periphery and in turn are surrounded by lymphocytes and multiplying fibroblasts. A fibroblast is a flat, elongated connective tissue cell. These cells form the fibrous supporting and binding tissues of the body. Extensive scarring or fibrosis eventually develops from productive lesions.

Apparently confusion exists as to the presence and location of *M. tuberculosis* in the various types of lesions associated with tuberculosis. Tubercle bacilli are relatively rare in productive lesions and in infiltrating macrophages. They are, however, present in fresh necrotic lesions and most frequently found in caseous material (necrotic tissue that is semi-solid and has a cheesy consistency) in association with lung cavities.

Healing.   The healing of tuberculous lesions may occur in several ways. These include calcification, fibrosis, and resolution. Generally, these types of healing are combined.

Calcification refers to a process by which calcium is deposited within the caseous centers of tuberculous lesions of long standing. It develops generally after two years.

Fibrosis or *scarring* accompanies most lesions of a tuberculous nature that undergo healing. Collagen is deposited during the process. As necrosis develops within a tuberculous lesion, this supportive tissue surrounds the caseous material, forming a capsule. Some clinicians and pathologists are of the opinion that these encapsulated lesions could be supporting viable tubercle bacilli. Therefore, they should never be considered as "healed," but rather as "inactive" or "stabilized."

Resolution probably accompanies the healing of all tuberculous lesions. The process includes the disappearance of infiltrating macrophages and even of the epitheloid cell tubercles described earlier.

When healing does not take place, the tuberculosis is considered to be "progressive." Established lesions can extend themselves by simple enlargement into surrounding tissue. This process, which is referred to as *local progression,* applies also to other types of spreading, such as bronchogenic (extension of lesions from the bronchi), lymphogenous, and hematogenous. These forms of spreading, together with the tissues and organs affected by them, are discussed in the section dealing with extrapulmonary tuberculosis.

According to pathologists, one important clinical complication of the local form of progression is the *pulmonary cavity*, which develops as the result of a tuberculous lesion spreading or extending into a bronchus, and its caseous material softening and flowing out of the region. Consequently, air fills in this area, and a tuberculous cavity forms.

Extrapulmonary Tuberculosis

Dissemination of tubercle bacilli to organs or structures other than the lungs proper may occur by several routes, including direct extension, hematogenous dispersals, and lymphogenous spread. In the so-called "bronchogenic spread," sputum-containing tubercle bacilli may spill over from the affected lung to the uninvolved one. Such infectious discharges may also on occasion be the source of *M. tuberculosis* in cases of tuberculosis of the larynx and trachea.

Miliary tuberculosis. When *hematogenous dispersal* is widespread and massive —thus producing generalized systemic involvement—the condition is called *miliary tuberculosis*. This state results from the simultaneous depositing of *M. tuberculosis* ("bacillary seeding") in numerous body tissues. Subsequently, small "millet-seedlike" lesions develop in these areas. Other forms of lesion also appear. In general, the development of lesions is influenced by factors including the immune and hypersensitive state of the individual, the size of the infecting dose, and the particular site involved in entering the circulation. Miliary tuberculosis is found most frequently in infants and children who experienced their first infection approximately one or two years earlier. The disease itself may vary from an overwhelming, acute infection to one which is of a mild, chronic, and relatively asymptomatic nature. Various tissues and organs can be affected through the different means of dissemination.

Lymphogenous dissemination is characterized by the leakage of small doses of tubercle bacilli from the lymphatics into the circulatory system. This introduction of bacilli is secondary to the primary infection. Subsequently, isolated foci develop in some tissues and organs. Such lesions may heal, or some years later may cause the development of extrapulmonary tuberculosis.

The incidence of extrapulmonary tuberculosis is lower than formerly in several areas of the world, especially the United States. Factors accounting for this situation include effective chemotherapeutic measures to prevent the spreading of tubercle bacilli to extrapulmonary locations, the effectiveness of programs to eradicate bovine tuberculosis, and improvements in diagnosis.

Skin Tests

Robert Koch's discovery of the tuberculin reaction in 1890 provided mankind with one of the most valuable diagnostic procedures for the control of tuberculosis. In addition to its obvious importance from the standpoint of differential diagnosis, the test serves as an extremely important epidemiological tool.

The basis of the tuberculin reaction is the development of a specific delayed type of hypersensitivity to certain products of *M. tuberculosis* and related mycobacteria during the course of an infection. These products are contained in culture extracts, and are referred to as *tuberculins*. The sensitivity which occurs in individuals may develop approximately one month after infection or later, and it usually remains for several years or for an entire lifetime.

Skin reactivity to the introduction of skin test material, e.g., Old Tuberculin (OT) or Purified Protein Derivative (PPD), may be suppressed by several factors or conditions. These include: (1) advanced age, (2) terminal or severe acute diseases (e.g., cancer), and (3) the administration of large quantities of cortisone. Infectious diseases such as measles, smallpox, vaccination against these diseases, or a rapidly progressive case of tuberculosis also may cause a similar type of skin reaction. *The tuberculin test reveals previous infection. but does not prove the presence of an active disease state.* Reports from many parts of the world indicate a relationship between the size of the skin reaction and the risk of developing active tuberculosis. Apparently the larger the reaction, the greater the possibility of active disease.

Preparations used for testing.   Two types of tuberculin, Old Tuberculin (OT) and Purified Protein Derivative (PPD) are widely employed for skin testing. The former material was originally described by Robert Koch, and incorporates the heat-sterilization of an *M. tuberculosis* culture. The active component in Old Tuberculin is a protein which is noted for its heat stability and retention of specificity for several years.

The second preparation, PPD, is a slightly more refined testing substance than OT. It is preferred because its strength lends itself to standardization of dosages; skin tests performed with the same dose are comparable. PPD contains an active protein component which is obtained from filtrates of autoclaved tubercule bacilli cultures.

Techniques for administration.   Three general types of procedures currently are employed in the performance of the tuberculin test: (1) intradermal injection (Mantoux), (2) jet injection, and (3) multiple puncture. The first of these methods, intradermal injection, serves as the standard procedure for comparison purposes with all other tests. Moreover, with the Mantoux test more accurate control of PPD or OT dosage is possible. The other two types of general methods are utilized for epidemiological (survey and screening) purposes.

Another procedure, known as the Vollmer patch test, also has had wide application because of its simplicity. Concentrated skin testing material, tuberculin, is applied in this case by means of a piece of filter paper which is held in place on the skin by adhesive tape. Such tests are examined and read 24 to 48 hours after the application of tuberculin. Unfortunately, the "patch test" is not considered to be reliable, and therefore is not a procedure of choice.

The standard dose used for differential diagnosis as well as for epidemiological studies is 5 tuberculin units (TU). The quantity of PPD used in milligrams per dose is 0.0001 or 0.1 microgram (μg). The dose is based on the milligrams of protein required for an approximate equivalent to a 1:2000 dilution of OT. When persons are suspected of having tuberculosis, a lower concentration is used first to circumvent a severe reaction. If a skin reaction is not observed within 2 to 3 days, the standard skin test dose is used.

Interpretations of skin testing reactions. The following interpretations and recording of skin test results are in keeping with the current recommendations of the National Tuberculosis and Respiratory Disease Association.

The intradermal introduction of tuberculin into sensitized persons usually results in the formation of an indurated (hard) area (Figure 33–6), which may or may not be associated with a surrounding reddened area (erythema). The intensity and size of the reaction varies according to the individual's sensitivity and the quantity of skin testing material introduced. Those persons exhibiting tuberculin sensitivity are called *reactors*. The degree of sensitivity can be determined from the size and accompanying features of the skin reaction, e.g., erythema and necrosis.

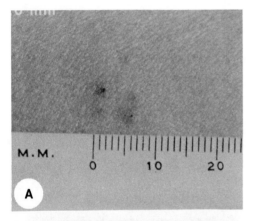

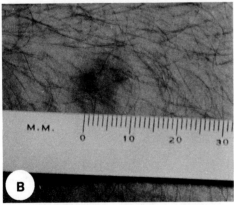

FIG. 33–6. The results of a Tuberculin Tine Test. The presence or absence of induration (hardened area) can be determined by visual observation or by stroking the region around the site of injection. A. The response to the skin testing material after 48 hours. B. The same individual 96 hours after injection. (Courtesy of Lederle Laboratories, Pearl River, N.Y.)

In recording the results of a skin test, notation should be made of: (1) the specific test method used, (2) the type and dose of skin testing material introduced, and (3) the size of the reaction (induration observed in millimeters). Readings should be made in a good light, and the patient's forearm should be slightly flexed.

The tuberculin test has practical significance, not only because it can serve as a diagnostic tool, but also because it can be used to screen large groups of people for tuberculosis and to detect infections and identify sources of infection. After initial infection with tubercule bacilli, the sensitivity to tuberculin develops in approximately 2 to 10 weeks. Once this state is acquired, it generally persists. The various factors which can affect its expression have been discussed earlier.

Laboratory Diagnosis

The microscopic demonstration of *Mycobacterium tuberculosis* in clinical specimens is essential to the diagnosis of tuberculosis. Because staining procedures constitute an important aspect of diagnosis, all glassware must be scrupulously clean.

Obtaining specimens. A wide variety of specimens can be utilized for the demonstration of tubercle bacilli; these include catheterized urine, cerebrospinal and pleural fluids, sputum, and tissue biopsy material. Sputum generally is the specimen of choice. In the case of children, specimens may be obtained with the aid of a laryngeal swab or gastric lavage. The latter procedure involves the introduction of a tube via the patient's nostril or mouth into the gastric area. A sterile syringe is used to draw the necessary material from this region.

Victims of tuberculosis may be too ill to produce sufficient sputum. Here the techniques of tracheal suction or nebulization with heated, hypertonic saline can be performed. Tracheal suction involves the introduction of 5 to 10 ml of sterile saline into the trachea of the individual. The patient subsequently coughs up the saline, together with sputum. A face mask or shield should be worn by the individual performing this procedure to guard him against the potentially infectious aerosol created by the patient.

The saline nebulization technique is a relatively simple one, and usually does not cause the patient any appreciable discomfort. In this method, sputum specimens are obtained after individuals have been subjected to a 10- to 15-minute period of inhaling a 10 per cent saline solution at 45°C.

The acid-fast staining procedure, otherwise known as the Ziehl-Neelsen technique (Color photograph 17), is the most widely used method for staining *M. tuberculosis* and related organisms. Certain laboratories which are equipped with fluorescence microscopes and the necessary accessories employ fluorescent dyes, such as auramine, for microscopic examination of specimens (see Chapter 6).

Preparing cultures. Filter membranes have been used to collect organisms from cerebrospinal and pleural fluids, after which they are placed on the surface of an appropriate medium.

With specimens such as sputum or gastric contents, concentration and digestion procedures are frequently necessary in order to free organisms which may be trapped within the specimen. Procedures used to obtain organisms for culture purposes include digestion with strong acid, or with alkali, enzymes, or mucolytic agents (Figure 33–7). Secondary microorganisms are eliminated from

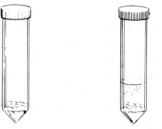

1. Sputum sample in 50 ml. plastic centrifuge tube.

2. Sample overlayered with Sputolysin.®

3. Vortex mixing.

4. Spin down.

5. Decant the supernatant solution.

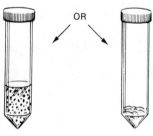

OR

6. For Acid-Fast bacilli, decontaminate as instructed.

7. Resuspend organisms in sterile diluent. Inoculate onto specific culture media for predominant organisms.

FIG. 33–7. An example of a sputum digestion procedure employing the mucolytic agent sputolysin. This is a concentrated sterile solution of Cleland's Reagent, dithiothreitol. Sputolysin liquifies sputum without causing any harmful effects to microorganisms. (Courtesy of Calbiochem, San Diego.)

specimens by a subsequent chemical treatment. *M. tuberculosis* possesses an unusual resistance to many chemical substances which is not shared by other organisms.

Several types of media are currently in use for *M. tuberculosis* isolation, with solid media preferred for purposes of primary isolation. Many of these preparations contain egg yolk or potato or both. A popular example of a buffered egg-potato medium would be Löwenstein-Jensen. Other preparations used in the cultivation of *M. tuberculosis* include Middlebrook Oleic Acid agar (7H–10), Petragnani, and Tarshis blood agar.

Culture preparations usually are incubated at 37°C and kept for 8 weeks, or longer if facilities permit. Weekly examinations are conducted during this time. An atmosphere of 3 to 10 per cent of carbon dioxide has been noted to enhance the growth of tubercle bacilli. In general, positive cultures usually become evident within 3 to 4 weeks.

Animal inoculations, specifically guinea pig, can also be used for the detection of *M. tuberculosis*. However, this procedure is not extensively used because of certain disadvantages, which include the expense of animal facilities as well as the animals and the existence of certain drug-resistant or atypical mycobacteria that do not produce diagnostically significant results in guinea pigs.

Guinea pig inoculations are used in situations where microscopic examinations of specimens are positive for tubercle bacilli, but cultures are negative, to differentiate *M. tuberculosis* from other mycobacteria, e.g., *M. avium* and *M. bovis,* and where contamination of sputum and urine specimens is a continual problem.

Identification. A definitive identification of *M. tuberculosis* usually is made if the following findings are present: (1) specimen inoculated guinea pigs show a positive skin test to OT, (2) organs of the injected animal, such as liver, lungs, and spleen, and draining lymph nodes exhibit gross tuberculosis lesions, and (3) acid-fast bacilli are present in lesions located in areas other than those near the site of inoculations. Several biochemical identification tests also are used. These include nitrate reduction and niacin production procedures. *M. tuberculosis* is positive for these tests.

Classification of Pulmonary Tuberculosis

The National Tuberculosis and Respiratory Disease Association has listed certain essential categories for a basic classification scheme. The following brief descriptions have been adapted from that publication.

Before any justifiable classification can be applied, the laboratory diagnosis of pulmonary tuberculosis must have been established. This refers specifically to the bacteriologic demonstration, cultural and microscopic, of *M. tuberculosis* in specimens obtained from a patient believed to be experiencing the disease.

Pulmonary tuberculosis, which includes all *M. tuberculosis*-associated lesions in the lungs, is generally divided into primary and reinfection tuberculosis. *Primary tuberculosis* develops uninterruptedly after the first implantation by *M. tuberculosis. Reinfection tuberculosis* is the most commonly occurring form of tuberculosis, and represents an entirely new episode in an individual in whom the primary infection has healed. Such infections may develop from: (1) the progression of the primary manifestation either immediately or after several years have elapsed (*endogenous*), (2) a "true reinfection" from an external source (*exogenous*), or (3) the superimposing of a new infection on an already active case of tuberculosis (*superinfection*). The third possibility is a rare occurrence.

A basic classification of pulmonary tuberculosis generally includes tuberculin conversion, the extent of disease, state of clinical activity, and therapeutic status.

Tuberculin converters. These are persons whose tuberculin skin tests change from a negative to a positive reaction within 12 months. Tuberculin converters do not exhibit any evidence of pulmonary tuberculosis, either on chest roentgenograms or on bacteriologic examinations.

Extent of disease. The total extent as well as the location of pulmonary lesions forms the basis of this category. Chest roentgenograms serve as the major source of such information.

Status of clinical activity. Both roentgenographic and bacteriologic findings serve as the basis for the various designations used to characterize the stages of clinical activity associated with pulmonary tuberculosis. The duration of such stages constitutes a significant part of the classification scheme.

Six classes of clinical activity and several subclasses are currently recognized. These include:

Active. Criteria such as: (1) the demonstration of *M. tuberculosis* in clinical specimens, (2) roentgenographic evidence of pulmonary lesions, or (3) the presence of complications, either singly or collectively. The duration of the activity and observations as to the degree of improvement should be indicated, if at all possible. Examples of these notations include "Active, unimproved" and "Active, improved."

Inactive. Two subclasses of this category exist, "Inactive, noncavitary" and "Inactive, cavitary." Patients put into the former category must produce negative results for both bacteriologic and roentgenographic examinations for at least 6 months. An active state cannot change to an inactive one in fewer than 6 months. However, reversion from an inactive state to active status can occur.

The class of "Inactive, cavitary" is a new one. Slight increases or decreases in cavity size, or slight variations in appearance of such cavities, are permitted in this category. Bacteriologic findings must be negative for a total of 18 months. The testing period must include a total of 15 consecutive months after the "Quiescent, cavitary stage."

Quiescent. Two subclasses of this category are recognized, "Quiescent, noncavitary," and "Quiescent, cavitary." The designations refer to specific classes which are intermediate between active and inactive stages. The associated bacteriologic findings are the same for both quiescent classes. Negative results are required at monthly intervals over a period of 3 consecutive months.

Quiescent, noncavitary status is assigned to individuals who not only have met the bacteriologic requirements mentioned above, but also exhibit on x-ray contracting or slightly clearing or stable lesions without "demonstrable cavitation." The second class in this category, "Quiescent, cavitary," differs from the former one only in permitting the presence of cavity. With quiescent, cavitary patients, their status may develop into an inactive, cavitary one, proceed to inactive, or unfortunately, may regress to active.

Activity undetermined. This designation is reserved for cases in which adequate bacteriologic and roentgenographic studies have not been performed. For public health purposes a provisional estimate of activity may be necessary. Tentative terms such as "probably active" or "probably inactive" can be utilized with persons whose status has not been definitely determined. Bacteriologic and roentgenographic observations in these cases must not contradict each other.

Dead. Notation of the cause of death, together with the results of autopsy findings (necropsy), may be used to supplement this class designation. In the event the cause of death was not tuberculosis, a final classification of the patient's clinical activity also should be included.

Therapeutic status. This classification category refers to particular procedures such as chemotherapy and surgical excision or collapse of the lung. These terms also should be used to discuss a patient's clinical status.

Prevention

Preventive measures used in tuberculosis have included casefinding and mass survey programs conducted among populations of apparently "healthy" individuals. Tuberculin testing and x-ray examinations are generally utilized for these purposes. Location of active cases can thereby be adequately determined.

The use of chemotherapeutic agents prophylactically (chemoprophylaxis) has been quite successful as a means of reducing the incidence of active tuberculosis. This approach has been used with "high risk" groups, such as recent contacts, infants, and tuberculin converters. BCG vaccination also has been employed for the protection of uninfected persons who are in contact with known tuberculous patients and when normal measures of chemoprophylaxis could not be performed. Because BCG vaccinations influence the diagnostic value of tuberculin testing, its use is under question.

Unfortunately, despite the availability of measures of treatment and early detection of tuberculosis, the infection is far from being eradicated. This is largely the consequence of several factors which include the nature of the disease itself (healthy-appearing persons may actually be infected and thereby serve as reservoirs for *M. tuberculosis*), limitations of detection and diagnosis, a general disinterest which may exist in a community, an unwillingness of infected individuals to be isolated and adequately treated and the development of drug-resistant infections. The antibiotic rifampin used in combination with other antituberculous agents has been successful in the treatment of drug-resistant infections.

QUESTIONS FOR REVIEW

1. Compare the different bacterial respiratory infections. Construct a table for this purpose and include the following categories:
   a. specific etiologic agent
   b. distinguishing clinical features
   c. Gram reaction
   d. medium of choice for isolation
   e. means of transmission
   f. availability of diagnostic skin test

   g. clinical specimen of choice
   h. means of prevention

2. Distinguish between the following:
   a. Schultz-Charlton reaction and the Dick test
   b. the Schick test and the Dick test
   c. the Mantoux test and BCG inoculation

3. What significance does the acid-fast staining procedure have in the diagnosis of respiratory disease? Which,

if any, respiratory system pathogen or pathogens are noted for their acid-fast reaction?

4. List examples of complications which can develop from a bacterial respiratory infection. How can such problems be prevented?

5. What are the reservoirs and sources of infectious agents in the following diseases?
   a. tuberculosis
   b. psittacosis
   c. diphtheria
   d. whooping cough

e. staphylococcal pneumonia
f. influenza
g. atypical primary pneumonia
h. lobar pneumonia
i. the common cold

7. What distinguishing property or properties does *Mycoplasma pneumoniae* have in comparison with other bacterial pathogens?

8. What are chlamydial respiratory infections? Is the etiology bacterial in nature? Explain. What differentiates psittacosis from ornithosis?

Mycotic and Viral Diseases of the Respiratory Tract

Fungus Diseases

Several fungus species are associated with respiratory diseases in humans (Table 34–1). Humans acquire these infections by inhaling spores from exogenous reservoirs, including dust, bird droppings, and soil. Certain fungi, e.g., *Coccidioides immitis,* are not widely distributed in nature, but appear to be found only in particular geographic regions. Other agents are ubiquitous. A selected number of these pathogens are discussed in this chapter, while additional ones are presented in other chapters. General aspects of treatment are given in Table 34–1.

Coccidioidomycosis

This fungus disease is also known by other names, such as desert fever, San Joaquin fever, and valley fever. Three distinct syndromes are known with this infection: the *acute,* the *chronic pulmonary,* and the *disseminated* forms. The disease occurs in Southern California and the southwestern United States, in South and Central America, and occasionally in other parts of the world. The incidence of infection is related to climatologic conditions in the endemic areas, with the peak of infection occurring in the dry, dusty summer months, especially after the end of a rather rainy winter season.

Means of transmission. Coccidioidomycosis generally is contracted from the inhalation of soil or dust containing the arthrospores (Figure 34–1*B*) of the causative agent, *Coccidioides immitis.* Domestic animals and rodents can develop the disease and may be partially responsible for its persistence in some areas.

Table 34–1   Fungi Associated with Human Respiratory Diseases

Respiratory Disease	Fungus Species	Possible Treatment
Aspergillosis, asthma, bronchiectasis, rhinitis	*Aspergillus fumigatus*	Amphotericin B
Bronchopulmonary candidiasis	*Candida albicans*	Amphotericin B
Chronic pneumonitis	*Cryptococcus neoformans*	Amphotericin B
Coccidioidomycosis	*Coccidioides immitis*	For disseminated form, Amphotericin B
Geotrichosis	*Geotrichum candidum*	Potassium iodide (orally) Sodium iodide (intravenously)
Histoplasmosis	*Histoplasma capsulatum*	1. Amphotericin B 2. Surgical removal of oral lesions
North American blastomycosis (Gilchrist's disease)	*Blastomyces dermatitidis*	1. Amphotericin B 2. Hydroxystilbamidine 3. Surgical procedures together with chemotherapy
Sporotrichosis of the lungs (rare)	*Sporotrichum schenckii*	Amphotericin B

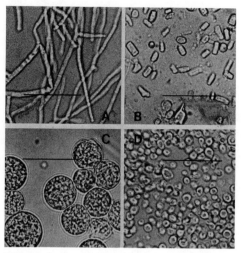

FIG. 34–1. Growth phases of *Coccidioides immitis* Selveria. *A.* Mycelia. *B.* Arthrospores. *C.* Spherules. *D.* Endospores. Bar markers represent 30 μm. (From Kong, Y. M., and Levine, H. B.: *Bacteriol. Rev.,* **31**:35–53, 1967.)

Clinical features. Approximately 10 to 18 days following the inhalation of *C. immitis* arthrospores, individuals experience so-called "flu-like" symptoms, which generally include chills, cough, fever, malaise, pain, and the presence of a purulent sputum. The latter is indicative of pneumonia. The majority of infected persons recover completely. However, in some individuals complications develop, such as residual pulmonary disease.

The disseminated form of coccidioidomycosis occurs only in about one of a thousand patients. The prognosis (future outlook) of disseminated coccidioidomycosis is very serious. Almost every tissue and organ of the body is vulnerable to attack by the fungus, including the bones, brain, lungs, meninges, and skin (Figure 34–2 and Color photograph 85). Infections may also occur in the mouth with lesions appearing on the tongue, palate or other areas. The patient may have had the disease for some time at a subclinical level, and only seeks professional advice after skin or mucous membrane involvement.

Diagnosis. Inside the body, arthrospores from the mycelial phase (Figure 34–1*A* and *B*) of *C. immitis* found in the dust germinate. This results in the formation of nonbudding spherules, each of which is 10 to 80 μm in diameter. When these spherules rupture, each can release up to 200 endospores (Figure 34–1*D*), which carry the disease to other parts of the body and result in secondary infections. A definitive diagnosis of coccidioidomycosis requires the demonstration of such *C. immitis* spherules (Figure 34–1*C*) in clinical specimens such as exudates, sputum, and tissue sections.

The cultivation of *C. immitis* is also of diagnostic importance. However, it should be kept in mind that the fungus is highly infectious, and must be handled with respect. The arthrospores (Color photograph 87) can be introduced into the laboratory environment if proper precautions and care are not observed.

C. immitis can be cultured on Sabouraud's glucose agar from either the arthrospores or the spherules. After 3 to 4 days of incubation a cottony white (Color photograph 86), moist colony with aerial mycelia develops and gradually turns brown with age.

Tentative diagnosis of this infection is possible by utilizing clinical features,

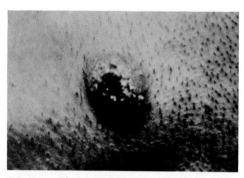

FIG. 34–2. The typical nodular, umbilicated skin lesion of coccidioidomycosis. (Courtesy of Dr. N. H. Rickles, Pathology Department, University of Oregon Dental School.)

epidemiological factors, positive skin test results with coccidioidin (Color photograph 59), and serological testing (e.g., complement-fixation and immunodiffusion). Skin tests usually are positive early in the disease, while complement-fixation tests become so after 3 months.

Immunity.   Recovery from primary coccidioidomycosis confers a solid, permanent immunity to further infection.

Histoplasmosis

This fungus disease is a granulomatous infection caused by *Histoplasma capsulatum*. Histoplasmosis occurs throughout the world, with a relatively high incidence in some countries, including Panama, Brazil, Argentina, the Philippines, Honduras, and Java. The disease is widespread in the United States and endemic in Missouri, Tennessee, Kentucky, Kansas, Iowa, Indiana, and southern Illinois. Extensive epidemiologic studies in these areas show positive histoplasmin skin tests in more than 75 per cent of the population. Histoplasmosis is no longer thought of as a rare and fatal disease, but rather as one that is widespread and generally mild. It may be a difficult disease to diagnose since it presents such a broad spectrum, ranging from an asymptomatic or mild infection to an acute fulminating disease, to a chronic pulmonary disease of long duration.

Means of transmission.   The infection is disseminated to human beings by spores from the fungus, which grows readily in acidic soil of areas with proper temperature and moisture.

Clinical features.   Mucocutaneous lesions usually indicate disseminated disease, however, an occasional patient presents a seemingly isolated lesion without apparent active disease elsewhere. It is rarely localized in the oral cavity. Respiratory infection is the common form of the disease.

In microscopic sections there are areas of central necrosis surrounded by granulomatous tissue with multinucleated giant cells, epithelioid cells, lymphocytes, and plasma cells. The organism is small, from 1 to 5 μm in diameter, oval to round (Figure 34–3A), and is seen within various phagocytic cells.

Diagnosis.   A definitive diagnosis requires the isolation in culture and microscopic identification of the fungus, and serological evidence.

H. capsulatum is dimorphic with a yeast-like or mycelial form seen when the conidia (spores) are introduced into a susceptible host. There they soon convert into yeast-like organisms and parasitize reticulendothelial cells, macrophages, and cells of the peripheral blood. Once in a cell, they increase in number by budding, resulting in small, yeast cells 1–3 μm in diameter which exhibit a clear area resulting from the shrinkage of the cytoplasm away from the rigid walls. This characteristic location and appearance is of great importance in making a diagnosis (Figure 34–3). In artificial media at room temperature the yeast-like form (Figure 34–4A) is converted to the mycelial form with a white to brown cottony appearance on Sabouraud's glucose medium. Microscopically there are branched hyphae whose spherical macroconidia have spiny projections 8 to 14 μm long (Figures 34–4B and C). The fungus is very resistant to environmental changes.

Serological evidence is obtainable through complement-fixation, immunodiffusion, and latex-agglutination tests.

North American Blastomycosis (Gilchrist's Disease)

This chronic systemic fungal disease is usually secondary to pulmonary involve-

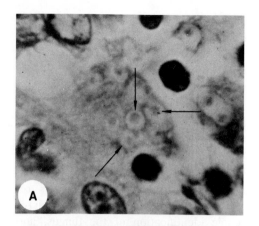

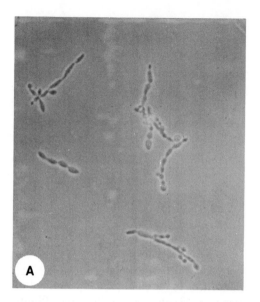

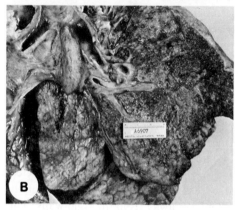

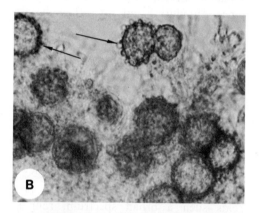

FIG. 34-3<u>A</u>. *Histoplasma capsulatum* in the parasitic stage within tissue. Note the clear areas (arrows) which result from shrinkage of the cytoplasm away from the rigid walls. <u>B.</u> The gross effects of *H. capsulatum* on the lung. (Courtesy of the Armed Forces Institute of Pathology, Washington, D.C., Neg. No. 58-1455-854965.)

ment. It rarely manifests itself as an intraoral lesion. The disease is essentially restricted to the North American continent and is more prevalent in the South Central and Mid-Atlantic sections and the Ohio-Mississippi River Valley. Sporadic cases have been reported from all states. Males aged 20 to 40 apparently are most often affected.

Clinical features.   The causative agent, *Blastomyces dermatitidis,* may take several forms. At least three clinical states are known, namely, pulmonary and dis-

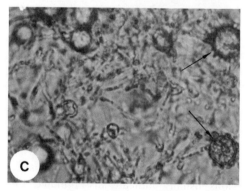

FIG. 34-4<u>A</u>. Yeast phase of *H. capsulatum* strain A811 under dark phase. <u>B</u> and <u>C.</u> Mycelial phase of *H. capsulatum* showing individual tuberculate macroconidia (arrows). (From Pine, L.: *Appl. Microbiol.,* **19**:413–420, 1970.)

seminated blastomycosis and a "primary cutaneous inoculation" form of infection. The latter is a rare occurrence and is characterized by the formation of a "chancriform lesion" or granuloma at the site of inoculation, and lymphadenopathy (lymph node enlargement) occurring regionally. Spontaneous healing generally occurs.

Pulmonary blastomycosis generally is mild, and generally self-healing. Many victims actually may be asymptomatic. However, pneumonitis progressing to cavitation and other complications, and ultimately terminating in the disseminated form of blastomycosis, can occur.

Disseminated blastomycosis generally originates from pulmonary involvement. Organisms can spread via the bloodstream to organs and tissues including those of the bones, central nervous system, gastrointestinal system, and the skin. A pustule generally is the initial skin manifestation, and can be quite conspicuous. Such lesions rupture, crust over, and peripherally enlarge. Sinuses, subcutaneous abscesses, and ulcers also may form.

Diagnosis. Laboratory diagnosis usually can be established by the demonstration of multinucleated, noncapsulated, thick-walled yeast cells from specimens including pustules in skin lesions, sputum, and biopsy material, together with successful isolation and cultivation on laboratory media.

Blastomyces dermatitidis, is a dimorphic fungus existing in tissue as a yeast, usually measuring from 8 to 15 μm in diameter with a thick wall 0.5 to 0.75 μm. A typical large bud is attached to the parent cell by a persistent wall 0.5 to 0.75 μm thick.

On Sabouraud's glucose medium incubated at room temperature, a white, filamentous colony forms. Mycelia appear white on this medium. Microscopically slender hyphae to which are attached smooth spherical 2 to 10 μm microconidia can be observed. On blood agar incubated at 37°C, the budding yeast phase of *B. dermatitidis* develops, producing colonies which are gray to tan, wrinkled, convex, glazed, and adhere to the medium. Initial isolation may require 30 to 35 days for growth; however, colonies may appear within 10 to 12 days.

Skin tests with dead yeast-phase organisms or a crude culture filtrate, blastomycin, may be used to indicate past or present infection. Unfortunately, the test is negative in many cases of the disease, especially early or late in the disease. It also produces cross-reactions with histoplasmin and coccidioidin.

Serological diagnosis can be performed with immunodiffusion techniques.

Virus Diseases

This portion of the chapter will be concerned with common viral agents (Table 34–2) which involve the respiratory tract not only as the principal site for their replication, but also as the system for their cytopathic effects. It is important to make this distinction because several viruses are able to grow in the upper respiratory epithelium or can use the tract for entry into the body. These are not discussed here.

In 1968, Rhodes and Van Rooyen reviewed the etiology of the major associated respiratory syndromes. Their main points can be summarized as follows:

(1) The number of viruses causing respiratory illness in humans and other animals is steadily increasing.

(2) One viral agent may produce more than one particular syndrome.

(3) The antigenic characteristics of several respiratory viruses, e.g., influenza and others, change periodically.

Table 34–2   Viral Agents and Commonly Associated Respiratory Tract Infections

Respiratory Tract Infection	Virus by Generic Designation[a]	Vernacular Family Designation	Type
Common Cold	*Coronavirus*	Coronavirus	Several
	Rhinovirus	Picornavirus	Several
Croup (acute laryngotracheo-bronchitis)	*Adenovirus*	Adenovirus	1, 2, 3, 5
	Myxovirus	Myxovirus	A
	Paramyxovirus	Paramyxovirus	1, 2, 3
	Respiratory syncytial virus[b]	Paramyxovirus	———
Influenza	*Myxovirus*	Myxovirus	A_2, B, C
Minor respiratory illnesses	*Adenovirus*	Adenovirus	1–6, 7, 14
	Bronchovirus	Paramyxovirus	———
	Echovirus	Picornavirus	Several
	Paramyxovirus	Paramyxovirus	1, 2, 3, 4
	Reovirus	Reovirus	1, 2, 3
Primary viral pneumonia[c]	*Adenovirus*	Adenovirus	3, 4, 7
	Bronchovirus	Paramyxovirus	———
	Myxovirus	Myxovirus	A_2
	Paramyxovirus	Paramyxovirus	1, 2

[a] Based on the results of isolations from cases of respiratory infections.
[b] This is the only designation for respiratory syncytial virus, or RS.
[c] This respiratory disease is distinguished from the common complication of many diseases, secondary viral pneumonia.

(4) Several factors of the host play a prominent role in determining susceptibility to respiratory illness; these include developmental, immunologic, physiologic, and socioeconomic features.

(5) Sharp distinctions in the symptomatology of the various respiratory diseases do not exist; symptoms do overlap.

Use of antibiotics.   In the treatment of various viral respiratory functions, antibiotics are given primarily to prevent secondary bacterial infections. This is done even though there is no clear evidence to demonstrate that these drugs reduce or eliminate the effects of the causative agents. Additional aspects of treatment are directed toward relieving the discomfort of the disease victim.

The symptomatology exhibited by individuals with viral respiratory infections are varied. In general, it includes chills, fever, general aches, malaise, some form of a nasal obstruction, and sore throat. Additional features of this class of diseases will be presented in the following discussion of selected respiratory infections caused by viruses.

The Common Cold

According to many authorities, acute afebrile diseases of the upper respiratory tract are the most frequent of human afflictions. In most cases these infections are not serious, only extremely uncomfortable, but as a group they cause the loss of millions of hours of work each year. The studies of many investigators have led to the general view that several different viruses can cause the common cold. Several of these etiologic agents have been designated as the *rhinoviruses* (from the Greek *rhino* meaning nose). It is important to note that these viruses are not the sole cause of the common cold, although they receive most attention in this chapter.

The rhinovirus-caused common cold syndrome appears to have a wide geographic distribution, as judged from the presence of antibodies in persons throughout the world. The transmission of rhinovirus infections seems to require a close and continued contact among individuals.

Clinical features. Rhinovirus-caused colds generally have a 2-day incubation period. Individuals with the illness usually exhibit increased amounts of a watery nasal discharge, in addition to a cough, coryza (head cold), headache, nasal obstruction of some type, sneezing, and a sore throat. The features of a generalized infection such as chills, fever, and general aches and pains are less frequently present.

Diagnosis. At present, the only practical method for identification is the isolation of the causative agent, using tissue culture cells, such as monolayer cultures of human embryo or primary monkey kidney. Nasopharyngeal specimens are employed as the specimens of choice. Serological tests, such as complement-fixation and neutralization procedures, have limited value.

Control. Attempts to develop vaccines against cold viruses have not been successful. Another approach to the problem of control has concentrated on the active inhibitor of viral activities, interferon. Here again, effective application has not been attained. The intake of large quantities of vitamin C has been suggested as an effective means of providing resistance toward respiratory illness under normal conditions. Further studies are currently underway to evaluate this control measure.

Attempts to control the spread of common cold agents through the use of disinfectant aerosols, irradiation with ultraviolet light, or the quarantine of infected persons, are generally of little value.

Croup
(Acute Laryngotracheobronchitis)

Croup is an acute infectious disease of children generally under 3 years of age. Males are affected more often than females. Croup may be mild or severe in its effects.

Several viruses and bacteria have been found to be etiologic agents of this disease (Table 34–2). Any one of the following agents may produce viral laryngotracheobronchitis: adenoviruses, myxoviruses (influenzaviruses), paramyxoviruses, respiratory syncytial agent (RS), or rhinoviruses.

Clinical features. Individuals with croup may exhibit a wide variety of symptoms, ranging from mild to severe. They can be categorized into the following three groups or degrees of severity. The first group comprises a cough, hoarseness, stridor (a high-pitched, harsh breathing sound) and additional symptoms of respiratory distress. The second includes fever, toxemia, and vomiting. The third is characterized by the general features of convulsions, cyanosis (blue coloration of the skin), dehydration, and restlessness. A local obstruction may also develop that necessitates a tracheotomy, a surgical procedure to produce an artificial tracheal opening for breathing. Children rarely die of croup if prompt treatment is carried out.

Diagnosis. Laboratory identification generally involves the inoculation of cell cultures and embryonated chicken eggs. Specimens used for this purpose include sputum and throat and tracheal washings. Serologic tests may also be carried out.

Influenza

Epidemics of influenza have plagued man and other animals for centuries. Widespread epidemics, or pandemics, occurred in 1847-1848, 1889-1891, and 1918-1919. The last-named flu epidemic produced such disastrous effects that approximately 20 million people died. Young adults from the 20 to 40 age group were affected to a very large extent. Although a significant accumulation of data incriminated a virus as the causative agent of the pandemic of 1918-1919, *Hemophilus influenzae,* the so-called influenza bacillus, still was regarded as the cause of the disease.

It was not until 1933 that Smith, Andrews, and Laidlaw reported their findings demonstrating that filtered, bacteria-free nasopharyngeal secretions from patients with influenza produced respiratory disease in ferrets inoculated intranasally. The findings were confirmed by several other laboratories of the world. Thus, the recovery of a virus contained in nasal washings, sputum, and other specimens from victims of influenza firmly established the viral nature of the disease. Moreover, it became clear that *H. influenzae*—as well as numerous other bacterial species including *Diplococcocus pneumoniae* and *Staphylococcus aureus*—in reality were secondary invaders in patients with influenza, and quite often were responsible for the fatal forms of pneumonia which developed.

Selected properties of influenza virus (myxoviruses). Several important discoveries were made shortly after the viral etiology of this respiratory disease was demonstrated. The use of the chicken embryo as an experimental animal made it possible not only to obtain large quantities of virus for vaccine production, but provided one inexpensive way to study the mechanism of influenza viral infection.

Another important development was the fortunate finding by Hirst in 1941 and also by McClelland and Hare that strains of influenza viruses can cause the agglutination of chicken red cells, (he-

magglutination or HA). These red cells were found to contain mucoprotein receptor sites with which the virus particles react. Each mucoprotein receptor is composed of a terminal N-acetylneuraminic acid group bound to an N-acetylgalactosamine residue which in turn is attached to a protein molecule. The viral enzyme which severs the virus from the receptor site is called neuraminidase. After this virus-mucoprotein interaction occurs, the viral agent destroys (hydrolyzes) the receptor site, thus making the red cells "inagglutinable" by fresh viruses of the same strain. This elution (removal) process exhausts the cellular receptor for the particular influenza strain originally causing the hemagglutination reaction. However, other influenza strains still may bring about the agglutination of these cells. This entire process is referred to as the property of "myxophily." All influenza viruses exhibit this characteristic. On the basis of this phenomenon, other viral agents can attach after another virus has been eluted. Thus, strains of influenza virus—*Myxovirus influenzae* A, B, or C—and certain parainfluenza viruses, e.g., mumps and Newcastle disease viruses, can form a *receptor gradient*. In other words, these viruses can be arranged in a series whereby each agent destroys the receptor sites for its own strain and those which happen to be below it, but not for those which are above it. A variety of erythrocytes are agglutinated by individual strains. For example, type A strains react with cells of chickens, dogs, ducks, human blood type O, guinea pigs, mice, and rats. Type A_2 strains, in addition to these, are also capable of agglutinating the erythrocytes of several other animals including cats, cows, monkeys, pigs, and rabbits.

The original strains of human influenza viruses, isolated in 1933 and prevalent for about 10 years, are referred to as Type A or A classic. As additional strains were discovered on the basis of antigenicity studies, other designations were created. These included types A_1 or A prime, A_2 or Asian (Figure 9–6F), B (Figure 1–2F2), and C. The major strains associated with human influenza are grouped under the types A, B, and C (Table 34–3).

Several antigens have been found to be associated with the viral particles of the myxoviruses, *Myxovirus influenzae* A, B, and C. These include the internal or nucleocapsid antigen, external or surface glycoprotein antigens, and the major structural protein of the viral envelope (M protein). The nucleocapsid (S) antigen corresponds to the virus's internal helical component, is immunologically identical to a soluble antigen in infected cells, and is assayed by complement-fixation procedures. The surface glycoprotein antigens are of two types. One of these corresponds to some of the projections on the virus particle's surface and is biologically and immunologically identical to the hemagglutinin. This antigen is measured by means of hemagglutination inhibition, neutralization, and complement-fixation tests (see Chapter 23). The other glycoprotein projections on the virus's surface correspond to the neuraminidase discussed earlier. Special biochemical tests are used for its detection. The M protein antigen is measured by complement-fixation and immunodiffusion procedures.

These antigens are of considerable practical importance. It appears that influenza viruses contain antigenically similar neuraminidase molecules, although their hemagglutinins (surface antigens) differ and periodically change. The latter observation demonstrated the existence of the phenomenon of antigenic variation or "antigenic drift." According to the various experts, it is believed that the emergence of new influenza virus strains is the result of "cyclic quantitative changes" in the hemagglutinin antigen. Such major antigenic changes in these surface molecules have rendered vaccines prepared from older established strains ineffective. The antibodies induced by such preparations did not react with the newly emerged viral strains responsible for the prevailing cases of influenza, since immunity is induced by the hemagglutinin on the viral particle's surface.

Dual infections with the various influenza viral types, i.e., A and C or C and B, have been reported.

Clinical features of uncomplicated influenza. In 1965 Stuart-Harris listed the major modes of influenza virus infections: *uncomplicated, complicated,*

Table 34–3 Human Influenza Virus Types (or Subtypes)

Viral Type or Subtypes	Years in which Strain Isolations Were Reported[a]	Number of Strains Involved
A (classic)	1933; 1934; 1943	3
A_1 (A Prime)	1940–1941; 1950; 1951; 1952–1953; 1955–1956; 1957	10
A_2 (Asian)[b]	1957; 1962; 1964; 1965	8
B	1940; 1943; 1944–1945; 1948; 1954; 1959; 1962; 1964; 1965	11
C	1947	1

[a] The human strains referred to here are those isolated in various geographic areas of the world. Generally, a strain (modern designation according to the World Health Organization) includes the type and subtype, the serial number, the geographic region where the isolation was made (e.g., India, Moscow, New Jersey, etc.) and the year of isolation. An example of the system would be A_2/Japan/305/57. Variations of this system and additional designations also are known.
[b] Often incorrectly called "Asiatic."

subclinical, and *asymptomatic* syndromes.

Generally the uncomplicated form of influenza has an incubation period which may vary from 1 to 4 days. Individuals suffering from the disease may experience a sudden onset of symptoms, including backache, chills, fever, headache, malaise, and some form of nasal congestion. The temperature rises rapidly to a peak and generally comes back to normal by the third day. The duration of the fever can vary; it may actually persist for 5 days. As the fever diminishes, respiratory symptoms increase. Victims of the disease may exhibit a dry, irritating cough, nasal congestion, a dry and sore throat, tracheitis, and a husky or hoarse voice.

Occasionally, during the early course of influenza, anorexia (loss of appetite), nausea, or vomiting are evident. Several other manifestations of the disease have been reported. These include chest pains, dizziness, insomnia, and sensitivity to light. Diarrhea is not a characteristic symptom of this disease. The so-called gastro-intestinal flu is not believed to be caused by influenza virus.

The duration of the average "attack" of uncomplicated influenza generally lasts anywhere from 7 to 10 days, depending upon the individual. Adults have been known to experience a feeling of debility following the disease. A prolonged cough also may persist well beyond the time that the other symptoms listed have subsided.

Stuart-Harris draws attention to the importance of the patient's age, state of health, and pregnancy status in determining the clinical pattern of influenza virus infections. Only the question of pregnancy will be discussed here. Apparently an attack of this respiratory disease may exert significant effects on both the expectant mother and her fetus. In the case of the mother, this is especially true if she has any of a number of pre-existing chest and heart diseases. Fetal abnormalities have been reported to occur with a greater than normal frequency in the offspring of mothers who had influenza during their gestation periods. It should be noted that the malformations associated with influenza are unlike those resulting from maternal rubella (German measles) infections.

Selected clinical features associated with the complications of influenza. Unfortunately, epidemics of this respiratory tract infection have been accompanied by a rise in mortality. The greatest proportional rise in deaths from complications has been caused by bronchitis and pneumonia. Complications have also been reported in organs other than the lungs, such as the components of circulatory and central nervous systems. The development of chest complications during the period of an influenza epidemic is determined by several factors, including the viral strain involved, the age and general health of the host, and the severity of the original attack of the disease.

Some people may actually have synchronous bacterial and viral infections, while other patients may acquire a bacterial pathogen while convalescing from influenza. In post-influenzal cases, *Streptococcus pneumoniae* is most often encountered, while in synchronous illnesses, *S. pneumoniae* and coagulase positive *Staphylococcus aureus* are found to be the most prominent invaders. In certain instances, however, the pneumonia is due to a pure *H. influenzae* infection.

Laboratory diagnosis. Generally a presumptive diagnosis of influenza is made on the basis of clinical and epidemiological findings. As laboratory confirmatory procedures are quite expensive, they are not used in cases of individual or sporadic infections. However, laboratory investigations are performed in studies of an epidemiological nature, and in determining the presence and the specific type of viral agent in a community. A diagnosis may be established with the aid of three general techniques. These procedures include: (1) isolation of the virus, (2) demonstration of an increase in specific antibody titer, and (3) detection of specific viral antigens in nasal secretions or sputum by immunofluorescent technique (see Chapter 23).

Viral isolations usually are performed by inoculating clinical specimens, e.g., nasal or throat washings or secretions, into the amniotic sac of 11- to 13-day-old chick embryos.

Serological diagnosis of influenza requires the demonstration of a significant increase in antibody levels between acute and convalescent sera. This may be accomplished by means of hemagglutination-inhibition (HI) tests and a type-specific complement-fixation procedure with viral ribonucleoprotein antigens.

Immunity. Persons recovering from a natural infection generally acquire a degree of resistance to the particular antigenic strain responsible for the respiratory illness. Unfortunately, new strains possessing new minor antigens develop and consequently cause successive attacks of influenza.

Prevention. Immunization of certain key individuals, such as police, nurses, physicians, and other health care personnel, usually is recommended before an epidemic strikes. Pregnant women, the elderly, and persons with debilitating diseases, such as chronic heart or respiratory diseases, should also be immunized. Mortality rates in persons 45 years of age and over have been relatively higher than in other age groups. As influenza can spread rapidly among residents of homes for the aged or nursing homes, the prophylactic use of vaccines cannot be overemphasized.

QUESTIONS FOR REVIEW

1. a. What fungus pathogens cause respiratory disease? Where can these diseases be found?
   b. Compare the methods of diagnosis and treatment associated with the various mycotic respiratory diseases.
   c. What factors contribute to a person's susceptibility to fungal diseases?

2. List five viral respiratory tract infections, together with their respective etiologic agents.

3. Discuss the measures used in the diagnosis, treatment, and prevention of viral respiratory system diseases.

4. a. What significance is associated with the antigenic variation found among the myxoviruses?
   b. How many viral types are in existence?
   c. Which viral types are currently within the general population?

5. Can complications develop from influenza? Explain.

Bacterial Diseases of the Gastrointestinal Tract

The human digestive system consists of a series of specific organs and glands which are designed to provide an adequate supply of nutrients to the individual. Once food is ingested, it is subjected to a series of reactions which comprise the processes of digestion, absorption, and elimination. As various portions of the digestive system are vulnerable to direct attack by microbial pathogens, or may be secondarily involved in a disease process, a brief survey of this system's component parts is warranted. This discussion will be followed by a consideration of the bacterial pathogens which can affect the human gastrointestinal (G-1) tract.

Structure and Function

The alimentary canal and certain accessory organs comprise the human digestive system. The alimentary canal extends from the mouth cavity to the anus. Its component parts include the oral cavity, pharynx, stomach, and small and large intestines (Figure 35–1). Accessory structures of the canal include the teeth, the salivary glands, the liver, the gallbladder, and the pancreas. Detailed discussions of the general features and infectious diseases of the oral cavity and pharynx are contained in Chapters 32 and 33.

Component Parts of the G-I Tract

The various portions of the digestive system possess a similar structure organiza-

tion, namely, an inner mucosa layer, a middle muscular layer, and an outer connective tissue layer.

The Stomach

This portion of the digestive system has a shape somewhat resembling a thick-walled J. The stomach is situated on the left side of the body just under the lower ribs. It is divided into three major portions, called the *cardiac region* (nearest the heart), the *fundus,* and the *pylorus,* the section leading to the opening of the small intestine (Figure 35–1). The inner mucous membrane of the stomach, the *mucosa,* contains millions of glands which secrete mucus and the various components of the gastric juice.

Food which enters the stomach from the esophagus must pass through the anteriorly located *cardiac sphincter.* This one-way constricting device remains closed until it receives the proper stimulus to open. The sphincter functions in preventing food from passing back into the esophagus.

The Small Intestine

This portion of the digestive system is a coiled tube measuring an average 7 meters or about 25 feet in length and 2.5 cm in diameter. Intestinal length is related to the type of diet. For example, meat-eaters (carnivores) have short intestines, while plant-eating animals (herbivores) have long ones. Man, an omnivore, has an in-

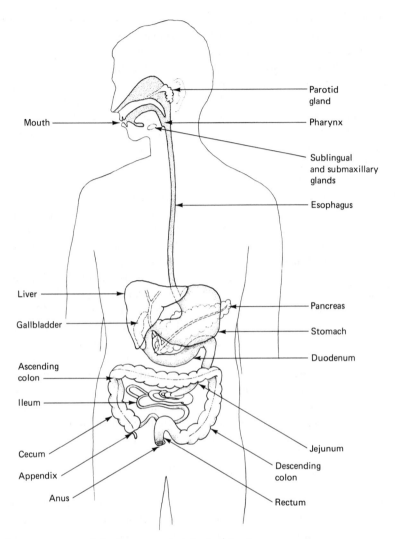

Parotid
gland

Mouth

Pharynx

Sublingual
and submaxillary
glands

Esophagus

Liver

Pancreas

Gallbladder

Stomach

Duodenum

Ascending
colon

Ileum

Jejunum

Cecum

Descending
colon

Appendix

Anus

Rectum

FIG. 35-1. The components of the human gastrointestinal tract.

testine of intermediate length. Length also varies greatly with the individual.

For purposes of study the small intestine is generally divided into three portions or "loops," the *duodenum* (1 foot in length), the *jejunum* (5 feet in length), and the *ileum* (approximately 19 feet in length). The duodenum is held in a fixed position by ligaments in the abdominal cavity that fasten it to the liver, stomach, and dorsal body wall. The rest of the small intestine and most of the large

intestine are fastened to the dorsal body wall by means of a thin, transparent membrane called the *mesentery*. The nature of this attachment leaves them relatively unrestricted.

By far the greater part of enzymatic digestion and most of the absorption take place in the small intestine. It appears that only alcohol and certain poisons, such as strychnine, are absorbed through the stomach wall. Food leaving the stomach passes through the so-called pyloric region into the duodenum. The entering acidified material is mixed with secretions produced by the liver and pancreas, as well as those which come from the small intestine itself, which are collectively referred to as *succus entericus*. Much of the entering material is composed of mucus, which aids the passage of the digesting food material through the intestine.

The highly absorptive nature of the small intestine is closely linked to its enormous surface area, which is composed of millions of small, fingerlike processes called *villi*. Each of these units contains capillaries and a small lymph vessel referred to as a *lacteal*. The capillaries are involved with the absorption of amino acids and simple sugars, while the lacteals are concerned with fatty acids and glycerol.

The Large Intestine (Colon)

As a matter of convenience, the large intestine is generally divided into the following regions: *ascending colon, transverse colon, descending colon,* and *rectum*. Food from the small intestine passes into the thicker-walled, larger diameter ascending colon. The small intestine opens into the large intestine from the side, not the top, thus leaving a "blind sac" at the beginning of the large intestine called the *caecum*. The *appendix,* a small finger-like projection, is located at the tip of the caecum.

The large intestine is primarily involved with the processing, storage, and elimination of food material remaining after digestion and absorption have occurred. Such matter consists of a so-called indigestible residue and large quantities of water. One of the functions of the large intestine is to absorb much of this water.

The rectum is the portion of the digestive system which functions in eliminating the waste products of digestion,

referred to as *feces*. In addition to the indigestible food elements, fecal matter contains large quantities of bacteria, heavy metals, and certain body secretions (e.g., bile). Elimination, or *defecation,* is both a voluntary and an involuntary act. Feces pass from the terminal part of the digestive system through the *anal sphincter.*

The Liver

One of the largest organs or glands found in the body, the liver is vitally important to the well-being of the individual. The liver is located in the upper portion of the abdominal cavity just beneath the diaphragm. Its many functions include: (1) bile formation, (2) the storage and interconversion of sugars, (3) regulation of blood glucose levels, (4) storage of vitamins, (5) production of prothrombin (important in blood coagulation), (6) formation of embryonic red blood cells, (7) removal of poisons from the bloodstream and their detoxification, and (8) deamination of amino acids (removal of the amino group).

Bile

The bile, or *gall,* is produced by all parts of the liver and stored in the gall bladder. Bile emulsifies fats so they can pass through the intestines, prevents food from decaying there, and stimulates the intestinal muscles. It passes into the small intestine by way of the *bile duct.* If this duct becomes clogged or blocked, the condition known as *jaundice* (a yellowing of body tissues) develops. This state has a variety of causes, including gallstones and infectious virus hepatitis.

The deep yellowish-orange color of human bile is largely determined by the proportions and presence of the two pigments *bilirubin* and *biliverdin,* which are derived from hemoglobin. Bilirubin is a golden red; biliverdin, which is oxidized bilirubin, is yellow-green.

The Pancreas

This digestive gland consists of a diffuse mass of tissue situated between the stomach and the duodenum. In addition to secreting pancreatic juice, the pancreas also is noted for the production of the two hormones *glucagon* and *insulin,* essential to carbohydrate metabolism. The pancreatic juice contains several important digestive enzymes. Its alkaline nature functions in neutralizing the stomach's hydrochloric acid, which enters the small intestine via the acidified food.

Bacterial Diseases

Representative bacterial diseases are shown in Table 35–1. The World Health Organization Expert Committee on Enteric Infections has adopted the designation *acute diarrheal disease* to signify a clinical condition in which there is ". . . a disturbance of intestinal motility and absorption which, once and by whatever means initiated, may become self-perpetuating as a disease through the production of dehydration and profound cellular disturbances, which in turn favor the containing passage of liquid stools." The specific bacterial pathogens that can cause this clinical state are shown in Table 35–1 along with other agents of gastrointestinal disease. Among the organisms associated with acute diarrheal disease are the etiologic agents of cholera, gastroenteritis, bacillary dysentery, infantile diarrhea, and traveler's diarrhea.

Today it is apparent that intestinal microflora may induce diarrhea in any of three ways: they may alter dietary foodstuffs or host secretions into end products that affect gut fluid movement; they may

penetrate the intestinal epithelium and ulcerate the bowel wall; or they may elaborate exotoxins that cause large shifts of water and electrolytes into the bowel without damaging the mucosa. It now appears that this last process may be implicated in many serious and not-so-serious diarrheal disorders. The features of representative disease states will be presented in this chapter.

A representative approach to the isolation and identification of gastrointestinal bacterial pathogens is presented in Figure 35–2. Significant differentiating physiological properties of the bacterial species related to these diseases are listed in Table 35–2.

Asiatic Cholera

Today, this bacterial disease is endemic principally in China, India, and certain other Far East countries. In the last century, cholera pandemics spread both eastward and westward, to involve the countries of Africa, Asia, Europe, and North America. During the current century, the disease appears to be more or less limited, as indicated, to India and surrounding areas, although epidemics have occurred in other parts of the world, including Egypt, Indonesia, Korea, and the Philippines.

Mode of transmission. The causative agents of cholera are the Gram-negative, slightly curved rods *Vibrio (comma) cholera* (Figure 35–3) and *V. El Tor.* The *El Tor* vibrio originally was considered to be a nonpathogenic variant of *V. cholerae.* This was largely because it was frequently found in water and it exhibited characteristics of other water-associated vibrios. The virulent nature of the *El Tor* vibrio became apparent when it was isolated from victims of localized outbreaks of cholera. The organism's designation was derived from the fact that it was

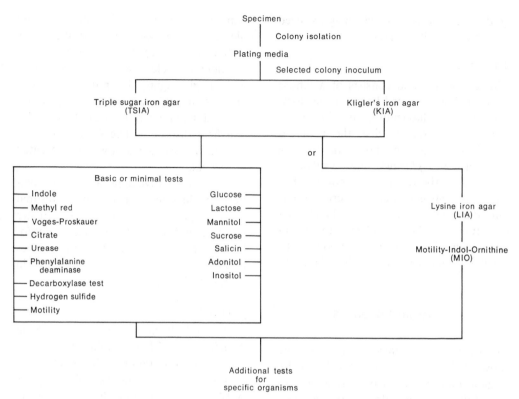

FIG. 35–2. A representative basic and preliminary biochemical approach to the identification of commonly encountered gastrointestinal bacterial pathogens. Many of the reactions, either individual or combined in multiple test systems (Chapter 28), are shown in Color photographs 37–42, 51–53, 88, 89, and 91. It should be noted that identification schemes vary among facilities and institutions. The decarboxylation tests listed are practical procedures for the detection of decarboxylases (enzymes) that remove carboxyl groups (COOH) from the amino acids arginine, lysine, and ornithine. (After *Differentiation of Enterobacteriaceae by Biochemical Reactions*, p. 12, Center for Disease Control, Atlanta, Georgia 30333, 1974.)

isolated at the El Tor quarantine station on the Gulf of Suez in 1905. Clinically, the infection produced by *V. El Tor* is indistinguishable from that of *V. cholerae*. Individuals acquire this disease through the ingestion of the causative organisms in food or water or by coming directly into contact with an infected person. Houseflies are also important in the dissemination of vibrios. Epidemics usually are associated with such sources of infection. There appear to be no long-term carriers.

Contamination of water supplies is, in general, caused by recent introduction of cholera organisms rather than the persistence of the agents in such an environment. Fish obtained from contaminated waters, if eaten without sufficient cooking, also constitute a source of disease agents.

Epidemics of cholera have been described as either *protracted* or *explosive*. Exposive epidemics occur when the pathogenic agents are transmitted by means of contaminated food, water, or aerosols. The protracted form of cholera occurs as a consequence of disease-causing organisms being spread by direct contact, or by contaminated objects (fomites).

Table 35–1 Representative Bacterial Diseases of the Gastrointestinal Tract

Disease	Etiologic Agent	Gram Reaction	Morphology	Possible Treatment
Asiatic cholera	*Vibrio cholera* *V. El Tor*	−	Vibrio	1. Maintain proper fluid and electrolyte balance 2. Antibiotics including chloramphenicol, streptomycin, and tetracyclines
Botulism	*Clostridium botulinum*	+	Rod	1. Antitoxin 2. Antibiotics to prevent secondary infection
Brucellosis (Malta fever, undulant fever)	*Brucella abortus, B. melitensis, B. suis*	−	Coccobacilli	Streptomycin and tetracyclines
Clostridial food poisoning	*Clostridium perfringens*	+	Rods	1. Measures to replace salt and water loss 2. Symptomatic
Enteric (paratyphoid) fever	*Salmonella schottmulleri* and other *Salmonella* spp.	−	Rods	Chloramphenicol, ampicillin
Gastroenteritis (salmonellosis)	*Salmonella typhimurium* and other *Salmonella* spp.	−	Rods	1. Restoration of fluid and electrolyte balance 2. Antibiotics, including chloramphenicol
Gastroenteritis (non-salmonella type)	*Escherichia coli, Proteus vulgaris*	−	Rods	Kanamycin
	Clostridium perfringens	+	Rods	1. Measures to replace salt and water loss 2. Symptomatic
	Streptococcus faecalis	+	Coccus	
	Vibrio parahaemolyticus	−	Vibrio	Antibiotic therapy is not widely used
	Yersinia enterocolitica	−	Coccobacillus	Chloramphenicol, gentamicin, and neomycin
Infantile diarrhea	*E. coli* strains designated enteropathogenic *E. coli* (EPEC)[a]	−	Rods	1. Maintain electrolyte and fluid balance 2. Antibiotics including colistin, carbenicillin, and tetracyclines
Leptospiroses	*Leptospira (icterohaemorrhagiae) interrogans* and other *Leptospira* spp.[b]	Generally not done	Spiral	1. Antibiotics including penicillin, chloramphenicol, and tetracyclines 2. Symptomatic 3. Restore fluid and electrolyte balance
Shigellosis (bacillary dysentery)	*Shigella boydii, S. dysenteriae, S. flexneri, S. sonnei,* and other *Shigella* spp.	−	Rods	1. Antibiotics including ampicillin, chloramphenicol, and tetracyclines 2. Maintain fluid and electrolyte balance
Staphylococcal enteritis	*Staphylococcus aureus*	+	Coccus	
Staphylococcal food poisoning	*Staphylococcus aureus*	+	Coccus	1. Measures to replace salt and water loss 2. Symptomatic
Traveler's diarrhea	Enterotoxin-producing *E. coli* strains	−	Rods	Symptomatic
Typhoid fever	*Salmonella typhi*	−	Rod	Antibiotics including chloramphenicol

[a] Current studies have demonstrated these strains to be responsible for diarrhea in adults.

[b] At this time of writing the taxonomy of *Leptospira* was under study by the Subcommittee on Leptospira of the International Committee on Systematic Bacteriology.

Table 35–2   Selected Physiological Properties of Gram-negative Bacterial Species
Associated with Gastrointestinal-System Disease States

| | Tests[a] | | | | | | | | | | | | |
| | | | | | | | | Fermentations | | | | | |
Organism	Indole	MR	VP	Citrate	Urease	PD	OD	Glu	Lac	Man	Su	H$_2$S	Mot.
Alcaligene faecalis	−	−	−	−	−	−	−	NC	NC	NC	NC	−	+
Escherichia coli	+	+	−	−	−	−	±	AG	AG	AG	AG	−	+
Enterobacter (Aerobacter) aerogenes	−	−	+	+	−	−	−	AG	AG	AG	AG	−	±
Proteus mirabilis	−	−	±	±	±	+	+	AG	NC	NC	AG	+	+
P. morgani	+	+	−	−	+	+	+	AG	NC	NC	NC	−	+
P. vulgaris	+	+	±	±	+	+	−	AG	NC	NC	AG	+	+
Pseudomonas aeruginosa	−	−	−	+	−	−	−	NC	NC	NC	NC	NC	+
Salmonella typhi	−	+	−	−	−	−	−	A	NC	A	NC	+	+
S. paratyphi A	−	+	−	−	−	−	+	AG	NC	AG	NC	−	+
S. schottmulleri (paratyphi B)	−	+	−	+	−	−	+	AG	NC	AG	NC	+	+
Shigella dysenteriae	±	+	−	−	−	−	−	A	−	−	−	−	−
Vibrio cholerae	+	−	−	−	−	−	−	A	NC	A	A	+ (Slow)	+
V. parahaemolyticus	+	+	−	+	−	−	+	A	NC	A	NC	−	+
Yersinia enterocolitica	±	+	−	−	+	−	+	A	NC	A	NC	−	+[b]

[a] Explanation of symbols: MR=methyl red; VP=Voges Proskauer; PD=phenylalanine deaminase; OD=ornithine decarboxylase; Glu=glucose; Lac=lactose; Man=mannose; Su=sucrose; H$_2$S=hydrogen sulfide; Mot=motility; − =negative; + =positive; ± =variable, dependent upon the strain of the organism; A=acid; AG=acid and gas; NC=no change or negative.

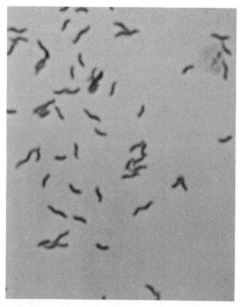

FIG. 35–3. The typical microscopic appearance of *Vibrio cholerae* as seen under the oil-immersion objective.

Cholera is more frequent during the warmer months of the year. Very few cases of this disease are found in the winter. In the endemic areas mentioned earlier, the occurrence of cholera appears to be related to a warm climate, high absolute humidity, and large population. When the monsoons bring heavy rainfall to these regions, the incidence of cholera is lowered substantially. This occurs because of the removal of contaminated matter by the rain.

The casual relationship of *V. cholerae* to gastrointestinal disease was demonstrated in 1883–1884 in the laboratory of Robert Koch. This discovery was a consequence of an accidental infection of a laboratory worker, acquired while *V. cholerae* was being isolated from clinical specimens (intestinal discharges of patients).

The causative agent. *V. cholerae* is a Gram-negative, non-spore-forming vibrio. Although individual cells may vary from short, thick rods to those which are long and thin, the organism generally measures from 0.3 to 0.6 μm in width and from 1.0 to 5.0 μm in length (Figure 35–3). *V. cholerae* is motile and grows abundantly on alkaline media, i.e., pH 9.

Clinical features. The incubation period for Asiatic cholera varies from 1 to 5 days. In most cases it is believed to be no longer than 3. Once the causative agents become established in the intestinal tube or cavity of the host, they infiltrate between the cells of the mucosal epithelium, and into the tubes of the various exocrine (ducted) glands.

It is fairly well accepted now that the diarrhea of cholera is due to the action of an exo-enterotoxin, choleragen, on an intact intestinal wall. The toxin stimulates adenyl cyclase activity, causing an increase in intracellular cyclic adenosine monophosphate (cAMP). This produces an active secretion of electrolytes, which accounts for the abnormally large movement of salts and water. In addition, excessive mucus is produced by the numerous globlet cells in the intestine. This material is rapidly released and imparts a rice-water appearance to the stools of cholera victims (rice-water stools). Large numbers of *V. cholerae* also are found in such waste material. Because of the sudden loss of large amounts of fluid—approximately 10 to 12 liters per day—the patient exhibits dehydration and a reduction of the blood's chloride content (hypochloremia). These losses of electrolytes and water are likely to cause collapse, shock, and death.

In general, three clinical forms of cholera, ranging from a mild state to more severe infections, are recognized. Complications of Asiatic cholera can involve systems other than the gastrointestinal tract. The central nervous, genitourinary, respiratory, and integumentary (i.e., skin) systems are examples of such regions. Individuals suffering from complications have experienced anemia, abortions, and neurologic involvement. Mortality rates are relatively high in the young and old.

Laboratory diagnosis. Several types of specimens are used in the identification of *V. cholerae* in suspected cases of cholera. Rectal swabs, the collection of stool material in suitable sterile containers with the aid of a sterile catheter, or a specimen from a formed stool are examples. In epidemiological investigations involving the examination of water for cholera agents, a specimen is first filtered through a membrane filter, which then is immersed into a tube with an appropriate medium.

Media used for the isolation of cholera vibrios include alkaline peptone water, gelatin agar, Monsur agar, and Monsur fluid medium. The alkaline peptone water is also utilized for the enrichment of other media. Several media used for the growth of vibrios of this type take advantage of the organisms' capability to tolerate a relatively high pH, and the presence of tellurite. Both of these factors are inhibitory to most coliforms. An example is Monsur's medium.

In addition to the cultivation of specimens on laboratory media, the direct examination of specimens also is utilized in the bacteriological identification of this pathogen. However, Gram's iodine or dilute carbol fuchsin stained preparations are preferable to distinguish *V. cholerae* from other microorganisms encountered. Once pure cultures are obtained, additional tests can be performed. These procedures, together with the reactions produced by *V. cholerae* and other gastrointestinal pathogens, are shown in Table 35–2.

Epidemiological studies also are conducted with respect to cholera. Sero- and phage-typing both can be used. In 1963, Mukerjee introduced a classification system with which to categorize *V. cholerae* strains into five types, numbered 1 through 5. The basis for classifying is susceptibility to lysis by four groups of "choleraphages." *Vibrio cholerae* can be differentiated from *V. El Tor* on the basis of phage susceptibility, and additional tests.

Prevention.   A cholera vaccine consisting of heat-killed organisms can provide protection. Unfortunately, this immunity is not long-lasting. Generally, 4 to 6 months of protection is believed possible. The vaccine is given in two 1 ml doses, 7 days apart.

In all probability the most effective measure to protect against cholera infection is to establish and maintain purified water supplies, thus eliminating the danger caused by contaminated water. In the areas where the disease prevails, this would greatly help in reducing the incidence of infection. In addition, of course, the elimination of flies, suitable treatment of patients during convalescence, and educating the general population as to the means of transmission could all be effective preventive measures.

Brucellosis

This disease, commonly referred to as undulant or Malta fever, occurs in countries bordering the Mediterranean Sea, the islands of Cyprus and Malta, the Scandinavian countries, Mexico, and the United States.

Mode of transmission.   Man acquires brucellosis through contact with the tissues or excretions of infected animals, or by the ingestion of contaminated meat or unpasteurized dairy products. Accidental inoculations of brucellae also have been reported. In general, the disease is not readily transmitted from human to human.

The causative agent.   The etiologic agents are placed in the genus *Brucella,* which was named after Sir David Bruce. He was the first to isolate the causative agent of Malta fever, a disease from which British soldiers were dying on the island of Malta in 1887. The genus is comprised of the three closely related species *B. abortus, B. suis,* and *B. melitensis.* These organisms cause Bang's disease or bovine brucellosis, swine (porcine) brucellosis, and caprine or goat brucellosis (Malta fever), respectively.

The brucellae are small, pleomorphic, Gram-negative coccobacilli. These organisms are nonmotile and non-spore-formers. All species are obligate parasites capable of maintaining an intracellular existence.

Laboratory diagnosis.   Clinical specimens that can be used for the isolation of *Brucella* species include blood, bone marrow, urine, tissue biopsy material from lymph nodes, and cerebrospinal, joint, and peritoneal fluids. Gram-stained smears of such clinical material also should be made. Other staining procedures, including a modified Ziehl-Nielsen (acid-fast) technique and fluorescent-antibody method, can also be used for direct microscopic examination of specimens. However, the number of organisms usually is quite small, so that cultivation is necessary to establish a definite diagnosis of brucellosis.

Repeated inoculations should be made in all suspected cases. In general, since *Brucella* species are slow growers, special media and techniques are necessary for their cultivation and differentiation. Trypticase soy broth and an atmosphere of 10 per cent carbon dioxide (capneic conditions) are generally used.

Several tests are used for species differentiation. It is now a well-established fact that certain *Brucella* strains do not produce typical reactions. Two methods have been specified as means to differentiate among such organisms; these are susceptibility to lysis by brucellaphage, and oxidative metabolic reactions. The phage used is the Tbilisi (Tb) strain. Only *B. abortus* is sensitive to it. Oxidative metabolic tests are not routinely performed in most modern diagnostic laboratories and will not be discussed further. These procedures require expensive materials and equipment, and are quite troublesome to perform.

Animal inoculations also may be used for the isolation of *Brucella* species. Usually male guinea pigs are employed. Inoculated animals are bled, after 6 weeks for the presence of brucella antibodies (agglutinins). If an animal's blood test is positive, it is sacrificed and examined for pathologic tissue changes, such as enlarged spleen and abscesses in the liver and genitalia.

Serological testing is also used in the identification of *Brucella*. Such confirmatory serology may take the form of the fluorescent-antibody technique, or a simple agglutination procedure. The latter can be either a slide or tube test.

Cases of human brucellosis also may be diagnosed with the aid of an agglutination test. Here phenolized suspensions of heat-killed *B. abortus* usually are used. A standard strain of this organism, 456, obtained from the National Institutes of Health (NIH) is employed. Titers greater than 1:80 are considered to be indicative of either past or current infections. It should be noted that recent skin tests or vaccination with brucellae or *Vibrio cholerae* preparations may produce misleading results.

Skin testing with brucella antigens (brucellergen), is also done for diagnostic purposes. As in the tuberculin test, the skin reaction is of the delayed type. Unfortunately, these tests appear to be limited in value, as false negative reactions (no reaction in cases of actual infection) can occur.

Prevention. Preventive measures against brucellosis are primarily directed toward the elimination of reservoirs. This generally involves immunization of natural reservoirs, such as cattle, goats, and hogs, and the segregation and even the destruction of serologically positive animals. The vaccination of humans against this disease has received limited application.

The routine pasteurization of dairy products also is an effective means of prevention. This procedure has markedly contributed to the reduced number of human cases in the United States.

Food Poisoning

The clinical state of food poisoning discussed here refers to the symptoms resulting from the consumption of food or drink contaminated by pathogenic bacteria or their toxic products. So-called "naturally" poisonous foods and conditions arising from the ingestion of foods sprayed with pesticides will not be considered.

In the past, there was a common tendency to label certain gastrointestinal upsets as *ptomaine poisoning*. The designation was used synonomously with food poisoning. This practice has declined as careful studies have demonstrated the presence of pathogenic microorganisms or their products in the foods consumed by stricken persons. Furthermore, there are serious doubts as to the actual existence of so-called "ptomaines."

The respective etiologies of the diseases referred to as common bacterial food poisoning are well established. These include botulism, *Clostridium perfringens* poisoning, salmonellosis and staphylococcal poisoning. Salmonellosis is an example of food infection or infectious food poisoning, while the other three states are examples of "bacterial intoxications." Additional microorganisms have been implicated in, or at least suspected of, causing gastrointestinal upsets; these include *Bacillus cereus,* certain *Escherichia coli* strains, and members of the Arizona group. Moreover, certain viruses have been incriminated in cases of food-borne illnesses. Only staphylococcal food poisoning, perfringens poisoning, and salmonellosis will be presented here.

Staphylococcal Food Poisoning

As indicated in other chapters, staphylococci are ubiquitous organisms. They are normally found in various regions of the human body, including the nose, skin, and throat. These bacteria do not cause intestinal infections, but rather probably the most common type of food poisoning. The "active agent" of this disease is one of several antigenically different enterotoxins produced by certain *Staphylococcus aureus* strains. Not all strains produce these toxins. At least 5 different enterotoxins have been reported. They are designated as enterotoxins A, B, C, D, and E.

Mode of transmission.   Staphylococcal food poisoning is worldwide in distribution and is not a communicable disease. Age, race, and sex are not considered to play any role in the occurrence of the state. Man shows symptoms of the disease after consuming food in which these organisms have grown well and produced a sufficient quantity of the toxic product. Types of food that can serve as a good growth medium for staphylococci include: (1) bakery goods, especially those with a custard or cream filling, (2) cured, processed, or leftover meats, (3) fish,

and (4) dairy products. Staphylococci gain access to such foods when they are left uncovered and are not refrigerated. In order for enterotoxin to be produced in sufficient concentration, food must remain at or above room temperature (25°C) for several hours.

The sources of disease agents include individuals with staphylococcal infections, human carriers, infected animals, and milk or milk products contaminated by carriers.

Clinical features.   The symptoms of staphylococcal poisoning develop shortly after the ingestion of the contaminated food. The time of onset, as well as the severity of symptoms, appears to depend on the quantity of enterotoxin consumed. Most individuals exhibit symptoms within 4 hours. Such persons may experience abdominal cramps, chills, cyanosis (bluish coloration of the skin), diarrhea, headache, nausea, and vomiting. These symptoms generally do not last long, perhaps 3 to 6 hours. Muscular cramps caused by the vomiting may still be present afterwards, however. Usually the person does not have much of an appetite, and has no further desire to eat the incriminated food.

Complications as well as deaths associated with this disease are rare.

Laboratory diagnosis.   Although a serological test has been developed for the detection of enterotoxin, it is not yet in common use. Presumptive evidence to show the involvement of foods in an outbreak of staphylococcal poisoning usually is obtained from examinations of such products for coagulase-positive *Staphylococcus aureus*. The presence of large numbers of such organisms is considered to be incriminating. This does not mean, however, that a small count of *S. aureus* clears the food product of suspicion. Procedures for the isolation of

S. aureus may use Mannitol-salt agar (Color photograph 62), Staphylococcus Medium No. 110 (SM 110), or egg yolk-pyruvate-tellurite-glycine agar (EYA), either singly or in a combination. Inoculated plates are incubated at 35°C for 24 to 30 hours. On EYA, *S. aureus* colonies usually are black and surrounded by clear zones. These areas indicate protein decomposition (proteolysis).

Quantitation of organisms in the suspected food can be made by taking a standard sample (10 g), preparing serial dilutions, plating 0.1 ml quantities onto the surface of several plates of a standard medium, and calculating the number of organisms by a standard formula. A percentage of the isolated staphylococci are tested for coagulase activity. It should be noted that enterotoxin-producing staphylococci are coagulase-positive, but not all coagulase-positive organism are toxin producers.

Prevention. Preventive measures against food poisoning include the proper covering and refrigeration of all foods after their preparation, and excluding persons with obvious skin infections or disorders from food handling, which includes the preparation as well as the serving of foods.

The true problems with staphylococcal food poisoning are not associated with food processing, but instead are related to the mishandling of food in food service establishments and in the home.

Perfringens Poisoning

Clostridium perfringens is more widely spread than any other pathogenic bacterium. Its principal habitats are the soil and the intestinal contents of humans and animals. This organism has been recognized since the late 1800s, when reports linked it with food poisoning; however, it was not until 1945 that *C. perfringens*

food-borne illness was reported. The illness received considerable attention in Great Britain in 1953 and has been recognized as a very important food poisoning organism in the United States since that time.

Clostridium perfringens, Type A, is known to cause a form of intoxication analogous to that associated with staphylococcal enterotoxin. A more severe form of disease, *enteritis necroticans,* is produced by *C. perfringens,* Type F. Strains of this bacterial species are divided into six types, A through F. The basis for this classification is the immunological specific toxin elaborated by each strain.

Mode of transmission. Outbreaks of perfringens poisoning have been associated with several types of food, including cooked meats and poultry dishes.

Clinical features. The incubation period for this disease is longer than for staphylococcal poisoning, but is generally less than 18 hours. The clinical course of perfringens poisoning is similar to the effects of staphylococcal enterotoxin.

Laboratory diagnosis. The demonstration of hundreds of thousands, or more, of *C. perfringens* per gram of suspected food specimen is considered as supportive evidence for clinical and epidemiological findings. Successful isolation of the same serotype of organisms from the incriminated food as from fecal specimens of victims of the disease provides additional support for the laboratory diagnosis.

Fluid thioglycollate medium (FTG) and blood-agar pour plates incubated anaerobically are generally used for this purpose. Following incubation, cultures are examined for the presence of Gram-positive rods. Spores usually are not produced by *C. perfringens* in FTG. Confirmation of the organism's identity is made by inoculating motility-nitrate medium.

C. perfringens is non-motile, but it reduces nitrate.

Quantitation of *C. perfringens* in foods can be performed as described for *S. aureus*. Media used for this purpose include TFG, tryptone-sulfite-neomycin (TSN) agar, and sulfite-polymyxin-sulfadiazine (SPS) agar.

Prevention. In general, preventive measures are similar to those described for staphylococcal poisoning.

Salmonellosis (Food Infection)

This disease, which bears no relationship to salmon, is primarily limited to the gastrointestinal tract. Outbreaks of salmonellosis usually are explosive in nature, and are associated with banquets, weddings, or other group-type meals. The suddenness of the disease tends to distinguish it from other infectious diseases involving the gastrointestinal system, such as amebic and bacillary dysentery.

Causative agent. Several species of *Salmonella* are known to be capable of producing this disease. Included in this group are *S. cholerasuis, S. enteritidis, S. newport, S. oranienburg,* and *S. typhimurium.* These organisms are Gram-negative, motile, non-spore-forming rods. At the present time the members of the genus *Salmonella* are divided into 13 major serological groups. All of these organisms have the same somatic or O antigens, which are components of their cell walls. The differentiation into several hundred serological types is based on differences which exist in their flagellar or H antigens. The basis for this type of categorization is the Kauffman-White scheme. Another antigen found with certain salmonellae is the Vi or virulence antigen, another somatic antigen. The presence of the Vi antigen is indicated by the failure of a strain to agglutinate with its corresponding O anti-serum.

While it interferes with serological reactions involving the O antigen, it is not functional with respect to serologically differentiating among the species of *Salmonella.*

Mode of transmission. Man acquires salmonellosis through his consumption of contaminated food or water. A variety of foods have been implicated as sources of causative agents in outbreaks; these include cream-containing bakery goods, ground meats, sausages, and eggs. Rodents such as mice and rats often are infected by salmonellae. Such animals, after recovery, may become carriers, and by means of their excreta contaminate certain foods for human consumption. This type of situation should be guarded against in establishments used for the preparation of food. The possibility of food contamination by human carriers also exists.

Clinical features. The symptoms of gastroenteritis develop suddenly, within about 48 hours after the ingestion of sufficient numbers of appropriate salmonellae. Infected persons experience abdominal pain, diarrhea, dizziness, fever, headache, nausea, and vomiting. Severe attacks of the disease leave victims with a definite degree of abdominal discomfort, poor appetite, and difficulty in digesting solid foods, which lasts for about a week. In general, recovery from gastroenteritis caused by the salmonellae occurs within a week.

Several of the symptoms associated with salmonella infections are linked in some way to the heat-stable endotoxins of these organisms of the salmonellae.

Laboratory diagnosis. Specimens of choice for isolation of the causative agent of salmonellosis include vomitus and feces. Blood cultures are seldom positive. In addition to culturing causative microorganisms on selective and/or differential media (Color photographs 89 and 91), their identification is accomplished through biochemical and serological methods (Table 35–2). It is important to make a comparison between antibody titers present early and later in the disease. The demonstration of an increase in O agglutinins (antibody concentrations or titer) toward the somatic (O) antigen, is possible within 1 or 2 weeks after infection. However, the increase may be of a very low order of magnitude. Moreover, the possible contribution by vaccinations also should be considered.

Prevention and control. Measures that can be taken against salmonellosis include: (1) the proper cooking of foods obtained from animal sources, such as ground meat and sausages; (2) suitable refrigeration and covering of prepared foods; (3) protecting food from contamination by mice, rats, or flies and related insects; (4) the periodic inspection of food handlers; and (5) suitable sanitation.

Once a case of salmonella food poisoning is discovered, it must be reported to public health authorities. This is extremely important, since suitable measures are called for in order to protect the public from an epidemic.

Vibrio parahaemolyticus Food Poisoning

The facultative halophile (salt-loving), Vibrio parahaemolyticus, is recognized as a public health hazard in seafoods of Japan, the United States, and various other countries. Recent outbreaks of food poisoning in the United States were associated with the consumption of crab or shrimp contaminated with this organism. Foods contaminated with V. parahaemolyticus through inadequate preparation

or handling may be held under conditions that favor the growth of bacteria and increase the risk to the consumer.

Mode of transmission. Under favorable growth temperatures, extensive multiplication may occur that probably increases the risk of food-borne illness. Restaurants and cafeterias commonly prepare seafood salads in advance of serving time and store them in the refrigerator until they are displayed on the serving line. Temperatures as high as 12.8°C in refrigerated showcases, 10°C in domestic refrigerators, and 15.6°C in coolers used in the blue crab industry have been recorded. Such deviations from optimum refrigerator temperatures might well permit multiplication of contaminating V. parahaemolyticus. Ingestion of contaminated seafood produces an acute diarrhea.

Clinical features. The manifestations of V. parahaemolyticus food poisoning appear within 8 to 48 hours after the ingestion of contaminated food or water. Common features of the disease state may include a sudden onset of diarrhea, fever, mild to moderate abdominal pain, loss of appetite, nausea, and vomiting. The duration of the condition is short, usually 2 to 5 days.

Laboratory diagnosis. Rectal swabs or stool specimens are heavily streaked on the surface of thiosulfatecitrate bile salts (TCBS) agar or of bromothymol blue-teepol (BTB-Teepol) agar plates. After incubation for 18 to 24 hours at 37°C, bluish green V. parahaemolyticus colonies appear. Specific identification of the organism involves the approach shown in Figure 35–2. Typical results of biochemical testing are listed in Table 35–2. A special test based on the hemolysis of human or rabbit erythrocytes is of value in distinguishing pathogenic vibrios from non-pathogenic ones. Currently, immunoserological tests are not considered to be practical.

Prevention. In general, suitable refrigeration of seafood would appear to be a likely preventative measure.

Leptospiroses

This group of diseases is produced by a large number of antigenically distinct members of the genus *Leptospira*. At least 80 different serotypes and subserotypes of the genus have been identified. In addition to pathogenic species (Table 35–3), the genus also contains saprophytes. The latter are collectively designated as *Leptospira biflexa*. Nonpathogenic leptospires can be distinguished from pathogenic forms on the basis of their inability to infect laboratory animals, and their ability to grow in media which are not supplemented with serum.

This genus is undergoing changes with respect to the designation of its species. The Leptospira subcommittee of the International Committee on Systematic Bacteriology has proposed recognition of two species thus far, the saprophyte *L. biflexa,* mentioned earlier, and the pathogen *L. interrogans.*

The causative agent. All *Leptospira* species, whether they are parasitic or saprophytic, are morphologically identical. *Leptospira* can be found in various bodies of water, such as lakes, ponds, and rivers, on decaying matter, and even in tap water in some situations. Leptospires measure approximately 4 to 20 μm (μ) in length, and 0.1 μm (μ) in width. These organisms are quite thin (*leptos* is from the Greek meaning thin), elongated structures consisting of many small coils tightly set together (Figure 35–4). Quite often leptospires are shaped like the letters C, S, and J. Finely tapered or so-called "hooked" ends are charac-

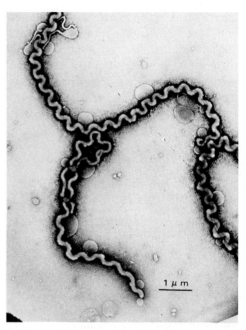

FIG. 35–4. Negatively stained cells of *Leptospira canicola*. Note the smooth, coiled shape of these organisms. (From Anderson, D. L., and Johnson, R. C.: *J. Bacteriol.,* **95**:2293–2309, 1968.)

teristically found in these organisms. In addition, leptospires possess a single straight axial filament that extends through the entire length of individual cells. Motility is generally observed in fresh specimens.

Staining of these organisms may be accomplished by means of a Giemsa stain preparation, or with silver stains.

The various *Leptospira* spp. are readily grown in artificial fluid media. However, as indicated earlier, pathogenic forms require the addition of a serum supplement. This requirement is usually fulfilled by the incorporation of 10 per cent heat-inactivated rabbit serum (heated at 56°C for 30 minutes). Other sources of this supplement are cattle, guinea pigs, and sheep. Naturally, these sera must be checked for the presence of leptospiral antibodies. Modified Stuart's, Fletcher's semi-solid, or Kort-

Table 35–3 Leptospira Species Capable of Causing Human Infection

Species	Disease	Known Reservoirs of Infection
L. australis	Canefield fever, field fever, mud fever, Pomona fever	Cattle, pigs, rats
L. autumnalis	Akiyami, autumnal fever, Fort Bragg fever, seven-day fever	Japanese field mice and moles
L. bataviae	Ricefield fever, swineherd's disease, Weil's disease	Cats, dogs, European harvest mice
L. hebdomadis	Akiyami B, Feld-fieber (fieldfever) B, seven-day fever	Field and meadow mice
L. icterohaemorrhagiae	Infectious or leptospiral jaundice, Weil's disease	Cattle, dogs, horses, a variety of rats including house, roof, and sewer areas, silver fox
L. canicola	Canicola fever	Dogs, fruit bats, house mice, rats
L. pyrogenes	Canefield fever, Leptospirosis febrilis	Black rats, fruit bats

hof's media are recommended for the isolation and cultivation of *Leptospira* spp.

Mention should also be made of the use of embryonated chick embryos for the cultivation of *Leptospira*. The inoculation of the chorioallantoic membrane (CAM) of this animal generally produces good growth (See Chapter 13 for a discussion of the animal and injection techniques).

Mode of transmission. The leptospiroses are considered to be examples of a zoonosis. Several species of wild rodents and domestic animals, including cattle, cats, and dogs, serve as reservoirs of infection (Table 35–3). While the natural hosts may experience a mild infection, they seldom die of the disease. A particular *Leptospira* species generally is quite well adapted to its host, and is capable of inhabiting the convoluted tubules of the animal's kidney without inflicting damage. Thus the periodic release of large numbers of leptospires in the animal's urine is not unusual. Man acquires the disease agent by coming into contact, either directly or indirectly, with this infected urine. *Leptospira* infections may result from bathing in, or falling into, stagnant bodies of water which have been contaminated by the infectious urine of rodents.

The organisms may gain access to the body tissues by first penetrating the mucous membranes of the eyes and nasopharynx, or by entering through skin abrasions, or cuts. Cases of the disease have been reported which involved consumption of contaminated food and water.

The infectious nature of the leptospires is favored only in alkaline environments. Acid conditions reduce their survival period.

Several factors have been reported to affect the incidence of human infections; these include age, sex, occupation, and seasonal variations. In general, adults are more likely to acquire leptospirosis because of a greater possibility of exposure. For example, newborn infants are not exposed to contaminated bodies of water which might be used for swimming, boating, or fishing. The age most commonly involved is between 20 and 30 years. The higher percentage of cases in males is caused by a greater occupational exposure. Typically male occupations—plumbing, gardening, meat packing, farming, etc.—afford more of an opportunity to be exposed to infected animals and contaminated bodies of water. No apparent difference in susceptibility between males and females has been reported.

In tropical areas, leptospirosis can occur throughout the year. In general, moisture and warmth are required by the various species of leptospira for survival. With environmental conditions of this sort, there is a much greater utilization of outdoor facilities not only for pleasure but also for work. Consequently, the potential for exposure also is higher. Cases of this disease are more frequent during the late summer and early winter months of the year.

Clinical features. Several species of *Leptospira* are associated with human infections. These disease states range from relatively mild to rather severe. Canicola fever, which is principally caused by *L. canicola*, is an example of a mild type of infection, while the classical Weil's disease is representative of a severe form of leptospiral infection. *L. icterohaemorrhagiae* is the primary cause of Weil's disease. The clinical features of these leptospiroses are described below.

Canicola Fever

In addition to *L. canicola,* canicola fever is less commonly caused by other species, including *L. grippotyphosa* and *L. hebdomadis*. Canicola fever has an incubation period of approximately 10 days. The appearance of general clinical symptoms is abrupt and includes anorexia (lack of appetite), chest pains, coryza (head cold), cough, difficulty in swallowing, fever ranging from 102° to 106°F, persistent headache, lymphadenopathy, muscular pains, nausea, general prostration, skin hemorrhages, stiff neck, and vomiting. The fever experienced by most infected persons lasts approximately 8 days, but in some cases it lasts 14 days. The fever may be continuous or remittent. About 20 per cent of cases show jaundice.

In addition to these clinical features, hemorrhagic manifestations (destruction of red blood cells), hematuria (blood in the urine), petechiae (small hemorrhages in the skin), and retinal hemorrhages also may be seen.

Disturbance of renal function is a common feature, not only of canicola fever, but of the other leptospiroses. Urinary output, however, is usually normal.

Recovery for the majority of infected persons varies between 4 and 5 weeks. Human infections seldom if ever are acquired from convalescing patients.

Weil's Disease (Spirochetal Fever, or Spirochetal Jaundice)

This infection, caused by *L. icterohaemorrhagiae*, is one of the most severe forms of human leptospirosis. The incubation period varies from 2 to 20 days, with the onset of clinical manifestations being rather abrupt. Three states of Weil's disease are recognized.

During the first stage many of the features described for canicola fever are exhibited by patients. However, a distinctive manifestation, jaundice, appears near the end of this period. (This disease state has various disease agents associated with it. Serodiagnosis is necessary to identify the specific *Leptospira* spp.). Furthermore, involvement of the central nervous system, kidneys, liver, and spleen commonly occurs. Infected persons may also have other symptoms, which include abdominal pain, gastrointestinal disturbances, conjunctivitis, sore throat, and pneumonia. Hemorrhages of the mucous membranes and skin usually indicate a very serious illness.

In the second state, characteristic manifestations include a lower fever, inflammations of the inner portions of the eyes, pronounced jaundice, and continued involvement of the gastrointestinal tract and kidneys. This period, which lasts approximately a week, is the most critical one in the infection. Heart failure and death can occur quite frequently. The patient's immunological response usually appears during this stage.

Patients in the third stage of Weil's disease generally experience the beginning of a restoration of normal functions. However, fever and jaundice may persist. Antibody titers usually increase during this time. The urinary excretion of leptospirae does occur, but usually ceases beyond the sixth week after the onset of symptoms.

The period for convalescence may be as short as 6 weeks, or as long as 6 months. Mortality rates vary considerably.

Laboratory diagnosis. Human leptospirosis can be definitely established by either isolating the disease agent from typical clinical specimens, such as blood and cerebrospinal fluid, or by demonstrating a significant rise in leptospiral antibody titer by serological tests including microscopic agglutination and complement-fixation. The latter involves obtaining two or more properly timed serum specimens taken at specified times during the course of the disease.

Detection of leptospirae in clinical specimens by direct microscopic examination can prove to be extremely difficult, because the concentration of such organisms is low. However, the chances of demonstrating leptospires can be increased with the use of differential centrifugation and the services of an experienced observer. Dark-field microscopy and staining techniques are routinely used. The latter type of procedures include silver-impregnation methods. Fluorescent-antibody techniques also have been employed. However, their value as routine diagnostic procedures is still under study.

It is important to note that failure to demonstrate the etiologic agents of leptospirosis by direct microscopy does not eliminate the possibility that these organisms are causing the disease state. Cultural and/or serological procedures should definitely be conducted to substantiate or refute the direct microscopic findings.

An extremely reliable method of detecting these microorganisms involves culturing blood specimens in appropriate artificial media, or inoculating them into laboratory animals.

Prevention. As indicated earlier, the natural reservoirs of leptospirosis are varied and numerous. Therefore, an attempt to eradicate them would be quite difficult. As an effective vaccine for this disease is not currently available for humans, preventive measures generally are directed toward reducing man's contact with contaminated water or urine from infected animals. Included among these preventive measures are the following: (1) the wearing of protective clothing, such as gloves, rubber boots, etc., while working with possibly contaminated objects or water supplies; (2) avoiding bodies of water which might be contaminated by infected animals; and (3) not using or ingesting water and food which may be contaminated.

Shigellosis (Bacillary Dysentery)

The principal causes of this acute infectious disease are the pathogenic shigellae. It is distinct from amebic and viral dysentery. The various species of *Shigella* are widely distributed, and are found primarily in the intestines of man, and occasionally of monkeys and other mammals. The most common causes of bacillary dysentary are *Shigella dysenteriae* (discovered by the Japanese bacteriologist Shiga in 1896), and *S. flexneri*. In general, the shigellae are far less invasive than the salmonellae. Additional distinguishing properties are listed in the Laboratory Diagnosis section.

Classifying shigellae on the basis of fermentation reactions has proved difficult in certain cases (Table 35–2). The use of newer media and approaches have removed many of such difficulties (Color photographs 51–53). Separation into species and serological types on the basis of antigenic composition has met with success. Four specific divisions or antigenic subgroups are recognized, called A, B, C, and D. Representative species of each group are shown in Table 35–4.

Mode of transmission. Since its description in the fourth century B.C., shigellosis has been found to be quite prevalent during several major military campaigns. This disease apparently occurs with a greater frequency than other forms of dysentery.

The human is the sole reservoir of infection; no lower animal reservoir is believed to exist. Although all age groups are susceptible to shigellae infection, children and males between the ages of 20 and 30 are more commonly infected. Predisposing factors related to the occurrences of shigellosis include lowered states of resistance, malnutrition, overcrowding, and poor sanitation.

Bacillary dysentery is usually contracted through the ingestion of contaminated food or water. The causative agents can be transmitted by feces, fingers, flies, or food.

Clinical features. The incubation period for shigellosis ranges from 1 to 14 days. The onset of symptoms is usually abrupt. An infected individual generally experiences abdominal pain, diarrhea, sharp fever (103°–104°F), and malaise. In severe forms of the disease, stools are primarily composed of blood, mucus, and pus, giving a "red currant jelly" appearance. A burning rectal sensation, dehydration, electrolyte imbalance, straining, and vomiting may accompany defecation. The average number of stools passed per day varies from 6 to 10.

The initial symptoms—abdominal pain, sharp fever, etc.—occur largely as a result of an acute inflammatory reaction involving the mucous membranes of the large intestine and associated structures. Although ulceration may result, septicemia does not. The infection remains localized and limited to these areas.

Individuals recovering from bacillary dysentery may become carriers of shigellae. This is an important consideration in the control and prevention of shigellosis, as they serve as reservoirs of causative agents between outbreaks.

Complications known to occur with shigellosis include the perforation of the bowel and massive bleeding.

The particular factors responsible for the pathogenicity in cases of shigellosis have not been fully determined, except for infections produced by *Shigella dysenteriae*. In addition to producing an endotoxin, which is characteristic of all shigellae, *S. dysenteriae* is known to form an exotoxin. This soluble, heat-labile protein is called the Shiga neurotoxin. It is one of the most powerful poisons known. When injected into experimental animals, the toxin causes hemorrhage, diarrhea, paralysis, and death.

Table 35–4
The Serological Groups of Shigella

Group	Representative Shigella Species	Common Name (if applicable)
A	*S. arabinotarda*	
	S. dysenteriae	Shiga bacillus
	S. schmitzii	Schmitz bacillus
B	*S. flexneri*	Flexner bacillus
C	*S. boydii*	Boyd bacillus
D	*S. sonnei*	Sonne bacillus

Laboratory diagnosis. Bacillary dysentery can be distinguished from other types of dysentery by means of microscopic examination of fecal specimens, cultivation, biochemical studies, and agglutination tests. Fecal matter from patients with diarrhea caused by other microorganisms, such as ameba, and *Escherichia coli*, generally does not contain large numbers of leukocytes, or large amounts of blood and mucus.

The laboratory verification of shigellosis is primarily based on the isolation and identification of the causative agent. Specimens of choice include feces or rectal swabs. Occasionally specimens are obtained directly from ulcerative intestinal lesions with the aid of a sigmoidoscope (a device for examining the large intestine and related structures). Cultures are generally made by inoculating deoxycholate agar, deoxycholate citrate agar, HE (Hektoen Enteric) agar (Color photograph 91), or other similar media. Although the shigellae are present in relatively large numbers during infections, they may not remain viable for a long period of time. Therefore, it is important to culture specimens soon after they are obtained. The final identification of these organisms is based on biochemical (Table 35–2) and specific agglutination tests. Fluorescent antibody procedures are under study.

The shigellae resemble the salmonellae in certain features. However, they can be differentiated from them on the basis of the following characteristics: (1) failure to produce gas during carbohydrate fermentations, (2) no production of hydrogen sulfide, (3) inability to utilize citrate, and (4) an absence of motility. In addition, *Shigella* spp. are antigenically different.

Prevention. The control of this disease involves far more than the appropriate use of antibiotics. Since human beings serve as the sole source of infectious agents, preventive measures must be directed towards infected persons, carriers, and items which may have been contaminated by them. The elimination of flies, the proper sanitary disposal of excreta, and the protection of food and water also are of great importance.

Unfortunately, vaccines have not been developed which could increase individual resistance. Thus, in situations of widespread shigellosis, the use of mass chemoprophylaxis may be necessary.

Typhoid Fever

The various species of the genus *Salmonella* are associated with at least three clinically distinguishable disease states in man: enteric fever, septicemias, and acute forms of gastroenteritis (infectious food poisoning) discussed earlier. Septicemias of this kind generally do not involve the gastrointestinal tract. Individuals so affected exhibit a high fever and a bacteremia. *Salmonella cholerasuis* is a commonly encountered etiological agent. All of these conditions are collectively called *salmonellosis*. Typhoid fever is the classic example of the enteric fevers. It is caused by the Gram-negative, motile, and non-spore-forming rod *Salmonella typhi*.

Mode of transmission. Humans acquire the infection through the ingestion of contaminated food or water. Flies and fomites also have been implicated as sources of the disease agent. In countries where adequate sanitation is maintained, typhoid fever appears either sporadically, or in an endemic form. Quite often the source of infectious agents is traced to carriers, individuals who do not have symptoms of the disease, but harbor the etiologic agent. In regions where sanitation is poor, with no purification of water supplies, improper waste disposal, and lack of pasteurization, typhoid epidemics can occur. All ages may be attacked.

Clinical features. The incubation period for typhoid fever generally varies from 10 to 14 days. Some unusual cases have been reported in which the disease occurred after 30 days of incubation. The onset of symptoms generally is gradual. This event apparently coincides with the entrance of *Salmonella typhi* into the victim's bloodstream, during the first or second week of infection.

Common early symptoms of the disease include abdominal distention, constipation, fever, which becomes progressively more severe and may reach 104°F, headache, loss of appetite, malaise, nausea, and vomiting. Diarrhea usually occurs during the second week of the infection. Fecal matter generally is yellowish to greenish in color and has a loose consistency. Blood may be present. *Salmonella typhi* can be found in stools during the entire period of the infection as well as during the period of convalescence. It is not unusual to recover such organisms from urine in the latter stages.

One characteristic feature of typhoid fever is the appearance of a rash, called "rose spots," on the trunk of the patient. Small, round, red macules occur in crops lasting approximately 2 to 3 days. At the height of the disease generalized tenderness is quite apparent. If treatment is not administered early, and the clinical symptoms are allowed to persist for several weeks, the patient will become gravely ill and perhaps even die. Complications that can develop during the course of typhoid fever include inflammation of the gall bladder (cholecystitis), perforation of the small intestine, hemorrhage in the small intestine, and pneumonia.

Salmonella typhi, as indicated earlier, can gain access to various tissues and organs via the bloodstream. These areas, such as the bone marrow, gall bladder, and spleen, can serve as future sources of reinfection. Thus another complication of typhoid fever is the relapse. This state occurs when organisms gain access to the bloodstream from the previously mentioned "foci of infection."

Laboratory diagnosis. See the section dealing with *Salmonella* food infection.

Enteric Bacteria Species and Disease States of Increasing Frequency

Several enteric or so-called coliform bacilli are normal, nonpathogenic inhabitants of the gastrointestinal tract. However, certain related strains or species are associated with infections or other pathological states involving the human urogenital and intestinal system. This group of Gram-negatives includes *Citrobacter freudii,* enteropathogenic *Escherichia coli,* enterotoxin-producing *E. coli, Providencia* species (spp.), *Serratia* spp., *Vibrio parahaemolyticus,* and *Yersinia enterocolitica.* Several of these organisms and the disease states associated with them will be described in the following paragraphs.

Proteus spp. Members of this genus are noted for their pronounced motility and ability to ferment a number of sugars, with the exception of lactose (Table 35–2). These organisms have a feature known as *swarming* or *intermediate spreading* on moist agar surfaces. The property is associated with their active motility. The production of ammonia from urea (urease test) (Color photograph 37) and the formation of hydrogen sulfide (Color photographs 51 and 91*C*) are biochemical properties used to differentiate *Proteus* species from those of *Salmonella.*

The genus includes *P. mirabilis, P. rettgeri, P. morganii,* and *P. vulgaris.* The last two species are considered to be the most significant from a clinical standpoint.

Antigenically, *Proteus* species are heterogenous. They can be subdivided by means of serological methods into at least 98 flagellar (H antigen) types and 30 somatic (O antigen) groups. In addition, certain strains of the O antigen group possess specific soluble polysaccharide antigenic components. These organisms are indicated by the letter X. Three different groups are recognized as OX2, OX19, and OXK. The antigens of these strains are agglutinated by the sera of patients having certain rickettsial diseases. This group of diseases includes Rocky Mountain spotted fever, scrub typhus, and typhus. The basic reaction is the basis of the Weil-Felix test, which is of diagnostic importance to infections of this kind.

Pathogenic species of *Proteus* have been associated with attacks of enteritis, especially in infants. The drug of choice used in these cases has generally been chloramphenicol. Unfortunately, these organisms are known to be drug-resistant.

Infant Epidemic Diarrhea (Enteropathogenic *Escherichia coli*, EPEC)

Numerous reports have appeared of epidemic diarrhea occurring in newborn and young infants. These outbreaks in most cases were associated with specific enteropathogenic strains of *Escherichia coli*. In 1960, Neter listed eleven enteropathogenic serological groups (serotypes) as significant causative agents of the infantile enteritis. Among the various strains listed, the following ones were considered to be of particular importance: O26: B6; O55: B5; O111: B4; and O127: B8. Recently, additional O serotypes involved with this disease have been uncovered; these include 86, 112, 119, 124, and 128.

In the United States, enteropathogenic types of *Escherichia coli* (EPEC) are usu-ally associated with cases of infantile diarrhea. Studies from India, Vietnam in 1971, and Japan in 1967 showed that EPEC cause disease not only in children but in adults as well. EPEC can cause disease in humans by at least two mechanisms: by production of a cholera-like enterotoxin and by an invasion of intestinal epithelial lining.

Mode of transmission. Incidents of infant epidemic diarrhea pose a definite threat in hospital practice, especially when nurseries are involved. Unfortunately, outbreaks of this kind may be accompanied by a high mortality rate. In addition, controlling the spread of enteropathogenic strains is a difficult problem. Such organisms develop resistance to commonly used antibiotics.

Epidemic diarrhea usually predominantly affects newborns and infants under 2 years of age. Premature babies are attacked most severely. Although the disease can occur in older children and adults, the effects are not serious.

The disease may be acquired by infants as a secondary infection. Situations have been reported in which patients requiring hospitalization for other conditions (e.g., brain injuries and congenital defects) became infected. Pediatric and nursing staff members must always be on guard to prevent such conditions from occurring.

Sources of enteropathogenic *E. coli* include convalescent infant carriers, cats, dogs, and fomites.

Before November 1971, there were reports of water-borne outbreaks of EPEC in the United States, but no confirmed outbreaks were associated with foods. However, from 30 October to 10 December 1971, over 200 persons in more than 90 separate outbreaks suffered acute food poisoning symptoms. Imported Camembert or Brie cheese was found to be the source of the causative agents.

Clinical features. Infants with epidemic diarrhea can exhibit a variety of symptoms, including a bluish coloration of the skin, convulsions, dehydration, diarrhea, distended abdomen, jaundice, nausea, and vomiting. Fatalities can and do occur. Among the most critical problems to be dealt with are dehydration and electrolyte imbalance. Unfortunately, some parents seek medical care only after several days or even weeks of diarrhea, weight loss, and vomiting.

Enteropathogenic *E. coli* strains generally remain localized to the gastrointestinal tract. However, bloodstream invasion and subsequent spreading to other areas can take place during the course of this infection.

Laboratory diagnosis. The identification of enteropathogenic *Escherichia coli* depends on its isolation from a freshly obtained stool specimen on a suitable selective and differential medium such as Eosin-Methylene Blue (EMB) agar or Hektoen Enteric (HE) agar (Color photographs 88 and 91). Differentiation from other Gram-negatives involves the use of a number of biochemical tests (Figure 35–2 and Table 35–2). Slide agglutination tests employing appropriate antisera are used to confirm the biochemical testing results. Fluorescent antibody techniques have been employed for the screening of specimens.

Traveler's Diarrhea

In recent years evidence has accumulated to show that enterotoxin-producing *Es-*

cherichia coli can cause an acute dehydrating diarrhea resembling that produced in Asiatic cholera. The O serotypes isolated included 6, 15, and 78. Unlike the enteropathogenic *E. coli* (EPEC), enterotoxin-producing organisms are unable to invade the intestinal mucosa. Traveler's diarrhea, as the designation suggests, is acquired by individuals traveling from one part of the world to another. Recovery from the condition usually is without complications.

Yersinia enterocolitica Infections

The number of *Yersinia enterocolitica* infections diagnosed in humans has increased considerably during the last decade. There has been a steady increase in the recorded incidence of infection and in the number of countries that report *Y. enterocolitica* isolations. The clinical aspects of the disease have widened, and the various animal species in which this bacterium is found have increased.

Acute gastroenteritis is the most frequent *clinical* form of this infection. Other clinical conditions described are septicemia, polyarthritis, erythema nodosum, and abscesses.

The incidence of *Y. enterocolitica* isolated from fecal specimens in cases of acute bacterial gastroenteritis is reported by some specialists to have surpassed the incidence of *Shigella*, being second to *Salmonella*. Cases of gastroenteritis due to *Y. enterocolitica*, reported until 1972, have been either sporadic or confined to small family outbreaks. Since that time outbreaks have been described in Finland, Japan, and the United States.

QUESTIONS FOR REVIEW

1. Could antibiotics taken by mouth affect an individual's intestinal flora? Explain.

2. Differentiate between bacterial food poisoning and bacterial intoxication. Give examples of each.

3. a. What general symptoms are experienced by a victim of staphylococcal food poisoning?
   b. Would the heating of foods containing an enterotoxin inactivate the toxin? Explain.
   c. What types of foods provide good growth conditions for staphylococci?
   d. Are these foods the same for *Clostridium perfringens?*
   e. List at least two measures to prevent staphylococcal poisoning.

4. Discuss "ptomaine poisoning." Is it related to bacterial gastrointestinal diseases?

5. If you were assigned as part of your job to tour Spain, Egypt, India, Peru, and Mexico, what diseases associated with the gastrointestinal system might you encounter? What precautionary measures would be advisable?

6. What disease outbreaks would you expect as a consequence of natural disasters such as earthquakes and floods?

7. Distinguish between typhoid and typhus fevers.

8. Discuss infant diarrhea.

9. Compare reservoirs for the following diseases:
   a. Asiatic cholera
   b. bacillary dysentery
   c. staphylococcal poisoning
   d. infantile diarrhea
   e. brucellosis

10. What is the difference between *Vibro cholerae* and *V. El Tor?*

11. What protective mechanisms against bacterial diseases are provided by the human gastrointestinal system?

12. What foods are associated with *Vibrio parahaemolyticus?*

13. a. What is traveler's diarrhea?
    b. How does it differ from typhoid fever?

14. Propose an approach to begin the identification of a bacterial pathogen of the gastrointestinal tract.

Viral Infections Associated with the Gastrointestinal Tract

Various viral pathogens may infect portions of the gastrointestinal system (Table 36–1). Sometimes symptoms of a disease process may not be evident. When an infection does occur, the effects do not necessarily produce gastrointestinal disturbances, but may cause reactions involving other body structures, such as those of the nervous and respiratory systems.

Certain viruses invade the gastrointestinal system and simply utilize its parts for purposes of replication only. Viral involvement may accompany other types of infections, but direct evidence showing the relationship of viruses to outbreaks of gastrointestinal upsets, such as summer diarrhea, usually is lacking. Discussion here is limited to the main groups of pathogens known to invade this system.

Picornavirus Infections

Characteristics of the Group

Coxsackie-, echo-, and polio viruses are recognized as being capable of infecting the gastrointestinal system. Originally, these specific agents were named enteroviruses because of their obvious association with this system. It soon became apparent that several viruses in the group were able to infect the respiratory tract and central nervous system as well. Another group of pathogens primarily affecting the respiratory system was conse-

quently designated the rhinoviruses. All of these various viruses were placed into a more adequate group, the *picornaviruses*. *Pico* means small and *rna* comes from RNA, the type of nucleic acid found in this group. Coxsackieviruses were named after Coxsackie, New York, where the first isolations took place in 1948. The name ECHO was derived from certain of the properties of these viruses, namely E = enteric location; C = capable of causing cytopathic changes in tissues cells; H = human source; and O = orphan. At one time there were more viral agents than diseases, hence the term *orphan*.

Several pathogenic viruses of lower animals are also in the picornavirus group. These include the agents of encephalo-myocarditis of mice, Teschen disease of pigs, and foot-and-mouth disease (FMD).

Infections

In general, the majority of picornaviruses enter the human body via the oral route. A few, however, enter by means of the respiratory tract. The disease states produced by this group generally differ in the tissues involved, the types of lesions resulting from infection, and the severity of the attack. Similar disease states (e.g., aseptic meningitis) may be caused by different picornaviruses. As most of the infections produced by picornaviruses are discussed in greater detail in other chap-

Table 36–1   Viruses Associated with the Gastrointestinal System and Related Structures

Representative Disease	Viral Groups (if known)	Genus or Other Designation	Possible Treatment
Aseptic meningitis, herpangina	Picornaviruses	*Coxsackievirus*	No specific treatment. Measures to relieve pain and respiratory distress and to rehabilitate paralyzed limbs are carried out when needed
Aseptic meningitis, implicated in enteritis		*Echovirus*	No specific treatment. Measures to relieve pain and respiratory distress and to rehabilitate paralyzed limbs are carried out when needed
Aseptic meningitis, poliomyelitis		*Poliovirus*	No specific treatment. Measures to relieve pain, to improve respiratory impairment, and rehabilitate paralyzed limbs are carried out when needed
Cytomegalovirus inclusion disease (CMID)	Herpesviruses	*Cytomegalovirus*	No specific treatment, however gamma globulins and steroids have been used
Hepatitis, Type A (infectious hepatitis)		Virus, Type A., I.H. virus MS-1	No specific therapy. Supportive treatment including avoidance of physical stress, administration of vitamins and substances necessary to maintain caloric and fluid and electrolyte balances
Hepatitis, Type B (serum hepatitis)		Virus, Type B., S.H. virus MS-2	
Infectious mononucleosis	Herpesviruses		Bed rest. Administration of anti-inflammatory agents in cases of hemolytic anemia. Hospitalization of severe cases

SOURCE: Adapted from Lwoff, A., and Tournier, P.: "The Classification of Viruses," *Ann. Rev. Microbiol.,* 20:45, 1966.

ters, only the echoviruses will be briefly considered here.

Echoviruses

Originally 33 types of echoviruses were recognized. With further study, two of these viral agents, types 10 and 28, were reclassified and placed into the rhinovirus group.

Echoviruses produce a variety of diseases, including aseptic meningitis, acute respiratory infections, paralysis, encephalitis, rashes, enteritis, and epidemic diarrhea in infants. Infections with this group of viruses probably occur more frequently than most people realize. No effective control measures are currently available to limit their spread. Artificial immunizations have not been developed, primarily because of the difficulty of preparing a single vaccine that can immunize against the great number of echovirus types.

Laboratory diagnosis.   The isolation of echoviruses using rhesus monkey kidney cells (Figure 36–1) appears to be a most sensitive and reliable method of laboratory diagnosis. Specimens of choice include throat secretions and feces.

Serological tests can be employed for the identification of viral agents. The procedures most commonly used are the hemagglutination (HA), passive hemagglutination, hemagglutination inhibition (HI), and neutralization tests, described in Chapter 23. Generally speaking, such tests are expensive to perform.

Cytomegalovirus Inclusion Disease

The cytomegaloviruses (CMV), also known as the salivary gland viruses, comprise a group of highly species-specific infecting agents. Humans, monkeys, and other animals can fall victim to them. Both *in vitro* and *in vivo,* these viral pathogens generally produce a cellular response characterized by *cytomegaly* (increases in cellular size) and the presence of intranuclear inclusion bodies (Figure 36–2). These features were first described in 1904 by Jesionek and Kiolemenoglon, and independently by Ribbert.

Two distinct antigenic types of cytomegaloviruses from human sources have been identified. There is also a possibility of a third group.

In infants, infections may present a grave disease picture. Involvement of the salivary glands and portions of the gastrointestinal and urinary systems is indicated by morphologic and virologic laboratory findings. Instances of chronic infections or

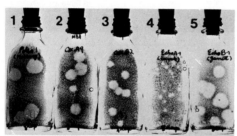

FIG. 36–1. Plaque formation patterns of selected picornaviruses (enteroviruses) on rhesus monkey cultures in bottles. (1) Poliovirus type 1 (Mahoney strain); (2) Coxsackie virus A9; (3) Coxsackie virus B2; (4) ECHO virus type 1 (Farouk strain); (5) ECHO virus type B7 (Garnett strain). Note the variation in plaque size between the different picornaviruses. (From Hsiung, G. D.: *Yale J. Biol. Med.*, **33**:359, 1961.)

generalized disease in older children and adults have been reported.

Cytomegalovirus properties. These viral agents have been grouped with the herpesviruses (see Chapter 31), primarily on the bases of the following: (1) viral particle morphology, (2) virion chemical composition, and (3) the characteristics of their intranuclear inclusion bodies (Figure 36–2).

Mode of transmission. The young infant appears to acquire CMV congenitally. Some instances of postnatal infection have also been reported. Cytomegalovirus has been found on postpartum examinations of mothers.

When CMV infection occurs with individuals beyond the newborn period, it has been associated with leukemia or other neoplastic (cancerous) diseases. Some cases have been reported in which generalized cytomegalic inclusion disease (CMID) produced complications in drug-induced suppression of the immune re-

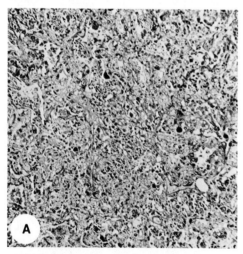

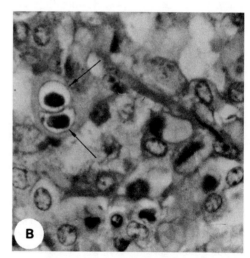

FIG. 36–2. Cytomegalovirus infection. <u>A</u>. The lung tissue shown clearly exhibits a narrowing of its alveolar spaces, which are filled with large cells and protein material (interstitial edema). <u>B</u>. The presence of intranuclear inclusions (arrows) in giant cells. (From Cangir, A., and Sullivan, M. P.: *JAMA*, **195**:1042, 1966. Courtesy of the University of Texas M. D. Anderson Hospital & Tumor Inst., Houston, Texas.)

sponse with organ transplantations. There is a strong suggestion that the use of steroids and related drugs may bring about an activation of a latent CMV infection.

Clinical features. Infected newborns show hepatitis, jaundice, increases in the sizes of both their livers and spleens (*hepatosplenomegaly*), mental retardation, and *thrombocytopenia purpura,* a disease state associated with a decrease in the number of blood platelets. Severely diseased infants also may suffer loss of sight due to a wasting away of the optic nerve and inflammation of the choroid and retinal layers of the eye. The clinical symptoms of CMV infection are quite similar if not identical to congenital toxoplasmosis (see Chapter 41).

Persons who acquire the virus postnatally often show no symptoms. The lungs of infants with interstitial pneumonitis have been found to contain CMV. Furthermore, documented cases of cytomegalovirus pneumonia have been reported to accompany malignant or clinical courses of CMID in leukemic infants who subsequently died.

Pathologic features. Characteristically, the primary change in tissues is the presence of enlarged cells which may contain several intranuclear inclusions. This situation has been found in tissues including kidney, lung, liver, pancreas, and salivary glands. An associated diffuse inflammatory cell filtrate is usually evident during the course of the disease. Extensive brain involvement and damage also may occur.

Laboratory diagnosis. Several infectious diseases, in addition to the previously mentioned congenital toxoplasmosis, may produce a clinical picture identical to that caused by CMV infection. Included among these agents are congenital syphilis and members of the TORCH group, which include toxoplasmosis, rubella, and the herpesviruses (see Chapter 37). Consequently, evidence of infection is best established by the recovery of cytomegalovirus. Specimens for this purpose include infected tissues, saliva, sputum, and urine. However, intranuclear inclusions may be present in the saliva of asymptomatic individuals, since latent CMV infections are fairly common in the population. Sputum specimens are of value only when obtained by a deep cough. The presence of intranuclear inclusions is not conclusive evidence without this stipulation. Cultures of human embryonic fibroblasts and adenoid and kidney cells have been employed for viral isolation.

Intranuclear inclusions are sometimes found in the urine sediments and bronchial and gastric washings of patients. This is primarily because of the common involvement of the associated organs during infection. Diagnostic serological tests also are used; they include immunofluorescence, indirect hemagglutination, and complement-fixation procedures.

Viral Hepatitis

This disease state, formerly known as acute catarrhal jaundice, generally is described as an infectious enteric and systemic infection in which the liver is characteristically involved. Traditionally, jaundice is the most prominent symptom exhibited by victims. The features of viral hepatitis are many, and range from viremia (viruses in the bloodstream) that does not seriously affect the liver, to a fulminating disease state ending in death within a few days.

It is customary to designate viral hepatitis in relation to a special etiologic agent, such as type A or infectious hepatitis (IH) and type B or homologous serum hepatitis (SH) viruses (also known as MS-1 and

Table 36–2   A Comparison of Diseases Caused by Infectious (IH) and
Serum (SH) Hepatitis Viruses

Property	Type A (Infectious Hepatitis) Virus	Type B (Serum Hepatitis) Virus
Age group most commonly affected	Children and young adults	All age groups
Clinical onset	Abrupt and with fever	Insidious and without fever
Communicability	Contagious	Not under normal conditions
Duration of carrier state	Unknown, however, believed to be over 8 months	May be as long as 5 years
Host	Human	Human
Immunity (resistance following infection)	Present	Questionable
Incidence	Seasonal	Throughout the year
Incubation period	15 to 40 days	60 to 160 days
Prevention by gamma globulin (prophylaxis)	Generally valuable	Questionable
Route of inoculation	Primarily oral, but parenteral also possible	Parenteral. Additional routes possible, e.g., personal contact, orally unrecognized inoculation, and aerolization of blood and other body fluids
Specimens in which virus is believed to be or is present	Blood and feces	Blood
Severity	Usually mild	Often severe
HB antigen	Absent	Present in early acute phase

MS-2, respectively). These microorganisms are separate viruses. Although they have several features in common (Table 36–2), they also differ from one another in several respects. The most important of these include: (1) the method of transmission, (2) the manner in which symptoms occur (onset of the disease), (3) the incubation period, and (4) the chemical composition.

Humans are apparently the only known natural hosts for viral hepatitis. A large number of infectious hepatitis cases have been associated with closed community environments including camps, nurseries, housing tracts, and schools. Outbreaks have also occurred in hospitals. Infectious hepatitis virus is spread by the fecal contamination of food or water. Serum hepatitis virus, on the other hand, is usually transmitted by almost any type of injection or related procedure. Moreover, doctors, nurses, technologists, or research technicians handling blood or blood products are particularly vulnerable to this disease agent. Before the significance of the proper sterilization of syringes and needles in preventing serum hepatitis was realized, several "epidemics" were reported from clinics giving routine injections. Unfortunately, even when suitable procedures are used, cases of the disease occur, especially in association with transfusions. The incidence of serum hepatitis varies from 0.2 to 1 per cent and possibly higher in situations of this type. The injection of 0.000025 ml of blood from a patient is sufficient to cause serum hepatitis.

A number of cases have been traced to instruments used in oral surgery. The practice of tattooing also has been incriminated in spreading the disease. Recent experimental studies have shown mosquitoes to be potential transmitters of the disease agent.

Properties of the hepatitis virus. At the time of writing, the information of type A virus was limited. Consequently, the emphasis is placed on type B virus.

Through electron microscopy several virus-like particles have been demonstrated. The first of these, originally referred to as the Australia (Au) antigen, appears only in patients with serum hepatitis. It was found to be a spherical particle (probably icosahedral) with an average diameter of 20 nanometers (20 nm). It is devoid of nucleic acids. A second particle, called the Dane particle, was identified in 1970 by D. S. Dane of London's Bland-Sutton Institute. It measures approximately 42 nm in diameter and is composed of an outer protein coat (which reacts with antibody specific for the viral surface antigen), and an inner core of 27 nm in diameter. The third particle, discovered by several groups but examined most thoroughly by Shao-nan Juang of Montreal's McGill University, has a diameter of 23 to 27 nm. It was discovered in the nuclei of liver cells from liver transplant patients who contracted hepatitis.

The emerging view which relates these different particles is that the Juang particle is the DNA- or RNA-containing viral core that replicates in the liver cell nucleus and there (presumably) causes the tissue damage associated with hepatitis B. Through some as-yet-unknown mechanism, the viral core migrates to the cell cytoplasm, where it is sheathed in the viral protein coat to become the Dane particle—the presumed transmissible form of the virus. This mode of replication is similar to that of mouse leukemia and of herpesviruses, whose protein coats are also synthesized in the cytoplasm. Evidence has been provided for the support of this concept by several studies.

Hepatitis B antigen. Hepatitis B antigen (HB Ag) is a lipoprotein found in the serum of many patients with Type B hepatitis. HB Ag is now the recommended designation for what previously has been referred to in the literature as Australia (Au) antigen, serum hepatitis antigen (SH), hepatitis antigen (HA) and hepatitis associated antigen (HAA). Full characterization of HB Ag is not yet completed.

Clinical features. The clinical spectrum (range of symptoms) of viral hepatitis is a broad one. At one end are victims of the infection who either have a viremia with little or no apparent evidence of disease, or exhibit several of the systemic symptoms but no jaundice (anicteric).

At the opposite end of this spectrum of clinical features are those individuals in whom the disease takes a rapid and fatal course. In such victims an overwhelming destruction of the liver occurs.

The incubation periods of serum hepatitis and infectious hepatitis viruses differ (Table 36–2). However, once jaundice (icteric) appears it is generally impossible to clinically distinguish one disease state from the other.

Viral hepatitis, Type A. This disease state usually begins with fatigue and a loss of appetite, which are sometimes accompanied by abdominal discomfort and muscular pains. Within 2 to 14 days, a yellowing of the body tissue (jaundice), dark urine, light stools, and tender liver enlargement may appear. Additional symptoms such as fever and chills also occur. In some individuals, jaundice may never be observed and the symptoms that appear suggest a flu-like illness. Most cases of Type A viral hepatitis (infectious hepatitis) are mild, and fever and other symptoms usually subside within a week's time. The jaundice normally clears in about 2 to 3 weeks.

Viral hepatitis, Type B. Although the clinical signs and symptoms of this disease are similar to those of Type A, the illness tends to be more severe, and hospitalization may be required for extended periods. The overwhelming destruction of the liver (fulminant hepatitis) which leads to death occurs more frequently in Type B hepatitis.

Other types of viral hepatitis. It should be noted in passing that other viral agents may produce liver injury. Infectious mononucleosis and cytomegalovirus are examples of recognized viral agents that cause hepatic damage, occasionally severe enough to be clinically recognized as hepatitis. In addition, it is well to keep in mind the possibility that agents as yet undiscovered (hepatitis virus types C, D, etc.) may account for some cases of hepatitis.

Laboratory diagnosis. The sera of many patients with serum hepatitis contain a specific antigen originally known as the Australia (Au) antigen because it was first found in the serum of an Australian Bushman. This substance, now referred to as HB Ag, has been found during the incubation period and in the early and late clinical courses of the disease. A definite need exists for an inexpensive test or tests, not only for diagnosis, but also for the detection of the antigen in blood donors capable of transmitting the infection. Such tests must be simple to perform, rapid, and sensitive.

At the present time, procedures which are used include complement-fixation, immunodiffusion techniques, hemagglutination and hemagglutination inhibition tests, electron microscopy, and radioimmunoassays. Radioimmunoassays (RIA) are among the most versatile and sensitive of the various procedures that employ antigens with radioactive labels for the measurement of antibody titers and/or the detection of antigens. One of these assays, the radioimmunoprecipitation (RIP) procedure, utilizes radioactively labeled viral antigen that is incubated with dilutions of the patient's antiviral antibody. The resulting viral antigen-antiviral antibody complex is then precipitated with anti-immunoglobulin (antibody against the antiviral antibody). The titer of the patient's antiviral antibody is determined by measuring the amount of radioactively labeled viral antigen that has been precipitated. While procedures of this type are quite sensitive, they also are expensive to perform. The complement-fixation test is recognized as being a sensitive and rapid method. Immunodiffusion techniques are less sensitive and slower. The hemagglutination and hemagglutination inhibition tests are comparable to the sensitivity and rapidity of most other diagnostic procedures.

A new agglutination test has recently been reported that incorporates specially coated latex spheres, which are added to a patient's serum preparation. The test can be performed fairly rapidly and it is claimed to be extremely sensitive, especially during the early stages of the disease. Furthermore, with this procedure, a differentiation between SH and IH viruses may be possible.

Currently no suitable laboratory test is available for type A virus detection. Some success, however, has been achieved with immune electron microscopy (see Chapter 23).

Prevention and control. Since under most circumstances it is impossible to differentiate between the two types of viral hepatitis, the preventive and control measures are applicable to both infectious and serum hepatitis.

In dealing with either suspected or

known cases of viral hepatitis it is customary to observe so-called "enteric precautions." Such measures include: (1) the hygienic disposal of feces, (2) the careful cleansing and disinfection of bedpans and toilet bowls, and (3) the proper sterilization of all dishes, eating utensils, bedclothes, and linen.

Preventing the parenteral transmission of viral hepatitis also requires rigorous observation of certain precautions. Nondisposable syringes, needles, tubing, and other types of equipment used for obtaining blood specimens, or for the administration of therapeutic agents, should be adequately sterilized before reuse. Most common means for chemical sterilization do not appear to be reliable for destroying hepatitis-causing viruses. Physical methods employed for this purpose are boiling in water for at least 20 minutes, heating at a temperature of 180°C for one hour, or autoclaving. Whenever possible, disposable equipment should be used for routine hospital and clinic procedures. *Disposable items also should be properly sterilized before being discarded.*

The possibility of transmitting viral hepatitis by means of blood or plasma transfusions is yet another problem facing physicians and hospitals. A patient with a history of jaundice should not be employed as a blood donor. Unfortunately, no method currently in use today is effective in rendering whole blood containing hepatitis virus free of the agent. On the other hand, the treatment of plasma with the chemical agent beta-propiolactone shows great promise. Plasma exposed to this chemical viricide and ultraviolet irradiation has been given to numerous patients without adverse reactions. In 1964, Lo Grippo and his associates reported only one case of clinical hepatitis among 425 patients receiving

plasma processed in this manner. The practice of pooling plasma and administering this product to patients is no longer an acceptable procedure. This is largely because of the obvious increased likelihood of transmitting the disease.

When given shortly after exposure, or early during the incubation period, the use of immune serum globulin has proved effective in the prevention of infectious hepatitis. This blood product is administered intramuscularly and in the recommended dose of 0.06 to 0.15 cc per pound of body weight. Gamma globulin usage in cases of serum hepatitis at this time is questionable.

Vaccine production. One of the most important steps in the production of a vaccine is to be able to grow the pathogen in question. Unfortunately, no one has been able to grow either of the hepatitis viruses. However, a vaccine that sidesteps this requirement has been prepared by employing viral antigens isolated from human carriers of hepatitis. The viral component in the vaccine is the hepatitis B surface antigen (HB_s Ag). It can be readily found in the blood plasma of patients with hepatitis B. Research studies with a variety of laboratory animals, including chimpanzees, have shown that the vaccine stimulates antibody production and provides protection against challenge doses of live virus. The preparation will probably be tested in humans in the near future.

Infectious Mononucleosis

This acute infectious disease has been found primarily in young adults, especially college students. It has often been called the "student's disease." Infectious mononucleosis involves components of the reticuloendothelial system (RES), including the lymph nodes and spleen. As the name of the disease implies, an increase in lymphocytes also is associated with the illness. These cells are abnormal, and can be classified on the basis of certain cytoplasmic and nuclear features. Such atypical lymphocytes are called Downey cells, and at least three classes are recognized. In general, the leukocyte levels are related to the course of the disease.

Etiology. The true cause and means of transmission have as yet not been determined. A likely candidate for an etiologic agent is a virus. Unfortunately, attempts to culture the agent have generally failed. In relatively recent studies concerned with certain virus-caused malignancies some rather interesting and promising findings were made. Strong evidence has been gathered to indicate that the agent known as Epstein-Barr virus (EBV), a DNA herpesvirus, is the cause of IM. This virus originally was detected in cell cultures derived from a type of malignancy of children called Burkitt's lymphoma.

In 1966 virologists Gertrude and Werner Henle observed that antibodies against EBV were present in the sera of approximately 80 per cent of a "low income" population in Philadelphia. Such antibodies apparently appeared during the early years of some children who showed no signs of clinical disease. The possible relationship of the EBV antibodies to infectious mononucleosis was suggested when a laboratory technician in the Henles' laboratory developed IM and the antibody titer to EBV rose at the same time. Additional findings have shown that young adults with antibodies toward Epstein-Barr virus do not develop IM, and that individuals lacking such antibodies are susceptible to infectious mononucleosis.

Considerable epidemiologic and serologic evidence has been accumulated to show the causal relationship between EBV and infectious mononucleosis. It can be summarized as follows:

(1) EBV can be regularly detected in established cell lines from individuals with infectious mononucleosis for several years after an attack of the disease.

(2) Antibody to EBV is absent from serum prior to illness and appears during the course of the infectious mononucleosis, often in rising titer.

(3) Early in the acute phase of illness, the antibody specific for EBV is IgM, indicating a primary immune response to the virus. After a period of approximately 70 days, IgG (antibodies) specific for EBV appears and is detectable for many years.

(4) Infectious mononucleosis occurs only in individuals without antibodies to EBV, and not in those persons with pre-existing antibodies to the virus.

(5) Clinical manifestations of infectious mononucleosis have appeared after the transmission of EBV by blood transfusions.

(6) EBV has been isolated from individuals with infectious mononucleosis as long as 16 months after onset of the disease.

Mode of transmission. According to Watson, infectious mononucleosis is chiefly transmitted by kissing (direct oral means) or by drinking from a commonly shared bottle or glass (indirect oral means) with the exchange of saliva and perhaps leukocytes. Experimental attempts to transmit the infection to animals and humans using various specimens, e.g., blood, gargle washings, and lymph nodes, have been unsuccessful.

Clinical features. The exact duration of the incubation period is unknown. However, indications are that it may range from 19 to 49 days. Victims of the disease may experience symptoms such as mild jaundice, slight fever, enlarged and tender lymph nodes, sore throat, headache, and general weakness. Some individuals may have abdominal pains, bleeding gums, and a slight cough. In general, once a person has had infectious mononucleosis an immunity is established. Definite recurrences are rare.

Complications. Varying reports of complications associated with infectious mononucleosis have appeared. These include anemia, convulsions, splenic rupture, cardiac involvement (inflammation of heart tissue), and inflammation of the gums.

Diagnosis. In addition to clinical features of this disease, certain laboratory findings are used for diagnostic purposes. These include the presence of atypical, large (thymus-dependent) lymphocytes, which were described earlier, and a characteristic positive test for heterophile antibodies—those which agglutinate sheep red blood cells (see Chapter 22). The antibody is an IgM globulin. Other so-called "Mono" serological tests also are in use. These include the ox hemolysin test, and

a procedure employing preserved (formalinized) horse blood cells. Confirmation of the presence of heterophile antibody in a patient's serum is accomplished with the aid of adsorption tests using guinea pig kidney and beef red cells. Infectious mononucleosis heterophile antibodies are absorbed by beef erythrocytes and not by guinea pig kidney cells. Other types of heterophile antibodies exhibit different agglutinating patterns.

Between 85 and 100 percent of patients with infectious mononucleosis will show evidence of liver involvement. This can be detected by abnormal liver function tests. The most sensitive indicators of acute liver damage include glutamic oxaloacetic transaminase (SGOT) and lactic dehydrogenase (LDH).

Treatment. Infectious mononucleosis is rarely fatal. Treatment procedures generally include bed rest, the administration of anti-inflammatory agents, such as corticosteroids, in case of hemolytic anemia, and the hospitalization of patients with severe complications.

QUESTIONS FOR REVIEW

1. What are enteroviruses?

2. a. Distinguish between infectious and serum hepatitis.
   b. What control measures can be employed to effectively prevent both diseases?
   c. Why do these diseases pose a particular problem as well as a danger to hospital personnel and patients?

3. Are vaccines or immunization procedures used for any gastrointestinal associated diseases? If so, list them.

4. What is cytomegalic inclusion disease (CMID)? Are there any predisposing factors associated with it?

5. Discuss infectious mononucleosis with respect to the following topics.
   a. causative agent
   b. diagnosis
   c. age group affected
   d. treatment and prevention

6. Is the liver vulnerable to infectious agents? Explain.

7. What general types of diagnostic methods are used for viral infections of the gastrointestinal tract?

8. What diseases are associated with the various members of the picorna group of viruses?

Microbial Diseases of the Reproductive and Urinary (Genitourinary) Systems

The Basic Anatomy of the Urinary System

This excretory system of man includes two *kidneys*, two *ureters*, the *urethra*, and the *urinary bladder* (Figure 37–1). The bean-shaped kidneys are compound tubular glands which secrete urine. This excretory product goes by way of two muscular tubes, the ureters, to the bladder, which stores the product until its elimination. Such urinary discharge takes place by way of the urethra to the out-side. The female urethra functions only in urination, while the male counterpart serves for the passage of both urine and semen.

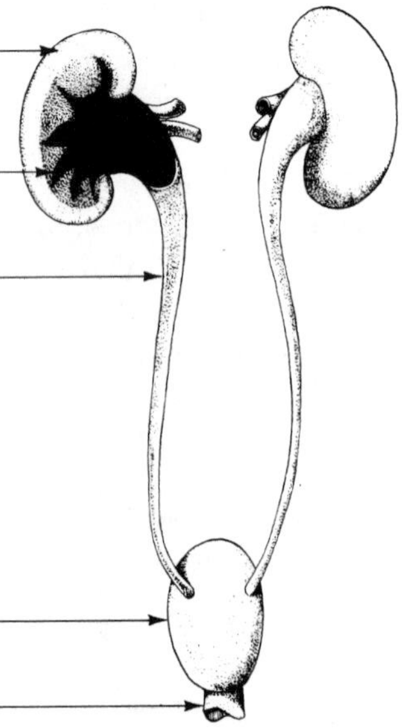

Upon examination of a kidney, the outer cortex and inner medulla can be seen (Figure 37–1). Much of the kidney consists of many closely packed *uriniferous tubules*. Some are *secretory* or *terminal tubules* and the others are *collecting tubules*. The secretory tubules, also known as *nephrons,* function in the formation of urine, while the collecting tubules serve as ducts to conduct urine to the *renal pelvis* and *ureter*.

Nephrons are considered to be both the structural and functional units of the kidney. Physiologically, each nephron can be divided into two structural divisions: the *Malpighian* or *renal corpuscle* and the *renal tubule* (Figure 37–2). The Malpighian corpuscle consists of a *glomerulus* (a tuft of capillaries), surrounded by a spherically expanded portion of a nephron, the *Bowman's capsule*. The renal tubule consists of three major regions: the *proximal convoluted tubule,* the *loop of Henle*, and the *distal convoluted tubule*. The renal capsule filters dissolved substances and some water out of the blood plasma, while the renal tubule is concerned with the reabsorption of water and the substances necessary for the maintenance of the body's normal internal environment.

Renal cortex

Renal medulla (pyramids)

Ureter

Urinary bladder

Uretha

FIG. 37–1. A diagrammatic representation of the human urinary system.

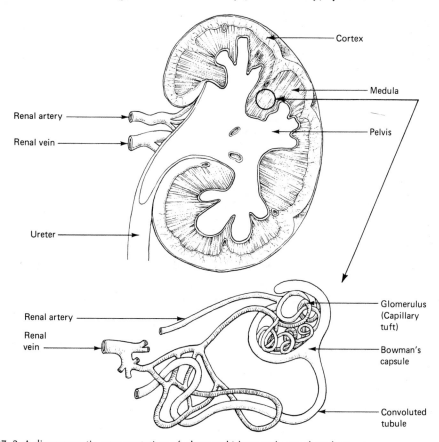

FIG. 37–2. A diagrammatic representation of a human kidney and a renal nephron.

The Functional Anatomy of the Female and Male Reproductive Systems

Female Reproductive System

An integral unit of the female reproductive system consists of two "button-shaped" organs called the *ovaries,* two *oviducts (Fallopian tubes),* the *uterus (womb),* and the *vagina* (Figure 37–3). The ovaries are situated near the kidneys on either side of the uterus. A mesentery or supporting membrane, *mesovarium,* serves to attach each ovary to the back of the broad ligament of the uterus.

Each ovary consists of a *medula* (interior) and of a *cortex* (outer region). Ova, or eggs, in various stages of development, are contained within the cortex.

In addition to producing sex cells, the ovaries also produce several important hormones, such as estradiol and progesterone.

When an ovum is released (*ovulation*), the egg is transported to the opening of the oviducts, known as the *ostium.* The oviducts convey the egg to the uterus. In case of fertilization, the cell implants itself in the uterine wall after about 3 months. The vagina is both a birth canal and a copulatory canal. This structure is a musculomembranous sheath extending from the uterus to the *vestibule* region. A thin fold of mucous membrane, called the *hymen,* may be found covering the external opening of the vagina. As the diagram of the female reproductive organs shows, the uterus projects into

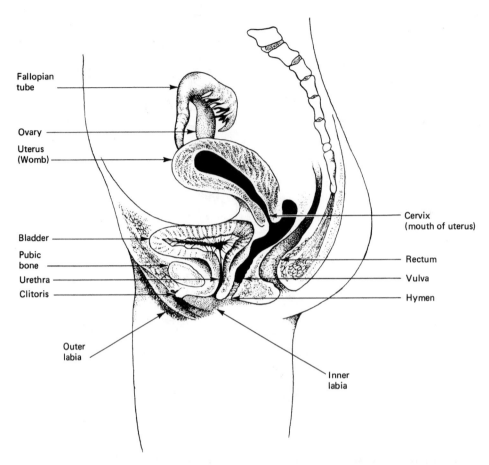

Fallopian tube

Ovary

Uterus (Womb)

Bladder

Pubic bone

Urethra

Clitoris

Outer labia

Cervix (mouth of uterus)

Rectum

Vulva

Hymen

Inner labia

FIG. 37–3. A diagrammatic representation of the female reproductive organs and related structures.

the upper portion of the vagina. This region is referred to as the *cervix* or *neck* of the uterus. The *fornix* is a circular recess between the cervix and the vaginal wall. It is not within the scope of this chapter to present details of menstruation and fertilization. However, references listed at the end of the text can be referred to for additional details.

The external genitalia of the female, collectively referred to as the *vulva,* include the *clitoris, labia majora, labia minora,* and vestibule. The clitoris, a small erectile organ homologous to the male penis, is situated at the anterior margin of the vulva. The labia majora

and the labia minora are longitudinal folds of skin (lips) which line the vaginal opening. The labia minora are situated between the labia majora. The vestibule occupies the region between the two labia minora, and contains the *glands of Bartholin.* These glands are responsible for the secretion of an alkaline fluid which functions as a lubricant during copulation.

Male Reproductive System

This system includes two oval glandular *testes,* a system of *ducts,* auxiliary glands, and the *penis* (Figure 37–4). The testes are located outside of the abdominal

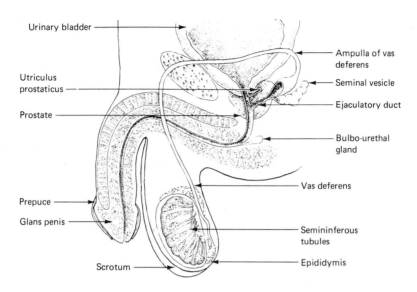

FIG. 37–4. A diagrammatic representation of the human male reproductive system.

cavity and are suspended by the *spermatic cords* in a cutaneous sac-like structure (pouch). The testes are divided into lobules which contain several *seminiferous tubules*. They produce *spermatozoa* and *testosterone* (male sex hormone). Mature sex cells (sperm) go from the seminiferous tubules to the duct called the *vas deferens,* or *ductus deferens,* by way of the *epididymis.* This latter structure is a coiled duct located on the upper surface of each *testis* (singular of "testes"). The vas deferens carries the sperm to the *urethra,* a tube which conducts both the sex cells and urine to the outside of the body via the penis (consult the earlier section of this chapter dealing with the urinary system).

The three auxiliary glands, namely, the *seminal vesicles,* the *prostate gland,* and the *bulbourethral glands of Cowper,* are concerned with the formation of *seminal fluid* or *semen.* The secretions of the seminal vesicles empty into the vas deferens, while those of the prostate and bulbourethral glands empty into the urethra.

Diseases of the Urinary Tract

The Flora of the Normal Urinary Tract

Experiments with various animals have shown that the normally sterile kidney is highly resistant to bacteria. Generally, many well-known urinary tract pathogens are unable to produce kidney infections. There are a few exceptions to this finding, including certain enterococci strains, *Escherichia coli, Proteus* species (spp.), and staphylococci.

In humans, bacteria are commonly present in the lower urethra. However, their numbers diminish in regions near the bladder. This is apparently caused by some antibacterial effect exerted by the urethral mucosa, plus the frequent flushing of its epithelial surface toward the outside by urine. Bladder urine is normally sterile. Urinary tract infections occur more often in females than in males. This may be because the male urethra is longer and, by virtue of its location, less likely to be subjected to fecal contamination.

A General Introduction to Urinary Tract Infections

Common urinary infections are summarized in Table 37–1. Bacteria commonly associated with urinary tract infections generally are representatives of the intestinal flora, called *coliforms*. Such organisms have been isolated from 80 per cent of the cases which either (1) have developed in the absence of urinary obstructions, or (2) have been unaffected by antibiotic therapy or urologic manipulations such as *catheterization*.

In cases where infection follows catheterization, *Pseudomonas* spp. infections are found in greater numbers with patients who have undergone urethral instrumentation. Infections caused by the enterococci, *Proteus* spp., and staphylococcus are believed to result from direct contact with infected individuals or contaminated articles, such as bedpans and catheters.

Anaerobic bacteria and several species of fungi also are known to cause urinary tract infections. The relationship of veneral diseases to this category of disease will be discussed in a later section of this chapter.

Predisposing conditions. Several clinical factors have been implicated as predisposing individuals to urinary tract infections. These include diabetes mellitus, neurologic diseases (e.g., polimyelitis and spinal cord injuries), toxemia of pregnancy, and lesions which interfere with urine outflow. Kidney stones, stricture, and tumors are examples of urinary obstructions.

Routes of infection. Although a controversy exists as to the pathways by which bacteria gain access to the kidney, three major routes of infection have been listed: *hematogenous* (via the blood), *lymphatic,* and *ascending urogenous* (via the ureter). Most clinical and experimental evidence indicates that the last-mentioned route is the most common pathway in pyelonephritis (inflammation of the kidney and pelvis). The infecting organism in large part determines the form and intensity of the resulting infection.

Sometimes it is possible to establish the means by which causative agents are acquired. For example, infections in women which develop shortly after marriage may be the consequence of mechanical injury to the female urethra during sexual intercourse. The onset of a typical acute infection is commonly associated with urinary tract instrumentation.

In the bladder cavity, bacteria find several factors that provide a favorable environment for their persistence in urine. These factors include (1) the availability of adequate nutrients, (2) the absence of surface phagocytosis (which commonly occurs in other tissues), (3) an optimal temperature for growth, and (4) a residual number of bacteria after emptying the bladder. Apparently a film composed of urine and bacteria, which coats the bladder surfaces, remains after urination and serves as an inoculum for newly formed urine. Various lines of evidence indicate that such contaminated urine can be a source of infectious agents for other regions of the urinary tract. Pathogens have been found capable of traveling in a direction opposite to normal urine flow.

Selected aspects of diagnosis. The presence of bacteria in freshly voided urine may have little or no significance unless they happen to be microorganisms such as *Mycobacterium tuberculosis* or *Salmonella* spp. Such urine, having passed through the urethra, will usually contain members of the region's normal flora, such as *Bacillus* spp., coliforms, diphtheroids, *Proteus* spp., staphylococci, streptococci, and yeasts.

Catheterized specimens cannot be relied upon as a source of uncontaminated urine, since the equipment used can come into contact with the urethra and consequently collect normal urethral flora. If the latter microorganisms never were involved in cystitis, prostatitis, pyelonephritis, and other urogenital infections, then various differential and selective media might be useful in the isolation and the identification of pathogens. Unfortunately, this is not the case; severe infections of the urogenital system may be caused by members of the normal flora.

Standard procedures. Through careful observation of clinical cases, urologists and microbiologists generally agree that the presence of more than 100,000 bacteria per milliliter of urine is strongly indicative of acute disease. The quantitation of microorganisms in urine specimens may be performed by means of standard dilutions using either the pour- or the streak (spread)-plate techniques, described in Chapter 12. In the clinical laboratory where numerous urine specimens are to be cultured, time generally does not permit use of the dilution process with pour-plates. However, the spread-plate technique is in common use. Time may still be a problem, especially if multiple dilutions must be made. The manipulations required can be reduced however, when it is assumed that a count of 100,000 (10^5) or more represents a significant finding. This can easily be obtained by making a 1:100 dilution of the specimen and placing 0.1 ml quantities of it on the surface of appropriate plating media, e.g., blood agar or EMB (eosin, methylene blue agar). About 100 colonies should appear. To determine the total number of organisms in 1 ml of urine would require multiplying the number of colonies (100) by the dilution factor (100 times 10 = 1,000), thus giving a final count of 100,000. The factor of 100 represents the 1:100 dilution, while the 10 represents the 0.1 ml of the diluted specimen plated on the medium. It is assumed that the 0.1 ml contains one-tenth of the bacteria in 1.0 ml of the original undiluted specimen.

Certain refinements have been made in procedures utilizing this principle of effective dilutions with small quantities of clinical specimens. *Calibrated loop techniques* are examples of such improvements. These procedures are based upon the delivery of 0.01 or 0.001 ml of urine to an appropriate medium by carefully calibrated microbiological loops.

Attempts have also been made in recent years to develop simplified procedures to accomplish effective dilutions without the use of pipettes or loops. One approach to this problem has been the placing of media into small cups or onto flat paddles which can then be dipped into the urine specimen (Color photograph 90). Here the surface of the agar medium is wetted by a small quantity of urine. After incubation, the number of resulting colonies can be counted and multiplied by a factor which depends upon the quantity of urine used to coat the surface of the agar.

In recent years several different types of reliable devices have become available from commercial sources to detect possible genitourinary-tract infections. They can serve as simple and convenient means with which to culture freshly voided urine and urogenital discharge specimens as soon as they are collected. Diagnostic culturing systems are available not only to determine the concentrations of bacteria in specimens, but also to detect the presence of specific medically important mi-

Table 37–1   Representative Diseases of the Urogenital System

Disease	Etiologic Agent	Gram Reaction	Morphology	Possible Treatment
Chancroid	Hemophilus ducreyi	−	Coccobacillus	Sulfonamides, chloramphenicol, streptomycin, tetracyclines
Cystitis (inflammation of the urinary bladder)	Escherichia coli, Proteus vulgaris, Pseudomonas aeruginosa	−	Rods	Sulfonamides, chloramphenicol, kanamycin, oral penicillin G, polymyxia
Gangrenous cystitis	E. coli, P. vulgaris, Salmonella typhosa	−	Rods	Sulfonamides, chloramphenicol, oral penicillin G
	Staphylococci and streptococci	+	Cocci	
Genital herpes	Herpesvirus hominis type 2	Not appropriate	Virus	
Glomerulonephritis (inflammation of kidney glomeruli)	Streptococcus pyogenes	+	Coccus	Chloramphenicol, erythromycin, lincomycin, penicillin, vancomycin
Gonorrhea	Neisseria gonorrhoeae	−	Coccus	Erythromycin, penicillin, tetracyclines
Granuloma inguinale	Calymmatobacterium granulomatis	−	Coccobacillus	Chloramphenicol, streptomycin, tetracyclines
Kidney cortex infections	Staphylococcus aureus	+	Coccus	Cephalothin, lincomycin, methicillin, nafcillin, vancomycin
Lymphogranuloma venereum	Chlamydia lymphogranulomatis	− or variable (not useful)	Coccobacillus	Sulfonamides
Nonspecific urethritis (inflammation of the urethra)	Candida albicans	+	Oval yeast	Amphotericin B
	Mycoplasma hominis and T-strains	−	Pleomorphic	Erythromycin, tetracyclines
	Staphylococci and streptococci	+	Cocci	
	Trichomonas (vaginalis) hominis	Not useful	Protozoan	Cephalothin, lincomycin, methicillin, penicillin, vancomycin
Postabortal sepsis	Anaerobic streptococci	+	Coccus	Erythromycin, chloramphenicol, lincomycin, penicillin, vancomycin
	Bacteroides spp.	−	Rods	Chloramphenicol, lincomycin, penicillin
	Clostridia	+	Rods	Chloramphenicol, penicillin, tetracyclines

Disease	Etiologic Agent	Gram Reaction	Morphology	Possible Treatment
Prostatitis (inflammation of the prostate gland)	E. coli, P. aeruginosa	−	Rods	Sulfonamides, gentamicin, oral penicillin G, polymyxin
	Neisseria gonorrhoeae	−	Coccus	Erythromycin, penicillin, tetracyclines
	Staphylococci and streptococci	+	Cocci	Cephalothin, lincomycin, methicillin, penicillin, vancomycin
	Mixed infections of the above organisms			Appropriate antibiotics
Puerperal sepsis (child-bed fever)	Anaerobic streptococci	+	Cocci	Chloramphenicol, erythromycin, penicillin, vancomycin
	Clostridia	+	Rods	Chloramphenicol, penicillin, tetracyclines
	E. coli, Proteus spp.	−	Rods	Sulfonamides, chloramphenicol, gentamicin, kanamycin
	Neisseria gonorrhoeae	−	Coccus	Erythromycin, penicillin, tetracyclines
Pyelonephritis (inflammation of the kidney and pelvis)	Bacteroides spp.; Enterobacter aerogenes, E. coli, Proteus spp., Pseudomonas aeruginosa	−	Rods	Chloramphenicol, gentamicin, kanamycin, polymyxin, tetracyclines
	Staphylococci and streptococci	+	Cocci	Chloramphenicol, kanamycin, methicillin, penicillin, vancomycin
Pyometria (pus formation in the uterus)	Anaerobic streptococci	+	Cocci	Chloramphenicol, erythromycin, penicillin, vancomycin
	Bacteroides spp.	−	Rods	Chloramphenicol, penicillin, tetracyclines
	Veillonella spp.	−	Cocci	Chloramphenicol, erythromycin, penicillin
Pyonephrosis (inflammation of the kidney with pus formation)	Anaerobic streptococci	+	Cocci	Chloramphenicol, penicillin, vancomycin
	Bacteroides spp.	−	Rods	Chloramphenicol, penicillin, tetracyclines
Syphilis	Treponema pallidum	Not useful	Spirochete	Erythromycin, penicillin, tetracyclines

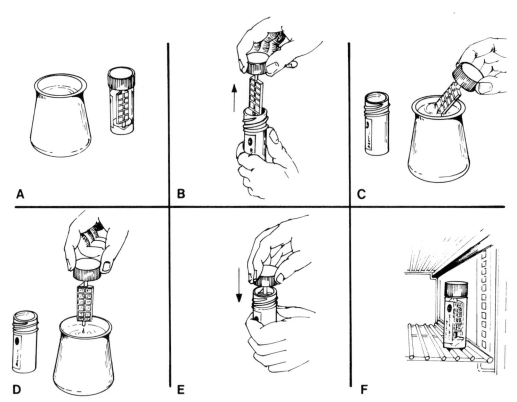

A   **B**   **C**

D   **E**   **F**

FIG. 37–5. A representative urine dip-slide procedure. _A_. The components of the procedure,
voided urine and a dip-slide in its container, are
shown. The dip-slide is removed from its container _B_ and inserted into the urine specimen

_C_. Excess urine is allowed to drip back into the
container _D_, and the dip-slide is placed back into
its container _E_ for incubation _F_. (After Pazin, G.
J., Wolinsky, A., and Lee, W. S.: _Amer Fam. Phys._,
11:85–96, 1975.)

croorganisms, including the following:
Candida albicans (a yeast), *Escherichia
coli, Neisseria gonorrhoeae, Pseudomonas
aeruginosa, Staphylococcus aureus, Streptococcus faecalis,* and *Trichomonas* (vaginalis) *hominis* (a protozoan).

By dipping the device into a freshly
voided urine sample and allowing a suitable incubation period at an appropriate
temperature, reliable counts that show the
number of bacteria present in the original
specimen can be obtained (Figure 37–5
and Color photograph 90). In determining the bacterial content, the assumption
is made that each colony appearing on
the slide represents the descendants of one

bacterium in the urine sample. Thus a
correlation can be made between the number of colonies on the medium's surface
and the number of bacteria in the urine.
Under normal conditions (i.e., the lack of
infections), bacterial counts of 20 or less
are obtained. Such findings are interpreted
to mean less than 10,000 bacteria per milliliter of sample. In cases of urinary-tract
infections counts exceeding 200 are possible. Significant counts range from 200
to over 1,000 (100,000 to 1,000,000 bacteria per milliliter of sample).

These devices can be used effectively
by laboratory personnel. Moreover, because of their ready-to-use feature, pa-

tients under the instructions of their physicians can also inoculate them, thus facilitating diagnosis and saving valuable time.

The simplest and most rapid of procedures is based on the observation of a Gram-stain preparation. A smear, approximately 1 centimeter square, is made with a well-mixed urine specimen, which then is air dried, heat fixed, and stained (see Chapter 6). If a careful microscopic examination of this smear indicates the presence of bacteria, the urine specimen probably will produce a count in excess of 100,000. The confidence level for this procedure is 70 to 80 per cent, and some clinical microbiologists claim a higher value.

Certain procedures or components of procedures that are used from time to time are unsuitable. These include the following: (1) the routine inoculation of urine specimens into any broth medium, (2) the direct inoculation of urine specimens into multiple differential media, (3) the use of miniaturized multiple test systems (Color photographs 52 and 53) or plates in a manner that does not produce isolated colonies from specimens containing large bacterial populations, and (4) the preparation of direct, unstandardized antibiograms.

Kidney (Renal) Diseases Caused by Bacteria

Two major types of infections affect kidney—those which produce a diffuse inflammation of the tissues, *pyelonephritis,* and those which primarily involve the organ's cortex. Detailed discussion of clinical and diagnostic features and the treatment of these disease states can be found in the appropriate texts listed in the reference section at the end of this book.

Acute Pyelonephritis

This is probably the most common disease of the kidney. It is an inflammation of one or both kidneys, involving the renal parenchyma (interstitial tissues), tubules, and the renal pelvis. Acute pyelonephritis generally is not considered a primary infection, but rather a complication brought on by an infectious process, such as respiratory disease or sepsis, elsewhere in the body.

Escherichia coli is the major cause of this condition. Some 60 to 80 per cent of acute pyelonephritis is attributed to this organism. Other bacteria that have also been associated with this infection include *Enterobacter aerogenes, Proteus* spp., *Pseudomonas aeruginosa,* staphylococci, and *Streptococcus pyogenes.* Most causes of acute pyelonephritis are "blood-borne." However, some infections have been reported to develop after the instrumentation of the urinary tract.

This renal infection appears to occur more often in females than in males. In the female, acute pyelonephritis is a common complication of lower urinary tract infections. However, the majority of cases are of a benign nature. Lesions generally heal spontaneously, leaving only small scars in the renal tissue. Nevertheless, it is important not to underrate these infections, as they may recur, or become chronic and eventually produce serious kidney damage.

Chronic Pyelonephritis

This disease state may seriously influence the future health of the affected individual. Most persons with chronic pyelonephritis undergo substantial scarring of the kidney, loss of renal substance, and severe reduction of kidney function. The bacteria causing this condition primarily are *E. coli* and *P. vulgaris.*

Kidney Cortex Infections

Infections of the renal or kidney cortical regions are quite different from pyelonephritis in several ways. The former are localized manifestations of the cortex which are definitely spread via the hematogenous route. Pyelonephritis, on the other hand, is a diffuse type of infection which is not necessarily acquired from the bloodstream.

In cortical infections, such as renal carbuncle and perirenal abscess, the primary source of disease agents quite often is a suppurative lesion of the skin (e.g., a boil or carbuncle) or a mucous membrane infection. Lesions associated with these states may be evident a number of weeks before kidney involvement. The microorganism most frequently present in such infections is *Staphylococcus aureus*. *E. coli* may be a secondary invader.

Diseases of the Urinary Bladder

This structure of the body exhibits a significant degree of resistance to infection. However, it can succumb to disease.

Cystitis

This inflammation of the bladder can be either acute or chronic. The acute form is one of the most common urinary tract lesions. However, it is considered to be a symptom rather than a specific disease. Consequently, the underlying etiological factor of acute cystitis must be uncovered. Attacks of this manifestation occur commonly among women.

Sources of bladder infection in the female include the gastrointestinal tract, infections of the cervix (cervicitis), and the uterus (endometritis), urethra, and vaginal involvement by the protozoan *Trichomonas hominis*. In males, the condition may be associated with several body structures, including the gastrointestinal tract, the kidneys, and the urethra. A frequent source of cystitis is an infection of the prostate. Several other factors that can contribute to the development of acute cystitis are foreign bodies self-introduced and certain diseases involving the blood and diabetes mellitus.

Microorganisms commonly associated with acute cystitis include *E. coli, P. vulgaris,* and *Ps. aeruginosa.*

Gangrenous Cystitis

This disease state may develop as a consequence of persistent acute cystitis. Various other causes also may produce gangrenous cystitis, including: (1) particular systemic infections such as bacterial dysentery and typhoid fever, (2) exposure to radium or x-ray, (3) trauma resulting from irrigations with strong chemical substances, and (4) operations involving the pelvic organs.

This condition has a high mortality associated with it. Several bacterial species may be found to produce gangrenous cystitis; these include *E. coli, P. vulgaris, S. typhi,* staphylococci, and streptococci.

Diseases of the Ureter

Infections of the ureter may develop independently, or may be a consequence of disease states involving the bladder, intra-abdominal organs, and kidneys. Inflammatory lesions of the ureter generally are associated with disease and related states of the kidney. These include acute and chronic pyelonephritis, tuberculosis, and calculous disease (various changes which are produced by kidney stones). Involvement occurs mostly through a direct extension from the other organs.

Individuals with ureter lesions may experience localized pain, tenderness, and pyuria. The treatment used in these cases generally includes the elimination of the original source of the problem. Therefore, depending on the clinical diagnosis, procedures such as antibiotic therapy and surgery may be necessary.

Nonspecific Urethritis (NSU)

This inflammation of the urethra is caused by microorganisms other than *Neisseria gonorrhoeae,* and by other factors including chemical agents (ingestion of alcoholic beverages or certain chemotherapeutic agents), and by trauma, such as passage of a cathether. Nonspecific urethritis is a very common disorder among females. Microorganisms which have been associated with the condition include the yeast *Candida albicans,* hemolytic staphylococci and streptococci, *Mycoplasma hominis,* T-strains of mycoplasma, and *Trichomonas hominis.* Mixed infections also occur.

Urinary Tract Infections Caused by Anaerobes

Several anaerobic organisms are known for their capability to cause infections of the kidney. These include members of the genera *Actinomyces, Bacteroides, Clostridium,* and *Streptococcus.* Diseases can come about from several causes, examples of which include ascending infection with "bowel organisms," bacteremia, the introduction of organisms during instrumentation and surgical procedures, and the lymphatic spread from the ileocecal region.

Kidney stones usually are found in instances of anaerobic kidney infections. Although *C. perfringens* has been isolated from such stones, it is believed that the majority of infections develop in the dead tissue associated with them. Anaerobes may complicate various clinical states, such as congenital defects and renal or bladder tumors.

Actinomycosis may be associated with generally normal kidneys. Such infections are chronic in nature. Individuals with kidney involvement generally experience fever, flank pain, malaise, and sweating. Diagnosis usually is made at the time of surgery, as culturing the causative agent from urine is extremely difficult. Penicillin or tetracycline is used in treatment.

Bacteroides and anaerobic streptococci are noted for an extremely destructive form of pyelonephritis. Reported after-effects include perinephric ("around the kidney") abscesses, pyonephrosis (pus in the kidney), and septicemia.

Clostridium-caused infections generally are wound complications of several types of surgical procedures, including nephrectomy (kidney removal) and prostatectomy (prostate removal, partial or total). Infections of this type can be mild or severe. An example of the latter would be gas gangrene of the urinary bladder.

Diseases of the Reproductive System

The reproductive organs and associated structures are subject to a wide variety of inflammatory conditions. The remaining portion of this chapter presents a number of representative nonvenereal infections and those referred to as the venereal or genitoinfectious diseases.

Anaerobic Infections of the Female Genital Tract

The normal bacterial flora of the vaginal region can include several anaerobic species belonging to the genera of *Bacteroides, Clostridium,* and *Streptococcus.* From this location, several of these microorganisms, as well as others, can penetrate the uterine or pelvic cavity when suitable anaerobic conditions prevail, and cause severe infections. Most of these result from the complications of malignancies of the puerperium (the confinement period following labor) and of septic abortion. Clostridia gain entrance to the uterus by means of unsterile instruments or other materials used in the performance of the abortive procedure.

Chronic and Subacute Pelvic Inflammatory Disease

This infection generally involves the Fallopian tubes and/or the ovaries. It is usually accompanied by varying degrees of pelvic peritonitis. Symptoms include abdominal pain, fever, and vaginal hemorrhage. Anaerobic streptococci and *Bacteroides* spp. usually cause the disease. It is believed that these effects may also result from a secondary infection by *Neisseria gonorrhoeae.*

Postabortal Sepsis

Several organisms have been associated with this infection, including anaerobic streptococci, *Bacteroides* spp., and clostridia. The last-named organisms are noted for production of the most dramatic effects, such as a severe form of uterine infection which can include inflammation of the uterine mucous membrane lining and muscles, with necrosis, perforation, peritonitis, and septicemia. Diagnosis here is proved by positive cultures obtained from various clinical specimens.

Puerperal (Childbirth) Sepsis

Postpartum (after birth) hemorrhage, premature rupture of membranes, and prolonged labor predispose mothers to puerperal sepsis. Microorganisms reported as causative agents include anaerobic streptococci, clostridia, *Escherichia coli, Neisseria gonorrhoeae,* and *Proteus* spp.

Endometritis generally constitutes the initial lesion. However, pathogens may gain entrance to the lymphatics and cause metastic (transferred) lung abscesses, pelvic thrombophlebitis (an inflammation of a vein which precedes thrombus formation), and septicemia.

Confirmation of clinical diagnosis involves aerobic and anaerobic cultures of blood and lochia (vaginal discharge appearing within the first 2 weeks after childbirth).

Pyometria

This frequent anaerobic pelvic infection, characterized by the accumulation of pus in the uterus, is considered a benign state. Microorganisms associated with the disease include anaerobic streptococci, *Bacteroides* spp., diphtheroids, and *Veillonella* spp. The condition has been noted in certain cases following menopause without malignancy, and in situations where uterine cavity irradiation has been performed. Symptoms of pyometra include bleeding, fever, pain, and a discharge of foul-smelling pus, often with bubbles.

Selected Diseases of the Male Reproductive System

Surface Infections of the Penis

Several nonvenereal infections are known to affect the penis. Inflammation of the glans penis (*balanitis*), and a similar condition of both the glans and the prepuce (*balanoposthitis*) are common examples. A variety of microorganisms can produce such infections. The treatment usually followed is circumcision and the administration of appropriate antibiotics. Diseases caused by other pathogens, e.g., *Herpesvirus,* are discussed elsewhere.

Diseases of the Prostate

The prostate, which is composed of glandular tissue and smooth muscle, surrounds the proximal portion of the male urethra. It is one of the most important of the male sex glands. Unfortunately, it is subject to various types of diseases. Some of these which are associated with microorganisms are described below.

Acute prostatitis. *Neisseria gonorrhoeae* was formerly considered to be the chief cause of acute inflammations of the prostate gland. Several other microorganisms, including *E. coli, P. aeruginosa,* staphylococci, and streptococci, have also been identified as etiologic agents of prostatic infections. Mixed infections have been commonly encountered.

Bacterial pathogens reach the prostate by routes similar to those listed for kidney infections. In cases of nonspecific urethra infections and gonorrhea, this gland becomes involved as a consequence of an acute urethral inflammation. Blood-borne infections of the prostate may occur as complications of boils, carbuncles, osteomyelitis, and epidemics of acute respiratory tract infections. The seminal vesicles (other accessory sex glands) may also be affected.

Chronic prostatitis. This infection of the prostate manifests itself more commonly in middle-aged males. Chronic prostatitis usually is a sequel to an acute infection of the gland. The bacteria producing this condition are similar to those associated with acute prostatitis.

Prostatic abscess. An abscess of the prostate gland can develop during the course of either an acute or chronic form of prostatitis. In the majority of cases, however, the condition arises as a complication of a pyogenic (pus-forming) infection located elsewhere, such as boils, carbuncles, and osteomyelitis. The bacteria associated with prostatic abscess formation are similar to those found to cause acute prostatitis.

The Venereal (Genitoinfectious) Diseases

Chancroid (Soft Chancre)

The Gram-negative coccobacillus *Hemophilus ducreyi,* which is occasionally referred to as Ducrey's bacillus, is the causative agent of chancroid. The disease is highly contagious, specific, and appears as a venereal ulcer occurring on the genitals. Chancroid bears no relation to the primary lesion of syphilis (hard or Hunterian chancre). Generally, *H. ducreyi* is transmitted by sexual contact. However, reports have appeared which implicate dressings and surgical instruments as possible sources of infection. Filth and poor sanitary habits are considered to be predisposing factors.

Clinical features. The incubation period of this venereal disease ranges from 1 to 3 days. Chancroid usually begins in the form of a pustule which eventually breaks down. This results in an irregular ulcer with steep, soft edges (Color photograph 102). Quite often an infected individual has multiple ulcers which enlarge and spread rapidly. Because these lesions do not possess indurated (hardened) edges, they are frequently referred to as "soft" chancres. The bases of these ulcers are gray in color and appear moth-eaten. It is not uncommon to observe a purulent, sometimes bloody discharge exuding from the lesion. Individuals with chancroid also may experience severe pain. The infection generally spreads to the inguinal lymph nodes (inguinal adenopathy) and may result in bubo formation (abscesses). Systemic infections do not occur.

Diagnosis. Chancroid generally is diagnosed on clinical grounds. This involves excluding other types of venereal infections, and the microscopic examination of specimens. The absence of indurated lesions and failure to detect spirochetes by means of dark-field microscopic examination generally eliminate the possibility of syphilis. *H. ducreyi* may be detected in Gram-stained smears prepared from ulcer specimens. Culturing of specimens in media containing blood or its derivatives also is a standard procedure. *H. ducreyi* is a Gram-negative bacillus, and produces hemolysis on blood agar.

A skin test employing a killed suspension of the causative agent is used in Europe as a means to differentiate between chancroid and other venereal diseases. Usually 48 hours are needed to demonstrate a positive reaction. It is characterized by redness and induration at the site of injection.

Gonorrhea

This highly infectious pyogenic disease is often referred to as a *specific urethritis*. It is caused by the Gram-negative "biscuit-shaped" diplococcus, *Neisseria gonorrhoeae* (Color photographs 92 and 93), which usually is situated intracellularly. This bacterium was first discovered in specimens from patients by Neisser in 1879. The disease primarily involves the genitourinary tract. However, various complications can develop, among them endocarditis, meningitis, and pyelonephritis. Once the disease is acquired, it may persist for many years if treatment is not administered.

The most common means by which adults contract gonorrhea is through sexual intercourse. In the male, the disease initially remains limited to the lining of the anterior urethra. However, with additional sexual relations, improper instrumentation during examinations, or self-medication, the infectious agents can be introduced into the posterior portion of the urethra. From this focus of infection other parts of the urogenital system can be readily invaded.

In the female, *N. gonorrhoeae* not only causes urethritis, but cervicitis (an inflammation of the cervix uteri), salpingitis (an inflammation of the Fallopian tubes), and vaginitis as well. In adult females, the designation of *external gonorrhea* is used when gonococcal involvement includes the Bartholin glands, the cervix, Skene's glands and ducts, and the urethra. If the infection spreads from these structures to the endometrium (the mucous membrane which lines the uterus), the endosalpinx (the membrane lining of the Fallopian tube), the ovaries, or the peritoneum, the term *internal gonorrhea* is employed. Many infected women do not show symptoms of the disease, however. Recent findings clearly indicate that the use of birth control pills increases the possibility of infection.

Unfortunately the eyes of newborns can become infected with *N. gonorrhoeae* while passing through the birth canal passage. This disease, known as *opthalmia neonatorum* (see Chapter 38), at one time was the major cause of blindness in many parts of the world. The use of Credé's solution (1 per cent silver nitrate) as well as other preparations, such as antibiotics, has greatly reduced the incidence of this infection.

Children can experience another manifestation of *N. gonorrhoeae, vulvo-vaginitis*. This type of gonococcal involvement is looked upon as an "institutional disease," as it has been found to be transmitted by contaminated towels or similar articles in hospitals, orphanages, and schools. It appears that, in relation to gonococcus infections of children, the conjunctiva and vagina are quite vulnerable. In the adult it is the internal genital organs and associated structures which possess this particular susceptibility. Vulvo-vaginitis is not exclusively caused by *N. gonorrhoeae;* hemolytic staphylococci and streptococci, as well as other microorganisms, have also been isolated from cases of vulvo-vaginitis. A new problem is presented by *N. gonorrhoeae* L-forms.

Clinical features. The incubation period for gonorrhea usually ranges from 3 to 7 days after exposure. Generally a thick, greenish-yellow urethral discharge appears (Figure 37–6). This material easily can be gathered and utilized for diagnostic purposes.

In rare instances gonococci may gain entry into the circulatory system and consequently cause widespread involvement of numerous areas of the body, which may end in fatality.

Diagnosis. The laboratory diagnosis of gonorrhea is dependent on the demonstration of the causative agent. Specimens of choice include endocervical secretions, the muco-purulent discharge from the vagina, and pus expressed from Skene's ducts and the urethra. Frequently, specimens must be transported under unfavorable circumstances or over considerable distances that may require several days. Recently a transport-growth system, known as Transgrow, has been developed for the transport of gonococcal-containing specimens. The bottle medium is inoculated with a specimen swab, the cap is tightly closed, and the preparation is incubated overnight. The medium can then be transported to the processing laboratory.

A definite laboratory identification is based on the results obtained with Gram-stained smears, and on culture characteristics. Fluorescent-tagged antibody procedures also are being utilized (Color

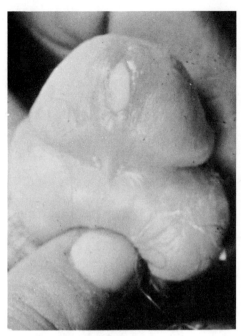

FIG. 37–6. The urethral discharge in an acute case of gonorrhea. (Courtesy of the Armed Forces Institute of Pathology, Washington, D.C., Neg. No. 218663–5–96.)

photographs 57 and 58). Smears of clinical specimens containing the causative agents should show Gram-negative diplococci, usually inhabiting leukocytes (Color photograph 92). Cultivation of the organism usually is performed on chocolate agar or Thayer and Martin medium (Figure 37–7). The latter preparation has been found to be quite efficient in the isolation of pathogenic members of *Neisseria*. Inoculated media are incubated at approximately 37°C in an atmosphere containing 2 to 8 percent CO_2. A candle jar can be used for this purpose. After growth has appeared, the plate containing the specimen is treated (the bacterial colonies are covered) with oxidase reagent (a 1 per cent solution of tetramethyl-p-phenylenediamine). Members of the genus *Neisseria* generally turn from a translucent off-white to a bright

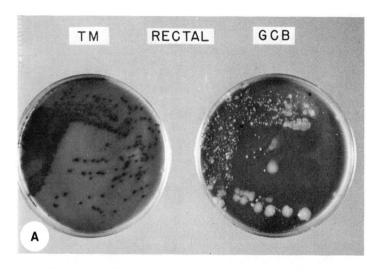

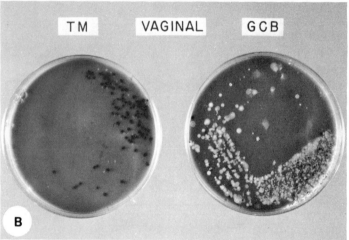

FIG. 37–7. The use of Thayer-Martin in the identification of *Neisseria gonorrhoeae* as compared with other media. *A*. Isolation from a rectal specimen. *B*. Isolation from a vaginal specimen. (Courtesy of Dr. D. S. Kellogg, Jr., National Communicable Disease Center, Atlanta, Georgia.)

purple color (Color photograph 94). Cultures exhibiting this type of reaction are called *oxidase positive*.

Other means are available to demonstrate this property include specially prepared tablets and paper strips containing the reagents. The application of the organisms in the form of a heavy suspension can produce positive results in a short time. However, certain precautions must be observed in working with these types of tests, as microorganisms other than the *Neisseria* may produce similar results.

Fermentation tests also are required to establish the identity of *N. gonorrhoeae* (Color photograph 96*A*). The organism produces acid from glucose, but not from maltose or sucrose.

Rapid diagnosis of gonorrhea can be made with the aid of specific florescein-tagged antibody preparations. However, this procedure has certain shortcomings. Clinical findings, together with a positive smear, constitute only a provisional (tentative) diagnosis. This is usually sufficient for the initiation of therapy.

An apparent association of disease-producing capability (virulence) with colonial morphology has been observed and reported for *N. gonorrhoeae*. In addition to forming distinctive colony types on agar media, virulent gonococci (designated T_1 and T_2) possess pili, resist phagocytosis by human leukocytes, are capable of attachment to various types of host cells (sperm), and can act as recipients for genetic transformation.

Prevention. Preventive measures for gonorrhea generally are directed toward detecting and treating the sexual contacts who transmitted the disease to the patients, and educating the public as to the means of transmission, availability of treatment, and other pertinent details.

Granuloma Inguinale (Granuloma Venereum)

This infection is caused by the Gram-negative *Calymmatobacterium* (*Donovania*) *granulomatis*. Originally the disease was believed to be limited to the tropics; however, several reports have proved it to be endemic in parts of the United States. The organism is presumed to be spread through sexual intercourse, although other means are thought to be possible. The disease itself is not highly contagious.

Clinical features. The disease initially appears in the form of a moist papule on, or in the vicinity of, the external genitalia. This lesion is painless. Involvement of the surrounding areas, e.g., mucous membrane and skin in and around the anus, genitalia, and groin, results from ulceration of the papule. The infection, however, remains limited to the areas mentioned.

Diagnosis. Examinations of Wright-stained smears of specimens from lesions demonstrate the presence of the organism in mononuclear cells. The oval, encapsulated organisms are frequently referred to as Donovan bodies. *C. granulomatis* cannot be initially isolated on artificial media. The general procedure involves primary isolation in the yolk sac of embryonated chick eggs. Subsequent adaptation to artificial media containing yolk material, and to other types of media, is possible. The microorganism is quite similar to *Klebsiella* spp.

Lymphogranuloma Venereum (LGV)

This disease is caused by *Chlamydia lymphogranulomatis*. Under normal conditions this microorganism is transmitted by sexual intercourse. However, infections can be acquired through non-venereal contacts, such as hands.

Lymphogranuloma venereum is also called by a variety of other names, including Duran-Nicholas-Favre disease, lymphogranuloma inguinale, fifth venereal disease, and venereal bubo. The last-mentioned term refers to the enlarged regional lymph nodes (buboes) which develop approximately 1 week to 2 months after the initial disease symptoms.

Clinical features. Lymphogranuloma venereum infection usually has an incubation period ranging from 3 days to 3 weeks. In males, a lesion appears on the glans and occasionally in the urethra; in females, the cervix, labia, or vaginal wall may be involved. Spreading of the pathogen to the regional lymph nodes results in inflammation and suppuration. Regional lymph nodes in the groin region of males frequently swell, thus giving rise to inguinal buboes. These buboes do not occur in infected females because the regional lymph nodes of the female are located within the pelvis.

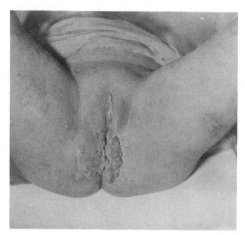

FIG. 37-8. Perianal lesions of lymphogranuloma venereum. (Courtesy of the Armed Forces Institute of Pathology, Washington, D.C., Neg. No. D4542-1.)

Healing with scar formation develops and eventually results in the obstruction of lymph channels. Characteristic effects of this phase of LGV include elephantiasis (massive enlargement) of the external genitalia in males, and rectal stricture (narrowing) in females (Figure 37-8).

Diagnosis. Procedures currently available for the diagnosis of LGV include: (1) isolation of the causative agent by the inoculation of bubo pus specimens into laboratory animals, (e.g., guinea pigs, mice, and chick embryos) followed by microscopic examination of appropriate specimens for the presence of inclusions, (2) the Frei test, a delayed hypersensitivity reaction elicited by infected persons after the intradermal inoculation of a skin test antigen (Lygranum), and (3) the complement-fixation test. With both the skin and complement-fixation tests, cross reactions can occur in cases of infections caused by other chlamydia, (such as psittacosis). However, these procedures can be modified to reduce or eliminate such cross reactivity (e.g., hydrochloric acid treatment of skin

test antigen) or to increase the specificity of the reaction (e.g., absorbing the complement-fixation test sera with a preparation of mixed *Chlamydia*).

Syphilis and the Other Treponematoses

Most health experts regard the treponematoses as one of the world's larger communicable disease problems. During the late 1940s and early 1950s a remarkably rapid decrease in the incidence of venereal syphilis was widely noted. This event coincided with the increased availability and use of penicillin. The general view held that syphilis was well on the road to eradication, and therefore would be relegated to the groups of historical diseases.

Unfortunately, during the 1960s this downward trend of reported cases reversed itself, to the point where syphilis is occurring in near epidemic proportions. The situation is amply demonstrated by noting that in 1956, 6,399 cases of early syphilis were reported in the United States, but in 1964, case reports reached a total of 22,969. Moreover, these numbers can only serve as minimum estimates, because, according to many public health authorities, untold numbers of cases go unreported. An extremely unfortunate aspect of the current status of syphilis is the increased involvement of teenagers and young adults, in the years from 15 to 24.

Historical aspects. A rather comprehensive treatment of the history and current knowledge of syphilis has been recently published by the Public Health Service, National Communicable Disease Center, in Atlanta, Georgia, as Public Health Service Publication No. 1660. Therefore, only, certain highlights of the historical background of the disease will be mentioned here.

The origin of syphilis is as much a

mystery today as it was after the great pandemic during the fourteenth and fifteenth centuries. Essentially, two major schools of thought have evolved as a result of academic disputes attempting to settle the origin of the disease. These two opposing views comprise the Columbian (American origin) and the Pre-Columbian theories. Proponents of the former school believe that syphilis was introduced into Europe as a consequence of Columbus' visit to Hispaniola (Haiti), an area in which the disease was considered endemic. The majority of Columbus' crew and six Indians who returned to Europe with the explorer are believed to have been the origin for the syphilization of Europe.

The Pre-Columbian theorists feel that syphilis occurred in Europe even prior to Columbus' voyage. The disease went unrecognized, probably because it either was confused with other infections or it occurred in a much milder form. As to the origin of syphilis, Pre-Columbian proponents affirm that the disease was present in Central Africa, as perhaps a nonvenereal "yaws-like" infection, and was brought to Europe by traders and travelers who visited endemic regions. Most authorities agree today that neither theory can sufficiently explain the rapid spread of syphilis, or the somewhat sudden transformation of an endemic disease into a new, fulminating epidemic infection.

Europe experienced a pandemic of syphilis in 1497. The disease manifested itself in an extremely severe form, which frequently resulted in death during the secondary stage. Apparently the disease was regarded as a totally new and previously unrecognized infection.

Beginning with the closing years of the fifteenth century, interest and concern associated with disease manifestations, mode of transmission, and treatment grew rapidly. The infection was called by a number of names which often implicated a political enemy as the source of the disease (the French disease, the Spanish disease). Other common designations included *bösen blattern* (the evil pox) and *la gross verole* (the great pox). Often different names were used, according to the social class of the patient. An Italian pathologist (and one of the first epidemiologists), Hieronymus Fracastoruis, wrote a poem "Syphilis Sive Morbus Gallicus," describing the plight of a mythical shepherd named Syphilis who was afflicted with the so-called French disease. This work had considerable merit in that it drew attention to the venereal nature of the disease, and also contained a representative version of the degree of knowledge pertaining to the infection available at the time. The term "syphilis" was introduced into the English language by the surgeon Thomas Gale in 1563. For many years, the descriptions of the clinical features of syphilis were extremely confusing. Concurrent infections with other venereal diseases were apparently quite common. To clear up the confusion, John Hunter, the famous English surgeon, inoculated himself with pus from a patient who had syphilis and gonorrhea. His descriptions of the course of syphilis were clouded by the manifestations of gonorrhea, and obviously did not alleviate the problem of diagnosis. Unfortunately, Hunter died in 1793 of classic cardiovascular syphilis.

Credit for finally distinguishing between syphilis and gonorrhea goes to Philippe Ricord in 1838.

Morphological and cultural properties. The causative agent of syphilis was discovered in 1905 by Fritz Schaudinn and Erich Hoffman. The spirochete nature of the microorganism caused them to name it *Spirochaeta pallida,* a designation which has since been changed to *Treponema pallidum.* This treponeme belongs to the order of Spirochaetales and the family of Treponemataceae.

The microorganism is one of three principal human pathogenic agents belonging to the genus *Treponema.* The others are *T. pertenue* and *T. carateum,* the causative agents of yaws and pinta, respectively (Table 37–2). The three species are morphologically and serologically indistinguishable. *T. pallidum* is a thin, delicate, spiral bacterium ranging in size from 6 to 15 μm in length, and possessing a uniform cylindrical thickness of about 0.25 μm, arranged in a number of tight body coils (6 to 14 turns or spirals). Upon dark-field examination of clinical specimens from primary and secondary syphilitic lesions, the spirality of the organism and its well-known corkscrew-like rotation (motility property) are easily recognized (Figure 37–9).

Structurally *T. pallidum* is believed to possess a cell wall similar, to an extent, to that found with other bacterial species. This contention is based on the results of chemical analyses of the spirochete which have demonstrated the presence of muramic acid (a common constituent of bacterial cell walls). *T. pallidum* consists of an outer membrane or sheath called a *periblast* or *periplast,* which surrounds the remaining inner components of the organism. The latter is sometimes collectively referred to as a *protoplasmic cylinder.* In addition, the spirochete has an axial filament, composed of 3 to 6 fibrils located between the periblast and protoplasmic cylinder. The structure is believed to be associated in some manner with the organism's locomotion.

Up to the present time all attempts to culture *in vitro* the treponemes pathogenic for humans have been unsuccessful.

FIG. 37–9. The typical appearance of *Treponema pallidum* with dark-field microscopy. Note the corkscrew feature of this organism. (Courtesy of Dr. D. S. Kellogg, Jr., National Communicable Disease Center, Atlanta, Georgia.)

T. pallidum has not been grown outside of human or other animal hosts. The utilization of chick embryos and tissue cultures for this purpose has met with failure. *T. pallidum* has however, been maintained in fluid media containing carbon dioxide, pyruvate, a reducing agent such as cysteine, serum albumin, and serum ultrafiltrate. Such cultures usually are incubated anaerobically at temperatures ranging from 25° (ordinary room temperature) to 37°C. The motility of organisms usually is not observed after the seventh day. *T. pallidum* also has been kept actively motile in special maintenance media containing thioglycollate for 22 days. Mention should be made of the successful *in vitro* cultivation achieved with avirulent strains of *T. pallidum,* namely, the Nichols, Noguchi, Reiter, and certain Kazan strains.

Transmission. Syphilis is transmitted through direct contact with infectious lesions in both the primary and secondary stages of the disease. These lesions may be either genital or oral. *T. pallidum* is capable of passing through abraded skin and intact mucous membranes. From the lesions, the spirochetes gain access to the circulatory system of the individual and are carried to every organ. Outside the body, this microorganism is extremely vulnerable to the effects of both physical and chemical agents. Examples of these destructive forces include heat, drying, storage at refrigerator temperatures (approximately 3 to 4°C), and ordinary soap and water.

Clinical features. The incubation period of syphilis ranges from 10 to 90 days after the initial invasion of the host. Several clinical features of this venereal disease are compared with those of other treponeme infections in Table 37–3.

The clinical manifestations of syphilis may conveniently be divided into three stages, primary, secondary, and tertiary.

Primary Syphilis. The primary lesion, or chancre, develops at the site of entry of *Treponema pallidum* within 2 to 6 weeks after exposure, and lasts for approximately 6 weeks (Color photograph 98). During this stage, the treponemes invade lymph nodes, and enter the bloodstream and are distributed throughout the body, producing a *spirochetemia*. Extragenital chancres commonly involve the lip (Color photograph 97), but also may involve the tongue or other mucosal sites. Such lesions are relatively painless.

The organisms are transmitted directly from an individual with syphilitic lesions of this nature, or possibly via contaminated articles such as food utensils. The immediate rapid spread of organisms throughout the body makes all attempts at local disinfection after contact ineffective, and of no prophylactic value.

Since the spirochetes are highly anaerobic and susceptible to adverse environmental effects such as drying, they must be transferred rapidly in a moist environment to produce the disease. The wet surface of the mucous membranes of the mouth provide ideal conditions for their growth. In all examinations of these tissues one must take protective measures against accidental exposure. It is good practice for the examiner to use two mouth mirrors or tongue blades and make a thorough inspection of the lips, tongue, and general oral region before placing bare fingers in a patient's mouth. A much safer procedure that must be used in all suspicious or proven cases of syphilis is to wear surgical gloves.

The primary chancre, which is also known as the *hard* or *Hunterian chancre,* begins as a single small, slightly elevated, round, red nodule on the tissue surface. It is usually painless. The central area breaks down, and the nodule ulcerates and discharges a fluid containing numerous treponemes.

These organisms can be demonstrated by dark-field examination (Figure 37–9) and are fully capable of infecting others. The spirochetes cannot be demonstrated in tissue sections except with special stains such as silver impregnation. Serological tests on the blood do not become positive until at least a week after the appearance of the chancre. Usually there is an accompanying lymphadenopathy (an enlargement of the lymph nodes) which becomes hardened. The enlargement of the lymph nodes is due to a hyperplasia, or increase, in all of the node elements and a widening of the sinusoids. The chancre heals spontaneously, leaving very little scarring unless there has been a superimposed secondary infection with pyogenic bacteria.

Secondary syphilis. One to 2 months following the appearance of the chancre, the generalized spread of the disease and widespread lymphadenopathy may become evident. Malaise accompanied by a rise in temperature, headaches, and various, skin rashes are common systemic disturbances (Color photograph 99).

Table 37–2 A Comparison of Selected Epidemiologic Features of the Treponematoses

| | | | | Mode of Transmission | | | |
| | | | | Biological | | | Mechanical |
Microorganism	Disease	Geographical Distribution	Age Group Affected	Venereal	Non-venereal	In utero	Flies, fomites, etc.
Treponema pallidum	Venereal syphilis	Worldwide	Sexually mature individuals and some newborns	Common	Not usually	Not uncommon	Extremely rare
T. pallidum	Endemic syphilis (Bejel)	Rural regions, prevalent in Africa, Australia, Mediterranean countries	Children 2 to 10 years of age	Not usually	Common	Rare	Probably not uncommon
T. pertenue	Yaws	Rural regions, mostly tropical areas	Children 4 to 15 years of age	Not usually	Common	Questionable	Possibly not uncommon
T. carateum	Pinta	Rural regions, humid tropical areas, only in the Americas	Individuals ranging in age from 10 to 30 years	Not reported	Common	Implicated	Implicated

Table 37–3 Summary of Selected Clinical Features of the Treponematoses

| | | Natural Course of Infection[a] | | | | | |
Disease	Incubation Period (range in days)	Initial Lesions	Latency Period	Late Benign Period	Cardiovascular Involvement	Central Nervous System Involvement	Communicability Period
Venereal syphilis	10–90	++	++	+	+	+	Variable during first stage of the disease; 2–4 years
Endemic syphilis (Bejel)	10–90	+	++	++	++	++	Variable, during periods when skin and mucous membrane lesions are present
Yaws	10–90	++	++	++	?	−	Variable, during stages when moist lesions are present
Pinta	7–20	+	+	++	?	−	Unknown, possibly when active lesions are present

[a] Explanation of symbols: ++=characteristically found, common; +=not uncommon; —=absent; ?=questionable, not proved.

Swollen grayish-white areas (the mucous patch) may develop on the mucous membranes of the lips, soft palate, tongue, or other areas. The typical mucous patch is a slightly elevated and flattened grayish-white area which can be removed, leaving an erythematous (red) zone of erosion and ulceration. This covering membrane is essentially a necrotic slough which covers the underlying inflammatory tissue. In the throat the chancres may have a creeping outline; they have been called "snail track ulcers." Such lesions contain large numbers of *T. pallidum* and are slow to heal.

In the secondary stage of syphilis, the mouth often contains numerous treponemes which are a ready source of infection for dentists, their assistants, or anyone else who places an unprotected finger in the mouth of one of these infected individuals.

Maculopapular (spotty) eruptions may also occur in the mouth, as well as on the skin. The oral lesions are often on the palate, but may involve the entire oral mucosa, as non-elevated or slightly elevated reddish areas. Microscopically, the tissue shows a nonspecific chronic inflammation, often associated with capillaries having thickened walls.

The secondary stage of syphilis can be confirmed clinically by demonstrating *T. pallidum* from mucous patches or by the serology, which is positive in almost all cases.

Tertiary syphilis. The *gummas,* which are soft, gummy tumors (Color photograph 101), and nodules of tertiary syphilis usually take 5 to 20 years to appear, but may occur, though rarely, within a short time following the secondary stage. Of the many changes which become apparent within tissues, two are most commonly seen:

A. *Syphilitic arteritis*: Small arteries become narrowed as a result of a fibrous thickening of their walls.

B. *Gumma* (plural, *Gummata*): These lesions (Color photograph 101) are a type of coagulation necrosis followed by scarring, and are assumed to be the direct result of a longstanding progressive decrease in the blood supply to the tissue (*ischemia*). Gummata may form in any tissue. Some involve the tongue, palate, and facial bones. These gumma may ulcerate, leaving typically rounded, "punched out" edges. When they occur in the palate they may eventually perforate, leaving an irregular opening into the nasal area which will interfere with speech.

Additional forms of syphilis

Late syphilis. This form of the venereal disease includes types known as latent syphilis, neurosyphilis, late benign syphilis, and cardiovascular syphilis.

The lesion of *late benign syphilis,* which is the gumma, usually does not produce death or total physical incapacity. However, when lesions arise in vital organs, complications occur which certainly are not benign. The gumma is believed to be a consequence of a hypersensitivity reaction to *T. pallidum.* It can involve any body organ. In addition, gummas may be found associated with the bones and skin of an infected individual. Serologic tests generally are highly reactive in this form of syphilis.

Congenital syphilis. This disease state occurs when *T. pallidum* crosses the placenta and infects the fetus. According to the Public Health Service Publication No. 1660, a situation of this nature may arise after the eighteenth week of gestation, when atrophy of the Langhan's cell layer of the placenta takes place. However adequate treatment of an infected mother before this time usually prevents

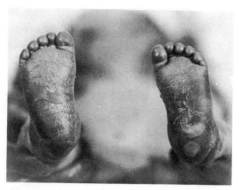

FIG. 37–10. Skin lesions of congenital syphilis appear soon after birth, frequently in the form of vesicles. These lesions can progress to superficial, crusted erosions. (Courtesy of the Armed Forces Institute of Pathology, Washington, D.C., Neg. No. 54–2488–7.)

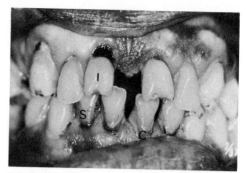

FIG. 37–11. Characteristic notched incisors (I) of congenital syphilis. Poor hygiene with considerable calculus (C) and stain (S) is also evident.

involvement of the fetus. If a woman conceives while she is in the primary or secondary stages of syphilis, her pregnancy in all probability will end in a stillbirth. When pregnancy occurs during the later stages of this infection, newborns may exhibit a variety of clinical manifestations ranging from fulminating fatal congenital infections to a normal, uninfected state.

Congenital syphilis is divided into two principal stages, early and late congenital syphilis. A primary stage is not present, as *T. pallidum* is directly introduced into the fetus via the placenta.

The effects of early congenital syphilis may include cutaneous (Figure 37–10) and mucous membrane lesions, hemolytic anemia, hepatosplenomegaly (enlarged liver and spleen), and the involvement of teeth (Figure 37–11 and Color photograph 101), bone and the central nervous system. These signs and symptoms appear before the child reaches 2 years of age.

The late form of congenital syphilis is defined by the persistence of manifestations beyond the age of 2. In approximately 60 per cent of cases, the disease is latent, and is characterized by reactive serologic reactions as the only manifestation. However, several signs of this stage of syphilis may appear. These include rare cardiovascular lesions, Clutton's joints (a painless involvement of the joints, usually the knees), interstitial keratitis, involvement of the bones and skin, Moon's molars (poor development of the cusps of the first molars), and neurosyphilis. Clutton's joints, eight-nerve deafness, and interstitial keratitis generally occur together near the beginning of puberty, and appear to be produced as a conseqeunce of a hypersensitivity response rather than by the purely destructive effects of *T. pallidum*.

Diagnosis. Syphilis has been called the "great imitator" by Osler. Without an accurate history and physical examination of the patient, this disease may go undiagnosed. Therefore, a complete examination and a routine serological test for syphilis (STS) are of utmost importance. Furthermore, in the clinical diagnosis of syphilis it is often necessary to distinguish the symptoms of the primary and secondary stages from other conditions or diseases which may be suggestive of *T. pallidum* infections.

In the case of suspected primary syphilis, a differential diagnosis should be conducted to rule out conditions including: (1) other venereal infections, e.g., chancroid, gonorrhea, granuloma inguinale, and lymphogranuloma venereum, (2) nonvenereal diseases, e.g., herpesvirus manifestations, mycotic infections, and scabies (a mite infestation), (3) extragenital chancres, (4) eruptions caused by drugs, e.g., antibiotics, barbiturates, salicylates, and sulfonamides, (5) carcinoma (cancer), and (6) traumatic injuries.

With the secondary stage of *T. pallidum* infections, in addition to several of the disease states listed for the primary stage of syphilis (drug manifestations, mycotic diseases, and scabies), differential diagnosis is necessary to eliminate several clinical states including: (1) alopecia (temporary loss of hair); (2) condylomata acuminata (wart-like lesions of a viral nature); (3) "id" (dermatophytid) reactions (hypersensitivity reactions associated with certain bacterial and mycotic infections); (4) infectious mononucleosis; (5) irritation of the iris, i.e., iritis; (6) lichen planus (papular skin disease); and (7) psoriasis. It must be remembered that any of these conditions can manifest themselves concurrently with the various stages of syphilis.

The laboratory diagnosis of the primary and secondary stages of syphilis can be made with the aid of dark-field microscopy. Care, however, must be exercised in order to differentiate *T. pallidum* from other spiral organisms which may be present in specimens. Nonpathogenic spirochetes also can be found in genital and oral regions.

The identification of *T. pallidum* is based on its characteristic morphological features and motility. Even if the organism is not demonstrated by the dark-field technique, this does not exclude the possibility of its presence. It may be

that: (1) the specimen was taken from a non-syphilitic lesion, (2) the patient had received some form of local or systemic treatment, (3) the examination was performed long after the appearance of the lesion, or (4) the lesion was a late manifestation of *T. pallidum*, which characteristically is known to contain relatively few spirochetes.

Serological tests also are of great importance in diagnosis. Since the initial application of the complement-fixation reaction by Wasserman, Neisser, and Bruck in 1906, over 200 tests for syphilis have been reported. However, only a select few of these are in common use (Table 37–4). With these procedures, syphilis generally can be diagnosed in almost every stage of the disease.

All of the general tests used in the diagnosis of *T. pallidum* infection are referred to collectively as *standard tests for syphilis (STS)*. All of these procedures are dependent on an antibody-antigen reaction. The type of antigen used can serve as a criterion for partial classification. On this basis two general categories of tests are formed—procedures utilizing treponemes or extracts of treponemes (*treponemal tests*), and methods employing normal tissue or other substances (*non-treponemal* or *reagin tests*).

Two types of antibodies produced by the host in response to *T. pallium* infection have been extensively studied. One of these substances is the reagin or Wasserman antibody. Its formation results from the interaction of the treponeme with the host's tissue. Antibodies of this nature react with a variety of non-treponemal substances. An example of such substances is cardiolipin, a highly purified preparation extracted from beef heart. The second type of antibody is produced in response to specific as well as group treponemal antigens. These substances are detected by the treponemal tests.

Table 37–4   Representative Serologic Tests Used in the Diagnosis of Syphilis

General Category of Tests Based on the Nature of Antigen	Serologic Reaction	Examples of Tests
Treponemal	Agglutination	*Treponemia pallidum* Agglutination
	Complement-fixation	Kolmer with Reiter Protein Antigen
		Reiter Protein Complement-Fixation
		Treponema pallidum Complement-Fixation
		Treponema pallidum Cryolysis Protein
	Immobilization	*Treponema pallidum* Immobilization (TPI)
	Immunofluorescence	Fluorescent Treponemal Antibody (FTA-200)
		Fluorescent Treponemal Antibody Absorption (FTA-ABS)
		Fluorescent-Antibody Dark Field (FADF)
Non-treponemal	Agglutination	Rapid Plasma Reagin
	Complement-fixation	Kolmer
	Flocculation	Kahn Standard
		Kline
		Mazzini
		Venereal Disease Research Laboratory (VDRL) Slide

SOURCE: Adapted from Public Health Service Publication No. 1660. This reference should be consulted for further discussions of these tests.

Procedures used in the recording and reporting of non-treponemal tests. Several different systems have been and are employed to record non-treponemal results. The following terminology and corresponding symbols are commonly used by laboratories. Positive reactions range from being *reactive* (R, 4+) to *weakly reactive* (WR, 3+, 2+, 1+). Negative reactions are designated as *nonreactive* (N, O, or −). Doubtful results are recorded as ±. When a quantitive examination—determination of the highest serum dilution which produces a reactive result—is needed, the outcome of the test is recorded by specifying the dilution (dils). If the serum was diluted in a twofold progression to an endpoint, i.e., 1:2, 1:4, 1:8, 1:16, 1:32, 1:64, 1:128, and so on, and if this specimen yielded a fully reactive result at the 1:64 dilution, the report would read 4+ or R at 64 dils.

Spinal fluid examination. The diagnosis as well as the evaluation of the treatment of neurosyphilis can only be accurately accomplished through the use of a spinal fluid examination. Utilization of this type of procedure can demonstrate the presence of *T. pallidum* involvement several months or years before more subjective or objective signs of neurologic disease become apparent.

Treatment.   Prior to Ehrlich's (Figure 37–12) entry into the field of syphilis therapy and his subsequent introduction of Arsphenamine or Salvarsan, mercury and potassium iodide were utilized in varying degrees by physicians. The former medication, despite its well-known toxicity, was still in use up to the time penicillin made its clinical appearance. (Ehrlich's development of chemotherapeutic compounds against infectious dis-

FIG. 37–13. Sir Alexander Fleming (1881–1955). In conjunction with Chain and Florey, he received the Nobel Prize in 1945 for his discovery and purification of penicillin. (Courtesy of the National Library of Medicine, Bethesda, Maryland.)

FIG. 37–12. Dr. Paul Ehrlich (1845–1915), the famous physician-chemist who provided one of the first effective drugs to combat syphilis. In 1908 he and Metchnikoff were jointly awarded the Nobel Prize in recognition of their investigations in immunology. (Courtesy of the National Library of Medicine, Bethesda, Maryland.)

ease agents was discussed more fully in Chapter 19.)

The modern-day management of syphilis would not have been possible had it not been for what is considered by many as the greatest single therapeutic advance in the history of infectious disease, Alexander Fleming's discovery of penicillin in 1929 (Figure 37–13). Not until 11 years later did the product become available for human use. In 1943, Dr. John Friend Mahoney, working in the Venereal Disease Research laboratory, re-ported the first successful results in the treatment of *T. pallidum* infections. This antibiotic remains the drug of choice for spyhilis. However, the oral administration of penicillin is not recommended, according to the Public Health Service Publication No. 1660.

Adequate doses of penicillin given during the primary and secondary stages effectively prevent the development of late lesions. Treatment of late latent and late symptomatic syphilis seemingly does completely eliminate the treponemes in all patients. Serological tests, especially specific reactions using *T. pallidum* as an antigen, such as the treponema-immobilization and fluorescent-antibody tests, remain positive in some cases of spyhilis. Syphilis is unique in that antibodies disappear upon recovery.

The bactericidal effect of penicillin is exerted only against growing organisms. *T. pallidum* grows slowly, with a generation time of approximately 30 hours. In the early stages of syphilis, when multiplication of treponemes is at its maximum, the penicillin may kill all of the organisms. In the late stages only a few organisms persist, which are probably not actively multiplying. Under such unfavorable circumstances the drug may be ineffective, allowing some treponemes to persist.

In the event that patients exhibit sensitivity to penicillin, other drugs may be employed. The more commonly used antibiotics are chlortetracycline, dimethylchlortetracycline, erythromycin, oxytetracycline, and tetracycline.

The procedure involved with syphilis in pregnant women is generally quite similar to that carried out in other cases of the disease. Usually one "adequate course" of penicillin treatment is all that is necessary. The dosages as well as the duration of treatment are dependent upon the stage of syphilis persent. All pregnant patients given treatment should be examined regularly, receiving monthly physical examinations and monthly serological testing.

"False-positive reactors" (Biologic false-positive reactors). Certain non-syphilitic persons can exhibit false-positive responses. A true false-positive reactor is characterized by his serum repeatedly producing reactive results with non-treponemal tests and yielding non-reactive results with treponemal tests (TPI and FTA-ABS). If this state persists for less than 6 months, the individual is referred to as an *acute false positive*. The designation of *chronic false positive* is assigned to a situation which is demonstrable for longer than 6 months. Any of several bacterial or viral dis-

eases could yield acute false positive reactions. These include infectious mononucleosis, tuberculosis, undulant fever, and measles. Recent immunizations or pregnancy may also produce this type of reaction. With respect to pregnancy it is also possible for maternal reagin to cross the placenta (placental transmission), to an uninfected fetus. Newborns having a history of this type are called *congenital false-positive reactors.*

Chronic false-positive reactions generally are associated with bacterial diseases, such as leprosy; protozoan infections, such as malaria and African sleeping sickness; and certain "autoimmune" diseases, such as lupus erythematosis. In addition, heroin addiction also has been implicated.

Endemic syphilis, pinta, and yaws. Endemic syphilis is known by several other names, including Bejel and Skerljevo. The disease, found primarily in tropical areas, is believed to be commonly transmitted through direct contact. The causative spirochete produces lesions during the early and late periods of the disease (Table 37–3). Involvement of the cardiovascular and central nervous systems as well as the skin generally occurs.

Pinta is a contagious disease caused by *Treponema carateum,* and it appears to be limited to tropical and subtropical regions, like Central and South America. The infection is believed to be transmitted through direct contact. Flies also have been implicated as possible vectors for the disease agent. The lesions (which primarily involve the feet, hands, and scalp) of this infection are described as being dry, scaly, and exhibiting a variety of colors. The name of the disease is derived from the Spanish verb *pintar,* which means to paint. These lesions at first are highly pigmented, and, then, after several years, appear to lose their color. Generally other body tissues or organisms are not invaded (Table 37–3). *T. carateum* is morphologically indistinguishable from *T. pallidum*. Wassermann antibodies are commonly detected, especially in the secondary and late stages of pinta. Penicillin is effective in the treatment of the disease.

Yaws also is a contagious disease, and is caused by *T. pertenue*. The infection is not transmitted by sexual contact, but by direct contact and possibly flies. Yaws is found in tropical areas, especially those with heavy rainfall. The characteristic lesion resembles a raspberry and consequently it has been referred to as a *framboise*. This disease is known by several other names, including *bouba* (Portuguese), *buba* (Spanish), *framboesia* (Dutch and German), and *pian* (French). Ulceration of the lesion eventually occurs, with the subsequent formation of a dry crust, followed by healing. Secondary eruptions usually manifest themselves within 2 to 4 weeks. The late stage of the disease is characterized by the involvement of the skin and bones. The cardiovascular and central nervous systems seldom appear to be affected. Congenital yaws is apparently a rare phenomenon. Serologic tests for syphilis are positive in yaws infections. Penicillin is effective in the treatment of diseased persons. Unfortunately, *T. pertenue* infections occur in areas where medical services are extremely limited.

Genital Herpes (Herpesvirus Type 2 Infection)

Ten years ago, a sexually transmitted viral infection called genital herpes was a rare condition, certainly considered minor in its ravages compared to the better-known and more virulent venereal bacterial diseases gonorrhea and syphilis. Currently, the incidence of this viral infection is increasing dramatically and is causing genuine alarm among public health experts. Herpesvirus Type 2 has been recognized as the causative agent of primary and recurrent infections involving the genital tract.

Clinical features. The symptoms of genital herpes usually appear about 6 days after sexual contact with an infected person. Initially some minor itching or rash occurs in the genital area. Most individuals ignore these symptoms. Shortly after this, a cluster of blister-like lesions may form, break open, and ulcerate. In females, these lesions can occur in the cervix, vulva, vagina, or urethra. In males, the penis and urethra are affected. Additional clinical effects that accompany genital herpes include fever, difficult and painful urination, swelling in the legs, and fatigue. Women infected with herpesvirus type 2 have a miscarriage rate of more than three times that of the general population. In pregnant women with genital herpes, delivery through an infected birth canal may expose the infant to the virus, causing death or irreversible brain damage.

The diagnostic laboratory procedures used with herpesviruses were discussed in an earlier chapter.

The TORCH Complex

Perinatal infection with toxoplasma (a protozoan), rubella virus, cytomegalovirus, and the herpesviruses may be clinically inapparent. Even when the infections are clinically apparent, the associated signs and symptoms may be indistinguishable. Furthermore, all of the agents can produce long-term ill effects in the infected fetus or newborn, so that prognosis must be guarded. Because the infections are often clinically inapparent, not only in the newborn but also in the mother, specific diagnosis is dependent on special laboratory testing. The acronym of "TORCH" was devised to focus attention on this group of microbial agents (*T,* toxoplasma; *R,* rubella virus; *C,* cytomegalovirus; *H,* herpesviruses, and *O,* others). Perinatal infections include those infectious disease states acquired by the embryo or fetus during the pregnancy period and by the newborn at the time of delivery. The specific features of these disease agents have been presented in other chapters.

QUESTIONS FOR REVIEW

1. How do microorganisms gain access to the tissues of the kidney?

2. Discuss the infections listed below as to causative agent or agents, sources of infection, and preventive measures you would think to be appropriate.
   a. acute pyelonephritis
   b. gangrenous cystitis
   c. acute prostatitis
   d. nonspecific urethritis

3. What types of urinary tract infections are associated with anaerobes?

4. Are there factors which can predispose an individual to some form of urinary tract infection? Explain.

5. Compare the venereal diseases discussed in this chapter as to causative agents, diagnosis, treatment, and prevention.

6. Can venereal diseases be transmitted by means other than sexual contact? Explain.

7. Which of the venereal diseases are known to exert harmful effects during pregnancy? Describe these manifestations and discuss preventive measures which can be taken.

8. What is a biological false-positive reactor? How is an individual of this type cleared of his label?

9. Consider the individuals listed below and their particular routines in answering this question: How can these persons acquire syphilis, gonorrhea, or LGV? If there can be no professional involvement, say so.
   a. barber
   b. physical therapist
   c. nurse
   d. x-ray technician
   e. physician
   f. dietician

10. Through what means might venereal diseases be eliminated totally? Discuss.

Selected Microbial Diseases of the Eye, Ear, and Central Nervous System

The eye and ear are special sense organs or *receptors* for obtaining information concerning both external and internal conditions. As these receptors are stimulated by external energy changes, they can be classified or categorized on the basis of the type of energy to which each selectively responds. Thus, the eye receives light and is a *photoreceptor*; the ear receives sound and is a *phonoreceptor*. The nose and taste buds are *chemoreceptors*.

The Eye

The eye consists of the eyeball and accessory appendages or organs (Figure 38–1). These appendages include the eyebrows, eyelids, conjunctiva, and the *lacrimal* apparatus that produces the tears.

The eyeball consists of three concentric coverings, which enclose the various transparent media through which light must pass in order to reach the photosensitive retina. The outermost covering protects the inner regions and gives form to the eyeball. This coat is made up of two regions, the transparent outer *cornea* and the *sclera* (white of the eye). Light rays pass through the cornea in order to enter the eyeball. The sclera, behind the cornea, is opaque and mainly protective in function.

The middle vascular covering, behind the cornea, is primarily nutritive in function. It is made up of: (1) the *chorioid proper*, (2) the *ciliary body*, and (3) the *iris*. The chorioid proper is a highly vascular and darkly pigmented membrane. It is located between the sclera and the visual portion of the retina. The ciliary body forms the thick central region of the vascular coat. The iris, the front portion of the covering, is thin, usually pigmented, and contains a central opening called the *pupil* (Figure 38–1). The iris is well known for its part in regulating the amount of light that reaches the retina.

The third and innermost coat, the *retina,* lines the vascular covering. The retina contains several cell layers, including *visual cells* (*rods* and *cones*), *ganglionic cells* (portions of which form the optic nerve), and *bipolar cells,* which are involved in the visual pathway from the eye to the brain.

Figure 38–1 shows other parts of the eye, including the *anterior chamber* (which contains the *aqueous humor*), the *posterior chamber* (which holds the *vitreous body* or *humor*), and the crystalline, circular, transparent *lens*.

The eyelids are movable folds which protect the eye from excessive light and injury, aid the pupil in controlling the amount of light reaching the retina, and contribute to the spreading of tears over the cornea, by the blinking reflex of the individual's response to the dryness of

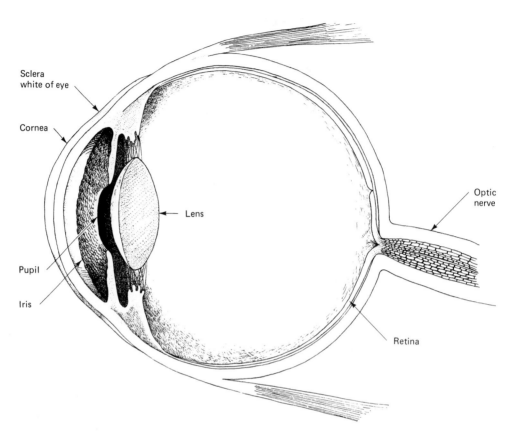

FIG. 38–1. Diagrammatic representations of the human eye. (Courtesy of National Institute of Nerological Diseases, Bethesda, Maryland.)

the cornea. Eyelids are equipped with two or three rows of stiff hairs, the eyelashes. Lashes of the upper lid are arranged in an upward direction, while the lower lashes turn downwards. The eyebrows are located at the junction of the forehead and the upper eyelid.

The conjunctiva is a mucous membrane which lines the inner part of the eyelid. Together, its two layers and three portions constitute an open *conjunctival sac* that provides a thin cover for the forepart of the sclera, the inner surfaces of the eyelids, and the cornea. Tears lubricate the conjunctiva and keep it free from particulate matter.

The *lacrimal glands,* which form a part of the lacrimal apparatus, are located above and to the side of the eyeball. Tears are secreted by these glands and are passed through a series of lacrimal ducts into the conjunctival sac. This secretion lubricates the front of the eye and thereby prevents drying of the cornea and the development of friction between the eyelids and the eyeball. In addition, tears exert a protective function by virtue of the presence of the enzyme lysozyme. Lysozyme exerts a certain degree of bactericidal action on certain saprophytic and pathogenic bacterial species.

The discussions of microbial-caused eye diseases will be limited to bacterial and viral states, since other microorganisms are rarely encountered. For extensive discussion of treatment and of diagnostic aspects, the reader is referred to the textbooks listed in the reference section for this chapter at the end of the text.

Normal Flora of the Conjunctiva

A small number of microorganisms can be isolated from the normal conjuctiva, including *Corynebacterium* spp., *Branhamella (Neisseria) catarrhalis,* staphylococci, and streptococci. Although almost any pathogenic bacterial species can cause ocular infection, such organisms may be present without producing any destructive effects. Several factors play a prominent role in protecting the human eye from infection: the bactericidal action of the lysozyme, the washing (flushing) mechanism, and the mechanical barrier of an intact mucous membrane.

Selected Bacterial Diseases of the Eye

Before more specific discussion, it should be mentioned that, in several types of ocular diseases, the practice of local eye hygiene may be totally effective without the use of any other type of treatment. Generally, local hygiene involves the removal of crusts and scales from the margins of the eyelids. The use of hot water compresses is most helpful for this purpose. It also is important to stress that prior to the application of ointments, crusts and scales always should be removed.

Several bacteria are known for their specific attraction to certain ocular structures (Table 38–1). Some of them are limited only to certain regions of the eye. *Neisseria gonorrhoeae* attacks the conjunctiva, but not the lacrimal apparatus; *Hemophilus aegypticus* is associated with the conjunctiva but not with the cornea. Furthermore, several bacterial species that do not cause primary invasion of the eye or associated appendages do produce secondary infections. Examples of such pathogens include *Brucella* spp., *Escherichia coli,* and *Proteus* spp. Several organisms, such as *Bacillus anthracis, Clostridium* spp., and *Mycobacterium tuberculosis,* which may produce infections of the eye, do so rarely.

Gonococcal Conjunctivitis

Neisseria gonorrhoeae may cause two types of conjunctiva involvement—opthalmia neonatorum (gonococcal conjunctivitis of the newborn) and conjunctivitis of the adult. Complications of these infections include corneal ulceration (keratitis), scarring, and blindness.

Ophthalmia neonatorum. Ophthalmia neonatorum develops as a consequence of the passage of the fetus through the birth canal of an infected mother. Usually both eyes of the newborn infant are involved. Characteristic features of the infection may include a sanious discharge (a combination of blood and pus), pseudomembrane formation, and swollen eyelids. The disease is highly contagious and infected individuals must be isolated.

Diagnosis. Diagnosis of gonococcal infection was discussed in Chapter 37. It should be emphasized that differentiation from other bacterial species (e.g., staphylococci and streptococci) should be carried out.

Prevention. Preventive measures generally consist of the administration of a 1 per cent silver nitrate solution (Crede's solution) into each thoroughly cleansed eye of the newborn infant. This procedure is given to every infant regardless of

Table 38–1   Representative Diseases of the Eye Caused by Bacteria

Disease	Etiological (Bacterial) Agent	Gram Reaction	Morphology	Possible Treatment
Blepharitis (inflammation of the eyelid margins and glands)	*Staphylococcus aureus*	+	Coccus	Cephalothin, methicillin, vancomycin
Chronic angular blepharo-conjunctivitis (inflammation of the eyelid, its margins, and glands)	*Moraxella lacunata* (Morax-Axenfeld bacillus)	−	Rod	Zinc salts, antibiotics including ampicillin, kanamycin, tetracyclines
Corneal ulcer	*Streptococcus (Diplococcus) pneumoniae*	+	Coccus	Erythromycin, penicillin
Dacryoadenitis (inflammation of the tear [lacrimal] glands)	*S. pneumoniae*	+	Coccus	Erythromycin, penicillin
Gonococcal conjunctivitis (inflammation of the eyelid) (conjunctiva)	*S. pneumoniae, S. aureus, Streptococcus pyogenes, S. mitis*	+	Cocci	Erythromycin, penicillin, cephalothin, methicillin, vancomycin
	Branhamella (Neisseria) catarrhalis, N. gonorrhoeae, N. meningitidis	−	Cocci	Erythromycin, penicillin, tetracyclines
Hordeolum (stye) (infection located at the edge of the eyelid)	*S. aureus*	+	Coccus	Erythromycin, penicillin
Keratitis (inflammation of the cornea)	*S. pneumoniae*	+	Coccus	Erythromycin, penicillin
	M. lacunata	−	Rod	Zinc salts, antibiotics including ampicillin, kanamycin, tetracyclines
	N. meningitidis	−	Coccus	Ampicillin, chloramphenicol, penicillin, tetracyclines
	S. mitis, S. aureus	+	Cocci	Cephalothin, methicillin, vancomycin
Ophthalmia neonatorum (conjunctivitis of the newborn)	*N. gonorrhoeae*	−	Coccus	Erythromycin, penicillin, tetracyclines
	S. aureus	+	Coccus	Cephalothin, lincomycin, methicillin, nafcillin
Orbital cellulitis (inflammation of tissue with the orbit of the eye)	*S. aureus, S. pyogenes*	+	Cocci	Cephalothin, erythromycin, methicillin, streptomycin, vaniomycin
Pinkeye (acute mucopurulent conjunctivitis)	*Hemophilus aegypticus*	−	Coccobacillus	Sulfonamides, streptomycin, tetracyclines

whether or not gonorrhea infection of the mother is suspected. Penicillin also has been used for prophylaxis. However, its use has not been widely accepted because instances of antibiotic sensitivity have been observed.

Gonococcal conjunctivitis in adults. In adults, the disease is generally similar to that of newborns, but there is likely to be greater involvement of the conjunctiva and cornea. Adults usually contract the disease by carrying organisms to the eye from a genitourinary infection.

Pinkeye

This bacterial disease is caused by *Hemophilus aegypticus,* also known as Kochs-Weeks bacillus. The organism was first discovered by Koch in 1884, as a secondary invader of trachoma infections in Egypt. Later, in 1886, Weeks reported the same microorganism as the etiologic agent of epidemic acute conjunctivitis. Pinkeye is a highly contagious variety of acute catarrhal conjunctivitis. The infection occurs more commonly during the warmer months of the year.

Symptoms of pinkeye infection include a copious discharge, redness and extreme swelling of the eyelids, and subconjunctival hemorrhages.

Diagnosis. A culture of this Gram-negative coccobacillus is necessary for diagnosis. The organism can be grown on Levinthal's medium or chocolate agar. On these media, the colonies of *H. aegypticus* appear small, glistening, and translucent. A sweet odor has been reported. Slight acid is produced from glucose and galactose, and nitrates are reduced to nitrites.

Moraxella Lacunata (Morax-Axenfeld Diplobacillus) Infections

This Gram-negative rod has particular importance for the ophthalmologist as it apparently causes eye diseases only. The bacterium was first described in 1896 by Morax, and independently reported by Axenfeld in 1897.

Clinical features. *M. lacunata* is known to characteristically cause chronic angular blepharoconjunctivitis. This disease is primarily one that affects adults, although reports have appeared of the involvement of newborns. Hot climates or hot dusty environments are closely associated with the disease.

Hypopyon keratitis (pus formation in the anterior chamber) is another manifestation of *M. lacunata*. This disease is found particularly in alcoholic and debilitated individuals.

Diagnosis. Diagnosis is possible by the demonstration of the organism's typical morphological features in smears of eye secretions. Culturally, the organism grows on enriched types of media, e.g., blood agar and Löffler's serum medium.

Morphologically *M. lacunata* usually appears in pairs, although occasionally short chains of rods may develop. This species is the largest Gram-negative organism causing ocular disease; however, in clinical specimens it looks short but stout. Furthermore, bipolar staining (intense staining of both ends of the cell, thus presenting an appearance similar to a microscopic safety pin) is common. *M. lacunata* is aerobic, non-motile, and non-spore-forming.

Pneumococcal Diseases

Streptococcus (Diplococcus) pneumoniae, in addition to causing upper respiratory tract infections, is known for its ability to produce severe diseases of the eye, including conjunctivitis, corneal ulcer, chronic dacryocystitis, keratitis, and postoperative infections of the eye.

Clinical features. *S. pneumoniae* apparently is the most common cause of central corneal ulcers (pneumococcal ulcer). The organism is primarily introduced through a corneal abrasion. Infections of this type have been reported to occur more commonly in farmers, miners, stonemasons, and persons working in related areas.

Diagnosis. Diagnosis of *S. pneumoniae* has been considered in the chapter concerned with bacterial respiratory diseases.

Staphylococcal Infections

Staphylococci in general are considered to be the most common etiologic agents of eye infections. Of the various eye diseases caused by staphylococci, blepharitis is the most common. Two clinical varieties of the infection are known, *ulcerative* and *squamous*. Staphylococci are considered to be the primary cause of the ulcerative state, and secondary invaders in the squamous. These manifestations can persist for several years and recur periodically. Complications which may develop include madarosis or loss of cilia (eyebrows and lashes), and tylosis ciliaris (lid margin thickening).

In addition to blepharitis, these Gram-positive cocci cause several diseases, including conjunctivitis in adults and newborns (staphylococcal ophthalmia neonatorum), hordeolum, keratitis, orbital cellulitis, and postoperative infections.

Diagnosis. The diagnostic features of staphylococci infections have already been discussed in several chapters. The essential features of a laboratory diagnostic procedure are shown in Color photographs 62–66.

Streptococcal Infections

Streptococci also are noted for their ability to cause certain diseases, including conjunctivitis, lacrimal sac abscess, and postoperative eye involvement. Orbital cellulitis produced by *S. pyogenes* is prevalent among children, and can develop from focal teeth infections, from pharyngitis, or from sinusitis.

Another streptococcal species, namely, *S. mitis* (Color photograph 46), also has been reported to cause several ocular infections, such as acute catarrhal conjunctivitis, chronic dacryocystitis, hypopyon keratitis, and postoperative involvement.

Diagnosis. The diagnosis of streptococci also has been presented in various chapters, therefore no discussion of this topic will be given here.

Eye Infections Caused by Viruses and the Chlamydia

Several viruses and certain members of the bacterial genus *Chlamydia* can cause some of the most common and destructive eye diseases of man (Table 38–2). Certain selected features of a representative number of these pathogens and the infections they cause are included here.

Selected Viral Infections

Epidemic keratoconjunctivitis (EKC). Human adenoviruses have a worldwide distribution. In general, these agents produce mild infections. Occasionally, involvement of the conjunctiva occurs as a consequence of direct contact with respiratory and ocular secretions. Reports also have implicated swimming pools in conjunctivitis and pharyngoconjunctival fever epidemics. Epidemic keratoconjunctivitis is commonly caused by *Adenovirus,* Type 8, and appears to be the result of a traumatic injury associated with dirt and dust in factories and shipyards. In addition, ophthalmologists, optometrists, and nurses may also transmit the disease agents with contaminated or improperly sterilized instruments.

Prevention. Control of keratoconjunctivitis primarily involves improvement of environmental conditions in working areas of factories, and the incorporation of suitable measures to prevent the spread of the disease during the examination and treatment of patients. An inactivated Type 8 vaccine has been effectively used in Japan to prevent this adenovirus infection.

Herpes corneales. *Herpesvirus hominis* (herpes simplex virus) is well known for its ability to cause a wide variety of lesions in humans. One group of clinical manifestations associated with the skin or mucous membranes (Chapters 31 and 32) includes a unilateral ulcer on the conjunctiva or cornea. This ocular infection, referred to as corneal herpes, may constitute an initial (primary) infection. A recurrent type is the most commonly encountered type of eye infection caused by *H. hominis* and develops in the presence of circulating antibodies.

Table 38–2   Common Eye Diseases Caused by Viruses and Chlamydia

Disease Manifestation	Etiologic Agent (Common Designation)	Possible Treatment
Conjunctivitis	Newcastle disease virus	Symptomatic
Conjunctivitis, keratitis, or a combination of both manifestations	Molluscum contagiosum virus (*Molluscovirus hominis*)	Symptomatic
Dendritic keratitis (associated with recurrent herpes); herpetic conjunctivitis (commonly found in children); purulent conjunctivitis; herpetic keratitis (corneal herpes)	*Herpesvirus hominis* (Herpes simplex virus)	5-iodo-2-deoxyuridine and other DNA synthesis inhibitors
Epidemic keratoconjunctivitis (EKC)	*Adenovirus,* Types 7 and 8	Symptomatic
Inclusion conjunctivitis	*Chlamydia oculogenitale*	Tetracyclines, sulfonamides
Non-purulent conjunctivitis	Measles virus	Symptomatic
Trachoma	*Chlamydia trachomatis*	Chlortetracycline, oxytetracycline, sulfonamides
Ulcerative blepharitis	Vaccinia	Symptomatic
Zoster ophthalmicus	Varicella — Herpes Zoster virus	Symptomatic The use of steroids is questionable

Infections Caused by the Chlamydia

The etiologic agents of trachoma and inclusion conjunctivitis formerly were designated as basophilic viruses. Now, however, these microrganisms are no longer classified as viruses, but as small intra-cellular bacteria. Laboratory differentiation of the two pathogens is not possible. Together, *Chlamydia trachomatis* and *C. oculogenitale* are referred to as the TRIC group of agents.

Trachoma.   Geographically, this contagious keratoconjunctivitis is prevalent in various semitropical and tropical parts of the world, including Africa, the Far East, the Middle East, and South America. The disease also occurs in certain regions of North America (e.g., the Southwest United States), as well as certain European countries. Although trachoma does not kill, it is the largest single cause of preventable blindness. The World Health Organization has estimated that nearly 400 million people suffer from this disease. In certain rural portions of northern India, for example, the infection rate may be as high as 80 to 90 per cent

of the area's total population. The incidence of trachoma is closely associated with poor sanitation and heavily populated areas. Transmission of the disease agents occurs by direct contact. Flies constitute important mechanical vectors for *C. trachomatis.*

Clinical features.   Trachoma is an inflammatory keratoconjunctivitis which manifests itself in an insidious manner. Typical effects associated with the infection include accumulation of blood vessels on the surface and penetration of scar tissue (*pannus formation*), tumor formation, and scarring (Figure 38–2). Secondary bacterial infections are commonly encountered. The disease generally remains limited to the conjunctiva and cornea, and does not spread widely.

Immunity.   Successful recovery from the disease does not provide a guarantee against additional infections. Apparently, immunity toward trachoma does not develop as a consequence of a clinical infection. The development of an effective vaccine to provide some degree of protection is currently under investigation.

Inclusion conjunctivitis. *C. oculogenitale* is a microorganism which causes clinical manifestations in the genital tract and in conjunctiva. The designation "inclusion blennorrhea" is used in relation to the genital infections, such as cervicitis and urethritis, while "inclusion conjunctivitis" is employed for conjunctival inflammations caused by this organism in babies and older individuals.

Females harboring *C. oculogenitale* may not exhibit any signs of infection. Mild vaginal discharges occasionally may be observed. Males acquiring the pathogenic agent usually produce a discharge, which may be a chronic or intermittent manifestation.

Inclusion conjunctivitis infection is contracted by babies on passage through the cervical canal. In the case of older individuals the disease can be acquired as a consequence of direct or indirect

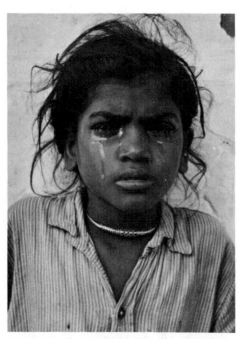

FIG. 38–2. A victim with trachoma and secondary bacterial infections. (Courtesy of World Health Organization, Geneva. Photo by Homer Page.)

contact with swimming pool patrons. This type of infection, which is frequently referred to as "swimming pool conjunctivitis," is quite mild and may heal without treatment. Generally, scarring does not occur.

The Ear

This organ of hearing is an intricate mechanism. Structurally, the ear can be divided into three parts: the external ear, middle ear, and internal ear (Figure 38–3).

The external ear serves to collect atmospheric sound waves. Basically it consists of an *auricle* (the expanded portion which is attached to the head) and the *external canal,* or *external acoustic meatus.*

The middle ear, or *tympanic cavity,* together with the outer ear, directs sound waves to the sense organ proper, the inner ear. This ellipsoidal, air-filled cavity possesses a large opening in its lateral wall which normally is closed by the *tympanic membrane* or *eardrum.* The *Eustachian tube* (or *auditory tube*) connects the tympanic cavity with the nasopharyngeal region. This tube also functions as a means with which to equalize the air tension in the middle ear with atmospheric pressure, and as a channel for middle ear drainage.

The tympanic cavity of each ear also possesses the three small bones (*ossicles*), the outermost *malleus* (hammer), the centrally located *incus* (anvil) and the innermost *stapes* (stirrup). The hammer is firmly attached to the tympanic membrane, while the stapes is inserted into the *oval window* (fenestra ovalis) of the temporal bone. Sound waves are conducted from the eardrum to the inner ear by means of these three small bones.

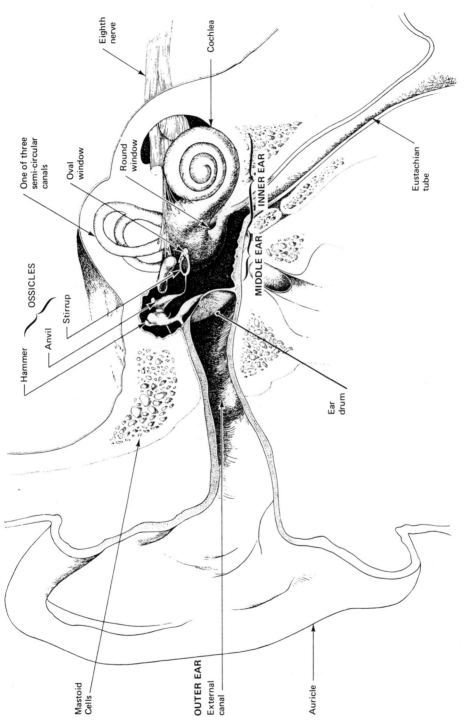

Eighth nerve

Cochlea

One of three semi-circular canals

Oval window

Round window

Eustachian tube

OSSICLES

Stirrup

Anvil

Hammer

MIDDLE EAR

INNER EAR

Ear drum

Mastoid Cells

OUTER EAR
External canal

Auricle

FIG. 38–3. A diagrammatic representation of the human ear. (Courtesy of Sonotone Corporation, Elmsford, N.Y.)

As mentioned earlier, the inner ear, or labyrinth, is the sense organ proper—the essential part of the ear. In addition, this structure has an important role in the maintenance of equilibrium. Anatomically, the inner ear consists of the *osseous labyrinth* and the *membranous labyrinth.*

Diseases of the Ear

Various microorganisms can cause infections of the ear. This section will primarily be devoted to those involving bacterial pathogens. Diseases associated with microorganisms are provided as frames of reference (Table 38–3).

Common symptoms associated with disease states of the ear include varying degrees of deafness, dizziness, involuntary rapid eye movements (*nystagmus*), pain, continuous or intermittent noises in the ear (*tinnitus aurium*), and a feeling of revolving in space or surroundings rotating about the victim of the disease (*vertigo*).

It is well known that individuals with nasopharyngeal (nose and throat) diseases are often predisposed to ear "affections." This is the case especially in situations of adenoid growths, Eustachian tube obstructions, various forms of otitis media, and paranasal sinus infections. Treatment must be directed not only towards the ear disease but also against the predisposing condition.

Furunculosis

This infection of the external meatus is commonly found in debilitated individuals and diabetics, but healthy persons can also experience this *Staphylococcus* manifestation. Furuncles, which are circumscribed inflammations of hair follicles or sebaceous glands enclosing an inner core, result from the introduction of these organisms either through scratching or from a discharge associated with purulent otitis. Recurrence of furunculosis is not uncommon.

Otitis Externa

This term represents a wide variety of conditions affecting the external ear. In general, otitis externa is considered to be a diffuse inflammation of the external auditory meatus. Several common modes of infection include scratching the ear with contaminated fingers, injury caused through the use of poorly fitted hearing aids, and improperly sterilized instruments used in ear examinations or in the removal of wax from the ear. Freshwater swimming has been recently implicated as a source of contamination. Several organisms have been associated with the disease. The most commonly encountered bacterial species are *Escherichia coli, Proteus* spp., *Pseudomonas* spp., *Staphylococcus aureus,* and hemolytic streptococci. Bacterial pathogens are now considered to be the most frequent cause of otitis externa. Formerly, fungi were believed to be the chief causative agents of the disease.

Several factors also have been implicated as important predisposing conditions for the development of otitis externa. Included in this group of factors are allergic states, dermatosis, endocrine dyscrasias (malfunctions), tumors, vitamin deficiencies, and irritants such as chlorine in swimming pools.

Acute Suppurative Otitis Media

Acute purulent otitis media is a common disease of childhood, though it is quite frequently overlooked. Generally the infection results from any and all inflammatory conditions involving the upper air passages. Contaminated water from swimming entering the middle ear from the nose or nasopharynx, injuries to the tympanic

Table 38–3   Representative Microbial Diseases of the Ear

Disease	Etiologic Agent	Gram Reaction	Morphology (if applicable)	Possible Treatment
Furunculosis (boils)	*Staphylococcus aureus*	+	Coccus	Cephalothin, lincomycin, methicillin, nafcillin, vancomycin
Myringitis (inflammation of the eardrum)	Mixed infections involving hemolytic streptococci and viruses	+	Cocci	Ampicillin, cephalothin, erythromycin, penicillin
Otitis externa (inflammation of the outer ear)	*Escherichia coli, Proteus* spp., *Pseudomonas* spp.	−	Rods	Chloramphenicol, gentamicin, kanamycin, penicillin, polymycin, tetracyclines
	Hemolytic streptococci, S. aureus	+	Cocci	Ampicillin, cephalothin, erythromycin, penicillin, vancomycin
	Mixed infections			
Otitis media (middle ear infection)	*Streptococcus (Diplococcus) pneumoniae*, beta-hemolytic streptococci, *S. aureus*	+	Cocci	Ampicillin, cephalothin, erythromycin, penicillin, vancomycin
	Hemophilus influenzae	−	Coccobacillus	Chloramphenicol, kanamycin, penicillin, streptomycin, tetracyclines
Otomycosis (mycotic infection of the external ear and ear canal)	*Aspergillus niger*	Not useful	Mold	
	Candida albicans	+	Yeast	Amphotericin B
Pharyngeal abscess	Beta-hemolytic streptococci, *S. aureus*	+	Cocci	Ampicillin, cephalothin, erythromycin, penicillin, vancomycin

membrane, skull fractures associated with the temporal bone, and certain complications of epidemic cerebrospinal meningitis all may produce this condition. Children apparently are predisposed to acute suppurative otitis media if they have adenoids in the nasopharynx, and if they possess a hereditary tendency toward catarrhal and suppurative involvement of the upper air passages.

Staphylococcus aureus, Hemophilus influenzae, and beta-hemolytic streptococci are the most common etiologic agents of this disease. *Streptococcus pneumoniae* also is known for its ability to produce acute suppurative otitis media.

Clinical features. Generally, pain is the primary manifestation. At first, the pain is limited to the ear, but then gradually "radiates" to involve the other portions of the head. Sneezing and yawning intensify the pain. Children, but not adults, generally exhibit a fever (101°F to 102°F) at the onset of the disease.

Individuals with this disease also complain of a full feeling in the ear and a continuous tinnitus. Vertigo does not commonly occur. Adults generally experience a severe headache, especially a frontal one, during the course of this disease. This symptom may be indicative of meningeal irritation.

Chronic Suppurative Otitis Media

This condition generally stems from an acute inflammation of the middle ear. Probably adequate treatment of the acute suppurative form of the disease would reduce the number of chronic cases. The causes of this disease are similar to those responsible for the acute infection.

The Nervous System

Three major components comprise the nervous system of man—the central, peripheral, and autonomic systems. Only a brief description of the first of these divisions will be given.

The central nervous system (CNS) consists of the *brain* and the *spinal cord* (medulla spinalis). The former structure is encased within the bony *cranium* (skull), and is continuous with the spinal cord, which is surrounded and protected by the segments of the vertebral column. Both the brain and spinal cord are hollow, contain *cerebrospinal fluid,* and enveloped by the three meninges (membranes), called the *dura mater* (outer), *arachnoid* (middle), and *pia mater* (inner), sheaths. Selected brain components are shown in Figure 38–4.

The acute infections of the nervous system can be either bacterial or viral. Viral infections usually are of a primary nature. Generally, however, brain abscess, meningitis, and other involvements of nervous tissue by *pyogenic* (pus-forming) bacteria occur as secondary infections. Such disease states develop from the dissemination of microorganisms from primary infections located elsewhere in the body, perhaps the lungs, middle ear, paranasal sinuses, or pelvis.

This section of the chapter will be concerned with CNS infections primarily caused by pyogenic bacteria and with selected viral diseases. Botulism, an intoxication rather than an infectious disease, is also presented. Chronic bacterial infections associated with *Mycobacterium tuberculosis* and *Treponema pallidum* are discussed in the respective chapters dealing with these organisms. This is true also of the involvement of the nervous system in certain mycotic diseases, e.g., coccidioidomycosis, crytococcosis, and torulopsis, and in protozoan infections including African sleeping sickness and toxoplasmosis (see Chapter 41).

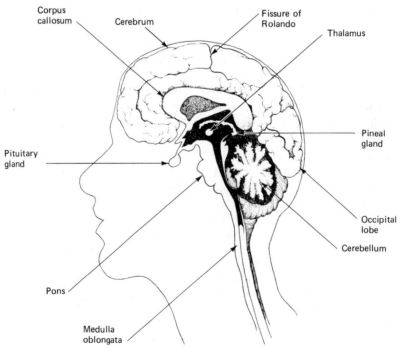

FIG. 38–4. A diagrammatic representation of a cross-section of the human brain.

Selected Bacterial Diseases of the Nervous System

Brain Abscess

Nervous tissue as well as the meninges respond to bacterial invasion as other tissues do. Pyogenic organisms gaining access to brain tissue produce an inflammatory reaction with pus formation, which results in an abscess.

Several bacteria have been associated with this type of infection, including the common pyogenic organisms *Escherichia coli, Streptococcus pneumoniae, Proteus* spp., *Staphylococcus aureus,* and *Streptococcus* spp.

Anaerobic agents also are important. According to Goldsand and Braude, they cause most, if not all, bacterial brain abscesses of a nontraumatic nature. The anaerobic diphtheroids and streptococci, *Bacteroides, Clostridium,* and *Veillonella* are involved. In terms of frequency, the anaerobic streptococci rank first, followed by *Bacteroides.* Brain abscesses caused by *Clostridium* are seldom found in civilian populations.

Most brain abscesses are complications which develop from chronic (old) suppurative foci located in other portions of the body, such as the lungs, middle ear, paranasal sinuses, pelvis, and pleura. Dissemination of organisms from these foci of infection can occur (1) by direct extension through bones, (2) via the perineural sheath of the olfactory nerves, and (3) by way of the venous system (by hematogenous routes). The majority of brain abscesses are associated with otitis media, mastoiditis, and cholesteatomas (tumors of the middle ear). The cerebral hemispheres are the most commonly involved with abscess formation. Apparently, this infection rarely occurs in the spinal cord.

Diagnosis. Bacteriological identification involves the collection of specimens such as blood and spinal fluid from persons suspected of having a brain abscess. Cultures of these specimens are incubated both aerobically and anaerobically.

Treatment. Bacterial brain abscesses are treated by drainage or excision of the abscess cavity and massive antibiotic therapy. Penicillin and tetracyclines have been used for the latter purpose.

Botulism

The disease's designation is derived from the Latin *botulus,* meaning "sausage." Uncooked sausages commonly were associated with disease for years. *Clostridium botulinum,* the causative agent of this disease, is known for its ability to produce a powerful neurotoxin when it grows under appropriate anaerobic conditions. Botulism is not considered to be an infectious disease. *C. botulinum* is not an invasive microorganism. However, persons who eat foods containing its toxin develop an intoxication. Botulism has been associated with a variety of food products, including improperly preserved or prepared home-canned fruits and vegetables, smoked fish, and uncooked fish and meats. Outbreaks of the disease also have occurred with commercial products. The neurotoxin causing botulism usually can be completely inactivated through heating at 100°C for 10 minutes. This fact accounts for the relatively low incidence of the disease. It should be noted that this procedure may not always be effective, as toxin inactivation also is a function of the toxin's concentration. Thus, individuals who cook canned products or processed fish at the aforementioned temperature and time period may not necessarily destroy the disease-producing property of the toxin.

It is important to note that foods contaminated by the toxin do not necessarily appear or smell any different from uncontaminated products. Furthermore, neither the gastric secretions (juices) of the stomach nor proteolytic enzymes of the duodenum will inactivate the toxin. This poison generally is absorbed both from the stomach and the small intestines. Intoxication via the respiratory tract with dried toxin also has been noted.

Six exotoxin types are known. Types A, B, E, and F are associated with human diseases, while the Types C and D have been reported to affect fowl and cattle, respectively. Most human cases and the highest mortality are caused by Types A and E toxins.

Clinical features. The manifestations of botulism usually begin approximately 18 to 96 hours after the ingestion of the toxin. Victims of the disease may have difficulty in speaking, dilated-fixed pupils, double vision, a dry mouth, inability to swallow, nausea, and vomiting. Paralytic manifestations involve the urinary bladder and all voluntary muscles. Death is caused by either cardiac arrest or respiratory failure. Individuals recovering from botulism experience a slow convalescence.

Laboratory diagnosis. Botulism in humans is diagnosed on the basis of clinical symptoms and a history of the ingestion of food types which are associated with the disease. A critical diagnosis of the disease is made by demonstration of the toxin's presence in the implicated food, or in the patient's serum. Procedures for this purpose utilize mice inoculations.

Samples of the suspected food also should be incubated anaerobically in or on appropriate media in order to demonstrate the presence of the causative agent. In the event *C. botulinum* is isolated, the organism should be tested for its ability to produce the neurotoxin. The specific identification of the toxin type is determined with the aid of mouse protection tests.

Treatment. Botulinum toxin blocks the release of acetylcholine by nerve fibers when a nerve impulse passes through the peripheral nervous system as a consequence of its being fixed to the "susceptible" efferent nerve endings of this system. Antitoxin cannot neutralize the neurotoxin once it has become fixed. Therefore, treatment should be initiated as soon as possible if botulism is suspected. Generally a polyvalent antitoxin preparation, which contains antitoxin Types A, B, and E, is used.

In the event respiratory paralysis develops, the procedures for tracheotomy and artificial respiration are utilized. Measures against secondary infections must also be taken.

Meningitis

Meningitis—inflammation of the membranes around the brain and spinal cord —can result from one of several mechanisms. These include the introduction of microorganisms through (1) penetrating injuries or (2) primary infections involving the skull and spinal column; (3) the direct extension of a disease process from primary foci of infection located in other parts of the body through bone via vascular channels, or along the perineural sheath of the olfactory nerves; and (4) by means of the bloodstream (hematogenous route) during the course of a septicemia.

Microorganisms present in the circulation of the individual experience great difficulty in entering the CNS. This is largely because of the so-called blood-brain barrier. Unless some form of injury or other condition occurs which could alter the premeability of this barrier, organisms are unable to penetrate. However, once infectious agents gain entrance to the brain and the adjacent meninges, the invasion and the destruction of the nervous tissue can proceed rapidly. The outcome of the disease, of course, depends upon the initial management of patients, which would require emergency measures including diagnostic and therapeutic procedures.

Meningeal inflammation can be classified into two types, *pachymeningitis* (inflammation of the dura mater), and *leptomeningitis* (inflammation of the pia mater and the arachnoid of the brain and spinal cord). The first of these conditions is a localized infection, and practically every case results from a direct extension of an infection located in the surrounding tissues. Usually inflammation of the dura mater occurs as a complication of infected skull fractures or as a related manifestation. The dura appears to limit the infection and prevents involvement of the leptomeninges. Although the infection may be effectively localized by the dura, it may spread to the leptomeninges or the brain by means of infected veins.

If pus is produced as part of the disease pattern, the infection is called *pyogenic meningitis.*

Acute purulent leptomeningitis can be caused by several pyogenic bacterial agents, including *Streptococcus pneumoniae, Escherichia coli, Hemophilus influenzae, Klebsiella* spp., *Listeria monocytogenes, Neisseria gonorrhoeae, N. meningitidis, Proteus* spp., *Pseudomonas aeruginosa, Salmonella* spp., *Serratia marcescens, Staphylococcus aureus,* and *Streptococcus* spp. At least 50 different organisms have been incriminated. Three bacterial species, namely *S. pneumoniae, H. influenzae,* and *N. meningitidis,* are the most commonly encountered agents.

Many of these pathogens reach the meninges by the routes discussed previously. However, mention should be made of situations in which organisms have been introduced through the injection of contaminated solutions, such as local anesthetics, into the cerebrospinal fluid. Certain *Pseudomonas* meningitis cases have been reported to occur in this manner.

The general clinical picture caused by many of these organisms is similar to that produced in meningococcal meningitis.

Meningococcal meningitis (cerebrospinal fever). *Neisseria meningitidis* is capable of causing the death of a human faster than any other infectious agent. Death of patients has been reported to occur in less than 2 hours after the manifestation of the first symptoms. Infections with meningococci frequently develop among closed populations, such as jails, military posts, schools, and ships. The transmission of the etiologic agent is believed to occur through droplets, in a manner similar to that found with other respiratory diseases. *N. meningitidis,* like certain other members of the genus, is unable to withstand the adverse effects of the environment for any appreciable lengths of time, and therefore, probably can cause infections only by some form of direct contact.

At the present time, on the basis of agglutination tests, four major serotypes of meningococci are recognized, called A, B, C, and D. Serotypes X, Y, Z, 29 E, and 135 also have been reported. Most major epidemics of the disease in the United States have been associated with Group A organisms. Groups B and C generally were active during the interim periods. The epidemiological picture has changed recently, and it is Group B organisms that are now the predominant agents causing meningococcal meningitis in the

United States. The frequency of infections produced by the other three groups is generally low.

Meningococcal meningitis has presented a serious problem in Africa since World War II. Group A organisms are predominant. The disease has been found in an area extending across Africa from the shores of the Atlantic Ocean to those of the Red Sea, and north of the equator to south of the Sahara. This region is referred to as the "meningitis belt."

Clinical features. Acute manifestations of meningococcal meningitis, especially the fulminant form, are considered true medical emergencies. The most common form of N. meningitidis disease is a subclinical infection of the nasopharynx (nasopharyngitis). Just how often these infections result in clinical symptoms cannot be accurately determined. However, such carriers serve as reservoirs of meningococci within the general community. Carrier states have been reported to persist for several months. On military bases, meningococcal carrier rates have involved 70 to 90 per cent of the recruits.

Clinically the particular form of this disease is important to the planning of specific therapy. In general, three clinical types or categories are recognized; meningitis, septicemia, and chronic meningococcemia.

Meningitis represents the most common form of N. meningitidis infection. Individuals with the disease usually experience fever, headache, and stiffness of the back of the neck. In young victims common features of the infection include chills, convulsions, irritability, and repeated vomiting. The progress of the disease is accompanied by increased meningeal irritation and rigidity (stiff neck). A rash also can develop and usually is found in approximately two-thirds of the patients who exhibit delirium, mental confusion, and coma. Furthermore, the cerebrospinal fluid from these patients generally contains large cell numbers (primarily polymorphonuclear leukocytes), and, in at least 50 per cent of the cases, N. meningitidis. A prompt and specific diagnosis is established with the latter finding.

Septicemia occurs either as a rapid fulminant variety of meningococcal infection, or as the primary stage before CNS invasion.

Chronic meningococcemia in general terms represents an equilibrium state between N. meningitidis and the host (patient).

Laboratory diagnosis. Prior to the initiation of therapy based on clinical findings, it is advisable to obtain blood and spinal fluid specimens for clinical and bacteriologic studies. Several other types of specimens can also be utilized, including material from exudates, nasopharynx, and skin lesions. Characteristically, these materials are used as inocula and are examined for evidence of a cellular response and the presence of pathogens.

In general, media utilized for purposes of isolating N. meningitidis include blood, chocolate, Mueller-Hinton agar, and Thayer-Martin (TM) medium. The latter two preparations are characteristically utilized in studies involving meningococcus carriers. TM selective medium is used to culture specimens suspected of containing a mixed flora. Cultures are incubated at 37°C in an atmosphere of 10 percent carbon dioxide. All members of the genus *Neisseria* exhibit a characteristic positive oxidase reaction (Color photograph 94) when tetramethyl-p-phenylenediamine is applied to the colonies of these organisms. The colonies usually undergo a series of color changes, eventually producing a magenta or dark red coloration. It is important to note that this oxidase test does not differentiate one species of *Neisseria* from another.

Morphologically *N. meningitidis* is a Gram-negative diplococcus. The organism produces acid only from glucose and maltose (Color photograph 96). Generally, in order to obtain these oxidation reactions with either *N. meningitidis* or *N. gonorrhoeae,* human or rabbit serum should be incorporated into the medium. The carbohydrate reactions of meningococcus can be utilized to differentiate the organism from most other species of the genus. Fluorescent antibody techniques also are used for the detection of *N. meningitidis.*

Treatment. Antimicrobial sensitivity tests must be carried out to ensure the adequate management of meningitis caused by enteric Gram-negative organisms, e.g., *E. coli, Proteus* spp., and *Salmonella* spp. as well as other bacterial species. Quite often, before results of such testing procedures can be obtained, some form of antimicrobial therapy must be instituted. However, such therapeutic measures should be modified when information of antibiotic sensitivities become available.

Prevention. Preventive measures against meningococcal infections are few. The isolation of carriers during times of epidemics would be extremely difficult in view of the sheer numbers of persons involved. Mass treatment, prophylactically, for substantial periods of time constitutes a danger in that resistant strains would more likely emerge. Vaccines appear to be one of the few possibilities to avert epidemics. Investigations are currently under way to develop preparations that would actively immunize individuals against meningococcus.

Meningitis caused by anaerobes. Generally speaking, this disease is only rarely caused by anaerobic bacteria, though several of the species associated with brain abscesses have been implicated with this disease manifestation. Included in this group of causative agents are *Actinomyces,* anaerobic streptococci, *Bacteroides,* and clostridia. Most meningitis caused by *Bacteroides* and anaerobic streptococci (Figure 38–5) has stemmed from middle ear or sinus infections. Clostridia generally are considered to be the etiologic agents of anaerobic meningitis arising as a complication of head injuries or surgery.

Laboratory diagnosis. The laboratory diagnosis of infections produced by anaerobic streptococci and *Bacteroides* usually is based on: (1) the findings obtained with a spinal fluid analysis, namely, the presence of a large numbers of cells, and a marked reduction in glucose content, and (2) bacteriologic identification. The Gram stain is of particular significance.

Neonatal meningitis. During the first 30 days of life, the incidence, morbidity, and mortality of pyogenic meningitis are higher than in any later time period. Newborn infants can be predisposed to this infection as a consequence of several factors, including: (1) complications associated with delivery, (2) maternal

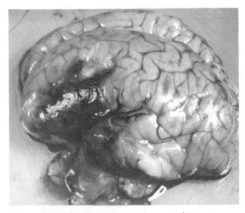

FIG. 38–5. Manifestation of anaerobic streptococci. (Courtesy of the Armed Forces Institute of Pathology, Washington, D.C., Neg. No. 54–13308–1.)

infections at the time of birth (perinatal disease states), and (3) prematurity. As this infection is both atypical and nonspecific in early symptomatology, a rapid and early diagnosis is extremely important.

Approximately 50 to 60 per cent of cases are caused by Gram-negative bacteria. *Escherichia coli* is the most commonly encountered of these pathogens. Other organisms of this group include species of *Klebsiella, Acinetobacter, Proteus, Pseudomonas,* and *Salmonella.* Gram-positive bacteria which have been found in cases of neonatal meningitis include *Listeria monocytogenes,* staphylococci, and Group A, B, and D hemolytic streptococci. The Gram-positive cocci account for approximately 20 to 30 percent of infections.

Diagnosis. Bacteriological isolation utilizes various specimens including blood, spinal fluid, and urine as well as fluid from the nasopharynx and skin lesions.

Treatment. Neonatal meningitis treatment is largely determined by the staining properties (Gram-stain reactions), the morphologic properties of organisms in direct smear preparations, and antibiotic sensitivity patterns of isolated organisms.

Selected Viral Infections of the Nervous System

Numerous viruses commonly are associated with nervous system involvement (Table 38–4). These pathogens are generally referred to as being neurotropic. Brief descriptions of selected syndromes and the viral agents associated with them are presented in Table 38–4. Viruses may gain access to the central nervous system by several means, including cellular blood components, cerebrospinal fluid, olfactory nerve fibers, and nerves. Certain neurotropic viral infections are described in this section. Those infections transmitted by arthropods (arbo-viruses) are discussed in Chapter 39.

Aseptic (Nonbacterial) Meningitis

This viral infection of the nervous system is considered to be not only one of the commonest syndromes, but also the easiest to recognize. Such infections are worldwide in distribution, occur in epidemic form, and primarily involve children. Several viral agents have been incriminated as causal agents (Table 38–4). It should be noted that a wide spectrum of clinical states can be caused by these viruses.

Table 38–4 Representative Nervous System Syndromes Caused by Viruses

Viral Syndrome	Brief Description	Viruses Commonly Associated with the Condition
Aseptic (nonbacterial) meningitis	Inflammation of the meninges (nonbacterial)	Coxsackie, echo, herpes simplex, mumps
Encephalitis	Inflammation of the brain	Eastern and Western Equine, Japanese B, Murray Valley, St. Louis, tick-borne encephalitis viruses
Ganglionitis	Inflammation of a ganglion	Varicella — Herpes Zoster (shingles)
Myelitis	Inflammation of the spinal cord	Picornaviruses
Postinfectious encephalitis	A complication during or subsequent to recovery from primary infection	Influenza, measles, mumps, rubella, varicella, variola
Postvaccination encephalitis	A complication following the administration of certain viral vaccine preparations	Rabies, smallpox, yellow fever vaccines

General clinical features. Symptoms associated with aseptic meningitis include fatigue, fever, headache, muscle pain, stiffness of the back and neck, nausea, vomiting, and general weakness.

Picornaviruses

The picornavirus group contains several viruses that can produce infections of the human nervous system, such as coxsackieviruses, echoviruses, polioviruses, foot-and-mouth disease virus, and rhinoviruses.

Poliomyelitis.   This viral infection has been found in every country where it has been sought. However, within the last few years, due to the use of the various types of polio vaccines, the incidence of the disease has been significantly reduced.

Three antigenic types, I, II, and III, are known. The most generally accepted view regarding the entry of poliovirus postulates that virus enters the body via the mouth and intestines. Multiplication of the organisms primarily takes place in the alimentary canal. The spreading of poliovirus to the nervous system occurs by way of the blood. Poliovirus is excreted in the feces before involvement of the nervous system develops. Several authorities also strongly believe in the transmission of poliovirus to the central nervous system by way of the peripheral nerves (the neural route). Several effects, ranging from a minor illness to paralysis, can occur as a result of poliovirus infection. Several of these clinical varieties of poliomyelitis are discussed below. The role of poliovirus in aseptic meningitis was mentioned earlier.

Clinical features.   The incubation period for this disease varies, but on the average fluctuates between 1 and 2 weeks. The most common form of poliomyelitis is the subclinical or abortive variety. Usually victims experience the nonparalytic disease manifestation for a very short period. Symptoms associated with subclinical infections include constipation, fever, headache, malaise, muscle pains, nausea, and vomiting.

Very few individuals with poliovirus infections develop paralysis. Of course, as in the case of other diseases, the final outcome of the infection is determined by several factors, including the virulence of the virus, the number of viruses, and the general resistance of the host. Persons exhibiting paralytic polio usually have had symptoms similar to those listed for the subclinical infection. Paralysis may affect any muscular system of the individual. For example, in the case of "bulbar" polio, the muscles innervated from the medulla are affected. The disease may assume a relatively mild course, producing weakness or paralysis of the facial muscles and others innervated by cranial nerves having centers in the medulla. With more serious forms of the infection, impairment of the circulatory and respiratory mechanisms develops. The term "bulbospinal" is employed in the event of spinal paralysis.

Paralytic polio often involves the limbs or trunk of the victim. Poliovirus is highly specific in attacking the anterior horn cells of the spinal cord, thus causing inflammation of the cord (myelitis).

The involvement of the muscles usually reaches a maximum within 3 days. The recovery of function of affected muscles may be apparent within 6 months. However, longer periods of 1 to 2 years also have been reported. In certain cases paralysis may persist throughout the individual's lifetime.

Poliomyelitis manifests itself differently in the young than in older persons. The development of the disease appears to be abrupt in children and gradual in adults. The muscle pain is more severe in older persons.

Mention should also be made here of factors which have been noted to either predispose or to aggravate paralytic poliomyelitis. These factors include physical exertion, especially during the preparalytic phase of the disease, pregnancy near term, routine intramuscular injections, and tonsillectomy.

Laboratory diagnosis. The diagnosis of paralytic poliomyelitis generally presents little difficulty, as the clinical symptoms are characteristic. However, in recent years problems have occurred. As a clinical diagnosis can be confirmed in the laboratory, it should be carried out. This is especially important because poliovirus can cause severe effects, including encephalitis and death. The diagnosis of subclinical or abortive infections requires laboratory confirmation.

Laboratory diagnosis is accomplished through virologic isolations and the use of neutralization tests. The isolation of poliovirus involves the inoculation of specimens, such as feces or nervous tissue from fatal cases, into tissue cultures (monkey kidney or human amnion cells). Poliovirus produces destructive changes in tissue cultures which are characteristic for the pathogen. Passive hemagglutination tests are currently under study.

Control. The effective control of poliomyelitis can be achieved by: (1) adequate diagnosis, classifications, and reporting of polio cases, (2) routine immunizations, (3) control of outbreaks, and (4) mass immunization programs.

Individuals recovering from polio infection usually acquire an active state of immunity to the viral type causing the disease.

The coxsackie viruses. The first coxsackie viral agent was isolated by Dalldorf and Sickles in 1948. The virus was recovered from suckling (unweaned) mice which were inoculated with fecal matter of children from Coxsackie, New York. Two main divisions or groups of these viruses are recognized, A and B. The former consists of 23 types, while the latter category is composed of 6 types. Coxsackie viruses exhibit the general characteristics described earlier for the picornavirus group. However, their pathogenicity for suckling mice rather than for adult animals is a feature which distinguishes them from the echoviruses and polioviruses.

Diseases caused by Group A coxsackie viruses include aseptic meningitis, herpangina (an ulcerative condition of the throat), minor respiratory illness, myocarditis, paralytic illness, and rubelliform rashes accompanied by fever. The diseases associated with the Group B coxsackie viruses include aseptic meningitis, epidemic pleurodynia, myocarditis, neonatal encephalomyocarditis, and paralytic illness.

In the majority of situations these disease agents are spread either directly or indirectly by contact with contaminated articles (fomites) and aerosols.

Laboratory diagnosis. The laboratory diagnosis of coxsackie infections includes animal inoculation for the recovery of virus, and serologic tests, such as neutralization and hemagglutination. Certain types of Group B (1, 3, and 5) are able to agglutinate human O red cells. This test is useful in the characterizing (typing) of viruses as well as in determining antibody titers (reponse to infection).

The echoviruses. This group of viruses is commonly found in the human gastrointestinal tract. They are considered to be the most common cause of aseptic meningitis, as nearly all strains comprising the group have been associated with the illness. Other disease effects caused by echoviruses include diarrhea, fever, and mild respiratory illness.

Evidence of infection is based on serologic tests performed with paired sera. This procedure is used to demonstrate a rise in antibody titer. The hemagglutination-inhibition or virus neutralization tests can be utilized for this purpose. Isolation of the virus from feces with the aid of tissue cultures, (e.g., human embryo kidney or primary monkey kidney cells) may also be useful.

Rabies (Hydrophobia)

This viral infection has been a dreaded disease since the time of the ancient civilizations of Egypt, Greece, and Rome. According to the fifth report of the WHO Expert Committee on Rabies, issued in 1966, rabies exists in two "epidemiologic" varieties: (1) the urban form, characteristically associated with dogs, and (2) the wildlife variety, which occurs in animals such as bats, coyotes, foxes, jackals, mongooses, skunks, and weasels.

The principal reservoir (source) of rabies virus is believed to be wild mammals. Humans and domesticated animals, such as cows, goats, horses, and sheep, acquire this disease accidentally. Saliva containing the rabies virus introduced into humans by the bite of a rabid animal is the principal means of transmission. Infection acquired through minor scratches and via the respiratory tract has also been reported. The virus found in nature which is responsible for the disease is called *street virus* or virus *de rage de rue*. Strains of this street virus passed through rabbits are known as *fixed virus* or *virus fixé*.

Clinical features. The incubation period of rabies in man is determined by factors including the quantity of virus introduced, the severity of the wound (depth), and the proximity of the wound to the brain. Apparently leg bites inflicted by rabid animals take longer to produce disease symptoms than bites involving the arm and head regions. Incubation periods reported vary from 6 days to 12 months.

General symptoms accompanying the disease include feelings of anxiety, headache, and insomnia. As the infectious process progresses, victims experience increasing difficulty in swallowing fluids (but not solids) to the point where the mere sight of such substances induces the well-known spasms associated with hydrophobia. Salivation becomes copious. Generalized convulsions, delirium, and coma also occur. The last two conditions may precede the death of the victim. Subclinical infections have not been reported to occur in humans.

Rabies in lower animals. The incubation period in dogs generally ranges from 2 to 8 weeks. Infected animals exhibit changes in their behavioral patterns, such as stumbling and gnawing on sticks and stones. In the "furious" type of rabies, dogs characteristically snap and bite, while in "dumb" rabies, they exhibit paralysis. The infection in dogs can be easily transmitted to other animals by biting. Often the saliva of infected dogs contains virus shortly before the disease symptoms appear.

Bat-transmitted rabies has been found to involve fruit-eating, insectivorous, and vampire bats. When these animals become rabid, they bite one another as well as other animals in the area.

Other important reservoirs of rabies are the wildlife populations of several countries. The infection can occur in either the furious or dumb varieties. The tendency of such rabid animals, such as skunks and wolves, to enter villages, cities, and even homes poses a continuous threat to the well-being of man and domestic animals.

Laboratory diagnosis. The laboratory diagnosis before death involves the inoculation of mice with saliva from patients suspected of having rabies, for the purpose of isolating the causative viral agent.

In fatal cases, specimens of the hippocampus and spinal cord are obtained and used to demonstrate the presence of rabies virus. These specimens are stained by the Seller's or fluorescent rabies antibody (FRA) techniques used to inoculate white mice. Histologic examinations are made of hippocampal and related tissues of mice which show signs of infection. The Seller's staining procedure is used to demonstrate Negri bodies. These are circular or oval, eosinophilic structures. Seller's stain is a mixture of basic fuchsin and methylene blue solutions.

Treatment. Various procedures have been utilized in the treatment of individuals bitten by rabid animals. The World Health Organization Expert Committee on Rabies recommends the following:

1. Animals suspected of being rabid should be confined, if possible, observed, and examined for at least 10 days. Treatment should not await the confirmation of rabies in the animal. However, the failure to detect the virus by a thorough laboratory investigation is a sufficient basis for stopping the course of vaccine injections.

2. Local treatment of bites should be carried out. Procedures would include the thorough washing of the wound with soap and water or other appropriate materials which are known for their viricidal effects (e.g., quaternary ammonium compounds). The topical administration of rabies antiserum or specific immune globulin preparations should be considered, and should be conducted or supervised by a physician.

3. The injection of rabies vaccine and antiserum should be instituted.

4. Preventive measures against tetanus and other bacterial infections also should be observed.

The vaccines used in antirabies treatment are of several types. The first of these, developed by Pasteur, utilized infected rabbit spinal cord material which was suspended over a desiccating agent in a closed jar. The purpose of this procedure was to destroy the viral agent. Today, many vaccines are prepared from the nervous tissues of various animals, such as calves, goats, horses, rabbits, and sheep. However, the method used for the inactivation of the virus is phenolization at different temperatures. Examples of such vaccines are the Fermi and Semple types. Other vaccines are also available which are prepared from duck embryos and suckling mice. The methods of inactivation used with these two preparations are exposure to β-propriolactone and ultraviolet irradiation, respectively.

In the treatment of individuals exposed to rabies virus, the injections of vaccines are given subcutaneously in the abdominal area (but not in the stomach, as many persons believe). The number of injections is determined by the location and the severity of the wound. Unfortunately, complications may develop with preparations containing nervous tissue (see Chapter 26). The most recent addition for treatment is Human Rabies Immune Globulin (HRIG), a form of passive (temporary) immunization.

Vaccines also are available for the immunization of humans and lower animals.

Control. The control of rabies can present several problems. However, certain measures recommended by the fifth report of the WHO Expert Committee on Rabies, if properly implemented, could help to significantly reduce the incidence of the disease. Included in their recommendations were the following: (1) prophylactic immunization not only of dogs, but also of cats; (2) the establishment of clinics in localities where rabies prevails; (3) the elimination of stray dogs, and the implementation of quarantine of dogs imported into "island communities," and (4) the incorporation of programs to eliminate or significantly reduce "proven" wildlife vectors.

Slow Virus Diseases

The concept of slow virus infections was first introduced by Sigurdsson in 1954 in his classic descriptions of several chronic diseases of Icelandic sheep. Since then additional slow virus infections have been described in humans and domestic animals. These disorders are characterized by an insidious onset and a chronic and determined progressive course that leads to a fatal outcome. Slow virus infections may be defined as a group of disease states caused by viruses in which the incubation periods are extremely long and in which the clinical expressions or course of the infections are relatively slow to appear. The outstanding feature of these infections is the persistence of a viral agent or its genetic components in a host who ultimately experiences cellular and tissue injury from the activities of the virus.

The reason for the long incubation periods of these diseases is unknown. The viral agents may be masked or hidden as a result of either immunoglobulin activity or an integrated effect of the virus that is not fully expressed.

The agents associated with this group of disease states were classified by Hanson in 1972 into two major categories, conventional and nonconventional, based on the recognized characteristics of the viruses. The conventional category includes the agents of lymphocytic choriomeningitis, herpesvirus-associated persistent infections, rabies, progressive multi-focal choriomeningitis, and subacute sclerosing panencephalitis (SSPE). All conventional agents show morphologic evidence of complete viral structure or substructure components. In addition, they provoke immune responses in the infected host and induce either degenerative or inflammatory changes in a variety of tissues. The unconventional group includes the agents of scrapie, kuru, Creutzfeldt-Jakob disease, and transmissible mink encephalopathy. These agents, unlike those of the conventional group, do not exhibit a virion structure or substructure, are not antigenic, and produce degenerative changes confined to the central nervous system. Representative associated disease states will be described.

Progressive multi-focal leukoencephalopathy (PMC). This disease is a rare central nervous system disorder of humans first described in 1958. It is characterized primarily by demyelination (destruction of the myelin of nerve tissue). Clinical features include memory loss, dysarthria (defective speech), and lack of coordination.

Subacute sclerosing panencephalitis (SSPE). SSPE is a rare disease that affects children and young adults. It usually develops several years after an initial exposure to natural measles virus or possibly to live measles vaccine. The relation between measles virus and SSPE is now well established. The virus has been isolated from brain biopsy material from patients with subacute sclerosing panencephalitis. Characteristic clinical features of the disease include behavioral changes, mental deterioration, loss of vision, and coma.

Creutzfeldt-Jakob disease (CJD). Most victims of CJD are between the ages of 35 and 65. The disease is characterized by progressive mental deterioration, ataxia (muscular coordination failure), and myoclonus (spasms in which there is rapid alternating rigidity and relaxation).

Kuru. The name of this disease, which means "to shiver," refers to the tremors that are associated with it. Kuru was originally discovered in a native tribe in New Guinea in 1957. In addition to tremors, the characteristics of the disease include progressive ataxia and mental deterioration. Death usually occurs within 6 to 9 months. Kuru primarily affects children and adult females. The natural transmission of the disease in the past was traced to the practice of cannibalism, which existed among tribes in the geographic area. The elimination of the practice has interrupted the natural transmission but has not resulted in the elimination of the disease.

The importance of slow virus infections lies in their potential application to other human diseases of unknown cause such as leukemia, multiple sclerosis, and Parkinson's disease, all of which affect large segments of the population.

QUESTIONS FOR REVIEW

1. What types of organisms comprise the normal flora of the conjunctiva? Are any of these normally pathogenic?

2. Describe or explain the following disease states of the eye. Wherever possible, indicate the organism or organisms known to be the causative agent.
   a. ophthalmia neonatorum
   b. hordeolum
   c. purulent conjunctivitis
   d. acute catarrhal conjunctivitis (pinkeye)
   e. dendritic keratitis
   f. pannus formation
   g. cellulitis of the eyelid
   h. blepharitis
   i. blepharoconjunctivitis

3. What is trachoma?

4. List the means of disease transmission for the infections given below.
   a. trachoma
   b. adult gonococcal conjunctivitis
   c. EKC
   d. angular blepharoconjunctivitis
   e. pinkeye
   f. central corneal ulcers
   g. inclusion conjunctivitis
   h. stye

5. What symptoms generally accompany ear diseases?

6. What are sources of infection for the following diseases?
   a. pinkeye
   b. otitis media
   c. otitis externa
   d. trachoma
   e. EKC

7. What is meningitis?

8. Discuss the laboratory identification of *Neisseria meningitidis*.

9. Discuss the viral diseases of the central nervous system. Include in your discussion the causative agent, the mode of transmission, diagnostic procedures used, and treatment.

10. What measures are currently available for the control of viral agents affecting the central nervous system?

11. What are slow virus infections? What significance do they have?

Infectious Diseases
Spread by Arthropod Bites

Many infectious diseases of humans and other animals can be transmitted through the bites of infected arthropods. All microbial types, with the exception of fungi, are represented in such arthropod transmissions. This chapter will present selected bacterial and virus infections known to be spread in this manner, and their control. Protozoan infections such as malaria and trypanosomiasis and certain helminth diseases are discussed in Chapters 41 and 42 respectively. Arthropods are important also in the transmission of plant disease agents.

Selected Bacterial Diseases

Bartonellosis (Carrión's Disease)

This human infection is caused by the small, motile, Gram-negative coccobacillus *Bartonella bacilliformis,* first observed by Barton in 1905. At first the clinical picture presented by the disease suggested two different types of infections. However, through the investigations of Carrión, it was learned that bartonellosis is a single disease entity with two states. In the first stage fever and a severe infectious anemia occur. This manifestation is called *Oroya fever.* The second stage of the disease appears as relatively benign wart-like eruptions and is known as *Verruga peruviana.* Both states of the disease are commonly called Carrión's disease.

Transmission. Transmission of *B. bacilliformis* to man is by the bite of sandflies (*Phlebotomus* spp.). Bartonellosis should not be confused with sandfly (*Phlebotomus*) fever, which is a viral infection transmitted by the same vector.

Table 39–1   Representative Bacterial Diseases (Other than Rickettsial) Transmitted by Arthropods

Disease	Etological Agent	Gram Reaction	Morphology	Geographical Distribution	Treatment
Bartonellosis (Carrión's disease)	*Bartonella bacilliformis*	—	Coccobacillus	South America, including Columbia, Ecuador, Peru	Antibiotics, including chloramphenicol, penicillin, streptomycin, tetracyclines
Plague	*Yersinia pestis*	—	Rod	Areas with wild rodents	Isolation antibiotics, including chloramphenicol, streptomycin, tetracyclines
Relapsing fever	*Borrelia recurrentis, B. duttonii*	Not done	Spirochetes	Normally, worldwide; notable exceptions, Australia, New Zealand, Oceania	Tetracyclines
Tularemia	*Francisella tularensis*	—	Rod	United States, Europe, Japan	Kanamycin, streptomycin

Clinical features. Carrión's disease has an incubation period of approximately 14 to 21 days. Symptoms of the infection include severe anemia, diarrhea, intermittent fever, headache, muscle pains, nausea, and vomiting. The skin lesions associated with the second stage may develop with or without the anemic stage. The mortality rate for untreated cases is reported to be approximately 40 per cent.

Diagnosis. *B. bacilliformis* can be cultured on a rich, semisolid nutrient agar medium containing hemoglobin and fresh rabbit serum. Blood smears stained by the Giemsa method also are utilized for diagnosis.

Relapsing Fever

Relapsing fever caused by the spirochetes of *Borrelia* (Figure 39–1) are either louse- or tick-borne infections. Louseborne disease is usually epidemic in nature and occur in the crowded conditions that develop during times of war and natural disasters. *Pediculus humanus var. capitis* and *var. vestimenti* are the louse vectors involved. The tick-borne infections are endemic and are primarily

limited to regions in which the vectors *Ornithodorus* spp. (Figure 39–2) live. Human infections with tick-borne borreliae are few, and largely confined to field workers, hunters, soldiers, and tourists.

No natural animal reservoir of *B. recurrentis* has been uncovered, although a variety of rodents have been implicated. A similar situation exists with *B. duttonii* (one of the tick-borne borreliae). A reservoir is created, however, when female ticks pass the borreliae to their eggs (transovarial passage). It should be noted that not all the larvae are necessarily infected.

Clinical features. Relapsing fever has an incubation period which varies from 3 to 10 days. The disease begins with the sudden onset of fever, which persists

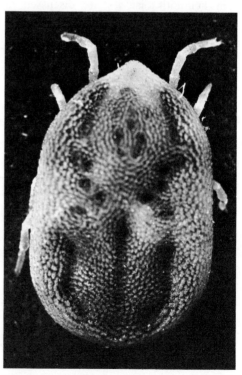

FIG. 39–2. *Ornithodorus* sp., a vector for tick-borne relapsing fever. (Courtesy of the Bureau of Vector Control, Berkeley, California.)

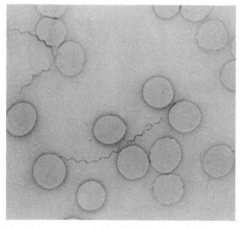

FIG. 39–1. Stained blood smear preparation of *Borrelia recurrentis.* The length of this organism can range from 8 to 40 μm and their width from 0.2 to 0.5 μm.

for approximately 4 days and ends abruptly. Large numbers of borreliae appear in the blood and urine during febrile periods, but disappear after the subsiding of the fever. Repeated febrile attacks, referred to as relapses, give the disease its name. Each of the successive episodes tends to be less severe than the previous ones, until they subside altogether. Tick-borne fevers have been reported to be more intense, shorter in duration, and involve the central nervous system more often than the louse-borne variety. In addition, the relapse episodes are greater in number.

Laboratory diagnosis. The *in vitro* cultivation of *Borrelia* spp. in artificial media has not met with appreciable success. The methods are designed for the maintenance of the organisms rather than for their multiplication.

Laboratory diagnosis is usually made from stained smears prepared from blood specimens obtained during a febrile episode (Figure 39–1). The Giemsa and Wright staining procedures are convenient for this purpose. Abnormal forms and accumulations of organisms into rosettes often are observed.

When microscopic examinations are negative, animal inoculations, utilizing either young white rats or mice, are employed. Blood specimens from patients are injected into these animals, and a spirochetemia usually will develop within 48 to 72 hours. The use of embryonated chick eggs has also been tried but certain difficulties have been encountered.

Diagnosis by serologic means has proved to be of little value.

Pasteurellosis

The genus of *Pasteurella* at one time contained four species primarily pathogenic for animals. The genus designation of two of these, *P. pestis* and *P. tularensis,* the respective etiologic agents of plague and tularemia, have been changed to *Yersinia* and *Francisella,* respectively. The other two organisms, *P. multocida* and *P. pseudo-tuberculosis,* rarely cause human infections. The diseases produced by these bacterial species are hemorrhagic septicemia and pseudo-tuberculosis pneumonia. All of these bacteria are small, non-spore-forming, Gram-negative rods.

Plague. For centuries *Yersinia pestis* has caused pandemics noted for their ravaging effects in Asia and Europe. The Great Plague, which began in 542, is believed to have been responsible for the deaths of over 100 million people in 50 years. The pandemic which reached its height of severity during the fourteenth century and became known as the Black Death has been considered the worst catastrophe to strike Europe, and perhaps the world. An estimated third of the world's population died in it. Serious outbreaks of plague continued to appear in Europe and Asia from 1360 to 1400. The name for the condition was coined because of the severe cyanosis (blue or purple color of the skin) which was observed to develop in the terminal stages of the disease. The last pandemic of the nineteenth century started in Central Asia in 1871, and spread to other parts of the world. Epidemics continue to occur occasionally in many regions of Asia and Africa. Reports of sporadic infections in South Africa, South America, and the southwestern United States have also appeared. Plague was apparently spread to South Africa from South America in 1899.

Y. pestis was identified as the causative agent of plague in 1894 by Yersin. In the same year, Kitasato also reported the finding of the plague bacillus. A certain degree of controversy, however, has developed as to the latter investigator's claim, since he reported a Gram-positive motile organism—a finding which is contrary to the current description of *Y. pestis.*

This bacterial infection primarily is a disease of rodents, both domestic and wild. However, several other mammalian species, including bats, cats, deer, kangaroos, monkeys, rabbits, and squirrels, can be infected. Recurrent epizootics apparently occur among various species of wild rodents, such as pack rats, prairie dogs, rabbits, and squirrels. This form of the disease, know as *sylvatic plague,* poses a serious threat to the well-being of man, since such infected animals are a source of disease agents for future epidemics.

Mode of transmission. The major direct sources for man are house rats, *Rattus rattus* and *R. r. diardi,* and the "ship's" rat, *R. r. alexandrinus.* Transmission of *Y. pestis* occurs through the bite of rat fleas primarily belonging to the genera of *Nosopsyllus* and *Xenopsylla.* Recent evidence has shown that the human flea, *Pulex irritans,* is the primary vector involved in bubonic plague epidemics. Infected fleas generally regurgitate microorganisms together with aspirated blood into the wound caused by their bites, and may deposit feces. *Y. pestis* does not reproduce within the tissues of the vector.

Clinical features. This disease takes two main forms in man, *bubonic plague* and *primary pneumonic plague.* In untreated cases the mortality rate for bubonic plague varies from 70 to 90 per cent. For primary pneumonic plague, it is 100 per cent. Death occurs quickly if treatment is not administered.

Bubonic plague is acquired through the bite of an infected flea. The injected microorganisms gain entrance to the re-gional lymph nodes, generally in the groin. These lymph nodes become enlarged and extremely tender, thus resulting in *bubo* formation (Figure 39–3). Such inflammed structures frequently are hemorrhagic and necrotic in appearance. The impairment of regional lymph node functioning enables the infectious agents to spread to other areas of the body via the circulation and cause secondary infections. In the event that death does not occur rapidly, internal organs such as the intestines, kidneys, liver, lungs, spleen, and occasionally the meninges also become involved. Although bubonic plague is not directly contagious from person to person, it can under certain conditions occur in epidemic proportions. This is especially the case when infected vectors have exhausted their source of rodent hosts.

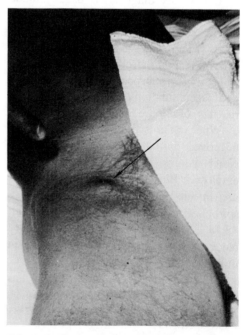

FIG. 39–3. The appearance of a plague bubo (arrow) on a victim's leg. (Courtesy of Mycology Section, Laboratory Division, Center for Disease Control, U.S. P.H.S.)

The second main form of the infection, pneumonic plague, is contagious, and it can spread directly from the infected person to uninfected persons, generally through respiratory droplets. Pneumonic plague is characterized by an acute lobar pneumonia which results in death within approximately 3 days. Cases in which pulmonary signs of infection were not noted until the apparent last day of the disease have been reported. A purple or bluish coloration of the skin (cyanosis) is a common feature of this form of plague.

Laboratory diagnosis. Specimens from infected individuals (e.g., sputum and aspirated fluid from lymph nodes) are stained by the Gram procedure and with Wayson's reagent. This reagent is a combination of the two stains carbolfuchsin and methylene blue. *Y. pestis* is a Gram-negative coccobacillus which exhibits a characteristic bipolar or "safety pin" appearance when stained by the latter method (Figure 39–4).

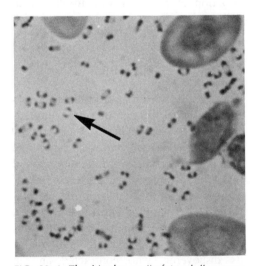

FIG. 39–4. The bipolar or "safety pin" appearance of *Yersinia* and *Pasteurella* species (spp.). (Courtesy of Drs. C. A. Manthei and K. L. Heddleston, U.S.D.A.)

Animal inoculations and the fluorescent-antibody technique also are used. The latter procedure is utilized for rapid diagnosis in plague pneumonia epidemics.

Y. pestis can be grown on blood agar. It produces acid but no gas from several carbohydrates, including galactose, glucose, levulose, maltose, and mannitol. Standard diagnostic serologic tests are not generally used for diagnosis.

Prevention. Vaccines either of an attenuated or killed type have been used to produce an artificially acquired active state of immunity. The Haffkine's vaccine, a killed preparation, is one of the most widely employed to immunize against plague.

The prophylactic use of sulfonamides also has proved effective.

Tularemia (Deer-fly fever, rabbit fever, and Ohara's disease). This infection caused by *Francisella* (*Pasteurella*) *tularensis* was first reported as occurring in ground squirrels from Tulare County, California (hence its name) by McCoy in 1911. One year later, McCoy and Chapin isolated and described the etiologic agent. The first human case of the disease was reported in 1914.

Mode of transmission. Man acquires tularemia by (1) handling the infected carcasses or rabbits (Figure 39–5*A*); (2) the bites of infected flies and ticks (*Amblyomma* spp. and *Dermacentor* spp.); (3) inhalation of infectious aerosols; or (4) contact with water contaminated by the bodies of infected rodents, e.g., beavers and water rats. Infections also have resulted from the bites of animals which have fed on diseased rabbits.

Clinical features. The incubation for tularemia varies from 3 to 10 days. Symptoms associated with the infection's onset include fever, headache, and general malaise. An ulcerating papule is often observed at the primary site of entry in the skin or mucous membranes (Figure 39–5B). The infectious agents gain access to the regional lymph nodes, which consequently enlarge, and may suppurate. Involvement of other tissues and organs, including the brain, liver, lungs, and spleen, occurs with the hematogenous spread of the microorganisms. Several

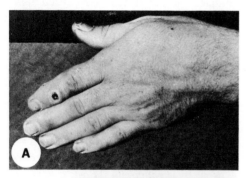

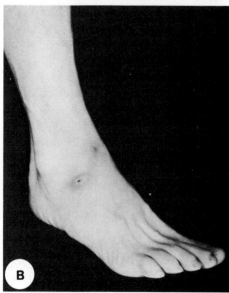

FIG. 39–5. Manifestations of tularemia. _A_. An infection resulting from the handling of an infected rabbit carcass. _B_. Site of primary involvement, in all probability resulting from an infected arthropod bite. (Courtesy of the Armed Forces Institute of Pathology, Washington, D.C., Neg. Nos. 85387–2 and AN 1147–1A.)

different forms of tularemia are known, including oculoglandular, pneumonic, typhoidal, and ulceroglandular.

Diagnosis. The causative organism of tularemia cannot be cultured on ordinary laboratory media. The amino acid cystine must be supplied. Media of choice include cystine-glucose-blood agar and coagulated egg yolk medium.

A definite identification of this Gram-negative organism is usually made with the aid of the fluorescent-antibody technique. Generally, the procedure is carried out with smear preparations of exudate taken from patients. Agglutination tests employing specific antisera also can be used.

Immunity. Generally speaking, recovery from tularemia produces a relatively permanent, naturally acquired active state of immunity in the victim. However, second episodes of infection have been reported. Relapses occur with tularemia even though high antibody titers are present in the infected individual. This situation is probably due to the intracellular location of the organisms, which prevents access to them by antibodies.

Rickettsia

The first discovery of rickettsia was largely a consequence of certain investigations by Ricketts in 1909 (Figure 39–6). While studying various aspects of the so-called Rocky Mountain spotted fever he observed the presence of extremely small, distinct, rod-like formations in the blood of patients and certain associated ticks. This pathogen later was named *Rickettsia rickettsii,* in honor of its discoverer, who contracted and in 1910 died of typhus fever.

Investigators in many countries extended the original discovery of rickettsia in the following 40 years to the point of

FIG. 39–6. Dr. H. T. Ricketts (1871–1910). (Courtesy of the National Library of Medicine, Bethesda, Maryland.)

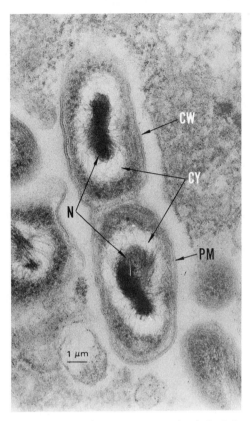

FIG. 39–7. An electron micrograph of *Coxiella burnetii* from a purified yolk sac suspension. The microorganism can be seen undergoing binary fission. Explanation of symbols: *CW*, cell wall; *CY*, cytoplasm; *N*, nucleus-like structure; *PM*, plasma membrane. (Courtesy of Drs. P. Burton and D. Paretsky, University of Kansas.)

describing over 30 varieties of these microorganisms pathogenic for man and lower animals. Moreover, several of these investigations have provided techniques for the isolation and cultivation of rickettsia, as well as methods for their identification and control, including vaccines and insecticides against vectors.

Rickettsia, as mentioned in Chapter 4, generally are described as small, obligate, intracellular parasites. With one known exception thus far—namely, *Rochalimaea quintana*, the causative agent of trench fever—rickettsia cannot be grown in a cell-free medium. These microorganisms grow well in the yolk sac of chick embryos, in certain laboratory animals, and in cell cultures. Depending upon the species, multiplication of rickettsia occurs in either the cytoplasmic or nuclear region of an infected cell. Division occurs by binary fission (Figure 39–7).

Morphologically, rickettsia are pleomorphic, and appear as rods or coccobacilli (Figure 39–8). These microorganisms are believed to be bacteria because of certain characteristics, including: (1) their Gram-negative nature; (2) the presence of at least 4 or 5 amino acids in the cell wall; (3) the possession of both DNA and RNA; (4) the inhibition of growth by several antibiotic substances; and (5) the presence of certain enzymes not derived from the host cell (e.g., enzymes associated with electron transport, the Krebs cycle, and protein synthesis). Electron microscopic studies (Figure 39–7) have clearly shown rickettsia to possess a cell wall, granular cytoplasm, near-central structures (presumably nuclei), and a plasma membrane.

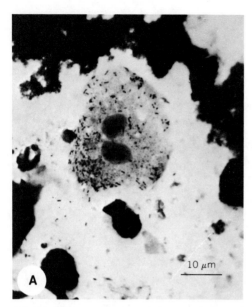

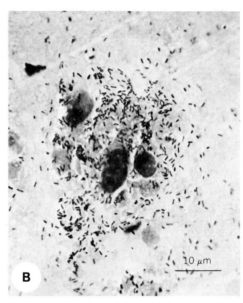

FIG. 39–8. Two examples of the morphological appearance of rickettsia in stained preparations. *A. Rickettsia australis*, the causative agent of North Queensland tick typhus. The preparation shown is from mouse peritoneum. *B. R. conorii*, the causative agent of Boutonneuse fever, in a smear prepared from an infected chick embryo yolk sac. (Courtesy of the Rocky Mountain Laboratory, U.S. Public Health Service, Hamilton, Montana.)

Transmission. One of the distinctive features of the majority of rickettsia is that their transmission, under natural conditions, is dependent upon a variety of arthropods (e.g., fleas, lice, mites, and ticks) (Table 39–2). An exception to this mode of spread is Q fever, which is primarily a droplet-transmitted infection. As multiplication of the rickettsial agents occurs in the arthropods responsible for their transmission, the arthropods can be considered as true natural vectors. Man is the only vertebrate reservoir for the rickettsia causing Brill's relapsing typhus (Brill's disease), epidemic typhus, and trench fever. In all other rickettsioses man acts as an accidental host only (Table 39–2). Therefore, the rickettsial diseases, with the exceptions previously noted, are zoonoses.

General clinical features. Most rickettsial infections involve the circulatory system. Effects that may develop during the course of a rickettsial infection include abortion, endocarditis, involvement of the central nervous system, kidney, and liver, inflammation of arteries, maculopapular rash, stupor, and terminal shock. Although no specific rickettsial toxin has been isolated, it is generally assumed that these and other effects must be caused by such a toxin substance. The particular clinical features of the various rickettsioses will be discussed in the sections concerned with the specific diseases.

Serologic tests. Procedures that can be employed in the diagnosis of rickettsial infections include complement-fixation, toxin neutralization tests, and the Weil-Felix test, which came into being during World War I. In 1916, Weil and Felix noted that the sera of epidemic typhus fever patients agglutinated the cells of a particular strain of the bacterium *Proteus*. It should be noted that urinary infections with *Proteus* spp. can cause the

Table 39–2 Selected Characteristics of Representative Rickettsioses Involving Man

Group Category and Disease	Etiologic Agent	Principal Vector or Means of Transmission	Geographical Distribution	Mammals Concerned in Normal Cycle
Louse-Borne Group				
Epidemic typhus	R. prowazekii	Pediculus capitis, P. corporis	Worldwide	Humans
Brill's disease	R. prowazekii	None	Europe, North America	Humans
Trench fever	Rochalimaea quintana	P. corporis	Africa, Europe, North America	Humans
_____a	R. canada	Haemaphysalis leporispalustris (tick)	Eastern Canada	Humans
Flea-Borne Group				
Endemic (murine) typhus	R. mooseri (typhi)	Xenopsyllus cheopis (rat flea)	Worldwide	Rodents
Tick-Borne Group				
Boutonneuse fever	R. conorii	Amblyomma variegatum, Rhipicephalus sanguineus, others	Africa, Europe, India, Middle East	Dogs, wild rodents
Queensland tick	R. australis	Ixodes holocyclus	Australia	Marsupials, wild rodents
Rocky Mountain spotted fever	R. rickettsii	Amblyomma spp., Dermocentor spp., Rhipicephalus sanguineus	Western hemisphere	Dogs, wild rodents
Mite-Borne Group				
Rickettsialpox	R. akari	Allodermanyssus sanguineus	Europe, North America	Wild rodents
Tsutsugamushi fever (scrub typhus)	R. tsutsugamushi (R. orientalis)	Trombicula spp.	Asia, Australia, Pacific Islands	Wild rodents
Q fever	Coxiella burnetii (R. burnetii)	Primarily droplet infection, although certain species of ticks have been implicated	Worldwide	Cattle, goats, sheep, wild rodents

NOTE: The specific rickettsial infections listed are arranged according to the arthropod vectors. This approach is one of the more commonly employed.

a The disease has not been named.

production of similar antibodies. It is important to keep this point in mind. The strains used were formerly isolated from the urine of similarly infected patients. Originally, the bacterial strain was designated as X-19. However, it was later learned that the somatic (O) antigen was involved in the reaction, hence the label OX-19. Additional strains, OX-2 and OX-K (Kingsburg), were subsequently found and utilized in the diagnosis of the rickettsioses. Table 39–3 lists the characteristic Weil-Felix reactions of selected rickettsial agents. In situations where the Weil-Felix reaction is not of significance in differentiating between certain rickettsial infections, other tests must be used. Direct immunofluorescent antibody tests are used for presumptive clinical diagnosis.

The use of chick embryo tissues for the cultivation of Rickettsia spp. has been proved to be valuable in several respects. Sensitive and reproducible plaque assay systems using chick embryo monolayers have been reported, which can be used to distinguish among certain groups of these microorganisms (Figure 39–9). In

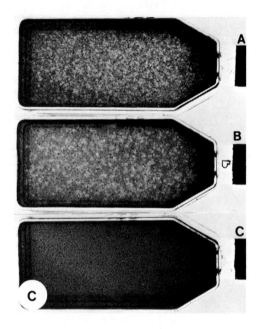

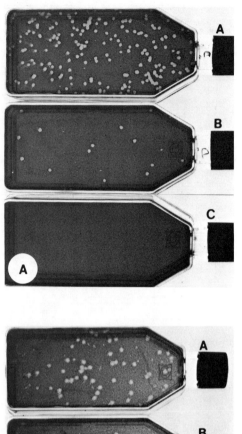

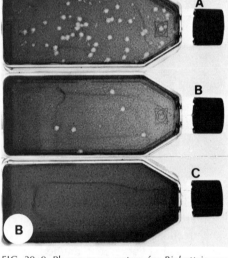

FIG. 39–9. Plaque assay system for *Rickettsia* spp. using chick embryo monolayers. *A*. Plaques formed by *R. conorii* (spotted fever group), the causative agent of Bountonneuse fever. *B*. The plaques produced by another spotted fever group member, *R. australis*. *C*. The plaques produced by *R. prowazekii* Breinl, a typhus group rickettsiae. The cultures from *A* to *B* contain lessening concentrations of organisms. An uninfected control (*C*) is at the bottom of each series. (From McDade, J. E., Stakebake, J. R., and Gerone, P. J.: *J. Bacteriol.,* **99**:910–912, 1969.)

general, members of a particular group produce similar plaque morphology.

The plaque assay technique has an additional advantage which has only recently been reported. With the aid of this method, it is more convenient to determine the antibiotic susceptibility of rickettsiae (Figure 39–10). The procedure appears to have great promise in several areas, including clinical and diagnostic microbiology, genetic studies, and the evaluation of new antibiotics.

Treatment.   Several chemotherapeutic agents have been found to be relatively effective in the treatment of certain rickettsial diseases; these include chloramphenicol doxycycline and erythromycin. Unfortunately, these drugs stop rickettsial growth, but do not kill the organisms.

Louse-Borne Typhus Fevers

As indicated in Table 39–2, three distinct disease entities are grouped under louse-borne rickettsial diseases—epidemic typhus, Brill's disease, and trench fever.

Table 39–3   Weil-Felix Reaction Patterns
of Selected Rickettsia

Rickettsial Species	Antigen Preparation[a]		
	OX-19	OX-2	OX-K
R. prowazekii	++	+	–
Rochalimaea quintana	–	–	–
R. mooseri	++	+	–
R. conorii	+	±	–
R. australis	+	±	–
R. tsutsugamushi	–	–	+
R. akari	–	–	–
Coxiella burnetii	–	–	–

[a] Explanation of symbols: ++ = an intense agglutination reaction; + = positive for agglutination; ± = variable reaction, but generally positive; – = negative response.

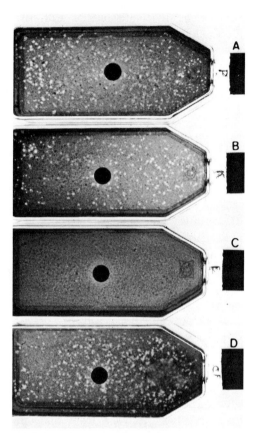

FIG. 39–10. Antibiotic sensitivity of *R. prowazekii* Breinl, as determined by the effect of antibiotics on plaque formation. From top to bottom antibiotic discs (dark circles) containing the following antibiotics and concentrations have been used in this test: *A*, penicillin (10 units); *B*, kanamycin (5 micrograms); *C*, erythromycin (15 micrograms), and *D*, cephalothin (30 micrograms). Note the marked effect of erythromycin. (From McDade, J. E.: *Appl. Microbiol.*, **18**:133–135, 1969.)

Both epidemic typhus and trench fever are associated with louse-infested individuals and the recent bites of infected lice. Brill's disease, on the other hand, is a clinical entity of a relapsing or sporadic nature which develops in persons who are not currently louse-infested. The rickettsial species *Rickettsia prowazekii* causes both epidemic typhus and Brill's disease. *Rochalimaea quintana* is the etiologic agent for trench fever.

Epidemic typhus fever.   The occurrence of *R. prowazekii* is traditionally linked to natural disasters, especially severe winters, famine, and war. In all of these situations, people are overcrowded and find it difficult to maintain adequate personal hygiene. The opportunities to bathe and wash clothes are limited. This provides an environment for body lice to flourish and for the transmission of typhus fever.

The transmission of epidemic typhus involves a man-to-louse-to-man cycle. The disease can develop in persons of any age. However, the effects of the infection are more severe in older individuals. Generally, under natural conditions the rickettsia are introduced into humans as a consequence of the body or head louse obtaining a blood meal. While the arthropod feeds, it defecates, thus releasing fecal matter containing infective organisms. As the bite of the louse causes an extreme itching sensation, the natural tendency is to scratch the affected area, and thereby inoculate oneself with the infectious feces. Although this is the way in which epidemic typhus is usually contracted, it is also possible to acquire an infection by inhaling dried, infected louse fecal matter, or having it blow into the eye, across the conjunctiva.

Clinical features. Typhus usually has an incubation period of approximately 10 to 12 days after a bite of an infected louse. Symptoms develop suddenly and include backache, chills, fever (ranging from 102° to 105°F), and general aches and pains. A rash, macular at first and later developing into a maculopapular form, occurs by the fourth to sixth day on the trunk (Figure 39–11) and spreads to the arms and legs. The face, palms, and soles are generally not involved.

In severe forms of the disease, prostration, renal insufficiency, and stupor have been reported. Complications may also develop, including secondary bacterial infections, encephalitis, and gangrene of the extremities. Recovery from epidemic typhus produces an immune state which also provides protection against endemic (flea-borne) typhus.

Laboratory diagnosis. Diagnosis is primarily by serological tests, e.g., complement-fixation and Weil-Felix tests.

Differentiation between *R. prowazekii* and *R. typhi* (*mooseri*), the causative agent of flea-borne typhus, may be necessary in certain cases. This can be accomplished by noting the differences in effects produced in laboratory animals (e.g., male guinea pigs, hamsters, and white rats) and toxin neutralization in mice. In male guinea pigs *R. typhi* produces a scrotal swelling while *R. prowazekii* does not.

Brill's disease. The first description of this disease was made in 1898 by Nathan

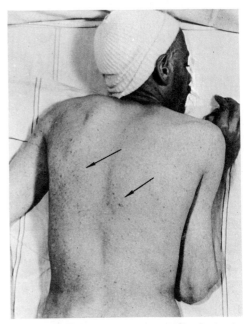

FIG. 39–11. Rash manifestation on the back of a victim of epidemic typhus. (Courtesy of the Armed Forces Institute of Pathology, Washington, D.C., Neg. No. 60–1001A.)

Brill. Individuals with the condition were mainly immigrants to the United States, and at the time of attack were not found to be louse-infested. Furthermore, several of these patients had a history of previous attacks of typhus. In 1934, the true nature of the clinical entity was provided by Zinsser, who showed the disease to be a relapsed state of a previously acquired *R. prowazekii* attack. This infection is also known as Brill-Zinsser disease, recrudescent epidemic typhus, or sporadic typhus.

Clinical features. The symptoms of the disease are generally milder and not as long-lasting as those of classic epidemic typhus.

Laboratory diagnosis. This is generally based on the isolation of *R. prowazekii* in guinea pigs, and serologic testing, e.g., agglutination and complement-fixation.

The Weil-Felix test appears to be negative quite often.

Trench fever.   This rickettsial disease, also known as His-Werner disease, Polish-Russian intermittent fever, and shank or shin fever, is commonly associated with wartime conditions, primarily during World War I and II. However, it has also been reported in Mexico and Tunisia. The transmission of the disease occurs in a manner similar to that described for epidemic typhus.

Clinical features.   The symptoms associated with the infection include chills, exhaustion, dizziness, fever (102° to 103°F), headache, pain in the shins and thighs, and pain behind the eyes. A rash also appears with the fever, but disappears within a few days.

Laboratory diagnosis.   The diagnosis is based on the recovery of *Rochalimeae quintana* from the feces of healthy lice allowed to feed on infected persons. This type of procedure is known as *xenodiagnosis* and is also used with certain protozoan infections, such as Chagas' disease. The Weil-Felix reaction is negative (Table 39–3).

Flea-Borne (Murine) Typhus Fever

This rickettsiosis is caused by *R. typhi.* It is found mainly in tropical and subtropical regions. However, as this disease is common in rats, the infection can occur wherever these rodents and the tropic rat flea *Xenopsyllus cheopsis* exist. Localities such as granaries, storehouses, and waterfront areas are likely candidates for the breeding sites of these animals.

The general transmission cycle of endemic typhus is from an infected rat to a flea to another rat. Man acquires the infection accidently; if a susceptible rat is not available, the infected rat flea uses man as its new host. Rickettsia are introduced into a susceptible human by the contamination of an infected flea bite with feces containing the infectious agents. This is a process similar to that described for epidemic (louse-borne) typhus.

Clinical features.   The symptoms of *R. typhi* are quite similar to those encountered in epidemic typhus. However, in general, they are much milder. The most characteristic feature is a severe headache.

Diagnosis.   Diagnosis of *R. typhi* infection includes laboratory animal inoculations and serologic tests.

The Tick-Borne Rickettsial Diseases

Several rickettsial infections are transmitted by ticks (Table 39–2). Rocky Mountain spotted fever was one of the first of such diseases described. Consequently, its manifestations were utilized as a basis for the classification of tick-borne rickettsial infections, and the category or division of the spotted fever group was named after it. In addition to specific antigenic characteristics, the tick-borne rickettsial species that cause spotted fevers have the characteristic feature of undergoing multiplication in both the cytoplasmic and nuclear regions of infected cells (Figure 39–12). Other rickettsia pathogenic for man reproduce only in the cytoplasm of cells.

Rocky Mountain spotted fever.   This disease, caused by *R. rickettsii,* was first recognized during the 1870s in Montana. Dogs, field mice, hares, rabbits, and squirrels all serve as reservoirs. Moreover, the tick vector itself serves as a reservoir, transmitting the rickettsial agents to future generations of ticks through transovarial passage. Representative tick vectors (Figure 39–13) and the

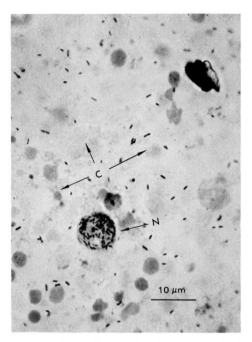

FIG. 39–12. *R. rickettsii.* Note the appearance of these rickettsia in both the cytoplasmic (C) and nuclear (N) cellular regions. (Courtesy of the Rocky Mountain Laboratory, U.S. Public Health Service, Hamilton, Montana.)

geographic regions involved are shown in Table 39–4.

Clinical features. Clinically this disease resembles typhus fever, except that the pattern of the rash's appearance begins peripherally, i.e., on the ankles, forehead, and wrists (Figure 39–14), and then spreads to the trunk. This is the reverse of the sequence of rash development observed with epidemic typhus fever.

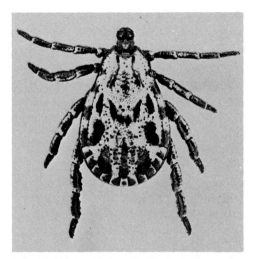

FIG. 39–13. An adult male *Dermacentor andersoni,* the Rocky Mountain wood tick. (Courtesy of the Rocky Mountain Laboratory, U.S. Public Health Service, Hamilton, Montana.)

Laboratory diagnosis. Diagnosis is based on the results obtained with complement-fixation tests and animal inoculations. The latter procedure is used to differentiate Rocky Mountain spotted fever from endemic and epidemic typhus fevers.

Mite-Borne Rickettsial Diseases

Tsutsugamushi fever (scrub typhus). This infection is an example of a zoonosis associated with rodents. The etiologic agent, *R. tsutsugamushi* (Figure 39–15), is also known as *R. orientalis.* Man acquires the disease when he is bitten by infected mites, *Trombicula akamushi*

Table 39–4   Representative Tick Vectors of Rocky Mountain Spotted Fever

Tick Species	Common Name	Geographic Region
Amblyomma americum	Lone Star tick	Southern United States
A. cajennense	Dog tick	Central and South America
Dermacentor andersoni	Rocky Mountain wood tick	Rocky Mountain areas, Canada
D. variabilis	American dog tick	Eastern United States
Rhipicephalus sanguineus	Brown dog tick	Central and South America

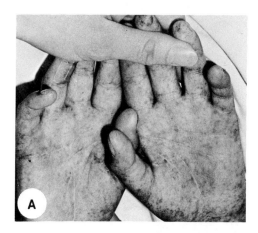

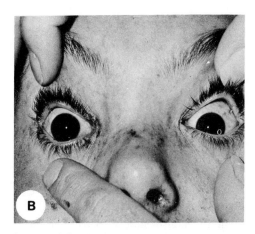

FIG. 39–14. Clinical features of Rocky Mountain spotted fever in children. *A*. The presence of a severe rash on a patient's hands. The skin on the fingertips of this child later became gangrenous. In general, the rash is most severe on the palms of the hands and soles of the feet. *B*. Another feature of the disease is conjunctivitis, regularly noted in children. The photograph also shows the petechial rash of the face and hemorrhagic crusts in the nose. (From Haynes, R. H., Sanders, D. Y., and Cramblett, H. G., Jr.: *J. Pediatrics*, **76**:685–693, 1970.)

(Figure 39–16), and other *Trombicula* species.

Clinical features. Scrub typhus usually has an incubation period ranging from 10 to 20 days after the bite of an infected mite. The primary lesion, an *eschar* (a localized necrotic lesion in the epidermis, extending into the dermis) develops 3 to 4 days before the acute symptoms of the disease. Clinical features of this infection resemble those of the typhus fevers. Complications such as deafness, mental disturbances, and polyneuritis can also occur.

Laboratory diagnosis. Laboratory diagnosis include serological tests (e.g., agglutination, complement-fixation, and Weil-Felix tests), inoculation of ground blood clot material into white mice, and

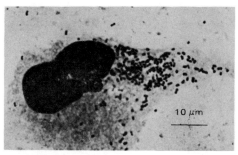

FIG. 39–15. *R. tsutsugamuchi* in a guinea pig testes smear preparation. Note the diplomorphological feature of the organisms. (Courtesy of the Rocky Mountain Laboratory, U.S. Public Health Service, Hamilton, Montana.)

FIG. 39–16. *Trombicula akamushi,* the mite vector for tsutsugamushi fever. (Courtesy of the Rocky Mountain Laboratory, U.S. Public Health Service, Hamilton, Montana.)

examination of stained smears of blood, cerebrospinal fluid, and urine. The Weil-Felix reaction for the OXK antigen is generally positive for *R. tsutsugamushi*.

Rickettsialpox. *R. akari* (Figure 39–17) is the causative agent for this rickettsial infection. The disease was first reported in 1946. Man acquires the infectious agents through the bite of a common mouse mite, *Allodermanyssus sanguineus* (Figure 39–18). In the U.S. the usual host for *A. sanguineus* is the common house mouse *Mus musculus*. Although *R. akari* is not transmitted by ticks, it is still grouped with other rickettsia comprising the Rocky Mountain spotted fever category of disease, because it shares several properties in common with the group, including antigenicity and pattern of multiplication.

Clinical features. Rickettsialpox has an approximate incubation period of 10 days after the bite of an infected mite. A small, hard, red lesion appears at the site which becomes a blister and eventually results in a scab. Within a week or so, symptoms of the disease suddenly appear and include backache, chills, fever (which may reach 104°F), and rash. The latter manifestation does not have a characteristic development or a distribution pattern, unlike epidemic typhus and Rocky Mountain spotted fever. Rickettsialpox has, at times, been misdiagnosed as chickenpox.

Laboratory diagnosis. Laboratory diagnosis involves the inoculation of infectious material (e.g., blood from the patients and blood obtained from diseased mice or the mite vector) into laboratory white mice. Passage of resulting organisms is carried out in the yolk sacs of embryonated chick eggs, or in the guinea pig.

Complement-fixation tests are used in

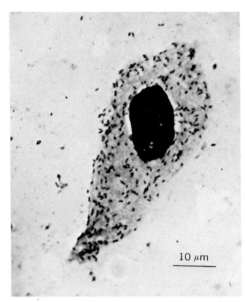

FIG. 39–17. *R. akari*, the causative agent of rickettsialpox. (Courtesy of the Rocky Mountain Laboratory, U.S. Public Health Service, Hamilton, Montana.)

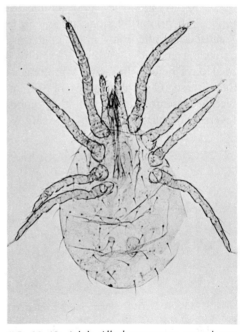

FIG. 39–18. Adult *Allodermanyssus sanguineus*. (Courtesy of the Rocky Mountain Laboratory, U.S. Public Health Service, Hamilton, Montana.)

convalescence, as the Weil-Felix reaction is negative due to the absence of specific antibodies.

Q ("Query") fever. This zoonotic rickettsial infection was first described in 1933 by Derrick in Australia. The etiologic agent for the disease is *R. burnetii,* also called *Coxiella burnettii.* Arthropods do not play a major role in the disease's transmission to man. Ticks are, however, considered important to the maintenance of the cycle of infection in wild rodents. Human infections occur through the inhalation of infectious discharges (droplet transmission) from diseased cattle, goats, and sheep. Infection thus can be either directly or indirectly acquired. Milk and eggs also have been incriminated in disease cycles.

Clinical features. Q fever has an approximate incubation period of 2 weeks. As in the case of other rickettsial infections, the onset of the disease is sudden. Symptoms associated with the disease include dry cough, fever (103° to 105°F), headache, and stiffness. A rash does not develop. Complications are unusual.

Laboratory diagnosis. Serologic tests, e.g., agglutination and complement-fixation tests, are performed with appropriate specimens, such as sera of humans and other animals, and from milk. Animal inoculations also utilize such specimens for the isolation of *R. burnetii.* In addition, serological testing should be carried out for purpose of differentiating Q fever manifestations from psittacosis and streptococcal infections.

The Arboviruses (Arthropod-Borne)

General Characteristics

At the present time well over 180 arboviruses have been reported. In all probability a sizeable number of these disease agents still remains to be isolated. (A new viral agent, the cause of Lassa fever, has been recently reported. Although little is known of its means of transmission, the possibility does exist that it is an arbovirus.) Historically, as a result of investigations by the U.S. Army Yellow Fever Commission headed by Major Walter Reed, the first arbovirus was discovered in 1901. Pursuing earlier findings, largely the observations of the Cuban physician Carlos Finlay, Reed and his colleagues Agramonte, Carroll, and Lazear clearly demonstrated not only the relationship of the mosquito *Aëdes aegypti* to the transmission of yellow fever but established the existence of the first human viral pathogen.

The arboviruses exhibit a unique capability in that they can multiply within the tissues of vertebrates and of certain blood-sucking arthropods. Viruses of this group, following their inoculation into the tissues of a susceptible vertebrate, multiply rapidly and soon produce a viral titer in the blood (*viremia*). In cases of human and certain lower animal infections, the virus may localize in the central nervous system of the host, which can result in extensive viral multiplication, tissue injury, encephalitis, and eventually death.

The general characteristics of this group of animal viruses include: (1) the possession of ribonucleic acid as the only form of nuclei acid; (2) enveloped virions with diameters ranging from 45 to 70 nm; (3) sensitivity to lipid solvents; and (4) ability to agglutinate erythrocytes of adult geese or newborn chickens under limited conditions associated with pH and temperature. On the basis of selected chemical and physical characteristics, an orderly grouping of a large number of arboviruses is emerging. In addition, several viruses initially isolated from arthropods have been removed from the arboviruses and have been placed into well established families such as the picornaviruses (coxsackie and polioviruses) and the reoviruses (respiratory agents). About 250 arboviruses are recognized at present. These viruses are arranged into the major groups A and B, the supergroup Bunyamwera, and several minor groups. The Bunyamwera supergroup includes the Bunyamwera C and California encephalitis groups (Table 39–5). Specific antigenic properties are also used for classification purposes. For example, viruses in groups A and B are classified on the basis of hemagglutination inhibition reactions (HAI), while those agents in group C are classified by their complement-fixation reactions. Additional characteristics of selected groups will be presented.

Group A Arboviruses

This group of viruses contains several pathogens that can cause severe encephalitis. A wide range of vertebrates and arthropods can be involved in their life cycles; these include domestic fowl, horses, man, rodents, snakes, and wild birds. Humans generally are considered to be only incidental hosts. Horses do not appear to be significant natural reservoirs either. Birds, however, are primary hosts, while snakes and certain rodents probably are secondary reservoirs for some members of this group of viruses. The majority of group A arboviruses are transmitted by mosquitoes. Hibernating mosquitoes have been reported to harbor viruses for several months.

Two general types of clinical syndrome have been observed with these viruses. One form, which is found with EEE, VEE, and WEE, consists of both a "systemic phase" with chills, fever, headache, and vomiting, and an "encephalitic phase" with stupor or coma, perhaps followed by slight paralysis. The second form is characterized by the systemic phase only.

Laboratory diagnosis of group A arbovirus infections usually involves viral isolation and serological tests, which include hemagglutination inhibition and neutralization tests.

Group B Arboviruses

This group of viruses is composed of at least 36 prototype strains. Most of these arboviruses are transmitted by culicine (*Culex*) mosquitoes, exhibit a host range and initial stages of pathogenesis similar to that of group A agents, and produce variable clinical syndromes. The viruses that comprise the Russian spring-summer complex are transmitted by ixodid ticks; other arthropods also have been implicated. Group B infections may produce three types of symptomatology: (1) acute central nervous system involvement manifested by encephalitis with death; (2) severe systemic illness affecting important visceral organs, including the kidneys and the liver; and (3) a milder form of systemic involvement characterized by fever, a rash, and severe muscle pains. Subclinical infections can also be produced by these viruses.

The diagnosis of group B arbovirus infection generally incorporates viral isolation techniques and serological testing.

Group C Arboviruses

This group of at least 11 viral agents is immunologically distinct from the other arbovirus groups. Animals implicated as natural reservoirs, on the basis of epidemiological investigations, include monkeys, oppossums, rats, and sloths. The full range of mosquito vectors has not been fully determined. Laboratory diagnosis involving virus isolations utilizes suckling and newly-weaned mice.

Table 39–5   Representative Groups of the Arbovirus

Group Designation	Disease	Vector M=Mosquito; Mi=Mite; P=Phlebotomus (Sandfly); T=Tick	Geographic Distribution
A[a]	Eastern equine encephalitis (EEE)	M	Argentina, Brazil, Dominican Republic, Guyana, Panama, Trinidad, United States
	Venezuelan equine encephalitis (VEE)	M	Brazil, Colombia, Equador, Panama, Trinidad, Venezuela
	Western equine encephalitis (WEE)	M	Argentina, Brazil, Canada, Guyana, Mexico, United States
B[a]	Dengue fever	M	Australia, Greece, New Guinea, Pacific Islands, Southeast Asia
	Japanese B encephalitis	M	Eastern Asian Mainland, Guam, India, Japan, Malaya
	Russian spring-summer encephalitis	T	Northern European Russia, Siberia
	Yellow fever	M	Africa, Central and South America, Trinidad
Bunyamwera	Bunyamwera	M	South Africa, Uganda
	Germiston	M	South Africa
	Guaroa	M	Brazil, Colombia
C	Apeu	M	Brazil
	Marituba	M	Panama
California encephalitis	California encephalitis	M	California
	Jamestown Canyon	M	Colorado
	Keystone	M	Florida
	Trivittatus	M	Florida, North Dakota
Changuinola	Changuinola	P	Panama
Phlebotomus fever	I-58	P	Iran
	Naples phlebotomus fever	P	Italy, Middle East, West Pakistan
Ungrouped diseases	Colorado tick fever	T	Western United States
	Hughes	T	Florida
Tacaribe	Junin	Mi	Argentina
	Lagos bat	?	Nigeria
	Lassa fever	?	Nigeria
	Rift Valley fever	M	Africa
	Tacaribe	M	Trinidad
	Uukuniemi	T	Finland

NOTE: Most of the groups listed contain many more viral agents than listed. This is only a representative sampling of both arbovirus groups and disease agents.

[a] These viruses are considered to be in one family and are referred to as Toga viruses (L. *toga*=coat).

Control of Arthropod-Transmitted Diseases

The control measures used for the majority of diseases discussed in this chapter are directed against the arthropod vectors (lice, mites, mosquitoes, sandflies, and ticks). This usually involves the use of insecticides, natural predators, and other functional means. Eradication programs designed to destroy the breeding sites or structures which provide protection are necessary to reduce the reproduction rates of vectors. Measures of this type will decrease successive generations.

Control measures also involve attacks on the reservoirs of infectious agents. This can be done through the use of traps and professional hunters. Furthermore, effective vaccines also can be used as prophylactic measures. Diseases such as certain rickettsial infections and yellow fever fall into this category.

QUESTIONS FOR REVIEW

1. What is relapsing fever?

2. What types of specimens are used in the diagnosis of:
   a. bartonellosis
   b. bubonic plague
   c. relapsing fever
   d. Rocky Mountain spotted fever
   e. pneumonic plague
   f. western equine encephalitis

3. Define or explain the following terms:
   a. sylvatic plague
   b. vector
   c. bubonic plague
   d. louse-borne relapsing fever
   e. pneumonic plague
   f. Brill's disease
   g. bubo
   h. Oroya fever

4. List the vectors and reservoirs for the following diseases.
   a. relapsing fever
   b. Q fever
   c. pneumonic plague
   d. Rocky Mountain spotted fever
   e. sylvatic plague
   f. eastern equine encephalitis
   g. epidemic typhus
   h. tsutsugamushi fever
   i. rickettsialpox
   j. tularemia

5. Characteristize the rickettsia. What distinguishing properties do these microorganisms possess?

6. Do rickettsia resemble viruses or bacteria more closely? Explain.

7. What effective methods are used in the control of the vectors and reservoirs associated with the diseases discussed in this chapter?

8. What are the distinguishing features of the arboviruses?

9. Which of the arthropod-borne diseases mentioned in this chapter are found in your immediate geographical area? What measures are utilized to control mosquito populations in your area?

10. What laboratory procedures are used in the diagnosis of the following diseases?
    a. pneumonic plague
    b. Q fever
    c. tularemia
    d. arbovirus infections

e. relapsing fever
f. bartonellosis
g. endemic typhus
h. tsutsugamushi fever

11. Are vaccines available for the arthropod-borne diseases? If so, indicate which diseases and the type or types of preparations (killed or attenuated).

12. Explain or define zoonosis.

13. What is an epizootic disease?

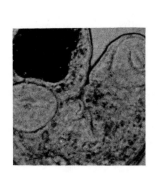

An Introduction to Medical Parasitology

DIVISION 8: Behavioral Objectives

After reading the chapters in this division, the individual should be able to:

1. Describe the structural properties and the major features of life cycles of medically important protozoa and helminths.

2. List the means of transmission for parasitic protozoa and helminths.

3. Summarize the commonly employed methods for the control and prevention of human protozoan and helminthic diseases.

4. Recognize the properties of medically important protozoa and helminths that are diagnostically significant.

Microorganisms and Oncogenesis

All the tissues of the human body are composed of individual cells of varying microscopic size. These cells must be able to divide and to reproduce in an exact and orderly manner for the well-being of the body to be maintained. Normal cell growth is inhibited by crowding: when sufficient cells have been produced in a given area, intercellular controls operate to stop further growth, a property called *contact inhibition*. If cellular reproduction becomes uncontrolled, growths or swellings, called *neoplasms* or *tumors,* develop. Tumors that form in a localized area and do not spread to other parts of the body are referred to as being *benign*. Growths that reproduce progressively in an unrestricted fashion and spread to other body regions are called *malignant* or *cancerous*. Cancer cells spread from one part of the body to others either by invading and destroying the normal tissue surrounding the malignancy (a direct extension process) or by *metastasis,* which involves the separation of cells from the major portion of a tumor and the spread of these cells to new sites.

Cancers have been recognized by physicians for several centuries. In ancient times they were relatively rare, and they remained a fairly insignificant cause of death until the present century. Today, however, cancers are the cause of approximately 16 percent of all deaths in the United States, and the figure is even higher in many European countries. This great increase, especially in the past few decades, is due in part to improved detection procedures and to environmental causes. The effects of environmental agents on human health is currently a subject of considerable interest. Of special concern to scientists are the long-term effects of chemical, physical, and microbial agents and, more specifically, their possible *oncogenic* (tumor-causing) and *carcinogenic* (cancer-producing) effects. Many factors have been recognized as being capable of modifying cellular nucleic acids and possessing carcinogenic potential.

Microbiology has had a great impact on several aspects of present-day cancer research. For example, certain microbial products have been shown to have cancer inhibitory (*carcinostatic*) properties. Moreover, recent progress in the understanding of the neoplastic process and its prevention has come from work with microorganisms and their interactions with respective hosts. This chapter will describe a limited number of aspects of tumor production and malignancy with which microorganisms have been associated. Consideration will first be given to basic terms.

The Forms of Human Cancer

It is not yet clear whether the condition referred to as cancer consists of several diseases having a common pattern of general symptoms or a single disease that can occur in many forms depending primarily upon the tissue from which it evolves. In any case, more than 100 clinically distinct types of cancer are recognized, each having a unique set of specific symptoms and requiring a specific course of therapy. These types can, however, be grouped into four major categories: carcinomas, leukemia, lymphomas, and sarcomas.

Carcinomas

These are solid tumors derived from epithelial tissues such as breasts, glands, skin, nerves, and the linings of the gastrointestinal, genital, respiratory, and urinary systems. Epithelial tissues comprise the internal and external body surface coverings and their derivatives.

Leukemia

This condition, also referred to as cancer of the blood, is characterized by the uncontrolled proliferation and accumulation of leukocytes (white blood cells). Just as there are many different types of leukocytes, there are many different types of leukemia. These include (1) acute and chronic lymphocytic leukemias (lymphoblastic leukemias), which are malignancies of lymphocytes (cells produced in the lymphoid organs—the spleen, lymph nodes, and thymus—and in the bone marrow) and (2) acute and chronic myelocytic leukemias (granulocytic or myelogenous leukemias), which are disorders of granulocytes. Granulocytes, produced by bone marrow, engulf and digest bacteria and other small particles.

Acute leukemias generally appear suddenly, with symptoms similar to those of a cold, and progress rapidly. The lymph nodes, spleen, and liver may become infiltrated with leukocytes and enlarged. Symptoms frequently include bone pain, paleness, a tendency to bleed easily, and a high susceptibility to infectious diseases. The most common causes of death, which occurs if the leukemia is not treated, are hemorrhaging and uncontrolled infections.

The chronic leukemias begin much more slowly, and several years may pass before significant symptoms appear. The symptoms are similar to those of the acute leukemias. The life expectancy of an individual who goes without treatment, however, is about 3 years after the onset of the condition.

In leukemias most of the leukocytes do not mature into functional cells. While leukemias constitute one of the most common malignancies of children, persons of any age can be victims.

Lymphomas

These are diseases in which abnormal numbers of lymphocytes are produced by the spleen and lymph nodes. The diseases are quite similar to leukemia, but in some lymphomas the immature lymphocytes aggregate in the lymphoid tissues. Hodgkin's disease is the best-known form of lymphoma.

Sarcomas

These diseases are characterized by tumors growing from bone, cartilage, connective tissue, fat, and muscle.

Characteristics of Cancerous States

Three major characteristics appear to define cancerous states: anaplasia, hyperplasia, and metastasis. Anaplasia is a structural abnormality in which involved cells do not mature and therefore resemble primitive or embryonic cells. Hyperplasia is an uncontrolled reproduction of cells.

Malignant cells do not respond to a host's signal to stop dividing; they consequently produce a localized accumulation of tissue. Metastasis refers to a malignant cell's ability to detach itself from a tumor, spread to another anatomical site, and establish a new tumor.

It is interesting to note that cancers are not in themselves fatal. In general, cancerous growths do not produce toxins or otherwise kill hosts directly. Cancers create a condition of malnutrition by utilizing nutrients needed by the tissues of the host. The malnutrition state produces a generalized emaciation and poor state of health called *cachexia*.

Viral Transformation

Viral transformation is the process by which normal cells are altered to become malignant cells as a consequence of virus infection. Transformed cells often undergo numerous alterations that can be expressed as changes in morphology, in metabolic functions, and in antigenicity. One of the important conclusions that some scientists have reached from animal experiments is that a virus must be integrated into the host cell's genome before it can transform the cell.

The introduction of certain cancer-inducing viruses into tissue culture systems readily produces cell transformation, however. The viral agent is often no longer recognizable in the cultures by its best-known properties, such as infectivity and antigenicity. Traces of the virus can be detected in the form of new antigens and viral DNA and RNA. Findings such as these suggest that standard, time-tested procedures for the isolation and identification of viral pathogens may not be adequate for human viral cancer agents.

Early History of the Role of Viruses in Oncogenesis and Malignancy

Acceptance of the concept that cancer can be caused by viruses has been difficult to obtain, despite the unequivocal and long-standing evidence from animal experiments. In 1908 V. Ellerman and O. Bang showed that leukemia in chickens could be transmitted by injecting bacteria-free filtrates from infected chickens into healthy chickens. Three years later, in 1911, Rous demonstrated a similar transfer of a chicken sarcoma. But the occurrence of virus-induced tumors in chickens was generally regarded as nothing more than a biological curiosity of domestic fowl. Such notions were shaken, however, by the discovery of the viral induction of wart-like tumors of epidermal tissue in rabbits (Shope, 1932) and by the discovery of the renal adenocarcinoma of the frog (Lucké, 1934). A few years later, in 1936, Bittner discovered a virus in mice (Figure 40–1) which was transmitted from mother to progeny through milk and which caused mammary-gland carcinomas. In 1951, Gross demonstrated that a lymphatic leukemia of mice was also virus-induced.

The murine (mouse) cancer viruses that were initially discovered were found to contain ribonucleic acid. More recent discoveries have shown that several deoxyribonucleic acid-containing viruses also cause cancer in mice and other rodents, such as the polyoma virus found in leukemic mice in 1959 and the subsequently discovered Simian virus 40 (SV40), a passenger virus in rhesus monkey kidney-tissue cultures. Virus-induced cancers in hamsters, mice, and rats by human adenoviruses were also

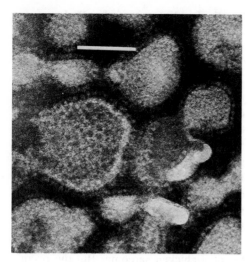

FIG. 40–1. The virion of mouse mammary tumor virus, which has a surface covered with spikes. The bar marker represents 0.1 μm. (From Sheffield, J. B.: *J. Virology,* **12**:616–624, 1973.)

reported. In addition, many new oncogenic viruses were discovered in the sixties. The following discussion presents selected features of the viruses associated with the viral etiology of oncogenesis.

Characteristics of Oncogenic RNA Viruses

Oncogenic RNA viruses (also called oncornaviruses and RNA tumor viruses) are generally divided into three main classes, labeled A, B, and C. Type A RNA viruses, which are not infectious, are a very small group of virus-like particles that have not been found outside the confines of cells and that have not been shown to be oncogenic. Type B RNA viruses have been associated primarily with certain tumors (carcinomas) of the breast. Type C RNA viruses, the most important class, have been shown to infect a large number of animal species. Most type C RNA viruses are oncogenic, causing mainly leukemias, lymphomas, and sar-

comas—all tumors arising in tissues such as bone, cartilage, connective tissue, and lymph nodes.

Differences Among Oncornaviruses

Distinctions among the various types of oncornaviruses have been based on morphology, although they can also be made on the basis of immunological differences and modes of maturation.

The type C RNA viruses consist of a roughly spherical, compact RNA core and associated proteins (nucleoid) surrounded by an electron-lucent lipid layer that gives electron micrographs of the virus a target-like appearance (Figure 40–2).

The nucleoid of type B viruses is more eccentric in shape, apparently because its major internal protein is about two-thirds larger than that of the type C viruses. The glycoprotein surface spikes of the type B viruses are larger and more regularly spaced than those of the type C viruses.

The type A particles occur in two subtypes, one found in cellular cytoplasm and one found in the reservoirs for lymph and other body fluids. Those found in the cytoplasm are believed to be immature forms of type B viruses, to which they are immunologically similar. The morphology of type A particles is similar to that of the other viruses, but the type A particles are encapsulated by a protein shell rather than by a lipid-containing membrane.

A principal difference between oncornaviruses and other animal RNA viruses lies in the size of the complete set of hereditary information contained in their chromosomes (genome). Oncornavirus genomes have a mass of about 12×10^6 daltons, compared to about 6×10^6 daltons for the paramyxoviruses and about 2×10^6 daltons for the poliomyelitis virus.

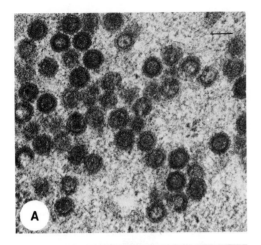

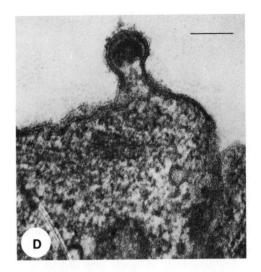

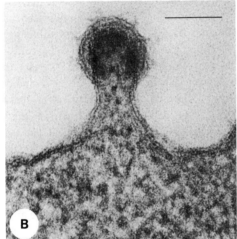

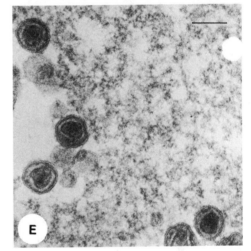

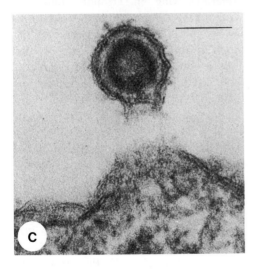

FIG. 40–2. Types B and C RNA production. Type C viruses have been implicated as causative agents of leukemia, lymphomas (diseases in which abnormal numbers of lymphocytes are produced), and sarcomas in a variety of avian and mammalian systems. _A_. Mouse mammary tumor virus (MMTV) in tissue culture. This virus is a type B particle. (Courtesy of Dr. T. M. Murad.) Electron micrographs _B_ through _E_ show type C virions released by a mammalian cell line. _B_. A budding particle from Chinese hamster tissue culture. _C_. A budding particle from a rat tissue culture preparation. _D_ and _E_. Free and budding particles from a pig cell line. Note the similarities in particle appearance. The scale represents 100 nm. (From Liever, M. M., Benveniste, R. E., Livingston, D. M., and Jodaro, G. J.: _Science_, **182**: 56–59, 1973.)

The Role of DNA Viruses in Carcinogenesis

Interest in the DNA viruses as human cancer virus candidates at first centered on the adenoviruses and papovaviruses. Adenoviruses, which cause respiratory infections in humans, and the papova (papilloma-polyoma-vacuolating) viruses, which may be responsible for a variety of tumors including the wart (see Chapter 31), produce tumors in experimental animals and transform animal cells in culture. Despite the fact that these viruses are widespread, there are few indications that implicate them in human cancers.

During the middle 1960s, however, the herpesviruses, a group of complex DNA viruses, attracted the attention of a number of investigators who were seeking to establish a link between cancer and viruses. At least three herpesviruses may be involved in human and lower-animal cancers and may thus serve as models for studying human disease.

One of the lower animal virus diseases is a malignant tumorous growth in the lymphoid system of chickens, known as Marek's disease. It has provided the first unequivocal proof that a herpesvirus is the cause of a cancer. Almost unknown a few years ago except among a handful of academic veterinary pathologists, Marek's disease became the scourge of U.S. commercial chicken flocks in the late 1960s. Joseph Marek, a Hungarian, described this disease state in 1901 but did not recognize it as a malignant one. In it, cells of the lymphoid system become cancerous and invade the nerve cells, resulting in paralysis of the fowl. As the disease progresses other organs are invaded, and the bird eventually dies. The virus that causes Marek's disease is extremely resistant to drying and may remain infectious for a long time after it has been liberated in bits of sloughed-off dead chicken skin (dander). The replication of the herpesvirus of Marek's disease takes place in non-malignant skin cells that normally die in any case. It is worth noting that in Marek's disease the tumor virus is not produced in the tumor cells. The virus transforms normal cells into tumor cells without necessarily producing viral progeny (a new generation of viruses).

An attenuated strain of the Marek's disease virus has been used for live-virus vaccines, with the result that Marek's disease has been effectively eradicated in treated flocks. This suggests that cancer vaccines for humans may be possible.

The herpesvirus that causes Marek's-disease tumor is immunologically related to a herpesvirus that is closely associated with a human cancer: Burkitt's lymphoma. In 1958 Denis Burkitt, a missionary surgeon working in Uganda, reported that a large number of African children between the ages of 4 and 16 suffered from tumors in the connective tissue of the jaw. These jaw sarcomas were thought to occur very rarely in Europe and in the U.S., but children of white missionaries living in Uganda sometimes acquired the disease. Although the lower jaw is most frequently the site of the tumor in Burkitt's lymphoma, tumors also arise at other sites, such as the upper jaw, the thyroid, the ovaries, the liver, and the kidneys. Intensive study of Burkitt's lymphoma began immediately after he published his report of this cancer.

Electron microscopic examinations of tumors for virus particles were fruitless, as were efforts to infect laboratory animals and tissue cultures with extracts of tumors. Efforts to establish tissue cultures with the cells from tumors also met with little success. Then M. A. Epstein and Y. M. Barr, as well as R. J. V. Pulvertaft, who

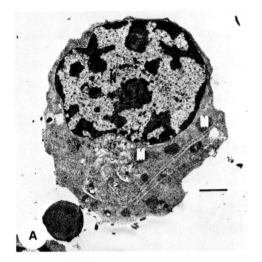

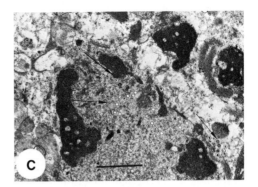

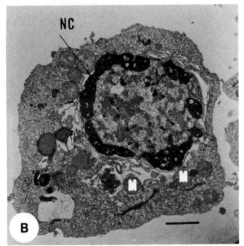

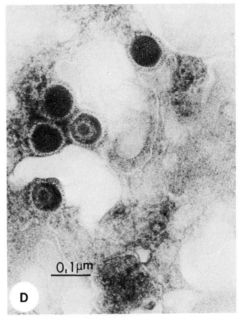

FIG. 40–3. Selected aspects of Epstein-Barr virus (EBV) infection. _A_. An ultrathin section of a non-virus-producing Burkitt lymphoma cell. The nucleus (N), cytoplasm, and organelles such as mitochondria (M) appear normal. _B_. An EBV-producing cell reveals ultrastructural changes in the nucleus, margination of chromatin (NC), and production of excess nuclear membrane. The cytoplasm contains swollen mitochondria. _C_.

Numerous virus capsids in various stages of maturation (arrows). _D_. Negative staining with 2 percent phosphotungstic acid (PTA), showing a heavy concentration of viral capsids. Material is from the fluid of a tumor cell culture. The bar markers shown in photos A, B, and C represent 1 μm. (Electron microscopy is the work of Muriel Lipman. From Miller, G.: J. Inf. Dis., **130**:187–205, 1974.)

worked independently of the other two investigators, undertook a series of tissue culture experiments using fresh tumor tissue flown in from Uganda. Electron microscopic examinations of some cells from these cultures clearly demonstrated the presence of herpesvirus particles. These particles have since been named Epstein-Barr virus (EBV).

The identification of a herpesvirus in Burkitt's lymphoma was a significant finding, since it is well known that certain herpesviruses are generally widespread in the human population. An interesting additional finding was reported in 1968 by Werner and Gertrude Henle and V. Diehl. These individuals discovered that infectious mononucleosis (the "kissing disease") not only is caused by a herpes-virus, but also is caused by an agent that cannot be distinguished from the Epstein-Barr virus. (See Chapter 36 for a discussion of this disease state.) Certainly one question raised by this finding has been: Do people who have had infectious mononucleosis (IM) have a greater probability of contracting cancer in later life? Thus far, it appears that a history of infectious mononucleosis is not associated with the incidence of cancer. Another interesting finding in the relationship between IM and EBV is that antibodies to Epstein-Barr virus are associated with protection against infectious mononucleosis and, conversely, IM occurs only in individuals who do not have antibodies against EBV.

Quite recently two groups of investigators showed that EBV can induce lymphoid tumors in monkeys. Since such experiments are hazardous and thus will not be carried out using humans, this is as far as experimentation can go in demonstrating that a virus from human cancer is in fact a cancer-causing agent. Demonstrating that a virus can induce a tumor is a different matter from finding a virus in a tumor. The prospect appears good that it will eventually be possible to show beyond a reasonable doubt that herpes-viruses can cause certain forms of human cancer. However, if and when human cancers are shown to be caused by viruses, the mechanism of action will still need to be determined.

Cancer Virus Hypotheses

Reverse Transcriptase

The discovery in 1970 of an enzyme that catalyzes the flow of genetic information from RNA $\rightarrow$ DNA in a surprising reversal of the usual DNA $\rightarrow$ RNA direction of genetic expression was of particular significance to cancer virus studies, because viruses known to cause cancer in animals have an RNA core. The enzyme, known as *reverse transcriptase,* provided for the first time a mechanism by which genetic material in the RNA of a virus can be incorporated into the DNA of a cell, where it might function like any gene. These RNA cancer viruses do not destroy cells, but if they are incorporated into a cell's genetic apparatus and then expressed, they could transform such a cell into a neoplastic one. Whether reverse transcriptase is unique to tumor cells is not totally known. However, it has served as a powerful tool with which to study cancer and other biological phenomena such as the differentiation process in normal, healthy developing cells.

Current RNA Cancer Hypotheses

There are three current RNA virus cancer hypotheses based on the assumption that viruses do, in fact, cause human cancer. These hypotheses have been developed to account for the way in which genetic information associated with a cancerous process is formed and expressed in cells. Before describing these hypotheses it should again be noted that cancer appears to be a number of different diseases. The demonstration of viral association with the causation of one type of cancer, or for that matter, of several types, should not be interpreted to mean that the problem of cancer will be solved. According to various studies the majority of cancers may be chemically induced.

Provirus hypothesis. Of the three current RNA cancer virus hypotheses, this one came first. It was formulated by Temin in the early 1960s. According to the provirus concept, after infection of a cell by an RNA tumor virus, the cell incorporates (integrates) the genetic information contained in the virus nucleic acid into its own DNA. By means of this reaction the cell acquires the capacity to produce oncogenic viruses and becomes transformed from a normal cell to a neoplastic one. It should be emphasized that the integration of viral genetic material takes place after a viral reverse transcriptase makes a DNA copy of the viral RNA. Once this step is performed the enzyme is no longer needed to establish the virus in the cell. Many researchers accept the provirus hypothesis as an accurate model of what can occur in lower animals. The possibility also exists that a similar set of reactions can develop in humans. RNA tumor viruses, for example, could possibly spread from one susceptible cell to another.

Oncogene hypothesis. This hypothesis, put forward in 1969 by Huebner and Todaro, states that the genetic information for cancer already exists in every cell and that such information is transmitted from parent to child. According to this model, then, infection of cells by C-type RNA viruses occurred millions of years ago during the course of evolution. Every cell is assumed to contain an oncogene, a region of DNA that is normally repressed (prevented from functioning). When the oncogene begins to function (becomes derepressed), possibly by a virus, by a chemical carcinogen, or by radiation, it expresses itself by bringing about the formation of a "transforming protein" (Figure 40–4). A transforming protein of this type could change a cell into a malignant one even though no viruses could be recovered from it.

The oncogene is pictured as only one portion of a larger structure, the virogene (Figure 40–4). The virogene consists of several segments of genetic information, which collectively must be activated in order for complete viruses to be made. This means, then, that the virogene would contain the necessary genetic information for the transforming protein, for the various components of the virus, and for the enzymes that go into the making of a complete virus. Thus it would not be necessary for the complete virogene to be expressed to produce a transformed cell. As a matter of fact, such complete expression could work against a virus-associated cancerous state, because the body might recognize and subsequently destroy the antigens of the whole virus, while it would be unable to act against the transforming protein of the oncogene.

Protovirus hypothesis. Temin proposed the protovirus hypothesis in 1970. In many ways it is similar to the oncogene concept. However, there are some distinguishing points. The protovirus hypothesis holds that cancer viruses arise from segments of genetic information randomly brought together through a variety of cellular and genetic events. These segments form the protovirus. An important point of the hypothesis is that cells do not come into being with all the genetic information necessary for the development of a malignancy. What they do have, however, is the potential for assembling such information.

As more and more information about the molecular processes of normal as well as malignant cells accumulates, the evidence in favor of each of the cancer virus hypotheses correspondingly increases. However, although evidence also is increasing in support of the presumption of a viral cause of human cancers, there is still sufficient reason to be skeptical. It is possible that a virus may be a necessary, but not a sufficient, contributor to the development of a cancerous state. Other factors, such as genetic disposition, immunological deficiency, or exposure to chemicals or radiation, may also be required. The need for two or more causes, acting together in the proper sequence, may help to explain why—if in fact viruses

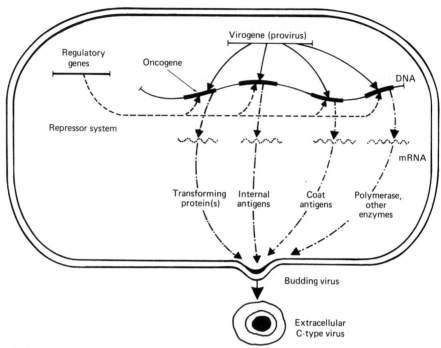

FIG. 40–4. A diagrammatic representation of the oncogene hypothesis. This view proposes that tumors are induced by transforming proteins, which are the products of virogene activity. A virogene has the capacity to produce a complete tumor virus. Theoretically, in normal cells oncogenes are turned off by regulatory genes that code for a repressor system. (After Culliton, B. J.: *Science,* **177**:44–47, 1972.)

are indeed involved—there is little evidence to show that cancer is a contagious condition.

Microbial Carcinogens

Although it is known that some fungi are harmful or toxic to plants and animals, a tendency to regard molds as harmless is rather common. However, in addition to the "side effects" of treatment with fungal antibiotics (Chapter 19), the health of humans and lower animals can be affected by contamination of foodstuffs by mycotoxins (Chapter 4 and 10). The available evidence from field and storage studies shows that the contamination of human as well as animal foods with carcinogenic mycotoxins such as aflatoxins is no longer only a suspected phenomenon. Extensive studies have shown that mycotoxins, especially aflatoxins, produce carcinogenic effects on organs such as the kidney, liver, intestines, stomach, and trachea.

In addition to the carcinogens produced by fungi, substances having carcinogenic properties are also synthesized or activated by bacteria.

Cancer Detection

The treatment of a cancerous state can be undertaken only after the condition is found. There are several ways to do this; however, there is no single test that will find all cases. One of the main methods used today involves certain routine screening tests, such as physical examinations, cervical smears (the Pap test) for women of childbearing age or older, x-rays, and proctoscopic examination of the rectum and lower bowel.

Fetal Antigen

Recently, biochemical tests for cancer have been growing in importance. Researchers have known for several years that a protein normally present only in human fetuses shows up in cancer patients. At first it was thought that the protein, named *carcinoembryonic antigen* (CEA), was found only in patients with cancer of the colon; then it was discovered with other types of cancers as well. Later, small amounts of CEA were found in individuals who seemed to be free of cancer. It now appears that the amount of CEA in a person's bloodstream seems related to the presence or absence of cancer.

Although CEA level does not signal any specific type of cancer (and may not, by itself, indicate cancer at all), it is already proving to be a valuable aid in monitoring treatment and in diagnosing a tumor's recurrence. Antigens such as CEA may eventually be used to indicate specific types of cancer, just as different microorganisms indicate specific diseases.

Other fetal antigens have been uncovered and associated with certain human cancers. These include α-fetoprotein, which is found in cases of liver and embryonic tumors, and γ-fetoprotein, which is found with patients having several different types of cancer.

Tumor-Specific Antigens (TSAs)

Immune reactions of humans to their cancers depend on tumor-specific antigens (TSAs) that are absent from or hidden in normal cells. Because these antigens are usually present in the surface membranes of tumor cells, the host can react against his or her tumor as if it were an allograft (a transplant involving genetically different members of the same species). Immunological surveillance by the host immune system in all probability eliminates many of the potentially neoplastic cells that develop during a so-called normal lifetime. However, individuals with certain impairments of this system have an increased probability of developing a tumor or related condition. Direct evidence for TSAs on human cancer cells has been provided by immunofluorescent procedures and other tests. Increasing evidence for the presence of these antigens on a wide variety of tumors and for host-associated immune responses to the TSAs has raised hopes for the development of diagnostic allergic skin tests or serological procedures for the early detection of cancers, as well as for some form of immunization against certain tumors.

The Use of Microbial Anti-tumor Activities for Treatment

The major forms of cancer treatment used today are surgery, radiation, and chemotherapy, or a combination of these treatments. However, for neoplastic disease there are limitations to these conventional methods, a realization that has resulted in the search for new measures of treatment. One approach, which attempts to stimulate the host's immune system to kill neoplastic cells, involves the use of non-specific immunological stimulators (NISs), incorporating microorganisms such as vaccinia virus, *Corynebacterium parvum,* and the Bacillus of Calmette and Guérin (BCG). Non-specific immunological stimulators appear to offer several advantages over the conventional approaches. Radiotherapy, hormonal therapy, and chemotherapy, all of which reduce immunological responsiveness, can harm patients severely by interfering with normal immunological function, particularly resistance to micro-organisms and/or their products. The non-specific stimulators can prevent or reverse such immunosuppression.

In order to show the value of stimulators, consideration will be given to BCG and its tumor-destruction effectiveness (Figure 40–5). Bacillus of Calmette and Guérin is a live attenuated organism derived from a bovine strain of *Mycobacterium tuberculosis*. There is a general consensus of opinion that an infection with BCG bacilli causes a change in the immunological apparatus of the host. One of the expressions of this altered state is an increased immunoglobulin response to unrelated antigens. Tumor inhibition requires the host to be able to develop and express an immune reaction of type IV (delayed hypersensitivity) to BCG antigens.

The current understanding of the cellular and molecular basis for BCG-mediated tumor destruction can be briefly summarized as follows. After injection of the host with BCG, sensitized T-lymphocytes develop that are able to recognize distinctive tubercle bacillus antigens. These lymphocytes react with the bacillus and produce a variety of potent molecules. Some of these molecules immobilize and activate macrophages, whereas others may be directly cytotoxic. If tumor cells are situated anatomically close to the bacteria, they are killed by activated macrophages and lymphotoxins. As a consequence of this reaction, immunity to specific tumor antigens may develop and in turn cause additional tumor cell death.

Living BCG has been used effectively in humans in some cases. Preparations also have proved effective in lengthening remissions in acute leukemia. Unfortunately, living BCG can cause disseminated disease in an immunosuppressed host.

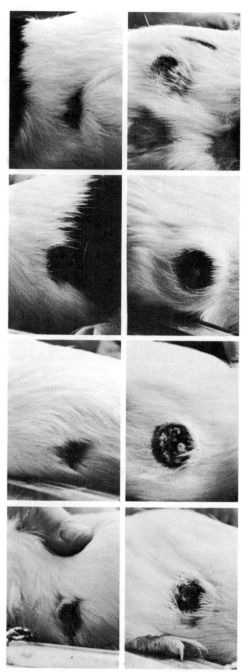

FIG. 40–5. Skin tumors in guinea pigs at the site of injection of BCG (Bacillus of Calmette and Guérin). The photographs on the right show the tumors 26 days after administration of 1 million (10^6) tumor cells. (From Bekierkunst, A., Wang, L., Toubiana, R., and Lederer, E.: *Inf. and Imm.*, **10**:1044, 1974.)

Although local reactions at the site of injections may be severe, they generally disappear. It seems that these adverse effects of using living BCG can be avoided by using lyophilized (freeze-dried), killed BCG alone or with other preparations having anti-tumor effects. One of these is the cord factor (trehalose-6,6'-dimycolate) obtained from mycobacterial cell walls.

Other bacterial sources of anti-tumor agents include bacterial endotoxins from *Salmonella enteritidis* and *Serratia marcescens*. These products of bacteria have been shown to inhibit tumor growth.

A Future Outlook

Proving that a virus causes human cancer has proved so elusive because both Koch's and Rivers' postulates, which have served for almost 100 and 44 years, respectively, as the criteria for establishing that a disease is caused by a given infectious agent, cannot be fulfilled. The first postulate requires the isolation of the etiologic agent from all infected organisms. But infectious particles cannot be recovered from most fresh tumor cells. Only after careful manipulations have been performed on tumor cells (for example, culturing them, sometimes with other kinds of cells) can infectious virus be demonstrated. This raises the possibility that the virus is a contaminant and is not involved in the development of the tumor itself.

Another postulate requires induction of the disease state in question in a suitable host by a pure preparation of the suspected etiologic agent. Such experiments normally are not performed on humans.

Thus investigators must rely on indirect or circumstantial evidence to prove the case against a suspected oncogenic virus. Today strategies include epidemiological studies, usually done in conjunction with immunological studies, to determine whether the virus has left traces of its presence in the form of antibodies against it in the patient's blood; study of tumor cells to detect the presence of viral DNA or RNA or of virus-associated antigens; comparison with virus-induced animal tumors; and study of the oncogenic potential of the virus both in cultured cells and in living animals, especially non-human primates.

In the event that human oncogenic viruses are isolated and obtained in sufficient quantities of pure form, there will be hope that the associated forms of cancer can be eliminated, or at least reduced in frequency, through either the development of effective vaccines or the discovery of ways with which to interrupt the primary routes of infection.

QUESTIONS FOR REVIEW

1. Distinguish between the following:
   a. carcinoma and leukemia
   b. sarcoma and lymphoma

2. What is reverse transcriptase? Of what significance is it to cancer virus studies?

3. Summarize the current RNA virus cancer hypotheses.

4. What is an oncogene?

5. Do oncogenic RNA viruses differ structurally from other RNA viruses?

6. Distinguish between a type-B and a type-C virus particle.

7. What role do DNA viruses have in carcinogenesis?

8. What promise do microorganisms hold for the treatment of tumors?

41

Medical Protozoology

Parasitology concerns itself with organisms (parasites) that live on or in other living organisms (hosts) from which they obtain nutrients and shelter. The close association or living together of two organisms is known as *symbiosis*. If the relationship is of mutual benefit to both individuals involved, it is called *mutualism*. If only one member of the pair benefits, while the other is neither benefited nor harmed, the situation is referred to as *commensalism*. Neither of these symbiotic relationships can be developed satisfactorily by a parasite, which usually does not settle into its environment as a result of chance, but is completely dependent on a host for survival. Some parasites multiply in tremendous numbers and eventually kill their host. This is an example of *unbalanced parasitism,* because the death of the host probably means the death of the parasite. The alternative to the self-destructive form of parasitism is one of *normal parasitism,* in which the parasite has a low level of virulence and the host's defense system limits the parasite's location and ability to reproduce. Thus a balanced relationship can be established between the two members of the association. A perfect or near-perfect host-parasite equilibrium requires the development of numerous complex adaptations over long periods of time.

Terminology

Some species are capable of either a parasitic or a free-living existence. Such organisms are referred to as *facultative* parasites. Other forms, known as *obligate* parasites, cannot complete their life cycles without the participation of the required host or hosts.

Numerous other descriptive terms are used to denote the special function, types of parasites or states of parasitoses encountered. The term *infection* is used in microbiology to indicate the relationship of a parasite to its host. The usage also is applicable to animal species which are endoparasites. However, the term *infestation* is used for parasites (*ectoparasites*) which attach to the skin or temporarily invade the superficial layers of the skin. Thus, a state of parasitosis is caused by either an infection or infestation with an animal parasite.

Temporary parasites invade a host intermittently during its life cycle only to obtain nutrients. *Incidental* parasites may establish an infection in a host that ordinarily is not parasitized. Other types of diagnosed parasites include *coprozoic* or *spurious* forms (foreign organisms which pass through the intestinal tract without causing an infection), and *pseudoparasites* (particles misdiagnosed as parasites).

Several different types of host are distinguished. For example, the *definitive* or *final host* harbors the adult or sexually mature parasite, while the *intermediate* one provides the environment for some or all of the immature or larval stages. Although man may constitute the only definitive host for several parasites, occasionally humans are accidental victims. In cases where other animal species act as hosts for these species which are parasitic for humans, such animals are called *reservoir* hosts.

The life cycles of parasites can be quite complex, involving several types and numbers of hosts. It appears that with more complicated life cycles the chances for survival of the parasite are greatly lessened. However, some parasites with complex life cycles compensate with adaptations including parthenogenesis and "overdeveloped" reproductive organs.

Distribution and Transmission

The distribution of parasites is influenced by the habits of suitable definitive hosts and by environmental conditions favoring the survival of the parasite, including temperature, moisture, and the availability of appropriate intermediate hosts. Many parasitic species are widely distributed in the tropical regions of the world. However, this condition appears to be disappearing, primarily because of the revolutionary changes in the international transportation of cargo and passengers. Opportunities for the distribution of parasites and their vectors have increased substantially.

Economic and social conditions also are important in the distribution of parasites. Low standards of living, inadequate sanitation, and ignorance of the means to control parasitic diseases favor the establishment of parasitoses.

The sources and transmission of parasitic diseases involve: (1) domestic or wild animals in which parasites can live (these are usually referred to as domestic and sylvatic reservoirs, respectively); (2) bloodsucking insects, of which mosquitoes, lice, and ticks are good examples; (3) various foods containing immature infective parasites; (4) contaminated soil or water; and (5) man and any portion of his environment which has been contaminated. It should be noted that the individual harboring a parasite can cause his own re-exposure with the same species of parasite, known as *autoinfection*.

The destructive effects depend on the number, size, degree of activity, location, and toxic products of the parasites. Consequently, symptoms may be absent, few, or severe. A wide range of symptoms can be encountered.

Treatment of Parasitic Infections

Several antiparasitic medications have been developed. However, as many of them are unlicensed, their use is limited in various countries, including the United States. Because more and more Americans appear to be traveling or working in tropical areas where parasitic disease agents abide, U.S. infection rates appear to be increasing. Therefore, it may become essential to have certain medications licensed for use and available to physicians. Two commercially available examples are Chloroquine hydrochloride used in cases of amebiasis and malaria, and Quinine dihydrochloride, used for malaria infections. Table 41–1 lists certain medications which have been used in the treatment of protozoan infections.

This chapter will emphasize the parasitic protozoan infections which have occupied the center of attention in recent years (Table 41–1). As the classification of protozoa is undergoing constant revision and improvement, references to classification will be based upon a system in common usage at the time of writing.

Table 41–1   Medically Important Protozoan Infections

Organism	Disease	Host Range	Location in the Body	Geographical Distribution	Possible Treatment
Ciliophora					
Balantidium coli	Balantidiasis	Humans, monkeys, pigs	Large intestine	Widespread	Antibiotics, including aureomycin and terramycin. Carbarsone
Mastigophora					
Giardia (lamblia) *intestinalis*	Giardiasis (sometimes associated with diarrhea)	Humans	Intestine	Widespread	Quinacrine hydrochloride (Atabrine), amodiaquine, metronidazole
Leishmania brasiliensis	Espundia (mucocutaneous leishmaniasis)	Humans, monkeys, dogs	Skin, mucous membranes	Central and South America	Pentavalent antimonial drugs Amphotericin B
L. donovani	Kala-azar (dum-dum fever)	Humans, several other mammals	Reticulo-endothelial system	Central Asia, China, India, South America, Tropical Africa	Sodium antimony gluconate Ethyl-stibamine Amphotericin B
L. tropica	Oriental sore	Humans, dogs	Skin	Central and South America, Mediterranean basin, Middle East, Far East, Africa	Pentavalent antimonial drugs
Trichomona (vaginalis) hominis	Vaginitis, prostatitis, genitourinary trichomoniasis	Humans	Vagina, prostate gland	Worldwide	Metronidazol, trichomycin, hamycin
Trypanosoma cruzi	Chagas' disease (South American trypanosomiasis)	Humans, cats, dogs, monkeys	Blood and reticulo-endothelial tissues	Central and South America	Compound Bayer 7602 (promising for young children)
T. gambiense	Gambian trypanosomiasis (African sleeping sickness)	Humans, monkeys	Blood, lymph, cerebrospinal fluid, spleen	Endemic in Central and Western Africa	For early stages: Aromatic diamidine suramin. For later stages: Mel B (a phenylarsonate derivative)
T. rhodesiense	Rhodesian trypanosomiasis (African sleeping sickness)	Humans, wild and domestic animals	Blood, lymph	Southeast Africa	Same

Organism	Disease	Host Range	Location in the Body	Geographical Distribution	Possible Treatment
Sarcodina					
Entamoeba gingivalis	Implicated in periodontitis	Humans, dogs, cats	Mouth	Widespread	No specific treatment
E. histolytica	Amebiasis	Humans, other mammals	Large intestine, liver	Worldwide; however, more common in tropical and subtropical areas	Chloroquine hydrochloride, metronidazole Chloroquine diphosphate (used for amebic hepatitis) Maintenance of fluid and electrolyte balance
Naegleria fowleri	Primary amoebic meningoencephalitis (PAME)	Humans	Central nervous system	Asia, Australia, Europe, and the United States	Amphotericin B
Sporozoa					
Plasmodium falciparum	Malignant tertian malaria (estivoautumnal)	Humans	Blood, liver	Tropical and subtropical areas	Amodiaquine hydrochloride (acute infection) Quinine dihydrochloride
P. malariae	Quartan malaria	Humans	Blood, liver	Tropical and subtropical areas, including Africa, Ceylon	Chloroquine phosphate (acute infection) Quinine dihydrochloride
P. ovale (rare species)	Tertian malaria (ovale malaria)	Humans	Blood, liver	Reported to be well established in Central and Western Africa and the Philippines. Also occurs sporadically in China, Greece, and Iran	Chloroquine phosphate (acute infection) Quinine dihydrochloride
P. vivax	Tertian (benign tertian or vivax) malaria	Humans	Blood, liver	East and West Africa, South America, United States	Chloroquine phosphate (acute infection) Quinine dihydrochloride
Uncertain Status					
Pneumocystis carinii	Subacute and chronic respiratory infections	Humans, cats, dogs, guinea pigs, mice, monkeys, sheep	Respiratory system	Increasing frequency	Pentamidine compounds
Toxoplasma gondii	Toxoplasmosis	Humans, cats, other mammals, certain birds	Nervous tissue, blood	Worldwide	Pyrimethamine and sulfonamides

Selected Characteristics of Parasitic Protozoa

Structurally, all protozoa are unicellular, possess one or more nuclei, and contain cytoplasmic inclusions such as endoplasmic reticula, mitochondria, ribosomes, and one or more vacuoles. While the vegetative or trophozoite ("troph") stage is common to all, several parasitic forms, such as *Entamoeba histolytica* and *Balantidium coli,* are capable of encystment.

The cytoplasm of trophozoites is surrounded by either a cell membrane or a specialized covering and contains the inclusions mentioned previously. The *cyst* can be described as a rounded, thick-walled structure containing these essential inclusions of the parasite. Encystment (1) provides protection against unfavorable conditions, (2) serves as a means of transmission, and (3) functions as a means for nuclear division and the parasite's multiplication.

Four main groups of human parasites belonging to the phylum of protozoa are recognized: the ciliates, flagellates, spore-formers, and the ameboid. Traditionally, each of these groups has been represented as a taxonomic class within the phylum. In recent years, however, there have been several changes in taxonomy. Some authorities assign subphylum or even phylum ranks to the main protozoan groups. In this chapter the following subphylum classification arrangement will be observed: *Ciliphora,* which includes the class of Ciliata (locomotion is by cilia); *Sarcomastigophora,* which includes the superclasses of Sarcodina (movement by pseudopodia) and Mastigophora (locomotion by flagella); and the *Sporozoa,* which includes the classes of Telosporea and Toxoplasmea. The majority of sporozoans do not have structures for locomotion. Features of specific parasitic protozoans will be described on an individual basis in the respective sections of this chapter.

The Ciliophora

Balantidium coli: Balantidiasis

Balantidium coli (Color photograph 114), first described by Malmsten in 1857, is the only ciliate considered by most authorities to be parasitic for man. Geographically, *Balantidium coli* is practically worldwide in distribution. The parasite lives in the large intestine, where it can invade the mucosa and submucosa, causing ulceration and frequently a fatal form of dysentery.

Means of transmission. Man acquires this parasite as a consequence of ingesting viable cysts from contaminated food. Once *B. coli* becomes established in a human host, its transmission from person to person is greatly enhanced in areas where sanitation is poor.

Life cycle. This protozoan possess two stages, the trophozoite and cyst. After cysts are ingested, the parasites in the host's intestine excyst, and the newly emerged trophozoites feed on various forms of organic matter, including starch-grains, bacteria, and the host's cells. Invasion of the surrounding tissue may occur. Encystment of *B. coli* trophs takes place with the dehydration of fecal matter containing them, either before or after feces evacuation from the large intestine. Subsequent contamination of food or water with such material may start the cycle again.

Clinical features and pathology. Infection with *B. coli* can produce intense abdominal pain, diarrhea, dysentery, loss of weight, and vomiting.

Once *B. coli* establishes itself, the parasite can penetrate the intestinal layers,

causing rapid destruction of tissue. Ulcerated areas can be rapidly invaded by
bacteria, and chronic ulcers similar to
those resulting from *Entamoeba histolytica* infections can develop.

Laboratory diagnosis. The finding of
cysts in stool specimens is considered as
diagnostic for *B. coli* infection (see Color
photograph 114).

Prevention of infection. Generally
speaking, the most practical methods
for the control of *B. coli* infection are:
(1) improvement of sanitary facilities,
(2) effective treatment of all infected
persons, and (3) increased efforts to
educate individuals in the dangers of contaminated food and water.

The Mastigophora

Before undertaking the study of the disease manifestations of human parasitic
flagellates, refer to Figure 41–1. This
figure presents the characteristic morphological forms of selected flagellates.

The *Leishmania* Parasites

This genus of flagellates is named in
honor of William Leishman, who in 1900
discovered the causative agent of kala-
azar, *Leishmania donovani.* Morphologically, the species of *Leishmania* cannot
readily be distinguished from one another. However, differentiation can be
made on the basis of clinical manifestations. At present, closely related forms
are considered either to be *dermotropic*
or *viscerotropic,* according to the part
of the body they invade. The dermotropic
species are referred to as belonging to the
"*L. tropica* species-complex."

Leishmania tropica. This microorganism, probably first observed by Cun-
ningham in 1885, causes the classical
cutaneous form of leishmaniasis called

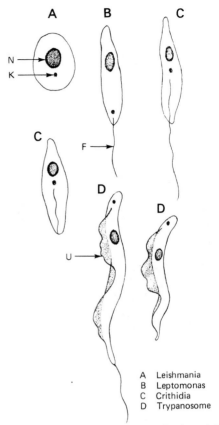

A   Leishmania
B   Leptomonas
C   Crithidia
D   Trypanosome

FIG. 41–1. Morphological forms of selected flagellates. _A_. The leishmanial form is oval or round,
and contains a nucleus (*N*) and a closely associated kinetoplast (basal structure of a flagellum),
but no flagellum or undulating membrane. _B_.
The *leptomonad* is elongated, and possesses an
anteriorly located kinetoplast (*K*) and a free flagellum (*f*), but no undulating membrane. _C_. The
crithidial form is characterized by an elongated
body, a kinetoplast just anterior to the nucleus,
and a flagellum. _D_. *Trypanosomal* form, in addition to the organelles of the crithidial stage, has
an undulating membrane (*U*).

the "Oriental sore" (Figure 41–2). Despite its name, the disease has an extensive
geographical distribution, including central Asia, the Congo basin, most of the
countries bordering on the Mediterranean Sea, the Middle East, the west coast
of Africa, and Central and South America.

Transmission and life cycle. *L. tropica*
is spread by the bite of various sandfly

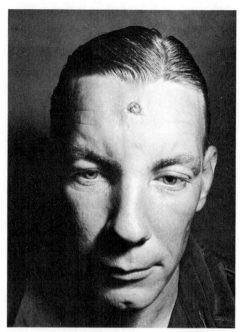

FIG. 41–2. Cutaneous lesion of leishmaniasis. (Courtesy of the Armed Forces Institute of Pathology, Washington, D.C., Neg. No. FA 4517.)

species belonging to the genus *Phlebotomus*. The arthropod acquires the leishmanial form of the parasite by feeding on an infected host (man or other suitable mammal). A transformation of the protozoan to the leptomonad stage occurs in the mid-gut of the sandfly. These forms multiply and may migrate to the buccal cavity of the insect. The parasites are then available for inoculation into a new host when the sandfly is ready for another blood meal.

Clinical features and pathogenicity. After an incubation period of 2 to 6 months, the inoculated area enlarges, forms a dry scab, and eventually gives rise to a more or less circular ulcer. Intense itching may be present during this time. The lesion is shallow and sharply defined. Secondary bacterial infection is commonly encountered. Untreated ulcers generally heal within 9 to 12 months

and leave depigmented scars at the inoculation site.

Diagnosis. Clinical aspects of the disease are utilized for diagnostic purposes. However, the parasites can be demonstrated in aspirated fluid specimens taken from the "ulcer bed." Staining the material, either with Leishman's or Giemsa stain, provides good results. An indirect fluorescent antibody test is also used routinely.

Prevention. Control measures include: (1) the use of insecticides to eliminate the arthropod vector, (2) treatment of infected individuals, and (3) the use of personal prophylactic devices such as insect repellants and sandfly nets. In addition, contaminated materials, such as dressings, clothing, and bedding, should be properly disinfected.

The other *Leishmania.* Table 41–1 lists the etiologic agents, the endemic areas, and the particular portions of the body which are involved in other leishmanial manifestations, such as kala-azar (visceral), and espundia (mucocutaneous). *L. donovani* is transmitted mainly by the bites of sandflies; however, as the causative agents have been observed in urine and feces of patients, other means may be possible. *L. brasiliensis* infection is contracted mainly by sandfly bites.

Laboratory diagnosis. Diagnosis in the case of kala-azar (Figure 41–3) is made by examination of blood films, bone marrow, or splenic tissues (Figure 41–3*B*). Serological diagnosis can be achieved adequately by the complement-fixation procedure or by an indirect fluorescent antibody test. Diagnosis of espundia is similar.

The Trypanosoma Parasites

T. gambiense and *T. rhodesiense:* African sleeping sickness. This disease

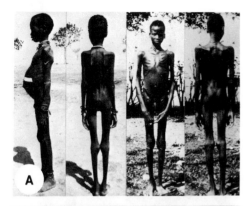

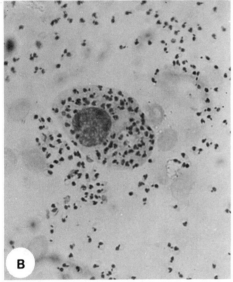

FIG. 41–3*A*. Two victims of kala-azar. (From Hoogstraal, H., and Heyneman, D.: *Amer. J. Trop. Med. & Hyg.,* **18**:1091, 1969.) *B*. *Leishmania donovani* in blood. (Courtesy of the Armed Forces Institute of Pathology, Washington, D.C., Neg. No. AFIP 55–17580-3.)

should not be confused with the virus-induced sleeping sickness infections, Eastern and Western equine encephalitis, which can be found in the United States and other parts of the world.

The manifestations of African sleeping sickness originally were recognized in two separate geographical regions, and were therefore considered to be two distinctly different clinical entities. Under ordinary laboratory conditions *Trypanosoma gambiense* and *T. rhodesiense* (the two human pathogenic species) are morphologically indistinguishable from *T. brucei*, which causes mild infections in several native game animals and more severe forms of the disease in domestic animals. A difference of opinion exists as to the taxonomic relationship between these species. Certain parasitologists consider all three species as strains of *T. brucei*, while other investigators distinguish only between *T. brucei* and *T. gambiense*. Closer attention will be paid here to the human parasitic species, in order to provide a clearer presentation of certain indiviual characteristics.

Historical aspects and geographical distribution. *T. gambiense*, the causative agent of Gambian trypanosomiasis, was first observed in 1901 by Forde. The discovery of *T. rhodesiense*, the causative agent of Rhodesian trypanosomiasis, was reported some eight years later in 1909 by Stephens and Fantham. *T. gambiense* is widely distributed in the western and central portions of Africa, while *T. rhodesiense* appears to be restricted almost entirely to the southeastern regions of the African continent.

Prevention. Preventive measures for these diseases are similar to those described previously for *L. tropica* infections.

Means of transmission and life cycle. Gambian trypanosomiasis is contracted by man through the bite of the tsetse fly, *Glossina palpalis*. The insect vectors for *T. rhodesiense*, *G. morsitans*, and *G. pallidipes* are closely related tsetse fly species (Figure 41–4). As the life cycles of both parasites appear to be quite similar, a general description will be provided. Trypanosomes are taken into the tsetse fly during a blood meal from an infected

FIG. 41–4. A tsetse fly, the vector of African sleeping sickness, perched on the end of a fingertip. (Courtesy of the World Health Organization, Geneva.)

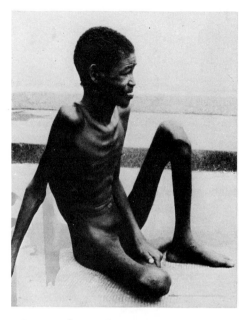

FIG. 41–5. The ravages of African sleeping sickness. (Courtesy of the World Health Organization, Geneva.)

host. The parasites pass into the insect's intestine, where they develop into both crithidial and trypanosomal forms. The flagellates soon migrate to the insect's salivary glands and develop into crithidia, which eventually transform into infective units called *metacyclic trypanosomes*. This last form is morphologically similar to the stage of the parasite as it appears in blood (Color photograph 112). The infected tsetse fly bites a susceptible host, and the cycle is thereby perpetuated.

Clinical features and pathology. Gambian sleeping sickness primarily involves the lymphatic and nervous system of man. The disease is chronic and may continue for several years (Figure 41–5). Occasionally, trypanosomes may be demonstrated in blood smears after an incubation period ranging from 6 to 14 days, even though the victim appears to be in good health. This asymptomatic stage, the low grade of parasitemia, may continue for several weeks.

In certain cases the disease aborts without the production of symptoms, while in other cases, the trypanosomes may invade the lymphatics and cause enlargement of the lymph nodes, liver,

and spleen. Winterbottom's sign, the enlargement of the posterior cervical lymph nodes, is a well-known characteristic of the disease.

Febrile attacks, during which time the parasites are present in large numbers, usually occur along with lymph node invasion. In addition to fever, parasitized individuals experience chills, disturbed vision, general weakness, headache, loss of appetite, and occasional skin eruptions, nausea, and vomiting.

If the disease progresses to the point of nervous system involvement, symptoms similar to those just mentioned manifest themselves. Furthermore, infected persons become extremely emaciated, readily fall asleep at any time—while eating, standing, etc.—and pass into a comatose state which is followed by death. The course of this disease may extend over several years, during which time exacerbations and remissions may occur.

Rhodesian trypanosomiasis presents very much the same clinical picture as seen in Gambian sleeping sickness. However, the infection has a much more rapid course, with death occurring in a year's time. Furthermore, the incubation period is quite short and there appears to be minimal glandular involvement. Winterbottom's sign may not be observed.

Laboratory diagnosis. Usually, diagnosis of trypanosomiasis includes the demonstration of the parasites in blood, in aspirated fluid from enlarged lymph nodes, or in spinal fluid (Color photograph 112). The clinical history and physical findings of patients also are extremely important. In the event that trypanosomes are difficult to find because they are present in low numbers, methods for concentrating the parasites can be used, such as zinc-sulfate flotation and Ritchie-formalin-ether concentration techniques.

Differentiation between the two forms of African sleeping sickness can occasionally be accomplished either on a geographical basis or on morphological grounds. Laboratory animals infected with *T. rhodesiense* will give rise to some parasites which have a posteriorly located nucleus, rather than the typical centrally situated nucleus of *T. gambiense*. An indirect fluorescent antibody test is available for serological diagnosis.

Prevention. Practical control measures which have been employed to reduce the incidence of the disease include: (1) destruction of breeding sites of the tsetse flies, (2) diagnosis and treatment of the disease in patients, (3) quarantine of infected individuals, (4) the wearing of protective clothing against the tsetse flies, and (5) prophylactic drug administration, especially in areas where the risk of infection is great.

T. cruzi: American trypanosomiasis—Chagas' disease. This disease, once considered to be rare and exotic, is now known to be a dangerous plague of the Americas.

Trypanosoma cruzi, the causative agent of Chagas' disease, was first discovered in 1908 by C. Chagas in the intestines of blood-sucking winged reduviid bugs (Color photograph 110). These arthropods were quite common in the huts of the Brazilian hinterland where Chagas was conducting his studies. Later the parasites were found in the blood of domestic animals and of several hundred patients apparently suffering from the manifestations of *T. cruzi*. Unfortunately, the discovery of the disease entity was seriously questioned, and after 1920 it was forgotten. A quarter-century later, Chagas' disease was rediscovered due to the investigations of Mazza and his colleagues, who recorded over 1,000 acute cases by 1944. The importance of Chagas' disease is emphasized by the World Health Report of 1962, which referred to "an estimated minimum of 7 million infected individuals."

T. cruzi is known to have a geographic distribution extending from southern portions of the United States through Mexico, Central America, and into South America to Argentina. Quite often various wild rodents, opossums, and armadillos harbor the parasite.

The disease is acquired by contaminated feces of a reduviid bug (triatoma) dropped into a bite wound caused by the arthropod. After the bug has taken its blood meal, the involved area itches intensely, and the reaction of scratching moves the feces into the wound.

The parasite can also penetrate through the ocular conjunctiva. Transfusions of blood from infected individuals in endemic areas is also an important means of the disease's transmission.

Infections are commonest among the very young. Both sexes are equally involved.

Clinical features and pathology. Based on an analysis of general pathological findings associated with *T. cruzi* infections, American trypanosomiasis can be differentiated into two separate pathological processes, the acute and chronic phases.

A person with the acute form of the disease (after a 1 to 2 week incubation), experiences general tiredness, headache, and a continuous or recurrent fever ranging from 37.4°–40°C (99° to 104°F) over a 4 to 5 week period. The most frequent signs of the disease affect the cardiovascular system and include tachycardia (fast heartbeat, much more intense than expected with the fever alone), cardiac enlargement, hypotension (low blood pressure), and heart failure. Coughing, diarrhea, and dysphagia (difficulty in swallowing) also are frequently encountered.

The pathological features of the acute phase of Chagas' disease are in accord with those of a typical septicemic and metastasizing process. The parasites occur in variable numbers in all the tissues and organs of the host. The heart is the most frequently and severely damaged organ. Involvement of the brain, liver, spleen, and spinal cord also occurs.

The chronic form of the disease occurs as the acute phase subsides. Parasites are not found in large numbers in the blood, due to the activation of the host's defense mechanisms. From a pathological viewpoint, most "chagasic" patients do not show any features characteristic of the chronic form of the disease.

Laboratory diagnosis. Two different stages of *T. cruzi* are distinguished in man: the trypansome or blood form, and the leishmania or tissue form. Diagnosis of the disease depends on the demonstration of the parasite in stained blood films (Color photograph 113), in biopsy specimens (e.g., muscle and lymph node tissues), or through the use of special concentration procedures.

The latter type of procedure includes culturing the parasite on artificial media, such as Novy-MacNeal-Nicolle (N.N.N.), and inoculation of suitable laboratory animals, or xenodiagnosis. In the xenodiagnosis procedure laboratory-reared reduviid bugs are allowed to feed on individuals suspected of having the disease. After several days of incubation, these bugs are examined for the presence of the intermediate stages of the parasite.

The complement-fixation test and certain other serological procedures also are used in diagnosis.

Prevention. Preventive measures are directed toward protecting individuals from being bitten by infected reduviid bugs, and toward the destruction of these vectors.

Genital and Intestinal Flagellates

Numerous flagellates capable of inhabiting man have been found in human fecal matter, in the mouth, and in the genital tract. For the most part their pathogenicity is doubtful, and many authorities consider them to be harmless commensals. However, two species, *Trichomonas hominis* and *Giardia intestinalis,* have been reported to be pathogenic.

Trichomonas vaginalis. Donné described this protozoan in 1836 (Figure 41–6 and Color photograph 120). The organism is found only in the genitourinary system, and has been acknowledged as the causative agent of the clinical entity genitourinary trichomoniasis. Several recent investigations have proved this dis-

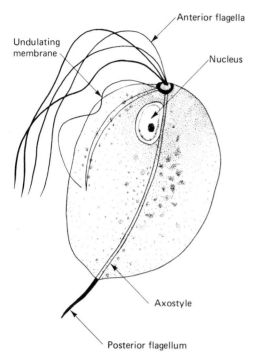

Undulating membrane

Anterior flagella

Nucleus

Axostyle

Posterior flagellum

FIG. 41–6. *Trichomonas hominis.* This protozoan has been observed to appear in the trophozoite stage only. Cysts have not been demonstrated to date.

ease to be a true venereal infection. Prostate involvement occurs in the male.

Temporary and permanent states of sterility have been reported to occur with long-lasting infections. However, in some cases successful therapy has enabled women to conceive and to give birth to normal children.

T. hominis infections can be acquired by newborn babies by way of an infected birth canal, or as a consequence of being exposed to highly unhygienic conditions. Reported infections of young girls appear to be rare. The disease seems to be as frequent in the human adult male as in the female. However, the symptoms in males generally are latent or subclinical, hence not obvious, while in acute stages in the female, a noticeable discharge is present.

Laboratory diagnosis. Clinical symptoms alone are not sufficient for diagnosis. Microscopic examination, including the Giemsa and Gram staining procedures, is definitely warranted. It is important to differentiate *Trichomonas* infection from similar states caused by *Neisseria gonorrhoeae, Staphylococcus,* and *Candida albicans.* Microscopic identification also is possible with the acridine orange staining technique (Color photograph 120).

Giardia (lamblia) intestinalis. A large percentage of individuals harboring this protozoan are asymptomatic (do not demonstrate symptoms). However, reports of some cases have definitely indicated involvement of the gall bladder and the production of gastroenteritis. The most common symptoms observed are abdominal cramps, flatulence, nausea, and alternating constipation and diarrhea. The disease can be found in most environments and appears to be more common in children than in adults.

Laboratory diagnosis. Diagnosis is made on the basis of demonstrating the cysts or trophozoites (Figure 41–7) in stool specimens. The trophozoite stage is generally rare, except in severe cases of profuse diarrhea.

The Sarcodina

Entamoeba histolytica: Amebiasis (Amebic Dysentery)

There is general confusion among parasitologists concerning this disease. The definition of amebiasis seems to vary, from individuals inhabited by various ameba to individuals harboring *Entamoeba histolytica* with or without clinical symptoms of disease. Misinterpretations of laboratory reports indicating

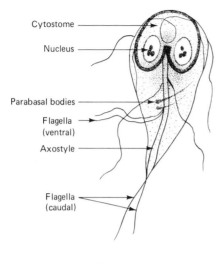

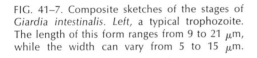

Trophozite

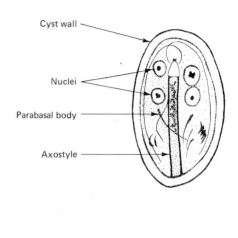

Cyst

FIG. 41–7. Composite sketches of the stages of *Giardia intestinalis. Left,* a typical trophozoite. The length of this form ranges from 9 to 21 μm, while the width can vary from 5 to 15 μm.

Right, an ovoid cyst. These structures vary in length from 8 to 14 μm and in width from 7 to 10 μm.

the presence of ameba in patients apparently have even resulted in unnecessary therapeutic treatments for patients.

Entamoeba histolytica was originally discovered and described by Lösch in 1875. Amebiasis is worldwide in its occurrence, with a higher morbidity rate in warmer climates where opportunities for exposure to the protozoan are greater. The true incidence of invasive amebiasis (tissue involvement) is apparently less than indicated by published figures. The most reliable basis for determining the disease's distribution should be the demonstration of amebic liver abscess. More definitive surveys and more adequately trained personnel are needed before an accurate determination of amebiasis distribution can be obtained.

Means of transmission. The most common means involved in the transmission of *E. histolytica* include contaminated water supplies, flies, infected foodhan-

dlers, and person-to-person contact. Obviously communities having poor sanitary conditions provide opportunities for repeated exposure.

Life cycle. Fully developed cysts (Figure 41–8*B* and Color photograph 118) are ingested by man. These forms exist in the alimentary canal and undergo a process of division, growth, and multiplication. The resulting trophozoites (Figure 41–8*A*) may penetrate deeply into the wall of the large intestine and multiply in this area. The parasites are known to feed well on red blood cells. Destruction of tissues leading to ulceration may or may not produce the classic symptoms of amebic dysentery. Involvement of the liver and other organs may also occur as a result of bloodstream invasion by the protozoan. Cyst formation results when trophozoites enter the intestinal lumen and encounter unfavorable conditions. It should be noted that if trophs are rapidly discharged from

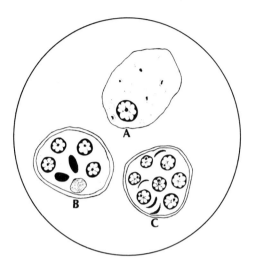

FIG. 41–8. Intestinal protozoa. _A_. Entamoeba histolytica trophozoite. Average diameter of these protozoans is slightly over 20μm. _B_. Cyst stage of the same microorganism. The "large race" measures approximately 12 to 20 μm. _C_. Cyst stage of Entamoeba coli, a nonpathogenic species which closely resembles, and often is incorrectly identified as, E. histolytica. E. coli cysts are larger than those of E. histoytica (10 to 35 μm in diameter), and contain splinter-shaped chromatoidal bodies and 1 to 8 nuclei.

this region, as in the acute diarrhea stage, these parasites die quickly.

Clinical features and pathology. Generally speaking, intestinal amebiasis may produce either no symptoms or nonspecific ones. However, individuals in the acute stage of the disease may have abdominal cramps, flatulence, diarrhea, feces containing blood and mucus, weight loss, and general fatigue. The degree of tissue invasion is important in the symptomatology picture. Numerous ulcerated areas may or may not be present. Perforation occurs in a small number of cases with severe symptoms.

Amebic hepatitis results from the parasites being carried to the liver by way of the circulatory system. Here,

organ enlargement, tenderness, fever, and loss of weight are observed. Pain becomes most severe with abscess formation. Pulmonary amebiasis may result from extension of liver involvement.

Laboratory diagnosis. Currently, the demonstration of trophozoites or cysts in stool specimens is diagnostic. Trophozoites with red blood cells in them are considered to be E. histolytica, for all practical purposes. In addition, several investigators have subdivided E. histolytica into races on the bases of differences in nuclear morphology, pathogenicity, and size. The small race of E. histolytica is referred to as E. hartmanni. Considering the possible modifying effects which the parasites' environment could exert, and the reports of cyst sizes which overlap, a more clearcut means of separating the races may be needed.

Several serodiagnostic tests, including the gel double diffusion and indirect fluorescent antibody procedures, are also being used. The sensitivity of all serological tests varies with the type of infection (e.g., abscesses, dysentery, etc.).

Prevention. Improvement in the level of sanitation in areas where it is needed should be carried out. Preventive measures should eliminate: (1) the possibility of flies and cockroaches gaining access to food, (2) infected food handlers, and (3) inadequate purification of water supplies. Attempts to educate individuals in personal hygienic habits and in the dangers in using as fertilizer human fecal matter which may be from infected persons should be expanded also.

Amoebic Meningoencephalitis

A "new" disease has been reported as being acquired from swimming in fresh or brackish water. Amoebic meningoencephalitis, caused by a small free-living amoeba, *Naegleria gruberi,* has epidemiologic features that suggest a water-borne origin. In fact, Butt in 1966 reported three fatal cases of primary amoebic meningoencephalitis in which the evidence indicated that the disease was acquired during warm weather by swimming and diving in fresh-water lakes or streams. Apley, Clarke, and Roome in 1970 reported a case of meningitis in a child that may have been acquired by playing in a mud puddle.

Laboratory diagnosis. The direct microscopic examination of fresh cerebrospinal fluid obtained aseptically is the procedure of choice. The detection of trophozoites is diagnostically significant. The indirect fluorescent antibody technique has recently been shown to be a valid identification method.

The Sporozoa

Malaria

Nearly a century has passed since the discovery of the first malarial parasite. The disease, suitably referred to as the greatest single killer of the human race, has been known from antiquity. Accounts of the disease's clinical manifestations date back to at least 1500 B.C. Hippocrates, while in Egypt, utilized the earlier records of malaria and noted the existence of differentiating fever cycles and other clinical features. With this information, he was able to divide the disease into quotidian, benign tertian, and quartan fevers. These designations denoted 24-, 48-, and 72-hour fever cycles, respectively. It is now known that they (and some other tertian fevers) are caused by infections with different species of the malarial parasite of the genus *Plasmodium.*

Advances in the knowledge of malaria from the etiologic standpoint were few until relatively modern times. One of

the truly remarkable discoveries in this connection was made by Alphonse Laveran. During the years 1878 to 1880, this young French medical officer demonstrated the malarial parasite in blood specimens from febrile patients. Unfortunately, Laveran's findings were not readily accepted, as other views of the disease's etiology were firmly entrenched in the minds of some of his contemporaries. In 1884, ignoring the existing scepticism, he demonstrated the protozoan parasite to the full satisfaction of such famous scientists as Chamberland, Pasteur, and Roux.

After Smith and Kilbourne demonstrated the tick transmission of Texas cattle fever in 1893 (Chapter 27) speculation grew concerning the involvement of mosquitoes in the malarial life cycle. One of the several notable resulting investigations was launched as a consequence of the efforts of Patrick Manson, who, in 1894, convinced surgeon Ronald Ross to test the mosquito-origin hypothesis. Ross's experiments, first with avian malaria and then with human parasites, demonstrated that malaria was mosquito-transmitted. Conclusive evidence was provided by later field trials conducted by British investigators in 1900.

Generally speaking, the potential distribution of human malaria can involve any area where: (1) *Anopheles* mosquitoes capable of supporting the parasite breed and are present in significant numbers, (2) reservoirs of the malarial parasite are available, and (3) adequate control measures directed against mosquitoes are either not practiced, or are ineffectively employed.

Four species of *Plasmodium* are known human pathogens: *P. falciparum, P. malariae, P. ovale,* and *P. vivax.* Their respective distributions are shown in Table 41–1. It should be noted that *Plasmodium* spp. are not equally extensive in distribution. Environmental conditions are known to influence the establishment of these as well as other arthropod-borne diseases.

Life cycle. A typical life cycle of malaria (Figure 41–9) begins with the sexual phase, *sporogony,* developing within the invertebrate host (anopheline mosquito).

Infective units (*sporozoites*) enter the bloodstream of man through the bite of a parasite-harboring female mosquito, and readily pass from the peripheral circulation into the parenchymal cells of the liver. Thus, the *pre-erythrocytic cycle,* or the first portion of the asexual phase, is initiated. (In the event liver involvement continues regularly in the course of the disease, after the original invasion of this organ, this cycle should be referred to as an exo-erythrocytic one.) The parasites grow and undergo repeated divisions, with the end result being the release of forms (*merozoites*) capable of invading red blood cells and thereby beginning the *erythrocytic* portion of the asexual cycle. Variations in this general cycle occur, depending upon *Plasmodium* species. For example, *P. falciparum* undergoes only one cycle which does not utilize red blood cells, i.e., one pre-erythrocytic generation, while other species can carry out several such cycles.

Erythrocytic schizogony (asexual development in red cells) is initiated by newly liberated *merozoites* invading the host's red cells. One such parasite assumes the shape of a signet ring in its new environment, grows, and develops into an ameboid, single-nucleus feeding form, known as a *trophozoite.* (See Color photographs 115, 116, and 117 for representation of these blood stages.) When the parasite attains its full size, mitotic divisions accompanied by cytoplasmic segmentation occurs. This ultimately results in the formation of a solid body composed of a varying number of merozoites. This structure is referred to as a *mature schizont.* The parasite-supporting red cell ruptures, and simultaneously releases the merozoites, the toxic metabolic products of the parasite, and the remains of the host cell into the general circulation. This group of substances is responsible for the chills and fever characteristic of the malarial syndrome. Periodicity of these well-known febrile cycles is not established during the early stages of the infection. It should be noted that the number of merozoites produced during this phase is constant for a particular species. Repetition of shizogony is caused by the newly liberated infective forms.

Certain merozoites, instead of continuing the asexual cycle, invade red cells and develop into female and male *gametocytes.* These forms circulate in the peripheral bloodstream, and are specifically available for ingestion by an anopheline mosquito. Under normal conditions a significantly large number of parasites are present during the time when mosquitoes take their blood meals. In the new host, they will undergo transformation into mature sex cells and participate in the sexual cycle or *sporogony.* Fertilization of a mature female cell (*macrogamete*) by a male cell (*microgamete*) results in the formation of a zygote. This structure becomes an *oökinete,* which is elongated and capable of movement. The oökinete penetrates the mosquito's stomach wall, rounds out, and develops into a stationary form known as a *oöcyst.* A series of divisions occur within this structure resulting in the production of many slender, thread-like, potentially infective sporozoites. Rupture of the oöcyst releases the sporozoites, which migrate throughout the mosquito's body. Those infective units entering the salivary glands of the arthropod can be

THE LIFE HISTORY OF PLASMODIUM VIVAX

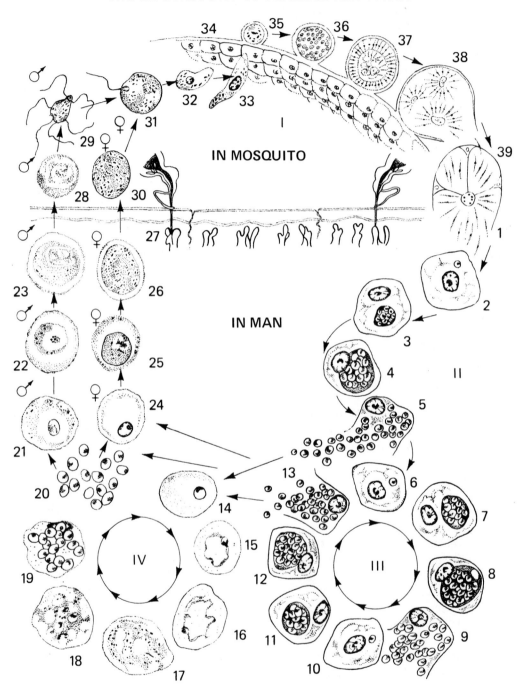

FIG. 41–9. Stages in the life cycle of the malaria parasite. An explanation of specific events as described in Wilcox, A.: *Manual for the Microscopical Diagnosis of Malaria in Man,* U.S. Department of Health, Education and Welfare, 1960.

1. Sporozoites from salivary gland of mosquito as they appear when inoculated into man at time of bite of the infected mosquito.

Pre-erythrocytic phase in man (primary phase).

2. Very young stage in cell. Parasite at this stage (2, 6, 10) not yet seen in man.

3, 4. Progressive growth of pre-erythrocytic phase tissue cells showing division of nucleus and increase in size of parasite.

5. Mature schizont of pre-erythrocytic phase in process of rupturing. Small merozoites enter red blood cells (14) to start erythrocytic cycle. These parasites also presumably enter other parenchymal cells (6) to start tissue cycle.

Erythrocytic cycle of parasite.

14. Young trophozoite (ring stage) in red blood cell.

15. Young growing trophozoite.

16. Growing ameboid trophozoite.

17. Mature trophozoite.

18. Immature schizont showing 6 divisions of chromatin.

19. Mature schizont showing 18 merozoites and accumulation of pigment.

20. Rupturing schizont. Some of the merozoites enter other red blood cells to carry on the erythrocytic cycle. Others enter red blood cells (21, 24) to form gametocytes (sexual stages). Arrows from 13 to 21 and 24 represent theory of formation of sex cells (gametocytes) from exo-erythrocytic merozoites.

21, 22, 23. Progressive stages of growth of the microgametocyte.

24, 25, 26. Progressive stages of growth of macrogametocyte.

Exo-erythrocytic (secondary) cycle in the tissues of man. It is believed that this phase accounts for relapses. (Arrow from 13 to 14 indicates initiation of blood cycle by exo-erythrocytic forms.)

6, 7, 8, 9. Progressive growth of one generation of this tissue phase.

10, 11, 12, 13. Another generation of this tissue phase. This event is indicative of continuous production in the tissues.

27. Skin of man.

Sporogonous cycle in the mosquito.

28. Microgametocyte released from red blood cells in mosquito's stomach.

29. Exflagellated microgametocyte.

30. Macrogametocyte released from red blood cell in the mosquito's stomach.

31. Microgamete entering macrogamete.

32. Fertilized parasite or zygote.

33. Elongated, motile, fertilized parasite, oökinete, penetrating wall of mosquito's stomach.

34. Tissue of mosquito's stomach showing epithelial cells and outer muscular wall.

35. First stage of oöcyst.

36, 37, 38. Progressive development of the oöcyst, terminating in 38 with rupture of cyst wall and release of sporozoites.

39. Cross-sections of mosquito's salivary gland, showing sporozoites within it.

40. Mosquito head. Upper picture represents mosquito sucking blood from human. Lower one represents injection of saliva by mosquito at the time of its biting another person. (Courtesy of the Laboratory of Parasite Chemotherapy, National Institute of Allergy and Infectious Diseases, National Institute of Health, Bethesda, Maryland.)

introduced into man when the mosquito uses its proboscis to obtain a blood meal. The malarial asexual cycle can then begin again.

Laboratory diagnosis. The classic symptoms of malaria mimic a large variety of other human infections. Therefore, at present the only completely reliable diagnostic procedure involves the demonstration of the parasite in blood films from infected individuals.

The color photographs 115, 116, and 117 show the various erythrocytic stages of the respective *Plasmodium* species. In order to lessen confusion for the beginner, certain important differentiating characteristics should be mentioned.

In the case of *P. falciparum* malaria, a peripheral blood smear usually will demonstrate the presence of ring stages and/or the sausage-shaped gametocytes (Color photograph 115). Furthermore, erythrocytes will exhibit multiple infections. In other words, several ring forms can be seen in one red cell.

Several features characterize *P. vivax* malaria. These properties include; (1) the presence of all erythrocytic development stages (a marked contrast to falciparum malaria), (2) enlargement of infected red cells, (3) the development of Schüffner's dots (erythrocytic stippling), and (4) the presence of an irregular pattern of 12 to 24 merozoites in the mature schizont stage.

P. malariae infection is recognized on the basis of (1) erythrocytes not being enlarged, (2) the absence of Schüffner's dots, and (3) the mature schizont stage being characterized by 7 to 9 merozoites arranged in a "rosette."

With *P. ovale* malaria, (1) red cells appear enlarged and oval in shape, (2) Schüffner's dots are present but appear to be of a coarser nature, and (3) the number of merozoites seen in the mature schizont stage range from 7 to 9.

The indirect fluorescent antibody and indirect hemagglutination tests are used in serological diagnosis of malaria.

Approach to treatment. Several effective drugs are in use against malaria. The choice of medication is determined by the particular situation, whether termination of an acute primary attack, suppressive or prophylactic therapy, or treatment of relapsing malaria. Moreover, intelligent therapy is dependent upon an accurate diagnosis and thorough knowledge of the effects of antimalarial drugs.

When a suppressive drug is used by an individual in a malarious area, the medication should not be discontinued on leaving the region, but continued for several weeks to ensure freedom from infection.

Contraindications are possible in various situations. Quite often these are dependent upon previously used medications. Resistance of malarial parasites also can be encountered. This is especially true with *P. falciparum*. Quinine appears to be one medication to which various strains of the aforementioned species are sensitive. Other approaches to treatment of resitant parasites includes the combination of particular drugs.

Prevention. Control of malaria involves measures which are not only directed against the vector of the disease, but also concern man (the definitive host). Eradication of the mosquito vector requires means for the destruction and elimination of breeding areas, larval stages, and adults.

Control measures in the case of humans include, the use of suppressive and prophylactic medications in endemic areas, prompt and adequate treatment of overt clinical attacks, and employing devices against mosquito bites.

During the late months of 1970 and early 1971, in certain counties of California several cases of malaria were traced to heroin addicts, with one of the major sources of the parasite being a returning veteran from Vietnam. Since addicts frequently share unsterilized syringes and needles, the transmission of the disease was easily accomplished. Suitable vectors are known to occur in these areas; however, fortunately, during these outbreaks of the disease, mosquitoes were not plentiful. Had these cases appeared in the summer months, statewide epidemics could have developed. The implications here are frightening in view of the high incidence of drug usage by soldiers returning from malaria zones, and the presence of suitable mosquito vectors in various regions of the United States.

Toxoplasma gondii

The etiologic agent of toxoplasmosis was originally discovered in 1908 by Nicolle and Manceaux, in a small North African rodent, the gondi (*Tenodactylus gondi*). The organism's name is derived in part from this animal. *T. gondii* exhibits a wide host range. In the late 1930s it was recognized that toxoplasma are associated with a type of infection that results in brain damage of the newborn. Infants may show evidence of the infection at birth or shortly thereafter.

Mode of transmission. *T. gondii* can be transmitted through the placenta (transplacental route). Other modes of transmission have created interest among investigators, particularly because the domesticated cat became implicated as a possible carrier of the disease agent. Recent evidence has indicated that cat feces contain one stage of the life cycle which has a high resistance to the environment as long as it is in the presence of moisture. The domesticated cat, which buries its excreta, usually in moist soil, provides a potential link in the transmission. Cat litter and sandboxes, in particular, may be a source of infection for the individuals who clean the box and inhale or ingest the cysts. Because toxoplasmosis was initially a disease of rodents, cats that eat infected mice can become infected in turn. A cat that is not permitted to roam or to eat raw meat is unlikely to acquire the infection.

While the cat is the one animal whose feces may be implicated in transmission, toxoplasma may be found in practically every mammal and in some birds. Therefore, ingestion of raw meat by humans or other animals can contribute to the spread of the disease agent.

Clinical features. Disease manifestations in most adults usually are considered to be of a benign nature. When symptoms occur, they are mild and include chills, fever, headache, extreme malaise, and myalgia (muscle pain). The disease simulates infectious mononucleosis. Newborn infants who contracted toxoplasma infection *in utero* commonly have serious defects involving the central nervous system. Common symptoms include convulsions, fever, hepatosplenomegaly, and pneumonitis. Unfortunately, in many cases complete recovery does not occur. Moreover, severe visual impairment, blindness, and mental retardation often develop, thus rendering children helpless invalids.

T. gondii is capable of both intracellular and extracellular development (Figure 41–10). Morphologically, extracellular forms are crescentic, with one end of the parasite more pointed than the opposite one (Figure 41–10 and Color photograph 111). Intracellular, *T. gondii* is

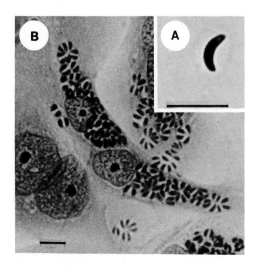

FIG. 41–10. Various stages of the parasite *Toxoplasma gondii*. The bar marker represents 10 μm. *A*. A stained preparation showing an artificially excysted sporozoite. *B*. The appearance of monkey kidney cells infected with *T. gondii* 25 days after inoculation. The infecting material was excysted sporozoites. Note the intracellular location of the parasites. (From Sheffield, H. G., and Melton, M. L., National Institute of Allergy and Infectious Diseases: *Science*, **167**:892, 1970. Copyright by the American Association for the Advancement of Science.)

smaller. Multiplication may take place within epithelial cells, leukocytes, cells of central nervous and reticuloendothelial systems. Pseudocysts, enlarged spherical masses of parasites enclosed by a membrane, may occasionally develop with their multiplication occurring within central nervous system cells.

Laboratory diagnosis. Diagnosis is difficult to obtain by direct examination of clinical specimens, such as blood or cerebrospinal fluid. One of the most widely used procedures in this connection is the Sabin-Feldman dye test. It is a serological test which employs living organisms, the patient's serum, and a solution of methylene blue. A positive reaction is indicated by the patient's serum. Apparently, antibodies against the disease agent make it "refractory" to staining. Positive results

here may serve as indications of either active infection or prior exposure to *Toxoplasma gondii*. Additional diagnostic procedures as being developed. Tests such as the indirect fluorescent antibody procedure also are being used for serodiagnostic purposes.

Prevention. Infection in a pregnant woman represents the greatest public health problem by virtue of transmission to the developing fetus. The following suggestions therefore are of particular importance to pregnant women.

(1) Avoid eating undercooked or raw meat.

(2) If a cat is already a family pet, and if a cat litter or sandbox is used, have another person clean and handle it.

(3) If a cat is to be purchased and kept as a family pet, keep it indoors and don't feed it raw meat products.

It should be noted that if serological testing shows that a woman prior to becoming pregnant has antibodies against *T. gondii*, the danger to the fetus is quite low.

A Parasite of Uncertain Systematic Status

The tissue parasite *Pneumocystis carinii* has received considerable attention in recent years. Although the true taxonomic position of this microorganism is still uncertain, many authorities consider it to be sporozoan in nature.

Pneumocystis carinii

This parasite is the etiologic agent of a subacute chronic pneumonitis infection involving the pulmonary alveolar spaces and surrounding supporting structures. The manifestations of *P. carinii* have occurred almost exclusively in children with congenital immunologic disorders, in patients with certain generalized vascular disorders, in debilitated infants, in newborn and premature infants, and in patients receiving immunosuppressive therapy for malignancies or organ transplantation. The etiologic agent was originally discovered in the guinea pig several years ago and has since been found in numerous other animals, including cats, dogs, mice, monkeys, and sheep. There are several similarities between human and animal *P. carinii* pneumonitis with respect to the morphology and the pathogenicity of the protozoan and histology of the diseased tissue. The organism infests the intraalveolar space of the lung as an opportunist and rarely penetrates tissue. To date all attempts at *in vitro* isolation have failed. This inability to cultivate *P. carinii* has prevented more extensive studies of the organism in relation to its habitat, life cycle, pathogenesis, and epidemiology. Various reports, however, clearly indicate that *P. carinii* has a worldwide distribution.

Mode of transmission. Although the mode of transmission for the parasite is not definitely established, the inhalation of *P. carinii* into the respiratory tract appears to be the most probable.

Clinical features. Clinically, there are no specific features by which *P. carinii* pneumonitis can be distinguished from other forms of pneumonitis. The clinical course of the disease usually takes 4 to 6 weeks. In premature babies, the illness is commonly recognized between the ninth and sixteenth weeks. The clinical findings include cough, cyanosis (bluish skin patches), intermittent fever, and tachypnea (rapid breathing). The customary x-ray finding demonstrates involvement of the lung area where blood vessels, bronchi, and nerves enter, progressing to a patchy infiltration of the lungs proper. Atelectasis, or areas of consolidation, may occur.

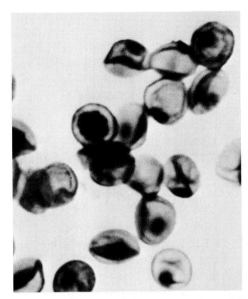

FIG. 41–11. Clusters of *Pneumocystis carinii* cysts. (Courtesy of Kim, H. K., and Hughes, W. T.: *Amer. J. Clin. Path.,* **60**:462–466, 1973.)

Laboratory diagnosis. As mentioned previously, *Pneumocystis carinii* has not been grown *in vitro*. Furthermore, reliable serologic tests are currently not available. Thus, precise diagnosis depends on the demonstration of the organism in pulmonary tissue (Figure 41–11 and Color photograph 119). There are three developmental stages of *P. carinii*: cyst, trophozoite, and sporozoite forms. Cysts are round, measure about 4 to 10 µm in diameter, and contain 1 to 8 sporozoites (Color photograph 119). The trophozoites vary in shape and range in size from 2 to 5 µm in diameter. A small amount of nuclear material in these forms, usually V-shaped, is generally located eccentrically. The three stages of *P. carinii* can be demonstrated through the use of Giemsa, Wright, or polychrome methylene blue stains. It should be noted, however, that knowledge of the morphology of *P. carinii* in the various stages of its life cycle is essential for the recognition of the organism with these stains.

QUESTIONS FOR REVIEW

1. Compare the structural and diagnostic features of the trophozoite and cyst stages of human protozoan parasites. Can such features be of diagnostic importance? Explain.

2. List several characteristics that all protozoa have in common.

3. Which protozoa possess a cyst stage in their life cycle?

4. Sleeping sickness can be caused by several microbial types. Name and compare at least six etiologic agents in relation to: (a) mode of transmission, (b) geographical distribution, (c) preventive and control measures, and (d) significance as a world problem.

5. If you were planning a world trip, including on your itinerary Arabia, Egypt, Greece, Japan, and India, to which protozoan diseases would you be exposed?

6. Which of the protozoan infections mentioned in this chapter are known to occur in the United States? In your state?

7. List at least three diagnostic features of the human species of *Plasmodium* which would enable one to determine the specific species causing an infection.

8. What is American trypanosomiasis?

9. Discuss both *Toxoplasma gondii* and *Pneumocystis carinii* infections from the standpoint of occurrence, diagnosis, and clinical significance.

10. Which of the protozoan parasites would you consider to pose serious problems for military personnel in Central America? In the Middle East? In the South Pacific? What effective control methods would you suggest?

11. What disease state would you suspect in the situations listed below?
    a. An individual exhibits the following symptoms: a drastic loss of weight, diarrhea, some abdominal pain, and the presence of blood in his stools.
    b. An individual who has just returned from a world tour, including Africa and South America, complains of the following: fever, disturbed vision, headaches, loss of appetite, nausea, and vomiting. On examination the person is found to have enlarged posterior lymph nodes, located in the neck.

12. What procedure or procedures would you perform in the laboratory to diagnose the conditions suggested by the symptoms described in question 11?

13. To classify *Trichomonas hominis* as a venereal disease agent is considered unjustified by some. Why? How else could this infectious protozoan be labeled?

42

Helminthic Diseases of Humans

One of the major subdivisions of medical parasitology is concerned with the study of helminths. This term is derived from the Greek word *helmins,* meaning worm, and is used for both parasitic and free-living species. The worms of medical importance discussed in this chapter include representative parasites from the phyla of Nemathelminthes (roundworms), also called Nematoda, and Platyhelminthes (flatworms, or flukes and tapeworms). Although several nematode species are known to be parasitic for plants and consequently can affect man through the spoilage and destruction of agricultural products, these worms will not be described here.

Structural Features of Parasitic Worms

Adaptation of a helminth to a parasitic existence is in large part determined by the development of certain structural and metabolic modifications. Many intestinal worms (and certain others) have an especially hardened integument (outer covering) enabling them to resist digestion by the host. Other modifications include (1) the possession of hooks, spines, cutting plates, various enzyme secretions, and additional weapons for purposes of attachment or penetration, and (2) the development of elaborate reproductive systems. The latter feature is represented by hermaphroditism in the case of cestodes (tapeworms) and a large number of trematodes (flukes). More detailed descriptions of specific helminths will be provided in the sections that follow.

The Nematodes

Parasitosis caused by roundworms can involve the skin and organs of the circulatory, digestive, nervous, and respiratory systems (Table 42–1). In short, practically every tissue of the body is vulnerable to attack by certain nematode species. Structurally, true nematodes are unsegmented, typically cylindrical and elongate, tapered at both ends, fundamentally bilaterally symmetrical, and do not possess any appendages. These parasites all have digestive, nervous, and reproductive systems. The digestive system is a complete one. With relatively few exceptions, the sexes are separate (*dioecious*). Excretory systems are not found in all nematodes, as adults of certain species lack such a system.

The worm's body is covered by a cuticle, which may exhibit ridges, striations, or wart-like structures. These various structures are used for purposes of classification. The sizes of roundworms vary widely. Some species are of microscopic size (see Color photograph 104), while others are several centimeters in length (Figure 42–1).

Table 42–1 Representative Medically Important Nematodes

Organism	Disease	Host Range	Location of Adult Forms in the Body	Geographical Distribution	Possible Treatment
Ancylostoma duodenale	Old World hookworm infestation	Primarily humans	Duodenum and jejunum	Chiefly found in Africa, Europe, the Orient	Bephenium hydroxymaphthoate (manufactured in Great Britain)
Ascaris lumbricoides	Ascariasis	Humans and other vertebrates	Small intestine	Worldwide	Thiabendazole, piperazine compounds
Brugia malayi	Malayan filariasis	Humans, other primates, cats	Lymphatics	Far East	Drugs for microfilariae: diethyl carbamazine (Hetrazan), 1-diethylcarbamyl-4-methyl piperazine. Drugs for adult worms: Suramine alone or with Hetrazan. Surgery and related procedures Corticosteroids
Dracunculus medinensis	Dracunculiasis (guinea worm infestation)	Humans, dogs, cats, several wild mammals	Skin, connective tissue	Certain areas of Africa and Asia, and rarely in South America	Nitrothiazole, appropriate antibiotics to prevent secondary infections
Enterobius vermicularis	Enterobiasis or oxyuriasis (pin- or seatworm infestation)	Humans, especially children	Large quantities occur in cecum and appendix. Female worm is especially found in the rectum	Widespread	Warm tapwater enemas Drugs include piperazine compounds, Pyrvinium Pamoate (Povan), thiabendazole
Loa loa	Loiasis (eye worm infection)	Humans, monkeys	Connective tissue, eyes	Central and West Africa	Diethylcarbamazine
Necator americanus	New World or American hookworm	Humans	Small intestine	Generally in Southern United States, Central and South America	Tetrachloroethylene
Onchocerca volvulus	Onchocerciasis	Humans	Skin, subcutaneous connective tissue, eyes	Africa, tropical America	Combination of diethylcarbamazine and Suramin
Strongyloides stercoralis	Strongyloidiasis	Humans, dogs, cats	Intestinal mucosa, lungs	Worldwide, but more commonly encountered in tropical areas	Thiabendazole
Trichinella spiralis	Trichinosis	Humans and several other mammals, including rats, rabbits, dogs, wolves	Small intestine	Worldwide, encountered in areas where pork is eaten	Thiabendazole (for larval migration) Corticosteroids
Trichuris trichiura	Whipworm infestation	Humans	Caecum	Worldwide	Thiabendazole
Wuchereria bancrofti	Bancroft's filariasis (elephantiasis)	Humans	Lymphatics	Australia, East Europe, Near East, Orient, Central and South America, Mediterranean and Central Africa	Corticosteroids

FIG. 42–1. *Ascaris lumbricoides.* Female worms range in size from 20 to 35 cm in length, while male specimens measure approximately 30 cm. (Courtesy of the Dow Chemical Company.)

The mouths' of primitive nematodes are surrounded by three lips. In *Ancylostoma duodenale* and *Necator americanus* (the Old and New World hookworms, respectively) these regions are highly modified into a buccal structure equipped with cutting plates or teeth (Figure 42–2). Such modifications, as well as others which will be mentioned, are of significance in nematode identification.

Life Cycle

The life cycles of nematodes vary. However, the stages involving the adult worm, the egg, and larvae are fundamental. With certain roundworms, non-operculate eggs (without lid) are discharged via the host's feces, mature on the ground, and may either be swallowed by a host or hatch out larvae which undergo further development and consequently become infective. With infective larvae, penetration of the host's skin leads to parasitosis. In still other nematode life cycles, larvae are discharged in fecal matter, and infective forms develop which also are capable of penetrating the host.

Some parasites utilize two hosts. For example, with *Trichinella spiralis,* the causative agent of trichinosis, all the stages of the worm's life cycle are completed in the pig. Man's infection depends on his ingesting encapsulated larvae in the striated muscles of this host, as inadequately cooked pork.

These and other examples of life cycles will be described in this section along with other properties of specific nematode species.

A

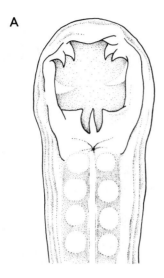

B

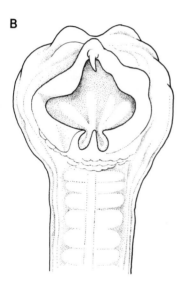

FIG. 42–2. A comparison of the modified buccal structures of hookworms. _A_. Anclylostoma duodenale. _B_. Necator americanus.

Larval Forms

Frequently, in describing the life cycles of these worms, references are made to _filariform_ and _rhabditiform_ larvae. These terms are based upon the type of esophagus the larval forms possess. The esophagus of filariform larvae can be described as a tube with a uniform caliber throughout; while the esophagus of rhabditiform

larvae is posteriorly expanded into a bulb, which has a valve mechanism.

The geographical distribution of medically important roundworms is shown in Table 42–1.

Representative Roundworm Infections

Ascariasis

Ascariasis has been recognized since the dawn of history. The nematode found in pigs is indistinguishable from that which infects man. It is the largest of the human intestinal roundworms (Figure 42–1).

Means of transmission. Adults can become infected with this worm by ingesting raw vegetables or water contaminated with fecal matter containing eggs (Figure 42–3) with infective larvae. Children also acquire the parasitosis by contaminating their hands with polluted soil, and then putting their fingers in their mouths.

Life cycle. Man's infection begins with ingestion of the parasite's ova, which are not infective until larvae develop within them. The eggs pass through the stomach and into the small intestine, where the

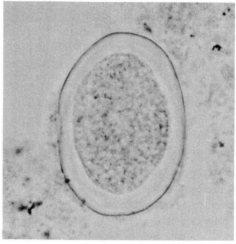

FIG. 42–3. _Ascaris lumbricoides_ ovum.

larvae, upon hatching, penetrate the intestinal wall. By entering the mesenteric venules or lymphatics, the parasites eventually reach the right side of the heart, and pass into the pulmonary vessels and into the lungs. The larvae moult twice, migrate up the respiratory tract to the epiglottis, pass over the esophagus, and down through the stomach to the small intestine. Here the last moult takes place, and the parasites develop into adult forms. The mature worms mate, eggs are deposited by the female, and the cycle begins again. The daily egg production per female round worm averages approximately 200,000.

Clinical symptoms and pathology. In ascariasis symptoms may be inapparent, especially in light infections. However, in a general type of infection a loss of weight, intermittent intestinal colic, obstruction of the intestinal lumen, peritonitis, and severe nervous involvement may be observed. *Ascaris* pneumonitis, a result of larval migration, can also develop; its symptoms include fever, dyspnea (labored breathing), a dry cough, and wheezing.

Laboratory diagnosis. The finding and identification of ova or adult worms in feces is sufficient for the diagnosis of ascariasis.

Prevention. Control measures primarily involve (1) improvement of sanitation in hyperendemic areas (2), treatment of human fecal matter (night soil) used as fertilizer, and (3) educating people as to the means of disease transmission.

Enterobius Vermicularis Infection (Pinworm, Seatworm)

Enterobiasis (oxyuriasis) has been known since ancient times. Its incidence has been found to be higher in temperate and colder climates than in tropical regions. Infections are more prevalent where large groups of individuals congregate, as in schools, mental institutions, and even large families. Children appear to have higher rates of enterobiasis than adults.

Transmission and life cycle. Oxyuriasis results from the ingestion of ova containing infective larvae. Such infections can be acquired through the handling of fomites, inhalation of eggs, or a transfer of ova to the mouth from the perianal region via the fingers.

After ova ingestion, infective larvae hatch in the small intestine and migrate to the cecal area of the large intestine. Here maturation and mating of the parasites occur. The female worm, carrying fertilized eggs (gravid), migrates to the perianal region, releasing masses of eggs as it crawls. Eventually the female's body ruptures. The deposited eggs are fully embryonated and infective.

The migration of worms produces a tickling or intense itching feeling, which causes the individual to scratch the area, commonly resulting in contamination of the fingers. Infection of other individuals by means of contaminated bedding or clothing is frequently encountered. The possibility also exists that larvae hatching in the perianal region eventually could migrate back into the large bowel. This type of infection is referred to as "retrofection."

Laboratory diagnosis. Diagnosis is based primarily on the demonstration of the characteristic ova of the parasite (Figure 42–4). The presence of eggs in the stools is not common. One of the most common techniques used to obtain eggs is the Scotch-tape procedure. The sticky surface of the tape is applied to the perianal region, usually with the aid of a test tube. The specimen containing-tape is affixed to a glass slide and then examined microscopically for the presence of ova.

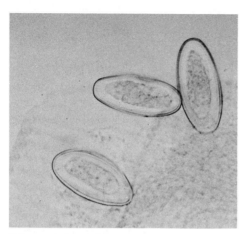

FIG. 42–4. *Enterobius vermicularis* ova. These eggs range in width from 20 to 32 μm and in length are approximately 50 to 60 μm.

Prevention. Preventive measures include treatment of all infected individuals and the development of good habits of personal hygiene.

Filariasis

The filaria are long, slender nematodes which invade portions of the lymphatic system and various other tissues of the human body. These helminths, as a group, undergo a unique stage in their life cycle, the production of motile larval forms called microfilaria (Color photograph 107). Although there are at least six species of filarias for which man is believed to be the definitive host, the discussion will be limited to the two most important forms of human infection, Bancroftian and Malayan filariasis. Selected characteristics of other filarian worms (e.g., *Loa loa* and *Onchocerca volvulus*) can be found in Table 42–1.

Historical aspects. Bancroftian filariasis has been known since 600 B.C. In 1878 Patrick Manson discovered that the causative agent, *Wuchereria bancrofti,* is transmitted by the bite of mosquitoes, specifically *Culex fatigans*—the first dem-

onstration of an arthropod's role as a vector of a parasite. *Brugia malayi,* the causative agent of Malayan filariasis, was first observed in 1927.

Transmission and life cycle. The filarias capable of infecting man have similar life cycles. Mosquito vectors include species of *Aëdes, Anopheles, Culex,* and *Mansonia.* Microfilaria (larval forms) are introduced into humans through the bites of an infected mosquito, which provides a suitable environment for the development of the parasite.

The microfilaria of *W. bancrofti* (Figure 42–5) appear in the peripheral circulation of man only at night ("nocturnal periodicity"). They are ingested by the appropriate species of mosquito during the course of a blood meal from an infected individual.

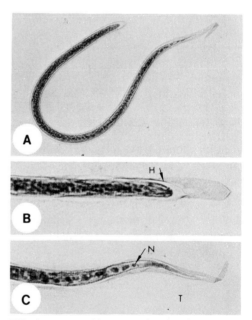

FIG. 42–5. Microfilaria. *A.* The sheathed *Wuchereria bancrofti* found in a patient with elephantiasis of the left scrotum. *B.* The head (H) region of the parasite, showing a sheath. *C.* The tail (T) portion of *W. bancrofti,* in which a sheath is also well defined. Note the nuclei (N). (From Vassilakos, P., and Cox, J. N.: *Internat. Acad. Cyto.,* **18**:62–64, 1974.)

Once in the body the microfilaria generally pass into the lymphatics, and occasionally into subcutaneous tissues, where they mature into adult male and female worms. After mating, the female releases her offspring into the lymphatic system of the host. The larvae become widely distributed in the bloodstream and exhibit the "nocturnal" pattern described. If suitable vectors do not ingest the microfilaria, the parasites will die and disappear from the circulation.

The life cycle of *B. malayi*—also known as *Wuchereria malayi* or *Filaria malayi*—is similar to that of *W. bancrofti,* except that these filaria are present in the peripheral blood for approximately 20 hours a day.

Symptoms and pathology. Clinically, effects of the disease vary with the host's general state of health, as well as the number of infective larvae, locations of the adult worms, and strain differences. Early effects of the disease include fever, lymphadentitis, and lymphangitis. The skin thickens during the course of the disease, and elephantiasis of the legs, scrotum, breasts, and vulva may occur, but elephantiasis is not an inevitable outcome. The obstruction of lymphatic drainage was formerly thought to be caused by the accumulation of living or dead adult worms. However, the possibility of an allergic tissue response toward the parasites has been suggested.

The clinical mainfestations of Malayan and Bancroftian filariasis are similar, except that the Malayan elephantiasis primarily involves the legs and is not as severe.

Laboratory diagnosis. Although clinical features are important, a true diagnosis is dependent upon the demonstration of the microfilaria in blood films (Color photograph 107). In regions where several filarial diseases are found, a differentiation among the parasites must be made. This is accomplished by structurally comparing the posterior ends of the microfilaria, noting (1) the presence or absence of a sheath, (2) the distribution, and (3) the number of nuclei present in this region of the parasite (Figure 42–5).

Prevention. Measures taken to prevent or control filariasis are similar to those which are observed with other arthropod-borne diseases.

Hookworm Infection

The term "hookworm" was coined on the basis of either the curved or bent anterior end of the worm, or the "hook-like" bursal rays (the supporting structures found in the posterior extremity of male worms) (Figure 42–6C shows a copulatory bursa).

Means of transmission and life cycle. The two hookworm species most important for man are *Ancylostoma duodenale* (the Old World hookworm) and *Necator americanus* (the American or New World hookworm). Both go through the same general life cycle. The ova of hookworms (Figure 42–6A) are passed in the fecal matter of an infected person. These eggs develop in the soil and give rise to rhabditiform larvae. With further growth, they develop into infective filariform larvae (Figure 42–6B). Under favorable conditions, the larvae may live for several months in the soil.

Man acquires a hookworm infection by these larvae penetrating his skin, often through the soles of the feet. Once in the body, the parasites are carried to the heart and lungs by the bloodstream. After further growth and development, the larvae penetrate the alveoli, ascend the respiratory tree, and are swallowed. Thus the parasites reach the small intestine, where they mature into adult male

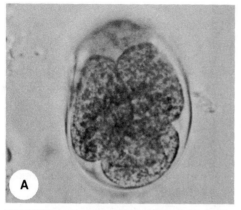

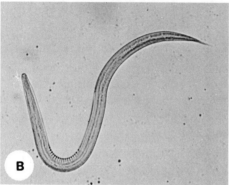

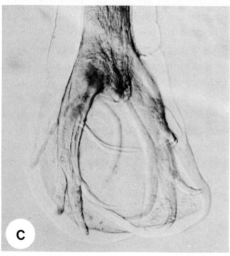

FIG. 42–6. Stages in the life cycle of hookworms. _A_. The ovum of *Necator americanus*. Hookworms range from 56 to 76 μm in length and 36 to 40 μm in width. _B_. An infective larva of *N. americanus*. These forms average 700 μm in length. _C_. The bursa of the male worm.

and female worms. Mating takes place in this area, the female lays eggs (which are passed out with the host's feces), and the cycle begins again.

Symptoms and pathology. The penetration of the skin by the rhabditiform larvae has been known to cause an allergic condition known as *ground itch*. This is more common with *N. americanus* than with the Old World species. In cases of large infecting larval doses, pneumonitis may occur.

Symptoms associated with this disease are for the most part dependent on the number of parasites present, and the general resistance of the host. With early infections, individuals may experience vague abdominal pains, colic, or nausea. Since the hookworms ingest the host's blood, chronic infections may cause significantly large blood loss, resulting in an iron deficiency anemic state.

Laboratory diagnosis. The recovery of hookworm ova is usually the basis of diagnosis. Eggs of *N. americanus* are slightly larger (64 to 76 by 40μm) than those of *A. duodenale* (56 to 60 by 36 to 40 μm).

Prevention. Control measures to prevent hookworm infections include (1) the use of footwear in endemic areas, (2) improvement of general sanitation (especially disposal of human fecal matter), (3) mass treatment of infected persons, and (4) increased attempts to educate individuals as to the parasite and its effects.

Trichinosis

Trichinella spiralis was first observed in its encapsulated larval form in the early 1800s. However, the pathologic significance of trichinosis in man was not truly recognized until 1860. In that year Zenker provided evidence of the serious and often fatal consequences of the disease.

Initially, *Trichinella spiralis* infection was found to be a public health problem in the pork-consuming populations of Europe. However, today, trichinosis has a much wider distribution, especially in the United States.

Transmission and life cycle. *T. spiralis* infection generally results from the consumption of improperly cooked or inadequately processed pork. The parasite exhibits very little host specificity, as evidenced by trichinal infections associated with bear meat and walrus flesh.

The ingestion of meat containing encysted larvae begins the parasite's life cycle in the host. The larvae excyst, invade the intestinal mucosa, and within a short period of time develop into adult male and female worms. Mating occurs and the female releases larvae (larviposits), which eventually enter the individual's bloodstream and consequently are distributed throughout the body.

These parasites quite often are filtered out in striated muscle, where they attain their full size and imbed themselves in a sheath derived from the host's muscle tissue. Several muscles of the host can be parasitized in this manner, including the diaphragm, deltoid, larynx, and pectoral. Many encapsulated larvae can remain viable for several years. However, the parasites eventually become calcified.

In the case of human infections, the full life cycle of the parasite usually involves two omnivorous mammals. *T. spiralis* is quite commonly found in rats and in swine raised on uncooked garbage or other products possibly containing the parasite.

Symptoms and pathology. The majority of individuals with trichinosis are asymptomatic. As with other parasitic infections, the clinical effects are dependent upon the number and location of larvae present in the body and the general health and resistance of the host. If symptoms do occur, usually diarrhea (with or without abdominal pain), eosinophilia (excess numbers of eosinophiles), fever, and nausea are observed.

With the invasion of muscular tissue, clinical findings again vary according to the intensity of the parasitosis. Manifestations which can develop include periorbital edema (swelling around the eyes), increasing eosinophilia, muscular pains, and respiratory difficulties. Splinter hemorrhages under the fingernails are very common. In severe cases, cardiac and neurologic involvement leads to death within 4 to 6 weeks after the onset of infection.

Laboratory diagnosis. Definite diagnosis of trichinosis is made on the basis of the demonstration of larvae in muscle biopsy material. Clinical symptoms and the patient's history are extremely important. The Bachman intradermal test (an immediate type of skin reaction) is of considerable value in following the progress of the disease and also in distinguishing trichinosis from other infections. This test involves the intracutaneous inoculation of a larvae extract. Both the biopsy examination and the skin test must be carried out at the appropriate time, which is approximately 3 to 4 weeks after the onset of the infection.

Prevention. To prevent infection with *Trichinella spiralis*, the proper cooking of pork and related products, and freezing pork at $-10°C$ or lower for longer than 24 hours are relatively effective.

The Platyhelminthes

The Cestodes

Tapeworms or cestodes comprise a specific class of the phylum Platyhelminthes, namely, Cestoidea. These worms are endoparasites which as adults live in the intestines of vertebrate hosts. Several species are capable of parasitizing man (Table 42–2).

The bodies of cestodes are flattened dorso-ventrally and consist of: (1) a *scolex* (head or attachment organ), which, depending on the particular species, may or may not be equipped with hooks and/or suckers; (2) a neck region (the zone of proliferation for body segments); and (3) the body, properly called the *strobila*. Figure 42–7 shows diagrammatically the relationship of these tapeworm parts to one another.

The hooks of the so-called *armed scolices* of tapeworms are attached to an anterior *rostellum* (Figure 42–8 and Color photograph 109) which may or may not be retractable. The armed scolex is characteristic of *Taenia solium* (Figure 42–8*A*), the pork tapeworm, while the unarmed structure is found in *Taenia saginata* (Figure 42–8*B*), the beef tapeworm. Still other tapeworm species, such as *Dibothriocephalus latus* (the fish tapeworm), possess heads which are in the form of a trenchlike groove (Figure 42–8*C*). Usually scolices of this nature exhibit weak suction power.

The strobila is composed of a series of *proglottids* (body segments) which, proceeding from the neck of the tapeworm, include (1) sexually immature units, (2) sexually mature segments, (Figure 42–9) and (3) gravid structures (the most distal) filled with ova. These body segments account for the ribbon-like appearance of these worms. Each pro-

Table 42–2   Representative Medically Important Cestodes

Organism	Disease	Host Range	Location in the Body	Geographical Distribution	Treatment
Dibothriocephalus latus (also known as *Diphyllobothrium latum*)	Dibothriocephaliasis (Diphyllobuthriasis)	Humans, dogs, cats, bears, other fish-consuming mammals	Intestine	Orient, Europe, United States, most of the great lakes of the world	Atabrine, carbon tetrachloride, oleoresin of aspidium
Echinococcus granulosis	Hydatid disease	Cattle, deer, dogs, foxes, horses, humans, jackals, pigs, rabbits, sheep, and wolves	Bone, brain, heart, kidney, liver, lungs, and spleen	Australia, Middle East, portions of South America, and United States	For adult worms, arecoline diphenthane, and 2% hydrogen peroxide; for cysts, surgical removal
Hymenolepsis diminuta	Hymenolepiasis diminuta	Rats, mice, humans, dogs	Intestine	Widespread. Sporadic in most instances	Oleoresin of male fern (contains either extract of plant and guinacrine)
Hymenolepsis nana	Hymenolepiasis nana	Rats, mice, humans	Intestine	United States, Asia, Europe. Sporadic in many instances	Atabrine and tetrachloroethylene
Taenia saginata[a]	Taeniasis saginata	Cysticercus in cows, adult worms in humans	Small intestine	Areas in which beef is consumed	Quinacrine hydrochloride (Atabrine)
Taenia solium	Taeniasis solium	Cysticercus in pigs, adult worms in humans	Small intestine	Areas in which beef is consumed	Antiphen, Atabrine

[a] According to T. C. Cheng, this cestode belongs more correctly in the genus of *Taeniarhynchus*. The full designation for the organism then would be *Taeniarhynchus saginatus*.

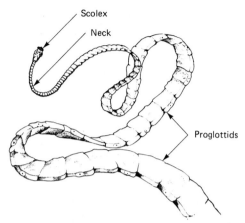

FIG. 42–7. A diagrammatic representation of a typical tapeworm.

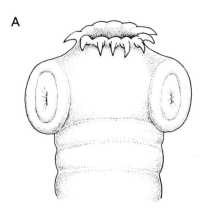

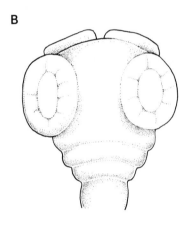

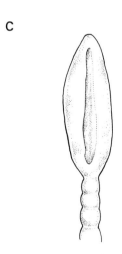

glottid usually possesses a complete set of female and male reproductive organs. In short, tapeworms are hermaphroditic. Fertilization may occur between proglottids of the same or different worms (*reciprocal fertilization*), or the sexual organs of a single body segment may carry out the process (*self-fertilization*).

Cestodes do not possess circulatory, digestive, respiratory, or skeletal organs. However, they do have ganglia and nerve cords. No specialized sense organs are known to occur.

The life cycles of cestodes, generally speaking, are complex. The majority of these parasites utilize a host other than man for the development of infective larvae. The eggs of the cestodes, with one exception (Figure 42–10*A*), are not operculated (Figure 42–10*B*). They vary in general appearance, as well as in the protective coverings of embryos (embryonic membranes). The embryo is referred to as the *oncosphere*. The life cycles of individual cestodes will be discussed more fully in the specific sections which follow.

Representative Tapeworm Infections

Dibothriocephaliasis (Diphylobothriasis). *Dibothriocephalus latus,* the broad

FIG. 42–8. Comparison of tapeworm scolices. <u>A</u>. *Taenia solium.* <u>B</u>. *T. saginata.* <u>C</u>. *Dibothriocephalus latus.*

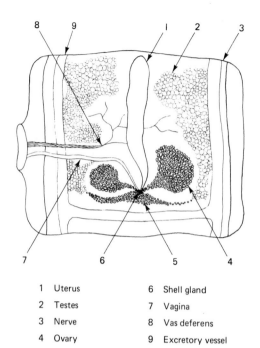

1	Uterus	6	Shell gland
2	Testes	7	Vagina
3	Nerve	8	Vas deferens
4	Ovary	9	Excretory vessel
5	Vitelline gland		

FIG. 42–9. Schematic representation of a mature proglottid from *Taenia solium*.

or fish tapeworm, is a relatively common parasite of man, dog, and fish-eating mammals in many parts of the world. While the tapeworm exhibits a worldwide distribution, it is encountered more commonly in fresh-water lake regions in central and northern Asia and Europe and in north-central Canada and the United States. Infections have also been reported in Alaska, Australia, and South America. Moreover, effects of the parasite have been found in individuals elsewhere who have eaten fish or associated products from endemic regions.

While symptoms of parasitosis are absent in many cases, the parasite may cause a condition closely resembling vitamin B_{12} deficiency (pernicious anemia). Other symptoms, including abdominal pains, enteritis (intestinal inflammation), and nervous involvement may be observed.

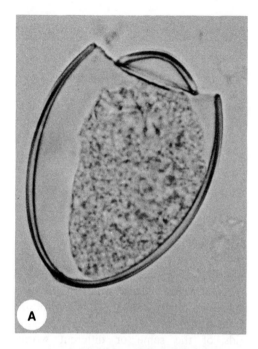

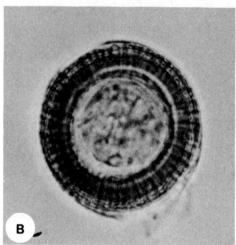

FIG. 42–10. Representative cestode eggs. *A*. The one exception to non-operculated eggs of tapeworms, *Dibothriocephalus latus*. Ova generally measure 70 μm in width. *B*. *Taenia saginata*. Ova generally measure 30 to 40 μm in diameter.

Mode of transmission and life cycle. Man and other suitable hosts, e.g., dogs and bears, acquire the infection by eating raw, improperly cooked, or pickled infected fresh-water fish. The parasite's life cycle is a complex one and usually involves two intermediate hosts. The cycle commences when unembryonated tapeworm eggs (Figure 42–10A) are discharged via the host's feces into a cool fresh-water environment.

These ova embryonate shortly (11 to 15 days), and then give rise to small ciliated embryos (embryophores). In order for the cycle to continue, the free-swimming larvae must be ingested by certain species of water fleas, such as *Cyclops*. In this first host, the parasite undergoes development by shedding its ciliated coat and being tranformed into a larval form known as a *procercoid*.

The infected crustaceans are eaten by any of a large variety of fishes, including perch, pike, salmon, and trout, thus providing an important environment for continued development of the parasite. The proceroid larvae migrate into the tissues of their second host and eventually develop into infective larvae. Ingestion of such parasitized fish by man completes the cycle, with the larvae developing into mature worms which are capable of egg production. Adult worms range in size from 3 to 10 or more meters in length. The fish tapeworm's scolex (Figure 42–8C) is quite different from other tapeworms of man. It has a somewhat "almond" shape with two deep grooves.

Laboratory diagnosis. The ova or, if found, the parasite's proglottids serve as the basis for diagnosis.

Prevention. Measures to prevent infection consist of: (1) thorough cooking of fish before eating, (2) elimination of reservoir hosts if possible, (3) treatment of infected individuals, and (4) removing the possibility of untreated sewage entering lakes and rivers. Freezing of fish for about 24 hours appears to be effective also.

Hydatid disease. *Echinococcus granulosis,* the hydatid worm, causes the most serious larval tapeworm infection in humans. A hydatid or hydatid cyst is the larval stage of the parasite. Adult *E. granulosis* are attached to the intestinal lining of carnivorous mammals such as dogs, foxes, and wolves. The complete strobila or body of the worm consists of a scolex (Color photograph 109), neck (one immature, one mature proglottids), and one or two gravid proglottids. The scolex contains four minute suckers and a double row of alternating hooklets. The gravid proglottids disintegrate in the small intestine of the final or definitive host, thereby providing a means by which the parasite's eggs can be eliminated in the feces.

Hydatid cyst is widely distributed throughout the temperate and subtropical regions of the world. The parasite is especially common in sheep-raising countries such as Australia, portions of South America, the Middle East, and the western United States.

Mode of transmission and life cycle. The important part of the life cycle from the standpoint of pathogenicity is the larval stage. Almost any mammal that ingests *E. granulosis* embryonated eggs can serve as a host for larval development. These intermediate hosts include camels, cattle, deer, horses, humans, mice, pigs, and rabbits. Herders of infected sheep and pigs are frequently exposed. In the intestine of the host, the eggs hatch and the liberated embryos make their way to various body organs, such as the brain, heart, kidneys, liver, and lungs, in which they become lodged. In these regions the larval form of the parasite is slowly transformed into a spherical fluid-filled sac or bladder, which is the cyst or hydatid. Cysts may grow to sizes that contain as much as 15 litres of fluid. The hydatid's inner lining can give rise to numerous scolices, which in turn may develop into daughter cysts. A hydatid of this type, which is surrounded by an intact, friable, multi-layered membrane covered with a host tissue, is called a *unilocular cyst*. If the host's membrane doesn't form, and the parasite digests its way through the organ in which it has become implanted, the hydatid is called an *alveolar cyst*. Alveolar cysts occur most frequently in the liver. Another type of cyst, called an *osseous cyst*, is formed when a hydatid develops with bone.

Damage caused by any cyst is related not only to its location but also to its size. It is possible for a hydatid to develop for several years before it causes serious injury. Ruptured cysts may produce a variety of allergic states, including anaphylaxis.

In the treatment of hydatid disease, chemotherapy is of little value. The standard procedure is surgical removal of the cyst. It should be noted that great care must be used in removing a cyst, since puncturing the structure would obviously result in the release of scolices into the body. Such scolices would then produce secondary growths.

Laboratory diagnosis. Diagnosis can involve several factors, including a patient's case history, symptoms, and x-ray findings, and the detection of free scolices from specimens such as aspirated hydatid fluid of stained preparations from a removed cyst (Color photograph 109). An intradermal skin test known as the Casoni test also can be used, as well as the indirect fluorescent antibody test, and the complement-fixation and other serological tests. The skin test is of an immediate type. The development of a positive reaction within 15 minutes after the introduction of a known amount of hydatid antigen

FIG. 42–11. A large hydatid cyst (arrows) of the liver in a dead animal which a shepherd has partially skinned to encourage sheepdogs to eat it. The cyst measures about 8 centimetres in diameter. (From Schantz, P. M., Clerou, R. P., Liu, I. K. M., and Schwabe, C. W.: *Amer. J. Trop. Med. Hyg.,* **19**:823, 1970.)

indicates current or previous infection. Indirect fluorescent antibody and immunoelectrophoresis procedures are currently under evaluation.

Prevention. Control measures are directed at domesticated dogs (the carriers of adult *E. granulosis*) and at hogs and sheep (the common reservoirs of the viable hydatid). Dogs become infected from eating the viscera of infected hogs and sheep (Figure 42–11). All infected carcasses should be incinerated, or treated chemically and buried deeply. Observation of personal hygiene practices, such as washing hands after handling dogs and, for children, avoiding contamination of fingers with a dog's excreta while playing with the animal, can prevent hydatid disease. Domestic dogs also should be periodically dewormed.

Taenia saginata infection. Beef or "unarmed"—hookless—tapeworm infections have been known since ancient times. The parasite is found among the beef-eating peoples of the world. Human infections more commonly occur with

Taenia saginata than with its counterpart in pork, *T. solium*. Man acquires the parasite by eating infected raw or lightly browned meats.

T. saginata lives in the small intestine and can measure from 5 to 25 meters in length. In general, the parasite is similar to *T. solium*. However, there are certain differences in the scolex (Figure 42–8), gravid proglottids, and the total length of strobila.

Transmission and life cycle. The life cycle of *T. saginata* is basically similar to that of *T. solium*. Embryonated ova are discharged in fecal matter and must be ingested by cattle, buffalo, or related animals. The eggs hatch within the small intestine, and the emerging parasites penetrate the animal's tissue and develop into an infective *cysticercus* (plural, cysticerci). This structure can be described simply as a fluid-filled bladder-like form containing miniature head of the parasite in an invaginated position. The stage is called *Cysticercus bovis*. Human infections with cysticerci are rare.

Adult worms develop in man as a consequence of ingesting infected meat, improperly cooked. The parasite attaches itself to the intestinal mucosa by means of its suckers. Usually, only one parasite is associated with an infection. However, cases in which more worms were involved have been reported.

Laboratory diagnosis. Diagnosis is based on determining the number of uterine side branches in gravid proglottids (Figure 42–12) obtained from stool specimens. Such proglottids can be examined in the living or stained states. The number of uterine branches characteristic for *T. saginata* is 15 to 20, averaging 18. This procedure is used because ova passed in feces are not only few in number, but indistinguishable from those of *T. solium*.

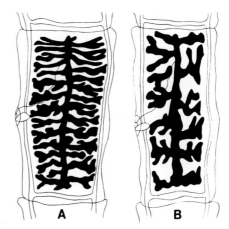

FIG. 42–12. A diagrammatic comparison of the gravid proglottids of tapeworms. *A. Taenia saginata. B. T. solium.*

Prevention. Measures against infection consist of avoiding ingestion of raw or improperly cooked meats, and sanitation improvement.

Taenia solium infection. Human infections with the "pork tapeworm" occur wherever raw or inadequately cooked infected pork is consumed. The disease is quite common in various parts of the world, including Central Europe, Mexico, and South America. Man acquires the parasite by swallowing the infective larval stage of the worm, *Cysticercus cellulosae*. This form of the parasite, like the cysticercus of *T. saginata*, is a fluid-filled bladder containing an invaginated miniature scolex.

The distinguishing characteristics of *T. solium* include its armed scolex (Figure 42–8*A*) and gravid proglottids (Figure 42–12*B*). The head of the worm is equipped with an alternating set of hooks, large and small, which produce a double ring appearance, and four prominent suckers. The gravid proglottids of the parasite contain 7 to 13 uterine branches in contrast to the average number of 18 for *T. saginata*.

Transmission and life cycle. Ingestion of ova by pigs or other animals initiates infection. In the small intestine of the animal, eggs hatch and liberate oncospheres which make their way to various tissues of the body. The parasites then develop into cysticerci. The term "measly pork" is used to describe the situation in which the tissues of the hog are heavily parasitized. Humans obtain the parasitic disease as a consequence of eating insufficiently cooked pork. In the intestine of man, the scolex of the bladderworm evaginates and, with the aid of suckers and hooks, the parasite can attach itself to the gut wall, and continue its development into an adult worm.

Clinical features. Symptoms associated with the infection may be extremely mild or totally absent. Of course, the exact extent of the parasitosis and the specific location of the parasites are determining factors.

Laboratory diagnosis. Finding of proglottids in fecal specimens and determining the number of uterine branches are of diagnostic significance. Serodiagnostic tests are currently being studied and evaluated.

Prevention. Preventive measures against infection are similar to those described for *T. saginata* infection.

The Trematodes

The Trematoda, or flukes, constitute another class of the phylum Platyhelminthes. Although thousands of species are known today, not all flukes are of medical significance. Table 42–3 lists a representative number of parasites belonging to this group which cause disease in man.

Generally speaking, most flukes (1) are flattened (somewhat in the form of a leaf or pear), (2) do not have a head or segmented body, (3) are covered by an external cuticular layer, and (4) species range in size from less than one millimeter to several centimeters, depending on the species.

As shown in Figure 42–13, these worms possess suckers and excretory, digestive, and reproductive systems. The digestive systems of the medically important parasites are incomplete. With one exception—the schistosomes (blood flukes)—all trematodes are hermaphroditic (monoecious). Sexual reproduction

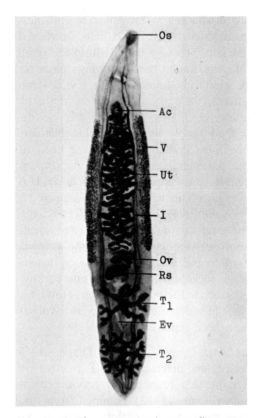

FIG. 42–13. The anatomy of a sexually mature *Clonorchis sinensis* (the Chinese liver fluke). This morphological type, the *distome* (possessing two suckers), is one of the most frequently encountered. Explanation of symbols: *Os,* oral sucker; *Ac,* ventral sucker; *V,* vitellaria; *Ut,* uterus; *I,* intestines; *Ov,* ovary; *Rx,* seminal receptacle; *T₁* and *T₂,* testes; *Ev,* excretory bladder. (Courtesy of Dr. Y. Komiya, Director, National Institute of Health, Tokyo, Japan.)

Table 42–3 Representative Medically Important Trematodes

Organism	Disease	Host Range	Location in the Body	Geographical Distribution	Treatment
Opisthorchis (Clonorchis) sinensis (Chinese liver fluke)	Clonorchiasis	Man, dogs, cats	Liver, bile ducts	China, Japan, Korea, Indochina	Hexachloroparaxylol 1, 4-Bis-trichloromethylbenzol
Fasciola hepatica (sheep liver fluke)	Fascioliasis	Man, sheep, goats, cattle	Liver, bile ducts	Sheep-raising regions	Hexachloroparaxylol
Fasciolopsis buski	Fasciolopsiasis	Man, pigs	Small intestine (duodenum, jejunum)	Orient	Hexachloroparaxylol, tetrachlorethylene
Heterophyes heterophyes	Heterophyiasis	Man, cats, dogs	Small intestine	Near East, Far East	Tetrachlorethylene, piperazine compounds
Metagonimus yokogawai	Metagoniminiasis	Man, cats, dogs, pigs	Small intestine	Far East, Siberia, Balkan states	Tetrachlorethylene
Opisthorchis felineus	Opisthorchiasis	Cats, occasionally man	Biliary and pancreatic ducts	Mainly in Central and Eastern Europe, U.S.S.R.	Thiabendazole, pyrvinium pamoate
Paragonimus westermani	Paragonimiasis	Man, cats	Lungs	Far East, Nigeria, Belgian Congo, Central America	Emetine hydrochloride combined with sulfonamide. Bithionol (2,2'-thiobis, 4,6-dichlorophenol)
Schistosoma haematobium	Schistosomiasis	Man, monkeys	Blood vessels, urinary bladder	Mainly Africa and Madagascar	Antimony compounds including antimony dimercaptosuccinate, and potassium antimony tartrate (tartaremetic)
Schistosoma japonicum	Schistosomiasis	Man, domestic animals	Blood vessels	Japan, China, Formosa, Philippines	Same as listed for *S. haematobium*
Schistosoma mansoni	Schistosomiasis	Man	Blood vessels, intestines	Generally, Africa, South America, including Puerto Rico and the Lesser Antilles	Same as listed for *S. haematobium*

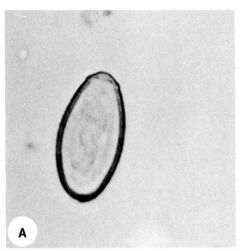

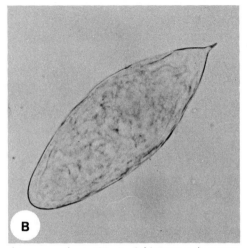

FIG. 42–14. A comparison of operculated and non-operculated ova of flukes. _A_. *Clonorchis sinensis*. Eggs of this parasite are approximately 29 μm in length and 16 μm in width. Notice the thin operculum (O). _B_. *Schistosoma haematobium*. These ova have dimensions of 110 to 175 μm in length and 40 to 70 μm in width. Note the terminal spine.

is the result of self-fertilization or cross-fertilization between two individual parasites.

Life Cycles

The majority of human-associated flukes produce operculated eggs (Figure 42–14*A*) and pass through four larval stages. The one exception to these characteristics are the schistosomes, which do not have operculated eggs and have only three larval stages (Figure 42–19).

It is important to note that, depending upon the location of the parasite in the host (e.g., *Paragonimus westermani* in the lungs, *Schistosoma haematobium* in the urinary bladder), the eggs of trematodes can be found in sputum, urine, or feces. By contrast, in the case of all man-associated cestodes, the eggs of adult worms are encountered in the feces of the host.

The individual larval stages of flukes are: (1) miracidium, (2) sporocyst, (3) redia, and (4) cercariae. The last three stages are found in fresh-water snails. In the case of certain trematode species,

such as *Opisthorchis (Clonorchis) sinensis, Fasciola hepatica,* and *Paragonimus westermani,* the last infective stage (known as metacercariae) can be found in crustaceans, in fishes, or on vegetation. The characteristic aspects of fluke development will be considered more fully for the individual species selected for discussion.

Representative Fluke Infestations

Clonorchiasis. Infections with the fluke *Clonorchis sinensis* are largely and commonly encountered in Oriental countries, including China, Indochina, Japan, and Korea. The causative agent of the disease was discovered by McConnel in 1865 in Calcutta, and was identified and named by T. S. Cobbold in the same year.

Means of transmission. The common practice of eating raw fish in the Orient appears to be the main means by which this infection is contracted. This is especially true in Japan and certain parts of China and Korea. The disease may also be acquired through the ingestion of improperly cooked, heavily infected fish.

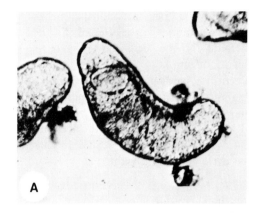

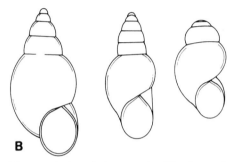

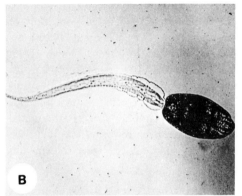

FIG. 42–15*A*. Actual photograph of *Parafossarulus manchouricus*. *B*. Drawings of shells belonging to first intermediate hosts of *Clonorchis sinensis*. Right, *P. manchouricus;* middle, *Bulimus* sp.; left, *Alocimua* sp. (Courtesy of Dr. Y. Komiya, Director, National Institute of Health, Tokyo, Japan.)

Life cycle. The ova of *C. sinensis*, once released by the host, do not hatch until they are ingested by suitable snail hosts, *Parafossarulus manchouricus* (Figure 42 15*A*) or *Bulimus* spp. (Figure 42–15*B*).

Within the snail, miracidia pass through the sporocyst, redia, and cercaria stages (Figure 42–16). The unforked cercariae leave the snail, and eventually attach to and penetrate an appropriate and available fish host, such as *Pseudorasbora* spp. (in Japan), *Zacco* spp. (in Taiwan), and *Acanthrohodeus* spp. (in China). As a consequence of the parasite's penetration, its tail becomes detached and is left behind on the outside of the host. This process is a rapid one, taking anywhere from 6 to 15 minutes for completion.

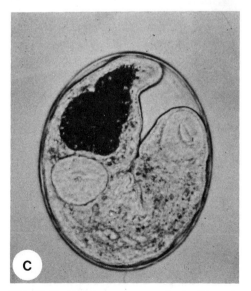

FIG. 42–16. Development stages in the life cycle of *C. sinensis*. *A*. Sporocyst. *B*. Stained cercaria. *C*. Metacercaria. (Courtesy of Dr. Y. Komiya, Director, National Institute of Health, Tokyo, Japan.)

Following penetration, the parasite encysts within the tissues of the fish, forming the metacercariae (Figure 42–16C). Infection of the final host occurs when the parasitized fish is eaten raw, or improperly cooked. Excystment occurs and the parasites develop into adult flukes in the digestive system of the new host. Once the fluke attains sexual maturity, the cycle can begin again.

Clinical symptoms and pathology. Taking into consideration various factors, such as the duration and intensity of the infestation and the general condition of the patient, certain classical symptoms and pathological effects have been reported. These include marked gastrointestinal disturbances, splenomegaly (enlarged spleen), cholecystitis (gallbladder inflammation) and hepatitis. Pathological changes have been reported involving the bile ducts, gallbladder, liver, spleen, and pancreas.

Laboratory diagnosis. When a patient's symptoms suggest clonorchiasis, diagnosis ultimately depends on the recovery and identification of *C. sinensis* ova. This is especially the case when there is the possibility of other diseases, including schistosomiasis and syphilis of the liver.

A direct smear can be made, using the fecal matter of the patient. However, in the event of a low-grade infection, sedimentation must first be carried out, as a means of concentrating the ova.

Prevention. Preventive measures in relation to clonorchiasis, as well as many other helminthic infestations, involves methods aimed at interrupting the life cycle of the parasite, the destruction of the adult flukes and ova, and the control of intermediate hosts. More public health education is needed, especially along the lines of sanitation improvements and persuading individuals in endemic areas

to stop eating raw or improperly cooked fish. This is quite a problem, as the custom is deeply rooted among Oriental peoples.

Paragonimiasis. It has been generally believed that the only lung fluke species developing in man is *Paragonimus westermani.* Recently, however, two more species have been reported as human pathogens. One of these, *P. skrjabini,* is the known causative agent of migratory subcutaneous nodular paragonimiasis.

Lung fluke infections are endemic primarily in the Orient and the surrounding areas, including Central China, Formosa (Taiwan), Japan, Korea, and the Philippines. Sporadic infestations have been reported in the Belgian Congo and Central America. *P. westermani* was first discovered by Kerbert in 1878.

Means of transmission. The most common means by which human paragonimiasis is contracted is by eating raw or partially cooked infected crabs. In addition, knives, strainers, chopping blocks, and other items used in the preparation and serving of dishes with infected crab can become contaminated with encysted metacercariae. Consequently, these kitchen utensils could serve as sources for fluke infestations.

Life cycle. Ova from *P. westermani* adults (Figure 42–17) are expelled from man via his sputum. This usually results from the rupturing of encapsulated cysts, which harbor the adult worms, into the bronchioles of the host. Eggs then are released and subsequently coughed up and spat out. Under suitable moist environmental conditions and optimum temperatures, miracidia develop and hatch in approximately 2 to 7 weeks. In the Far East, the rice and vegetable paddies serve as ideal areas for the development of this parasite.

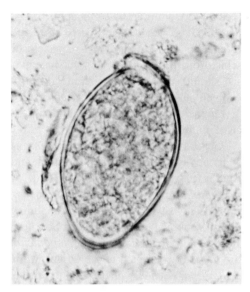

FIG. 42–17. *Paragonimus westermani* ovum. These eggs usually range in length from 80 to 120 μm and in width from 50 to 60 μm.

Emerging miracidia locate and penetrate their first intermediate host, a snail belonging to any one of a large number of genera, including *Brotea, Hua, Melania, Oncomelania, Pomatiopsis, Semisulcospira,* and *Thiara.* Shortly after invading the snail host, the miracidia undergo a development cycle and form a sporocyst generation. Following this larval stage, two generations of rediae are formed. The first of these develops within 4 weeks after injection, while the second generation of rediae make their appearances approximately 63 days after penetration.

Microcercous cercariae (larvae which are characterized by a short knoblike tail) escape from the snail about 78 days after the initial invasion. These cercariae crawl rather than swim to their second intermediate host, and are believed either to penetrate the crab at various vulnerable locations, e.g., joint folds, or to be ingested by the host. More than 11 species of crayfish and freshwater crabs have

been reported as being involved with this phase of *P. westermani's* life cycle. Members of the crab genera *Eriocheir, Parathelphusa, Potomon,* and *Sesarma* and those crayfish belonging to the genera *Cambaroides* and *Cambarus* are usually second intermediate hosts.

Once inside the new host, metacercarial cysts are formed in such areas as the gills, heart, liver, muscles of the legs, and general body. A crab-eating host, such as man, acquires the parasites as a consequence of eating uncooked or poorly cooked crayfish or crabs. Excystment of the metacercariae occurs in the intestine of the definitive host, usually within one hour after ingestion. Emerging immature flukes bore through the intestine into the coelom (body cavity), penetrate the diaphragm, and finally enter the lungs, where they encapsulate. It is also possible, according to several reports, for *P. westermani* to become lodged in other body structures, such as the brain, intestines, liver, and urinary system. Mature adult flukes subsequently produce ova, and upon their expulsion from the host, the cycle begins once more.

Clinical symptoms and pathology. The characteristic symptoms of paragonimiasis is a cough and blood-stained sputum. During the early stages of this disease, almost all patients exhibit pleurisy and occasionally pneumothorax (lung collapse). Nonspecific symptoms such as anemia and eosinophila also have been reported. The pathologic manifestations associated with this disease, as with any disease in general, are affected by factors as the number of parasites and the duration of the infection. Nevertheless, ulcerating abscesses involving cutaneous, mucous, and serous surfaces, fibrous cyst formation, and cystic dilatation of the bronchi are representative of the reported pathologic findings.

Laboratory diagnosis. Unequivocal diagnosis of paragonimiasis depends upon the finding of *P. westermani* ova (Figure 42–17) in sputum or stool specimens. In recent years, however, an increasing number of serologic tests also have been widely applied. Many of these have served as supplementary diagnostic methods. Included in this group are techniques such as an immediate-type intradermal test (I.D.), agglutination, and complement-fixation tests. The antigens employed here are extracts of adult or larval forms. The I.D. test is especially useful in differentiating paragonimiasis from pulmonary tuberculosis or other chest disease manifestations. The complement-fixation and agglutination tests can serve as indicators of cure after therapy. Both of these tests turn negative within 3 to 9 months after a complete recovery from *P. westermani* infection.

Prevention. Several control methods have been suggested for the eradication of *P. westermani* infections, including: (1) destruction of intermediate hosts, (2) mass treatment of human hosts in endemic areas to destroy adult flukes, and (3) increased education as to the dangers involved in eating of raw crabs, and the possibility of contamination during the preparation of food. It has been concluded that paragonimiasis could gradually die out with a thorough mass treatment of victims with bithionol in endemic areas.

Schistosomiasis (bilharziasis). Infection with blood flukes (the schistosomes) is considered one of the most important parasitic diseases of man. Three human-infecting species cause the disease entity, namely, *Schistosoma haematobium, S. japonicum,* and *S. mansoni.* The first species listed was discovered by Bilharz in 1852, while *S. japonicum* was first recovered from man by Fujinami in 1904. Sambon proposed the basis for the establishment of the third species of schistosome. Nevertheless, schistosomiasis should not be considered a newly evolved disease entity, especially since *S. haematobium* has been found in ancient mummies.

Generally speaking, *S. haematobium* is endemic in various parts of Africa and Madagascar. Sporadic infection with *S. haematobium* organism have been reported in several countries, including Saudi Arabia, Israel, Syria, and Southern Portugal. Infections with *S. japonicum* are generally confined to the Orient, while *S. mansoni* is widely distributed in Africa,

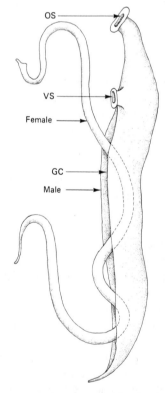

FIG. 42–18. A composite sketch of typical adult schistosomes. Note the following anatomical parts: *GC,* gynecophoric canal; *OS,* oral sucker; *VS,* ventral sucker.

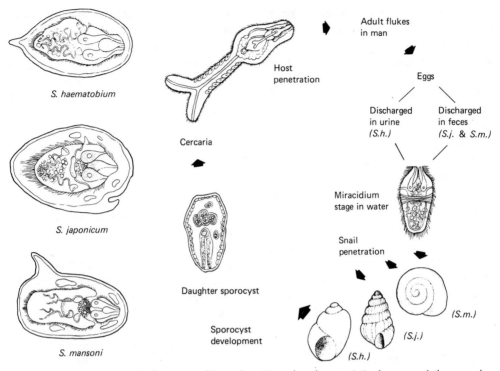

FIG. 42–19. A comparison of schistosome life cycles. Note the characteristic features of the eggs belonging to the three different species. (*S.m.* = *S. mansoni*; *S.j.* = *S. japonicum*; *S.h.* = *S. haematobium*.)

Madagascar, Brazil, Venezuela, Puerto Rico, and the Dominican Republic. Immigration from Puerto Rico has made it a major health problem in New York City.

Means of transmission. Man acquires schistosomiasis as a consequence of working or wading in waters containing infective cercariae (Figure 42–19). These larvae escape from their snail intermediate host and penetrate the unbroken skin of a mammalian host. Once inside the new host, the parasites mature (Figure 42–18) and migrate to various tissue locations in the body.

Life cycle. A comparison of the life cycles of the three causative agents is given in Figure 42–19. As a definite degree of similarity exists among the schistosome species, only *S. japonicum* life's cycle will be described in detail here.

The life cycle of *S. japonicum* begins when ova containing fully developed miracidia are passed by an infected man in his feces. If the fecal matter comes into contact with water, the miracidium becomes extremely active, ruptures the egg, and escapes into the watery surroundings. The miracidium swims about in its environment in search of an appropriate snail host, such as *Oncomelania* spp. Upon finding the intermediate host, these larval forms penetrate, lose their ciliated covering, develop into sporocysts, and migrate to the visceral mass of the mollusc. The sporocysts multiply rapidly, and within 2 weeks large numbers of minute daughter sporocysts develop.

Unlike other flukes of medical importance, schistosomes do not produce rediae at any time during their life cycles. The final larval stage, cercariae, arise from sporocysts. Once formed, these fork-tailed cercariae escape from the snail and swim freely in a water environment looking for an appropriate host. In penetrating the unbroken skin of a mammalian host, the fork-tails of the cercariae are discarded.

With the aid of their various enzyme secretions, and their capacity to alternately contract and elongate, these parasites migrate through the body, entering small lymphatic vessels and eventually reaching the systemic circulation. Subsequently, the young flukes are carried to the portal system where they mature in the sinusoids of the host's liver. Then they return to the circulatory system, specifically to the superior mesenteric veins. Here copulation occurs, and the female flukes enter the smaller branches of the vein to lay eggs. These deposited eggs can become dislodged and carried by the blood to intestinal blood vessels. From this location, the ova penetrate the intestinal wall, causing traumatic injury (Color photograph 108), then enter the intestinal lumen and leave their host via the feces.

Clinical symptoms and pathology. No notable differences in symptomatology are evident between the schistosome species. The major clinical manifestations include systemic intoxication, fever, night sweats, diarrhea or dysentery, excruciating epigastric pain, and an increase in liver size. In the case of *S. haematobium,* hematuria and bladder colic are characteristically encountered.

The form as well as the severity of pathologic changes in cases of human schistosomiasis are apparently related not only to the numbers of parasites present and the tissues involved, but also to the particular sensitivity of the host animal. Generally, the deposition of eggs causes local traumatic injury and hemorrhage. Ulceration and necrosis of intestinal tissues are characteristically encountered.

Migrating flukes usually produce little or no appreciable damage. However, involvement of the liver by schistosomes may cause enlargement and extreme tenderness of this organ. Invasion of the lungs can produce pneumonia. Pathologic manifestations in the urinary and reproductive systems can be quite extensive in the case of *S. haematobium.* These effects include (1) fibrosis of the muscular and subcutaneous coats of the urinary bladder, (2) constriction of the urethral lumen, (3) formation of bladder stones, and (4) obstruction of the scrotal lymphatics. Chronic schistosomiasis has been implicated as a prominent factor in the development of malignancies of the urinary bladder.

Diagnosis. The ova of the schistosomes are quite characteristic. Diagnosis in the majority of cases is made by the identification of eggs from fecal or urine specimens. Another means of diagnosis involves causing the fluke's miracidia to hatch and identifying the larval forms. Another technique is the rectal biopsy test. A small piece of tissue is removed and examined for the presence of ova. This latter test has value in diagnosing infections of long standing. Complement-fixation and skin testing can also be employed as supplementary procedures. In addition, routine use of the indirect fluorescent antibody test is increasing.

Prevention. Control measures for schistomiasis include (1) improvements in sanitary practices to prevent contamination of agricultural products by infected human fecal matter, (2) the incorporation of appropriate molluscicides to kill snail vectors, and (3) the use of improved means to educate people as to the dangers of soil and water pollution. The latter measure involves disseminating knowledge of proper sanitary disposal methods for human wastes, and the discontinuation of the use of human and animal feces as agricultural fertilizer.

"Swimmer's itch" (schistosome dermatitis). The cercariae of several fluke species which are normally parasitic in birds and in mammals other than man can be encountered in fresh-water streams, ponds, lakes, and seashore regions. These larvae are apparently not as host-specific as the other developmental larvae of flukes, such as miracidia, and may even penetrate the skin of available vertebrates.

Maturation of the parasite does not occur in the human, but its penetration of the skin causes a dermatitis characterized by numerous small red pustules and intense itching. The life cycle of these dermatitis-producing schistosomes does not differ substantially from those found normally in humans. Although man is an accidental host for these parasites, "swimmer's itch" is not an uncommon disease entity.

The cercariae of the following species may be involved in this form of parasitism," *Austrobilharzia* spp., *Gigantobilharzia* spp., *Schistosomatium* spp., *Trichobilharzia* spp.

No specific chemotherapy is available for schistosome dermatitis. However, calamine or caladryl lotion may be applied to relieve the intense itching. Although the itching and eruptions usually disappear within a short period, small scars may form. These last for only a few weeks.

Control measures are primarily directed against the snail hosts, *Hymnaea* spp., *Nassarius* spp., and *Physa* spp. Copper sulfate is commonly employed. Care must be exercised in its application, however, as the chemical molluscicide is quite toxic for various forms of aquatic life.

QUESTIONS FOR REVIEW

1. What properties of helminths enable them to adapt to a parasitic existence?

2. From a medical standpoint, what helminthic structures are of diagnostic significance?

3. Compare roundworms, flukes, and tapeworms as to the following characteristics:
   a. general structural features
   b. life cycles
   c. reservoirs
   d. diagnosis

4. a. What general measures are used in the control of helminthic diseases?
   b. Why are certain diseases of this type difficult to eradicate? Explain.
   c. What major means can be used to eliminate the Chinese liver fluke from a particular region?

5. Do helminthic diseases affect only the gastrointestinal system? Which ones do not?

6. If you were going to tour various parts of the world, including Africa, Central America, the South Pacific,

and the Orient, which helminthic diseases might your encounter?

7. a. What are microfilariae?
   b. What diseases are associated with them?
   c. How are these agents transmitted?

8. Distinguish between armed and unarmed scolices.

9. What is a cysticercus?

10. What is "swimmer's itch"? Is this a fatal type of infection?

11. How would you diagnostically differentiate between tuberculosis and paragonimiasis?

12. a. What relationship does fertilizing crops with human excreta have to the occurrence of helminthic diseases?
    b. Are fomites of significance in the transmission of these diseases?

Glossary

A

abscess: A localized collection of pus.

accretion: The process whereby substances accumulate externally onto surfaces.

acid-fastness: A particular property of certain bacteria that retain the primary stain (carbol fuchsin) and are difficult to decolorize with acid alcohol.

acne vulgaris: A chronic skin condition characterized by inflammed sebaceous glands.

acquired immunity: Resistance acquired after birth.

active immunization: The production of antibodies in response to a direct antigenic stimulus.

acute: Short in duration, with a rapid onset and relative severity.

adaptation: The ability to adjust.

adjuvant: A substance used to prolong and intensify an antigenic stimulus.

adoptive immunity: An experimental phenomenon produced by the transfer of cells capable of synthesizing immunoglobulins.

aerobe: A microorganism whose growth requires the presence of free oxygen.

aerotolerant: Able to grow in the presence of free oxygen (e.g., streptococci).

agammaglobulinemia: A congenital immunological abnormality characterized by the absence of gamma globulin.

agar-agar: A dried polysaccharide extract of red algae, used as the solidifying agent in various microbiological media.

agglutination: The visible clumping of cellular or particle-like antigens by homologous antibodies (e.g., blood typing).

agglutinins: Antibodies that cause agglutination.

agglutinogen: The particulate antigen involved in the agglutination reaction.

algal bloom: A large accumulation of algae in one area.

allele: Alternate gene.

allergens: The antigenic substances that cause allergies.

allergic rhinitis: Hay fever.

allergy: Any altered activity of an individual caused by contact with animate or inanimate substances.

allotypes: Genetic variations.

alopecia: Temporary loss of hair.

amino acid: A nitrogenous organic compound that serves as a basic unit of structure of a protein molecule.

amphibionts: Obligately parasitic, but not pathogenic, organisms found on man and lower animals.

amphitrichous: Having one flagellum at each end of a cell.

anabolism: Processes of metabolism which are synthetic in nature and result in the formation of cell materials (e.g., protein, nucleic acid, lipids).

anaerobe: A microorganism that grows only or best in the absence of free oxygen.

anamnestic response: The sudden secondary rise in antibody concentration produced by a second injection of antigen some time after the initial exposure.

anaphylaxis: An immediate type of allergic reaction resulting in the release of histamine and other pharmacologically active agents.

anemia: A deficiency of erythrocytes, hemoglobin content of cells, or both.

Angstrom (Å) unit: A unit of length measuring 10^{-8} cm (1/100,000,000 cm).

aniline dye: A synthetic organic dye.

antibiogram: An evaluation of an organism's sensitivity to a series of antimicrobial agents.

antibiotic: A microbial metabolic product which has antimicrobial activity.

antibody (immunoglobulin): A protein synthesized by lymphatic tissue cells in response to an antigenic stimulus (foreign macromolecules).

antigen: A foreign substance which induces the formation of antibodies. Chemically such stimulants are protein, polysaccharide, or a combination of the two.

antiseptic: Against or opposing sepsis (infection), putrefaction, or decay. An antimicrobial agent used for decontamination of body surfaces by preventing or arresting microbial growth.

antiserum: Serum containing specific antibodies.

antitoxin: An antibody capable of neutralizing the toxin or toxoid which stimulated its production.

arboviruses: Viruses transmitted by arthropods.

arthropod: An invertebrate animal having jointed body and limbs (e.g., insects).

arthrospore: A thin-walled asexual spore formed from the fragmentation of hyphae.

Arthus reaction: A localized form of anaphylaxis.

ascarid: A form of roundworm belonging to the genus *Ascaris*.

ascospore: A sexual spore of ascomycetes.

aseptic meningitis: Nonbacterial inflammation of the meninges.

atelectasis: A collapsed condition of the lung.

atopy: An allergic response which develops in individuals accidentally absorbing certain allergic substances; conditions of this nature show a familial distribution and may be inheritable.

atrichous: Lacking flagella.

attenuated: Weakened; reduced in virulence.

auto-antibodies: Immunoglobulins produced against body components.

autoclave: An apparatus utilizing pressurized steam for sterilization.

autogenous vaccine: A preparation of organisms isolated from the patient to be treated.

autograph: The tissue used for transplantation from healthy areas to denuded areas of the same individual. The recipient is also the donor in this case.

auto-immunization: A state resulting from the production of antibodies (auto-antibodies) against the host's body components (auto-antigens).

autolysis: Cellular disintegration caused by the organism's own enzymes.

autotroph: An organism that is able to synthesize all of its organic components from inorganic sources.

avirulent: Unable to produce disease.

B

bacteremia: The demonstrated presence of bacteria in the blood.

bactericidal: Lethal to bacteria.

bacterin: A nonliving immunizing preparation consisting of either killed bacteria or extracts of such cells.

bacteriocin: An antimicrobial substance which will kill sensitive members of other strains of the same organism. Its production is by certain bacteria, under the genetic control of an episome.

bacteriology: The science of microorganisms whose general characteristics include (1) an undifferentiated unicellular arrangement, (2) non-mitotic nuclear division, (3) no nuclear membrane, and (4) a usual upper size of 2-3 μm.

bacteriophage: Viruses which infect bacteria.

bacteriostatic: Inhibitory to bacterial growth.

balanitis: Inflammation of the glans penis.

balanoposthitis: Inflammation of both the glans penis and the prepuce.

basal granule (body or organelle): The structure which gives rise to a flagellum or cilium.

base pair: A purine together with its complementary pyrimidine in DNA and RNA. For example, adenine pairs with thymine, and guanine with cytosine.

basidium: A club-shaped specialized cell of the fungus group basidiomycetes on which are borne the basidiospores.

B-cell: A lymphocyte from the bursa of Fabricius (that is, of the immunoglobulin-forming type).

BCG: Bacillus of Calmette and Guérin, an attenuated bovine strain of living tubercle bacilli used as a vaccine.

Bence-Jones protein: A light chain immunoglobulin subunit found in the urine of patients with a malignancy involving lymphoid tissue.

benign: Mild in nature; not malignant.

BGA: Bordet-Gengou agar.

binary fission: An asexual reproductive process in which one cell splits into two independent daughter cells.

Binomial System of Nomenclature: The scientific method of naming organisms. Each organism is given a two-part designation of genus and species.

biochemical mutants: A general term applied to mutants that have defects in biochemical pathways; generally applied to mutants defective in the production or degradation of small molecules.

Biochemical Oxygen Demand (BOD): The oxygen-consuming property of water.

biochemistry: The science of chemical compounds and reactions accompanying the vital functions of living things.

biophysics: The science of physical phenomena as applied to living organisms.

biopsy: The removal of tissue, its microscopic examination and identification.

bipolar staining: Intense staining of both ends of a cell.

blastospore: An asexual reproductive cell formed by a budding process.

blepharitis: Inflammation of eyelid margins and glands.

blight: A general term describing the manifestations observed in certain plant diseases. Sudden wilting, spotting, and death of plant parts or the entire plant are representative of the symptoms observed.

blood group antigens: Antigens that are genetically determined and that are associated with the surface of red blood cells.

Brownian movement: A peculiar jiggling motion of particles and bacteria in suspension, caused by the bombardment of molecules in the suspending fluid.

brucellergen test: Skin test for the diagnosis of brucellosis.

buboes: Enlarged regional lymph nodes.

bubonic plague: A disease state in man characterized by lymphatic involvement.

buccal: Pertaining to the cheek or mouth.

buffer: Any substance present in a preparation which tends to control the change in pH when either an acid or alkali is added.

bullae: Blisters.

bursa of Fabricius: A cloacal organ in fowl from which the immunoglobulin-synthesizing B-lymphocytes originate.

C

calcification: Deposit of calcium salts in soft tissue and bone.

calculus: An abnormal accumulation of mineral salts.

capneic cultivation: Growth under increased levels of CO_2.

capsid: The symmetrical protein coat that surrounds the nucleic acid core of viruses.

capsomere: The smallest subunit of a viral protein coat (capsid).

capsule: A component of certain yeasts and bacteria found external to their cell walls.

carbohydrate: A class of organic compounds of carbon, hydrogen, and oxygen, with the latter two components in a ratio of 2:1. Sugars, starches, and cellulose are examples.

carbuncle: A circumscribed skin and tissue inflammation which terminates in slough and pus formation.

carcinogen: Any cancer-producing substance.

carcinogenesis: The induction of cancer.

cardinal temperatures: Those temperatures which refer to the minimum, optimum and maximum levels characteristic of a particular organism.

caries: Gradual decay of a bone or tooth associated with the inflammation of bone or progressive decalcification of teeth.

carnivores: Meat eaters.

carrier: An individual harboring a disease agent without apparent symptoms.

caseation: The process by which the body converts necrotic tissue into a granular amorphous mass resembling cheese.

catabolism: The chemical reactions by which food materials or nutrients are converted into simpler substances for the production of energy and cell materials.

catalase: An enzyme that catalyzes the decomposition of hydrogen peroxide.

catalyst: A substance which is able to speed up or cause a reaction to occur without itself being altered permanently.

catarrhal: Characterized by the outpouring of mucus.

catheter: A tubular surgical device used for the withdrawal of fluids from a body cavity or structure.

cellulitis: Inflammation of connective tissue.

central dogma: The colloquial phrase given to a major theme of molecular biology—that the flow of information follows the pattern DNA → RNA → protein.

centrioles: Minute bodies found in eucaryotic cells which act as poles for the spindle fibers that develop during mitosis.

cercariae: The free-swimming larval stage of trematodes (flukes), with a main body and a tail.

cervicofacial: Pertaining to the neck and face.

cestodes: Tapeworms.

chancre: (Hunterian) the primary lesion of syphilis.

chemotaxis: Reaction to chemical stimuli, whereby cells are either attracted or repelled by the chemical.

chemotherapy: The treatment of disease by the use of chemicals which destroy the causative agents but should not injure the patient.

chiasmata: The crossing-over process during meiosis, resulting in the exchange of portions of chromosomes.

chitin: A complex polysaccharide which is the principal component of the exoskeletons of certain shellfish, arthropods, and of the cell walls of some fungi.

cholecystitis: Gallbladder inflammation.

chorioretinitis: Inflammation of the vascular coat (choroid) and the light-sensitive portion (retina) of the eye.

chromatic aberration: A distortion of an image due to light rays of different wavelengths being brought into focus at different points.

chromogenic: Pigment-producing.

chronic: Of long duration.

cilia: Short, hairlike processes projecting from cells.

ciliophora: A class of protozoa that possess cilia at some stage in their life cycle.

cisterna: The space between two unit membranes.

clone: A family of cells derived from a single parental cell by repeated divisions; the offspring of a single cell.

coagulase: An extracellular enzyme that causes citrated or oxalated plasma to clot.

coagulase-reacting factor (CRF): An accessory factor in plasma which must be present for coagulase activity.

coenzyme: The simpler portion of an enzyme which is necessary for the enzyme's activation.

colic: Abnormal abdominal pain.

colicin: One kind of bacteriocin; a protein produced by one strain of enteric bacteria that kills other strains of enteric bacteria.

coliform: Gram-negative rods, including *Escherichia coli* and similar species, that normally inhabit the colon (large intestine). Commonly included in the coliform group are *Enterobacter aerogenes, Klebsiella* sp., and other related bacteria.

colonization: Establishment of a site of reproduction of microbes on a material, animal, or person without necessarily resulting in tissue invasion or damage.

commensalism: The association between two organisms in which one is benefited and the other is neither harmed nor benefited.

competent cell: A bacterial cell that is capable of taking up and integrating high-molecular-weight DNA into its own chromosome in DNA-mediated transformation.

complement: A complex protein found in blood which is capable of destroying bacteria and certain other cells when it is combined with an antigen-antibody complex.

complement fixation: The inactivation of complement caused by its combining with an antigen-antibody complex. The reaction is the basis of certain diagnostic tests.

congenital: Existing at time of birth or shortly after.

conidiospores: Fungal spores borne on specialized structures called conidiophores.

conjunctiva: The mucous membrane that lines the inner surface of the eyelids and exposed surfaces of the eyeball.

consolidation: Solidification, as of the lung in pneumonia.

contact dermatitis: A particular form of delayed hypersensitivity which may be associated with simple chemicals, metals, certain drugs, cosmetics, insecticides, or the active components of plants such as poison ivy and poison oak.

contaminated: Soiled with infectious material.

contractile vacuole: A pulsating vacuole formed in certain protozoa, which helps to maintain proper osmotic balance in the cell.

Coombs tests: Serological tests used to detect incomplete antibodies. The procedures have clinical importance in cases of hemolytic anemia and erythroblastosis fetalis.

cord factor: A toxic substance produced by tubercle bacilli.

corticosteroids: Natural (or synthetic) compounds from the adrenal cortex which are anti-inflammatory and immunosuppressive.

coryza: Acute inflammation of the nasal mucous membrane.

counterstain: A dye used in differential staining techniques to impart color to organisms not retaining the primary stain.

crepitation: Creaking sounds.

cristae: The inner membrane layers of mitochondria which form folds or plates.

crithidial: Morphological form of the hemoflagellates in which the cell is spindle-shaped, possesses an undulating membrane and a flagellum, and the kinetoplast is located between the nucleus and the flagellum.

crossmatching: Procedures used to determine the blood compatabilities of prospective donors and recipients.

crust: Dried blood, pus, or serum combined with cellular and bacterial debris.

culture media: Artificial food material upon which microorganisms are grown.

curettage: Removal of tissue with a spoon-shape instrument (curet).

cyanophages: Viruses of blue-green algae.

cyanosis: Blue or grey-to-purple discoloration of the skin due to oxygen deficiency in the blood.

cyst: A walled sac or pouch which contains fluid, semisolid or solid material, or a resting structure formed by certain microorganisms.

cystitis: Inflammation of the urinary bladder.

cytochrome: Respiratory pigment widely distributed in nature, containing iron for oxidation-reduction activity.

cytology: The science dealing with the structure and function of cells.

cytomegaly: Increase in the size of cells.

cytopathic effect (CPE): Morphological changes in tissue culture cells caused by a pathogen, usually a virus.

cytotropic antibodies: The specific circulating antibodies associated with the wheal-and-flare, or erythema, response.

D

dacryoadenitis: Inflammation of the tear glands.

dalton: A unit of weight equal to the weight of a single atom of hydrogen.

DDT: An insecticide, dichlorodiphenyl trichloroethane, that is toxic to humans and other animals when swallowed or absorbed through the skin.

debilitated: State of weakness.

debridement: Surgical removal of devitalized tissue and foreign material.

deciduous teeth: First or temporary teeth.

decontamination: Removal or inactivation of pathogenic microorganisms and their toxic products.

deep-seated (systemic) mycoses: Fungus infections of the subepithelial tissues.

defective virus: A virus that lacks a part of its nucleic acid and thereby cannot direct the replication and release of complete, infective virions.

definitive: Final.

delayed hypersensitivity: A form of allergy characterized by several factors including the absence of circulating antibodies, reactions taking place from 24 to 48 hours, transfer possible in humans by a non-antibody "active" transfer factor, and lack of an inhibition of the reaction by antihistimines.

denaturation: A change in the secondary or tertiary structure of a macromolecule, such as a protein or nucleic acid, that affects solubility and various biological activities.

de nova: New.

dental caries: Tooth decay.

dermatophytoses: General designation given to skin diseases caused by fungi; such organisms are frequently called dermatophytes.

dermis: The portion of the skin lying just beneath the surface layers and containing nerves, blood vessels, and connective tissue.

dermotropic: Having an affinity for the skin.

desiccation: Drying.

detergent: Natural or synthetic compounds which are surface active materials (includes soap and quaternary ammonium compounds).

dextran: A branched polysaccharide of D-glucose subunits; often found as a storage product in bacteria and yeast.

diabetes mellitus: Disease caused by an inability of the pancreas to produce insulin.

diaminopimelic acid: A chemical found in nature only in procaryotic organisms, particularly in the cell-wall mucocomplex of bacteria.

diarrhea: The frequent passage of loose, watery stools.

diatomaceous earth: A filtering material composed of the remains of diatoms.

Dick test: Skin test to determine susceptibility to scarlet fever.

differential blood count: A procedure to determine the respective numbers of the various white blood cell types.

differential medium: A growth medium for microorganisms in which the appearance of certain organisms is altered so that they can be distinguished from one another.

diluting: The process of increasing the proportion of solvent to particulate matter or other material being diluted.

dilution (serial): Successive dilutions of a specimen.

dimorphism: The property of exhibiting two forms in different environments.

dipicolinic acid: A compound of bacterial spores which contributes to heat resistance.

diploid: Having chromosomes in pairs; twice the haploid number.

disinfection: The treatment of certain materials to reduce the level of contamination with particular reference to pathogens.

disseminated: Spread.

donor cell: The bacterial cell that transfers its chromosome, or a portion of its DNA, to another cell (the recipient cell).

droplet nucleus: The saliva, sputum, etc., remaining after evaporation of a discharged droplet.

D value: The time required to kill 90 per cent of the microorganisms in a suspension at a specific temperature.

dysentery: Intestinal disorders characterized by inflammation of the mucous membrane.

dysphagia: An inability or difficulty in swallowing.

dyspnea: Difficulty in breathing.

E

ecology: The study of the interrelationship of an organism and its environment.

ecosystem: All of the organisms in a habitat plus all of the factors in the environment with which the organisms interact.

ectoparasite: A parasite that lives or feeds on the outer surface of the host's body.

ectothrix infection: The growth of a fungus within and on the external portions of the hair shaft.

eczema: A condition characterized by a blistery skin rash, with weeping of fluid and formation of crusts, usually due to an allergy.

edema: An accumulation of fluids in tissue causing localized or generalized swelling.

Eh: The oxidation-reduction potential of a given system or the tendency of that system to take up or give out electrons, as compared to a standard hydrogen electrode.

electron transport system: A series of oxidation-reduction reactions in which electrons are transported from a substrate to a final acceptor, usually O_2, and ATP is formed.

electrophoresis: The migration of protein particles in an electrical field.

elephantiasis: Pronounced swelling due to obstruction of the lymphatic vessels.

encephalitis: Inflammation of the brain.

encephalomyelitis: Acute inflammation of the brain and spinal cord.

encystment: The process by which certain protozoa and helminths produce a resting structure, the cyst.

endemic: Present more or less continuously in a community.

endocarditis: Inflammation of the membrane lining of the heart valves and/or chambers.

endodontics: The specialty of dentistry dealing with the cause, diagnosis, and treatment of diseases involving the dental pulp.

endogenous: Arising from within.

endometritis: Inflammation of the uterus.

endoplasmic reticulum: Interconnected membranes within the cytoplasm of an eucaryotic cell.

endospore: A spore within the bacterium.

endothrix infection: The growth of a fungus only within the hair shaft.

endotoxin: A poisonous substance usually released after an organism disintegrates.

enteritis: Inflammation of the intestines, more particularly the mucous and submucous membranes of the small intestines.

enterocolitis: Inflammation of the intestines and colon.

enterotoxin: An exotoxin of certain strains of staphylococci that causes food poisoning.

envelope (bacterial): The cellular component that encloses the cytoplasm, including the cytoplasmic membrane, cell wall, and capsule, if present.

envelope (viral): The outer lipid-containing layer possessed by some virions; obtained from modified host-cell membranes when the virus leaves the host.

enzyme: An organic catalytic substance that causes changes in other substances without undergoing any alteration itself.

eosinophilia: An increase in the number of eosinophiles.

epidemic: An outbreak of a disease that appears rapidly and attacks a large number of persons in a community at approximately the same time.

epidemiology: The division of medical science concerned with defining and explaining the interrelationships of the host, agent, and environment in causing disease.

episome: A particle of functional DNA which can exist either covalently bonded to the bacterial chromosome or in an extrachromosomal state.

erythematous: Pertaining to the formation of red spots on the skin.

erythroblastosis fetalis: A condition resulting from a blood incompatibility between a mother and her fetus.

erythrocytic schizogony: Asexual reproduction by binary fission of a microorganism within a red blood cell, as in malaria.

eschar: A localized necrotic lesion extending into the dermis.

etiology: Cause.

eucaryote: An organism characterized by a nuclear membrane, membranous organelles, and mitotic division.

eutrophication: Nutrient enrichment leading to over-production of algae.

evolution: The development of an organism from its original or rudimentary state to its present or completed state.

exanthem: Rash.

exfoliate: To scale off dead tissue.

exoenzyme: An enzyme which is secreted by the cell to the environment.

exogenous: Arising from without.

exotoxin: A poisonous protein product released during the lifetime of an organism or on its disintegration.

exudate: Material such as pus composed of fluid from the vascular system, cells, and sometimes products of tissue breakdown.

F

fastidious organism: An organism that has complex nutritional and environmental requirements.

F^+ cell: A bacterial cell that can transfer the extrachromosomal F (fertility) particle to a recipient (F^-) cell.

F^- cell: A bacterial cell that does not contain an F particle but that can act as a recipient and receive one from an F^+ cell.

febrile: Of or relating to fever.

feces: Body wastes discharged from the large intestine through the anus.

fermentation: The enzymatic decomposition of complex organic compounds under anaerobic conditions.

ferritin: An electron-dense protein having a molecular weight of 700,000 and containing about 23 per cent iron.

F_{ab} fragment: A fragment of an immunoglobulin consisting of one light chain and one-half of the heavy chain.

fibroblast: A flat, elongated cell with cytoplasmic processes at each end.

fibrosis: The formation of fibrous tissue.

filariform: Resembling the slender, threadlike nematodes lacking the esophageal bulb.

filiform: Hairlike or filamentous.

filtrate: A liquid passed through a filter.

filtration: Passage of a liquid through a porous membrane for the removal of particles, or the use of certain types of glass to remove particular wavelengths of light.

fixation: The process of preserving a specimen.

flatulence: Excessive gas in the stomach and intestines.

floc: A mass of microorganisms caught together in slime produced by certain bacteria; generally found in waste treatment plants.

flora: Microorganisms present in a given location (e.g., intestinal flora).

fluke: A short, flattened parasite worm of the class *Trematoda.*

fluorescent antibody: An immunoglobulin coupled to a fluorescent dye for use in ultraviolet microscopy.

fomites: Inanimate contaminated objects.

Forssman antigen: Specific guinea pig tissue antigen which causes the production of antibodies that can lyse sheep erythrocytes in the presence of complement. The presence of such antibodies forms the basis of one diagnostic test for infectious mononucleosis.

frequency: The number of light wave vibrations occurring in one second.

fulminating: Occurring suddenly with greatly increasing intensity.

furuncle: Localized inflamed area having a soft center and eventually a pus discharge.

G

gametes: Germ or sex cells.

gammopathies: Abnormalities in immunoglobulin synthesis.

gastritis: Inflammation of the stomach.

gastroenteritis: Inflammation of the stomach and intestines.

gel diffusion: A form of precipitin test incorporating agar gel bases to stabilize the precipitates formed.

gene: A hereditary determinant present on a chromosome; a unit of genetic information.

genetic code: The composition and sequence of all the sets of three nucleotides which code for the amino acids. The sequence of three nucleotides which codes for one amino acid is termed a *code word.*

genome: The entire set of genetic information material.

genotype: The number and kinds of genes possessed by an organism.

genus: A category of related organisms, usually containing several species; the first name of an organism in the binomial system of classification.

germination: The sprouting of a spore.

Giemsa stain: A stain (composed of the dyes azure and eosin) used for the demonstration of chlamydia, rickettsia, and protozoa.

gingiva: The tissues which surround the bases of the teeth; gums.

gingivitis: Inflammation of the gums.

glomerulonephritis (acute hemorrhagic nephritis): Inflammation of the capillary loops in the glomeruli of the kidney.

glycolysis: Anaerobic process of glucose breakdown with the formation of pyruvic acid or lactic acid and the production of energy.

gnotobiotics: The study of animals that have been born and raised in a germ-free environment.

graft: The tissue to be transplanted.

granuloma: A tumor or growth usually composed of fleshy masses with many small blood vessels and varying amounts of inflammation.

growth curve: A graphic representation of the growth (changes in population) of microorganisms in an *in vitro* system.

gum-boil (parulis): An abscess involving the tissue under the tough fibrous membrane surrounding a bone (periosteum).

gumma: Granuloma found in the late stages of syphilis.

gymnoplast (protoplast): A bacterial cell lacking a cell wall.

H

halophilic organism: Literally, a "salt-loving" organism which will grow in a medium that contains NaCl. (The growth of other bacteria is inhibited by NaCl.)

H (Hauch) antigen: Flagellar antigen found with flagellated bacteria.

haploid: A single set of unpaired chromosomes in a nucleus.

haptene: Generally speaking, a substance that does not provoke an antibody response but, depending on other properties, may react *in vitro* with homologous antibody.

helminth: Worm.

hemadsorption: The adhering of erythrocytes to various types of microorganisms or to virus-infected tissue culture cells.

hemagglutination: The clumping of red blood cells.

hemagglutinins: The antibodies involved in the agglutination of erythrocytes.

hematemesis: Black vomit.

hematocrit: An apparatus for determining the volume of red blood cells in centrifuged, oxalated blood.

hematuria: The presence of blood in the urine.

hemolysin: In general terms, any biological agent that will cause the disruption of red blood cells.

hemolysis: The disruption of red blood cells with the leakage of hemoglobin.

hepatitis: Inflammation of the liver.

hepatosplenomegaly. Enlarged liver and spleen.

herbivores: Plant eaters.

hetero: A prefix meaning *different*.

heterotroph: An organism which is incapable of utilizing CO_2 as its sole source of carbon and which requires one or more organic compounds for its nutrition.

hetrophile antigens: Antigenic substances that are present in various tissues and cause the production of antibodies which react with the tissues of several mammals, fish, and plants.

histamine: A cell associated substance which is a powerful capillary dilator and stimulates gastric juice production.

histone: A basic protein usually associated with nuclear material.

Hodgkin's disease: A neoplastic, lymphoproliferative disorder characterized by a progressive loss of T-lymphocyte function.

homo: A prefix meaning *same*.

homograft: The tissue obtained from a donor and transplanted on or in the recipient.

homologous: Derived from the same system or species.

hordeolum (stye): Infection located at the edge of the eyelid.

hyaluronidase: An enzyme found in association with certain body tissues, bacteria, and helminths. It functions in dissolving the material which holds body cells together (hyaluronic acid).

hydrocephalus: Accumulation of cerebrospinal fluid within the brain.

hydrolysis: A chemical reaction in which a substance is split by the addition of water to the molecule.

hyperemia: The presence of excess blood in any part of the body.

hypergammaglobulinemia: A state in which immunoglobulin levels are elevated.

hyperplasia: Abnormal increase in the number of cells resulting in the formation of tumors.

hypersensitivity: Any altered activity caused by contact with animate or inanimate substances.

hypertonic solution: A solution more concentrated than isotonic and with a greater osmotic pressure than the system with which it is compared.

hypertrophy: Abnormal increase in the size of an organ or tissue. This state results from an increase in cell division, cellular enlargement, or both.

hyphae: The filaments or threads which make up a mycelium.

hypogammaglobulinemia: A state in which less than the normal amounts of antibodies are present.

hypotonic solution: A solution less concentrated than isotonic and with a lower osmotic pressure than the system with which it is compared.

I

id (trichophytid) reaction: Sterile skin eruptions caused by an allergic reaction in infected persons to fungal products.

immediate type of hypersensitivity: An allergic state generally characterized by the presence of circulating antibodies, development of reactions within 24 hours, passive transfer by serum from sensitized person, and inhibition by antihistaminic drugs.

immunity: The state of being resistant to the action of foreign proteins and microorganisms.

immunoblast: A cell intermediate between the lymphocyte and the plasma cell.

immunoelectrophoresis: A technique incorporating the elements of electrophoresis and double gel-diffusion. It is used in the separation and identification of proteins.

immunofluorescence: Fluorescence resulting from a reaction between a substance and specific immunoglobulins that are bound to a fluorescent dye.

immunogen: Antigen.

immunoglobulins: In general, any protein exhibiting antibody activity or having antigenic determinants in common with antibody molecules.

immunology: The study of immunity to disease.

immunopoietic: Antibody forming.

immunosuppression: Nonspecific inhibition (suppression) of the ability to make an immune response, resulting in an overall depression of the response to all or most antigenic substances.

impetigo: A bacterial disease of the skin, often highly contagious, characterized by small blisters, weeping of fluid, and formation of crusts.

incision: An even cut made for surgical purposes.

induration: An area of hardened tissue.

industrial microbiology: The use of microorganisms, or a microbiological technique, in a commercial enterprise.

infectious disease: A microorganism's interference with the normal functioning of a host's physiochemical processes.

infestation: The attachment to or temporary invasion of the superficial skin layers by parasites.

inflammation: Tissue reaction to injury; a defensive response to irritation.

infusion: The cold water extraction of nutrients from yeast, plant, or animal tissues; the introduction of liquid into a vein.

inorganic: Not of organic origin.

inspissation: The coagulation of serum or egg-containing media at temperatures below boiling to prevent bubble formation in the medium and inactivation of labile components.

interferon: A protein capable of exerting antiviral action. It is induced by certain viruses, other microbes, and certain inert materials.

interstitial pneumonitis: Inflammation occurring in spaces within the structure of the lungs.

in utero: Within the uterus.

in vitro: In glass; in essence, experiments performed under artificial conditions.

in vivo: In the living body or organism.

involution forms: Abnormal or unusual shapes.

iodoform: Organic preparation of iodine used as a local analgesic and antiseptic.

ionization: The process of becoming electrically charged.

ischemia: Localized obstruction of circulation.

isoantigens: Antigens of the same species.

isograft: The transplantation of tissue between genetically identical animals.

isohemagglutination: The clumping reactions between red blood cells (agglutinogens) and antibodies (agglutinins) from the same species.

isohemolysins: Antibodies involved with the lysis of red blood cells.

isolation: Quarantine.

isotonic solution: A preparation having the same concentration as the environment with which it is compared.

J

jaundice: Yellowing of body tissues.

K

keloids: Tumorous growths.

keratin: Insoluble protein which is the principal component of the epidermis, hair, and nails.

keratitis: Inflammation of the cornea.

kinetoplast: A nucleic acid-containing structure associated with the basal body of some flagellated organisms.

kinins: Basic peptides formed by several enzymes called kallikreins. Kinins function in anaphylactic reactions.

Koch phenomenon: The sequence of events observed by Koch upon the injection of tubercle bacilli into sensitized and nonsensitized animals. (See text for further discussion.)

Koch's Postulates: A definite sequence of experimental steps which shows the causal relationship between a specific organism and a specific disease.

Koplik's spots: Small, bluish-white spots surrounded by a reddened area on the mucous membrane of the cheeks and lips, and present at the onset of measles.

Krebs (citric acid) cycle: A series of aerobic enzymatic reactions by which pyruvic acid produced in glycolysis is converted into energy, CO_2 and H_2O.

L

labile: Unstable.

laceration: Tear or irregular wound.

lacrimal: Pertaining to tears.

lamellae: Thin plates or discs.

larva: An immature form of certain animals which differs morphologically from the adult form.

latent: Quiet; not active.

lavage: The washing out of a body cavity (e.g., stomach) in order to remove irritants, poisons, or swallowed pathogens, in particular, *Mycobacterium tuberculosis.*

legume: Any of a group of plants (including peas, beans, and clover) with pods that split in two when mature; some can develop a symbiotic relationship with nitrogen-fixing bacteria.

lepromin test: A skin test of the delayed hypersensitive type used in the diagnosis of leprosy.

lethal: Deadly.

leucopenia: Abnormal decrease of white blood cells, usually below 5000 per ml.

leukocytosis: An increase in white blood cells.

lichen: An association of a fungus and an alga resulting in a new structural entity. The new formation is morphologically distinct from either of its microbial components, and possesses separate chemical and physiological characteristics.

life cycle: The events that comprise the life of an organism which follow in succession.

lingual: Pertaining to the tongue.

linkage: The presence of multiple genes on the same chromosome.

lipid: An organic compound consisting of fats and other substances of similar properties.

litmus: A blue dye prepared from lichens which is used as a pH indicator.

lobar: Pertaining to a lobe of the lung.

locus: A spot or place.

lophotrichous: The presence of tufts of flagella at one end of a bacterium.

lymphadenitis: Inflamation of a lymph node.

lymphangitis: Inflammation of lymphatic vessels.

lymphocyte: A white blood cell without cytoplasmic granules in which a compact nucleus may occupy most or all of the cell.

lymphoma: A tumor or neoplastic disorder of lymphoid tissue.

lymphosarcoma: Cancer in the lymphatic system.

lyophilization: The process of freeze-drying.

lysis: Destruction of cells.

lysogenic conversion: An alteration in the phenotype of an organism due to the infection by a lysogenic bacteriophage.

lysogeny: The state in which the bacteriophage genome persists in direct association with the bacterial genome. A lytic cycle may occur at some later time.

lysozyme: An enzyme known for its destructive action on the murein sacculus of bacteria.

lytic bacteriophage: Bacterial virus which infects a host and ultimately causes its destruction.

M

macroconidia: Large asexual spores formed by splitting off from the end of a mycelial branch.

macrogamete: A female sex cell.

macule: Round, small, colored area of the skin.

maculopapules: Slightly raised macules.

malaise: General discomfort, uneasiness.

mandibular: Pertaining to the lower jaw.

maxilla: Jawbone.

medical sepsis: Refers to procedures used to reduce the transmission of pathogens.

meiosis: A sequence of complex nuclear changes with two mitotic divisions, resulting in the production of four haploid cells, usually gametes.

meningitis: Inflammation of the membranes covering the brain and spinal cord.

merozoite: The asexual reproduction cell in malaria organisms.

mesophiles: Microorganisms which grow best at temperatures between 20° and 37°C.

messenger RNA (m-RNA): Ribonucleic acid (RNA) which serves as a template for protein synthesis.

metabolism: The sum total of chemical reactions in cells by which energy is provided for vital processes and new cell substances are assimilated.

metacercariae: An encysted form of cercariae found with certain flukes (trematodes).

metachromatic granules: Intracellular particles or volutin which stain blue to red with aged methylene blue dye and have been reported to consist of nucleoprotein, polyphosphate, or combinations of these and other materials.

metastasis: Dissemination of a disease.

metazoa: Animals whose bodies consist of many cells.

metric system: Standardized decimal measurement based upon the meter as a unit of length, the gram as a unit of weight, and the liter as a unit of liquid measure.

microaerophilic: Microorganisms which grow best in the presence of low concentrations of oxygen.

microbiota: Microorganisms found in a particular area.

microcephaly: Abnormal smallness of the head.

microconidia: Small asexual spores arising from a hyphal branch.

microgamete: Male sex cell.

micrometer (μm): One millionth (10^{-6}) part of a meter or 10^{-3} of a millimeter.

micrometry: A method by which dimensions of cells, their components or other items are measured.

micron (μ): One thousandth (10^{-3}) of a millimeter. The symbol μm is currently being used for the unit the micron represents.

microphage: A phagocytic cell capable of engulfing bacteria or debris.

miliary tuberculosis: Generalized systemic involvement in tuberculosis.

minimum inhibitory concentration: (MIC): The lowest concentration of a drug which will prevent growth of a standard microbial suspension.

miracidium: A highly ciliated larval stage found with flukes trematodes).

mitochondrion: A cellular organelle consisting of an outer membrane and an inner one folded into cristae.

mitosis: The process in which genetic material is duplicated and equally distributed in newly formed cells.

Monera: Kingdom of protocaryotic organisms with unicellular or simple colonial organization.

monotrichous: Having a single flagellum.

morbidity: The number of cases of a disease per unit of the population within a given time period.

mordant: A substance used to make a dye stain more intensely.

mortality rate: The numbers of deaths caused by a particular disease per unit of the population within a given time period.

M protein: A component of certain bacterial cell walls which is associated with a protective function for the organism.

murein sacculus: The rigid layer of a bacterial cell wall.

mutation: A sudden change in the genetic code resulting in an hereditable characteristic differing from the parent cells.

myalgia: Pain or tenderness of the muscles.

mycelium: An interwoven mat of hyphae.

mycology: The study of fungi.

mycosis: A fungus infection.

myelitis: Inflammation of the spinal cord.

myringitis: Inflammation of the eardrum.

N

nanometer (nm): 10^{-6} millimeters or 10^{-9} meter. This designation has in most cases replaced the millimicron (mμ).

necrosis: Death of a cell or a tissue.

neoplasm: A mass of new tissue which grows independently of surrounding tissue.

nosocomial infections: Hospital-acquired infections.

nucleocapsid: The structure composed of the capsid and the enclosed nucleic acid of a virus particle.

nucleolus: A small body in a cell nucleus.

nucleoside: Any of a class of compounds composed of a carbohydrate and purine or pyrimidine base.

nucleotide: Any of a class of compounds consisting of a carbohydrate, and purine, or pyrimidine and phosphoric acid.

nucleus: The cellular structure containing the chromosomes.

numerical taxonomy: A technique for determining the relationships among organisms by determining the number of characteristics that the organisms have in common.

nystagmus: Involuntary rapid eye movements.

O

obligate: Necessary or required.

occlusal: Pertaining to the biting or grinding surface of a tooth.

oncogenic: Cancer-producing.

onychomycosis: Infection of the toenails and fingernails.

Operon concept: A concept for cellular regulation, involving a group of genes under the control of operator and repressor genes.

ophthalmia neonatorum: Conjunctivitis of the newborn.

opportunists: Microorganisms that cause infection only under especially favorable conditions (e.g., when defense mechanisms are not fully functioning).

organelle: A specialized part of a cell which performs a specific function.

organic: Pertaining to an organ or organs.

organic substance: A substance derived from living organisms. Carbohydrates, fats, proteins are examples.

oropharynx: The lower part of the pharynx which is continuous with the mouth and visible by direct vision.

osmotic pressure: The pressure which develops when two solutions of different concentrations are separated by a semipermeable membrane.

osteomyelitis: Inflammation of bone marrow.

otitis externa: Outer ear infection.

otitis media: Middle ear infection.

ototoxic: Affecting the sense of hearing.

Ouchterlony test: An immunodiffusion test based on diffusion of both antigen and antibody through gels.

ovum: Egg.

oxidation: The loss of electrons or hydrogen.

oxidative phosphorylation: The generation of energy in the form of ATP that results from the passage of electrons through the electron transport chain to a final electron acceptor.

P

paleomicrobiology: The study of microorganisms based upon fossil remains.

pandemic: Affecting the majority of the population of a large region or epidemic concurrently in many different parts of the world.

papilla: A nipple; any soft, small protuberance on the skin with tactile functions.

papule: Pimple.

para-aminobenzoic acid (PABA): The vitamin required for folic acid synthesis.

parasite: An organism that lives within, upon, or at the expense of another organism.

parasitemia: The presence of parasites in the blood.

parasitology: The study of protozoa and higher forms of life (worms) which cause human disease.

parasporal body: Structure formed during sporulation in certain bacteria, which is adjacent to the spore.

paronychia: Infection of marginal structures about the nail.

parotid gland: Largest of the salivary glands, located in tissues on the side of the face below and to the front of the ear.

passive immunization: The transfer of antibodies from an immunized donor to a nonimmune recipient.

Pasteurization: The processes of heating food or other substances under controlled conditions of time and temperature (for example, 63°C for 30 minutes) in order to kill non-sporeforming pathogens and reduce the numbers of other microbes.

pathogenesis: The sequence of changes that ends in disease.

pathogenic: Capable of producing disease.

pellagra: A niacin deficiency disease.

peptide bond: The covalent bond that joins an amino group of one amino acid to the carboxyl group of another amino acid, with the formation of water.

periblast: An outer membrane which surrounds the inner components of spirochetes.

periodontal: Pertaining to tissues around the teeth.

periostitis: Inflammation of the membrane surrounding bone.

peritonitis: Inflammation of the membrane lining the abdominal cavity.

peritrichous: Flagella located around cell wall.

permeability: The capacity of a membrane or other structure to allow passage of substances through it.

petechiae: Small hemorrhages in the skin.

phage: A bacterial virus (bacteriophage).

phagocyte: A white blood cell capable of ingesting solid particles.

phagocytosis: Cellular engulfment of foreign particles.

phenol: A disinfectant and antiseptic chemical.

phenol coefficient: The ratio of the highest dilution of a germicide being evaluated showing kill in 10 but not in 5 minutes to a comparable phenol dilution.

phenotype: Physical expression of the genetic makeup of an organism.

phlebitis: Inflammation of a vein.

phloem: A type of plant vascular tissue.

photosynthesis: The sum total of the metabolic processes by which light energy is utilized to convert CO_2 and reduce inorganic compound to organic compounds, $(6H_2X + 6CO_2 \rightarrow C_6H_{12}O_6 + 6X)$.

phycology: The study of algae.

phylum (phyla): A large division of related families in the classification of living organisms. The classification is subdivided progressively from World $\rightarrow$ Kingdoms $\rightarrow$ Subkingdoms $\rightarrow$ Phyla $\rightarrow$ Classes $\rightarrow$ Orders $\rightarrow$ Families $\rightarrow$ Genera $\rightarrow$ Species.

physiology: The science of the functions of cells, tissues, and organs of living organisms.

phytoplankton: The algae which compose plankton.

picornaviruses: Small viruses which contain RNA.

pilus (fimbria): Projections on bacterial cells which are not organs of locomotion.

pinocytosis: The absorption of liquids by phagocytic cells.

placenta: The structure in the uterus through which the fetus derives its nourishment.

plaque (dental): A collection of bacteria tightly adhering to a tooth surface; responsible for dental caries.

plaque (viral): A clear area in a layer or monolayer of cells; plaques are created by viral lysis of infected cells within the clear area.

plasma: The liquid part of lymph and blood.

plasma cell: A cell 10 to 20 μm in diameter which can actively synthesize immunoglobulins and which can be distinguished morphologically from similar cells.

plasma membrane: Membrane surrounding the cytoplasm.

plastid: A structure which is the center of chemical activity involved in cell metabolism.

platelets: Small blood components which take part in clotting.

pleomorphic: Having many shapes.

pleural: Referring to the membrane surrounding the lungs.

pleurisy: Inflammation of the serous membrane that covers the lungs and may cause painful adhesions.

pleuritis: Inflammation of the membrane that covers the lungs.

PMNL: Polymorphonuclearleukocyte.

pneumonic plague: Respiratory symptoms caused by the plague bacillus.

pneumonitis: Inflammation of the lungs.

pneumothorax: An accumulation of gas or air in the pleural cavity which may collapse the lung.

polyhedron: Many sided figure.

polyneuritis: Inflammation of two or more nerves.

polysaccharide: A carbohydrate composed of more than three molecules of monosaccharides.

portals of exit: Sources of infectious body fluids.

post-partum: Following delivery.

Prausnitz-Küstner (P-K) reaction: An example of the passive transfer of atopy.

precipitin reaction: The interaction of soluble antigens with homologous antibodies.

proglottid: Tapeworm segment.

prognosis: A prediction of the course of a disease and the general outlook based upon that prediction.

properdin: One type of bactericidal heat-sensitive protein found in serum. Complement and magnesium ions are necessary for its activity.

prophylaxis: Observance of rules or procedures necessary to prevent disease.

prostration: Absolute exhaustion.

protease: An enzyme which attacks protein.

protein: High molecular-weight polymers composed of amino acids.

procaryote: An organism characterized by a lack of nuclear membrane, the absence of organized membranous organelles, and the presence of simple flagella.

protoplast: A bacterial cell lacking a cell wall.

pruritis: Severe itching.

pseudo-mycelium: Chains of yeast cells of *Candida* spp. which appear as short hyphae. This is best observed in cornmeal tween 80 agar.

psoriasis: Chronic inflammatory skin disease characterized by the formation of silvery scaling patches.

psychomotor retardation: Delayed response of voluntary muscles.

psychrophiles: Microorganisms which grow well between 0° and 30°C. The optimum temperature is usually above 25°C.

ptomaine poisoning: An incorrect term for food poisoning.

puerperal sepsis: Infection following childbirth.

purified protein derivative (PPD): Substance obtained from cultures of *Mycobacterium tuberculosis* or related organisms and used in skin testing.

pustule: Small elevated skin lesion containing pus.

putrefaction: The anaerobic decomposition of protein resulting in foul odors.

pyelonephritis: Inflammation of the kidneys.

pyemia: A septicemic state resulting in the localized collection of pus in the host's tissues.

pyoderma: Supperative condition of the skin.

pyogenic: Pus producing.

pyometria: Retained pus in the uterus.

pyuria: Pus cells in the urine.

Q

quantasome: The elementary photosynthetic particle associated with the membranous structures comprising the grana of chloroplasts.

Quellung reaction: An immunological test used to identify certain encapsulated bacteria.

R

radicular: Of or pertaining to a root.

radioimmunoassay: An immunologic test that utilizes radiolabeled antigen, antibody, complement, or other reactants.

reagin: A term used for skin sensitizing antibody or the nonprotective antibody produced in victims of syphilis.

recombination: A process in which the transfer of genetic material occurs between two organisms.

replica plating: A technique for transferring organisms from a large number of separated colonies from one medium to another.

reservoir host: A nonclinical source of infectious agents.

resistance transfer factors (RTF): A set of genes which are associated with R factors and which carry the genetic information for the transfer of these R factors.

reverse isolation: A procedure used to protect highly susceptible patients from pathogens found in a hospital environment.

reverse transcriptase: An enzyme that synthesizes DNA complementary to an RNA template.

R factor: A transferable plasmid, found in many enteric bacteria, which carries genetic information for resistance to one or more chemotherapeutic agents; often associated with a transfer factor that is responsible for conjugation with another bacterium and for transfer of the R factor.

rhinitis: Inflammation of the nose.

ribosome: Intracellular ribonucleoprotein structures important in protein synthesis.

rickets: Vitamin D deficiency disease.

risus sardonicus: A smile produced by spasm of the facial muscles.

Rivers' Postulates: A procedure similar to that associated with Koch's Postulates, but involving viruses.

rosette technique: A test that involves immunoglobulin-producing or immunoglobulin-binding cells and a cellular antigen.

rough forms (of bacteria): Noncapsulated bacteria which produce dull to granular colonies.

rouleaux formation: Aggregation of red blood cells, much like a roll of coins.

S

Sabin-Feldman dye test: A serological test used in the diagnosis of toxoplasmosis.

Sabouraud's glucose medium: A preparation commonly used to grow fungi.

salpingitis: Inflammation of the fallopian tubes.

sanious: Foul-smelling discharge from an ulcer containing blood and pus.

sanitation: The use of procedures to promote and establish conditions favorable for health.

saprophyte: Any organism which derives its nutrition from dead or decaying organic matter.

scarlatina: A milder form of scarlet fever.

Schick test: Injection of diphtheria toxin beneath the skin to test for susceptibility.

Schilling's hemogram: Method of performing a differential blood cell count by separating the polymorphonuclear neutrophiles (PMNLs) into four categories based on the number and arrangement of nuclei.

schizogony: The asexual phase of a malarial parasite's life cycle.

schizomycetes: The fission fungi or bacteria.

Schüffner's dots: A stippling of red blood cells which is frequently found in cases of vivax malaria.

Schultz-Charlton test: The skin test used to assist in the diagnosis of scarlet fever.

scolex: The head of a tapeworm.

scrofula: Tuberculosis of the cervical lymph nodes.

scurvy: Vitamin C deficiency disease.

second set reaction: The rapid destruction of a second homograft.

secretors: Persons whose blood group substances are found in various tissues and body fluids.

sedimentation constant (S): A measure of the relative sedimentation rate of molecules in a gravitational field. These constants are expressed in Svedberg (S) units. Generally the higher the value the greater is the molecular weight of the molecule.

selective medium: A growth medium for microorganisms in which some component will inhibit the growth of certain organisms and enhance the growth of others.

semi-gymnoplast (spheroplast): Yeast or bacterial cell with insufficient cell wall material to confer osmotic stability.

septic: Pertaining to a condition caused by pathogens or their poisonous products.

septicemia: The association of bacteria in the blood with toxic symptoms of a host.

septum: Crosswall.

sequelae: Conditions following and resulting from a disease.

serology: The study of the nature and behavior of humoral antibodies.

serotonin: Cell associated substance that functions in anaphylaxis.

serum: The yellow fluid that forms when blood coagulates.

serum sickness: One example of immediate-type of hypersensitivity. It is associated with sensitivity to foreign protein.

Shwartzman reaction: Local hemorrhagic and necrotic inflammation developing from injections or certain types of exposure to Gram-negative associated substances. It is not induced by an immune mechanism.

simple staining: A procedure using only one dye.

sinus: Any cavity having a relatively narrow opening.

sinusoid: Resembling a sinus.

slime layer: A gelatinous, nonstructural covering of the cell wall of certain bacteria.

sludge: The precipitated solid matter produced by water and sewage treatment.

smear: A thin film of material spread on a clean glass slide.

somatic antigen: An antigen associated with the body of a cell.

spherical aberration: A distortion of an image caused by peripheral light rays passing through a lens not being brought to the same focus as those appearing near the center of the lens. It is a geometric defect in a lens.

spheroplast: A yeast or bacterial cell with insufficient cell wall material to confer osmotic stability.

spirochete: A corkscrew-shaped bacterium.

spirochetemia: The presence of spirochetes in the blood.

splenomegaly: Increased size of the spleen.

spontaneous generation: A theory holding that certain forms of life arose spontaneously from non-living matter.

sporadic: Irregular.

sporangium: A closed structure within which asexual spores (sporangiospores) are produced.

sporogony: The sexual phase of the malarial parasite's life cycle.

sporozoite: An elongated, sickle-shaped body formed in an oöcyst as the result of the sexual reproduction phase of malaria in mosquitoes.

starter culture: A growth of one or more microorganisms selected to perform a particular fermentation or other industrial process.

sterilization: The destruction of all living forms.

stomatitis: Inflammation of the oral mucosa.

stridor: High-pitched, harsh breathing sound.

strobila: The body of a tapeworm.

STS: Standard tests for syphilis.

stupor: Suppression of the sense of feeling.

sub-acute bacterial endocarditis (SBE): A disease process involving inflammation of the heart valves and inner lining of the heart.

subclinical infection: A state in which the individual doesn't experience all of the characteristic symptoms of a particular disease, or such effects are less severe.

sublingual: Below the tongue.

substrate: A substance acted upon, as by an enzyme.

superficial fungi: Fungi which predominantly attack the hair, nails, and mucosal surfaces.

supernatant: The fluid over a precipitate or sediment.

suppuration: Pus formation.

surgical asepsis: Practices used to sterilize objects and general areas of operation.

sylvatic plague: Plague as present in the wild rodent population.

symbiosis: The living together of two organisms in intimate association.

symptomatic treatment: Treatment of expected symptoms.

synchronous: Occurring at the same time.

syndrome: A set of symptoms which occur together.

synergy: Joint action of two or more organisms in bringing about changes that neither can cause alone.

syngamy: Sexual reproduction.

synthetic medium: A medium composed of known compounds.

T

tachycardia: Fast heartbeat.

tachypnea: Abnormal rapidity of respiration rate.

taxonomy: The classification of organisms.

temperate bacteriophage: A bacterial virus which may induce either lytic or lysogenic cycles within the appropriate host.

template: The molecule that serves as the pattern for the synthesis of another molecule. Macromolecular synthesis involves templates.

tetanospasmin: The neurotoxin of *Clostridium tetani*.

thallus: The vegetative body of a thallophyte, with no differentiation into roots, stems, or leaves.

thermal death point: The temperature which will sterilize a microbial suspension after ten minutes.

thermal death time: The time required for a particular temperature to sterilize a microbial suspension.

thermoduric: Capable of surviving exposure to high temperatures.

thermolabile: Sensitive to heat.

thermophile: Microorganism which grows best at temperatures ranging from 50° to 70°C.

thrombocytopenia purpura: A disease state in which there is a decrease in the number of blood platelets.

thymus gland: A gland associated with antibody production.

tincture: A diluted alcoholic solution of a particular chemical which is mentioned in the name.

tinnitus aurium: Continuous or intermittent noises.

titer: The potency of a biological reactant commonly expressed in units/ml. The level of antibodies frequently are given in this way.

T-lymphocyte: A thymus-derived lymphocyte that is responsible for cell-mediated hypersensitivity.

tonus: The normal degree of tension and vigor present in muscle.

toxemia: The presence of toxins in the blood.

toxin: A poisonous substance.

toxoid: A converted bacterial toxin. The resulting preparation is non-toxic, but still antigenic.

tracheotomy: A surgical procedure used to create an artificial tracheal opening for breathing.

transduction: The incorporation by a recipient bacterium into its chromosome of genetic material obtained from a donor bacterium and carried by a bacterial virus.

transformation: The experimental conversion of a bacterial type by means of free, extracellular bacterial DNA.

translucent: Permitting passage of light, but not transparent.

transovarial passage: With respect to diseases this refers to the transmitting of infectious agents to offspring through eggs.

trophozoite: The vegetative cell of a protozoan (i.e., active feeding stage).

tubercle: A nodule.

tuberculin: A general term for a bacteria-free soluble protein fraction extract prepared from killed tubercle bacilli.

tuberculin converters: Persons whose tuberculin skin tests change from a negative to a positive reaction within twelve months.

tuberculin reaction: The representative skin response associated with delayed-type hypersensitivity.

turbidity: Cloudiness.

U

ulcer: A rounded or irregularly shaped area of inflammatory tissue destruction in the epithelial lining of a surface.

ultracentrifuge: A high-velocity centrifuge used to separate colloidal or submicroscopic particles such as proteins or viruses.

ultrafiltration: A method for the removal of all of the very smallest of particles from a solution.

ultraviolet light (UV): Electromagnetic radiation with a wavelength of 175 to 350 nm (shorter than visible light). Certain wavelengths absorbed by nucleic acids result in mutation or in death of cells.

umbilicated: Elevated lesion, or structure with a depressed center.

unit membrane: The basic structure of all cell membranes, which measure 75 Å in thickness and consist of two lipid layers separated by a protein layer.

urease reaction: A test for the presence of urease, an enzyme which hydrolyzes urea to CO_2 and NH_3.

urticaria: An inflammatory reaction, characterized by the eruption of pustules, temporary wheals, and severe itching.

uvula: The small, fleshy mass hanging from the soft palate, above the tongue and at the entrance to the oropharynx.

V

vacuole: A clear area in a cell's cytoplasm.

V.D.R.L. (Venereal Disease Research Laboratory) test: A precipitation test for the diagnosis of syphilis.

vector: A carrier of pathogenic agents, especially an arthropod.

vertigo: A sensation of either the surroundings revolving around an individual or vice versa.

vesicle: A blister.

viable: Living

viremia: A large concentration of viruses in the blood.

virion: A fully infectious virus particle.

virulence: Ability to produce disease.

viscerotropic: An affinity for internal organs of the chest or abdominal cavity.

Voges-Proskauer (VP) reaction: A biochemical test for the detection of acetylmethylcarbinol. It is of value in the identification of various enteric bacteria.

W

wavelength: The distance between the top of one wave (crest) and the identical phase of a succeeding wave.

Weil-Felix test: An agglutination test used in the diagnosis of rickettsial diseases.

wheal: A flat, reddened, elevated area on the skin, frequently characterized by itching and short duration.

wheal and erythema reaction: The flat, elevated swollen skin response observed in certain immediate-type hypersensitivities.

whey: The liquid remaining after milk has been coagulated by acidification or enzymatic activity.

Widal test: A slide agglutination test used in the diagnosis of typhoid and paratyphoid fevers.

X

xenodiagnosis: A procedure using laboratory-reared reduviid bugs in the diagnosis of Chagas' disease. These arthropod vectors feed on a person suspected of having the infection. After a suitable incubation period, these vectors are examined microscopically for the presence of *T. cruzi.*

Z

Ziehl-Neelsen stain: Acid-fast procedure.

zoonoses: Diseases which primarily affect lower animals, but which can be transmitted to man by natural means.

zooplankton: A collective term for the non-photosynthetic microorganisms present in the drifting flora and fauna of a body of water.

zygospore: The spore resulting from the union of two similar sex cells.

zygote: The organism resulting from fertilization.

References

Considerable thought and effort have been given to selecting sources of factual material for readers interested in further study.

Those works providing information of a general nature pertinent to the subject matter found in several chapters have been placed into the "General References" section. Those publications more closely related to the topics presented in the individual chapters have been placed in the "Specific References" section and are listed by chapter.

General References

AINSWORTH, G. C., SPARROW, F. K., and SUSSMAN, A. S. (eds.): *The Fungi: An Advanced Treatise,* Vol. IV A and B. Academic Press, New York, 1973.

ANTHONY, C. P., and KOLTHOFT, N. J.: *Textbook of Anatomy and Physiology.* The C. V. Mosby Company, St. Louis, 9th ed., 1975.

BUCHANAN, R. E., and GIBBONS, N. E. (co-eds.): *Bergey's Manual of Determinative Bacteriology.* The Williams & Wilkins Co., Baltimore, 8th ed., 1974.

CRONQUIST, A.: *Basic Botany.* Harper & Row, New York, 1973.

DAVIS, B. D., DULBECCO, R., EISEN, H. N., GINSBERG, H. S., WOOD, W. B., JR., and MCCARTY, M.: *Microbiology.* Hoeber Medical Division. Harper & Row, New York, 2nd ed., 1973.

DOYLE, W. T.: *Nonvascular Plants: Form and Function.* Wadsworth Publishing Company, Inc., Belmont, Cal., 1965.

FENNER, F., MCAUSLAN, B. R., MIMS, C. A., SAMBROOK, J., and WHITE, D. O.: *The Biology of Animal Viruses.* Academic Press, New York, 1974.

FRAENKEL-CONRAT, H., and WAGNER, R. R. (eds.): *Comprehensive Virology,* Vol. I. Descriptive Catalogue of Viruses. Plenum Press, New York, 1974.

FRAZER, D.: *Viruses and Molecular Biology.* The Macmillan Company, New York, 1967.

GOTH, A.: *Medical Pharmacology: Principles and Concepts.* The C. V. Mosby Company, St. Louis, 7th ed., 1974.

HAYAT, M. A. (ed.): *Principles and Techniques of Electron Microscopy,* Vol. IV. Van Nostrand Reinhold, New York, 1974.

KARLSON, P.: *Introduction to Modern Biochemistry.* Academic Press, New York, 4th ed., 1975.

LENNETTE, E. H., SPAULDING, E. H., and TRUANT, J. P. (eds.): *Manual of Clinical Microbiology.* American Society for Microbiology, Washington, D.C., 2nd ed., 1974.

OLSEN, O. W.: *Animal Parasites: Their Life Cycles and Ecology.* University Park Press, Baltimore, 3rd ed., 1974.

PERLMAN, D. (ed.): *Advances in Applied Microbiology,* Vol. XVII. Academic Press, Inc., New York, 1974.

RHINESMITH, H. S., and CIOFFI, L. A.: *Macromolecules of Living Systems.* Reinhold Publishing Company, New York, 1968.

ROSE, N. R., MILGROM, F., and VAN OSS, C. J. (eds.): *Principles of Immunology.* Macmillan Publishing Co., Inc., New York, 1973.

SLEIGH, M.: *The Biology of Protozoa.* American Elsevier Publishing Co., Inc., New York, 1973.

STANIER, R. Y., DOUDOROFF, M., and ADELBERG, E. A.: *The Microbial World.* Prentice-Hall, Inc., Englewood Cliffs, N.J., 1970.

VAN DER HOEDEN, J.: *Zoonoses.* American Elsevier Publishing Company, Inc., New York, 1964.

Specific References

CHAPTER 1

BEVERIDGE, W. I. B.: *The Art of Scientific Investigation.* Vintage Books, A Division of Random House, New York, 1957.

KLUYVER, A. J., and VAN NIEL, C. B.: *The Microbes' Contribution to Biology.* Harvard University Press, Cambridge, Mass., 1956.

PORTER, J. R.: "The Scientific Journal—300th Anniversary," *Bact. Rev.,* **28**:211, 1964.

WAKSMAN, S. A.: "Microbiology as a Field of Science and Application," *Amer. Sci.,* **57**:364, 1969.

CHAPTER 2

BULLOCH, W.: *The History of Bacteriology.* Oxford University Press, London, 1960.

CLARK, P. F.: *Pioneer Microbiologist of America.* University of Wisconsin Press, Madison, Wis., 1961.

LECHEVALIER, H. H., and SOLOTOROVSKY, M.: *Three Centuries of Microbiology.* McGraw-Hill Book Company, New York, 1974.

CHAPTER 3

AINSWORTH, G. C., and SNEATH, P. H. A. (eds.): *Microbial Classification.* Twelfth Symposium of the Society for General Microbiology, Cambridge University Press, London, 1962.

Evolution in the Microbial World. Twenty-fourth Symposium of the Society General Microbiology. Cambridge University Press, New York, 1974.

FOX, S. W. (ed.): *The Origins of Prebiological Systems.* Academic Press, Inc., New York, 1965.

KEOSIAN, J.: *The Origin of Life.* Reinhold Publishing Company, New York, 1964.

MANDEL, M.: "New Approaches to Bacterial Taxonomy: Perspective and Prospects," *Ann. Rev. Microbiol.,* **23**:239, 1969.

OPARIN, A. I.: *The Origin of Life,* Republication of the 1938 edition (The Macmillan Company, New York). Dover Publications Inc., New York, 1953.

SKERMAN, V. B. D.: *A Guide to the Identification of the Genera of Bacteria,* Williams & Wilkins Co., Baltimore, 2nd ed., 1967.

SNEATH, P. H. A., and SOKAL, R. R.: *Numerical Taxonomy.* W. H. Freeman & Co., San Francisco, 1973.

SOKAL, R. R., and SNEATH, P. H. A.: *Principles of Numerical Taxonomy.* W. H. Freeman, San Francisco, 1963.

SWAIN, F. M.: "Paleomicrobiology," *Ann. Rev. Microbiol.,* **23**:455, 1969.

CHAPTER 4

AHMADJIAN, V., and HALE, M. E.: *The Lichens.* Academic Press, New York, 1973.

ALEXOPOULOS, C. J. and BOLD, H. C.: *Algae and Fungi.* The Macmillan Company, New York, 1967.

BONNER, J. T.: *The Cellular Slime Molds.* Princeton University Press, Princeton, N.J., 2nd ed., 1967.

DIENER, T. O.: "Viroids: The Smallest Known Agents of Infectious Diseases," *Annu. Rev. Microbiol.,* **28**:28, 1974.

DODGE, J. D.: *The Fine Structure of Algal Cells.* Academic Press, Inc., New York, 1973.

MANWELL, R. D.: *Introduction to Protozoology.* St. Martin's Press, Inc., New York, 1961.

ORMSBEE, R. A.: "Rickettsiae (as Organisms)," *Ann. Rev. Microbial,* **23**:275, 1969.

CHAPTER 5

ANGUS, J. A.: "I. Bacterial Pathogens as Microbial Insecticides," in Symposium on Microbial Insecticides, *Bact. Rev.,* **29**:364, 1965.

FRAZIER, W. C.: *Food Microbiology.* McGraw-Hill Book Company, New York, 1958.

HEDEN, C. G.: "Defenses against Biological Warfare," *Ann. Rev. Microbiol.,* **21**:639, 1967.

LEDERBERG, J.: "Biological Warfare: A Global Threat," *Amer. Sci.,* **59**:195, 1971.

PALMER, C. M.: *Algae in Water Supplies.* U.S. Department of Health, Education, and Welfare, Washington, D.C., 1962.

RHEINHEIMER, G.: *Aquatic Microbiology.* Interscience. Wiley, New York, 1974.

TAYLOR, G. R.: "Space Microbiology," *Annu. Rev. Microbiol.,* **28**:121, 1974.

CHAPTER 6

BARTHOLOMEW, J. W., and MITTWER, T.: "The Gram Stain," *Bact. Rev.,* **16**:1, 1952.

GOLDMAN, M.: *Fluorescent Antibody Methods.* Academic Press, Inc., New York, 1968.

HAYAT, M. A.: *Principles and Techniques of Scanning Electron Microscopy.* Biological Applications. Van Nostrand Reinhold, New York, 1974.

KAY, D. (ed.): *Techniques for Electron Microscopy.* Blackwell Scientific Publications, Oxford, 2nd ed., 1965.

WREN, L. A.: *Understanding and Using the Phase Microscope.* Unitron Instrument Company, Newton Highlands, Mass., 1963.

CHAPTER 7

HALL, J. L., FLOWERS, T. J., and ROBERTS, R. M.: *Plant Cell Structure and Metabolism.* Longman Group, Ltd., London, 1974.

LOEWY, A. G., and SIEKEVITZ, P.: *Cell Structure and Function.* Holt, Rinehart & Winston, Inc., New York, 1969.

PORTER, K. R., and BONNEVILLE, M. A.: *Fine Structure of Cells and Tissues.* Lea & Febiger, Philadelphia, 4th ed., 1973.

SLEIGH, M. A. (ed.): *Cilia and Flagella.* Academic Press, New York, 1974.

THOMAS, L.: *The Lives of a Cell: Notes of a Biology Watcher.* The Viking Press, New York, 1974.

CHAPTER 8

BARKER, A. N., GOULD, G. W., and WOLF, J. (eds.): *Spore Research, 1973.* Academic Press, New York, 1974.

BRAUN, V., and HANTKE, K.: "Biochemistry of Bacterial Cell Envelopes," *Annu. Rev. Biochem.,* **43**:89, 1974.

GUZE, L. B.: *Microbial Protoplasts, Spheroplasts, and L-Forms.* Williams & Wilkins Co., Baltimore, 1967.

MANILOFF, J., and MOROWITZ, H. J.: "Cell Biology of the Mycoplasmas," *Bact. Rev.,* **36**:263–290, 1972.

SALTON, M. R. J.: *The Bacterial Cell Wall.* American Elsevier Publishing Company, Inc., New York, 1964.

SHIVELY, J. M.: "Inclusion Bodies of Prokaryotes," *Annu. Rev. Microbiol.,* **28**:167, 1974.

SINGER, S. J.: "The Molecular Organization of Membranes," *Annu. Rev. Biochem.,* **43**:805, 1974.

SUSSMAN, A. S., and HALVORSON, H. O.: *Spores: Their Dormancy and Germination.* Harper & Row Publishers, Inc., New York, 1966.

CHAPTER 9

ADAMS, M. H.: *Bacteriophages.* Interscience Publishers, Inc., New York, 1959.

BRADLEY, D. E.: "Ultrastructure of Bacteriophages and Bacteriocins," *Bact. Rev.,* **31**:230, 1967.

KNIGHT, C. A.: *Molecular Virology.* McGraw-Hill Book Co., New York, 1974.

RIFKIN, D. B., and QUIGLEY, J. P.: "Virus-Induced Modification of Cellular Membranes Related to Viral Structure," *Annu. Rev. Microbiol.,* **28**:325, 1974.

SHATKIN, A. J.: "Animal RNA Viruses: Genome Structure and Function," *Annu. Rev. Biochem.,* **43**:643, 1974.

"The Molecular Biology of Viruses," *Symp. Soc. Gen. Microbiol.,* **18**, Cambridge University Press, New York, 1968.

CHAPTER 10

CONANT, N. F., SMITH, D. T., BAKER, R. D., and CALLAWAY, J. L.: *Manual of Clinical Mycology.* W. B. Saunders Co., Philadelphia, 3rd ed., 1971.

GRELL, K. G.: *Protozoology.* Springer-Verlag, New York, 1973.

MEGLITSCH, P. A.: *Invertebrate Zoology.* Oxford University Press, London, 2nd ed., 1972.

CHAPTER 11

FRIDKIN, M., and PATCHORNIC, A.: "Peptide Synthesis," *Annu. Rev. Biochem.,* **43**:419, 1974.

HASCHEMEYER, R. H., and DE HARVEN, E.: "Electron Microscopy of Enzymes," *Annu. Rev. Biochem.,* **43**:279, 1974.

STEWART, P. R., and LETHAM, D. S. (eds.): *The Ribonucleic Acids.* Springer-Verlag, New York, 1973.

CHAPTER 12

Anaerobe Laboratory: *Outline of Clinical Methods in Anaerobic Bacteriology.* Anaerobe Laboratory, Virginia Polytechnic Institute, Blacksburg, 1972.

Bioquest: *BBL Manual of Products and Laboratory Procedures.* Bioquest, Division of Becton, Dickinson and Co., Cockeysville, Md., 5th ed., 1968.

Difco: *Manual of Dehydrated Culture Media and Reagents.* Difco Laboratories, Detroit, Mich., 9th ed., 1953.

STEWART, J. A.: *Methods of Media Preparation for the Biological Sciences.* Charles C. Thomas, Springfield, Ill., 1974.

CHAPTER 13

KUCHLER, R. J. (ed.): *Animal Cell Culture and Virology.* Dowden, Hutchinson, and Russ, Inc., Stroudsburg, Pa., 1974.

CHAPTER 14

MANDELSTAM, J., and McQUILLEN, K.: *The Biochemistry of Bacterial Growth.* John Wiley & Sons, Inc., New York, 1968.

CHAPTER 15

DOELLE, H. W.: *Bacterial Metabolism,* Academic Press, Inc., New York, 1969.

MILDVAN, A. S.: "Mechanism of Enzyme Action," *Annu. Rev. Biochem.,* **43**:357, 1974.

SCHEKMAN, R., WEINER, A., and KORNBERG, A.: "Multi-enzyme Systems of DNA Replication," *Science,* **186**:987, 1974.

CHAPTER 16

ADELBERG, E. A. (ed.): *Papers on Bacterial Genetics.* Little, Brown & Co., Boston, 1960.

BARKSDALE, L., and ARDEN, S. B.: "Persisting Bacteriophage Infections, Lysogeny and Phage Conversions," *Annu. Rev. Microbiol.,* **28**:265, 1974.

Cold Spring Harbor Symposia on Quantitative Biology: *Chromosome Structure and Function,* Vol. XXXVIII. Cold Spring Harbor Laboratory, Cold Spring Harbor, New York, 1974.

DULANEY, E. L. and LASKIN, A. I. (eds.): *The Problems of Drug-Resistant Pathogenic Bacteria.* Ann. N.Y. Acad. Sci., Vol. 182, 1971.

HAYES, W.: *The Genetics of Bacteria and Their Viruses.* John Wiley and Sons, Inc., New York, 1968.

JACOB, F.: *The Logic of Life: A History of Heredity.* (Translated from the French by B. E. Spillman.) Pantheon Books, New York, 1973.

KORNBERG, A.: *DNA Synthesis.* W. H. Freeman & Co., San Francisco, 1974.

LEVINTHAL, M.: "Bacterial Genetics Excluding *E. coli,*" *Annu. Rev. Microbiol,* **28**:219, 1974.

CHAPTER 17

CORUM, C. J. (ed.): *Federal Regulations and Practical Control Microbiology for Disinfectants, Drugs and Cosmetics.* Society for Industrial Microbiology, no location listed, 1969.

CURSON, I.: "Endodontic Techniques. 6. Root Canal Instruments and Their Sterilization," *Brit. Dent. J.,* **121**:289, 1966.

GRAHAME, R.: "Sterilization of Instruments and Dressing in General Practice," *Lancet,* **1**:1109, 1965.

LAWRENCE, C. A., and BLOCK, S. S. (eds.): *Disinfection, Sterilization, and Preservation.* Lea and Febiger, Philadelphia, 1971.

McLUNDIE, A. C., KENNEDY, G. D. C., STEPHAN, K. W., and KENNEDY, T. F.: "Sterilization in General Dental Practice," *Brit. Dent. J.,* **124**:214, 1968.

SHAPTON, D. A., and BOARD, R. G. (eds.): *Safety in Microbiology.* Academic Press, New York, 1972.

SPAULDING, E. H.: *Recommendations for Chemical Disinfection of Medical and Surgical Materials.* Biophysics Section, Technology Branch, National Communicable Disease Center, Atlanta, Georgia, 1966.

CHAPTER 18

Accepted Dental Remedies. Council on Dental Therapeutics of the American Dental Association, 30th ed., 1964.

BLAKEMORE, W. S.: "Symposium: Filtered Laminar Airflow Technology," *Devel. Ind. Microbiol.,* **11**:45, 1970.

GREEN, H. G., DENNIS, H. J., and PELLEN, G. B., JR.: "Central Sterilization for the Dental Clinic," *Military Med.,* **131**:1483, 1966.

LANE, C. R., COOK, G. T., KELSEY, J. C., and BEEBY, M. M.: "High Temperature Sterilization for Surgical Instruments," *Lancet,* **2**:358, 1964.

PHILIPS, I., and TAYLOR, T. A.: "Sterilization of Surgical Instruments in a 'Flash Autoclave'," *Lancet,* **2**:840, 1965.

QUENZEL, L. B., HAYWARD, J. M., and BARNETT, J. W.: "Hot Air Sterilization at 200°," *J. Appl. Bact.,* **30**:518, 1967.

CHAPTER 19

BARRY, A. L., GARCIA, F., and THRUPP, L. D.: "An Improved Single-Disk Method for Testing the Antibiotic Susceptibility of Rapidly Growing Pathogens." *Amer. J. Clin. Pathol.,* **53**:149–158, 1970.

"Antibiotic Susceptibility Testing," Seminar, *Bulletin 0334,* Difco Laboratories, Detroit, 1970.

Laboratory Reference Manual: Garamycin. Schering Corporation, Bloomfield, N.J., 1969.

"Antimicrobial Susceptibility Testing," *Pfizer Diagnostics Technical Bulletin,* Chas. Pfizer & Co., Inc., New York, 1970.

BAUER, A. W., KIRBY, W. M. M., SHERRIS, J. C., and TRUNK, M.: "Antibiotic Sensitivity Testing by a Standardized Single-Disk Method," *Amer. J. Clin. Path., 45*:493, 1966.

BLUMBERG, M., and STROMINGER, J. L.: "Interaction of Penicillin with the Bacterial Cell. Penicillin: Binding Proteins and Penicillin-Sensitive Enzymes," *Bact. Rev., 38*:291–335, 1974.

FINEGOLD, S. M., DAVIS, A., ZIMENT, I., and JACOBS, I.: "Chemotherapy guide," *Calif. Med., 111*:362, 1969.

HARWICK, H. L., WEISS, P., and FEKELY, F. R., JR.: "Application of Microtitration Techniques to Bacteriostatic and Bacteriocidal Antibiotic Susceptibility Testing," *J. Lab. Clin. Med., 72*:511, 1968.

JONES, S. R.: "Antiviral Chemotherapy," *Annu. Rev. Med., 25*:251.

PRATT, W. B.: *Fundamentals of Chemotherapy.* Oxford University Press, Inc., London, 1973.

SALTON, M. R. J., and TOMASZ, A. (eds.): *Mode of Action of Antibiotics on Microbial Walls and Membranes,* Vol. 235. N.Y. Acad. Sci., New York, 1974.

SCHMIDT, R. M., and ROSENKRANZ, H. S.: "Antimicrobial Activity of Local Anesthetics: Lidocaine and Procaine," *J. Inf. Dis., 121*:597, 1970.

SUTTER, V. L., KWOK, Y.-Y., and FINEGOLD, S. M.: "Standardized Anti-Microbial Disc Susceptibility Testing of Anaerobic Bacteria. I. Susceptibility of *Bacteroides fragilis* to Tetracycline." *Appl. Microbiol., 23*:268–275, 1972.

THRUPP, L. D.: "New Cephalosporins and 'Expanded-Spectrum' Penicillins," *Annu. Rev. Pharmacol., 14*:435, 1974.

TILLES, J. G.: "Antiviral Agents," *Annu. Rev. Pharmacol., 14*:469, 1974.

CHAPTER 20

DINGLE, J. T.: *Lysosomes in Biology and Pathology.* American Elsevier Publishing Co., New York, 3rd ed., 1973.

ISAACS, A., and LINDENMANN, J.: "Virus Interference. I. The Interferon," *Proc. Roy, J. B.,* London, 147:258, 1957.

MILLER, J. F. A. P.: "The Thymus and the Development of Immunologic Responsiveness," *Science, 144*:1544, 1964.

WILKINSON, P. C.: *Chemotaxis and Inflammation.* Churchill Livingstone, Edinburgh, Scotland (distributed in the U.S. by Longman, Inc., New York), 1974.

CHAPTER 21

BALOWS, A., DeHAAN, R. M., DOWELL, V. R., JR., and GUZE, L. B. (eds.): *Anaerobic Bacteria: Role in Disease.* Charles C. Thomas, Publisher, Springfield, Ill., 1974.

KADIS, S., MONTIE, T. C., and AJL, S. J. (eds.): *Microbial Toxins,* Vol. II A. Academic Press, Inc., New York, 1971.

MUDD, S.: *Infectious Agents and Host Reactions.* W. B. Saunders Company, Philadelphia, 1970.

ROBBINS, S. L.: *Pathologic Basics of Disease.* W. B. Saunders Co., Philadelphia, 1974.

SMITH, H.: "Mechanisms of Virus Pathogenicity," *Bact. Rev., 36*:291–310, 1972.

CHAPTER 22

"Antibodies," *Cold Spring Harbor Symp. Quant. Biol., 32*:entire issue, 1967.

DAY, E. D.: *Foundations of Immunochemistry.* Williams & Wilkins Co., Baltimore, 1966.

OUCHTERLONY, O.: *Handbook of Immunodiffusion and Immunoelectrophoresis.* Ann Arbor Science Publishers, Ann Arbor, Michigan, 1968.

SELA, M. (ed.): *The Antigens.* Academic Press, New York, 1973.

SMITH, G. P., HOOD, L., and FITCH, W. M.: "Antibody Diversity," *Ann. Rev. Biochem., 40*:943, 1971.

CHAPTER 23

CHERRY, W. B., GOLDMAN, M., and CARSKI, T. R.: *Fluorescent Antibody Techniques in the Diagnosis of Communicable Diseases.* Public Health Service Publication No. 729. Government Printing Office, Washington, D.C., 1960.

FARR, R. S., and MINDEN, P.: "The Measurement of Antibodies," *Ann. N. Y. Acad. Sci., 154*:107, 1968.

FREDERICK, J. F. (Chairman): "Gel. Electrophoresis," *Ann. N. Y. Acad. Sci., 121*:(entire issue), 1964.

GOLDMAN, M.: *Fluorescent Antibody Methods.* Academic Press, Inc., New York, 1968.

LANDSTEINER, K.: *The Specificity of Serological Reactions.* Harvard University Press, Cambridge, Mass., rev. ed., 1945.

MAYER, M. M.: "Mechanism of Haemolysis by Complement," in WOLSTENHOLME, G. E. W., and KNIGHT, J. (eds.): *Complement.* Little, Brown & Co., Boston, 1965.

ROSE, N. R., and BIGAZZI, P. E. (eds.): *Methods in Immunodiagnosis.* John Wiley & Sons, New York, 1973.

CHAPTER 24

QUEENAN, J. T.: *Modern Management of the Rh Problem.* Hoeber Medical Division, Harper & Row, Publishers, Inc., Scranton, Pa., 1967.

SIMMONS, A.: *Technical Hematology.* J. B. Lippincott Company, Philadelphia, 1968.

WINTROBE, M. M.: *Clinical Hematology.* Lea & Febiger, Philadelphia, 5th ed., 1961.

CHAPTER 25

GOODFRIEND, L., SEHON, A. H., and ORANGE, R. P. (eds.): *Mechanisms in Allergy: Reagin-Mediated Hypersensitivity.* Marcel Dekker, Inc., New York, 1973.

LEVINE, B. B.: "Immunochemical Mechanisms of Drug Allergy," *Ann. Rev. Med.,* **17**:23, 1966.

ROITT, I. M.: *Essential Immunology.* Blackwell Scientific Publications, Oxford, 2nd ed., 1974.

UHR, J. W.: "Delayed Hypersensitivity," *Physiol. Rev.,* **46**:359, 1966.

CHAPTER 26

American Academy of Pediatrics: *Report of the Committee on the Control of Infectious Diseases.* American Academy of Pediatrics, Evanston, Ill., 1966.

FALLERONI, A. E.: "Treatment of Allergic Emergencies," *Modern Treatment,* **5**:782, 1968.

MICHEL, M. I.: "Reactions to Routine Immunizations," *Modern Treatment,* **5**:879, 1968.

PARISH, H. J., and CANNON, D. A.: *Antisera, Toxoids, Vaccines, and Tuberculins in Prophylaxis and Treatment.* Published for the Wellcome Foundation, Ltd., by E. & S. Livingstone, Ltd., Edinburgh and London, 1961.

CHAPTER 27

BURNET, F. M.: *Natural History of Infectious Diseases.* Cambridge University Press, Cambridge, 2nd ed., 1953.

FRIEDMAN, G. D.: *Primer of Epidemiology.* McGraw-Hill Book Co., New York, 1974.

GORDON, J. (ed.): *Control of Communicable Diseases in Man.* American Public Health Association, New York, 10th ed., 1965.

GREGORY, P. H., and MONTEITH, J. L. (eds.): *Airborne Microbes.* Seventeenth Symposium, Soc. Gen. Microbiol., London, 1967.

HERS, J. E., and WINKLER, K. C. (eds.): *Airborne Transmission and Airborne Infection.* Concepts and methods presented at the Seventh International Symposium on Aerobiology at Enschede, the Netherlands. John Wiley & Sons, New York, 1973.

Pictorial Keys to Some Arthropods and Mammals of Public Health Importance. U.S. Dept. HEW, Public Health Service Center, Atlanta, Georgia, 1964.

Proceedings of the International Conference on Nosocomial Infections, Center for Disease Control, American Hospital Association, Chicago, 1971.

WILLIAMS, R. E. O., BLOWERS, R., GARROD, L. P., and SHOOTER, R. A.: *Hospital Infection.* Yearbook Medical Publishers, Inc., Chicago, 2nd ed., 1966.

CHAPTER 28

BAILEY, R. W., and SCOTT, G. E.: *Diagnostic Microbiology.* C. V. Mosby Co., St. Louis, 1970.

BARTLETT, R. C.: *Medical Microbiology: Quality Cost and Clinical Relevance.* John Wiley & Sons, New York, 1974.

DOWELL, V. R., JR., and HAWKINS, T. M.: *Laboratory Methods in Anaerobic Bacteriology: CDC Laboratory Manual.* DHEW Publ. No. (CDC) 74-8272. Center for Disease Control, Atlanta, 1974.

PRIER, J. E., BARTOLA, J., and FRIEDMAN, H.: *Quality Control in Microbiology.* University Park Press, Baltimore, 1975.

CHAPTER 29

CARITHERS, H. A., CARITHERS, C. M., and EDWARDS, R. O., JR.: "Cat-scratch Disease," *JAMA,* **207**:312, 1969.

ECKMANN, L.: *Principles of Tetanus*. Hans Huber Publishers, Bern and Stuttgart, 1967.

FORKNER, C. E.: *Pseudomonas Aeruginosa Infections*. Grune & Stratton, Inc., New York, 1960.

HILL, G. J.: *Leprosy in Five Young Men*. Colorado Associated University Press, Boulder, Colorado, 1971.

LENDRUM, F. C.: "The Name 'Leprosy'," *Amer. J. Trop. Med. & Hyg.*, **1**:999, 1952.

SAUER, G. C.: *Manual of Skin Diseases*. J. B. Lippincott Co., Philadelphia, 3rd ed., 1973.

WHO Expert Committee on Leprosy. *WHO Tech. Report Series,* No. 319, 1966.

CHAPTER 30

LEWIS, G. M., and WHEELER, C. E.: *Practical Dermatology*. W. B. Saunders Company, Philadelphia, 3rd ed., 1967.

MOSS, E. S., and McQUOWN, A. L.: *Atlas of Medical Mycology*. Williams & Wilkins Co., Baltimore, 1970.

WINNER, H. I., and HURLEY, R.: *Candida Albicans*. Little, Brown & Co., Boston, 1964.

WOLSTENHOLME, G. E. W., and PORTER, R.: *Systemic Mycoses*. Little, Brown & Co., Boston, 1968.

CHAPTER 31

COOPER, L. Z., and KRUGMAN, S.: "The Rubella problem," *Disease-a-Month,* Feb. 1, Yearbook Medical Publishers Inc., Chicago, 1969.

DOCHERTY, J. J., and CHOPAN, M.: "The Latent Herpes Simplex Virus," *Bact. Rev.*, **33**:337–355, 1974.

ENDERS, J. F.: "Measles Virus: Historical Review, Isolation, and Behavior in Various Systems," *Am. J. Dis. Child.*, **103**:282, 1962.

WELLER, T. H., ALFORD, C. A., JR., and NEVA, F. A.: "Changing Epidemiologic Concepts of Rubella, with Particular Reference to Unique Characteristics of the Congenital Infection," *Yale J. Med. & Biol.*, **37**:455, 1965.

CHAPTER 32

BEATY, N. N.: "Bacterial Endocarditis" in Conn, H. F. (ed.): *Current Therapy*. W. B. Saunders Company, Philadelphia, 1969.

BISSET, K. A., and DAVIS, G. H. G.: "The Oral Actinomycetes," *Arch. Oral Biol.*, **1**:80, 1959.

BJORN, H., and CARLSSON, J.: "Observations on Dental Plaque Morphogenesis," *Odont. Rev.*, **15**:23, 1964.

BURNETT, G. W., and SCHERP, H. W.: *Oral Microbiology and Infectious Disease*. Williams and Wilkins Co., Baltimore, 3rd ed., 1968.

COHEN, L.: "Oral Candidiasis," *Oral Surg.*, **20**:316, 1965.

GILMOUR, M. N., HOWELL, A., JR., and BIBBY, G. B.: "The Classification of Organisms Termed Leptotrichia (Leptothrix) buccalis, I," *Bact. Rev.*, **25**:131, 1961.

HUEBNER, R. J., COLE, R. M., BEEMAN, E. A., BELL, J. A., and PEERS, J. H.: "Herpangina. Etiologic Studies of a Specific Infectious Disease," *JAMA*, **145**:628, 1961.

KRASSE, B., JORDAN, H. V., EDWARDSSON, S., SVENSSON, I., and TRELL, L.: "The Occurrence of Certain 'Caries-inducing' Streptococci in Human Dental Plaque Material with Special Reference to Frequency and Activity of Caries," *Arch. Oral Biol.*, **13**:911, 1968.

LOE, H.: "Epidemiology of Peridontal Disease," *Odont. T.*, **71**:479, 1963.

McCARTHY, C., SNYDER, M. L., and PARKER, R. B.: "The Indigenous Oral Flora of Man. The Newborn to the One-Year-Old Infant," *Arch. Oral Biol.*, **10**:61, 1965.

MECKELL, A. H.: "The Formation and Properties of Organic Films on Teeth," *Arch. Oral Biol.*, **10**:585, 1965.

NOLTE, W. A.: *Oral Microbiology*. C. V. Mosby Co., St. Louis, 1968.

RIZZO, A. A., and MERGENHAGEN, S. E.: "Studies of the Significance of Local Hypersensitivity in Periodontal Disease," *Periodon.*, **3**:271, 1965.

TIECKE, R. W. (ed.): *Oral Pathology*. McGraw-Hill Book Company, New York, 1965.

WILLIAMS, N. B.: "Microbial Ecology of the Oral Cavity," *J. Dent. Res.*, **42**:509, 1963.

CHAPTER 33

Diagnostic Standards and Classification of Tuberculosis. National Tuberculosis and Respiratory Disease Association, New York, 1969.

EATON, M. D.: "Pleuropneumonia-like Organisms and Related Forms," *Ann. Rev. Microbiol.*, **19**:379, 1965.

HAMIL, E. R.: "The Role of the Nurse in the Control of Staphylococcal Infections in Hospitals," *Calif. Health*, **17**:July 15, 1959.

HAYFLICK, L. (Consulting Editor and Conference Chairman): "Biology of the Mycoplasma," *Ann. N.Y. Acad. Sci.,* **143** (Art. 1):1, 1967.

Introduction to Respiratory Disease. National Tuberculosis and Respiratory Disease Association, New York, 1964.

IVLER, D. (Conference Chairman): "The Staphylococci: Ecologic Perspectives," *Ann. N.Y. Acad. Sci.,* **128**:1, 1965.

MORTIMER, E., FISCHER, P., JENKINS, N., and McGIRR, D.: "Staphylococcus in the Nursery," *Amer. J. Nurs.,* **61**:56, 1961.

PAGE, M. I.: "The Present Problem of Diphtheria Control in the United States," *Amer. J. Pub. Health,* **52**:68, 1962.

RILEY, R., and O'GRADY, F.: *Airborne Infections: Transmission and Control.* The Macmillan Company, New York, 1961.

ROSENTHAL, S. R., AFREMOW, M. L., NIKURS, L., LOEWINSOHN, E., LEPPMAN, M., KATELE, E., LIVERIGHT, D., THORNE, M.: "BCG Vaccination and Tuberculosis in Students of Nursing," *Amer. J. Nurs.,* **63**:88, 1963.

SOUTH, J.: *Tuberculosis Handbook for Public Health Nurses.* National Tuberculosis Association, New York, 4th ed., 1965.

UHR, J. W. (ed.): *The Streptococcus, Rheumatic Fever, and Glomerulonephritis.* Williams & Wilkins Co., Baltimore, 1964.

YOUMANS, G. P.: "The Pathogenic 'Atypical' Mycobacteria," *Ann. Rev. Microbiol.,* **17**:473, 1963.

CHAPTER 34

MACKENZIE, J. S., and HOUGHTON, M.: "Influenza Infections During Pregnancy: Association with Congenital Malformations and with Subsequent Neoplasms in Children, and Potential Hazards of Live Virus Vaccines." *Bact. Rev.,* **38**:356–370, 1974.

STUART-HARRIS, C. H., and ANDREWES, C.: *Influenza and Other Virus Infections of the Respiratory Tract.* Williams & Wilkins Company, Baltimore, 1965.

CHAPTER 35

ALSTON, J. M., and BROOM, J. C.: *Leptospirosis in Man and Animals.* E. & S. Livingstone, Ltd., London, 1958.

DACK, G. M.: *Food Poisoning.* University of Chicago Press, Chicago, 1956.

DALRYMPLE-CHAMPNEYS, W.: *Brucella Infection and Undulant Fever in Man.* Oxford University Press, New York, 1960.

DE, S. N.: *Cholera.* Oliver & Boyd, London, 1961.

GREENGARD, J., GHABRIAL, S., and METZGER, W.: "Epidemic Diarrhea in Infancy," *Med. Times,* **90**:38, 1962.

HOBBS, B. C., and CHRISTIAN, J. H. B.: *The Microbiological Safety of Food.* Academic Press, New York, 1973.

MACLELLAN, J. D.: "The Histotoxic Clostridial Infections of Man," *Bact. Rev.,* **26**:177, 1962.

TENNANT, B. (ed.): "Neonatal Enteric Infections Caused by Escherichia Coli," *Ann. N.Y. Acad. Sci.,* **176**:5, 1971.

CHAPTER 36

ALLEN, J. G., and SAYMAN, W. A.: "Serum Hepatitis from Transfusions of Blood," *JAMA,* **180**:1079, 1962.

CANGIR, A., and SULLIVAN, M. P.: "The Occurrence of Cytomegalovirus Infections in Childhood Leukemia," *JAMA,* **195**:616, 1966.

HAVENS, P. R., JR.: "Viral Hepatitis," *Ann. Rev. Med.,* **14**:57, 1963.

HOAGLAND, R. J.: *Infectious Mononucleosis.* Grune & Stratton, Inc., New York, 1967.

HSIUNG, G. D.: "Further Studies on Characteristics of ECHO Viruses," *Ann. N.Y. Acad. Sci.,* **101**:413, 1962.

KRUGMAN, S., GILES, J. P.: "Viral Hepatitis: New Light on an Old Disease," *JAMA,* **212**:1019, 1970.

PLOTKIN, S. A., CARP, R. I., and GRAHAM, A. F.: "The Polioviruses of Man," *Ann. N.Y. Acad. Sci.,* **101**:357, 1962.

PRIER, J. E., and FRIEDMAN, H.: *Australia Antigen.* University Park Press, Baltimore, 1973.

CHAPTER 37

BREWER, J. I., and DECOSTA, E. J.: *Textbook of Gynecology.* Williams & Wilkins Co., Baltimore, 4th ed., 1967.

ELLIOTT, H., and RYZ, K.: *Venereal Diseases: Treatment and Nursing.* Bailliere Tindall, London (The William & Wilkins Co., Baltimore, exclusive U.S. agents), 1972.

KAMPMEIER, R. H.: "Venereal Disease in the Teenages," *Medical Aspects of Human Sexuality,* **2**:14, 1968.

NATIONAL COMMUNICABLE DISEASE CENTER: *Syphilis: A Synopsis.* Public Health Service Publication No. 1660, U.S. Government Printing Office, Washington, D.C., 1968.

SANFORD, J. P.: "Management of Urinary Tract Infections," *Med. Times,* **96**:715, 1968.

CHAPTER 38

HORSTMANN, D. M.: "Epidemiology of Poliomyelitis and Allied Diseases," *Yale J. Biol. and Med.,* **36**:5, 1963.

JAWETZ, E.: "Agents of Trachoma and Inclusion Conjunctivitis," *Ann. Rev. Microbiol.,* **18**:301, 1961.

NAGANO, Y., and DAVENPORT, F. M.: *Rabies.* University Park Press, Baltimore, 1971.

SULKIN, S. E., and ALLEN, R.: *Virus Infection in Bats.* Monographs in Virology, Vol. 8. S. Karger, Basel, Switzerland, 1974.

ZEMAN, W., and LENNETTE, E. H. (eds.): *Slow Virus Diseases.* The Williams & Wilkins Co., Baltimore, 1974.

CHAPTER 39

FELSENFELD, O.: "Borreliae, Human Relapsing Fever, and Parasite-Vector-Host Relationships," *Bact. Rev.,* **24**:46, 1965.

ZDRODOVSKII, P. F., and GOLINEVICH, H. M.: *The Rickettsial Diseases.* (Translated from the Russian by B. Haigh.) Pergamon Press, Inc., Elmsford, N.Y., 1960.

CHAPTER 40

BEERS, R. F., JR., TILGHMAN, R. C., and BASSETT, E. G. (eds.): *The Role of Immunological Factors in Viral and Oncogenic Processes.* Johns Hopkins University Press, Baltimore, 1974.

CARTER, S. K., and SLAVIK, M.: "Chemotherapy of Cancer," *Annu. Rev. Pharmacol.,* **14**:157, 1974.

RAFFERTY, K.: "Herpes Viruses and Cancer," *Sci. Amer.,* **229**:26, 1973.

TOOZE, J. (ed.): *The Molecular Biology of Tumor Viruses.* Cold Spring Harbor Laboratory, Cold Spring Harbor, New York, 1973.

CHAPTERS 41 AND 42

BRAY, R. A.: *"Leishmania,"* *Annu. Rev. Microbiol.,* **28**:189, 1974.

BROWN, H. W.: *Basic Clinical Parasitology.* Appleton-Century-Crofts, Inc., New York, 3rd ed., 1969.

ELSDON-DEW, R.: "The Epidemiology of Amoebiasis," *Adv. Parasit.,* **6**:1, 1968.

GARNHAM, P. C. C.: *Malaria Parasites and Other Haemosporidia.* Blackwell Scientific Publications, Oxford, 1966.

JIROVEC, O., and PETRU, M.: "Trichomonas Vaginalis and Trichomoniasis," *Adv. Parasit.,* **6**:117, 1968.

KOBERLE, F.: "Chagas' Disease and Chagas' Syndromes: The Pathology of American Trypanosomiasis," *Adv. Parasit.,* **6**:63, 1968.

MARKELL, E. K., and VOGE, M.: *Medical Parasitology.* W. B. Saunders Company, Philadelphia, 1965.

McKELVEY, J. J., JR.: *Man Against Tsetse: Struggle for Africa.* University Press, Ithaca, New York, 1973.

PAN AMERICAN HEALTH ORGANIZATION: *Immunologic Aspects of Parasitic Infections.* World Health Organization, Washington, D.C., 1967.

Index

Explanation of symbols: f, figure; t, table.